Handbook
of Steel
Construction

Tenth Edition

cisc icca

Canadian Institute of Steel Construction
Institut canadien de la construction en acier

Tenth Edition

First Printing March 2010
Second Revised Printing March 2011
Third Printing November 2011

ISBN 978-0-88811-154-8

PRINTED IN CANADA

CONTENTS

PART ONE
CSA S16-09 – Design of Steel Structures

PART TWO
CISC Commentary on CSA S16-09

PART THREE
Connections and Tension Members

PART FOUR
Compression Members

PART FIVE
Flexural Members

PART SIX
Properties and Dimensions

PART SEVEN
CISC Code of Standard Practice and Miscellaneous Data

PART EIGHT
General Index

CONTENTS

FOREWORD

The Canadian Institute of Steel Construction is a national industry organization representing the structural steel, open-web steel joist and steel plate fabricating industries in Canada. Formed in 1930 and granted a Federal charter in 1942, the CISC functions as a non-profit organization promoting the efficient and economic use of fabricated steel in construction.

As a member of the Canadian Steel Construction Council, the Institute has a general interest in all uses of steel in construction. CISC works in close co-operation with the Steel Structures Education Foundation (SSEF) to develop educational courses and programs related to the design and construction of steel structures. The CISC supports and actively participates in the work of the Standards Council of Canada, the Canadian Standards Association, the Canadian Commission on Building and Fire Codes and numerous other organizations, in Canada and other countries, involved in research work and the preparation of codes and standards.

Preparation of engineering plans is not a function of the CISC. The Institute does provide technical information through its professional engineering staff, through the preparation and dissemination of publications, and through the medium of seminars, courses, meetings, videos and computer software. Architects, engineers and others interested in steel construction are encouraged to make use of CISC information services.

CISC is located at:

3760 14th Avenue, Suite 200
Markham, Ontario, L3R 3T7

and may also be contacted via one or more of the following:

Telephone: (905) 946-0864
Fax: (905) 946-8574
E-mail: *info@cisc-icca.ca*
Website: *www.cisc-icca.ca*

PREFACE

This handbook has been prepared and published by the Canadian Institute of Steel Construction. It is an important part of a continuing effort to provide current and practical information to assist educators, designers, fabricators and others interested in the use of steel in construction.

The First Edition of the CISC Handbook of Steel Construction was published in 1967, with the Second through Sixth editions following each new edition of the CSA structural steel design standard, now called CSA S16-09. The first printing of the Seventh Edition introduced CSA G40.21-350W as the basic steel grade for W and HP shapes, while the second revised printing of that same edition also included ASTM specifications A992 and A572 grade 50. The Eighth Edition was expanded to include Hollow Structural Sections produced in accordance with ASTM Specification A500 grade C. The Ninth Edition accompanied the National Building Code of Canada (NBCC) 2005, while this Tenth Edition is intended to be used in conjunction with the NBCC 2010.

Part 1 is a reprint of CSA S16-09 "Design of Steel Structures". To assist in understanding the requirements of this standard, Part 2 provides a Commentary prepared by CISC. Part 3 contains information on bolts and welds with tables for design and evaluation of various structural framing connections. Design tables for eccentric loads on weld groups have been revised to incorporate more recent research. Parts 4 and 5 contain information on compression and flexural members, respectively. In Part 6, section properties and dimensions data are provided for currently produced rolled and welded shapes. The CISC Code of Standard Practice, Seventh Edition, leads the information found in Part 7 and features new appendices on architecturally exposed structural steel and digital modelling.

Permission to reprint portions of their publications, granted by the Canadian Standards Association and the American Institute of Steel Construction, Inc., is gratefully acknowledged. The contributions of Alfred Wong and Adam Korzekwa, who helped make publication of this book possible, are sincerely appreciated.

Although no effort has been spared in an attempt to ensure that all data in this book is factual, and that numerical values are accurate to a degree consistent with current structural design practice, the Canadian Institute of Steel Construction does not assume responsibility for errors or oversights resulting from use of the information contained herein. Anyone making use of the contents of this book assumes all liability arising from such use. Suggestions for improvement of this publication will receive full consideration for future printings.

Charles Albert
Editor
March 2010

DESIGNATIONS

Standard designations should always be used to identify structural steel products on drawings and other documents. In Canada, the official designation is the metric (SI) designation, and examples of correct designations for most of the commonly used steel products are provided below. These designations should be used on all design drawings, for detailing purposes and for ordering material.

Shape		**Examples**
Welded Wide-Flange Shapes		WWF900x169
W Shapes		W610x113
Miscellaneous M Shapes		M200x9.7
Standard Beams (S Shapes)		S380x64
Standard Channels (C Shapes)		C230x20
Miscellanous Channels (MC Shapes)		MC250x12.5
Structural Tees	- cut from WWF Shapes	WWT250x138
	- cut from W Shapes	WT155x43
	- cut from M Shapes	MT100x4.9
Bearing Piles (HP Shapes)		HP250x62
Equal-Leg angles		L102x102x9.5
Unequal-Leg angles		L127x89x9.5
Plates (thickness × width)		PL8x500
Square bars (side, mm)		Bar 25⌹
Round bars (diameter, mm)		Bar 25 ϕ
Flat Bars (thickness × width)		Bar 5x60
Round Pipe (outside diameter × thickness)		DN300x9.52†
Hollow Structural Sections	- Rectangular	HSS152x102x9.5 CSA G40.21 Class C *
	- Square	HSS152x152x9.5 CSA G40.21 Class C *
	- Round	HSS141x9.5 CSA G40.21 Class C *
Cold-Formed C-Sections		CFC305S89-468M

* *HSS steel grades: CSA G40.21 Class C or H, or ASTM A500 Grade C*

† *This designation has been suggested by the U.S. National Institute of Building Sciences.*

GENERAL NOMENCLATURE

Explanations of the nomenclature used in many sections of this book appear in those specific sections. In addition, the following symbols are included here for convenience. See also CSA S16-09 Clause 2.2.

A	Area
A_b	Cross-sectional area of one bolt based on nominal diameter
A_e	Effective area of section in compression to account for elastic local buckling
A_f	Flange area
A_n	Net area
A_p	Concrete pull-out area of a shear stud
A_{sc}	Cross-sectional area of a steel shear connector
A_w	Web area; shear area; effective throat area of weld
a	Centre-to-centre distance between transverse web stiffeners; depth of concrete compression zone
a/h	Aspect ratio; ratio of distance between stiffeners to web depth
B	Bearing force in a member or component under specified load
B_f	Bearing force in a member or component under factored load
B_r	Factored bearing resistance of a member or component
b	Width of stiffened or unstiffened compression elements; design effective width of concrete slab; overall flange width
b_{el}	width of stiffened of unstiffened compression elements
C	Ratio of connection resistance to the resistance of a single bolt or fillet weld of unit size and length (for computing the resistance of eccentrically loaded bolt or weld groups)
C_e	Euler buckling load
C_f	Compressive force in a member or component under factored load; factored axial load
C_r	Factored compressive resistance of a member or component
C'_r	Compressive resistance of concrete acting at the centroid of the concrete area in compression
C_w	Warping torsional constant
C_y	Axial compressive load at yield stress
c	Distance from neutral axis to outer fiber of structural shape
D	Outside diameter of circular sections; diameter of rocker or roller; stiffener factor; fillet weld size (millimetres)
d	Depth; overall depth of a section; diameter of bolt or stud
E	Elastic modulus of steel (200 000 MPa assumed)
E_c	Elastic modulus of concrete
e	End distance; lever arm between the compressive resistance, C_r, and tensile resistance, T_r
e'	Lever arm between the compressive resistance, C'_r, of concrete and tensile resistance, T_r, of steel
F_a	Acceleration-based site coefficient, as defined in the NBCC
F_{cr}	Critical plate buckling stress
F_s	Ultimate shear strength
F_u	Specified minimum tensile strength (MPa)
F_v	Velocity-based site coefficient, as defined in the NBCC
F_y	Specified minimum yield stress, yield point or yield strength
f'_c	Specified compressive strength of concrete at 28 days (MPa)

g	Transverse spacing between fastener gauge lines (gauge distance)
h	Clear depth of web between flanges; height of stud
I	Moment of inertia
I_E	Earthquake importance factor of the structure (see Clause 27 of S16-09 and the NBCC)
$I_E F_a S_a(0.2)$	Specified short-period spectral acceleration ratio (see Clause 27 of S16-09)
$I_E F_v S_a(1.0)$	Specified one-second spectral acceleration ratio (see Clause 27 of S16-09)
I_t	Transformed moment of inertia of a composite beam
I_{ts}	Transformed moment of inertia of a composite beam based on the modular ratio, n_s
I_x, I_y	Moment of inertia about axis x-x, y-y
J	St. Venant torsional constant
K	Effective length factor
K_x, K_y	Effective length factor with respect to axis x-x, y-y
KL	Effective length
k	Distance from outer face of flange to web toe of fillet of rolled shapes
k_1	Distance from centreline of web to flange toe of fillet of rolled shapes
L	Length
L_{cr}	Maximum unbraced length adjacent to a plastic hinge
L_u	Maximum unsupported length of compression flange for which no reduction in factored moment resistance, M_r, is required (for simply-supported beams under uniform moment). See also CSA S16-09 Clause 13.6(e).
L_x, L_y	Unsupported length with respect to axis x-x, y-y
M_f	Bending moment in a member or component under factored load
M_{f1}	Smaller factored end moment of a beam-column; factored bending moment at a point of concentrated load
M_{f2}	Larger factored end moment of a beam-column
M_p	Plastic moment $= ZF_y$
M_r	Factored moment resistance of a member or component
M'_r	Factored moment resistance of a member of a given unbraced length greater that L_u
M_{rc}	Factored moment resistance of a composite beam
M_w	Strength reduction factor for multi-orientation fillet welds to account for ductility incompatibility of the individual weld segments
M_y	Yield moment $= SF_y$
m	Number of faying surfaces or shear planes in a bolted joint, equal to 1 for bolts in single shear and 2 for bolts in double shear
N	Length of bearing of an applied load
n_s	Modular ratio of modulus of elasticity of steel to age-adjusted effective modulus of elasticity of concrete (for computing shrinkage deflections of composite beams)
P	Concentrated load
P_f	Factored axial load
Q	Ratio of plate resistance to weld resistance per unit length (for computing the resistance of welded connections subject to out-of-plane eccentricity)
Q_r	Sum of the factored resistances of all shear connectors between points of maximum and zero moment
q_r	Factored resistance of a shear connector
R	End reaction or concentrated transverse load applied to a flexural member
r	Radius of gyration
$\bar{r}_o$	Polar radius of gyration of a singly-symmetric section about the shear centre (see Clause 13.3.2 of S16-09)

r_u, r_v	Radius of gyration with respect to axis u-u, v-v
r_x, r_y	Radius of gyration with respect to axis x-x, y-y
r_z	Radius of gyration with respect to axis z-z
S	Elastic section modulus
$S_a(T)$	5% damped spectral response acceleration, expressed as a ratio to gravitational acceleration, for a period of T in seconds, as defined in the NBCC
S_x	Elastic section modulus with respect to axis x-x
S_y	Elastic section modulus with respect to axis y-y
s	Centre-to-centre spacing (pitch) between successive fastener holes in line of stress
T_f	Tensile force in a member or component under factored load
T_r	Factored tensile resistance of a member or component; factored tensile resistance of the steel acting at the centroid of that part of the steel area in tension
t	Thickness
U	Amplification factor for stability analysis of beam-columns
U_t	Factor to account for efficiency of the tensile area
V_f	Shear force in a member or component under factored load
V_r	Factored shear resistance of a member or component
V_s	Slip resistance of a bolted joint
W	Total uniformly distributed load; concentrated load
w	Web thickness; load per unit of length
Z	Plastic section modulus of a steel section
α_1	Ratio of average stress in a rectangular compression block to the specified concrete strength
β	Coefficient for weak-axis bending in beam-columns
β_x	Asymmetry parameter for singly-symmetric beams (see Clause 13.6(e) of S16-09)
θ	Angle of axis of weld segment with respect to the line of applied force (in degrees)
κ	Ratio of the smaller to the larger factored end moment, positive for double curvature and negative for single curvature
λ	Non-dimensional slenderness ratio in column formula
ϕ	Resistance factor
Ω	Section property used in computing the flexural-torsional buckling resistance of a singly-symmetric section (see Clause 13.3.2 of S16-09)
ω	Coefficient used to determine equivalent uniform bending effect in beam-columns
Δ	Deflection of a point of a structure

ASTM	American Society for Testing and Materials
CISC	Canadian Institute of Steel Construction
CPMA	Canadian Paint Manufacturers' Association (*now known as the Canadian Paint and Coatings Association*)
CSCC	Canadian Steel Construction Council
CSA	Canadian Standards Association
NBCC	National Building Code of Canada
RCSC	Research Council on Structural Connections
SSEF	Steel Structures Education Foundation
SSPC	Steel Structures Painting Council (*now known as the Society for Protective Coatings*)
SSRC	Structural Stability Research Council

PART ONE
CSA S16-09
DESIGN OF STEEL STRUCTURES

General

This Standard is reprinted with the permission of the Canadian Standards Association and contains all errata and revisions approved at time of printing. The reprint includes CSA S16-09 "Design of Steel Structures" (September 2009) along with Update No. 1 (October 2010).

CSA Standards are subject to periodic review, and amendments will be published by CSA from time to time as warranted. Check the CISC website (*www.cisc-icca.ca*) for future errata to the S16 Standard.

For information on requesting interpretations, see Note (5) to the Preface to CSA S16-09.

CSA Standard

S16-09
Design of steel structures

CANADIAN STANDARDS ASSOCIATION

®*Registered trade-mark of Canadian Standards Association*

Published in September 2009 by Canadian Standards Association
A not-for-profit private sector organization
5060 Spectrum Way, Suite 100, Mississauga, Ontario, Canada L4W 5N6
1-800-463-6727 • 416-747-4044

Visit our Online Store at www.ShopCSA.ca

Legal Notice for Standards

100%

The Canadian Standards Association (CSA) prints its publications on Rolland Enviro100, which contains 100% recycled post-consumer fibre, is EcoLogo and Processed Chlorine Free certified, and was manufactured using biogas energy.

To purchase CSA Standards and related publications, visit CSA's Online Store at **www.ShopCSA.ca** or call toll-free 1-800-463-6727 or 416-747-4044.

ISBN 978-1-55491-224-7
Technical Editor: M. Braiter

© Canadian Standards Association — 2009

Contents

Technical Committee on Steel Structures for Buildings

R.B. Vincent	Canam Group Inc., Boucherville, Québec	*Chair*
M.I. Gilmor	Canadian Institute of Steel Construction, Markham, Ontario	*Vice-Chair* *Secretary*
P.C. Birkemoe	University of Toronto, Toronto, Ontario	
R. Bjorhovde	The Bjorhovde Group, Tucson, Arizona, USA	*Associate*
M. Bruneau	State University of New York at Buffalo, Buffalo, New York, USA	
B.D. Charnish	Halcrow Yolles, Toronto, Ontario	
C. Christopoulos	University of Toronto, Toronto, Ontario	*Associate*
M.P. Comeau	Campbell Comeau Engineering Limited, Halifax, Nova Scotia	
R.G. Driver	University of Alberta, Edmonton, Alberta	
T. Fraser	Anvil Corporation, Bellingham, Washington, USA	
G. Frater	Canadian Steel Construction Council, Markham, Ontario	*Associate*
G. Grondin	University of Alberta, Edmonton, Alberta	*Associate*
R. Hounslow	XL Ironworks, Surrey, British Columbia	
M. Hrabok	University of Saskatchewan, Saskatoon, Saskatchewan	
M. Lasby	Hatch, Vancouver, British Columbia	*Associate*
R.A. MacCrimmon	Hatch, Niagara Falls, Ontario	

D. MacKinnon	Canadian Institute of Steel Construction, Markham, Ontario	*Associate*
J. Mark	M&G Steel, Oakville, Ontario	
A. Metten	Bush, Bohlman & Partners, Vancouver, British Columbia	
G.S. Miazga	Waiward Steel Fabricators Limited, Edmonton, Alberta	
C.J. Montgomery	Cohos Evamy, Edmonton, Alberta	
B. Moss	Roswell & Associates Engineers Ltd., Sault Ste. Marie, Ontario	
P.K. Ostrowski	Ontario Power Generation Inc., Toronto, Ontario	
J. A. Packer	University of Toronto, Toronto, Ontario	*Associate*
C. Rogers	McGill University, Montréal, Québec	
R.M. Schuster	University of Waterloo, Waterloo, Ontario	*Associate*
C.R. Taraschuk	National Research Council Canada, Ottawa, Ontario	
A. Tiruneh	Alberta Municipal Affairs and Housing, Edmonton, Alberta	*Associate*
R. Tremblay	École Polytechnique, Montréal, Québec	
T. Verhey	Walters Inc., Hamilton, Ontario	
E. Whalen	CWB Learning Centre, Mississauga, Ontario	
A. Wong	Canadian Institute of Steel Construction, Markham, Ontario	*Associate*
R. Yuen	City of Calgary, Calgary, Alberta	
P.A. Zubick	Waiward Steel Fabricators Ltd., Edmonton, Alberta	*Associate*
M. Braiter	Canadian Standards Association, Toronto, Ontario	*Project Manager*

△ *Preface*

This is the seventh edition of CSA S16, *Design of steel structures*. It supersedes the previous limit states editions published in 2001, 1994, 1989, 1984, 1978, and 1974. These seven limit states design editions were preceded by seven working stress design editions published in 1969, 1965, 1961, 1954, 1940, 1930, and 1924. The 1969 working stress design edition was withdrawn in 1984, from which point the design of steel structures in Canada has been carried out using limit states design principles.

This Standard is appropriate for the design of a broad range of structures. It sets out minimum requirements and is expected to be used only by engineers competent in the design of steel structures.

The 2001 edition of this Standard and its interim revision in 2005 involved significant rewriting. The intent of the 2009 edition is to make less significant changes while updating the Standard with current research and practice. Some specific changes to this Standard include the following:

(a) Annex K has been added to provide guidance for design under fire conditions.

(b) To be in line with CAN/CSA-A23.3, the resistance factor, ϕ, for concrete has been increased from 0.6 to 0.65 and α factor has been introduced to modify the stress block intensity. These changes have a minor influence on the resistance of composite beams and columns.

(c) Resistance expressions have been added to the flexural buckling of singly symmetric sections (e.g., channels, Tees, and angles) and the flexural buckling of asymmetric sections (e.g., built-up angles).

(d) Clause 13.3.3 has been added to provide guidance on the design of single-angle braces in compression.

(e) The calculation of the coefficient, ω_2, for unsupported beams with a moment gradient has been updated to reflect current research.

(f) The shear design provisions for beams without web stiffeners have been separated from web-stiffened beams.

(g) Clause 13.4.1.3 has been added for shear resistance of tubular members.

(h) Block shear requirements have been expanded and revised to better reflect recent test results.

(i) Clause 13.14 has been added to provide the resistance for bolts and welds in combination.

(j) Clause 15 for trusses, Clause 16 for open-web steel joists, and Clause 20 for plate walls have been reviewed and modified for practical considerations.

(k) Bending and axial compression plus bending requirements for composite columns have been rewritten.

(l) Clause 27.8 has been added to cover buckling restrained brace frames under seismic loading. These braces contain an internal steel core that can yield under axial load but is restrained such that it does not buckle in compression by a larger diameter shaft that does not participate in the axial resistance. These braces have similar response in compression and tension.

(m) The height limits for conventional construction ($R_d = 1.5$) have been extended, provided a variety of conditions are satisfied. The restrictions are such that this extension would mostly apply to industrial buildings.

(n) The criteria used for seismic design are now required to be stated on drawings.

(o) The concept of the "protected zone" for seismic systems has been introduced. The provision of protected zones will assist in preventing local failures during rapidly reversing seismic loads.

(p) The factor, R_y, applied to the specified yield stress of steels, has been increased for HSS brace members to reflect test results of the actual yield of members containing these sections.

(q) Minimum cross-section slenderness requirements for columns both in and outside the braced frames and buckling restrained braced frames in seismic active regions are now specified. The aim is to provide a degree of ductility for those columns that might experience bending moments due to movements of the building under seismic loading. Columns in single and multi-storey brace bay buildings are no longer class 4.

(r) A number of improvements and additions have been made for ductile eccentric braced frames and ductile plate walls. New seismic requirements have been introduced for limited-ductility plate walls.

(s) Infill panels of ductile plate walls may now have perforations and corner cut-outs.

(t)   The bolt edge distances for plates cut with plasma, laser, and water jet are now the same as those cut with gas.

(u)   All column bases now require a minimum of four anchor rods unless special precautions are taken.

(v)   Annex L has been added to provide designers with guidance to reduce the risk of brittle fracture.

A commentary on this Standard, prepared by the Canadian Institute of Steel Construction with contributions from many members of the Technical Committee, comprises Part 2 of the Institute's *Handbook of Steel Construction*.

This Standard is intended to be used with the provisions of the 2010 edition of the *National Building Code of Canada (NBCC)*, specifically Clause 7, which references the *NBCC* for load factors, load combinations, and other loading provisions.

This Standard was prepared by the Technical Committee on Steel Structures for Buildings, under the jurisdiction of the Strategic Steering Committee for Structures (Design), and has been formally approved by the Technical Committee.

September 2009

Notes:

(1) *Use of the singular does not exclude the plural (and vice versa) when the sense allows.*

(2) *Although the intended primary application of this Standard is stated in its Scope, it is important to note that it remains the responsibility of the users of the Standard to judge its suitability for their particular purpose.*

(3) *This publication was developed by consensus, which is defined by CSA Policy governing standardization — Code of good practice for standardization as "substantial agreement. Consensus implies much more than a simple majority, but not necessarily unanimity". It is consistent with this definition that a member may be included in the Technical Committee list and yet not be in full agreement with all clauses of this publication.*

(4) *CSA Standards are subject to periodic review, and suggestions for their improvement will be referred to the appropriate committee.*

(5) *All enquiries regarding this Standard, including requests for interpretation, should be addressed to Canadian Standards Association, 5060 Spectrum Way, Suite 100, Mississauga, Ontario, Canada L4W 5N6.*

   Requests for interpretation should

   (a) define the problem, making reference to the specific clause, and, where appropriate, include an illustrative sketch;

   (b) provide an explanation of circumstances surrounding the actual field condition; and

   (c) be phrased where possible to permit a specific "yes" or "no" answer.

   Committee interpretations are processed in accordance with the CSA Directives and guidelines governing standardization and are published in CSA's periodical Info Update, which is available on the CSA Web site at www.csa.ca.

S16-09
Design of steel structures

1 Scope and application

1.1 General
This Standard provides rules and requirements for the design, fabrication, and erection of steel structures. The design is based on limit states. The term "steel structures" refers to structural members and frames that consist primarily of structural steel components, including the detail parts, welds, bolts, or other fasteners required in fabrication and erection. This Standard also applies to structural steel components in structures framed in other materials. The clauses related to fabrication and erection, serve to show that design is inextricably a part of the design-fabrication-erection sequence and cannot be considered in isolation. For matters concerning standard practice pertinent to the fabrication and erection of structural steel not covered in this Standard, see Annex A.

1.2 Requirements
Requirements for steel structures such as bridges, antenna towers, offshore structures, and cold-formed steel structural members are given in other CSA Standards.

1.3 Application
This Standard applies unconditionally to steel structures, except that supplementary rules or requirements may be necessary for
(a) unusual types of construction;
(b) mixed systems of construction;
(c) steel structures that
   (i) have great height or spans;
   (ii) are required to be movable or be readily dismantled;
   (iii) are exposed to severe environmental conditions;
   (iv) are exposed to severe loads such as those resulting from vehicle impact or explosion;
   (v) are required to satisfy aesthetic, architectural, or other requirements of a non-structural nature;
   (vi) employ materials or products not listed in Clause 5; or
   (vii) have other special features that could affect the design, fabrication, or erection;
(d) tanks, stacks, other platework structures, poles, and piling; and
(e) crane-supporting structures.

1.4 Other standards
The use of other standards for the design of members or parts of steel structures is neither warranted nor acceptable except where specifically directed in this Standard. The formulas provided in this Standard may be supplemented by a rational design based on theory, analysis, and engineering practice acceptable to the regulatory authority, provided that nominal margins (or factors) of safety at least equal to those intended in the provisions of this Standard are maintained. (See Annex B.)

1.5 Terminology
In CSA Standards, "shall" is used to express a requirement, i.e., a provision that the user is obliged to satisfy in order to comply with the standard; "should" is used to express a recommendation or that which is advised but not required; "may" is used to express an option or that which is permissible within the limits of the standard; and "can" is used to express possibility or capability. Notes accompanying clauses do not include requirements or alternative requirements; the purpose of a note accompanying a clause is

to separate from the text explanatory or informative material. Notes to tables and figures are considered part of the table or figure and may be written as requirements. Annexes are designated normative (mandatory) or informative (non-mandatory) to define their application.

2 Definitions and symbols

2.1 Definitions

The following definitions apply in this Standard:

Approved — approved by the regulatory authority.

Brace point — the point on a member or element at which it is restrained (see Clause 9).

Camber — the deviation from straightness of a member or any portion of a member with respect to its major axis.

Note: *Frequently, camber is specified and produced in a member to compensate for deflections that will occur in the member when loaded (see Clause 6.3.2). Unspecified camber is sometimes referred to as bow.*

Concrete — portland cement concrete in accordance with CSA A23.1.

Deck or **decking** — the structural floor or roof element spanning between adjacent joists and directly supported thereby. The terms "deck" and "decking" include cast-in-place or precast concrete slabs, profiled metal deck, wood plank or plywood, and other relatively rigid elements suitable for floor or roof construction (see Clause 16).

Designer — the professional engineer responsible for the design.

Erection tolerances — tolerances related to the plumbness, alignment, and level of the piece as a whole. The deviations are determined by considering the location of the ends of the piece (see Clause 29).

Fabrication tolerances — tolerances allowed from the nominal dimensions and geometry, such as cutting to length, finishing of ends, cutting of bevel angles, and out-of-straightness such as sweep and camber for fabricated members (see Clause 28).

Factors —

> **Importance factor, I** — a factor applied severally to loads due to snow and rain, wind, or earthquake for both the ultimate and serviceability limit states. It is based on the importance of the structure as defined by its use and occupancy (see Clause 6.2.2).

> **Load factor, α** — a factor, given in Clause 7.2, applied to a specified load for the limit states under consideration that takes into account the variability of the loads and load patterns and the analysis of their effects.

> **Resistance factor, ϕ** — a factor, given in Clause 13.1, applied to a specified material property or the resistance of a member, connection, or structure that, for the limit state under consideration, takes into account the variability of material properties, dimensions, quality of work, type of failure, and uncertainty in prediction of member resistance.
> **Note:** *To maintain the simplicity of the design formulas in this Standard, the type of failure and the uncertainty in prediction of member resistance have been incorporated in the expressions of member resistance (see Annex B for a more detailed discussion).*

Fatigue limit state — the limiting case of the slow propagation of a crack within a structural element that can result either from live load effects (load-induced fatigue effect) or as the consequence of local distortion within the structure (distortion-induced fatigue effects).

Firm contact — the condition that exists on a faying surface when plies are solidly seated against each other but not necessarily in continuous contact (see Clause 23.2).

Inspector — a qualified person who acts for and on behalf of the owner or designer on all inspection and quality matters within the scope of the contract documents.

Joist shoe — the connection assembly located at the junction of the top chord and the end diagonal that allows the joist to bear on its support (see Clause 16).

Limit states — those conditions of a structure under which the structure ceases to fulfill the function for which it was designed.

> **Fatigue limit states** — conditions that concern safety and are related to crack propagation under cyclic loading.

> **Serviceability limit states** — conditions that restrict the intended use and occupancy of the structure and include deflection, vibration, and permanent deformation.

> **Ultimate limit states** — conditions that concern safety and include overturning, sliding, fracturing, and exceeding load-carrying capacity.

Loads —

> **Companion load** — a specified variable load that accompanies the principal load in a given load combination.

> **Factored load** — the product of a specified load and its load factor.

> **Gravity load** (newtons) — a load equal to the mass of the object (kilograms) being supported multiplied by the acceleration due to gravity, **g** (9.81 m/s^2).

> **Notional lateral load** — a fictitious lateral load, as given in Clause 8.4, that allows the stability of the frame, with failure modes involving in-plane bending, to be computed based on the actual length ($K = 1$) for beam-columns.

> **Principal load** — the specified variable load or rare load that dominates in a given load combination.

> **Specified loads (D, E, H, L, L$_{-c}$, C, C$_d$, C$_T$, P, S, T, and W)** — those loads prescribed by the regulatory authority (see Clause 6.2.1).

Mill tolerances — variations allowed from the nominal dimensions and geometry with respect to cross-sectional area, non-parallelism of flanges, and out-of-straightness such as sweep or camber in the product as manufactured and given in CSA G40.20.

Modulus of elasticity of concrete — the ratio of stress to strain in the elastic range of a stress-strain curve for concrete and, with density, γ_c, between 1500 and 2500 kg/m^3, is taken as follows:

$$E_c = \left(3300\sqrt{f_c'} + 6900\right)\left(\frac{\gamma_c}{2300}\right)^{1.5}$$

For normal density concrete with compressive strength, f_c', between 20 and 40 MPa, the modulus of elasticity may be taken as follows:

$$E_c = 4500\sqrt{f_c'}$$

Protected zone — areas of members in a seismic force resisting system that undergo large inelastic strains and in which limitations apply to fabrication and attachments. See Clause 27.1.9.

Regulatory authority — a federal, provincial/territorial, or municipal ministry, department, board, agency, or commission that is responsible for regulating by statute the use of products, materials, or services.

Resistance —

    Factored resistance, ϕR — the product of the nominal resistance and the appropriate resistance factor.

    Nominal resistance, R — the nominal resistance of a member, connection, or structure as calculated in accordance with this Standard and based on the specified material properties and nominal dimensions.

Segmented member — a member with a constant cross-section when axial loads are applied between in-plane lateral supports or frame connections, and a member with cross-section changes between in-plane lateral supports or frame connections.

Seismic design storey drift — the storey drift obtained from the lateral deflections obtained from a linear elastic analysis multiplied by $R_d R_o / I_e$ (see Clause 27).

Snug-tightness — the condition that brings the plies into firm contact commonly attained by a few impacts of an impact wrench, or the full effort of an ironworker using an ordinary spud wrench (see Clause 23).

Span of an open-web steel joist — the centre-to-centre distance of joist bearings or shoes (see Clause 16).

Sweep — the deviation from straightness of a member or any portion of a member with respect to its minor axis.

Tie joists — joists that are designed to resist gravity loads only and, in accordance with Clause 16.5.12.2, have at least one end connected to a column to facilitate erection.

Truss — a triangulated framework loaded primarily in flexure (see Clause 15).

2.2 Symbols
The following symbols are used throughout this Standard. Deviations or additional nomenclature are noted where they appear.

A = area

A_{ar} = cross-sectional area of an anchor rod based on its nominal diameter

A_b = cross-sectional area of a bolt based on its nominal diameter; cross-sectional area of a plate wall beam

A_c = transverse area of concrete between longitudinal shear planes; cross-sectional area of concrete in composite columns; cross-sectional area of a plate wall column; effective area of concrete slab

A_{cv} = critical area of two longitudinal shear planes, one on each side of the area A_c, extending from the point of zero moment to the point of maximum moment

A_e = effective area of section in compression to account for elastic local buckling (see Clause 13.3.5)

A_f = flange area

A_g = gross area

A_{gv} = gross area in shear for block failure (see Clause 13.11)

A_m = area of fusion face

A_n	= net area; the tensile area of a rod
A_{ne}	= effective net area reduced for shear lag
A_p	= concrete pull-out area
A_r	= area of reinforcing steel
A_s	= area of steel section, including cover plates; area of bottom (tension) chord of a steel joist; area of a stiffener or pair of stiffeners
A_{sc}	= cross-sectional area of a steel shear connector; cross-sectional of the yielding segment of the steel core of a buckling restrained brace
A_{se}	= effective steel area (see Clause 18.3.2)
A_{st}	= area of steel section in tension
A_w	= web area; shear area; effective throat area of a weld
a	= centre-to-centre distance between transverse web stiffeners; depth of the concrete compression zone
a'	= length of cover plate termination
a/h	= aspect ratio; ratio of distance between stiffeners to web depth
B	= bearing force in a member or component under specified load
B_f	= bearing force in a member or component under factored load
B_r	= factored bearing resistance of a member or component
b_l	= longer leg of angle in Clause 13.3.3
b_s	= shorter leg of angle in Clause 13.3.3
b	= overall width of flange; design effective width of concrete or cover slab
b_{el}	= width of stiffened or unstiffened compression elements
b_c	= width of concrete at the neutral axis specified in Clause 18.2.3; width of column flange
b_e	= effective flange width in Clause 18.3.2
b_f	= width of flange
C	= compressive force in a member or component under specified load; axial load
C_e	= Euler buckling strength
	= $\pi^2 EI/L^2$
C_{ec}	= Euler buckling strength of a concrete-filled hollow structural section
C_f	= compressive force in a member or component under factored load; factored axial load
C_{fs}	= sustained axial load on a composite column
C_p	= nominal compressive resistance of a composite column when $\lambda = 0$ (see Clause 18.3.2)
C_r	= factored compressive resistance of a member or component; factored compressive resistance of steel acting at the centroid of that part of the steel area in compression
C_{rc}	= factored compressive resistance of a composite column
C_{rcm}	= factored compressive resistance that can coexist with M_{rc} when all of the cross-section is in compression
C_{rco}	= factored compressive resistance with $\lambda = 0$
C_r'	= compressive resistance of concrete acting at the centroid of the concrete area assumed to be in uniform compression; compressive resistance of a concrete component of a composite column
C_w	= warping torsional constant, mm^6
C_y	= axial compressive load at yield stress
c	= cohesion stress for concrete (1.0 MPa) in accordance with Clause 11.5.2(c) of CAN/CSA-A23.3
c_1	= coefficient used to determine slip resistance
D	= outside diameter of circular sections; diameter of rocker or roller; stiffener factor; dead load

d	= depth; overall depth of a section; diameter of a bolt or stud
d_b	= depth of beam
d_c	= depth of column
E	= elastic modulus of steel (200 000 MPa assumed); earthquake load and effects (see Clause 6.2.1)
E_c	= elastic modulus of concrete
E_c'	= age adjusted effective modulus of electricity of concrete
E_{ct}	= effective modulus of concrete in tension
e	= end distance; lever arm between the compressive resistance, C_r, and the tensile resistance, T_r; length of link in eccentrically braced frames
e'	= lever arm between the compressive resistance, C'_r, of concrete and tensile resistance, T_r, of steel
F	= strength or stress
F_a	= acceleration-based site coefficient (see Clause 27 and the *NBCC*)
F_{cr}	= critical plate-buckling stress in compression, flexure, or shear
F_{cre}	= elastic critical plate-buckling stress in shear
F_{cri}	= inelastic critical plate-buckling stress in shear
F_e	= Euler buckling stress; elastic buckling stress
F_s	= ultimate shear stress
F_{sr}	= allowable stress range in fatigue
F_{srt}	= constant amplitude threshold stress range
F_{st}	= factored axial force in the stiffener
F_u	= specified minimum tensile strength
F_v	= velocity-based site coefficient (see Clause 27 and the *NBCC*)
F_y	= specified minimum yield stress, yield point, or yield strength
F_{ye}	= effective yield stress of section in compression to account for elastic local buckling (see Clause 13.3.5)
F_y'	= yield level, including effect of cold-working
F_{yr}	= specified yield strength of reinforcing steel
f_c'	= specified compressive strength of concrete at 28 days
f_{sr}	= calculated stress range at detail due to passage of the fatigue load
G	= shear modulus of steel (77 000 MPa assumed)
g	= transverse spacing between fastener gauge lines (gauge distance)
H	= weld leg size; permanent load due to lateral earth pressure (see Clause 6.2.1)
h	= clear depth of web between flanges; height of stud; storey height
h_c	= clear depth of column web
h_d	= depth of steel deck
h_s	= storey height
I	= moment of inertia
I_b	= moment of inertia of a beam
I_c	= moment of inertia of a column
I_E	= earthquake importance factor of the structure (see Clause 27 and the *NBCC*)
I_e	= effective moment of inertia of a composite beam
I_g	= moment of inertia of a cover-plated section
I_S	= importance factor for snow load as defined in Table 4.1.6.2 of the *NBCC*
I_s	= moment of inertia of OWSJ or truss

I_t	= transformed moment of inertia of a composite beam
I_w	= importance factor for wind load as defined in Table 4.1.7.1 of the *NBCC*
I_{yc}	= moment of inertia of compression flange about the y-axis (see Clause 13.6(e))
I_{yt}	= moment of inertia of tension flange about the y-axis (see Clause 13.6(e))
J	= St. Venant torsional constant
K	= effective length factor
K_z	= effective length factor for torsional buckling
KL	= effective length
k	= distance from outer face of flange to web-toe of fillet of I-shaped sections; factor as specified in Clause 18.3.2
k_a	= coefficient used in determining inelastic shear resistance
k_b	= buckling coefficient; required stiffness of the bracing assembly
k_s	= mean slip coefficient
k_v	= shear buckling coefficient
L	= length or span; length of longitudinal or flare bevel groove weld; live load; length of connection in direction of loading; centre-to-centre distance between columns in a plate wall; length of member between work points at truss chord centrelines in Clause 13.3.3.
L_c	= length of channel shear connector
L_{cr}	= maximum unbraced length adjacent to a plastic hinge
L_u	= longest unbraced length with which a beam will reach either $M_r = \phi M_p$ or $M_r = \phi M_y$, depending on the class of the cross-section (see Clause 13.6(e))
L_{yr}	= shortest unbraced length with which a singly symmetric beam will undergo elastic lateral-torsional buckling (see Clause 13.6(e))
M	= bending moment in a member or component under specified load
M_a	= factored bending moment at one-quarter point of unbraced segment
M_b	= factored bending moment at mid-point of unbraced segment
M_c	= factored bending moment at three-quarter point of unbraced segment
M_f	= bending moment in a member or component under factored load
M_{f1}	= smaller factored end moment of a beam-column; factored bending moment at a point of concentrated load
M_{f2}	= larger factored end moment of a beam-column
M_{fc}	= bending moment in a girder, under factored load, at theoretical cut-off point
M_{max}	= maximum factored bending moment magnitude in unbraced segment
M_p	= plastic moment resistance
	= ZF_y
M_{pb}	= plastic moment of a beam
M_{pc}	= plastic moment of a column
M_r	= factored moment resistance of a member or component
M_{rc}	= factored moment resistance of a composite beam; factored moment resistance of a column reduced for the presence of an axial load
M_u	= critical elastic moment of a laterally unbraced beam
M_w	= strength reduction factor for multi-orientation fillet welds to account for ductility incompatibility of the individual weld segments
M_y	= yield moment resistance
	= SF_y

M_{fc} = bending moment in a girder, under factored load, at theoretical cut-off point

M_{yr} = yield moment resistance of a singly symmetric beam including the effects of residual stresses (see Clause 13.6(e))

m = number of faying surfaces or shear planes in a bolted joint

= 1.0 for bolts in single shear

= 2.0 for bolts in double shear

N = length of bearing of an applied load; number of passages of moving load

N' = number of passages of moving load at which $F_{sr} = F_{srt}$

N_{fi} = number of cycles that would cause failure at stress range level i

n = number of bolts; number of shear connectors required between the point of maximum positive bending moment and the adjacent point of zero moment; parameter for compressive resistance; number of threads per inch; number of stress range cycles at a given detail for each passage of the moving load; modular ratio, E/E_c

n' = number of shear connectors required between any concentrated load and nearest point of zero moment in a region of positive bending moment

n_s = modular ratio, E/E_c'

n_t = modular ratio, E/E_{ct}

P = force to be developed in a cover plate; pitch of threads; permanent effects caused by prestress (see Clause 6.2.1)

P_f = factored axial force

p = fraction of full shear connection

Q_r = sum of the factored resistances of all shear connectors between points of maximum and zero moment

q_r = factored resistance of a shear connector

q_{rr} = factored resistance of a shear connector in a ribbed slab

q_{rs} = factored resistance of a shear connector in a solid slab

R = end reaction or concentrated transverse load applied to a flexural member; nominal resistance of a member, connection, or structure; transition radius

R_d = ductility-related force modification factor that reflects the capability of a structure to dissipate energy through inelastic behaviour (see Clause 27 and the NBCC)

R_o = overstrength-related force modification factor that accounts for the dependable portion of reserve strength in a structure (see Clause 27 and the NBCC)

R_y = factor applied to F_y to estimate the probable yield stress

r = radius of gyration

r_t = radius of gyration of a compression flange plus one-third of web area in compression due to major axis bending (see Clause 13.6(e)(i))

r_x = radius of gyration of a single-angle member about its geometric axis parallel to the connected leg in Clause 13.3.3

r_y = radius of gyration of a member about its weak axis

r_y' = radius of gyration of a member about its minor principal axis

S = elastic section modulus of a steel section; variable load due to snow (see Clause 6.2.1)

$S_a(0.2)$ = 5% damped spectral response acceleration, expressed as a ratio to gravitational acceleration, for a period of 0.2 seconds (see Clause 27 and the NBCC)

$S_a(1.0)$ = 5% damped spectral response acceleration, expressed as a ratio to gravitational acceleration, for a period of 1 second (see Clause 27 and the NBCC)

S_e = effective section modulus as defined in Clause 13.5(c)

s = centre-to-centre longitudinal spacing (pitch) of any two successive fastener holes; longitudinal stud spacing; vertical spacing of tie bars (see Clause 18.3.1)

T = tensile force in a member or component under specified load; load effects due to contraction, expansion, or deflection (see Clause 6.2.1); period of a structure (see Clause 27 and the *NBCC*)

T_f = tensile force in a member or component under factored load

T_r = factored tensile resistance of a member or component; in composite construction, factored tensile resistance of the steel acting at the centroid of that part of the steel area in tension

T_y = axial tensile load at yield stress

t = thickness; thickness of flange; average flange thickness of channel shear connector

t_b = thickness of beam flange

t_c = concrete or cover slab thickness; thickness of column flange

t_p = thickness of plate

U_t = factor to account for efficiency of the tensile area (see Clause 13.11)

U_1 = factor to account for moment gradient and for second-order effects of axial force acting on the deformed member

U_2 = amplification factor to account for second-order effects of gravity loads acting on the laterally displaced storey

V = shear force in a member or component under specified load

V_f = shear force in a member or component under factored load

V_h = total horizontal shear to be resisted at the junction of the steel section or joist and the slab or steel deck; shear acting at plastic hinge locations when plastic hinging occurs

V_p = plastic shear resistance
  = $0.55wdF_y$

V_r = factored shear resistance of a member or component

V_{re} = probable shear resistance of a steel plate wall

V_s = slip resistance of a bolted joint

V_{st} = factored shear force in column web to be resisted by stiffener

W = wind load

w = web thickness; width of plate; infill plate thickness (see Clause 20)

w' = sum of thickness of column web plus doubler plates

w_c = column web thickness

w_d = average width of flute of steel deck

w_f = width of flare bevel groove weld face

w_n = net width (i.e., gross width less design allowance for holes within the width)

X_u = ultimate strength as rated by the electrode classification number

x = subscript relating to strong axis of a member; distance from flange face to centre of plastic hinge

$\bar{x}$ = eccentricity of the weld with respect to centroid of the element

x_o, y_o = principal coordinates of the shear centre with respect to the centroid of the cross-section

y = subscript relating to weak axis of a member; distance from centroid of cover plate to neutral axis of cover-plated section; distance from centroid of the effective area of concrete slab to elastic neutral axis

Z = plastic section modulus of a steel section

z = subscript related to Z-axis of a member

α = load factor; angle of inclination from vertical (see Clause 20)

α_f = angle between shear friction reinforcement and shear plane in concrete

α_1 = ratio of average stress in rectangular compression block to the specified concrete strength

β = value used to determine bracing stiffness; angle in radians as specified in Clause 18.2.3; coefficient for weak axis bending in beam-columns as specified in Clause 13.8.2

β_x = asymmetry parameter for singly symmetric beams as specified in Clause 13.6(e)

γ = fatigue life constant

γ' = fatigue life constant at which $F_{sr} = F_{srt}$

γ_c = density of concrete

Δ_b = displacement of the bracing system at the point of support under force C_f (may be taken as Δ_o)

Δ_f = relative first-order lateral (translational) displacement of the storey due to factored loads

Δ_o = initial misalignment of the member at a brace point (see Clause 9.2) taken as the maximum tolerance specified in Clause 29.3.7 over the total length between the brace points on either side of the brace being designed

Δ_s = deflection due to shrinkage of concrete

εf = free shrinkage strain of concrete

κ = ratio of the smaller to the larger factored end moment, positive for double curvature and negative for single curvature (see Clauses 13.6 and 13.8)

λ = non-dimensional slenderness parameter in column formula; modification factor for concrete density

λ_p = non-dimensional slenderness parameter as specified in Clause 18.3.2

μ = coefficient of friction for concrete (1.4) in accordance with Clause 11.5.2(c) of CAN/CSA-A23.3

ρ = density of concrete; slenderness ratio

ρ_e = equivalent slenderness ratio of a built-up member

ρ_i = maximum slenderness ratio of the component part of a built-up member between interconnectors

ρ_o = slenderness ratio of a built-up member acting as an integral unit

ρ_v = ratio of shear friction reinforcing steel in concrete extending from the point of zero moment to the point of maximum moment

ΣC_f = sum of factored axial compressive loads of all columns in the storey

ΣV_f = sum of factored lateral loads above the storey; total first-order storey shear

σ = effective normal stress for concrete in accordance with Clause 11.5.3 of CAN/CSA-A23.3

σ_{ct} = tensile stress in concrete

ϕ = resistance factor as defined in Clause 2.1 and specified in Clause 13.1

ω_h = non-dimensional column flexibility parameter for plate walls

ω_L = non-dimensional boundary member flexibility parameter for extreme panels of plate walls

ω_1 = coefficient to determine equivalent uniform bending effect in beam-columns (see Clause 13.8)

ω_2 = coefficient to account for increased moment resistance of a laterally unsupported doubly symmetric beam segment when subject to a moment gradient (see Clause 13.6(a))

ω_3 = coefficient to account for modified moment resistance of a laterally unsupported singly symmetric beam segment when subject to a moment gradient (see Clause 13.6(e))

2.3 Units

Equations and expressions appearing in this Standard are compatible with the following SI (metric) units:
(a) force: N (newtons);
(b) length: mm (millimetres);
(c) moment: N•mm; and
(d) strength or stress: MPa (megapascals).

3 Reference publications

This Standard refers to the following publications, and where such reference is made, it shall be to the edition listed below, including all amendments published thereto.

CSA (Canadian Standards Association)
CSA A23.1/A23.2-09
Concrete materials and methods of concrete construction/methods of test and standard practices for concrete

CAN/CSA-A23.3-04
Design of concrete structures

CAN/CSA-A660-04 (R2009)
Certification of manufacturers of steel building systems

B95-1962 (withdrawn)
Surface Texture (Roughness, Waviness, and Lay)

G40.20-04/G40.21-04 (R2009)
General requirements for rolled or welded structural quality steel/structural quality steel

CAN/CSA-G164-M92 (withdrawn)
Hot Dip Galvanizing of Irregularly Shaped Articles

G189-1966 (withdrawn)
Sprayed Metal Coatings for Atmospheric Corrosion Protection

S136-07
North American specification for the design of cold-formed steel structural members

S304.1-04
Design of masonry structures

W47.1-09
Certification of companies for fusion welding of steel

W48-06
Filler metals and allied materials for metal arc welding

W55.3-08
Certification of companies for resistance welding of steel and aluminum

W59-03 (R2008)
Welded steel construction (metal arc welding)

W178.1-08
Certification of welding inspection organizations

W178.2-08
Certification of welding inspectors

ASTM International (American Society for Testing and Materials)
A 27/A 27M-08
Standard Specification for Steel Castings, Carbon, for General Application

A 108-07
Standard Specification for Steel Bar, Carbon and Alloy, Cold-Finished

A 148/A 148M-08
Standard Specification for Steel Castings, High Strength, for Structural Purposes

A 216/A 216M-08
Standard Specification for Steel Castings, Carbon, Suitable for Fusion Welding, for High-Temperature Service

A 307-07b
Standard Specification for Carbon Steel Bolts and Studs, 60 000 PSI Tensile Strength

A 325-09
Standard Specification for Structural Bolts, Steel, Heat Treated, 120/105 ksi Minimum Tensile Strength

A 325M-09
Standard Specification for Structural Bolts, Steel, Heat Treated 830 MPa Minimum Tensile Strength [Metric]

A 352/A 352M-06
Standard Specification for Steel Castings, Ferritic and Martensitic, for Pressure-Containing Parts, Suitable for Low-Temperature Service

A 490-08b
Standard Specification for Structural Bolts, Alloy Steel, Heat Treated, 150 ksi Minimum Tensile Strength

A 490M-08
Standard Specification for High-Strength Steel Bolts, Classes 10.9 and 10.9.3, for Structural Steel Joints [Metric]

A 514/A 514M-05
Standard Specification for High-Yield-Strength, Quenched and Tempered Alloy Steel Plate, Suitable for Welding

A 521/A 521M-06
Standard Specification for Steel, Closed-Impression Die Forgings for General Industrial Use

A 572/A 572M-07
Standard Specification for High-Strength Low-Alloy Columbium-Vanadium Structural Steel

A 668/A 668M-04
Standard Specification for Steel Forgings, Carbon and Alloy, for General Industrial Use

A 958-00 (2006)
Standard Specification for Steel Castings, Carbon and Alloy, with Tensile Requirements, Chemical Requirements Similar to Standard Wrought Grades

A 992/A 992M-06
Standard Specification for Structural Steel Shapes

A 1011/A 1011M-09a
Standard Specification for Steel, Sheet and Strip, Hot-Rolled, Carbon, Structural, High-Strength Low-Alloy, High-Strength Low-Alloy with Improved Formability, and Ultra-High Strength

F 436-09
Standard Specification for Hardened Steel Washers

F 959-09
Standard Specification for Compressible-Washer-Type Direct Tension Indicators for Use with Structural Fasteners

F 1554-07
Standard Specification for Anchor Bolts, Steel, 36, 55, and 105-ksi Yield Strength

F 1852-08
Standard Specification for "Twist Off" Type Tension Control Structural Bolt/Nut/Washer Assemblies, Steel, Heat Treated, 120/105 ksi Minimum Tensile Strength

F 2280-08
Standard Specification for "Twist Off" Type Tension Control Structural Bolt/Nut/Washer Assemblies, Steel, Heat Treated, 150 ksi Minimum Tensile Strength

CISC (Canadian Institute of Steel Construction)
Code of Standard Practice for Structural Steel (2009)

Crane-Supporting Steel Structures: Design Guide, 2nd ed. (2nd revised printing, January 2009)

Handbook of Steel Construction, 10th ed. (2010)

Hollow Structural Section: Connections and Trusses — A Design Guide, 2nd ed. (June 1997)

Steel Joist Facts, 2nd ed. (1980)

CISC/CPMA (Canadian Institute of Steel Construction/Canadian Paint Manufacturing Association)
Note: *The Canadian Paint Manufacturing Association is now the Canadian Paint and Coatings Association*
1-73a (1975)
A Quick-Drying One-Coat Paint for Use on Structural Steel

2-75 (1975)
A Quick-Drying Primer for Use on Structural Steel

National Research Council Canada
National Building Code of Canada, 2010

User's Guide — NBC 2010: Structural Commentaries (Part 4)

RCSC (Research Council on Structural Connections)
Guide to Design Criteria for Bolted and Riveted Joints, 2nd ed. (2001)

Specification for Structural Joints Using ASTM A325 or A490 Bolts, 2000

SSPC (Society for Protective Coatings)
SP 1 (2004)
Solvent Cleaning

SP 2 (2004)
Hand Tool Cleaning

SP 3 (2004)
Power Tool Cleaning

SP 5/NACE No. 1 (2007)
White Metal Blast Cleaning

SP 6/NACE No. 3 (2007)
Commercial Blast Cleaning

SP 7/NACE No. 4 (2007)
Brush-Off Blast Cleaning

SP 10/NACE No. 2 (2007)
Near-White Blast Cleaning

SP 11 (2004)
Power Tool Cleaning to Bare Metal

SP 12/NACE No. 5
Surface Preparation and Cleaning of Metals by Waterjetting Prior to Recoating

SP 14/NACE No. 8
Industrial Blast Cleaning

Structural Stability Research Council
Guide to Stability Design Criteria for Metal Structures, 5th ed., 1998

Other publications
Frank, K. H. and Fisher, J. W. "Fatigue Strength of Welded Cruciform Joints", *Journal of the Structural Division, ASCE.* Vol.105, ST9, pp. 1727-1740, September 1979.

4 Structural documents

4.1 General
The term "structural documents" may include drawings, specifications, computer output, and electronic and other data.

4.2 Structural design documents

4.2.1
The structural design documents shall show a complete design of the structure with members suitably designated and located, including such dimensions and details as necessary to permit the preparation of fabrication and erection documents. Floor levels, column centres, and offsets shall be dimensioned. Structural design drawings shall be to a scale adequate to convey the required information.

4.2.2
In addition to the information required by the applicable building code, the structural design documents shall include, but not be limited to, the following information, as applicable:
(a) the design standards used;
(b) the material or product standards (see Clause 5);
(c) the design criteria for snow, wind, seismic, and special loads;
(d) the specified live and superimposed dead loads;
(e) the type or types of construction (see Clause 8);
(f) the structural system used for seismic design and the seismic design criteria (see Clause 27);
(g) the requirements for roof and floor diaphragms;

(h)   the design criteria for open-web steel joists (see Clause 16);

(i)   the design criteria for crane-supporting structures (see Annex C);

(j)   all load-resisting elements essential to the integrity of the completed structure and the details necessary to ensure the effectiveness of the load-resisting system in the completed structure;

(k)   the camber of beams, girders, and trusses;

(l)   the governing combinations of shears, moments, axial forces, and torsions to be resisted by the connections;

(m)   the size and location of stiffeners, reinforcement, and bracing required to stabilize compression elements;

(n)   the types of bolts, the pretensioning requirements, and the designation of joints as bearing or slip-critical (see Clause 22.2);

(o)   the type and configuration details of structural connections that are critical for ductile seismic response; and

(p)   the locations and dimensions of protected zones (see Clause 27.1.9).

4.2.3
Revisions to design documents shall be clearly indicated and dated.

4.2.4
Provided that all requirements for the structural steel are shown on the structural documents, architectural, electrical, and mechanical documents may be used as supplements to the structural documents to define the detail configurations and construction information.

4.3 Fabrication and erection documents

4.3.1 Connection design details
Connection design details shall be prepared before the preparation of shop details and submitted to the structural designer for confirmation that the intent of the design is met. Connection design details shall provide details of standard and non-standard connections and other data necessary for the preparation of shop details. Connection design details shall be referenced to the design documents, erection drawings, or both.

4.3.2 Shop details
Shop details shall
(a)   be prepared before fabrication and submitted to the structural designer for review;
(b)   provide complete information for the fabrication of various members and components of the structure, including the
    (i)   required material and product standards;
    (ii)   location, type, and size of all mechanical fasteners;
    (iii)   bolt installation requirements;
    (iv)   welds; and
(c)   provide the locations and dimensions of the protected zones and a complete description of the fabrication operations that are prohibited in protected zones.

4.3.3 Erection diagrams
Erection diagrams shall be submitted to the designer for review. Erection diagrams are general arrangement drawings that should show the principal dimensions of the structure, piece marks, sizes of the members, all steel load-resisting elements essential to the integrity of the completed structure, size and type of bolts, field welds, bolt installation requirements, elevations of column bases, all necessary dimensions and details for setting anchor rods, and any other information necessary for the assembly of the structure. Erection diagrams shall provide the locations and dimensions of the protected zones and a complete description of the erection operations that are prohibited in protected zones.

4.3.4 Erection procedures

Erection procedures shall outline the construction methods, erection sequence, temporary bracing requirements, and other engineering details necessary for shipping, erecting, and maintaining the stability of the steel frame. Erection procedures shall be supplemented by drawings and sketches that identify the location of permanent and temporary load-resisting elements essential to the integrity of the partially completed structure. Erection procedures shall be submitted for review when so specified.

4.3.5 Fieldwork details

Fieldwork details shall be submitted to the designer for review. Fieldwork details shall provide complete information for modifying fabricated members in the shop or on the job site. All operations required to modify the member shall be shown on the fieldwork details. If extra materials are necessary to make modifications, shop details shall be required.

5 Material — Standards and identification

5.1 Standards

5.1.1 General

Acceptable material and product standards and specifications for use under this Standard are specified in Clauses 5.1.3 to 5.1.10. Materials and products other than those specified may be used if approved. Approval shall be based on published specifications that establish the properties, characteristics, and suitability of the material or product to the extent and in the manner of those covered in specified standards and specifications.

5.1.2 Strength levels

The yield strength, F_y, and the tensile strength, F_u, used as the basis for design shall be the specified minimum values as given in the material and product standards and specifications. The levels reported on mill test certificates shall not be used as the basis for design.

5.1.3 Structural steel

Structural steel shall meet the requirements of CSA G40.20/G40.21, ASTM A 572, or ASTM A 992/A 992M.

5.1.4 Sheet steel

Sheet steel shall meet the requirements of ASTM A 1011/A 1011M.

Other standards for structural sheet are listed in Section A2 of CSA S136. Only structural-quality sheet standards that specify chemical composition and mechanical properties shall be acceptable for conformance with this Standard. Mill test certificates that list the chemical composition and the mechanical properties shall be available, upon request, in accordance with Clause 5.2.1(a).

5.1.5 Cast steel

Cast steel shall meet the design requirements for weldability, strength, ductility, toughness, and surface finish.
Note: *Reference standards include ASTM A 27/A 27M, ASTM A 148/A 148M, ASTM A 216/A 216M, ASTM A 352/A 352M, and ASTM A 958.*

5.1.6 Forged steel

Forged steel shall meet the requirements of ASTM A 521/A 521M or ASTM A 668/A 668M.

5.1.7 Bolts and bolt assemblies

Bolts and bolt assemblies shall meet the requirements of ASTM A 307, ASTM A 325, ASTM A 325M, ASTM A 490, ASTM A 490M, ASTM F 1852, or ASTM F 2280.

Note: *Before specifying metric bolts, the designer should check on their availability in the quantities required.*

5.1.8 Welding electrodes

Welding electrodes shall meet the requirements of CSA W48, as applicable.

5.1.9 Studs

Studs shall meet the requirements of ASTM A 108.

5.1.10 Anchor rods

Anchor rods shall meet the requirements of CSA G40.20/G40.21 or ASTM F 1554.

5.2 Identification

5.2.1 Methods

The specifications (including type or grade, if applicable) of the materials and products used shall be identified by the following means, except as specified in Clauses 5.2.2 and 5.2.3:

(a) mill test certificates or producer's certificates satisfactorily correlated to the materials or products to which they pertain; and

(b) legible markings on the material or product made by its producer in accordance with the applicable material or product standard.

5.2.2 Unidentified structural steel

Unidentified structural steel shall not be used unless approved by the building designer. If the use of unidentified steel is authorized, F_y shall be taken as 210 MPa and F_u shall be taken as 380 MPa.

5.2.3 Tests to establish identification

Unidentified structural steel may be tested to establish identification when permitted by the building designer. Testing shall be done by an approved testing agency in accordance with CSA G40.20. The test results, taking into account both mechanical properties and chemical composition, shall form the basis for classifying the steel as to specification. Once classified, the specified minimum values for steel of that specification grade shall be used as the basis for design (see Clause 5.1.2).

5.2.4 Affidavit

The fabricator, if requested, shall provide an affidavit stating that the materials and products that have been used in fabrication conform to the applicable material or product standards called for by the design drawings or specifications.

6 Design requirements

6.1 General

6.1.1 Limit states

Steel structures designed in accordance with this Standard shall be safe from collapse during construction and designed to be safe and serviceable during the useful life of the structure. Limit states define the various types of collapse and unserviceability that are to be avoided. Those concerning safety are called the ultimate limit states (strength, overturning, sliding, and fracture) or the fatigue limit state (crack propagation), and those concerning serviceability are called the serviceability limit states (deflections, vibration, and permanent deformation). The object of limit states design calculations is to keep the probability of reaching a limit state below a certain value previously established for the given type of structure. This is achieved in this Standard by the use of load factors applied to the specified loads (see Article 4.1.2.1 of the *National Building Code of Canada* [*NBCC*]) and resistance factors applied to the specified resistances (see Clause 13 and Annex B).

The various limit states are specified in Clause 6. Some of these relate to the specified loads and others to the factored loads. Camber, provisions for expansion and contraction, and corrosion protection are further design requirements related to serviceability and durability. All limit states shall be considered in the design.

6.1.2 Structural integrity

The general arrangement of the structural system and the connection of its members shall be designed to provide resistance to disproportionate collapse as a consequence of local failure. The requirements of this Standard generally provide a satisfactory level of structural integrity for steel structures.

Note: *Further guidance can be found in Commentary I,* User's Guide — NBC 2010: Structural Commentaries *(Part 4).*

6.2 Loads

6.2.1 Specified loads

Except as provided for in Clause 7.1, the loads and influences specified in Article 4.1.2.1 of the *NBCC* shall be considered in the design of structural steelwork, taking into consideration that the regulatory authority might specify other loads in some circumstances.

6.2.2 Importance factors based on use and occupancy

The specified snow, wind, and earthquake loads shall be multiplied by the importance factors for the different importance categories for buildings in accordance with Article 4.1.2.1 of the *NBCC*. For buildings having a Low Importance Category, the factor of 0.8 for the ultimate limit states may be applied to the live load, *L*.

6.3 Requirements under specified loads

6.3.1 Deflection

6.3.1.1

Steel members and frames shall be proportioned so that deflections are within acceptable limits for the nature of the materials to be supported and for the intended use and occupancy. Consideration shall be given to the differential deflections of adjacent parallel framing members in the same plane.

Note: *In the absence of a more detailed evaluation, see Annex D for recommended values for deflections.*

6.3.1.2

Roofs shall be designed to withstand any additional loads likely to occur as a result of ponding (see also Clause 6.2.1).

Note: *Further guidance can be found in Commentary I,* User's Guide — NBC 2010: Structural Commentaries *(Part 4).*

6.3.2 Camber

6.3.2.1

Camber of beams, trusses, or girders, if necessary, shall be stipulated on the design drawings. Generally, trusses and crane girders with a span of 25 m or greater should be cambered for approximately the dead-plus-half-live-load deflection.

Note: *See Clause 16 for requirements for open-web joists, Clause 15 for requirements for trusses, and Clause 28.6 for fabrication tolerances.*

6.3.2.2

Any special camber requirements necessary to bring a loaded member into proper relation with the work of other trades shall be stipulated on the design drawings.

Note: *See also Clause 6.3.1.1. See Clause 16.12.2.5 for maximum deviation in elevation between adjacent joists.*

6.3.3 Dynamic effects

6.3.3.1

Suitable provision shall be made in the design for the effect of live loads that induce impact, vibration, or both. In severe cases, e.g., structural supports for heavy machinery that causes substantial impact or vibration when in operation, the possibility of harmonic resonance, fatigue, or unacceptable vibration shall be investigated.

6.3.3.2

Special consideration shall be given to floor systems susceptible to vibration, e.g., large open floor areas free of partitions, to ensure that such vibration is acceptable for the intended use and occupancy.

Note: *For further information, see Annex E.*

6.3.3.3

Unusually flexible structures (generally those whose ratio of height to effective resisting width exceeds 4:1) shall be investigated for lateral vibrations under dynamic wind load. Lateral accelerations of the structure shall be checked to ensure that such accelerations are acceptable for the intended use and occupancy.

Note: *Information on lateral accelerations under dynamic wind loads can be found in Commentary I, User's Guide — NBC 2010: Structural Commentaries (Part 4).*

6.3.4 Resistance to fatigue

Structural steelwork shall be designed to resist the effects of fatigue under specified loads in accordance with Clause 26.

6.4 Requirements under factored loads

6.4.1 Strength

Structural steelwork shall be proportioned to resist moments and forces resulting from the application of the factored loads acting in the most critical combination, taking into account the resistance factors specified in Clause 13.1.

6.4.2 Overturning

The building or structure shall be designed to resist overturning resulting from the application of the factored loads acting in the most critical combination, taking into account the importance category of the building as specified in Clause 6.2.2 and the resistance factors specified in Clause 13.1.

6.5 Expansion and contraction

Suitable provision shall be made for expansion and contraction commensurate with the service and erection conditions of the structure.

6.6 Corrosion protection

6.6.1

Steelwork shall have sufficient corrosion protection to minimize any corrosion likely to occur in the service environment.

6.6.2

Interiors of buildings conditioned for human comfort may be generally assumed to be non-corrosive environments; however, the need for corrosion protection shall be assessed, and protection shall be furnished in those buildings where it is deemed to be necessary.

6.6.3

Corrosion protection of the inside surfaces of enclosed spaces permanently sealed from any external source of oxygen shall not be necessary.

6.6.4

The minimum required thickness of steelwork situated in a non-corrosive environment and therefore not requiring corrosion protection shall be in accordance with Clause 11.

6.6.5

Corrosion protection shall be provided by means of suitable alloying elements in the steel, by protective coatings, or by other effective means, either singly or in combination.

6.6.6

Localized corrosion likely to occur from trapped water, excessive condensation, or other factors shall be minimized by suitable design and detail. Where necessary, positive means of drainage shall be provided.

6.6.7

If the corrosion protection specified for steelwork exposed to the weather, or to other environments in which progressive corrosion can occur, is likely to require maintenance or renewal during the service life of the structure, the steelwork so protected, exclusive of fill plates and shims, shall have a minimum thickness of 4.5 mm.

6.7 Requirements under fire conditions

Structural steelwork shall be designed using one of the methods specified in Annex K.

Note: *Qualification testing (see Annex K) complies with the "acceptable solutions" in the NBCC (Division B, Acceptable Solutions, Part 3, Fire Protection, Occupant Safety and Accessibility). Engineering analysis (see Annex K) is an "alternative solution" that complies with the requirements of the NBCC (Division A, Compliance, Objectives and Functional Statements).*

6.8 Brittle fracture

The risk of brittle fracture in steel structures subjected to dynamic tensile stresses at low temperatures (during both construction and service life) shall be assessed.

Note: *See Annex L for guidance on material selection and details to minimize the risk of brittle fracture.*

7 Factored loads and safety criterion

7.1 Safety during erection and construction

Suitable provision shall be made for loads imposed on the steel structure during its erection. During subsequent construction, suitable provision shall be made to support the construction loads on the steel structure with an adequate margin of safety.

7.2 Safety criterion and effect of factored loads for the ultimate limit states

7.2.1

The structural steelwork shall be designed to have sufficient strength or stability, or both, such that factored resistance is greater than or equal to the effect of factored loads, as follows:

$$\phi R \geq \Sigma \alpha_i S_i$$

where the factored resistance is determined in accordance with the applicable clauses of this Standard, and the effect of factored loads for the ultimate limit states is determined in accordance with Division B, Article 4.1.3.2 of the *NBCC*.

7.2.2

The effect of factored loads in force units shall be determined from the structural effect due to the specified loads, including importance factors due to use and occupancy (see Clause 6.2), multiplied by the load factors, α, for load combination cases in accordance with Division B, Article 4.1.3.2 of the *NBCC*.

8 Analysis of structure

8.1 General

In proportioning the structure to meet the design requirements of Clause 6, the methods of analysis specified in Clause 8 shall be used. The distribution of internal forces and bending moments shall be determined both under the specified loads to satisfy the requirements of serviceability and fatigue specified in Clause 6 and under the factored loads to satisfy strength and overturning requirements specified in Clause 7.

8.2 Types of construction

8.2.1 General

Three basic types of construction and associated design assumptions, i.e., "rigidly connected," "simple," and "semi-rigid" (see Clauses 8.2.2 to 8.2.4) may be used for all or part of a structure under this Standard. The distribution of internal forces and bending moments throughout the structure shall depend on the type or types of construction chosen and the forces to be resisted.

8.2.2 Rigidly connected and continuous construction

In this construction, the beams, girders, and trusses are rigidly connected to other frame members or are continuous over supports. Connections shall be generally designed to resist the bending moments and internal forces calculated by assuming that the angles between intersecting members remain unchanged as the structure is loaded.

8.2.3 Simple construction

Simple construction assumes that the ends of beams, girders, and trusses are free to rotate under load in the plane of loading. Resistance to lateral loads, including stability effects, shall be ensured by a suitable system of bracing or plate walls or by the design of part of the structure as rigidly connected or semi-rigid construction.

8.2.4 Semi-rigid (partially restrained) construction

8.2.4.1

In this construction, the angles between connected members change under applied bending moments and redistribute the moments between members while maintaining sufficient capacity to resist lateral loads and to provide adequate stability of the framework in accordance with Clause 8.4.

8.2.4.2

The design and construction of semi-rigid frameworks shall meet the following requirements:

(a) The positive and negative moment/rotation response of the connections up to their maximum capacity shall have been established by test and either published in the technical literature or be available from a reputable testing facility.

(b) The design of the structure shall be based on either linear analysis employing the secant stiffness of connections at ultimate load or incremental analyses following the non-linear test response of the connections.

(c) Consideration shall be given to the effects of repeated vertical and horizontal loading and load reversals, with particular regard to incremental strain in connections and low-cycle fatigue.

8.3 Analysis methods

8.3.1 Elastic analysis

Under a particular loading combination, the forces and moments throughout all or part of the structure may be determined by an analysis that assumes that individual members behave elastically.

8.3.2 Plastic analysis

Under a particular loading combination, the forces and moments throughout all or part of the structure may be determined by a plastic analysis, provided that

(a) the steel used has $F_y \leq 0.85 F_u$ and exhibits the stress-strain characteristics necessary to achieve moment redistribution;

(b) the width-to-thickness ratios meet the requirements of Class 1 sections as specified in Clause 11.2;

(c) the members are braced laterally in accordance with the requirements of Clause 13.7;

(d) web stiffeners are supplied on a member at a point of load application where a plastic hinge would form;

(e) splices in beams or columns are designed to transmit 1.1 times the maximum calculated moment under factored loads at the splice location or $0.25M_p$, whichever is greater;

(f) members are not subject to repeated heavy impact or fatigue; and

(g) the influence of inelastic deformation on the strength of the structure is taken into account (see Clause 8.4).

8.4 Stability effects

8.4.1

The translational load effects produced by notional lateral loads, applied at each storey, equal to 0.005 times the factored gravity loads contributed by that storey, shall be added to the lateral loads for each load combination. The notional lateral loads shall be applied in both orthogonal directions independently when the three-dimensional effects of loading are included in the analysis of the structure.

8.4.2

The analyses referred to in Clause 8.3 shall include the sway effects in each storey produced by the vertical loads acting on the structure in its displaced configuration. The second-order effects that are due to the relative translational displacement (sway) of the ends of a member shall be determined from a second-order analysis. Elastic second-order effects may be accounted for by amplifying translational load effects obtained from a first-order elastic analysis by the factor

$$U_2 = \frac{1}{1 - \left[\dfrac{\Sigma C_f \Delta_f}{\Sigma V_f h} \right]}$$

Note: *For combinations including seismic loads, U_2, see Clause 27.1.8.2.*

9 Stability of structures and members

9.1 Stability of structures

The structural system shall be adequate to
(a) resist the forces caused by factored loads;
(b) transfer the factored loads to the foundations;
(c) transfer forces from walls, floors, or roofs acting as shear-resisting elements or diaphragms to adjacent lateral-load-resisting elements; and
(d) resist torsional effects.
    (See also Clause 8.4.)

9.2 Stability of members

9.2.1 Initial misalignment at brace point

The initial misalignment of the member at a brace point, Δ_o, shall be taken as the maximum tolerance specified in Clause 29.3 over the total length between the brace points on either side of the brace being designed.

9.2.2 Displacement of bracing systems

The displacement of the bracing system at the brace point, Δ_b, is the sum of the brace deformation, the brace connection deformation, and the brace support displacement. This displacement is due to the brace force and any other forces acting on the brace and shall be calculated in the direction perpendicular to the braced member at the brace point.

9.2.3 Function of bracing

Bracing systems provide lateral support to columns, the compression flange of beams and girders, or the compression chords of joists or trusses.

    Bracing systems, including bracing members and their connections and supports, shall be proportioned to resist the forces that develop at the brace points and limit the lateral displacement of the brace points.

    Bracing for beams shall provide lateral restraint to the compression flange, except that at cantilevered ends of beams and beams subject to double curvature, the restraint shall be provided at both top and bottom flanges unless otherwise accounted for in the design.

9.2.4 Twisting and lateral displacements

Twisting and lateral displacements shall be prevented at the supports of a member or element unless accounted for in the design.

9.2.5 Simplified analysis

Bracing systems shall be proportioned to have a strength perpendicular to the longitudinal axis of the braced member in the plane of buckling equal to at least 0.02 times the factored compressive force at each brace point in the member or element being braced, unless a detailed analysis is carried out in accordance with Clause 9.2.6 to determine the appropriate strength and stiffness of the bracing system. Any other forces acting on the bracing member shall also be taken into account. The displacement Δ_b shall not exceed Δ_o.

9.2.6 Detailed analysis

9.2.6.1 Second-order method

Forces acting in the member bracing system and its deformations shall be determined by means of a second-order elastic analysis of the member and its bracing system. This analysis shall include the most critical initial deformed configuration of the member and shall consider forces due to external loads. In the analysis, hinges may be assumed at brace points in the member or element being braced.

The displacement Δ_b shall not exceed Δ_o unless a greater value can be justified by analysis.

9.2.6.2 Direct method

Unless a second-order analysis is carried out in accordance with Clause 9.2.6.1 or a simplified analysis is carried out in accordance with Clause 9.2.5, bracing systems shall be proportioned at each brace point to have a factored resistance in the direction perpendicular to the longitudinal axis of the braced member in the plane of buckling equal to at least

$$P_b = \frac{\beta[\Delta_o + \Delta_b]C_f}{L}$$

where

P_b = force used to design the bracing system (when two or more points are braced, the forces P_b alternate in direction)

β = 2, 3, 3.41, 3.63, or 4 for 1, 2, 3, 4, or more equally spaced braces, respectively, unless a lesser value can be justified by the analysis

Δ_o = initial misalignment

Δ_b = displacement of the bracing system, assumed to be equal to Δ_o for the initial calculation of P_b

C_f = maximum factored compression in the segments bound by the brace points on either side of the brace point under consideration

L = length between braces

For flexural members, P_b shall be increased, as appropriate, when loads are applied above the shear centre or for beams in double curvature.

After P_b and any other forces acting on the bracing member are applied, the calculated displacement of the bracing system, Δ_b, shall not exceed Δ_o unless justified by analysis.

9.2.7 Slabs or decks

When bracing of the compression flange is affected by a slab or deck, the slab or deck and the means by which the calculated bracing forces are transmitted between the flange or chord and the slab or deck shall be adequate to resist a force in the plane of the slab or deck. This force, which shall be taken as at least 0.05 times the maximum force in the flange or chord unless a lesser amount can be justified by analysis, shall be considered to be uniformly distributed along the length of the compression flange or chord.

9.2.8 Accumulation of forces

Consideration shall be given to the probable accumulation of forces, C_f, when the bracing system restrains more than one member. When members are erected with random out-of-straightness, the initial misalignment may be taken as

$$(0.2+0.8/\sqrt{n})\Delta_o$$

where

n = number of members or elements being braced

This reduction shall not be applied when member initial misalignments are dependent on each other and are likely to be in the same direction and of the same magnitude.

9.2.9 Torsion

Bracing systems for beams, girders, and columns designed to resist loads causing torsion shall be proportioned in accordance with Clause 14.10. Special consideration shall be given to the connection of asymmetric sections such as channels, angles, and Z-sections.

10 Design lengths and slenderness ratios

10.1 Simple span flexural members

Beams, girders, and trusses may be designed on the basis of simple spans, whose length may be taken as the distance between the centres of gravity of supporting members. Alternatively, the span length of beams and girders may be taken as the actual length of such members measured between centres of end connections. The length of trusses designed as simple spans may be taken as the distance between the extreme working points of the system of triangulation employed. The design of columns or other supporting members shall provide for the effect of any significant moment or eccentricity arising from the manner in which a beam, girder, or truss is connected or supported.

10.2 Continuous span flexural members

Beams, girders, or trusses having full or partial end restraint due to continuity or cantilever action shall be proportioned to carry all moments, shears, and other forces at any section, assuming the span, in general, to be the distance between the centres of gravity of the supporting members. Supporting members shall be proportioned to carry all moments, shears, and other forces induced by the continuity of the supported beam, girder, or truss.

10.3 Members in compression

10.3.1 General

A member in compression shall be designed on the basis of its effective length, KL (the product of the effective length factor, K, and the unbraced length, L).

Unless otherwise specified in this Standard, the unbraced length, L, shall be taken as the length of the compression member between the centres of restraining members. The unbraced length may differ for different cross-sectional axes of a compression member. At the bottom storey of a multi-storey structure or for a single-storey structure, L shall be taken as the length from the top of the base plate to the centre of restraining members at the next higher level.

The effective length factor, K, depends on the potential failure modes, whether by bending in-plane or buckling, as specified in Clauses 10.3.2 and 10.3.3.

Note: *See also Clause 9 on the effectiveness of the brace or support point.*

10.3.2 Failure mode involving bending in-plane

The effective length shall be taken as the actual length ($K = 1.0$) for beam-columns that would fail by in-plane bending, provided that, when applicable, the sway effects, including notional load effects, are included in the analysis of the structure to determine the end moments and forces acting on the beam-columns.

10.3.3 Failure mode involving buckling

The effective length for axially loaded columns that would fail by buckling and for beam-columns that would fail by out-of-plane (lateral-torsional) buckling shall be based on the rotational and translational restraint afforded at the ends of the unbraced length (see Annexes F and G).

10.4 Slenderness ratios

10.4.1 General

The slenderness ratio of a member in compression shall be taken as the ratio of the effective length, KL, to the corresponding radius of gyration, r. The slenderness ratio of a member in tension shall be taken as the ratio of the unbraced length, L, to the corresponding radius of gyration.

10.4.2 Maximum slenderness ratio

10.4.2.1
The slenderness ratio of a member in compression shall not exceed 200.

10.4.2.2
Except as specified in Clauses 15.2.6 and 16.5.6.1, the slenderness ratio of a member in tension shall not exceed 300. This limit may be waived if other means are provided to control flexibility, sag, vibration, and slack in a manner commensurate with the service conditions of the structure, or if it can be shown that such factors are not detrimental to the performance of the structure or of the assembly of which the member is a part.

11 Width (or diameter)-to-thickness — Elements in compression

11.1 Classification of sections

11.1.1
For the purposes of this Standard, structural sections shall be designated as Class 1, 2, 3, or 4, depending on the maximum width (or diameter)-to-thickness ratios of the elements subject to compression, and as otherwise specified in Clauses 11.1.2 and 11.1.3, as follows:
(a) Class 1 sections permit attainment of the plastic moment and subsequent redistribution of the bending moment;
(b) Class 2 sections permit attainment of the plastic moment but need not allow for subsequent moment redistribution;
(c) Class 3 sections permit attainment of the yield moment; and
(d) Class 4 sections generally have elastic local buckling of elements in compression as the limit state of structural resistance.

11.1.2
Class 1 sections, when subject to flexure, shall have an axis of symmetry in the plane of loading and, when subject to axial compression, shall be doubly symmetric.

11.1.3
Class 2 sections, when subject to flexure, shall have an axis of symmetry in the plane of loading unless the effects of asymmetry of the section are included in the analysis.

11.2 Maximum width (or diameter)-to-thickness ratios of elements subject to compression
The maximum width (or diameter)-to-thickness ratios of elements subject to axial compression shall be as specified in Table 1 and those of elements subject to flexural compression shall be as specified in Table 2, for the specified section classification.

Sections that exceed the limits presented in Table 1 or Table 2 shall be classified as Class 4 sections. The factored axial compressive resistance of Class 4 sections shall be calculated in accordance with Clause 13.3.5. The factored bending resistance of Class 4 sections shall be calculated in accordance with Clause 13.5.

11.3 Width and thickness

11.3.1
For elements supported along only one edge parallel to the direction of compressive force, the width, b_{el}, shall be taken as follows:
(a) plates: shall be the distance from the free edge to the first row of fasteners or line of welds;
(b) legs of angles, flanges of channels and Z's, and stems of T's: the full nominal dimension; and
(c) flanges of beams and T's: one-half of the full nominal dimension.

11.3.2
For elements supported along two edges parallel to the direction of compressive force, the width shall be taken as follows:
(a) flange or diaphragm plates in built-up sections: the width, b_{el}, shall be the distance between adjacent lines of fasteners or lines of welds;
(b) flanges, b_{el}, and webs, h, of rectangular hollow sections (HSS) shall be the nominal outside dimension less four times the wall thickness;
(c) webs of built-up sections: the width, h, shall be the distance between adjacent lines of fasteners or the clear distance between flanges when welds are used; and
(d) webs of hot-rolled sections: the width, h, shall be the clear distance between flanges.

11.3.3
The thickness of elements, t or w, shall be taken as the nominal thickness. For tapered flanges of rolled sections, the thickness shall be taken as the nominal thickness halfway between a free edge and the corresponding face of the web.

12 Gross and net areas

12.1 Application
Members in tension shall be proportioned on the basis of the areas associated with the potential failure modes. Members in compression shall be proportioned on the basis of the gross area associated with the potential failure mode.
Note: *For beams and girders, see Clause 14.*

12.2 Gross area
Gross area shall be calculated by summing the products of the thickness and the gross width of each element (flange, web, leg, plate), as measured normal to the axis of the member.

12.3 Net area

12.3.1 General
The net area, A_n, shall be determined by summing the critical net areas, A_n, of each segment along a potential path of minimum resistance calculated as follows:
(a) for a segment normal to the force (i.e., in direct tension):

$$A_n = w_n t$$

(b) for a segment inclined to the force between openings (e.g., bolt holes) but not parallel to the force:

$$A_n = w_n t + \frac{s^2 t}{4g}$$

12.3.2 Allowance for bolt holes

In calculating w_n, the width of bolt holes shall be taken as 2 mm larger than the specified hole dimension. If drilled holes are used, this allowance may be waived.

12.3.3 Effective net area — Shear lag

12.3.3.1

When fasteners transmit load to each of the cross-sectional elements of a member in tension in proportion to their respective areas, the effective net area shall be taken as the net area, i.e., $A_{ne} = A_n$.

12.3.3.2

When bolts transmit load to some but not all of the cross-sectional elements and when the critical net area includes the net area of unconnected elements, the effective net area shall be taken as follows:

(a) for WWF, W, M, or S shapes with flange widths not less than two-thirds the depth, and for structural tees cut from these shapes, when only the flanges are connected with three or more transverse lines of fasteners:

$$A_{ne} = 0.90A_n$$

(b) for angles connected by only one leg with
(i)   four or more transverse lines of fasteners:

$$A_{ne} = 0.80A_n$$

(ii) fewer than four transverse lines of fasteners:

$$A_{ne} = 0.60A_n$$

(c) for all other structural shapes connected with
(i)   three or more transverse lines of fasteners:

$$A_{ne} = 0.85A_n$$

(ii) two transverse lines of fasteners:

$$A_{ne} = 0.75A_n$$

12.3.3.3

When a tension load is transmitted by welds, the effective net area, A_{ne}, shall be computed as the sum of the effective net areas of the elements, A_{n1}, A_{n2}, and A_{n3}, as applicable, but shall not exceed A_g. The net areas of the connected plate elements shall be defined as follows:

(a) for elements connected by transverse welds, A_{n1}:

$$A_{n1} = wt$$

(b) for elements connected by longitudinal welds along two parallel edges, A_{n2}:
(i)   when $L \geq 2w$:

$$A_{n2} = 1.00wt$$

(ii) when $2w > L \geq w$:

$$A_{n2} = 0.50wt + 0.25Lt$$

(iii) when $w > L$:

$$A_{n2} = 0.75Lt$$

where

L = average length of welds on the two edges

w = plate width (distance between welds)

(c) for elements connected by a single longitudinal weld, A_{n3}:

(i) when $L \geq w$:

$$A_{n3} = \left(1 - \frac{\overline{x}}{L}\right)wt$$

(ii) when $w > L$:

$$A_{n3} = 0.50Lt$$

where

$\overline{x}$ = eccentricity of the weld with respect to centroid of the connected element

L = length of weld in the direction of the loading

The outstanding leg of an angle shall be considered connected by the (single) line of weld along the heel.

12.3.3.4

Larger values of the effective net area may be used if justified by test or rational analysis.

12.3.4 Angles

For angles, the gross width shall be the sum of the widths of the legs minus the thickness. The gauge for holes in opposite legs shall be the sum of the gauges from the heel of the angle minus the thickness.

12.3.5 Plug or slot welds

In calculating the net area of a member across plug or slot welds, the weld metal shall not be taken as adding to the net area.

12.4 Pin-connected members in tension

12.4.1

In pin-connected members in tension, the net area, A_n, across the pin hole, normal to the axis of the member, shall be at least 1.33 times the cross-sectional area of the body of the member. The net area of any section on either side of the axis of the member, measured at an angle of 45° or less to the axis of the member, shall be not less than 0.9 times the cross-sectional area of the body of the member.

12.4.2

The distance from the edge of the pin hole to the edge of the member, measured transverse to the axis of the member, shall not exceed four times the thickness of the material at the pin hole.

12.4.3

The diameter of a pin hole shall be not more than 1 mm larger than the diameter of the pin.

13 Member and connection resistance

13.1 Resistance factors
Unless otherwise specified, resistance factors, ϕ, applied to resistances specified in this Standard shall be taken as follows:
(a)   structural steel: $\phi = 0.90$ and $\phi_u = 0.75$;
(b)   reinforcing steel bars: $\phi_r = 0.85$;
(c)   bolts: $\phi_b = 0.80$;
(d)   shear connectors: $\phi_{sc} = 0.80$;
(e)   beam web bearing, interior: $\phi_{bi} = 0.80$ (see Clause 14.3.2);
(f)   beam web bearing, end: $\phi_{be} = 0.75$ (see Clause 14.3.2);
(g)   bearing of bolts on steel: $\phi_{br} = 0.80$;
(h)   weld metal: $\phi_w = 0.67$;
(i)   anchor rods: $\phi_{ar} = 0.67$; and
(j)   concrete: $\phi_c = 0.65$.
The factored resistances so determined, in order to meet the strength requirements of this Standard, shall be greater than or equal to the effect of factored loads determined in accordance with Clause 7.2.

13.2 Axial tension
The factored tensile resistance, T_r, developed by a member subjected to an axial tensile force shall be taken as follows:
(a)   the least of
    (i) $T_r = \phi A_g F_y$;
    (ii) T_r = resistance determined using Clause 13.11; and
    (iii) $T_r = \phi_u A_{ne} F_u$; and
(b)   for pin connections: $T_r = 0.75 \phi A_n F_y$.

13.3 Axial compression

13.3.1 Flexural buckling of doubly symmetric shapes
The factored axial compressive resistance, C_r, of doubly symmetric shapes meeting the requirements of Table 1 shall be taken as

$$C_r = \phi A F_y \left(1 + \lambda^{2n}\right)^{-1/n}$$

where

n = 1.34 for hot-rolled, fabricated structural sections and hollow structural sections manufactured in accordance with CSA G40.20, Class C (cold-formed non-stress-relieved)

       = 2.24 for doubly symmetric welded three-plate members with flange edges oxy-flame-cut and hollow structural sections manufactured in accordance with CSA G40.20, Class H (hot-formed or cold-formed stress-relieved)

λ $= \sqrt{\dfrac{F_y}{F_e}}$

F_e $= \dfrac{\pi^2 E}{\left(\dfrac{KL}{r}\right)^2}$

   Doubly symmetric shapes that can be governed by torsional buckling shall also meet the requirements of Clause 13.3.2.

13.3.2 Flexural, torsional, or flexural-torsional buckling

The factored compressive resistance, C_r, of asymmetric, singly symmetric, and cruciform or other doubly symmetric sections not covered under Clause 13.3.1 shall be computed using the expressions given in Clause 13.3.1 with a value of $n = 1.34$ and the value of F_e taken as follows:

(a) for doubly symmetric sections (e.g., cruciform) and axisymmetric sections (e.g., Z-sections), the least of F_{ex}, F_{ey}, and F_{ez};

(b) for singly symmetric sections (e.g., double angles, channels, and T-sections), with the y-axis taken as the axis of symmetry, the lesser of F_{ex} and F_{eyz}

where

$$F_{eyz} = \frac{F_{ey} + F_{ez}}{2\Omega}\left[1 - \sqrt{1 - \frac{4 F_{ey} F_{ez} \Omega}{\left(F_{ey} + F_{ez}\right)^2}}\right]$$

(c) for asymmetric sections (e.g., bulb angles), the smallest root of

$$\left(F_e - F_{ex}\right)\left(F_e - F_{ey}\right)\left(F_e - F_{ez}\right) - F_e^2\left(F_e - F_{ey}\right)\left(\frac{x_o}{\bar{r}_o}\right)^2 - F_e^2(F_e - F_{ex})\left(\frac{y_o}{\bar{r}_o}\right)^2 = 0$$

where
F_{ex}, F_{ey}, and F_{ez} are calculated with respect to the principal axes

$$F_{ex} = \frac{\pi^2 E}{\left(\dfrac{K_x L_x}{r_x}\right)^2}$$

$$F_{ey} = \frac{\pi^2 E}{\left(\dfrac{K_y L_y}{r_y}\right)^2}$$

$$F_{ez} = \left(\frac{\pi^2 E C_w}{\left(K_z L_z\right)^2} + GJ\right)\frac{1}{A\bar{r}_o^2}$$

where

K_z = effective length factor for torsional buckling, conservatively taken as 1.0

$$\bar{r}_o^2 = x_o^2 + y_o^2 + r_x^2 + r_y^2$$

$$\Omega = 1 - \left[\frac{x_o^2 + y_o^2}{\bar{r}_o^2}\right]$$

where

x_o, y_o = principal coordinates of the shear centre with respect to the centroid of the cross-section

Note: *For equal-leg double angles connected back-to-back to a common gusset plate, flexural-torsional buckling is not a controlling limit state.*

13.3.3 Single-angle members in compression

13.3.3.1 General

The factored compressive resistance, C_r, of single-angle members may be calculated neglecting the effects of eccentricity if the appropriate slenderness as specified in Clause 13.3.3.2 or 13.3.3.3 is used, provided that

(a) members are loaded at the ends in compression through the same one leg;

(b) members are attached by welding or by minimum two-bolt connections; and

(c) there are no intermediate transverse loads.

The factored compressive resistance, C_r, of single-angle members meeting the requirements of Table 1 shall be taken as

$$C_r = \phi A F_y \left(1 + \lambda^{2n}\right)^{-1/n}$$

where

n = 1.34

λ = $\sqrt{\dfrac{F_y}{F_e}}$

F_e = $\dfrac{\pi^2 E}{\left(\dfrac{KL}{r}\right)^2}$

13.3.3.2 Individual members and planar trusses

For equal-leg angles or unequal-leg angles with leg length ratios (b_l/b_s) less than 1.7 and connected through the longer leg that are individual members or are members of planar trusses with adjacent web members attached to the same side of the gusset plate or chord:

(a) $0 \le \dfrac{L}{r_x} \le 80 : \dfrac{KL}{r} = 72 + 0.75\dfrac{L}{r_x}$

(b) $\dfrac{L}{r_x} > 80 : \dfrac{KL}{r} = 32 + 1.25\dfrac{L}{r_x} \le 200$

For unequal-leg angles with leg length ratios (b_l/b_s) less than 1.7 and connected through the shorter leg, KL/r shall be increased by adding $4[(b_l/b_s)^2 - 1]$. KL/r shall be not less than $0.95L/r_y'$.

where

L = length of member between work points at truss chord centrelines

b_l = longer leg of angle

b_s = shorter leg of angle

r_x = radius of gyration of single-angle member about geometric axis parallel to connected leg

r_y' = radius of gyration of single-angle member about minor principal axis

13.3.3.3 Box and space trusses

For equal-leg angles or unequal-leg angles with leg length ratios (b_l/b_s) less than 1.7 and connected through the longer leg that are members of box or space trusses with adjacent web members attached to the same side of the gusset plate or chord:

(a) $0 \le \dfrac{L}{r_x} \le 75 : \dfrac{KL}{r} = 60 + 0.8\dfrac{L}{r_x}$

(b) $\dfrac{L}{r_x} > 75 : \dfrac{KL}{r} = 45 + \dfrac{L}{r_x} \le 200$

For unequal-leg angles with leg length ratios (b_l/b_s) less than 1.7 and connected through the shorter leg, KL/r shall be increased by adding $6[(b_l/b_s)^2 - 1]$. KL/r shall be not less than $0.82L/r_y'$.

13.3.3.4 Other members

Single-angle members with different end conditions from those described in Clause 13.3.3.1, leg length ratios (b_l/b_s) greater than 1.7, adjacent web members attached to opposite sides of the gusset plate or chord, or transverse loading shall be designed for compressive resistance, C_r, with Clause 13.3.2, accounting for the effects of eccentricity.

13.3.4 Segmented members in compression

The factored compressive resistance of segmented columns shall be determined using a rational method. Notional loads need not be applied between in-plane lateral supports.

13.3.5 Members in compression subjected to elastic local buckling

The factored compressive resistance, C_r, for sections that exceed the width (or diameter)-to-thickness ratios specified in Table 1 shall be determined as either:

(a) $C_r = \phi A_e F_y \left(1 + \lambda^{2n}\right)^{-1/n}$

   where

   $\lambda \quad = \quad \sqrt{\dfrac{F_y}{F_e}}$

with an effective area, A_e, calculated using reduced element widths meeting the maximum width-to-thickness ratio specified in Table 1; or

(b) $C_r = \phi A F_{ye} \left(1 + \lambda_{ye}^{2n}\right)^{-1/n}$

   where

   $\lambda_{ye} \quad = \quad \sqrt{\dfrac{F_{ye}}{F_e}}$

with an effective yield stress, F_{ye}, determined from the maximum width (or diameter)-to-thickness ratio meeting the limit specified in Table 1.

   The elastic buckling stress, F_e, shall be calculated using Clause 13.3.1, 13.3.2, or 13.3.3, as applicable, and using gross section properties.

13.4 Shear

13.4.1 Webs of flexural members with two flanges

13.4.1.1 Elastic analysis

The factored shear resistance, V_r, developed by the web of a flexural member shall be taken as

$$V_r = \phi A_w F_s$$

where

A_w = shear area (dw for rolled shapes and hw for girders, $2ht$ for rectangular HSS)
and F_s is as follows:

(a) for unstiffened webs:

    (i)   when $\dfrac{h}{w} \le \dfrac{1014}{\sqrt{F_y}}$:

$$F_s = 0.66F_y$$

    (ii)   when $\dfrac{1014}{\sqrt{F_y}} < \dfrac{h}{w} \le \dfrac{1435}{\sqrt{F_y}}$:

$$F_s = \dfrac{670\sqrt{F_y}}{(h/w)}$$

    (iii) when $\dfrac{h}{w} > \dfrac{1435}{\sqrt{F_y}}$:

$$F_s = \dfrac{961\,200}{(h/w)^2}$$

(b) for stiffened webs:

    (i)   when $\dfrac{h}{w} \le 439\sqrt{\dfrac{k_v}{F_y}}$:

$$F_s = 0.66F_y$$

    (ii)   when $439\sqrt{\dfrac{k_v}{F_y}} < \dfrac{h}{w} \le 502\sqrt{\dfrac{k_v}{F_y}}$:

$$F_s = F_{cri}$$

    (iii) when $502\sqrt{\dfrac{k_v}{F_y}} < \dfrac{h}{w} \le 621\sqrt{\dfrac{k_v}{F_y}}$:

$$F_s = F_{cri} + k_a(0.50F_y - 0.866F_{cri})$$

(iv) when $621\sqrt{\dfrac{k_v}{F_y}} < \dfrac{h}{w}$:

$$F_s = F_{cre} + k_a(0.50F_y - 0.866\, F_{cre})$$

where

k_v = shear buckling coefficient, as follows:

(1) when $a/h < 1$

$$k_v = 4 + \frac{5.34}{(a/h)^2}$$

(2) when $a/h \geq 1$

$$k_v = 5.34 + \frac{4}{(a/h)^2}$$

where

a/h = aspect ratio = ratio of the distance between stiffeners to web depth

$$F_{cri} \quad = \quad 290\frac{\sqrt{F_y k_v}}{(h/w)}$$

k_a = aspect coefficient

$$= \quad \frac{1}{\sqrt{1+(a/h)^2}}$$

$$F_{cre} \quad = \quad \frac{180\,000\, k_v}{(h/w)^2}$$

13.4.1.2 Combined shear and moment in stiffened web beams

Transversely stiffened web members depending on tension field action to carry shear shall be proportioned to satisfy the requirements of Clause 14.6 for combined shear and moment.

13.4.1.3 Tubular members and concrete-filled tubular members

The shear resistance, V_r, of Class 1 and 2 tubular members and concrete-filled tubular members where local wall buckling is prevented shall be taken as

$$V_r = 0.66\phi\,(A/2)F_y$$

where

A = cross-sectional area of the tubular member portion of the concrete-filled member

13.4.2 Plastic analysis

In structures designed on the basis of a plastic analysis as defined in Clause 8.3.2, the factored shear resistance, V_r, developed by the web of a flexural member subjected to shear shall be taken as

$$V_r = 0.8\,\phi A_w F_s$$

where F_s is determined in accordance with Clause 13.4.1.1.

13.4.3 Webs of flexural members not having two flanges

The factored shear resistance for cross-sections not having two flanges (e.g., solid rectangles, rounds, and Ts) shall be determined by rational analysis. The factored shear stress at any location in the cross-section shall be taken as not greater than $0.66\phi F_y$ and shall be reduced where shear buckling is a consideration.

13.4.4 Pins

The total factored shear, V_r, resistance of the nominal area of pins shall be taken as

$V_r = 0.66\phi A F_y$

13.4.5 Gusset plates and coped beams

The shear resistance of gusset plates and the shear resistance at the ends of coped beams shall be computed in accordance with Clause 13.11.

13.5 Bending — Laterally supported members

The factored moment resistance, M_r, developed by a member subjected to uniaxial bending moments about a principal axis where effectively continuous lateral support is provided to the compression flange, or where the member has no tendency to buckle laterally, shall be taken as follows:

(a) for Class 1 and Class 2 sections (except that singly symmetric I-sections and T-sections shall not yield under service loads):

$$M_r = \phi Z F_y$$
$$= \phi M_p$$

(b) for Class 3 sections:

$$M_r = \phi S F_y$$
$$= \phi M_y$$

(c) for Class 4 sections:

(i) when both the web and compression flange slenderness exceed the limits for Class 3 sections, the value of M_r shall be determined in accordance with CSA S136. The calculated value, F'_y, applicable to cold-formed members, shall be determined using only the values for F_y and F_u that are specified in the relevant structural steel material standard;

(ii) when the flanges meet the requirements of Class 3 but the web slenderness exceeds the limit for Class 3, the requirements of Clause 14 shall apply; and

(iii) when the web meets the requirements of Class 3 but the flange slenderness exceeds the limit for Class 3, M_r shall be calculated as follows:

$$M_r = \phi\, S_e\, F_y$$

where

S_e = effective section modulus determined using an effective flange width of $670t / \sqrt{F_y}$ for flanges supported along two edges parallel to the direction of stress and an effective width of $200t / \sqrt{F_y}$ for flanges supported along one edge parallel to the direction of stress. For flanges supported along one edge, b_{el}/t shall not exceed 60

Alternatively, the moment resistance may be calculated using an effective yield stress determined from the flange width-to-thickness ratio meeting the Class 3 limit.

13.6 Bending — Laterally unsupported members

Where continuous lateral support is not provided to the compression flange of a member subjected to uniaxial strong axis bending, the factored moment resistance, M_r, of a segment between effective brace points shall be determined as follows:

(a) For doubly symmetric Class 1 and 2 sections, except closed square and circular sections:

(i) when $M_u > 0.67M_p$:

$$M_r = 1.15\phi M_p \left[1 - \frac{0.28M_p}{M_u} \right] \leq \phi M_p$$

(ii) when $M_u \leq 0.67M_p$:

$$M_r = \phi M_u$$

where the critical elastic moment of the unbraced segment, M_u, is given by

$$M_u = \frac{\omega_2 \pi}{L} \sqrt{EI_y\, GJ + \left(\frac{\pi E}{L} \right)^2 I_y C_w}$$

where

$$\omega_2 = \frac{4M_{max}}{\sqrt{M_{max}^2 + 4M_a^2 + 7M_b^2 + 4M_c^2}} \leq 2.5$$

where

C_w = warping torsional constant, taken as 0 for rectangular hollow structural sections

J = St. Venant torsional constant

L = length of unbraced segment of beam

M_{max} = maximum factored bending moment magnitude in unbraced segment

M_a = factored bending moment at one-quarter point of unbraced segment

M_b = factored bending moment at midpoint of unbraced segment

M_c = factored bending moment at three-quarter point of unbraced segment

ω_2 = coefficient to account for increased moment resistance of a laterally unsupported doubly symmetric beam segment when subject to a moment gradient

Where the bending moment distribution within the unbraced segment is effectively linear, the equivalent moment factor, ω_2, may be taken as

$$1.75 + 1.05\kappa + 0.3\kappa^2 \leq 2.5$$

where

κ = ratio of the smaller factored moment to the larger factored moment at opposite ends of the unbraced length (positive for double curvature and negative for single curvature)

For unbraced beam segments loaded above the shear centre between brace points, where the method of load delivery to the member provides neither lateral nor rotational restraint to the member, the associated destabilizing effect shall be taken into account using a rational method. For loads applied at the level of the top flange, in lieu of a more accurate analysis, M_u may be determined using $\omega_2 = 1.0$ and using an effective length, for pinned-ended beams, equal to 1.2L and, for all other cases, 1.4L.

(b) For doubly symmetric Class 3 and 4 sections, except closed square and circular sections, and for channels:

(i) when $M_u > 0.67M_y$:

$$M_r = 1.15\phi M_y \left[1 - \frac{0.28M_y}{M_u} \right]$$

but not greater than ϕM_y for Class 3 sections and the value specified in Clause 13.5(c)(iii) for Class 4 sections; and

(ii)   when $M_u \leq 0.67M_y$:

$$M_r = \phi M_u$$

where M_u and ω_2 are as specified in Item (a)(ii).

(c) For closed square and circular sections, M_r shall be determined in accordance with Clause 13.5.

(d) For cantilever beams, a rational method of analysis taking into account the lateral and torsional restraint conditions at the supports and tip of the cantilever, as well as the loading conditions and the flexibility of the backspan, shall be used.

(e) For singly symmetric (monosymmetric) Class 1, 2, or 3 I-sections and T-sections, lateral-torsional buckling strength shall be checked separately for each flange that experiences compression under factored loads at any point along its unbraced length, as follows (except that these sections shall not yield under service loads):

(i)   when $M_u > M_{yr}$:

$$M_r = \phi \left[M_p - (M_p - M_{yr}) \left(\frac{L - L_u}{L_{yr} - L_u} \right) \right] \leq \phi M_p$$

except for Class 3 sections, as well as Class 1 and 2 T-sections where at any point within the unbraced segment the stem tip is in compression, where M_p is replaced with M_y

where

M_{yr} = $0.7S_x F_y$ with S_x taken as the smaller of the two potential values

L_{yr} = length L obtained by setting $M_u = M_{yr}$

L_u = $1.1r_t \sqrt{E / F_y} = \dfrac{490r_t}{\sqrt{F_y}}$

where

r_t = $\dfrac{b_c}{\sqrt{12\left(1 + \dfrac{h_c w}{3b_c t_c}\right)}}$

where

h_c = depth of the web in compression

b_c = width of compression flange

t_c = thickness of compression flange

(ii)   when $M \leq M_{yr}$

$$M_r = \phi M_u$$

where the critical elastic moment of the unbraced segment, M_u, is given by

$$M_u = \frac{\omega_3 \pi^2 E I_y}{2L^2} \left[\beta_x + \sqrt{\beta_x^2 + 4\left(\frac{GJL^2}{\pi^2 E I_y} + \frac{C_w}{I_y} \right)} \right]$$

and where in lieu of more accurate values the section properties β_x and C_w may be evaluated as

$$\beta_x = 0.9(d-t)\left(\frac{2I_{yc}}{I_y} - 1\right)\left(1 - \left(\frac{I_y}{I_x}\right)^2\right)$$

$$C_w = \frac{I_{yc}I_{yt}(d-t)^2}{I_y}$$

where

β_x = asymmetry parameter for singly symmetric beams

I_{yc} = moment of inertia of the compression flange about the y-axis

I_{yt} = moment of inertia of the tension flange about the y-axis

and when singly symmetric beams are in single curvature

ω_3 =ω_2 for beams with two flanges

=1.0 for T-sections

in all other cases

ω_3 =$\omega_2\,(0.5 + 2\,(I_{yc}/I_y)^2)$ but ≤ 1.0 for T-sections

For unbraced beam segments loaded above the section mid-height and between brace points, where the method of load delivery to the member provides neither lateral nor rotational restraint to the member, the associated destabilizing effect shall be taken into account using a rational method.

For other singly symmetric shapes, a rational method of analysis shall be used.

(f)   For biaxial bending, the member shall meet the following requirement:

$$\frac{M_{fx}}{M_{rx}} + \frac{M_{fy}}{M_{ry}} \le 1.0$$

13.7 Lateral bracing for members in structures analyzed plastically

Members in structures or portions of structures in which the distributions of moments and forces have been determined by a plastic analysis shall be braced to resist lateral and torsional displacement at all hinge locations. However, bracing shall not be required at the location of the last hinge to form in the failure mechanism assumed as the basis for proportioning the structure. The laterally unsupported distance, L_{cr}, from braced hinge locations to the nearest adjacent point on the frame similarly braced shall not exceed the following:

(a)   for static plastic analysis and for seismic design in accordance with Clauses 27.3 and 27.7.9.3:

$$\frac{L_{cr}}{r_y} = \frac{25\,000 + 15\,000\kappa}{F_y}$$

(b)   for seismic design in accordance with Clauses 27.2 and 27.9:

$$\frac{L_{cr}}{r_y} = \frac{17\,250 + 15\,500\kappa}{F_y}$$

where κ is as specified in Clause 13.6(a).

Except as specified in Items (a) and (b), the maximum unsupported length of members in structures analyzed plastically need not be less than that permitted for the same members in structures analyzed elastically.

13.8 Axial compression and bending

13.8.1 General
In Clause 13.8, a distinction is made between braced and unbraced frames. A frame is classified as braced when its sway stiffness is at least five times that of the frame with moment connections instead of bracing.
Note: *For segmented members, the in-plane compressive resistance may be determined assuming pinned end connections. See Clause 13.3.4.*

13.8.2 Member strength and stability — Class 1 and Class 2 sections of I-shaped members
Members required to resist both bending moments and an axial compressive force shall be proportioned so that

$$\frac{C_f}{C_r} + \frac{0.85 U_{1x} M_{fx}}{M_{rx}} + \frac{\beta U_{1y} M_{fy}}{M_{ry}} \leq 1.0$$

where

C_f and M_f = the maximum load effects, including stability effects as specified in Clause 8.4
$\beta \quad = 0.6 + 0.4\lambda_y \leq 0.85$

The capacity of the member shall be examined for
(a) cross-sectional strength (members in braced frames only) with $\beta = 0.6$, in which case
    (i) C_r shall be as specified in Clause 13.3, with the value $\lambda = 0$;
    (ii) M_r shall be as specified in Clause 13.5 (for the appropriate class of section); and
    (iii) U_{1x} and U_{1y} shall be as specified in Clause 13.8.4, but not less than 1.0;
(b) overall member strength, in which case
    (i) C_r shall be as specified in Clause 13.3, with the value $K = 1$, except that for uniaxial bending, C_r shall be based on the axis of bending (see also Clause 10.3.2);
    (ii) M_r shall be as specified in Clause 13.5 (for the appropriate class of section);
    (iii) U_{1x} and U_{1y} shall be taken as 1.0 for members in unbraced frames; and
    (iv) U_{1x} and U_{1y} shall be as specified in Clause 13.8.4 for members in braced frames; and
(c) lateral torsional buckling strength, when applicable, in which case
    (i) C_r shall be as specified in Clause 13.3 and based on weak-axis or torsional-flexural buckling (see also Clause 10.3.3);
    (ii) M_{rx} shall be as specified in Clause 13.6 (for the appropriate class of section);
    (iii) M_{ry} shall be as specified in Clause 13.5 (for the appropriate class of section);
    (iv) U_{1x} and U_{1y} shall be taken as 1.0 for members in unbraced frames;
    (v) U_{1x} shall be as specified in Clause 13.8.4, but not less than 1.0, for members in braced frames; and
    (vi) U_{1y} shall be as specified in Clause 13.8.4 for members in braced frames.
In addition, the member shall meet the following requirement:

$$\frac{M_{fx}}{M_{rx}} + \frac{M_{fy}}{M_{ry}} \leq 1.0$$

where M_{rx} and M_{ry} are as specified in Clause 13.5 or 13.6, as appropriate.

13.8.3 Member strength and stability — All classes of sections except Class 1 and Class 2 sections of I-shaped members
Members required to resist both bending moments and an axial compressive force shall be proportioned so that

$$\frac{C_f}{C_r}+\frac{U_{1x}M_{fx}}{M_{rx}}+\frac{U_{1y}M_{fy}}{M_{ry}}\le 1.0$$

where all terms are as specified in Clause 13.8.2.

The capacity of the member shall be examined for the following cases in the manner specified in Clause 13.8.2:
(a) cross-sectional strength (members in braced frames and tapered members only);
(b) overall member strength; and
(c) lateral-torsional buckling strength.

In addition, for braced frames the member shall meet the following requirement:

$$\frac{M_{fx}}{M_{rx}}+\frac{M_{fy}}{M_{ry}}\le 1.0$$

where M_{rx} and M_{ry} are as specified in Clause 13.5 or 13.6, as appropriate.

13.8.4 Value of U_1
In lieu of a more detailed analysis, the value of U_1 for the axis under consideration, accounting for the second-order effects due to the deformation of a member between its ends, shall be taken as

$$U_1=\left[\frac{\omega_1}{1-\dfrac{C_f}{C_e}}\right]$$

where ω_1 is as specified in Clause 13.8.5 and

$$C_e=\frac{\pi^2 EI}{L^2}$$

13.8.5 Values of ω_1
Unless otherwise determined by analysis, the following values shall be used for ω_1:
(a) for members not subjected to transverse loads between supports:

$$\omega_1 = 0.6 - 0.4\kappa \ge 0.4$$

where
κ = ratio of the smaller factored moment to the larger factored moment at opposite ends of the member length (positive for double curvature and negative for single curvature)
(b) for members subjected to distributed loads or a series of point loads between supports:
$$\omega_1 = 1.0$$
(c) for members subjected to a concentrated load or moment between supports:
$$\omega_1 = 0.85$$

For the purpose of design, members subjected to a concentrated load or moment between supports (e.g., segmented columns) may be considered to be divided into segments at the points of load (or moment) application. Each segment shall then be treated as a member that depends on its own flexural stiffness to prevent sidesway in the plane of bending considered, and ω_1 shall be taken as 0.85. In calculating the slenderness ratio for use in Clause 13.8, the total length of the compression member shall be used.

Note: *For references to more exact methods often justified for crane-supporting columns and similar applications, see Annex C.*

13.9 Axial tension and bending

13.9.1

Members required to resist both bending moments and an axial tensile force shall be proportioned so that

$$\frac{T_f}{T_r} + \frac{M_f}{M_r} \leq 1.0$$

where M_r is as specified in Clause 13.5.

13.9.2

Additionally, the following shall apply to laterally unsupported members:

(a) $\dfrac{M_f}{M_r} - \dfrac{T_f Z}{M_r A} \leq 1.0$ for Class 1 and Class 2 sections

(b) $\dfrac{M_f}{M_r} - \dfrac{T_f S}{M_r A} \leq 1.0$ for Class 3 and Class 4 sections

where M_r is as specified in Clause 13.6.

13.10 Load bearing

The factored bearing resistance in newtons, B_r, developed by a member or portion of a member subjected to bearing shall be taken as follows:

(a)   on the contact area of accurately cut or fitted parts:

$$B_r = 1.50 \phi F_y A$$

(b)   on expansion rollers or rockers:

$$B_r = 0.000\,26\phi \left(\frac{R_1}{1 - \dfrac{R_1}{R_2}} \right) L F_y^2$$

where

F_y = specified minimum yield point of the weaker part in contact

R_1 and L = radius and length, respectively, of the roller or rocker

R_2 = radius of the groove of the supporting plate

13.11 Block shear — Tension member, beam, and plate connections

The factored resistance for a potential failure involving the simultaneous development of tensile and shear component areas shall be taken as follows:

$$T_r = \phi_u \left[U_t A_n F_u + 0.6 A_{gv} \frac{(F_y + F_u)}{2} \right]$$

where
(a) U_t is an efficiency factor, and $U_t = 1.0$ is used for symmetrical blocks or failure patterns and concentric loading or is taken from the following Table for specific applications;

Connection type	U_t
Flange-connected Ts	1.0
Angles connected by one leg and stem-connected Ts	0.6
Coped beams	
One bolt line	0.9
Two bolt lines	0.3

(b) A_n is the net area in tension, as specified in Clause 12; and
(c) A_{gv} is the gross area in shear.
For steel grades with $F_y > 485$ MPa, $(F_y + F_u)/2$ shall be replaced with F_y in the determination of T_r.
The second term of the expression in this Clause may be used to calculate the potential plate tear-out resistance of one or more bolts along parallel planes tangent to the bolt hole(s) and directed towards the edge of the plate.

13.12 Bolts and local connection resistance

13.12.1 Bolts in bearing-type connections

13.12.1.1 General
For bolts subject to shear or tension, ϕ_b shall be taken as 0.80.

13.12.1.2 Bolts in bearing and shear
The factored resistance developed at the bolts in a bolted joint subjected to bearing and shear shall be taken as the lesser of
(a) the factored bearing resistance at bolt holes B_r (except for long slotted holes loaded perpendicular to the slot), B_r, as follows:

$$B_r = 3\phi_{br}ntdF_u$$

or

(b) the factored bearing resistance perpendicular to long slotted holes, B_r, as follows:

$$B_r = 2.4\phi_{br}ntdF_u$$

where
ϕ_{br} = 0.8
F_u = tensile strength of the connected material
The reduced bearing resistance of holes close to the edge in the direction of the loading shall be accounted for by appropriate consideration of the resistance requirements of Clause 13.11.
Note: *See also Clauses 13.2 and 13.11 for resistances of bolted parts and Clause 22.3 for limiting end and edge distances.*
(c) the factored shear resistance of the bolts, V_r, as follows:

$$V_r = 0.60\phi_b nmA_bF_u$$

When the bolt threads are intercepted by a shear plane, the factored shear resistance shall be taken as $0.70V_r$.

For lap splices with $L \geq 15d$, where d is the bolt diameter and L is the joint length between centres of end fasteners, the shearing resistance of the bolts shall be multiplied by $1.075–0.005 \, L/d$, but by not less than 0.75.

Note: *The specified minimum tensile strength, F_u, for bolts is given in the relevant ASTM Standard, e.g., for*

    (a) *ASTM A 325M, F_u is 830 MPa;*
    (b) *ASTM A 490M, F_u is 1040 MPa;*
    (c) *ASTM A 325 bolts 1 inch or less in diameter, F_u is 825 MPa;*
    (d) *ASTM A 325 or ASTM F 1852 bolts greater than 1 inch in diameter, F_u is 725 MPa; and*
    (e) *ASTM A 490 or ASTM F 2280 bolts, F_u is 1035 MPa.*

13.12.1.3 Bolts in tension

The factored tensile resistance developed by a bolt in a joint subjected to tensile force, T_f, shall be taken as

$$T_r = 0.75\phi_b A_b F_u$$

The calculated tensile force, T_f, is independent of the pretension and shall be taken as the sum of the external load plus any tension caused by prying action.

Note: *See also Clause 26.5 for bolts in tension subjected to load combinations involving fatigue.*

13.12.1.4 Bolts in combined shear and tension

A bolt in a joint that is required to develop resistance to both tension and shear shall be proportioned so that

$$\left(\frac{V_f}{V_r}\right)^2 + \left(\frac{T_f}{T_r}\right)^2 \leq 1$$

where V_r is as specified in Clause 13.12.1.2 and T_r is as specified in Clause 13.12.1.3.

13.12.2 Bolts in slip-critical connections

13.12.2.1 General

For a slip-critical connection under the forces and moments produced by specified loads, slip of the assembly shall not occur. In addition, the effects of factored loads shall not exceed the resistances of the connection as specified in Clause 13.12.1.

13.12.2.2 Shear connections

The slip resistance, V_s, of a bolted joint, subjected to shear, V, shall be taken as

$$V_s = 0.53c_1 k_s mn A_b F_u$$

where

c_1 = a coefficient that relates the specified initial tension and mean slip to a 5% probability of slip for the method used to pretension the bolts

k_s = the mean slip coefficient as determined by tests carried out in accordance with "Testing method to Determine the Slip Coefficient for Coatings Used in Bolted Joints", Annex A, of RCSC's *Specification for Structural Joints Using ASTM A325 and A490 Bolts*

See Table 3 for values of k_s and c_1.

When long slotted holes are used in slip-critical connections, slip resistance shall be taken as $0.75 \, V_s$.

13.12.2.3 Connections in combined shear and tension

A bolt in a joint that is required to develop resistance to both tension and shear shall be proportioned so that the following relationship is satisfied for the specified loads:

$$\frac{V}{V_s} + 1.9\frac{T}{nA_bF_u} \le 1.0$$

where V_s is the slip resistance specified in Clause 13.12.2.2.

13.13 Welds

13.13.1 General

The resistance factor, ϕ_w, for welded connections shall be taken as 0.67.

Note: *See Table 4 for matching electrode classifications for CSA G40.21 steels.*

13.13.2 Shear

13.13.2.1 Complete and partial joint penetration groove welds, and plug and slot welds

The factored shear resistance shall be taken as the lesser of
(a) for the base metal:

$$V_r = 0.67\phi_w A_m F_u$$

(b) for the weld metal:

$$V_r = 0.67\phi_w A_w X_u$$

where
A_m = shear area of effective fusion face
A_w = area of effective weld throat, plug, or slot

13.13.2.2 Fillet welds

The factored resistance for direct shear and tension- or compression-induced shear shall be taken as

$$V_r = 0.67\phi_w A_w X_u(1.00 + 0.50\sin^{1.5}\theta)M_w$$

where
θ = angle, in degrees, of axis of weld segment with respect to the line of action of applied force (e.g., 0° for a longitudinal weld and 90° for a transverse weld)
M_w = strength reduction factor for multi-orientation fillet welds. For joints with a single weld orientation, $M_w = 1.0$; for joints with multiple weld orientations, for each segment

$$M_w = \frac{0.85 + \theta_1/600}{0.85 + \theta_2/600}$$

where
θ_1 = orientation of the weld segment under consideration
θ_2 = orientation of the weld segment in the joint that is nearest to 90°

Weld returns that are not accounted for in the joint capacity need not be considered a weld segment in the context of this clause.

Where over-matched electrodes are used, the base metal capacity at the fusion face shall also be checked and may be considered to have the following strength:

$$V_r = 0.67 \phi_w A_m F_u$$

13.13.2.3 Flare bevel groove welds for open-web steel joists

The factored resistance for direct shear and tension- or compression-induced shear shall be taken as

$$V_r = 0.67 \phi_w A_w F_u$$

where

A_w = $0.50 w_f L$ (or as established by procedure qualification tests)

     where

      w_f =   width of flare bevel groove weld face

F_u =   least ultimate tensile strength of the components in the joint

13.13.3 Tension normal to axis of weld

13.13.3.1 Complete joint penetration groove weld made with matching electrodes

The factored tensile resistance shall be taken as that of the base metal.

13.13.3.2 Partial joint penetration groove weld made with matching electrodes

The factored tensile resistance shall be taken as

$$T_r = \phi_w A_n F_u \le \phi A_g F_y$$

where

A_n =   nominal area of fusion face normal to the tensile force

When overall ductile behaviour is desired (member yielding before weld fracture), the following shall apply:

$A_n F_u > A_g F_y$

13.13.3.3 Partial joint penetration groove weld combined with a fillet weld, made with matching electrodes

The factored tensile resistance shall be taken as

$$T_r = \phi_w \sqrt{\left(A_n F_u\right)^2 + \left(A_w X_u\right)^2} \le \phi A_g F_y$$

where

A_g =   gross area of the components of the tension member connected by the welds

13.13.4 Compression normal to axis of weld

13.13.4.1 Complete and partial joint penetration groove welds made with matching electrodes

The compressive resistance shall be taken as that of the effective area of base metal in the joint. For partial joint penetration groove welds, the effective area in compression shall be taken as the nominal area of the fusion face normal to the compression plus the area of the base metal fitted in contact bearing (see Clause 28.5).

13.13.4.2 Cross-sectional properties of continuous longitudinal welds

Continuous longitudinal welds made with matching electrodes may be considered as contributing to the cross-sectional properties A, S, Z, and I of the cross-section.

13.13.4.3 Welds for hollow structural sections

The provisions of Appendix L of CSA W59 may be used for hollow structural sections.

13.14 Welds and high-strength bolts in combination

The factored shear resistance of a joint that combines welds and bolts in the same plane, $V_{r,joint}$, shall be taken as the largest of

(a) $V_{friction} + V_{r,trans} + 0.85V_{r,long}$;

(b) $V_{friction} + V_{r,long} + 0.5V_{r,bolt}$; and

(c) $V_{r,bolt}$.

where

$V_{friction}$	=	plate friction resistance component
	=	$0.25V_s$ when the bolts are pretensioned in accordance with Clause 23.8
	=	0 when the bolts are not pretensioned
$V_{r,trans}$	=	transverse weld resistance component
	=	V_r determined from Clause 13.13.2.2 for $\theta = 90°$
$V_{r,long}$	=	longitudinal weld resistance component
	=	V_r for combination joints with only longitudinal welds and bolts, with V_r determined from Clause 13.13.2.2 for $\theta = 0°$
$V_{r,bolt}$	=	bolt shear resistance component
	=	V_r determined from Clause 13.12.1.2

14 Beams and girders

14.1 Proportioning

Beams and girders consisting of rolled shapes (with or without cover plates), hollow structural sections, or fabricated sections shall be proportioned on the basis of the properties of the gross section or the modified gross section. No deduction need be made for fastener holes in webs or flanges unless the reduction of flange area by such holes exceeds 15% of the gross flange area, in which case the excess shall be deducted. The effect of openings other than holes for fasteners shall be considered in accordance with Clause 14.3.3.

14.2 Flanges

14.2.1
Flanges of welded girders should consist of a single plate or a series of plates joined end-to-end by complete penetration groove welds.

14.2.2
Flanges of bolted girders shall be proportioned so that the total cross-sectional area of cover plates does not exceed 70% of the total flange area.

14.2.3
Fasteners or welds connecting flanges to webs shall be proportioned to resist horizontal shear forces due to bending combined with any loads that are transmitted from the flange to the web other than by direct bearing. Spacing of fasteners or intermittent welds in general shall be in proportion to the intensity of the shear force and shall not exceed the maximum for compression or tension members, as applicable, in accordance with Clause 19.

14.2.4
Partial-length flange cover plates shall be extended beyond the theoretical cut-off point, and the extended portion shall be connected with sufficient fasteners or welds to develop a force in the cover plate at the theoretical cut-off point not less than

$$P = \frac{AM_{fc}\,y}{I_g}$$

where

P = required force to be developed in cover plate

A = area of cover plate

M_{fc} = moment due to factored loads at theoretical cut-off point

y = distance from centroid of cover plate to neutral axis of cover-plated section

I_g = moment of inertia of cover-plated section

Additionally, for welded cover plates, the longitudinal welds connecting the cover-plate termination to the beam or girder shall be designed to develop the force, P, within a length, a', measured from the actual end of the cover plate, determined as follows:

(a) when there is a continuous weld equal to or larger than three-fourths of the cover-plate thickness across the end of the plate and along both edges of the cover plate, a' shall be taken as the width of the cover plate;

(b) when there is a continuous weld smaller than three-fourths of the cover-plate thickness across the end of the plate and along both edges, a' shall be taken as 1.5 times the width of the cover plate; and

(c) when there is no weld across the end of the plate but there are continuous welds along both edges, a' shall be taken as 2 times the width of the cover plate.

14.3 Webs

14.3.1 Maximum slenderness
The slenderness ratio, h/w, of a web shall not exceed $83\,000/F_y$

where

F_y = specified minimum yield point of the compression flange steel

This limit may be waived if analysis indicates that buckling of the compression flange into the web will not occur at factored load levels.

14.3.2 Web crippling and yielding

The factored bearing resistance of the web shall be taken as follows:

(a) for interior loads (concentrated load applied at a distance from the member end greater than the member depth), the smaller of

   (i) $B_r = \phi_{bi} w (N + 10t)F_y$

   (ii) $B_r = 1.45\phi_{bi} w^2 \sqrt{F_y E}$

(b) for end reactions, the smaller of

   (i) $B_r = \phi_{be} w (N + 4t)F_y$

   (ii) $B_r = 0.60\phi_{be} w^2 \sqrt{F_y E}$

where

ϕ_{bi} = 0.80

ϕ_{be} = 0.75

N = length of bearing

   Where the bearing resistance of the web is exceeded, bearing stiffeners shall be used (see Clause 14.4).

14.3.3 Openings

14.3.3.1

Except as specified in Clause 14.1, the effect of all openings in beams and girders shall be considered in the design. At all points where the factored shear or moments at the net section would exceed the capacity of the member, adequate reinforcement shall be added to the member at these points to provide the required strength and stability.

14.3.3.2

Unreinforced circular openings may be located in the web of unstiffened prismatic Class 1 and Class 2 beams or girders without considering net section properties, provided that

(a) the load is uniformly distributed;

(b) the section has an axis of symmetry in the plane of bending;

(c) the openings are located within the middle third of the depth and the middle half of the span of the member;

(d) the spacing between the centres of any two adjacent openings, measured parallel to the longitudinal axis of the member, is a minimum of 2.5 times the diameter of the larger opening; and

(e) the factored maximum shear at the support does not exceed 50% of the factored shear resistance of the section.

14.3.3.3

If the forces at openings are determined by an elastic analysis, the procedure shall be in accordance with published, recognized principles.

14.3.3.4

The strength and stability of the member in the vicinity of openings may be determined on the basis of assumed locations of plastic hinges, such that the resulting force distributions satisfy the requirements of equilibrium, provided that the analysis is carried out in accordance with Items (a), (b), and (f) of Clause 8.3.2. However, for I-type members, the width-to-thickness ratio of the flanges may meet only the requirements of Class 1 or 2 sections, provided that the webs meet the width-to-thickness limit of Class 1 sections.

14.3.4 Effect of thin webs on moment resistance

When the web slenderness ratio, h/w, exceeds $1900/\sqrt{M_f/\phi S}$, the flange shall meet the width-to-thickness ratios of Class 3 sections in accordance with Clause 11, and the factored moment resistance of the beam or girder, M_r', shall be determined as follows:

$$M_r' = M_r\left[1 - 0.0005\frac{A_w}{A_f}\left(\frac{h}{w} - \frac{1900}{\sqrt{M_f/\phi S}}\right)\right]$$

where

M_r = factored moment resistance determined in accordance with Clause 13.5 or 13.6, but not to exceed ϕM_y

When an axial compressive force acts on the girder in addition to the moment, the constant 1900 in the expression for M_r' shall be reduced by the factor $(1 - 0.65C_f/\phi C_y)$ (see also Clause 11.2).

14.4 Bearing stiffeners

14.4.1

Pairs of bearing stiffeners on the webs of single-web beams and girders shall be required at points of concentrated loads and reactions wherever the bearing resistance of the web is exceeded (see Clause 14.3.2). Bearing stiffeners shall also be required at unframed ends of single-web girders having web depth-to-thickness ratios greater than $1100/\sqrt{F_y}$. Box girders may employ diaphragms designed to act as bearing stiffeners.

14.4.2

Bearing stiffeners shall bear against the flange or flanges through which they receive their loads and shall extend approximately to the edge of the flange plates or flange angles. They shall be designed as columns in accordance with Clause 13.3, assuming that the column section consists of the pair of stiffeners and a centrally located strip of the web equal to not more than 25 times its thickness at the interior stiffeners, or a strip equal to not more than 12 times its thickness when the stiffeners are located at the end of the web. The effective column length, KL, shall be taken as not less than three-fourths of the length of the stiffeners in calculating the ratio KL/r. Only that portion of the stiffeners outside of the angle fillet or the flange-to-web welds shall be considered effective in bearing. Angle bearing stiffeners shall not be crimped. Bearing stiffeners shall be connected to the web to develop the full force required to be carried by the stiffener into the web or vice versa.

14.5 Intermediate transverse stiffeners

14.5.1

Intermediate transverse stiffeners, when used, shall be spaced to suit the shear resistance determined in accordance with Clause 13.4, except that at girder end panels or at panels adjacent to large openings, the tension-field component shall be taken as zero unless means are provided to anchor the tension field.

14.5.2

Except as specified in Clause 14.5.1, the maximum distance between stiffeners, when required, shall not exceed the values shown in Table 5.

14.5.3

Intermediate transverse stiffeners may be furnished singly or in pairs. Width-to-thickness ratios shall meet the requirements of Clause 11. The moment of inertia of the stiffener, or pair of stiffeners if so furnished, shall be not less than $(h/50)^4$ taken about an axis in the plane of the web. The gross area, A_s, of intermediate stiffeners, or pairs of stiffeners if so furnished, shall be as follows:

$$A_s = \frac{aw}{2}\left[1 - \frac{a/h}{\sqrt{1+(a/h)^2}}\right]CYD$$

where

a =   centre-to-centre distance of adjacent stiffeners (i.e., panel length)

w =   web thickness

h =   web depth

C = $\left[1 - \frac{310\,000\,k_v}{F_y\,(h/w)^2}\right]$ but not less than 0.10

where

k_v =   shear buckling coefficient (see Clause 13.4.1.1)

F_y =   specified minimum yield point of web steel

Y =   ratio of specified minimum yield point of web steel to specified minimum yield point of stiffener steel

D =   stiffener factor

   =   1.0 for stiffeners furnished in pairs

   =   1.8 for single-angle stiffeners

   =   2.4 for single-plate stiffeners

When the greatest shear, V_f, in an adjacent panel is less than that permitted by Clause 13.4.1.1, this gross area requirement may be reduced by multiplying by the ratio V_f/V_r.

14.5.4

Intermediate transverse stiffeners shall be connected to the web for a shear transfer per pair of stiffeners (or per single stiffener when so furnished), in newtons per millimetre of web depth, h, not less than $1 \times 10^{-4}hF_y^{1.5}$, except that when the largest calculated shear, V_f, in the adjacent panels is less than V_r, this shear transfer may be reduced in the same proportion. However, the total shear transfer shall not be less than the value of any concentrated load or reaction required to be transmitted to the web through the stiffener. Fasteners connecting intermediate transverse stiffeners to the web shall be spaced not more than 300 mm from centre to centre. If intermittent fillet welds are used, the clear distance between welds shall not exceed 16 times the web thickness or four times the weld length.

14.5.5

When intermediate stiffeners are used on only one side of the web, the stiffeners shall be attached to the compression flange. Intermediate stiffeners used in pairs shall have at least a snug fit against the compression flange. When stiffeners are cut short of the tension flange, the distance cut short shall be equal to or greater than four times but not greater than six times the girder web thickness. Stiffeners should be clipped to clear girder flange-to-web welds.

14.6 Combined shear and moment

Transversely stiffened girders depending on tension-field action to carry shear shall be proportioned such that

(a) $0.727\dfrac{M_f}{M_r} + 0.455\dfrac{V_f}{V_r} \le 1.0$;

(b) $\dfrac{M_f}{M_r} \le 1.0$; and

(c) $\dfrac{V_f}{V_r} \le 1.0$

where

M_r = value determined in accordance with Clause 13.5 or 13.6, as applicable

V_r = value determined in accordance with Clause 13.4

14.7 Rotational restraint at points of support
Beams and girders shall be restrained against rotation about their longitudinal axes at points of support.

14.8 Copes

14.8.1
The effect of copes on the lateral torsional buckling resistance of a beam or girder shall be taken into account.

14.8.2
The effect of copes in reducing the net area of the web available to resist transverse shear and the effective net area of potential paths of minimum resistance shall be taken into account (see Clause 13.11).

14.9 Lateral forces
The flanges of beams and girders supporting cranes or other moving loads shall be proportioned to resist any lateral forces produced by such loads.

14.10 Torsion

14.10.1
Beams and girders subjected to torsion shall have sufficient strength and rigidity to resist the torsional moment and forces in addition to other moments or forces. The connections and bracing of such members shall be adequate to transfer the reactions to the supports.

14.10.2
The factored resistance of I-shaped members subject to combined flexure and torsion may be determined from moment-torque interaction diagrams that take into account the normal stress distribution due to flexure and warping torsion and the St. Venant torsion. Assumed normal stress distributions shall be consistent with the class of section.

14.10.3
Members subject to torsional deformations required to maintain compatibility of the structure need not be designed to resist the associated torsional moments, provided that the structure satisfies the requirements of equilibrium.

14.10.4
For all members subject to loads causing torsion, the torsional deformations under specified loads shall be limited in accordance with Clause 6.2.1. For members subject to torsion or to combined flexure and torsion, the maximum combined normal stress, as determined by an elastic analysis, arising from warping torsion and bending due to the specified loads shall not exceed F_y.

15 Trusses

15.1 Analysis

15.1.1 Simplified method
The simplified method assumes that all members are pin-connected and loads are only applied at the panel points, except that bending effects due to transverse loads applied between panel points are assessed by taking into account any continuity of the members. This method may be used when compression members are at least Class 3.

15.1.2 Detailed method
The detailed method accounts for the actual loading and joint fixity. The detailed method shall be used for trusses
(a)   with panels adjacent to abrupt changes in the slope of a chord;
(b)   with Vierendeel panels;
(c)   with panels at abrupt changes in transverse shear; or
(d)   designed for fatigue.

15.2 General requirements

15.2.1 Effective lengths of compression members
The effective length for buckling in the plane of the truss shall be taken as the distance between the lines of intersection of the working points of the web members and the chord. The effective length for buckling perpendicular to the plane of the truss shall be equal to the distance between the points of lateral support. For built-up members, see Clause 19.
Note: *For the effective lengths of compression members in trusses comprising hollow structural sections, see CISC's* Hollow Structural Section: Connections and Trusses — A Design Guide.

15.2.2 Joint eccentricities
Bending moments due to joint eccentricities shall be taken into account. The eccentricity of work points at a joint or at a support shall be taken into account.

15.2.3 Stability
Trusses shall be braced to ensure their lateral stability. Brace members that support compression chords at discrete points shall meet the requirements of Clause 9.2. Ends of compression chords that are not attached to a supporting member shall be braced laterally, unless it can be demonstrated that the support is not necessary.

15.2.4 Chord members
Splices may occur at any point in chord members.

15.2.5 Web members
The factored resistances of the first compression web member subject to transverse shear, and its connections, shall be determined with their respective resistance factors, ϕ, multiplied by 0.85.
    The bending moments due to truss geometric distortions of end compression web members of bottom bearing trusses shall be included in the design. The simplified method may be used.
    Splices may occur at any point in web members.

15.2.6 Compression chord supports
Truss web members that provide support to a compression chord in the plane of the truss shall be designed for an additional force equal to 0.02 of the chord force, unless the brace force has been determined by rigorous analysis.

15.2.7 Maximum slenderness ratio of tension chords

The maximum slenderness ratio shall be limited to 240, except when other means are provided to control flexibility, sag, vibration, and slack in a manner commensurate with the service conditions of the structure.

15.2.8 Deflection and camber

Except for the deflection due to flexural deformation of Vierendeel panels, deflections may be determined from the axial deformations of the truss members. For camber, see Clause 6.3.2.

15.3 Composite trusses

Trusses designed to act compositely with the slab or cover slab shall also meet the requirements of Clause 17.

16 Open-web steel joists

16.1 Scope

Clause 16 specifies requirements for the design, manufacture, transportation, and erection of open-web steel joists used in the construction of buildings. Joists intended to act compositely with the deck slab shall also meet the requirements of Clause 17. Clause 16 shall be used only for the design of joists having an axis of symmetry in the plane of the joist.

16.2 General

Open-web steel joists are steel trusses of relatively low mass with parallel or slightly pitched chords and triangulated web systems proportioned to span between walls, structural supporting members, or both, and to provide direct support for floor or roof deck. In general, joists are manufactured on a production line that employs jigs, with certain details of the members being standardized by the individual manufacturer. When specified, joists can be designed to provide lateral support to compression elements of beams or columns, to participate in lateral-load-resisting systems, or as continuous joists, cantilevered joists, or joists having special support conditions.

16.3 Materials

Steel used for joists shall be a weldable structural grade meeting the requirements of Clause 5.1. Structural members cold-formed to shape may use the effect of cold-forming in accordance with Clause A7 of CSA S136. The calculated value of F_y' shall be determined using only the values for F_y and F_u that are specified in the relevant structural steel material standard. Yield levels reported on mill test certificates or determined in accordance with Clause F3 of CSA S136 shall not be used as the basis for design.

16.4 Design documents

16.4.1 Building structural design documents

The building structural design documents shall include, as a minimum, the following:
(a)   the uniformly distributed specified live and dead loads, unbalanced loading conditions, any concentrated loads, and any special loading conditions, e.g., non-uniform snow loads, ponding loads, horizontal loads, end moments, net uplift, downward wind load, bracing forces to provide lateral support to compression elements of beams or columns, allowances for mechanical equipment, and deflection limits;
(b)   joist spacing, camber (see Clause 6.3.2), joist depth, and shoe depth;
(c)   where joists are not supported on steel members, maximum bearing pressures or sizes of bearing plates;
(d)   anchorage requirements in excess of the requirements of Clause 16.5.12;
(e)   bracing required by Clause 16.5.6.2 (if any);

(f) method for and spacing of attachments of steel deck to the top chord (the documents shall indicate the special cases where the deck is incapable of supplying lateral support to the top chord [see Clause 16.8.1]);

(g) minimum moment of inertia to provide satisfactory design criteria for floor vibrations, if applicable (see Clause 6.3.3.2);

(h) any other information necessary for designing and supplying the joists; and

(i) a note that no drilling, cutting, or welding is to be done unless approved by the building designer.

Note: *The building drawings should include a note warning that attachments for mechanical, electrical, and other services should be made using approved clamping devices or U-bolt-type connectors.*

16.4.2 Joist design documents

Joist design documents prepared by the joist manufacturer shall show, as a minimum, the

(a) specified loading;
(b) factored member loads;
(c) material specification;
(d) member sizes;
(e) dimensions;
(f) spacers;
(g) welds;
(h) shoes;
(i) anchorages;
(j) bracing;
(k) bearings;
(l) field splices;
(m) bridging locations;
(n) camber; and
(o) coating type.

16.5 Design

16.5.1 Loading for open-web steel joists

The factored moment and shear resistances of open-web steel joists at every section shall not be less than the moment and shear due to the loading conditions specified by the building designer in the documents described in Clause 16.4.1(a) or to the factored dead load plus the following factored live load conditions, considered separately:

(a) for floor joists, an unbalanced live load applied on any continuous portion of the joist to produce the most critical effect on any component;

(b) for roof joists, an unbalanced loading condition with 100% of the snow load plus other live loads applied on any continuous portion of the joist and 50% of the snow load on the remainder of the joist to produce the most critical effect on any component;

(c) for roof joists, wind uplift;

(d) for roof joists, 100% of the snow load plus 40% of the downward wind load (companion load); and

(e) the appropriate factored concentrated load (from the *NBCC*) applied at any one panel point to produce the most critical effect on any component.

16.5.2 Design assumptions

Open-web steel joists shall be designed for loads acting in the plane of the joist applied to the top chord assumed to be prevented from lateral buckling by the deck. For the purpose of determining axial forces in all members, members may be assumed to be pin-connected and the loads may be replaced by statically equivalent loads applied at the panel points.

The resistance of the deck connections as well as the resistance of the deck shall be verified by the joist designer to ensure that adequate lateral support is provided to the top chord of a joist as determined in accordance with Clause 9.2.7. When additional stability elements are necessary, they shall be designed in accordance with Clause 9.2.6.2.

16.5.3 Verification of joist manufacturer's design

When the adequacy of the design of a joist cannot be readily demonstrated by a rational analysis based on accepted theory and engineering practice, the joist manufacturer may verify the design by test. The test shall be carried out as described in the testing procedure in Part 5 (steps 1 to 4) of Steel Joist Facts (CISC 1980). The test loading shall be 1.10/0.90 times the factored loads used in the design.

16.5.4 Member and connection resistance

Member and connection resistance shall be calculated in accordance with Clause 13, except as otherwise specified in Clause 16.

16.5.5 Width-to-thickness ratios

16.5.5.1

The width-to-thickness ratios of compressive elements of hot-formed sections and cold-formed HSS shall be governed by Clause 11. The width-to-thickness ratios of compressive elements of cold-formed sections shall be governed by CSA S136.

16.5.5.2

For the purpose of determining the appropriate width-to-thickness ratio of compressive elements supported along one edge, any stiffening effect of the deck or the joist web shall be neglected.

16.5.6 Bottom chord

16.5.6.1

The bottom chord shall be continuous and, when in tension, may be designed as an axially loaded tension member unless subject to eccentricities in excess of those permitted under Clause 16.5.10.4 or subject to applied load between panel points. The governing radius of gyration of the tension chord or any component thereof shall be not less than 1/240 of the corresponding unsupported length. For joists with the web in the y-plane, the unsupported length of chord for computing L_x/r_x shall be taken as the panel length centre-to-centre of panel points, and the unsupported length of chord for calculating L_y/r_y shall be taken as the distance between bridging lines connected to the tension chord. Joist shoes, when anchored, may be assumed to be equivalent to bridging lines. A bottom chord subjected to concentrated loads between panel points shall be designed, when the chord is in tension, in accordance with Clause 13.9 and, when the chord is in compression, in accordance with Clause 16.5.7.3, respectively.

16.5.6.2

The bottom chord shall be designed in accordance with Clause 16.5.7.3 for the resulting compressive forces when
(a) net uplift is specified;
(b) joists are made continuous or cantilevered;
(c) end moments are specified; or
(d) it provides lateral support to compression elements of beams or columns.

   Bracing, when required, shall be provided in accordance with Clause 9.2. For joists with net uplift, a single line of bottom-chord bridging shall be provided at each end of the joists near the first bottom chord panel points unless the ends of the bottom chord are otherwise restrained. (See also Clause 16.7.9(a)).

16.5.7 Top chord

16.5.7.1

The top chord shall be continuous and may be designed for axial compressive force alone when
(a) the panel length does not exceed 610 mm;
(b) concentrated loads are not applied between the panel points; and

(c)   not subject to eccentricities in excess of those permitted under Clause 16.5.10.4.

When the panel length exceeds 610 mm, the top chord shall be designed as a continuous member subject to combined axial and bending forces.

16.5.7.2

The slenderness ratio, KL/r, of the top chord or of its components shall not exceed 90 for interior panels or 120 for end panels. The governing KL/r shall be the maximum value determined by the following:

(a)   for the x-x (horizontal) axis, L_x shall be the centre-to-centre distance between panel points and K shall be taken as 0.9;

(b)   for the y-y (vertical) axis, L_y shall be the centre-to-centre distance between the attachments of the deck. The spacing of attachments shall be not more than the design slenderness ratio of the top chord times the radius of gyration of the top chord about its vertical axis and not more than 1000 mm. K shall be taken as 1.0; and

(c)   for the z-z (skew) axis of individual components, L_z shall be the centre-to-centre distance between panel points or spacers, or both, and K shall be taken as 0.9. Decking shall not be considered to fulfill the function of batten plates or spacers for top chords consisting of two separated components, where r = the appropriate radius of gyration.

16.5.7.3

Compression chords shall be proportioned such that

$$\frac{C_f}{C_r} + \frac{M_f}{M_r} \leq 1.0$$

where

M_r =   value specified in Clause 13.5

C_r =   value specified in Clause 13.3

At the panel point, C_r may be taken as $\phi A F_y$ and Clause 13.5(a) may be used to determine M_r provided that the chord meets the requirements of a Class 2 section and $M_f/M_p < 0.25$.

For top chords with panel lengths not exceeding 610 mm, M_f resulting from any uniformly distributed loading may be neglected.

The chord shall be assumed to be pinned at the joist supports.

16.5.7.4

Top chords in tension whose panel lengths exceed 610 mm shall be designed in accordance with Clause 13.9.

16.5.7.5

When welding is used to attach steel deck to the chord of a joist, the flat width of any chord component in contact with the deck shall be at least 5 mm larger than the nominal design dimensions of the deck welds, measured transverse to the longitudinal axis of the chord.

16.5.7.6

When mechanical fasteners are used to attach steel deck to the chord of a joist, the minimum chord thickness shall be specified by the designer.

16.5.8 Webs

16.5.8.1

Webs shall be designed in accordance with Clause 13 to resist the shear at any point due to the factored loads specified in Clause 16.5.1. Particular attention shall be paid to possible reversals of force in each web member.

16.5.8.2

The length of a web member shall be taken as the distance between the intersections of the neutral axes of the web member and the chords. For buckling in the plane of the web, the effective length factor shall be taken as 0.9 if the web consists of individual members. For all other cases, the effective length factor shall be taken as 1.0.

16.5.8.3

The factored resistances of the first compression web member subject to transverse shear, and its connections, shall be determined with their respective resistance factors, ϕ, multiplied by 0.85.

16.5.8.4

The vertical web members of a joist with a modified Warren geometry shall be designed to resist an axial force equal to the calculated sum of the compressive force in the web member plus 0.02 times the force in the compression chord at that location.

16.5.8.5

The slenderness ratio of a web member in tension need not be limited.

16.5.8.6

The slenderness ratio of a web member in compression shall not exceed 200.

16.5.9 Spacers and battens

Compression members consisting of two or more sections shall be interconnected so that the slenderness ratio of each section calculated using its least radius of gyration is less than or equal to the design slenderness ratio of the built-up member. Spacers or battens shall be an integral part of the joist.

16.5.10 Connections and splices

16.5.10.1

Component members of joists shall be connected by welding, bolting, or other approved means.

16.5.10.2

Connections and splices shall develop the factored loads without exceeding the factored member resistances specified in Clause 16. Butt-joint splices shall develop the factored tensile resistance, T_r, of the member.

16.5.10.3

Splices may occur at any point in chord or web members.

16.5.10.4

Members connected at a joint should have their centroidal axes meet at a point. Where this is impractical and eccentricities are introduced, such eccentricities may be neglected if they do not exceed the following:

(a) for continuous web members, the greater of the two distances measured from the neutral axis of the chord member to the extreme fibres of the chord member; and

(b) for non-continuous web members, the distance measured from the neutral axis to the back (outside face) of the chord member.

   When the eccentricity exceeds these limits, provision shall be made for the effects of the total eccentricity. Eccentricities assumed in design shall be taken as the maximum fabrication tolerances and shall be included with the shop details.

16.5.11 Bearings

16.5.11.1
Bearings of joists shall be proportioned so that the factored bearing resistance of the supporting material is not exceeded.

16.5.11.2
Where a joist bears, with or without a bearing plate, on solid masonry or concrete support, the bearing shall meet the requirements of CSA S304.1 for masonry and CAN/CSA-A23.3 for concrete.

16.5.11.3
Where a joist bears on a structural steel member, the end of the shoe shall extend at least 65 mm beyond the edge of the support, except that when the available bearing area is restricted, this distance may be reduced, provided that the shoe is adequately proportioned and anchored to the support.

16.5.11.4
The joist shoe and the end panel of the joist shall be proportioned to include the effect of the eccentricity between the centre of the bearing and the intersection of the centroidal axes of the chord and the end diagonal.

16.5.11.5
Bottom bearing joists shall have their top and bottom chords held adequately in position at the supports.

16.5.12 Anchorage

16.5.12.1
Joists shall be properly anchored to withstand the effects of the combined factored loads, including net uplift. As a minimum, the following shall be provided:
(a) when anchored to masonry or concrete:
   (i)   for floor joists, a 10 mm diameter rod at least 300 mm long embedded horizontally; and
   (ii) for roof joists, a 20 mm diameter anchor rod 300 mm long embedded vertically with a 50 mm, 90° hook, or a 20 mm diameter headed anchor rod; and
(b) when supported on steel, one 20 mm diameter bolt, or a pair of fillet welds satisfying the minimum size and length requirements of CSA W59; the connection shall be capable of withstanding a horizontal load equal to 10% of the reaction of the joist.

16.5.12.2
Tie joists may have their top and bottom chords connected to a column. Unless otherwise specified by the building designer, tie joists shall have top and bottom chord connections that are each at least equivalent to those required by Clause 16.5.12.1. Either the top or bottom connection shall utilize a bolted connection.

16.5.12.3
Where joists are used as a part of a frame, the joist-to-column connections shall be designed to carry the moments and forces due to the factored loads.

16.5.13 Deflection

16.5.13.1
Steel joists shall be proportioned so that deflection due to specified loads is within acceptable limits for the nature of the materials to be supported and the intended use and occupancy. Such deflection limits shall be as specified in Clause 6.3.1 unless otherwise specified by the building designer.

16.5.13.2
The deflection shall be calculated based on truss action, taking into account the axial deformation of all of the components of the joists.

16.5.14 Camber
Unless otherwise specified by the building designer, the nominal camber shall be 0.002 of the span. Negative cambers to satisfy roof drainage requirements shall be designed for appropriate rainwater ponding loads.

Note: *For manufacturing tolerances, see Clause 16.10.9. For maximum deviation between adjacent joists, or joists and adjacent beams or walls, see Clause 16.12.2.5. For special camber requirements, see Clause 6.3.2.2.*

16.5.15 Vibration
The building designer shall give special consideration to floor systems where unacceptable vibration can occur. When requested, the joist manufacturer shall supply joist properties and details to the building designer (see Annex E).

16.5.16 Welding
Welding shall meet the requirements of Clause 24. Specific welding procedures for joist fabrication shall be accepted by the Canadian Welding Bureau.

16.6 Stability during construction
Means shall be provided to support joist chords against lateral movement and to hold the joist in the vertical or specified plane during construction.

16.7 Bridging

16.7.1 General
Bridging transverse to the span of joists may be used to meet the requirements of Clause 16.6 and also to meet the slenderness ratio requirements for chords. Bridging shall not be considered "bracing" as described in Clause 9.2.

16.7.2 Installation
All bridging and bridging anchors shall be completely installed before any construction loads, except for the weight of the workers necessary to install the bridging, are placed on the joists.

16.7.3 Types
Unless otherwise specified or approved by the building designer, the joist manufacturer shall supply bridging that may be of the diagonal or horizontal type.

16.7.4 Diagonal bridging
Diagonal bridging consisting of crossed members running from the top chord to the bottom chord of adjacent joists shall have a slenderness ratio, L/r, of not more than 200, where L is the length of the diagonal bridging member or one-half of this length when crossed members are connected at their point of intersection, and r is the least radius of gyration. All diagonal bridging shall be connected adequately to the joists by bolts or welds.

16.7.5 Horizontal bridging

A line of horizontal bridging shall consist of a continuous member perpendicular to the joist span attached to either the top chord or the bottom chord of each joist. Horizontal bridging members shall have a slenderness ratio of not more than 300.

16.7.6 Attachment of bridging

Attachment of diagonal and horizontal bridging to joist chords shall be by welding or mechanical means capable of resisting an axial load of at least 3 kN in the attached bridging member. Welds shall meet the minimum length requirements specified in CSA W59.

16.7.7 Anchorage of bridging

Each line of bridging shall be adequately anchored at each end to sturdy walls or to main components of the structural frame, if practicable. Otherwise, diagonal and horizontal bridging shall be provided in combination between adjacent joists near the ends of bridging lines.

16.7.8 Bridging systems

Bridging systems, including sizes of bridging members and all necessary details, shall be shown on the erection diagrams. If a specific bridging system is required by the design, the design drawings shall show all information necessary for the preparation of shop details and erection diagrams.

16.7.9 Spacing of bridging

Diagonal and horizontal bridging shall be spaced so that the unsupported length of the chord between bridging lines or between laterally supported ends of the joist and adjacent bridging lines does not exceed
(a) $170r$ for chords in compression; and
(b) $240r$ for chords always in tension

where

r　=　applicable chord radius of gyration about its axis in the plane of the web

Ends of joists anchored to supports may be assumed to be equivalent to bridging lines. If ends of joists are not so anchored before deck is installed, the distance from the face of the support to the nearest bridging member in the plane of the bottom chord shall not exceed $120r$. There shall not be less than one line of horizontal or diagonal bridging attached to each joist spanning 4 m or more. If only a single line of bridging is required, it shall be placed at the centre of the joist span. If bridging is not used on joists less than 4 m in span, the ends of such joists shall be anchored to the supports to prevent overturning of the joist during placement of the deck.

16.8 Decking

16.8.1 Decking to provide lateral support

Decking shall bear directly on the top chord of the joist. If not sufficiently rigid to provide lateral support to the compression chord of the joist, the compression chord of the joist shall be braced laterally in accordance with Clause 9.2.

16.8.2 Deck attachments

Attachments considered to provide lateral support to top chords shall meet the requirements of Clause 9.2.3. The spacing of attachments shall not exceed
(a)   the design slenderness ratio of the top chord times the radius of gyration of the top chord about its vertical axis; and
(b)   1 m.

16.8.3 Diaphragm action

Where decking is used in combination with joists to form a diaphragm for the purpose of transferring lateral applied loads to vertical bracing systems, special attachment requirements shall be fully specified on the building design drawings.

16.8.4 Cast-in-place slabs

Cast-in-place slabs used as decking shall have a minimum thickness of 65 mm. Forms for cast-in-place slabs shall not cause lateral displacement of the top chords of joists during installation of the forms or the placing of the concrete. Non-removable forms shall be positively attached to top chords by means of welding, clips, ties, wedges, fasteners, or other suitable means at intervals not exceeding 1 m; however, there shall be at least two attachments in the width of each form at each joist. Forms and their method of attachment shall be such that the cast-in-place slab, after hardening, is capable of furnishing lateral support to the joist chords.

16.8.5 Installation of steel deck

16.8.5.1

To facilitate attachment of the steel deck, the location of the top chord of the joist shall be confirmed by marking the deck at suitable intervals or by other means.

16.8.5.2

The installer of the steel deck to be fastened to joists by arc spot welding shall be a company certified by the Canadian Welding Bureau to the requirements of CSA W47.1.

The welding procedures shall be accepted by the Canadian Welding Bureau.

The welders shall have current qualifications for arc spot welding issued by the Canadian Welding Bureau.

16.9 Shop coating

Joists shall have a shop coating meeting the requirements of Clause 28.7.3.3, unless otherwise specified by the building designer.

16.10 Manufacturing tolerances

16.10.1

The tolerance on the specified depth of the manufactured joist shall be ±7 mm.

16.10.2

The deviation of a panel point from the design location, measured along the length of a chord, shall not exceed 13 mm. The centroidal axes of the bottom chord and the end diagonals carrying transverse shear should meet at the first bottom panel point even when the end diagonal is an upturned bottom chord (see Clause 16.5.10.4).

16.10.3

The deviation of a panel point from the design location, measured perpendicular to the longitudinal axis of the chord and in the plane of the joist, shall not exceed 7 mm.

16.10.4

The connections of web members to chords shall not deviate laterally more than 3 mm from that assumed in the design.

16.10.5
The sweep of a joist or any portion of the length of the joist, upon completion of manufacture, shall not exceed 1/500 of the length on which the sweep is measured.

16.10.6
The tilt of bearing shoes shall not exceed 1 in 50 measured from a plane perpendicular to the plane of the web and parallel to the longitudinal axis of the joist.

16.10.7
The tolerance on the specified shoe depth shall be ±3 mm.

16.10.8
The tolerance on the specified length of the joist shall be ±7 mm. The connection holes in a joist shall not vary from the detailed location by more than 2 mm for joists 10 m or less in length or by more than 3 mm for joists more than 10 m in length.

16.10.9
The tolerance in millimetres on the nominal or specified camber shall be $\pm\left(6 + \dfrac{L}{4000}\right)$.

The minimum camber in a joist shall be 4 mm. The range in camber for joists of the same span shall be 20 mm.

16.11 Inspection and quality control

16.11.1 Inspection
Material and quality of work shall be accessible for inspection at all times by qualified inspectors representing the building designer. Random in-process inspection shall be carried out by the manufacturer and all joists shall be thoroughly inspected by the manufacturer before shipping. Third-party welding inspection shall be in accordance with Clause 30.5.

16.11.2 Identification and control of steel
Steel used in the manufacture of joists shall be identified in the manufacturer's plant as to its specification (and grade, where applicable) by suitable markings, recognized colour-coding, or a system devised by the manufacturer that will ensure to the satisfaction of the building designer that the correct material is being used.

16.11.3 Quality control
Upon request by the building designer, the manufacturer shall provide evidence of having suitable quality control measures to ensure that the joists meet all specified requirements. When testing is part of the manufacturer's normal quality control program, the loading criteria shall be 1.0/0.9 times the factored loads for the specific joist design.

16.12 Handling and erection

16.12.1 General
Care shall be exercised to avoid damage during strapping, transport, unloading, site storage, stacking, and erection. Dropping of joists shall be avoided. Special precautions shall be taken when erecting long, slender joists, and hoisting cables should not be released until the member is stayed laterally by at least one line of bridging. Joists shall have all bridging attached and permanently fastened in place before the application of any loads. Construction loads shall be adequately distributed so as not to exceed the capacity of any joist. Field welding shall not cause damage to joists, bridging, deck, and supporting steel members.

16.12.2 Erection tolerances

16.12.2.1
The maximum sweep of a joist or a portion of the length of a joist upon completion of erection shall not exceed the limit specified in Clause 16.10.5 and shall be in accordance with the requirements of Clause 29.

16.12.2.2
All members shall be free from twists, sharp kinks, and bends.

16.12.2.3
The deviation of joists as erected from the location in the plan shown on the erection diagrams shall not exceed 15 mm.

16.12.2.4
The deviation of the bottom chord with respect to the top chord, normal to the specified plane of the web of a joist, shall not exceed 1/50 of the depth of the joist.

16.12.2.5
The maximum deviation in elevation between the tops of any three adjacent joists shall not be greater than 0.01 times the joist spacing and not greater than 25 mm. The deviation is the vertical offset from the top of the centre joist to the line joining the tops of the centres of the adjacent joists. The maximum shall also apply to joists adjacent to beams or walls.

17 Composite beams, trusses, and joists

17.1 Application
Clause 17 shall apply to composite beams consisting of steel sections, trusses, or joists interconnected with either a reinforced concrete slab or a steel deck with a concrete cover slab. Trusses and joists designed to act compositely with the slab or cover slab shall also meet the requirements of Clauses 15 and 16, respectively.

17.2 Definitions
The following definitions apply in Clause 17:

Cover slab — the concrete above the flutes of the steel deck. All flutes are filled with concrete so as to form a ribbed slab.

Effective cover slab thickness, t — the minimum thickness of concrete measured from the top of the cover slab to the top of the steel deck. The minimum thickness shall be 65 mm unless the adequacy of a lesser thickness has been established by appropriate tests.

Effective slab thickness, t — the overall slab thickness, provided that the slab is cast
(a) with a flat underside;
(b) on corrugated steel forms having a height of corrugation not greater than 0.25 times the overall slab thickness; or
(c) on fluted steel forms whose profile has the following characteristics:
   (i) the minimum concrete rib width is 125 mm;
   (ii) the maximum rib height is 40 mm but not more than 0.4 times the overall slab thickness; and
   (iii) the average width between ribs does not exceed 0.25 times the overall slab thickness nor 0.2 times the minimum width of concrete ribs.

In all other cases, "effective slab thickness" means the overall slab thickness minus the height of flute corrugation.

Flute — the portion of the steel deck that forms a valley.

Rib — the portion of the concrete slab that is formed by the flute.

Slab — a reinforced cast-in-place concrete slab at least 65 mm in effective thickness. The area equal to the effective width times the effective slab thickness should be free of voids or hollows except for those specifically permitted in the definition of effective slab thickness.

Steel deck — a load-carrying steel deck consisting of a
(a) single fluted element (non-cellular deck); or
(b) two-element section consisting of a fluted element in conjunction with a flat sheet (cellular deck).
The maximum depth of the deck shall be 80 mm and the average width of the minimum flute shall be 50 mm. A steel deck may be of a type intended to act compositely with the cover slab in supporting applied load.

Steel joist — an open-web steel joist suitable for composite design (see Clause 16).

Steel section — a steel structural section with a solid web or webs suitable for composite design. Web openings may be used only if their effects are fully investigated and accounted for in the design.

Steel truss — a steel truss suitable for composite design (see Clause 15).

17.3 General

17.3.1 Deflections
Calculation of deflections shall take into account the effects of creep of concrete, shrinkage of concrete, and increased flexibility resulting from partial shear connection and from interfacial slip. These effects shall be established by test or analysis, where practicable. Consideration shall also be given to the effects of full or partial continuity in the steel beams and concrete slabs in reducing calculated deflections.

In lieu of tests or analysis, the effects of partial shear connection and interfacial slip, creep, and shrinkage may be assessed as follows:
(a) for increased flexibility resulting from partial shear connection and interfacial slip, the deflections shall be calculated using an effective moment of inertia given by

$$I_e = I_s + 0.85p^{0.25}(I_t - I_s)$$

where

I_s = moment of inertia of a steel beam, or of a steel joist or truss adjusted to include the effect of shear deformations, which may be taken into account by decreasing the moment of inertia based on the cross-sectional areas of the top and bottom chords by 15% or by a more detailed analysis

p = fraction of full shear connection

= 1.00 for full shear connection

I_t = transformed moment of inertia of composite beam based on the modular ratio $n = E/E_c$

(b) for creep, elastic deflections caused by dead loads and long-term live loads, as calculated in Item (a), need to be increased by 15%; and
(c) for shrinkage of concrete, using a selected free shrinkage strain, strain compatibility between the steel and concrete, and an age-adjusted effective modulus of elasticity of concrete as it shrinks and creeps, the deflection of a simply supported composite beam, joist, or truss shall be calculated as follows:

$$\Delta_s = \frac{L^2}{8}\psi = \frac{L^2}{8}c\frac{\varepsilon_f A_c y}{n_s l_{es}}$$

where

L = span of the beam, joist, or truss

ψ = curvature along length of the beam, joist, or truss due to shrinkage of concrete

c = empirical coefficient used to match theory with test results (accounting for cracking of concrete in tension, the non-linear stress-strain relationship of concrete, and other factors)

ε_f = free shrinkage strain of concrete

A_c = effective area of concrete slab

y = distance from centroid of effective area of concrete slab to centroidal axis of the composite beam, joist, or truss

n_s = modular ratio, E/E'_c

where

E'_c = $E_c/(1+\chi\phi)$

= age-adjusted effective modulus of elasticity of concrete

where

χ = aging coefficient of concrete

ϕ = creep coefficient of concrete

l_{es} = $l_s + 0.85p^{0.25}(l_{ts} - l_s)$

= effective moment of inertia of composite beam, truss, or joist based on the modular ratio n_s

where

l_{ts} = transformed moment of inertia based on the modular ratio n_s

Note: *For typical values of c, ε_f, χ, and ϕ, see Annex H.*

17.3.2 Vertical shear

The web area of steel sections or the web system of steel trusses and joists shall be proportioned to carry the total vertical shear, V_f.

17.3.3 End connections

End connections of steel sections, trusses, and joists shall be proportioned to transmit the total end reaction of the composite beam.

17.4 Design effective width of concrete

17.4.1

Slabs or cover slabs extending on both sides of the steel section or joist shall be deemed to have a design effective width, *b*, equal to the lesser of
(a) 0.25 times the composite beam span; or
(b) the average distance from the centre of the steel section, truss, or joist to the centres of adjacent parallel supports.

17.4.2

Slabs or cover slabs extending on one side only of the supporting section or joist shall be deemed to have a design effective width, *b*, not greater than the width of the top flange of the steel section or top chord of the steel joist or truss plus the lesser of
(a)   0.1 times the composite beam span; or
(b)   0.5 times the clear distance between the steel section, truss, or joist and the adjacent parallel support.

17.5 Slab reinforcement

17.5.1 General

Slabs shall be adequately reinforced to support all loads and to control both cracking transverse to the composite beam span and longitudinal cracking over the steel section or joist. Reinforcement shall not be less than that required by the specified fire-resistance design of the assembly.

17.5.2 Parallel reinforcement

Reinforcement parallel to the span of the beam in regions of negative bending moment of the composite beam shall be anchored by embedment in concrete that is in compression. The reinforcement of slabs that are to be continuous over the end support of steel sections or joists fitted with flexible end connections shall be given special attention. Reinforcement at the ends of beams supporting ribbed slabs perpendicular to the beam shall be not less than two 15M bars or equivalent.

17.5.3 Transverse reinforcement — Concrete slab on metal deck

Unless it is known from experience that longitudinal cracking caused by composite action directly over the steel section or joist is unlikely, additional transverse reinforcement or other effective means shall be provided. Such additional reinforcement shall be placed in the lower part of the slab and anchored so as to develop the yield strength of the reinforcement. The area of such reinforcement shall be not less than 0.002 times the concrete area being reinforced and shall be uniformly distributed.

17.5.4 Transverse reinforcement — Ribbed slabs

17.5.4.1

Where the ribs are parallel to the beam span, the area of transverse reinforcement shall be not less than 0.002 times the concrete cover slab area being reinforced and shall be uniformly distributed.

17.5.4.2

Where the ribs are perpendicular to the beam span, the area of transverse reinforcement shall be not less than 0.001 times the concrete cover slab area being reinforced and shall be uniformly distributed.

17.6 Interconnection

17.6.1

Except as permitted by Clauses 17.6.2 and 17.6.4, interconnection between steel sections, trusses, or joists and slabs or steel decks with cover slabs shall be attained by the use of shear connectors as specified in Clause 17.7.

17.6.2

Uncoated steel sections, trusses, or joists that support slabs and are totally encased in concrete shall not require interconnection by means of shear connectors, provided that
(a)   a minimum of 50 mm of concrete covers all portions of the steel section, truss, or joist except as specified in Item (c);
(b)   the cover in Item (a) is reinforced to prevent spalling; and

(c) the top of the steel section, truss, or joist is at least 40 mm below the top and 50 mm above the bottom of the slab.

17.6.3

Studs may be welded through a maximum of two steel sheets in contact, each not more than 1.71 mm in overall thickness, including coatings (1.52 mm in nominal base steel thickness plus zinc coating not greater than nominal 275 g/m²). Otherwise, holes for placing studs shall be made through the sheets as necessary. Welded studs shall meet the requirements of CSA W59.

17.6.4

Methods of interconnection other than those specified in Clause 17.7 that have been adequately demonstrated by test and verified by analysis may be used to effect the transfer of forces between the steel section, truss, or joist and the slab or steel deck with cover slab. In such cases, the design of the composite member shall conform, to the extent practicable, to the design of a similar member employing shear connectors.

17.6.5

The diameter of a welded stud shall not exceed 2.5 times the thickness of the part to which it is welded unless test data satisfactory to the designer are provided to establish the capacity of the stud as a shear connector.

17.7 Shear connectors

17.7.1 General

The resistance factor, ϕ_{sc}, to be used with the shear resistances specified in Clause 17.7 shall be taken as 0.80. The factored shear resistance, q_r, of other shear connectors shall be established by tests acceptable to the designer.

17.7.2 End-welded studs

17.7.2.1

End-welded studs shall be headed or hooked with $h/d \geq 4$. The projection of a stud in a ribbed slab, based on its length prior to welding, shall be at least two stud diameters above the top surface of the steel deck. The factored resistance of end-welded studs shall be as specified in Clauses 17.7.2.2 and 17.7.2.4.

17.7.2.2

In solid slabs

$$q_{rs} = 0.50\phi_{sc}A_{sc}\sqrt{f_c'E_c} \leq \phi_{sc}A_{sc}F_u$$

where

q_{rs} = factored shear resistance

F_u = 450 MPa for commonly available studs (CSA W59 Type B studs)

17.7.2.3

In ribbed slabs with ribs parallel to the beam

(a) when $3.0 > w_d/h_d \geq 1.50$:

$$q_{rr} = q_{rs}\left[0.75 + 0.167\left(\frac{w_d}{h_d} - 1.5\right)\right] \leq q_{rs}$$

(b)   when $w_d/h_d < 1.50$:

$$q_{rr} = \phi_{sc}\left[0.92\frac{w_d}{h_d}dh(f_c')^{0.8} + 11sd(f_c')^{0.2}\right] \le 0.75q_{rs}$$

where

s   = longitudinal stud spacing

17.7.2.4

In ribbed slabs with ribs perpendicular to the beam
(a)   when $h_d = 75$ mm:

$$q_{rr} = 0.35\phi_{sc}\rho A_p\sqrt{f_c'} \le q_{rs}$$

(b)   when $h_d = 38$ mm:

$$q_{rr} = 0.61\phi_{sc}\rho A_p\sqrt{f_c'} \le q_{rs}$$

where

A_p = concrete pullout area, taking the deck profile and stud burnoff into account. For a single stud,
          the apex of the pyramidal pullout area, with four sides sloping at 45°, shall be taken as the centre
          of the top surface of the head of the stud. For a pair of studs, the pullout area has a ridge
          extending from stud to stud

ρ = 1.0 for normal-density concrete (2150 to 2500 kg/m^3)

         = 0.85 for semi-low-density concrete (1850 to 2150 kg/m^3)

17.7.2.5

The longitudinal spacing of stud connectors in solid slabs and in ribbed slabs when ribs of formed steel
deck are parallel to the beam shall be not less than six stud diameters. The spacing of studs shall not
exceed 1000 mm (see also Clause 17.8).
    The transverse spacing of stud connectors shall be not less than four stud diameters.

17.7.3 Channel connectors

In solid slabs of normal-density concrete with $f_c' \ge 20$ MPa and a density of at least 2300 kg/m^3, the
following shall apply:

$$q_{rs} = 45\phi_{sc}(t + 0.5w)L_c\sqrt{f_c'}$$

The spacing of the shear connectors shall be in accordance with Clause 17.9.8.

17.8 Ties

Mechanical ties shall be provided between the steel section, truss, or joist and the slab or steel deck to
prevent separation. Shear connectors may serve as mechanical ties if suitably proportioned. The maximum
spacing of ties shall not exceed 1000 mm. The average spacing in a span shall not exceed 600 mm or be
greater than that required to achieve any specified fire-resistance rating of the composite assembly.

17.9 Design of composite beams with shear connectors

17.9.1

The composite beam shall consist of steel section, truss or joist, shear connectors, ties, and slab or steel deck with cover slab.

The flat width of the top chord or that of a component member of the top chord shall be not less than $1.4d + 20$ mm

where

d = diameter of the stud connector

17.9.2

The properties of the composite section shall be based on the maximum effective area (equal to effective width times effective thickness), neglecting any concrete area in tension. If a steel truss or joist is used, the area of its top chord shall be neglected in determining the properties of the composite section and only Clause 17.9.3(a) shall apply.

17.9.3

The factored moment resistance, M_{rc}, of the composite section with the slab or cover slab in compression shall be calculated as follows, where $\phi = 0.90$, the resistance factor for concrete, $\phi_c = 0.65$, and $\alpha_1 = 0.85 - 0.0015 f'_c$ (but not less than 0.67):

(a) Case 1 — full shear connection and plastic neutral axis in the slab, i.e., $Q_r \geq \phi A_s F_y$ and $\phi A_s F_y \leq \alpha_1 \phi_c b t f'_c$

where
Q_r = sum of the factored resistances of all shear connectors between points of maximum and zero moment

$$M_{rc} = T_r e' = \phi A_s F_y e'$$

where

e' = the lever arm and is calculated from the equation

$$a = \frac{\phi A_s F_y}{\alpha_1 \phi_c b f'_c}$$

(b) Case 2 — full shear connection and plastic neutral axis in the steel section, i.e., $Q_r \geq \alpha_1 \phi_c b t f'_c$ and $\alpha_1 \phi_c b t f'_c < \phi A_s F_y$

$$M_{rc} = C_r e + C'_r e''$$

where

$$C_r = \frac{\phi A_s F_y - C'_r}{2}$$

$$C'_r = \alpha_1 \phi_c b t f'_c$$

(c) Case 3 — partial shear connection, i.e., $Q_r < \alpha_1 \phi_c b t f'_c$ and $\phi A_s F_y$

$$M_{rc} = C_r e + C'_r e''$$

where

$$C_r = \frac{\phi A_s F_y - C_r'}{2}$$

$$C_r' = Q_r$$

where

e' = the lever arm and is calculated from the equation

$$a = \frac{C_r'}{\alpha_1 \phi_c bf_c'}$$

17.9.4

No composite action shall be assumed in calculating
(a) flexural strength when Q_r is less than 0.4 times the lesser of $\alpha_1 \phi_c btf_c'$ and $\phi A_s F_y$; and
(b) deflections when Q_r is less than 0.25 times the lesser of $\alpha_1 \phi_c btf_c'$ and $\phi A_s F_y$.

17.9.5

For full shear connection, the sum of the factored resistances of all shear connectors distributed between the point of maximum bending moment and each adjacent point of zero moment, Q_r, shall equal or exceed the total horizontal shear, V_h, at the junction of the steel section, truss, or joist and the concrete slab or steel deck, calculated as $V_h = \phi A_s F_y$ or $V_h = \alpha_1 \phi_c btf_c'$ for Cases 1 and 2, as specified in Items (a) and (b), respectively, of Clause 17.9.3.

17.9.6

For partial shear connection, the total horizontal shear, V_h, as specified in Clause 17.9.3(c), shall be calculated as $V_h = Q_r$.

17.9.7

Composite beams employing steel sections and concrete slabs may be designed as continuous members. The factored moment resistance of the composite section, with the concrete slab in the tension area of the composite section, shall be the factored moment resistance of the steel section alone, except that when sufficient shear connectors are placed in the negative moment region, suitably anchored concrete slab reinforcement parallel to the steel sections and within the design effective width of the concrete slab may be included in calculating the properties of the composite section. The total horizontal shear, V_h, to be resisted by shear connectors between the point of maximum negative bending moment and each adjacent point of zero moment shall be taken as $\phi_r A_r F_{yr}$.

17.9.8

The number of shear connectors to be located on each side of the point of maximum bending moment (positive or negative, as applicable), distributed between that point and the adjacent point of zero moment, shall be not less than

$$n = \frac{V_h}{q_r}$$

Shear connectors may be spaced uniformly, except that in a region of positive bending the number of shear connectors, n', required between any concentrated load applied in that region and the nearest point of zero moment shall be not less than

$$n' = n\left(\frac{M_{f1} - M_r}{M_f - M_r}\right)$$

where

M_{f1} = positive bending moment under factored load at concentrated load point

M_r = factored moment resistance of the steel section alone

M_f = maximum positive bending moment under factored load

17.9.9

In the end panels of composite joists and trusses, the top chord shall be designed to resist all factored forces, ignoring any composite action unless adequate shear connectors are placed over the seat or along a top chord extension to carry horizontal shear. Studs shall not be placed closer than their height to the end of the concrete slab.

17.9.10

The shear that is to be developed on the longitudinal shear surfaces, A_{cv}, of composite beams with solid slabs or with cover slabs and steel deck parallel to the beam shall be taken as

$$V_u = \Sigma q_r - \alpha_1 \phi_c f_c' A_c - \phi_r A_r F_{yr}$$

where

A_r = area of longitudinal reinforcement within the concrete area, A_c

For normal-weight concrete, the factored shear resistance along any potential longitudinal shear surfaces in the concrete slab shall be taken as

$$V_r = \left(0.80 \phi_r A_r F_{yr} + 2.76 \phi_c A_{cv} \right) \leq 0.50 \phi_c f_c' A_{cv}$$

where

A_r = area of transverse reinforcement crossing shear planes, A_{cv}

17.10 Design of composite beams without shear connectors

17.10.1

Uncoated steel sections or joists supporting concrete slabs and encased in concrete in accordance with Clause 17.6.2 may be proportioned based on the assumption that the composite section supports the total load.

17.10.2

The properties of the composite section for determination of load-carrying capacity shall be calculated using ultimate strength methods, neglecting any area of concrete in tension.

17.10.3

As an alternative method of design, encased simple-span steel sections or joists may be proportioned based on the assumption that the steel section, truss, or joist alone supports 0.90 times the total load.

17.11 Unshored beams

For composite beams that are unshored during construction, the stresses in the tension flange of the steel section, truss, or joist due to the loads applied before the concrete strength reaches $0.75 f_c'$ plus the stresses at the same location due to the remaining specified loads considered to act on the composite section shall not exceed F_y.

17.12 Beams during construction

The steel section, truss, or joist alone shall be proportioned to support all factored loads applied prior to hardening of the concrete without exceeding its calculated capacity under the conditions of lateral support or shoring, or both, to be furnished during construction.

18 Composite columns

18.1 Resistance prior to composite action

The factored resistance of the steel member prior to the attainment of composite action shall be determined in accordance with Clause 13.

18.2 Concrete-filled hollow structural sections

18.2.1 General

18.2.1.1 Scope

Clause 18.2 applies to composite members consisting of steel hollow structural sections completely filled with concrete, provided that

(a) the width-to-thickness ratio of the walls of rectangular hollow structural sections does not exceed

$$\frac{1350}{\sqrt{F_y}};$$

(b) the outside diameter-to-thickness ratio of circular hollow structural sections does not exceed $28\,000/F_y$; and

(c) the concrete strength is between 20 and 80 MPa for axially loaded columns and between 20 and 40 MPa for columns subjected to axial compression and bending.

18.2.1.2 Axial load on concrete

The axial load assumed to be carried by the concrete at the top level of a column shall be only that portion applied by direct bearing on concrete. At the bottom of a column, a base plate or other means shall be provided for load transfer. At intermediate floor levels, direct bearing on the concrete shall not be considered necessary.

18.2.1.3 Composite action in bending

Full composite resistance as specified in Clause 18.2.3 may be developed at the ends of concrete-filled hollow structural members in bending or combined axial-bending, e.g., at column bases, only if the connection is able to transfer the forces from both the steel and concrete elements to the adjacent structural elements.

18.2.2 Compressive resistance

The factored compressive resistance of a composite concrete-filled hollow structural section shall be taken as

$$C_{rc} = (\tau \phi A_s F_y + \tau' \alpha_1 \phi_c A_c f_c')(1 + \lambda^{2n})^{-1/n}$$

where

τ $= \tau'$

$\quad = 1.0$, except for circular hollow structural sections with a height-to-diameter ratio (L/D) of less than 25 for which

$$\tau = \frac{1}{\sqrt{1 + \rho + \rho^2}}$$

and $\tau' = 1 + \left(\dfrac{25\rho^2 \tau}{D/t}\right)\left(\dfrac{F_y}{\alpha_1 f_c'}\right)$

where

$$\rho = 0.02\,(25 - L/D)$$

$$\alpha_1 = 0.85 - 0.0015f'_c \text{ (but not less than 0.67)}$$

$$\lambda = \sqrt{\frac{C_p}{C_{ec}}}$$

where

$$C_p = C_{rc}, \text{ computed with } \phi = \phi_c = 1.0 \text{ and } \lambda = 0$$

$$C_{ec} = \frac{\pi^2 EI_e}{(KL)^2}$$

where

$$EI_e = EI_s + \frac{0.6E_c I_c}{1 + C_{fs}/C_f}$$

where

I_s and I_c = moment of inertia of the steel and concrete areas, respectively, as computed with respect to the centre of gravity of the cross-section

E_c = modulus of elasticity of concrete as defined in Clause 2.1

C_{fs} = sustained axial load on the column

C_f = total axial load on the column

$$n = 1.80$$

18.2.3 Bending resistance

The factored bending resistance of a composite concrete-filled hollow structural section shall be taken as

$$M_{rc} = C_r e + C'_r e'$$

where

(a) for a rectangular hollow structure section:

$$C_r = \frac{\phi A_s F_y - C'_r}{2}$$

$$C'_r = 1.18\,\alpha_1\,\phi_c\,a\,(b - 2t)\,f'_c$$

$$C_r + C'_r = T_r$$

$$= \phi A_{st} F_y$$

Note: *The concrete in compression is taken to have a rectangular stress block of intensity f'_c over a depth of a.*

(b) for a circular hollow structural section:

$$C_r = \phi F_y\,\beta\,\frac{Dt}{2}$$

$$C'_r = 1.18\alpha_1\phi_c f'_c\left[\frac{\beta D^2}{8} - \frac{b_c}{2}\left(\frac{D}{2} - a\right)\right]$$

$$e = b_c\left[\frac{1}{(2\pi - \beta)} + \frac{1}{\beta}\right]$$

$$e' = b_c\left[\frac{1}{(2\pi - \beta)} + \frac{b_c^2}{1.5\beta D^2 - 6b_c(0.5D - a)}\right]$$

where

β = value in radians found from the recursive equation

$$\beta = \frac{\phi A_s F_y + 0.295 \alpha_1 \phi_c D^2 f_c' \left[\sin(\beta/2) - \sin^2(\beta/2) \tan(\beta/4) \right]}{\left(0.148 \alpha_1 \phi_c D^2 f_c' + \phi D t F_y \right)}$$

$$b_c = D \sin\left(\frac{\beta}{2}\right)$$

$$a = \frac{b_c}{2} \tan\left(\frac{\beta}{4}\right)$$

Conservatively, M_{rc} may be taken as

$$M_{rc} = \left(Z - 2 t h_n^2\right) \phi F_y + \left[\frac{2}{3}(0.5D - t)^3 - (0.5D - t)h_n^2\right] 1.18 \alpha_1 \phi_c f_c'$$

where

Z = the plastic modulus of the steel section alone

$$h_n = \frac{1.18 \alpha_1 \phi_c A_c f_c'}{2.36 D \alpha_1 \phi_c f_c' + 4t(2\phi F_y - 1.18 \alpha_1 \phi_c f_c')}$$

α_1 = value as defined in Clause 18.2.2

18.2.4 Axial compression and bending

Composite concrete-filled hollow structural sections required to resist both bending moments and axial compression shall be proportioned analogously to members conforming to Clause 13.8.2 so that

$$\frac{C_f}{C_{rc}} + \frac{B \omega_1 M_f}{M_{rc}\left(1 - \dfrac{C_f}{C_{ec}}\right)} \leq 1.0 \text{ and}$$

$$\frac{M_f}{M_{rc}} \leq 1.0$$

where

$$B = \frac{C_{rco} - C_{rcm}}{C_{rco}}$$

where

C_{rco} = factored compressive resistance with $\lambda = 0$

C_{rcm} = $1.18 \, \alpha_1 \phi_c A_c f_c'$

where

α_1 = value as defined in Clause 18.2.2

M_{rc} = value as defined in Clause 18.2.3

18.3 Partially encased composite columns

Note: *The Canam Group Inc. holds patents on the partially encased composite columns described in this Clause. Canam Group Inc. will make available any patent rights to interested applicants, wherever located, either as a free licence or on reasonable terms and conditions.*

18.3.1 General

Clause 18.3 applies to doubly symmetrical composite members consisting of three-plate built-up steel H-sections, with plain tie bars welded between the flange tips at regular intervals, in which the cells between the column flanges and the web are completely filled with concrete in the field during construction, provided that

(a) members are axially loaded;

(b) concrete is of normal density and has a compressive strength, f'_c, between 20 and 70 MPa;

(c) $A_s + A_r \leq 0.20$ of the gross cross-sectional area;

(d) the full width of flange, b_f, is between 0.9 and 1.1 times the section depth, d;

(e) the flanges and the web are of equal thickness, t;

(f) the flange width-to-thickness ratio is not greater than 32;

(g) a pair of continuous fillet welds, sufficient to develop the shear yield capacity of the web, connects the web to each flange;

(h) the vertical spacing of tie bars, s, does not exceed the lesser of 500 mm or two-thirds of the least dimension of the cross-section. The area of a tie bar shall be taken as the greatest of

    (i) 63 mm^2;

    (ii) $0.01 b_f t$; and

    (iii) 0.5 mm^2 per mm of tie bar spacing;

(i) the tie bars are welded to the flanges to develop the yield strength of the tie bars and the cover of the tie bars is at least 30 mm;

(j) out-of-straightness of the flanges, as measured between any two adjacent ties along the column edges, does not exceed 0.005 times the tie spacing;

(k) the specified yield strength of structural steel, F_y, does not exceed 350 MPa;

(l) the specified yield strength of reinforcement, F_{yr}, does not exceed 400 MPa; and

(m) the clear height-to-width ratio of the column does not exceed 14.

18.3.2 Compressive resistance

The factored compressive resistance of a partially encased three-plate built-up composite column shall be taken as

$$C_{rc} = (\phi A_{se} F_y + 0.95 \alpha_1 \phi_c A_c f'_c + \phi_r A_r F_{yr})(1 + \lambda^{2n})^{-1/n}$$

where

A_{se} = effective steel area of the steel section

    = $(d - 2t + 2b_e)t$

    where

$$b_e = \frac{b_f}{\left(1 + \lambda_p^3\right)^{1/1.5}} \leq b_f$$

        where

$$\lambda_p = \frac{b_f}{t}\sqrt{\frac{F_y}{720\ 000k}}$$

           where

$$k = \frac{0.9}{(s/b_f)^2} + 0.2(s/b_f)^2 + 0.75$$

α_1 = value specified in Clause 18.2.2

A_r = area of longitudinal reinforcement

λ = $\sqrt{\dfrac{C_p}{C_{ec}}}$

where

C_p = C_{rc} computed with ϕ, ϕ_c, and $\phi_r = 1.0$ and $\lambda = 0$

C_{ec} = value specified in Clause 18.2.2

n = 1.34

18.3.3 Bending resistance

The factored bending resistance of a partially encased three-plate built-up composite column shall be taken as

$$M_{rc} = C_r e + C'_r e'$$

where

C_r = $\dfrac{\phi A_s F_y - C'_r}{2}$

$C_r + C'_r$ = T_r

= $\phi A_{st} F_y$

$C'_r = 1.18 \alpha_1 \phi_c a(b - t)\, f'_c$ for strong axis bending

$C'_r = 1.18 \alpha_1 \phi_c a(b - 2t)\, f'_c$ for weak axis bending

Note: *The concrete in compression is taken to have a rectangular stress block of intensity f'_c over a depth of a.*

18.3.4 Axial compression and bending

Partially encased three-plate built-up composite columns required to resist both bending moments and axial compression shall be proportioned so that

$$\frac{C_f}{C_{rc}} + \frac{M_{fx}}{M_{rcx}} + \frac{M_{fy}}{M_{rcy}} \leq 1$$

18.3.5 Special reinforcement for seismic zones

18.3.5.1

Columns larger than 500 mm in depth in buildings where the specified one-second spectral acceleration ratio ($I_E F_a S_a(1.0)$) is greater than 0.30 shall be reinforced with longitudinal and transverse bars.

18.3.5.2

The longitudinal bars specified in Clause 18.3.5.1 shall

(a) have an area not less than 0.005 times the total gross cross-sectional area;

(b) be at least two in number in each cell; and

(c) be positioned against the tie bars and at a spacing not greater than the tie spacing, s.

18.3.5.3

The transverse bars specified in Clause 18.3.5.1 shall

(a) be U-shaped 15M bars arranged to provide corner support to at least every alternate longitudinal bar in such a way that no unsupported longitudinal bar is farther than 150 mm clear from a laterally supported bar;

(b) have ends welded to the web of the steel shape, in line with the ends of the transverse bars located in the opposite cell, or ends anchored within the concrete core located on the opposite side of the web; and

(c)   have a vertical spacing not greater than the tie spacing, s, or 16 times the diameter of the smallest longitudinal bar.

18.4 Encased composite columns

18.4.1 General
Clause 18.4 applies to doubly symmetrical steel columns encased in concrete, provided that
(a)   the steel shape is a Class 1, 2, or 3 section;
(b) $A_s \geq 0.04$ of the gross cross-sectional area;
(c) $A_s + A_r \leq 0.20$ of the gross cross-sectional area;
(d)   the concrete is of normal density and has a compressive strength, f'_c, between 20 and 55 MPa;
(e)   the specified yield strength of structural steel, F_y, does not exceed 350 MPa; and
(f)   the specified yield strength of reinforcement, F_{yr}, does not exceed 400 MPa.

18.4.2 Compressive resistance
The factored compressive resistance of a steel concrete-encased composite column shall be taken as

$$C_{rc} = (\phi A_s F_y + \alpha_1 \phi_c A_c f'_c + \phi_r A_r F_{yr})(1 + \lambda^{2n})^{-1/n}$$

where
α_1 =   value specified in Clause 18.2.2
A_r =   value specified in Clause 18.3.2
λ =   value specified in Clause 18.3.2
n =   value specified in Clause 18.3.2

18.4.3 Reinforcement

18.4.3.1
The concrete encasement shall be reinforced with longitudinal bars and lateral ties extending completely around the structural steel core. The clear cover shall not be less than 40 mm.
   The longitudinal bars shall
(a)   be continuous at framed levels when considered to carry load;
(b)   have an area not less than 0.01 times the total gross cross-sectional area;
(c)   be located at each corner; and
(d)   spaced on all sides not further apart than $525t/\sqrt{F_y}$ times one-half the least dimension of the composite section.

18.4.3.2
The lateral ties shall
(a)   be 15M bars, except that 10M bars may be used when no side dimension of the composite section exceeds 500 mm; and
(b)   have a vertical spacing not exceeding the least of the following:
      (i)   two-thirds of the least side dimension of the cross-section;
      (ii)   16 longitudinal bar diameters; or
      (iii) 500 mm.

18.4.4 Columns with multiple steel shapes
Where the composite cross-section includes two or more steel shapes, the steel shapes shall be considered built-up members subject to the requirements of Clause 19 until the concrete strength reaches $0.75f'_c$.

18.4.5 Load transfer

The portion of the total axial load resisted by the concrete shall be developed by direct bearing at connections. The bearing strength of concrete may be taken as $1.95\phi_c\alpha_1 f'_c A_L$, where A_L is the loaded area, provided that the concrete is restrained against lateral expansion.

18.4.6 Bending resistance

The bending resistance of encased composite columns may be determined according to the Structural Stability Research Council's *Guide to Stability Design Criteria for Metal Structures*.

19 Built-up members

19.1 Members in compression

19.1.1

All components of built-up compression members and the transverse spacing of their lines of connecting bolts or welds shall meet the requirements of Clauses 10 and 11.

19.1.2

Component parts that are in contact with one another at the ends of built-up compression members shall be connected by
(a) bolts spaced longitudinally not more than four diameters apart for a distance equal to 1.5 times the width of the member; or
(b) continuous welds having a length of not less than the width of the member.

19.1.3

Unless closer spacing is required for transfer of load or sealing inaccessible surfaces, the longitudinal spacing in-line between intermediate bolts or the clear longitudinal spacing between intermittent welds for the outside plate component of built-up compression members shall not exceed the following, where t is the thickness of the outside plate:
(a) when the bolts or intermittent welds are staggered on adjacent lines: $525t/\sqrt{F_y}$, but not more than 450 mm; and
(b) when the bolts on all gauge lines or intermittent welds along the component edges are not staggered: $330t/\sqrt{F_y}$, but not more than 300 mm.

19.1.4

Compression members composed of two or more shapes in contact or separated from one another shall be interconnected in such a way that the slenderness ratio of any component, based on its least radius of gyration and the distance between interconnections, shall not exceed that of the built-up member. The compressive resistance of the built-up member shall be based on
(a) the slenderness ratio of the built-up member with respect to the appropriate axis, when the buckling mode does not involve relative deformation that produces shear forces in the interconnectors; or
(b) an equivalent slenderness ratio, with respect to the axis orthogonal to that in Item (a), when the buckling mode involves relative deformation that produces shear forces in the interconnectors, taken as follows:

$$\rho_e = \sqrt{\rho_o^2 + \rho_i^2}$$

where
ρ_e = equivalent slenderness ratio of the built-up member
ρ_o = slenderness ratio of the built-up member acting as an integral unit

ρ_i = maximum slenderness ratio of component part of the built-up member between interconnectors

For built-up members composed of two interconnected shapes, e.g., back-to-back angles or channels, in contact or separated only by filler plates, the maximum slenderness ratio of component parts between fasteners or welds shall be based on an effective length factor of 1.0 when the fasteners are snug-tight bolts and 0.65 when welds or pretensioned bolts are used.

For built-up members composed of two interconnected shapes separated by lacing or batten plates, the maximum slenderness ratio of component parts between fasteners or welds shall be based on an effective length factor of 1.0 for both snug-tight and pretensioned bolts and for welds.

For compound compression members, connections at the ends and interconnectors should be capable of transferring the shears and moments through a rigid connection up to the factored load levels.

19.1.5

For starred angle compression members interconnected at least at the one-third points, Clause 19.1.4 need not apply.

19.1.6

The fasteners and interconnecting parts, if any, of members identified in Clause 19.1.4 shall be proportioned to resist a force equal to 0.01 times the total force in the built-up member.

19.1.7

It is possible that the spacing requirements of Clauses 19.1.3, 19.2.3, and 19.2.4 will not always provide a continuous tight fit between components in contact. When the environment is such that corrosion could be a serious problem, it is possible that the spacing of bolts or welds will need to be less than the specified maximum.

19.1.8

Open sides of compression members built up from plates or shapes shall be connected to each other by lacing, batten plates, or perforated cover plates.

19.1.9

Lacing shall provide a complete triangulated shear system and may consist of bars, rods, or shapes. Lacing shall be proportioned to resist a shear normal to the longitudinal axis of the member of not less than 0.025 times the total axial load on the member plus the shear from transverse loads, if any.

19.1.10

The slenderness ratio of lacing members shall not exceed 140. The effective length for single lacing shall be the distance between connections to the main components; for double lacing connected at the intersections, the effective length shall be half of that distance.

19.1.11

Lacing members shall be inclined preferably to the longitudinal axis of the built-up member at an angle of not less than 45°.

19.1.12

Lacing systems shall have diaphragms in the plane of the lacing and as near to the ends as practicable, as well as at intermediate points where lacing is interrupted. Such diaphragms may be plates (tie plates) or shapes.

19.1.13

End tie plates used as diaphragms shall have a length not less than the distance between the lines of bolts or welds connecting them to the main components of the member. Intermediate tie plates shall be at least one-half the specified length of end tie plates. The thickness of tie plates shall be at least 1/60 of the width between lines of bolts or welds connecting them to the main components, and the longitudinal spacing of the bolts or clear longitudinal spacing between welds shall not exceed 150 mm. At least three bolts shall connect the tie plate to each main component or a total length of weld not less than one-third the length of tie plate shall be used.

19.1.14

Shapes used as diaphragms shall be proportioned and connected to transmit a longitudinal shear equal to 0.05 times the axial compression in the member from one main component to the other.

19.1.15

Perforated cover plates may be used in lieu of lacing and tie plates on open sides of built-up compressive members. The net width of such plates at access holes may be assumed to resist axial load, provided that
(a) the width-to-thickness ratio is as specified in Clause 11;
(b) the length of the access hole does not exceed twice its width;
(c) the clear distance between access holes in the direction of load is not less than the transverse distance between lines of bolts or welds connecting the perforated plate to the main components of the built-up member; and
(d) the periphery of the access hole has a minimum radius of 40 mm at all points.

19.1.16

Battens consisting of plates or shapes may be used on open sides of built-up compression members that do not carry primary bending in addition to axial load. Battens shall be provided at the ends of the member, at locations where the member is laterally supported along its length, and elsewhere as required by Clause 19.1.4.

19.1.17

Battens shall have a length of not less than the distance between lines of bolts or welds connecting them to the main components of the member and shall have a thickness of not less than 1/60 of this distance if the batten consists of a flat plate. Battens and their connections shall be proportioned to resist the following simultaneously:

(a) a longitudinal shear force $V_f = \dfrac{0.025\, C_f d}{na}$; and

(b) a moment $V_f = \dfrac{0.025\, C_f d}{na}$

where
d = longitudinal centre-to-centre distance between battens
n = number of parallel planes of battens
a = distance between lines of bolts or welds connecting the batten to each main component

19.2 Members in tension

19.2.1

Members in tension composed of two or more shapes, plates, or bars separated from one another by intermittent fillers shall have the components interconnected at fillers spaced so that the slenderness ratio of any component between points of interconnection shall not exceed 300.

19.2.2

Members in tension composed of two plate components in contact or a shape and a plate component in contact shall have the components interconnected so that the spacing between connecting bolts or clear spacing between welds does not exceed the lesser of 36 times the thickness of the thinner plate or 450 mm (see Clause 19.1.3).

19.2.3

Members in tension composed of two or more shapes in contact shall have the components interconnected so that the spacing between connecting bolts or the clear spacing between welds does not exceed 600 mm, except where it can be determined that a greater spacing would not affect the satisfactory performance of the member (see Clause 19.1.3).

19.2.4

Members in tension composed of two separated main components may have perforated cover plates or tie plates on the open sides of the built-up member. Tie plates, including end tie plates, shall have a length of not less than two-thirds of the transverse distance between bolts or welds connecting them to the main components of the member and shall be spaced so that the slenderness ratio of any component between the tie plates does not exceed 300. The thickness of tie plates shall be at least 1/60 of the transverse distance between the bolts or welds connecting them to the main components, and the longitudinal spacing of the bolts or welds shall not exceed 150 mm. Perforated cover plates shall meet the requirements of Items (b), (c), and (d) of Clause 19.1.15.

19.3 Open box-type beams and grillages

Two or more rolled beams or channels used side by side to form a flexural member shall be connected at intervals of not more than 1500 mm. Through-bolts and separators may be used, provided that, in beams having a depth of 300 mm or more, not fewer than two bolts are used at each separator location. When concentrated loads are carried from one beam to the other or distributed between the beams, diaphragms having sufficient stiffness to distribute the load shall be bolted or welded between the beams. The design of members shall provide for torsion resulting from any unequal distribution of loads. Where beams are exposed, they shall be sealed against corrosion of interior surfaces or spaced sufficiently far apart to permit cleaning and coating.

20 Plate walls

20.1 General

20.1.1 Definition

A plate wall is a lateral-force-resisting structural system consisting of a framework of columns and beams, with relatively thin infill plates in the plane of the frame connected all around to the surrounding members. Frame connections between the beams and columns may be moment-resisting or simple shear connections.

20.1.2 Lateral resistance

Lateral storey shears are considered to be carried by a combination of frame action, if applicable, and post-buckling tension fields that develop in the infill plates parallel to the direction of the principal tensile stresses. Axial forces and moments develop in the beams and columns of plate walls as a result of the
(a) response of the wall to the overall bending and shear; and
(b) tension field action in the adjacent infill plates.

20.2 Seismic applications

Under seismic loading, plate walls shall meet the additional requirements of Clauses 27.9 or 27.10, as appropriate.

20.3 Analysis

Forces and moments in the members and connections, including those resulting from tension field action, may be determined from a plane frame analysis, with the infill plates represented by a series of inclined pin-ended strips.

20.4 Angle of inclination

20.4.1
When the aspect ratio of the panel lies within the limits $0.6 \leq L/h \leq 2.5$, the angle of inclination from the vertical, α, of the inclined pin-ended strips may be taken as 40°. Otherwise, it shall be determined as follows and shall be between 38° and 45°:

$$\tan^4 \alpha = \frac{1 + \dfrac{wL}{2A_c}}{1 + wh\left(\dfrac{1}{A_b} + \dfrac{h^3}{360 I_c L}\right)}$$

where

w = infill plate thickness
L = centre-to-centre distance between columns
A_c = cross-sectional area of column
h = storey height
A_b = cross-sectional area of beam
I_c = moment of inertia of column

20.4.2
A single angle of inclination taken as the average for all the panels may be used to analyze the entire plate wall.

20.5 Limits on column and beam flexibilities

20.5.1
The column flexibility parameter at each panel, ω_h, shall be determined as follows and not exceed 2.5:

$$\omega_h = 0.7h\left(\frac{w}{2LI_c}\right)^{0.25}$$

This requirement is met by providing columns with moments of inertia, I_c, greater than or equal to $0.0031 wh^4/L$.

20.5.2
The boundary member flexibility parameter for the extreme panels, ω_L, shall be determined as follows:
(a) not exceed 2.5 at the top panel of the plate wall;
(b) not exceed 2.0 at the bottom panel of the plate wall; and
(c) be greater than $0.84\omega_h$:

$$\omega_L = 0.7\left(\left(\frac{h^4}{I_c} + \frac{L^4}{I_b}\right)\frac{w}{4L}\right)^{0.25}$$

These requirements are met by providing a beam with a moment of inertia, I_b, greater than or equal to

$\dfrac{wL^4}{650L - (wh^4/I_c)}$ for the top beam and $\dfrac{wL^4}{267L - (wh^4/I_c)}$ for the bottom beam, if present. See also Clause 20.9.2.

20.6 Infill plates

The factored tensile resistance of the inclined infill plate strips shall be calculated in accordance with Clause 13.2.

20.7 Beams

Beams shall be proportioned to resist bending moments and axial compressive forces in accordance with Clause 13.8. Infill plates shall not be deemed to provide lateral support to adjacent beams. Either Class 1 or 2 sections may be used, except as required by Clause 27.9.3.1.

20.8 Columns

Columns shall be Class 1 sections and proportioned to resist bending moments and axial forces in accordance with Clause 13.8 or 13.9, as appropriate. Infill plates shall not be deemed to provide lateral support to adjacent columns.

20.9 Anchorage of infill plates

20.9.1

At the top panel, the vertical component of the infill plate tension field shall be anchored to a beam meeting the requirements of Clause 20.5.2.

20.9.2

At the bottom panel, the vertical component of the infill plate tension field shall be anchored by connecting the infill plate directly to the substructure or to a beam that meets the requirements of Clause 20.5.2.

20.9.3

At the bottom panel, the horizontal component of the infill plate tension field shall be transferred to the substructure.

20.10 Infill plate connections

Infill plates shall be connected to the surrounding beams and columns. These connections and, if required, any infill plate splices shall be in accordance with Clause 13.12 or 13.13. The factored ultimate tensile strength of the infill plate strips shall be developed by the connections.

21 Connections

21.1 Alignment of members

Axially loaded members that meet at a joint shall have their centroidal axes intersect at a common point if practicable. Bending resulting from joint eccentricity shall be taken into account.

21.2 Unrestrained members

Except as otherwise indicated in the structural design documents, all connections of beams, girders, and trusses shall be designed and detailed as flexible and ordinarily may be proportioned for the reaction shears only. Flexible beam connections shall accommodate end rotations of unrestrained (simple) beams. To accomplish this, inelastic action at the specified load levels in the connection is permitted.

21.3 Restrained members

When beams, girders, or trusses are subject to both reaction shear and end moment due to full or partial end restraint or to continuous or cantilever construction, their connections shall be designed for the combined effect of shear, bending, and axial load.

When beams are rigidly framed to the flange of an I-shaped column, stiffeners shall be provided on the column web if the following bearing and tensile resistances of the column are exceeded:

(a) opposite the compression flange of the beam:

$$B_r = \phi_{bi} w_c \left(t_b + 10 t_c\right) F_{yc} < \frac{M_f}{d_b}$$

except when the column has a Class 3 or 4 web, in which case the following shall apply:

$$B_r = \frac{640\,000 \phi_{bi} w_c \left(t_b + 10 t_c\right)}{\left(h_c / w_c\right)^2}$$

(b) opposite the tension flange of the beam:

$$T_r = 7 \phi t_c^2 F_{yc} < \frac{M_f}{d_b}$$

where

w_c = thickness of column web

t_b = thickness of beam flange

t_c = thickness of column flange

F_{yc} = specified yield point of column

d_b = depth of beam

h_c = clear depth of column web

The stiffener or pair of stiffeners opposite either beam flange shall develop a force, F_{st}, equal to $(M_f / d_b) - B_r$.

Stiffeners shall also be provided on the web of columns, beams, or girders if V_r calculated from Clause 13.4.2 is exceeded, in which case the stiffener or stiffeners shall transfer a shear force, V_{st}, equal to $V_f - 0.8 \phi A_w F_s$

The stiffeners shall be connected so that the force in the stiffener is transferred through the stiffener connection. When beams frame to one side of the column only, the stiffeners need not be longer than one-half of the depth of the column. When an axial tension or compression force is acting on the beam, its effects (additive only) shall be considered in the design of the stiffeners.

21.4 Connections of tension or compression members
The connections at ends of compression members not finished to bear or of tension members shall be designed for the full factored load effect.

21.5 Bearing joints in compression members
Where columns or other compression members bear on bearing plates or are finished to bear at splices, there shall be sufficient fasteners or welds to hold all parts securely in place in order to provide a satisfactory level of structural integrity (see Clauses 6.1.2, 28.5, and 29.3.9). The flanges of single web members shall be connected.

21.6 Lamellar tearing
Corner or T-joint details of rolled structural members or plates involving transfer of tensile forces in the through-thickness direction resulting from shrinkage due to welding executed under conditions of restraint shall be avoided where possible. If this type of connection cannot be avoided, measures shall be taken to address the possibility of lamellar tearing.

21.7 Placement of fasteners and welds

Except in members subject to fatigue (see Clause 26) and in braces subject to seismic loads (see Clause 27.5.4.1), disposition of fillet welds to balance the forces about the neutral axis or axes for end connections of single-angle, double-angle, or similar types of axially loaded members shall not be required. Eccentricity between the centroidal axes of such members and the gauge lines of bolted end connections may also be neglected. In axially loaded members subject to fatigue, the fasteners or welds in end connections shall have their centroid on the centroidal axis of the member unless provision is made for the effect of the resulting eccentricity.

21.8 Fillers

21.8.1 Fillers in bolted connections

21.8.1.1

When load-carrying fasteners pass through fillers with a total thickness greater than 19 mm, the fillers shall be extended beyond the splice material and the filler extension shall be secured by sufficient fasteners to distribute the total force in the connected element uniformly over the combined cross-section of the connected element and the filler. Alternatively, an equivalent number of fasteners shall be included in the connection.

21.8.1.2

When load-carrying fasteners pass through fillers with a total thickness between 6.4 and 19 mm, the shear capacity of the fasteners shall be reduced to account for bending in the fasteners by R_v as follows:

R_v = 1.1 − 0.0158t

where

t = thickness of the fillers

Alternatively, the fillers shall be extended beyond the splice material and the filler extension shall be secured by sufficient fasteners to distribute the total force in the connected element uniformly over the combined cross-section of the connected element and the filler or an equivalent number of fasteners shall be included in the connection.

21.8.1.3

When load-carrying fasteners pass through fillers with a total thickness less than or equal to 6.4 mm, the shear capacity of the fasteners need not be reduced.

21.8.2 Fillers in welded connections

In welded construction, any filler with a total thickness greater than 6 mm shall extend beyond the edges of the splice plate and shall be welded to the part on which it is fitted with sufficient weld to transmit the splice plate load, applied at the surface of the filler, as an eccentric load. Welds that connect the splice plate to the filler shall be sufficient to transmit the splice plate load and shall be long enough to avoid overloading the filler along the toe of the weld. Any filler that is 6 mm or less in thickness shall have its edges made flush with the edges of the splice plate, and the required weld size shall be equal to the thickness of the filler plate plus the size necessary to transmit the splice plate load.

21.9 Welds in combination

If two or more of the general types of weld (groove, fillet, plug, or slot) are combined in a single connection, the effective capacity of each shall be calculated separately with reference to the axis of the group in order to determine the factored resistance of the combination.

21.10 Fasteners and welds in combination

21.10.1 New connections
The strength of a joint that combines welds and bolts in the same plane shall be proportioned in accordance with Clause 13.14.

21.10.2 Existing connections
The strength of a joint that combines welds and bolts in the same plane shall be proportioned in accordance with Clause 13.14.

21.11 High-strength bolts (in slip-critical joints) and rivets in combination
In making alterations, rivets and high-strength bolts in slip-critical joints may be considered as sharing forces caused by specified dead and live loads.

22 Design and detailing of bolted connections

22.1 General
Clause 22 deals primarily with ASTM A 325, ASTM A 325M, ASTM A 490, ASTM A 490M, ASTM F 1852, and ASTM F 2280 bolt assemblies and equivalent fasteners. The bolts may be required to be installed to a specified minimum tension, depending on the type of connection.

22.2 Design of bolted connections

22.2.1 Use of snug-tightened high-strength bolts
Snug-tightened high-strength bolts may be used in connections other than those specified in Clause 22.2.2 (see Clause 23.7).

22.2.2 Use of pretensioned high-strength bolts
Pretensioned high-strength bolts (ASTM A 325, ASTM A 325M, ASTM A 490, ASTM A 490M, ASTM F 1852, and ASTM F 2280) shall be used in
(a) slip-critical connections where slippage cannot be tolerated (e.g., connections subject to fatigue or frequent load reversal, or connections in structures that have rigorous deflection or stiffness limit states);
(b) shear connections proportioned in accordance with the seismic requirements of Clause 27;
(c) all elements resisting crane loads;
(d) connections subject to impact or cyclic loading;
(e) connections where the bolts are subject to tensile loading (see Clause 13.12.1.3); and
(f) connections using oversize or long slotted holes (unless specifically designed to accommodate movement).

22.2.3 Joints subject to fatigue loading
Joints subject to fatigue loading shall be proportioned in accordance with Clause 26.

22.2.4 Effective bearing area
The effective bearing area of bolts shall be the nominal diameter multiplied by the length in bearing. For countersunk bolts, half of the depth of the countersink shall be deducted from the bearing length.

22.2.5 Fastener components

22.2.5.1 Structural bolt assemblies

Except as specified in Clause 22.2.5.3, bolts, nuts, and washers for structural bolt assemblies shall meet the requirements of ASTM A 325, ASTM A 325M, ASTM A 490, ASTM A 490M, ASTM F 1852, or ASTM F 2280.

22.2.5.2 Galvanized bolt assemblies

Galvanized ASTM A 325 and ASTM A 325M bolt assemblies shall meet the special galvanizing requirements of ASTM A 325 and ASTM A 325M.

22.2.5.3 Alternatives to ASTM A 325, ASTM A 325M, ASTM A 490, and ASTM A 490M bolt assemblies

Other fasteners may be used if they meet the chemical and mechanical requirements of ASTM A 325, ASTM A 325M, ASTM A 490, or ASTM A 490M and have body diameters and bearing areas under the head and nut specified in those Standards. Such fasteners may differ in other dimensions and their use shall be subject to the approval of the designer.

22.3 Detailing of bolted connections

22.3.1 Minimum pitch

The minimum distance between centres of bolt holes shall be 2.7 times the bolt diameter.

22.3.2 Minimum edge distance

The minimum distance from the centre of a bolt hole to an edge shall be as specified in Table 6.

22.3.3 Maximum edge distance

The maximum distance from the centre of any bolt to the nearest edge of parts in contact shall be 12 times the thickness of the outside connected part, but not greater than 150 mm.

22.3.4 Minimum end distance

In the connection of tension members having more than two bolts in a line parallel to the direction of load, the minimum end distance (from the centre of the end fastener to the nearest end of the connected part) shall be governed by the edge distance values specified in Table 6. In members having one or two bolts in the line of load, the end distance shall be not less than 1.5 bolt diameters.

22.3.5 Bolt holes

22.3.5.1

Holes may be punched, sub-punched, sub-drilled and reamed, or drilled, as permitted by Clause 28.4. The nominal diameter of a hole shall be not more than 2 mm greater than the nominal bolt size. This requirement may be waived to permit the use of the following bolt diameters and hole combinations in bearing-type or slip-critical connections:
(a) a 3/4 in diameter bolt or an M20 bolt in a 22 mm hole;
(b) a 7/8 in diameter bolt or an M22 bolt in a 24 mm hole; and
(c) a 1 in diameter bolt or an M24 bolt in a 27 mm hole.

Oversized or slotted holes may be used with high-strength bolts 16 mm in diameter and larger when approved by the designer.

22.3.5.2

Joints that use enlarged or slotted holes shall be proportioned in accordance with Clauses 13.11, 13.12, and 23 and meet the following requirements:

(a) Oversize holes shall be 4 mm larger than bolts 22 mm and less in diameter, 6 mm larger than bolts 24 mm in diameter, and 8 mm larger than bolts 27 mm and greater in diameter. Oversize holes shall not be used in bearing-type connections but may be used in any or all plies of slip-critical connections. Hardened washers shall be used under heads or nuts adjacent to the plies containing oversize holes.

(b) Short slotted holes shall be 2 mm wider than the bolt diameter and have a length that does not exceed the oversize diameter requirements of Item (a) by more than 2 mm. Short slotted holes may be used in any or all plies of slip-critical or bearing-type connections and without regard to direction of loading in slip-critical connections, but shall be normal to the direction of the load in bearing-type connections. For pretensioned bolts, hardened washers shall be used under heads or nuts adjacent to the plies containing the slotted holes.

(c) Long slotted holes shall be 2 mm wider than the bolt diameter, shall have a length greater than that allowed in Item (b) (but not more than 2.5 times the bolt diameter in only one of the connected parts at an individual faying surface of either a slip-critical or bearing-type connection), and may be used in

    (i) slip-critical connections without regard to the direction of loading (slip resistance shall be decreased in accordance with Clause 13.12.2.2); and

    (ii) bearing-type connections with the long dimension of the slot normal to the direction of loading, provided that structural plate washers or a continuous bar not less than 8 mm in thickness covers long slots that are in the outer plies of joints. The plate washers or bar shall have a size sufficient to completely cover the slot after installation. Plate washers or bars shall not be required for bearing-type connections in double shear.

(d) When pretensioned ASTM A 490 or ASTM A 490M bolts greater than 26 mm in diameter are used in oversize or slotted holes, hardened washers shall be at least 8 mm thick.

22.3.5.3

The maximum and minimum edge distance for bolts in slotted or oversize holes (as permitted in Clause 22.3.5.1) shall meet the requirements of Clauses 22.3.2 to 22.3.4, assuming that the fastener can be placed at any extremity of the slot or hole.

23 Installation and inspection of bolted joints

23.1 ASTM A 307 bolts

Nuts on ASTM A 307 bolts shall be snug-tightened. When so specified by the designer, nuts shall be prevented from working loose by the use of lock washers, locknuts, jam nuts, thread burring, welding, or other methods approved by the designer.

23.2 Connection fit-up

When assembled, all joint surfaces, including those adjacent to bolt heads, nuts, and washers, shall be free of scale (tight mill scale excepted), burrs, dirt, and foreign material that could prevent firm contact of the parts. Connections using high-strength bolts shall be in firm contact when assembled and shall not be separated by gaskets or compressible materials.

23.3 Surface conditions for slip-critical connections

The condition of the contact surfaces for slip-critical connections, as specified in Table 3, shall be as follows:

(a) For clean mill scale, the surfaces shall be free of oil, paint, lacquer, or any other coating for all areas within the bolt pattern and for a distance beyond the edge of the bolt hole that is the greater of 25 mm or the bolt diameter.

(b) For Classes A and B, the blast-cleaning and the coating application shall be the same as those used in the tests to determine the mean slip coefficient.

(c) For Class C, hot-dip galvanizing shall be done in accordance with CAN/CSA-G164 and the surface subsequently roughened by hand wire-brushing. Power wire-brushing shall not be used.

(d) For all other coatings, the surface preparation and coating application for the joint shall be the same as those used in the tests to determine the mean slip coefficient.

Coated joints shall not be assembled before the coatings have cured for the minimum time used in the tests to determine the mean slip coefficient.

23.4 Minimum bolt length

The length of bolts shall be such that the point of the bolt will be flush with or outside the face of the nut when completely installed.

23.5 Use of washers

23.5.1

ASTM F 436 hardened washers shall be used under the turned element

(a) as required by Clause 23.5.2;

(b) for pretensioned ASTM F 1852 and ASTM F 2280 bolts; and

(c) for bolt arbitration inspection procedures.

23.5.2

When high strength bolts are pretensioned, ASTM F 436 hardened washers shall

(a) be used to cover oversize or slotted holes (see Clause 22.3.5);

(b) be used with ASTM F 959 washers, as applicable;

(c) be placed under the head and nut when used with steel having a specified minimum yield point of less than 280 MPa and the bolts are either ASTM A 490, ASTM A 490M, or ASTM F 2280; and

(d) be not less than 8 mm in thickness, when either ASTM A 490, ASTM A 490M, or ASTM F 2280 bolts greater than 26 mm in diameter are used in oversize and slotted holes.

23.5.3

If necessary, washers may be clipped on one side to a point not closer than 7/8 of the bolt diameter from the centre of the washer hole.

23.5.4

ASTM F 436 bevelled washers shall be used to compensate for lack of parallelism where, in the case of A ASTM 325, ASTM A 325M, and ASTM F 1852, bolts, an outer face of bolted parts has more than a 5% slope with respect to a plane normal to the bolt axis. In the case of ASTM A 490, ASTM A 490M, and ASTM F 2280 bolts, bevelled washers shall be used to compensate for any lack of parallelism due to the slope of the outer faces.

23.6 Storage of fastener components for pretensioned bolt assemblies

Fastener components shall

(a) be stored in closed containers;

(b) be returned to protected storage at the end of the work shift when not incorporated into the work;

(c) not have the as-delivered condition altered in any fashion, including cleaning; and

(d) not be incorporated into the work if rust or dirt resulting from plant or job site conditions accumulates unless they are cleaned, relubricated, and requalified with a bolt tension calibrator. ASTM F 1852 and ASTM F 2280 bolt assemblies shall not be relubricated, except by the manufacturer.

23.7 Snug-tightened high-strength bolts

High-strength bolts that are not required to be pretensioned shall be installed in properly aligned holes to a snug-tight condition (for slotted holes, see Clause 22.3.5.2).

23.8 Pretensioned high-strength bolts

23.8.1 Installation procedure

Pretensioned bolts shall be installed to at least the minimum bolt tensions specified in Table 7, in accordance with the following procedure:

(a) After the holes in a joint are aligned, sufficient bolts shall be placed to secure the member.

(b) Bolts shall be placed in the remaining open holes and snug-tightened, with joint assembly progressing systematically from the most rigid part of the joint to its free edges (re-snugging may be necessary in large joints)

(c) When all bolts are snug-tight, each bolt in the joint shall be pretensioned, with pretensioning progressing systematically from the most rigid part of the joint to its free edges in a manner that will minimize relaxation of previously pretensioned bolts.

23.8.2 Turn-of-nut method

After the snug-tightening procedure is completed, each bolt in the connection shall be pretensioned additionally by the applicable amount of relative rotation specified in Table 8. During this operation there shall be no rotation of the part not turned by the wrench unless the bolt and nut are match-marked to enable the amount of relative rotation to be determined.

23.8.3 Use of ASTM F 959 washers

When ASTM F 959 washers are used (also known as direct tension indicator washers), the pretension of the bolt in accordance with Table 7 shall be verified using a tension calibrator. Prior to installation of ASTM F 959 bolt assemblies, a sample of not fewer than three complete bolt assemblies of each combination of diameter, length, grade, and lot to be used in the work shall be placed individually in a bolt-tension calibrator at the site of installation to verify that the pretensioning method develops a tension that is equal to or greater than 1.05 times the minimum tensions specified in Table 7. The pre-installation verification procedure shall be performed at the start of the work and whenever the lot of fastener assembly is changed.

23.8.4 Use of ASTM F 1852 and ASTM F 2280 bolts

Prior to installation of ASTM F 1852 and ASTM F 2280 bolt assemblies in joints requiring pretension, a sample of not fewer than three complete bolt assemblies of each combination of diameter, length, grade, and lot to be used in the work shall be placed individually in a bolt-tension calibrator at the site of installation to verify that the pretensioning method develops a tension that is equal to or greater than 1.05 times the minimum tensions specified in Table 7. The pre-installation verification procedure shall be performed at the start of the work and whenever the lot of fastener assembly is changed.

During the snug-tightening procedure, care shall be taken to avoid severing the splined ends. Bolts with severed ends shall be replaced. After the snug-tightening procedure is completed, each bolt in the joint shall be pretensioned.

23.9 Inspection procedures

23.9.1

The inspector shall determine that the requirements of Clauses 23.1 to 23.7 are met. Tensioning of bolts shall be observed during their installation to ascertain that the proper procedures are employed.

In addition, the following shall apply:

(a) for snug-tight connections, the inspection need ensure only that the bolts have been tightened sufficiently to bring the connected elements into firm contact;

(b) for bolts pretensioned by the turn-of-nut method, the turned element of all bolts shall be visually examined for evidence that they have been pretensioned;

(c) for ASTM F 959 washers, the washers shall be inspected to ensure that adequate deformations have been achieved in accordance with the manufacturer's installation procedures; and

(d) for ASTM F 1852 and ASTM F 2280 bolt assemblies, the splined ends shall be inspected for twist-off.

Note: *For pretensioned connections, see Annex I if there is disagreement concerning the results of inspection of bolt-tensioning procedures.*

23.9.2

Bolt tensions exceeding those specified in Table 7 shall not be cause for rejection.

24 Welding

24.1 Arc welding

Arc welded joints shall be designed in accordance with

(a) Clause 13.13 for factored resistance to static loading; and

(b) Clause 26 for resistance to fatigue loading.

For all other aspects of welding, the requirements of CSA W59 shall be followed.

24.2 Resistance welding

The resistance of resistance-welded joints shall be in accordance with CSA W55.3. Related welding practice shall meet the welding standards approved by the Canadian Welding Bureau as specified in CSA W55.3.

24.3 Fabricator and erector qualification

Fabricators and erectors responsible for welding structures fabricated or erected under this Standard shall be certified by the Canadian Welding Bureau to the requirements of CSA W47.1 (Division 1 or Division 2), CSA W55.3, or both, as applicable. Part of the work may be sublet to a Division 3 fabricator or erector; however, the Division 1 or Division 2 fabricator or erector shall retain responsibility for the sublet work.

24.4 Joint surface conditions

Joints that are to be welded shall be kept free of all foreign matter, including paint, primer, and other coatings that could be detrimental to achieving a sound weldment. Welding procedures for welding over coatings shall be developed and qualified in accordance to CSA W47.1. Such welding procedures shall indicate the paint/coating product identifier, manufacturer, and maximum coating thickness.

Consideration for low hydrogen applications shall be made.

Note: *These procedures can apply to*

    (a) welding of joist shoes to supporting members;

    (b) joist bridging;

    (c) metal deck to supporting members; and

    (d) shear connectors.

25 Column bases and anchor rods

25.1 Loads
Suitable provision shall be made to transfer factored axial loads, including uplift, shears, and moments, to footings and foundations. Forces present during construction and in the finished structure shall be resisted.

25.2 Minimum number of anchor rods
Columns shall be fitted with at least four anchor rods. When four anchor rods are not feasible, special precautions shall be taken.

25.3 Resistance

25.3.1 Concrete in compression
The compressive resistance of concrete shall be determined in accordance with Clause 10.8 of CAN/CSA-A23.3. When compression exists over the entire base plate area, the bearing pressure on the concrete may be assumed to be uniform over an area equal to the width of the base plate multiplied by the length minus 2e, where e is the eccentricity of the column load. Where eccentricity exists about both column axes, the width of the base plate shall also be reduced by twice the eccentricity in that direction.

25.3.2 Tension

25.3.2.1 Anchor rods
The factored tensile resistance of an anchor rod shall be taken as

$$T_r = \phi_{ar} A_n F_u$$

where

ϕ_{ar} = 0.67

A_n = the tensile area of the rods

= $0.85 A_g$

25.3.2.2 Pull-out
Full anchorage shall be obtained when the factored pull-out resistance of the concrete is equal to or greater than the factored tensile resistance of the rods.

Note: *For methods of transferring the tensile forces from the anchors to the concrete, see CAN/CSA-A23.3.*

25.3.3 Shear

25.3.3.1 Shear transfer mechanisms
Shear resistance may be developed by friction between the base plate and the foundation unit or by bearing of the anchor rods or shear lugs against the concrete. The requirements of CAN/CSA-A23.3 shall be deemed to be met when
(a) loads are transferred by friction;
(b) shear lugs bear against the concrete; and
(c) shear acts toward a free edge.

25.3.3.2 Anchor rods in bearing
The factored bearing resistance of an anchor rod shall be taken as

$$B_r = 1.4 \phi_c A f_c'$$

where

ϕ_c = 0.65

A = bearing area = product of the rod diameter, d, and depth, in accordance with CAN/CSA-A23.3.

25.3.3.3 Anchor rods in shear

The factored shear resistance of an anchor rod shall be taken as

$$V_r = 0.60\phi_{ar}A_{ar}F_u$$

where

A_{ar} = cross-sectional area of the anchor rod based on its nominal diameter

When the rod threads are intercepted by the shear plane, the factored shear resistance shall be taken as $0.70V_r$.

25.3.4 Anchor rods in shear and tension

An anchor rod required to develop resistance to both tension and shear shall be proportioned so that

$$(V_f/V_r)^2 + (T_f/T_r)^2 \le 1$$

where

V_f = portion of the total shear per rod transmitted by bearing of the anchor rods on the concrete

25.3.5 Anchor rods in tension and bending

An anchor rod required to develop resistance to both tension and bending shall be proportioned to meet the requirements of Clause 13.9.1. The tensile and moment resistances, T_r and M_r, shall be based on the properties of the cross-section at the critical section. M_r shall be taken as $\phi_{ar}SF_y$.

25.3.6 Moment on column base

The moment resistance of a column base shall be taken as the couple formed by the tensile resistance determined in accordance with Clause 25.3.2 and by the concrete compressive resistance determined in accordance with Clause 25.3.1.

25.4 Fabrication and erection

25.4.1 Fabrication

25.4.1.1 Base plate holes

Base plate holes may be drilled, machined, or thermally cut. The surfaces of thermally cut holes shall meet the requirements of Clause 28.2.

Holes in base plates for anchor rods shall be of sufficient size to meet or exceed the placement tolerances for anchor rods. The Designer shall provide details of corrective work if base plate holes are to be adjusted to suit as-cast locations of anchor rods.

25.4.1.2 Bases resting on masonry or concrete

The bottom surfaces of bearing plates and column bases that rest on masonry or concrete foundations and are grouted to ensure full bearing need not be planed.

25.4.1.3 Rolled steel bearing plates

Finishing of steel-to-steel contact bearing surfaces shall meet the requirements of Clauses 28.5 and 29.3.9. Plates 55 mm or less thick may be used without machining. Plates more than 55 mm thick may be straightened by pressing or machined at bearing locations.

25.4.2 Erection

25.4.2.1 Setting column bases
Column bases shall be set on level finished floors, pre-grouted levelling plates, levelling nuts, or shim packs that are adequate to transfer the construction loads. Steel shim packs may remain in place unless otherwise specified by the Designer.

25.4.2.2 Tensioning of anchor rods
Nuts on anchor rods need be installed only to a snug-tight condition unless otherwise specified by the Designer. If pre-tension is required, the method of tensioning and the pre-tension value shall be defined by the Designer.

26 Fatigue

26.1 General
In addition to meeting the fatigue requirements of Clause 26, all members and connections shall meet the requirements for the static load conditions using the factored loads. Specified loads shall be used for all fatigue calculations. A specified load less than the maximum specified load but acting with a greater number of cycles can govern and therefore shall be considered. Members and connections subjected to fatigue loading shall be designed, detailed, and fabricated so as to minimize stress concentrations and abrupt changes in cross-section. The life of the structure shall be taken as 50 years, unless otherwise specified by the owner.

26.2 Proportioning
In the absence of more specific requirements by the owner or designer, the requirements of Clause 26 shall be used to proportion members and parts. Fatigue resistance shall be provided only for repetitive loads.

26.3 Live-load-induced fatigue

26.3.1 Calculation of stress range
The controlling stress feature in load-induced fatigue is the range of stress to which the element is subjected. This is calculated using ordinary elastic analysis and the principles of mechanics of materials. More sophisticated analysis shall be required only in cases not covered by Table 9, e.g., major access holes and cut-outs. Stress range is the algebraic difference between the maximum stress and minimum stress at a given location; thus, only live load induces a stress range.

The load-induced fatigue requirements of Clause 26 need be applied only at locations that undergo a net applied tensile stress. Stress ranges that are completely in compression need not be investigated for fatigue.

26.3.2 Design criteria
For load-induced fatigue and constant amplitude fatigue loading, the following design requirement shall apply:

$$F_{sr} \geq f_{sr}$$

where

F_{sr} = fatigue resistance

$$= \left(\frac{\gamma}{nN}\right)^{1/3} \geq F_{srt}$$

$$= \left(\frac{\gamma'}{nN}\right)^{1/5} \geq F_{srt}$$

where

γ and γ' = fatigue life constants (see Clause 26.3.4).

n = number of stress range cycles at given detail for each application of load

N = number of applications of load

F_{srt} = constant amplitude threshold stress range (Clauses 26.3.3 and 26.3.4)

f_{sr} = calculated stress range at the detail due to passage of the fatigue load

26.3.3 Cumulative fatigue damage

The total damage that results from variable amplitude fatigue loading shall satisfy

$$\sum \left[\frac{(nN)_i}{N_{fi}}\right] \leq 1.0$$

where

$(nN)_i$ = number of expected stress range cycles at stress range level i, F_{sri}

N_{fi} = number of cycles that would cause failure F_{sri}, obtained from Figure 1 for the appropriate fatigue category. Alternatively, it can be calculated as follows:

$N_{fi} = \gamma F_{sri}^{-3}$ for $F_{sri} \geq F_{srt}$

and

$N_{fi} = \gamma' F_{sri}^{-5}$ for $F_{sri} \leq F_{srt}$

The summation shall include both stress cycles above and below F_{srt}.
The fatigue constants nN' and γ' shall be as specified in Table 10.

26.3.4 Fatigue constants and detail categories

The fatigue constants γ, γ', nN', and F_{srt} shall be as specified in Table 10 and shown in Figure 1. The detail categories shall be obtained from Table 9 and are illustrated in Figure 2.

For high-strength bolts, see also Clause 13.12.1.3.

26.3.5 Limited number of cycles

Except for fatigue-sensitive details with high stress ranges (probably with stress reversal), special considerations beyond those specified in Clause 26.1 need not apply in the event that the number of stress range cycles, nN, over the life of the structure, expected to be applied at a given detail, is less than

the greater of γ/f_{sr}^3 or 20 000.

26.4 Distortion-induced fatigue

26.4.1

Members and connections shall be detailed to minimize distortion-induced fatigue that can occur in regions of high strain at the interconnection of members undergoing differential displacements. Whenever practicable, all components that make up the cross-section of the primary member shall be fastened to the interconnection member.

26.4.2

Plate girders with $h/w > 3150/\sqrt{F_y}$ shall not be used under fatigue conditions.

26.5 High-strength bolts

A high-strength bolt subjected to tensile cyclic loading shall be pretensioned to the minimum preload specified in Clause 23.8. Connected parts shall be arranged so that prying forces are minimized. The prying force per bolt shall not exceed 30% of the externally applied load.

The permissible maximum applied nominal axial stress, including amplification by prying under specified loads, based on the nominal area of the bolt, shall not exceed 214 MPa for ASTM A 325, ASTM A 325M, and ASTM F 1852 bolts and 262 MPa for ASTM A 490, ASTM A 490M, and ASTM F 2280 bolts.

The total maximum cyclic service load that may be applied to a bolt is calculated as the product of the permissible maximum nominal stress above and the nominal area of a bolt. Thus calculated, the service load per bolt, including the amplification by prying, shall not exceed this maximum applied service load on a pretensioned bolt.

27 Seismic design

27.1 General

27.1.1 Scope

Clause 27 specifies requirements for the design of members and connections in the seismic-force-resisting system of steel-framed building structures. With the exception of Clause 27.11, Clause 27 applies to buildings for which seismic design loads are based on a ductility-related force modification factor, R_d, greater than 1.5. Clause 27 shall be applied with the requirements of the *NBCC*. Alternatively, the maximum anticipated seismic loads may be determined from non-linear time-history analyses using appropriate structural models and ground motions. Height restrictions shall not apply when the seismic forces are determined from non-linear time-history analyses or to buildings with specified short-period spectral acceleration ratios ($I_E F_a S_a(0.2)$) less than 0.35, unless otherwise specified in Clause 27 or the *NBCC*.

Clause 27 may be applied to structures other than building structures provided that the structure includes a clearly defined seismic-force-resisting system and that a level of safety and seismic performance comparable to that required by Clause 27 for building structures is provided.

27.1.2 Capacity design

Unless otherwise specified in Clause 27, seismic-force-resisting systems shall be designed according to capacity design principles to resist the maximum anticipated seismic loads, but such loads need not exceed the values corresponding to $R_d R_o = 1.3$.

In capacity design,
(a) specific elements or mechanisms are designed and detailed to dissipate energy;
(b) all other elements are sufficiently strong for this energy dissipation to be achieved;
(c) structural integrity is maintained;
(d) elements and connections in the horizontal and vertical load paths are designed to resist the seismic loads;
(e) diaphragms and collector elements are capable of transmitting the loads developed at each level to the vertical seismic-force-resisting system; and
(f) these loads are transmitted to the foundation.

Connections along the horizontal load path that are designed for forces corresponding to $R_d R_o = 1.3$ shall have a ductile governing ultimate limit state.

27.1.3 Seismic load path

Any element that significantly affects the load path or the seismic response shall be considered in the analysis and shown on the structural drawings.

27.1.4 Members and connections supporting gravity loads

Structural members and their connections that are not considered to form part of the seismic-force-resisting system shall be capable of supporting gravity loads when subjected to seismically induced deformations.

Splices in gravity columns not part of the seismic-force-resisting system shall have a factored shear resistance in both orthogonal axes equal to the sum of $0.2ZF_y/h_s$ of the columns above and below the splices.

Note: *The gravity loads to be supported are those considered in combination with the earthquake loading.*

27.1.5 Material requirements

27.1.5.1

Steel used in the energy-dissipating elements described in Clauses 27.2 to 27.10 shall comply with Clauses 5.1.3 and 8.3.2(a). F_y shall not exceed 350 MPa unless the suitability of the steel is determined by testing or other rational means. F_y shall not exceed 480 MPa in columns in which the only expected inelastic behaviour is at the column base. Other material may be used if approved by the regulatory authority.

Note: *F_y is the specified minimum yield stress. See Clause 5.1.2.*

27.1.5.2

For buildings with specified short-period spectral acceleration ratios ($I_E F_a S_a(0.2)$) greater than 0.55, rolled shapes with flanges 40 mm or thicker, or plates and built-up shapes over 51 mm in thickness, used in energy-dissipating elements or welded parts, shall have a minimum average Charpy V-notch impact test value of 27 J at 20 °C, unless it can be demonstrated that tensile stresses, including local effects, are not critical. The impact tests shall be conducted in accordance with CSA G40.20, with the following exceptions:

(a) the central longitudinal axis of the test specimens in rolled shapes shall be located as near as practicable to midway between the inner flange surface and the centre of the flange thickness at the intersection with the web mid-thickness; and

(b) one impact test sample shall be taken from each 15 tonnes or less of shapes produced from each heat, or from each ingot for shapes rolled from ingots.

27.1.5.3

Welds of primary members and connections in buildings with specified short-period spectral acceleration ratios ($I_E F_a S_a(0.2)$) greater than 0.35 shall be made with filler metals that have a minimum average Charpy V-notch impact test value of 27 J at –30 °C as certified in accordance with CSA W48 or a manufacturer's certificate of conformance. This requirement may be waived for buildings with specified short-period spectral acceleration ratios ($I_E F_a S_a(0.2)$) less than or equal to 0.55 when the welds are loaded primarily in shear.

27.1.6 Bolted connections

Bolted connections shall

(a) have pretensioned high-strength bolts;

(b) have surfaces of Class A or better, when designed as bearing-type connections;

(c) not be considered to share load with welds;

(d) not have long slotted holes;

(e) not have short slotted holes unless the load is normal to the slot; and

(f) have end distances in the line of seismic force not less than two bolt diameters when the bearing force due to seismic load exceeds 75% of the bearing resistance (see Clause 13.12.1.2).

The requirements of this Clause may be waived when fastener and connection details conform to those of a tested assembly.

27.1.7 Probable yield stress

The probable yield stress shall be taken as R_yF_y. The value of R_y shall be taken as 1.1, and the product R_yF_y as not less than 460 MPa for HSS sections or 385 MPa for other sections, unless the probable yield stress, taken as an average yield stress, is obtained in accordance with CSA G40.20.

Width-to-thickness limits of energy-dissipating elements shall be based on F_y, with F_y taken as not less than 350 MPa.

27.1.8 Stability effects

27.1.8.1

The effects of notional loads and P-delta effects shall be taken into account when sizing the energy-dissipating elements or mechanisms of the seismic-force-resisting system. Notional loads and P-delta effects shall also be considered when determining the limiting forces corresponding to $R_dR_o = 1.3$. Notional loads and P-delta effects need not be considered when determining member forces induced by yielding of the energy-dissipating elements or mechanisms of the seismic-force-resisting system.

The notional loads shall be calculated in accordance with Clause 8.4.1.

27.1.8.2

When the provisions of the *User's Guide — NBC 2010: Structural Commentaries (Part 4)* are applied in calculating P-delta effects, the value of U_2 in Clause 8.4.2 may be taken as

$$U_2 = 1 + \left(\frac{\sum C_f R_d \Delta_f}{\sum V_f h} \right)$$

Structural stiffness shall be provided such that U_2 does not exceed 1.4.

27.1.9 Protected zones

Structural and other attachments that could introduce metallurgical notches or stress concentrations shall not be used in areas designated as protected zones unless engineered and forming part of the design system or forming part of a test assembly that satisfies the physical test requirements of Clause 27.2.5.1. Discontinuities created by fabrication or erection operations shall be repaired.

Welded shear studs and decking attachments that penetrate the beam flange shall not be placed on the beam flanges within protected zones unless approved by the Designer. Arc-spot welds necessary to secure decking may be used.

Protected zones shall be indicated on the structural design documents and shop details (see Clauses 4.2.2, 4.3.2, and 4.3.3).

27.2 Type D (ductile) moment-resisting frames, $R_d = 5.0$, $R_o = 1.5$

27.2.1 General

27.2.1.1

Ductile moment-resisting frames can develop significant inelastic deformation through plastic hinging in beams a short distance from the face of columns. Plastic hinges in columns shall be used only at the base, except in single-storey buildings.

Note: *Plastic deformation in joints is limited by Clause 27.2.4. See Clause 27.9 for cantilever column structures.*

27.2.1.2
Energy-dissipating elements shall be proportioned and braced to enable them to undergo large plastic deformations.

27.2.1.3
In Clauses 27.2.2 to 27.2.4, the effects of bearing of slabs on column flanges shall be considered in determining the flexural resistance of, and the loading produced by, composite beams.

27.2.2 Beams
Beams are expected to develop plastic hinges typically at a short distance from the face of columns (see Clause 27.2.5) and shall
(a)　be Class 1 sections; and
(b)　be laterally braced in accordance with Clause 13.7(b) unless alternative bracing is demonstrated as satisfactory in accordance with Clause 27.2.5.1. The value of κ shall be based on the bending moment distribution for combined gravity and seismic loads. The bending moments due to seismic load may be taken as varying linearly from a maximum at one end of the beam to zero at the other, unless another value can be justified.

The forces acting on other members and connections due to plastic hinging shall be calculated using $1.1R_y$ times the nominal flexural resistance, ZF_y, except when connections and associated design procedures referenced in Annex J are selected.

Beams in single-storey buildings need not meet the requirements of this Clause if plastic hinges develop near the top of columns instead of in the beams.

27.2.3 Columns

27.2.3.1
Columns shall be Class 1 or 2. When a column is expected to develop plastic hinging, it shall be Class 1 and meet the following requirements:
(a)　the column shall be laterally braced in accordance with Clause 13.7(b), using $\kappa = 0.0$, unless other values of κ can be justified by analysis;
(b)　when the specified one-second spectral acceleration ratio ($I_E F_v S_a(1.0)$) is greater than 0.30, the factored axial load shall not exceed $0.30AF_y$ for all seismic load combinations; and
(c)　the column shall meet the requirements of Clause 27.2.8.

Non-dissipating structural elements adjacent to plastic hinges in columns shall be able to resist forces corresponding to $1.1R_y$ times the nominal flexural resistance of the columns. This nominal flexural resistance shall be taken as $1.18M_{pc} (1 - C_f/\phi C_y)$, but shall not be greater than the nominal plastic moment resistance of the column, M_{pc}, where C_f is as specified in Clause 27.2.3.2.

27.2.3.2
Columns shall resist the gravity loads together with the forces induced by plastic hinging of the beams. The following shall apply at each beam-to-column intersection:

$$\Sigma M'_{rc} \geq \Sigma \left(1.1\ R_y M_{pb} + V_h \left(x + \frac{d_c}{2} \right) \right)$$

where
$\Sigma M'_{rc}$ = sum of the column factored flexural resistances at the intersection of the beam and column centrelines

and

$$M'_{rc} = 1.18\phi M_{pc} \left(1 - \frac{C_f}{\phi C_y} \right) \leq \phi M_{pc}$$

where

M_{pb} = nominal plastic moment resistance of the beam

V_h = shear acting at that plastic hinge location when $1.1R_yM_{pb}$ is reached at beam hinge locations

x = distance from the centre of a beam plastic hinge to the column face, which shall correspond to that of the assembly used to demonstrate performance in accordance with Clause 27.2.5.1

M_{pc} = nominal plastic moment resistance of the column

C_f = results from summation of V_h acting at and above the level under consideration

Columns in single-storey buildings need not meet the requirements of this Clause if plastic hinges develop near the top of columns.

27.2.3.3
When the axial force calculated in accordance with Clause 27.2.3.2 is tensile, column splices having partial-joint-penetration groove welds shall
(a) be capable of resisting twice the calculated tensile force;
(b) have flange connections that are each capable of resisting at least $0.5A_fR_yF_y$, where A_f is the flange area of the smaller column at the splice; and
(c) be located at least one-fourth of the clear distance between beams but not less than 1 m from the beam-to-column joint.

27.2.4 Column joint panel zone

27.2.4.1
When plastic hinges form in adjacent beams, the panel zone shall resist forces arising from beam moments of

$$\Sigma\left(1.1R_yM_{pb} + V_h\left(x + \frac{d_c}{2}\right)\right)$$

where the summation is for both beams at a joint, and M_{pb}, V_h, and x are as specified in Clause 27.2.3.2.
In single-storey buildings, when plastic hinges form near the top of columns, panel zones shall resist forces arising from moments corresponding to plastic hinge moments of $1.1R_y$ times the nominal flexural resistance of the column.

27.2.4.2

27.2.4.2.1
The horizontal shear resistance of the column joint panel zone shall be taken as follows when detailed in accordance with Clause 27.2.4.3:

$$V_r = 0.55\phi d_c w' F_{yc}\left[1 + \frac{3\,b_c t_c^2}{d_c d_b w'}\right] \leq 0.66\phi d_c w' F_{yc}$$

where the subscripts b and c denote the beam and the column, respectively.

27.2.4.2.2
If Clause 27.2.4.2.1 does not apply, the resistance shall be taken as $V_r = 0.55\phi d_c w' F_{yc}$.

27.2.4.3

The following requirements shall also apply:

(a) Joint panel zones designed in accordance with Clause 27.2.4.2.1, where the specified short-period spectral acceleration ratio ($I_E F_a S_a$ (0.2)) is equal to or greater than 0.55, shall be detailed in such a way that the sum of panel zone depth and width divided by the panel zone thickness shall not exceed 90.

(b) Joint panel zones designed in accordance with Clause 27.2.4.2.2 shall satisfy the width-to-thickness limit of Clause 13.4.1.1(a)(i).

(c) Doubler plates shall be groove- or fillet-welded to develop their full shear resistance.

In calculating width-to-thickness ratios, doubler plate thickness may be included with web thickness only when the doubler plate is connected to the column web near the centre of the panel.

27.2.4.4

When connections and associated design procedures referenced in Annex J are selected, the provisions of Clauses 27.2.4.1 to 27.2.4.3 need not apply.

27.2.5 Beam-to-column joints and connections

27.2.5.1

The beam-to-column joint shall maintain a strength at the column face of at least the nominal plastic moment resistance of the beam, M_{pb}, through a minimum interstorey drift angle of 0.04 radians under cyclic loading. Satisfaction of this requirement shall be demonstrated by physical testing.

When reduced beam sections are used, or when local buckling limits the flexural strength of the beam, the beam need only achieve $0.8M_{pb}$ at the column face when an interstorey drift angle of 0.04 radians is developed under cyclic loading.

Note: *Physical testing procedures used to demonstrate the required behaviour and specific details and design procedures for connections that will achieve the specified performance are referenced in Annex J.*

27.2.5.2

The factored resistance of the beam web-to-column connection shall equal or exceed the effects of gravity loads combined with shears induced by moments of $1.1R_y ZF_y$ acting at plastic hinge locations, except when connections and associated design procedures referenced in Annex J are selected.

27.2.5.3

In single-storey buildings, when the column frames into the underside of the beam and plastic hinging is expected near the top of a column, the connection shall meet the requirements of Clause 27.2.5.1.

27.2.6 Bracing

The following bracing requirements apply:

(a) Beams, columns, and beam-to-column joints shall be braced by members proportioned in accordance with Clause 9.2 where $C_f = 1.1R_y F_y$ times the cross-sectional area in compression. The possibility of complete load reversals shall be considered.

(b) When plastic hinges occur in the beam, lateral bracing at the joints shall be provided at least at the level of one beam flange. If bracing is not provided at the level of both beam flanges, the transverse moments produced by the forces that would otherwise be resisted by the lateral bracing shall be included in the seismic load combinations. Attachments in the hinging area shall meet the requirements of Clause 27.2.8.

(c) When plastic hinges occur near the top of the column, lateral bracing at the joints shall be provided at the level of both beam flanges.

(d) When no lateral support can be provided to the joint at the level considered, the following shall apply:

(i) the column maximum slenderness ratio shall not exceed 60; and

(ii)   transverse moments produced by the forces otherwise resisted by the lateral bracing shall be included in the seismic load combinations.

27.2.7 Fasteners
Fasteners connecting the separate elements of built-up flexural members shall have resistance adequate to support forces corresponding to moments of $1.1R_yZF_y$ at the plastic hinge locations.

27.2.8 Protected zones
The regions at each end of the beams subject to inelastic deformations and in columns where inelastic deformations are anticipated shall be designated as protected zones and meet the requirements of Clause 27.1.9.

The protected zone of the beams shall be defined as the area from the face of the column flange to one-half of the beam depth beyond the theoretical hinge point. Abrupt changes in beam flange cross-sections shall be avoided in protected zones, unless specially detailed reduced beam sections are provided that satisfy Clause 27.2.5. Bolt holes in beam webs, when detailed in accordance with the individual connection requirements of this Standard, may be used.

Where the theoretical hinge point falls within the column, the protected zone of the columns shall be defined as the area from the face of the cap or base plate to one-half of the column depth beyond the theoretical hinge point or the column depth, whichever is greater.

27.3 Type MD (moderately ductile) moment-resisting frames, R_d = 3.5, R_o = 1.5
Moderately ductile moment-resisting frames can develop a moderate amount of inelastic deformation through plastic hinging in the beams at a short distance from the face of columns. The requirements of Clause 27.2 shall apply to such frames, except that
(a)   with respect to Clause 27.2.2,
   (i)   the beams shall be Class 1 or 2 sections; and
   (ii)   the bracing shall meet the requirements of Clause 13.7(a);
(b)   with respect to Clause 27.2.3.1(b), the factored axial load shall not exceed $0.50AF_y$; and
(c)   with respect to Clause 27.2.5.1, the minimum interstorey drift angle shall be 0.03 radians.

27.4 Type LD (limited-ductility) moment-resisting frames, R_d = 2.0, R_o = 1.3

27.4.1 General
Limited-ductility moment-resisting frames can develop a limited amount of inelastic deformation through plastic hinging in the beams, columns, or joints. This system may be used in buildings
(a)   not exceeding 60 m in height where the specified short-period spectral acceleration ratio $(I_EF_aS_a (0.2))$ is greater than or equal to 0.35; and
(b)   not exceeding 30 m in height where the specified short-period spectral acceleration ratio $(I_EF_aS_a (0.2))$ is greater than 0.75 or where the specified one-second spectral acceleration ratio $(I_EF_aS_a (1.0))$ is greater than 0.30.

27.4.2 Beams and columns

27.4.2.1
Beams shall be Class 1 or 2. Columns shall be Class 1. Except at roof level, beams shall frame into the columns.

27.4.2.2

When the specified short-period spectral acceleration ratio ($I_E F_a S_a (0.2)$) is greater than 0.55 or the building is greater than 60 m in height, columns shall satisfy the requirements of Clause 27.2.3.2. However, when Clause 27.2.3.2 is applied, the term $1.1 R_y M_{pb}$ may be replaced by M_{pb}. In addition, the beams shall be designed so that for each storey, the storey shear resistance is not less than that of the storey above.

27.4.3 Column joint panel zone

The horizontal shear resistance of the column joint panel zone shall be that specified in Clause 27.2.4.2.

27.4.4 Beam-to-column connections

27.4.4.1

The beam-to-column joints shall meet the requirements of Clause 27.2.5.1, except that the minimum interstorey drift angle shall be 0.02 radians. Alternatively, beam-to-column joints shall meet the requirements of Clauses 27.4.4.2 to 27.4.4.6.

27.4.4.2

Beam-to-column connections shall have a moment resistance equal to the lesser of
(a) $R_y M_{pb}$; or
(b)   the effect of the gravity loads combined with the seismic load multiplied by 2.0, provided that the controlling limit state is ductile.

   Joints with welded flanges designed in accordance with Item (a) shall have a welded web connection.

Note: *The requirement specified in Item (a) is considered to be met when complete-penetration groove welds made with matching electrodes in accordance with Clause 13.13.3.1 are used between the beam flanges and the column flanges, with the beam web connected by a welded joint.*

27.4.4.3

Columns shall be I-shaped sections. The tensile resistance of the column flange shall be taken as $0.6 T_r$, as specified in Clause 21.3.

27.4.4.4

Weld backing bars and run-off tabs shall be removed and repaired with reinforcing fillet welds. Top-flange backing bars may remain in place if continuously fillet welded to the column flange on the edge below the complete joint penetration groove weld. Neither partial-joint-penetration groove welds nor fillet welds shall be used to resist tensile forces in the connections.

27.4.4.5

Beam-to-column connections shall resist shear forces resulting from the gravity load together with shears corresponding to moments at each end equal to those specified in Clause 27.4.4.2.

27.4.4.6

For single-storey buildings in which columns frame under the beam, the roles of beam and column shall be considered.

27.5 Type MD (moderately ductile) concentrically braced frames, $R_d = 3.0$, $R_o = 1.3$

27.5.1 General

Moderately ductile concentrically braced frames can dissipate moderate amounts of energy through yielding of bracing members.

27.5.2 Bracing systems

27.5.2.1 General
Moderately ductile concentrically braced frames include
(a) tension-compression bracing systems (see Clause 27.5.2.3);
(b) chevron braced systems (see Clause 27.5.2.4);
(c) tension-only bracing systems (see Clause 27.5.2.5); and
(d) other systems, provided that stable inelastic response can be demonstrated.
Knee bracing and K-bracing, including those systems in which pairs of braces meet a column on one side between floors, are not considered to be moderately ductile concentrically braced frames.

27.5.2.2 Proportioning
At all levels of any planar frame, the diagonal bracing members shall be proportioned in such a way that the ratio of the sum of the horizontal components of the factored tensile brace resistances in opposite directions is between 0.75 and 1.33.

27.5.2.3 Tension-compression bracing
Except where the specified short-period spectral acceleration ratio ($I_E F_a S_a$ (0.2)) is less than 0.35, tension-compression concentric bracing systems shall not exceed 40 m in height. In addition, when the height exceeds 32 m, the factored seismic forces shall be increased by 3% per metre of height above 32 m.

27.5.2.4 Chevron bracing
Chevron bracing systems comprise pairs of braces, located either above or below a beam, that meet the beam at a single point within the middle half of the span. Chevron bracing systems shall meet the requirements of Clause 27.5.2.3.
The beams to which the chevron bracing is attached shall
(a) be continuous between columns;
(b) have both top and bottom flanges laterally braced at the brace connection; and
(c) resist bending moments due to gravity loads (assuming no vertical support is provided by the bracing members) in conjunction with bending moments and axial forces induced by forces of T_u and C'_u in the tension and compression bracing members, respectively. In the case of buildings not exceeding four storeys, the tension brace force may be taken as $0.6T_u$, provided that the beam is a Class 1 section. When braces are connected to the beam from above, the case where the brace compression force is equal to C_u shall also be considered.
The beam-to-column connections shall resist the forces corresponding to the loading described in Item (c) for beams. However, when the tension brace force is less than T_u, the connections shall resist the gravity loads combined with forces associated with the attainment of R_y times the nominal flexural resistance of the beam at the brace connection.
The lateral braces at the brace connection shall resist a transverse load of 0.02 times the beam flange yield force.
Note: *See Clause 27.5.3.4 for the probable tensile, compressive, and post-buckling compressive resistances of bracing members, T_u, C_u, and C'_u, respectively.*

27.5.2.5 Tension-only bracing
The braces in tension-only bracing systems are designed to resist, in tension, 100% of the seismic loads and are connected at beam-to-column intersections. These systems shall
(a) not exceed 20 m in height and, when the height exceeds 16 m, the factored seismic forces shall be increased by 3% per metre of height above 16 m;
(b) have all columns that are continuous and of constant cross-section over the building height; and
(c) have column splices proportioned for the full moment resistance of the cross-section and for a shear force of $2.0ZF_y/h_s$, where Z is the plastic modulus of the column and h_s is the storey height.
Although the braces are proportioned on the basis of tension loading only, this system shall meet the other requirements of Clause 27, including Clauses 27.5.3 to 27.5.5.

27.5.3 Diagonal bracing members

27.5.3.1 Brace slenderness

The slenderness ratio, KL/r, of bracing members shall not exceed 200.

When the specified short-period spectral acceleration ratio ($I_E F_a S_a (0.2)$) is equal to or greater than 0.75 or the specified one-second spectral acceleration ratio ($I_E F_v S_a (1.0)$) is equal to or greater than 0.30, the slenderness ratio of HSS bracing members shall not be less than 70.

Note: *The effects of translational and rotational restraints at the brace ends or along the brace length should be accounted for in the calculation of KL.*

27.5.3.2 Width (diameter)-to-thickness ratios

When the specified short-period spectral acceleration ratios ($I_E F_a S_a (0.2)$) are equal to or greater than 0.35, width-to-thickness ratios shall not exceed the following limits:

(a) when $KL/r \leq 100$:
   (i) for rectangular and square HSS: $330/\sqrt{F_y}$;
   (ii) for circular HSS: $10\,000/F_y$;
   (iii) for legs of angles and flanges of channels: $145/\sqrt{F_y}$; and
   (iv) for other elements: Class 1;
(b) when $KL/r = 200$
   (i) for HSS members: Class 1;
   (ii) for legs of angles: $170/\sqrt{F_y}$; and
   (iii) for other elements: Class 2; and
(c) when $100 < KL/r < 200$, linear interpolation may be used.

When the specified short-period acceleration ratio ($I_E F_a S_a (0.2)$) is less than 0.35, HSS shall be Class 1 and all other sections shall be Class 1 or 2. The width-to-thickness ratio for legs of angles shall not exceed $170/\sqrt{F_y}$.

Back-to-back legs of double-angle bracing members for which buckling out of the plane of symmetry governs, the width-to-thickness ratio shall not exceed $200/\sqrt{F_y}$ irrespective of the specified short-period acceleration ratio ($I_E F_a S_a (2)$).

27.5.3.3 Built-up bracing members

For buildings with specified short-period spectral acceleration ratios ($I_E F_a S_a (0.2)$) equal to or greater than 0.35, the slenderness ratio of the individual parts of built-up bracing members shall not be greater than 0.5 times the governing effective slenderness ratio of the member as a whole. If overall buckling of the brace does not induce shear in the stitch fasteners that connect the separate elements of built-up bracing members, the slenderness ratio of the individual parts shall not exceed 0.75 times the governing effective slenderness ratio of the member as a whole.

If overall buckling of the brace induces shear in the stitch fasteners, the stitch fasteners shall have a resistance adequate to support one-half of the yield load of the smaller component being joined, with this force assumed to act at the centroid of the smaller member. Bolted stitch connections shall not be located in the anticipated plastic hinge regions of bracing members.

27.5.3.4 Probable brace resistances

For the purpose of evaluating forces on connections and other members upon yielding and buckling of the bracing members in capacity design, the probable tensile resistance of bracing members, T_u, shall be taken as equal to $A_g R_y F_y$; the probable compressive resistance of bracing members, C_u, shall be taken as equal to the lesser of $A_g R_y F_y$ and $1.2C_r/\phi$, where C_r is computed using $R_y F_y$; and the probable post-buckling compressive resistance of bracing members, C'_u, shall be taken as equal to the lesser of $0.2A_g R_y F_y$ and C_r/ϕ, where C_r is computed using $R_y F_y$.

Each of the two loading conditions,

(a) the compression acting braces attaining their probable compressive resistance, C_u; and
(b) the compression acting braces attaining their probable buckled resistance, C'_u,

shall be considered as occurring in conjunction with the tension acting braces developing their probable tensile resistance, T_u.

For chevron bracing, when plastic hinging in the beam is permitted by Clause 27.5.2.4(c) or 27.6.2.2, the brace tensile force need not exceed the greater of that corresponding to plastic hinging in the beam and that corresponding to C_u of the compression brace.

When the forces corresponding to $R_d R_o = 1.3$ are computed, the redistribution of forces due to brace buckling shall be considered.

27.5.4 Brace connections

27.5.4.1 Eccentricities
Eccentricities in connections of braces to gusset plates or other supporting elements shall be minimized.

27.5.4.2 Resistance
The factored resistance of brace connections shall equal or exceed both the probable tensile resistance of the bracing members in tension, T_u, and the probable compressive resistance of the bracing members in compression, C_u, specified in Clause 27.5.3.4. For chevron bracing, the brace tension force may be reduced as specified in Clause 27.5.3.4.

The net section fracture resistance of the brace shall be adequate to resist the tension resistance, T_u. The net section factored resistance of the brace may be multiplied by R_y/ϕ, where R_y shall not exceed 1.2 for HSS and 1.1 for other shapes. This multiplier shall not be applied to the factored resistance of any cross-section reinforcement.

27.5.4.3 Ductile hinge rotation
Brace members or connections, including gusset plates, shall be detailed to provide ductile rotational behaviour, either in or out of the plane of the frame, depending on the governing effective brace slenderness ratio. When rotation is anticipated in the bracing member, the factored flexural resistance of the connections shall equal or exceed $1.1 Z R_y F_y$ of the bracing member and the net section factored bending resistance of an unreinforced brace may be multiplied by R_y/ϕ. This requirement may be satisfied in the absence of axial load.

27.5.5 Columns, beams, and connections other than brace connections

27.5.5.1
The factored resistance of columns, beams, and connections other than brace connections shall equal or exceed the effects of gravity loads and the brace forces corresponding to the brace probable resistances specified in Clause 27.5.3.4. For chevron bracing, the beams shall be designed in accordance with Clause 27.5.2.4 and the brace tension force may be reduced as specified in Clause 27.5.3.4.

27.5.5.2
Columns in multi-storey buildings using the systems specified in Items (a) to (c) of Clause 27.5.2.1 shall be continuous and of constant cross-section over a minimum of two storeys, except as required by Clause 27.5.2.5.

Columns outside of the braced bays shall meet the requirements of Class 1, 2, or 3 flexural members.

Columns in braced bays shall meet the requirements of Class 1 or 2 beam-columns. Column resistances in the braced bays shall satisfy the requirements of Clause 13.8 including an additional bending moment in the direction of the braced bay of $0.2 Z F_y$ in combination with the computed bending moments and axial loads. Splices in columns in braced bays shall be designed to provide the required axial, shear, and flexural resistances including the effects of the additional bending moments in the direction of the braced bays of $0.2 Z F_y$ acting either in the same or the opposite directions at the column ends.

27.5.5.3
Partial-joint-penetration groove weld splices in columns subject to tension shall meet the requirements of Items (a) and (b) of Clause 27.2.3.3.

27.5.6 Protected zones
The protected zone of bracing members shall
(a) be designated to include the full brace length;
(b) be designated to include elements that connect braces to beams and columns; and
(c) meet the requirements of Clause 27.1.9.

27.6 Type LD (limited-ductility) concentrically braced frames, R_d = 2.0, R_o = 1.3

27.6.1 General
Concentrically braced frames of limited ductility can dissipate limited amounts of energy through yielding of bracing members. The requirements of Clause 27.5 shall be met, except as modified by Clauses 27.6.2 to 27.6.6.

27.6.2 Bracing systems

27.6.2.1 Tension-compression bracing
Except where the specified short-period spectral acceleration ratio ($I_E F_a S_a$(0.2)) is less than 0.35, tension-compression concentric bracing systems shall not exceed 60 m in height. In addition, when the height exceeds 48 m, the factored seismic forces shall be increased by 2% per metre of height above 48 m.

Tension-compression bracing, in which pairs of braces meet a column on one side between floors, may be used in limited-ductility concentrically braced frames provided that the columns meet the requirements of Clause 27.6.6.

27.6.2.2 Chevron bracing
Chevron bracing systems shall not exceed 60 m in height.

Structures of 20 m or less in height need not meet the requirements of Clause 27.5.2.4(c) provided that the braces and beam-to-column connections are proportioned to resist the forces that develop when buckling of the compression brace occurs, and provided that when a beam is attached to braces from below, it is a Class 1 section and has adequate nominal resistance to support the tributary gravity loads, assuming no vertical support is provided by the bracing members.
Note: *Clause 27.6.2.1 also applies to chevron bracing systems.*

27.6.2.3 Tension-only bracing
Tension-only systems shall meet the following requirements:
(a) not exceed 40 m in height and, when the height exceeds 32 m, the factored seismic forces shall be increased by 3% per metre of height above 32 m; and
(b) in multi-storey structures, have all columns fully continuous and of constant cross-section over a minimum of two storeys.

27.6.3 Diagonal bracing members

27.6.3.1
In single- and two-storey structures, the slenderness ratio of bracing members connected and designed in accordance with Clause 27.5.2.5 shall not exceed 300.

27.6.3.2

The requirements of Clause 27.5.3.2 may be modified as follows:
(a)   when the brace slenderness ratio exceeds 200 (as permitted by Clause 27.6.3.1), the width-to-thickness limits of Clause 27.5.3.2 need not apply; and
(b)   for buildings less than 40 m in height and with specified short-period spectral acceleration ratios ($I_E F_a S_a$ (0.2)) less than 0.45, braces need not be more compact than Class 2. The width-to-thickness ratio of the legs of angles shall not exceed $170/\sqrt{F_y}$.

27.6.4 Bracing connections

The requirements of Clause 27.5.4.3 shall not apply to buildings with specified short-period spectral acceleration ratios ($I_E F_a S_a(0.2)$) less than 0.55 if the brace slenderness ratio is greater than 100.

27.6.5 Columns, beams, and other connections

For buildings with specified one-second spectral acceleration ratios ($I_E F_a S_a(1.0)$) not greater than 0.30, the design forces for column splices in Clause 27.1.4 need not be taken into account.

27.6.6 Columns with braces intersecting between floors

Columns with braces intersecting between floors shall resist the simultaneous effects of
(a)   the gravity loads;
(b)   the axial loads, shear forces, and bending moments induced by yielding and buckling of the bracing members at the design storey drift as obtained from non-linear incremental analysis, assuming that yielding develops in the tension-acting bracing members located at any one level along the height of the storey; and
(c)   an out-of-plane transverse load at each brace-to-column intersecting point equal to 10% of the load in the compression members meeting at the intersecting points.
Horizontal struts shall be provided between columns at the brace intersecting point levels in the plane of the bracing bents for transferring loads between tension-acting braces along the height of the storey.

27.7 Type D (ductile) eccentrically braced frames, R_d = 4.0, R_o = 1.5

27.7.1 General

Ductile eccentrically braced frames can dissipate energy by yielding of links.

27.7.2 Link beam

27.7.2.1

The link beam shall contain a segment (the link) designed to yield, either in flexure or in shear, prior to yielding of other parts of the eccentrically braced frame.

27.7.2.2

A link shall be provided at least at one end of each brace. A link shall not be required in roof beams of frames over five storeys in height.

27.7.2.3

Link beams shall be Class 1 and designed for the coexisting shears, bending moments, and axial forces. Link beams may have Class 2 flanges and Class 1 webs when $e \leq 1.6M_p/V_p$, where e is the length of the link and $V_p = 0.55wdF_y$, for links with wide-flange cross-sections, or $0.55(2w)dF_y$, for links with built-up tubular cross-sections.

27.7.2.4

The web or webs of the link shall be of uniform depth and have no penetrations, splices, attachments, reinforcement, or doubler plates, other than the stiffeners required by Clause 27.7.6.

For links with built-up tubular rectangular cross-sections, complete-joint-penetration groove welds shall be used to connect the webs to the flanges. Inaccessible backing bars need not be removed in these joints.

27.7.2.5

Flanges of tubular links shall satisfy $b/t \leq 0.64\sqrt{E/F_y}$, where b is the clear flange width. Webs shall satisfy $h/w \leq 1.67\sqrt{E/F_y}$. The moment of inertia of tubular links associated to horizontal, out-of-plane bending shall not be less than 0.67 times the link moment of inertia associated to bending in the vertical plane.

27.7.3 Link resistance

The shear resistance of the link shall be taken as the lesser of

$\phi V_p'$ and $2\phi M_p'/e$

where

$$V_p' = V_p \sqrt{1 - \left(\frac{P_f}{AF_y}\right)^2}$$

where

V_p = $0.55wdF_y$ for links with wide-flange cross-sections

= $0.55(2w)dF_y$ for links with built-up tubular cross-sections

P_f = axial force in the link

= C_f or T_f

A = gross area of the link beam

$$M_p' = 1.18M_p \left(1 - \frac{P_f}{AF_y}\right) \leq M_p$$

e = length of the link

27.7.4 Link length

The link length shall be not less than the depth of the link beam. When $P_f/(AF_y) > 0.15$, the link length shall be as follows:

(a) when $\dfrac{A_w}{A} \geq 0.3\dfrac{V_f}{P_f}$:

$$e \leq \left[1.15 - 0.5\frac{P_f}{V_f}\frac{A_w}{A}\right]\left(\frac{1.6M_p}{V_p}\right)$$

(b) when $\dfrac{A_w}{A} < 0.3\dfrac{V_f}{P_f}$:

$$e \leq \frac{1.6M_p}{V_p}$$

where

A_w = area of web

  = $(d - 2t)w$ for links with wide-flange cross-sections

  = $(2d - 2t)w$ for links with tubular cross-sections

27.7.5 Link rotation

The inelastic component of the rotation of the link segment relative to the rest of the beam, taken as three times that of the elastic drift determined for factored seismic loading, Δ_f, shall not exceed the following limits:
(a) when $e \leq 1.6M_p/V_p$: 0.08 radians;
(b) when $e \geq 2.6M_p/V_p$: 0.02 radians; and
(c) when $1.6M_p/V_p < e < 2.6M_p/V_p$, linear interpolation may be used.

27.7.6 Link stiffeners

27.7.6.1 Links with wide-flange cross-sections

27.7.6.1.1
Full-depth web stiffeners shall be provided on both sides of the beam web at the ends of the link. The stiffeners shall have a combined width of not less than $b_f - 2w$ and a thickness of not less than $0.75w$ or 10 mm, whichever is larger.

27.7.6.1.2
Intermediate link web stiffeners shall be full depth and when
(a) $e \leq 1.6M_p/V_p$, spaced at intervals not exceeding $(30w - 0.2d)$ when the link rotation angle is 0.08 radians, or $(52w - 0.2d)$ when the rotation angle is 0.02 radians, or less (for intermediate rotation angles, spacing shall be determined by linear interpolation);
(b) $2.6M_p/V_p < e < 5M_p/V_p$, placed at a distance of $1.5b_f$ from each end of the link;
(c) $1.6M_p/V_p < e < 2.6M_p/V_p$, provided as in Items (a) and (b); and
(d) $e \geq 5M_p/V_p$, are not required.

27.7.6.1.3
Intermediate web stiffeners shall be required on only one side of the web for link beams less than 650 mm in depth and on both sides of the web for beams 650 mm or greater in depth. One-sided stiffeners shall have a thickness of not less than w or 10 mm, whichever is larger, and a width of not less than $0.5(b_f - 2w)$.

27.7.6.1.4
Fillet welds connecting stiffeners to the beam web shall be continuous and develop a stiffener force of A_sF_y. Fillet welds connecting intermediate stiffeners to the flanges shall develop a force of $0.50A_sF_y$. Welds connecting the stiffeners at the link ends to the flanges shall develop a force of A_sF_y.

27.7.6.2 Links with built-up tubular cross-sections

27.7.6.2.1
Full-depth web stiffeners shall be provided on one side of each link web at the diagonal brace connection. These stiffeners shall have a combined width not less than $(b - 2w)$ and a thickness not less than $0.75w$ or 13 mm, whichever is larger.

27.7.6.2.2

Intermediate link web stiffeners shall be full depth and when

(a) $e \le 1.6 M_p/V_p$, and $0.64\sqrt{E/F_y} \le h/w \le 1.67\sqrt{E/F_y}$, spaced at intervals not exceeding $20w-(d-2t)/8$, on one side of each web; and

(b) $h/w \le 0.64\sqrt{E/F_y}$, are not required.

27.7.6.2.3

Fillet welds connecting stiffeners to the beam web shall be continuous and develop a stiffener force of $A_s F_y$.

27.7.7 Lateral support for link

Except for links with built-up tubular rectangular cross-sections for which lateral bracing is not required, lateral support shall be provided to both top and bottom flanges at the ends of a link. These lateral supports shall have factored resistance equal to at least $0.06 b_f t R_y F_y$.

27.7.8 Link beam-to-column connection

27.7.8.1

When a link is directly connected to a column, the link-to-column connection shall be demonstrated by physical tests as being capable of undergoing cyclic inelastic rotation equal to at least 1.2 times the inelastic component of the rotation as specified in Clause 27.7.5.

Note: *Physical testing procedures to be used to demonstrate the required behaviour are referenced in Annex J.*

27.7.8.2

The demonstration of performance required by Clause 27.7.8.1 may be waived when

(a) a link is separated from a column by a short distance in which the beam is reinforced to ensure elastic behaviour of the connection, and the beam within this length remains elastic under the forces produced by the strain-hardened link (see Clause 27.7.10.2);

(b) the link length does not exceed $1.6 M_p/V_p$; and

(c) full-depth web stiffeners are provided at the end of the reinforced section.

27.7.8.3

Except for connections designed in accordance with Clause 27.7.8.1 and 27.7.8.2, link beam-to-column connections may be designed for shear and torsion only. The factored torsional resistance shall equal or exceed $0.02 b_f t d F_y$.

27.7.9 Beam outside the link

27.7.9.1

The beam outside the link shall be Class 1 or 2.

27.7.9.2

The beam outside the link shall resist forces corresponding to $1.30 R_y$ times the nominal strength of the link. When subject to these forces, the beam resistance may be taken as the factored resistance multiplied by R_y/ϕ.

Note: *The nominal shear strength of the link is equal to the lesser of V_p' and $2M_p'/e$ (see Clause 27.7.3).*

27.7.9.3

The beam outside of the link shall be provided with sufficient lateral support to maintain stability of the beam under the forces defined in Clause 27.7.9.2. If yielding is anticipated at the link end of this outer beam segment, bracing shall be provided in accordance with Clause 13.7(a). Lateral bracing shall be provided to both top and bottom flanges and have factored resistances at least equal to $0.02 b_f t R_y F_y$.

27.7.10 Diagonal braces

27.7.10.1
Diagonal brace sections shall be Class 1 or 2.

27.7.10.2
Each diagonal brace and its end connections shall have a factored resistance to support axial force and moment produced by the strain-hardened link. The forces developed in the link shall be taken as $1.30R_y$ times the nominal strength of the link for links with wide-flange cross-sections and $1.45R_y$ times the nominal strength of the link for links with built-up tubular cross-sections.

27.7.11 Brace-to-beam connection
No part of the brace-to-beam connection shall extend into the link. The intersection of the brace and beam centrelines shall be at the end of or within the link. If the brace is designed to resist a portion of the link end moment, full end restraint shall be provided. The beam shall not be spliced within or adjacent to the connection between beam and brace.

27.7.12 Columns

27.7.12.1
Column sections shall be Class 1 or 2.

27.7.12.2
Columns shall be designed to resist the cumulative effect of yielding links together with the gravity loads. The link forces for links with wide-flange cross-sections shall be taken as $1.15R_y$ times the nominal strength of the link, except that in the top two storeys the force shall be taken as $1.30R_y$ times the nominal value. The link forces for links with built-up tubular cross-sections shall be taken as $1.30R_y$ times the nominal strength of the link, except that in the top two storeys the force shall be taken as $1.45R_y$ times the nominal value.

Column sections in braced bays shall be Class 1 or 2. Column resistances in the braced bays shall satisfy the requirements of Clause 13.8 assuming an additional bending moment in the direction of the braced bay of $0.2ZF_y$ in combination with the computed bending moments and axial loads. In the top two storeys, the additional bending moment shall be taken as equal to $0.4ZF_y$.

27.7.12.3
Splices in columns in braced bays shall be designed to provide the required axial, shear, and flexural resistances including the effects of the additional bending moments in the direction of the braced bays of $0.2ZF_y$ acting either in the same or the opposite directions at the column ends.

Splices that incorporate partial-joint-penetration groove welds shall be located at least one-fourth of the clear distance between beams but not less than 1 m from the beam-to-column joints. When tension occurs in columns due to the link-induced forces, column splices having partial-joint-penetration groove welds shall be designed in accordance with Items (a) and (b) of Clause 27.2.3.3.

27.7.13 Protected zone
Link beams shall be designated as a protected zone. The protected zone shall extend to one-half of the depth of the beam beyond the ends of the link beams. Welding on link beams may be used for attachment of link stiffeners. The protected zone shall meet the requirements of Clause 27.1.9.

27.8 Type D (ductile) buckling restrained braced frames, R_d = 4.0, R_o = 1.2

27.8.1 General
Ductile buckling restrained braced frames can develop significant inelastic deformation through axial yielding in tension and compression of the core of the buckling restrained bracing members.

27.8.2 Bracing systems
Knee bracing and K-bracing, including systems in which pairs of braces meet a column on one side between floors, shall not be considered to be buckling restrained braced frames.

Except where the specified short-period spectral acceleration ratio ($I_E F_a S_a (0.2)$) is less than 0.35, buckling restrained braced frames shall not exceed 40 m in height unless stable inelastic response can be demonstrated.

27.8.3 Bracing members

27.8.3.1
The braces shall consist of a structural steel core and a system that restrains the steel core from buckling. The steel core shall be designed to resist the entire axial force in the brace. The factored axial tensile and compression resistances (T_r and C_r, respectively) of the steel core to be used for design of the core shall be taken as follows:

$$T_r = C_r = \phi A_{sc} F_{ysc}$$

where

A_{sc} = cross-sectional area of the yielding segment of the steel core

F_{ysc} = specified minimum yield strength or actual yield strength of the steel core, determined from a coupon test in accordance with CSA G40.21

27.8.3.2
Splices shall not be used in the steel core. Plates used in the steel core that are 50 mm thick or greater shall satisfy the minimum notch toughness requirements of Clause 27.1.5.

27.8.3.3
The buckling restraining system shall be able to resist, without buckling, the forces and deformations that will develop in the brace at deformations corresponding to 2.0 times the seismic design storey drift.

27.8.3.4
The probable tensile, T_{ysc}, and compressive, C_{ysc}, resistances of the bracing members, including strain hardening and friction effects, shall be taken as follows:

$$T_{ysc} = \omega A_{sc} R_y F_{ysc}$$

$$C_{ysc} = \beta \omega A_{sc} R_y F_{ysc}$$

where

ω = a strain hardening adjustment factor obtained by dividing the maximum force developed in the buckling restrained brace in the qualification testing specified in Clause 27.8.6, up to a deformation corresponding to 2.0 times the seismic design storey drift, by $A_{sc} R_y F_{ysc}$

β = a friction adjustment factor obtained by dividing the maximum force developed in the buckling restrained brace in the qualification testing specified in Clause 27.8.6, up to a deformation corresponding to 2.0 times the seismic design storey drift, by $\omega A_{sc}R_yF_{ysc}$

R_y may be taken as equal to 1.0 if F_{ysc} is determined from a coupon test as part of the qualification testing specified in Clause 27.8.6.

27.8.4 Brace connections

The factored resistance of brace connections shall equal or exceed the probable tensile and compressive resistances of the bracing members.

The design of connections shall include consideration of local and overall buckling and shall be consistent with the bracing forces and details considered in the qualification testing required by Clause 27.8.6.

27.8.5 Beams, columns, and connections other than brace connections

27.8.5.1

The factored resistance of beams, columns, and connections other than brace connections shall equal or exceed the effect of gravity forces and the brace connection forces specified in Clause 27.8.4, assuming the redistribution of loads when the bracing members develop their probable tensile and compressive resistances.

27.8.5.2

Columns in multi-storey buildings shall be continuous and of constant cross-section over a minimum of two storeys.

Column sections outside of the braced bays shall be Class 1, 2, or 3.

Column sections in braced bays shall be Class 1 or 2. Column resistances in the braced bays shall satisfy the requirements of Clause 13.8 assuming an additional bending moment in the direction of the braced bay of $0.2ZF_y$ in combination with the computed bending moments and axial loads. Splices in columns in braced bays shall be designed to provide the required axial, shear, and flexural resistances including the effects of the additional bending moments in the direction of the braced bays of $0.2ZF_y$ acting either in the same or the opposite directions at the column ends.

27.8.5.3

Partial-joint-penetration groove weld splices in columns subject to tension shall meet the requirements of Items (a) and (b) of Clause 27.2.3.3.

27.8.6 Testing

Individual buckling restrained brace members and buckling restrained braced frames shall be able to develop their resistance without buckling and with positive strain hardening up to deformations corresponding to 2.0 times the seismic design storey drift, and shall exhibit values of ω and β greater than 1.0. Satisfaction of these requirements shall be demonstrated by physical testing. Qualifying test results shall consist of at least two successful cyclic tests, one a test of a brace subassemblage (including brace connection rotational demands at the specified performance) and the other a uniaxial or subassembly test. Both requirements may be based on

(a) tests reported in research or documented tests performed for other projects; or
(b) tests conducted specifically for the project.

Note: *Physical testing procedures and acceptance criteria that can be used to demonstrate the required behaviour and specific details and design procedures for connections that will achieve the specified performance are provided in Appendix T of the AISC 2005 Seismic Provisions for Structural Steel Buildings.*

27.8.7 Protected zone

The steel core of bracing members and the elements that connect the steel core to beams and columns shall be designated as protected zones and shall meet the requirements of Clause 27.1.9.

27.9 Type D (ductile) plate walls, R_d = 5.0, R_o = 1.6

27.9.1 General

Ductile plate walls are composed of infill plates framed by rigidly connected columns and beams. They can develop significant inelastic deformation by the yielding of the infill plates and plastic hinging in beams a short distance from the face of columns. Plastic hinges in columns shall be allowed only at the base.

The requirements of Clause 20 shall apply unless otherwise specified by Clause 27.9.

27.9.2 Infill plates

27.9.2.1 Shear resistance

The infill plate shall be designed to resist 100% of the applied factored storey shear force. The factored shear resistance of infill plates shall be taken as

$$V_r = 0.4\phi F_y wL\sin2\alpha$$

27.9.2.2 Probable yield force

The forces acting on other members and connections due to yielding of the infill plates shall be calculated as R_y times the tension yield resistance of the infill plates, but these forces need not exceed the value corresponding to $R_d R_o$ = 1.3.

27.9.2.3 Perforated infill plates

Unreinforced circular perforations may be located in infill panels if the
(a) perforations are of equal diameter, D, and are regularly spaced vertically and horizontally over the entire area of the infill plates to form a regular grid of staggered holes to allow development of continuous diagonal tension fields at 45°;
(b) shortest centre-to-centre distance between the perforations, S_{diag}, is such that $D/S_{diag} \leq 0.6$; and
(c) the distance between the first holes and infill plate connections to the surrounding beams and columns is at least D, but does not exceed $(D + 0.7S_{diag})$.
The factored shear resistance of infill plates with circular perforations shall be taken as

$$V_r = 0.4(1 - 0.7D/S_{diag})\phi F_y wL_i \sin2\alpha$$

27.9.2.4 Infill plates with corner cut-outs

Quarter-circular cut-outs may be located at the upper corners of the infill plates if
(a) the infill plates are connected to a reinforcement arching plate that follows the edge of the cut-outs and are designed to allow development of the full strength of the solid infill plate;
(b) the radius of the corner cut-outs is less than one-third of the infill plate clear height; and
(c) beams and columns are designed to resist the compression or tension axial forces acting at the end of the arching reinforcement.

27.9.3 Beams

27.9.3.1

Beams may develop plastic hinges (typically at a short distance from the faces of columns) in accordance with Clause 27.2.5.1, except that the minimum interstorey drift angle shall be 0.02 radians.

Beams shall be Class 1 sections braced in accordance with Clause 13.7(b).

27.9.3.2

Beams at every storey shall have sufficient flexural resistance such that at least 25% of the applied factored storey shear force is resisted by beams and columns forming a moment-resisting frame. Axial loads in beams and gravity load effects on beams need not be considered in calculating this resistance.

27.9.3.3

Beam resistances shall meet the requirements of Clause 13.8, considering the axial loads and bending moments induced by the gravity and lateral loads and the tension force in the infill plate determined in accordance with Clause 27.9.2.2. The effects of the tension force in the infill plate acting on the beams and the columns shall be considered in the calculation of the beam axial loads.

27.9.3.4

The factored resistance of the beam web-to-column connection shall equal or exceed the effects of gravity loads and tension forces in the infill plates, as determined in accordance with Clause 27.9.2.2, acting above and below the beams, combined with shears induced by moments of $1.1R_yM_{pb}$ acting at plastic hinge locations. The moments acting in the beam plastic hinges may be taken as $1.18(1.1R_yM_{pb})(1-C_f/\phi C_y)$, where C_f is the beam axial load due to the tension forces in the infill plates and C_y is the axial yield resistance of the beam.

27.9.4 Columns

27.9.4.1

Columns shall be Class 1 sections braced in accordance with Clause 13.7(b).

27.9.4.2

Columns shall resist the effects of gravity loads together with the axial loads, shear forces, and bending moments due to the tension forces in the infill plates as determined in accordance with Clause 27.9.2.2, as well as the forces induced by the beams as determined in accordance with Clause 27.9.3.4.

Note: *Shear yielding can govern and should be prevented.*

27.9.4.3

Column splices shall develop the full flexural resistance of the smaller section at the splice, together with the shear force consistent with plastic hinging at column ends, assuming double curvature. Splices shall be located as close as practicable to one-fourth of the storey height above the floor.

27.9.4.4

The columns shall be stiffened so that plastic hinging forms in the columns above the base plate or foundation beam.

27.9.5 Column joint panel zones

The horizontal shear resistance of the column joint panel zone shall meet the requirements of Clauses 27.2.4.2 and 27.2.4.3.

27.9.6 Beam-to-column joints and connections

Beam-to-column joints and connections shall meet the requirements of Clause 27.4.4, except that Clause 27.4.4.2(b) shall not apply.

27.9.7 Protected zones

Infill plates, the region at each end of the beams subject to inelastic straining, and column bases where inelastic deformations are anticipated shall be designated as protected zones and shall meet the requirements of Clause 27.1.9. The protected zone of beams shall be defined as the area from the face of the column flange to one-half of the beam depth beyond the theoretical hinge point. Bolt holes in beam webs, when detailed in accordance with the individual connection requirements of this Standard, may be used.

27.10 Type LD (limited-ductility) plate walls, R_d = 2.0, R_o = 1.5

Limited-ductility plate walls dissipate a limited amount of energy by yielding of the infill plates and supporting members. The requirements of Clause 27.9 shall be met, except as follows:
(a) Type LD plate walls shall be limited to 60 m in height;
(b) beams need not be rigidly connected to the columns;
(c) beams may be Class 1 or Class 2;
(d) Clauses 27.9.3.1 and 27.9.3.2 shall not apply; and
(e) if beams are not rigidly connected to columns, Clauses 27.9.5 and 27.9.6 shall not apply and shears induced by moments of $1.1R_yM_{pb}$ acting at plastic hinge locations as specified in Clause 27.9.3.4 need not be considered.

27.11 Conventional construction, R_d = 1.5, R_o = 1.3

27.11.1

Structural systems in this category have some capacity to dissipate energy through localized yielding and friction that inherently exists in traditional design and construction practices. Except as otherwise specified in Clause 27.11, the requirements of Clauses 27.1 to 27.10 and 27.12 shall not apply to these systems.

Diaphragms and connections of primary framing members and diaphragms of the seismic-load-resisting system of steel-framed buildings with specified short-period spectral acceleration ratios ($I_EF_aS_a(0.2)$) greater than 0.45 designed to resist seismic loads based on a force reduction factor, R_d, of 1.5 shall be
(a) proportioned so that the expected connection failure mode is ductile; or
(b) designed to resist gravity loads combined with the seismic load multiplied by R_d.

The connection design load need not exceed the gross section strength of the members being joined, as determined using the probable yield stress R_yF_y.

27.11.2

Cantilever column structures composed of single or multiple beam-columns fixed at the base and pin-connected or free at the upper ends shall
(a) have Class 1 section columns;
(b) have U_2 not greater than 1.25; and
(c) have base connections designed to resist a moment of $1.1R_y$ times the nominal flexural resistance of the column, but need not exceed the value corresponding to R_dR_o = 1.0.

27.11.3

When the specified short-period spectral acceleration ratio ($I_EF_aS_a(0.2)$) is greater than or equal to 0.35, structural systems other than cantilever column structures as specified in Clause 27.11.2, and not part of an assembly occupancy building as specified in the *NBCC*, may exceed 15 m in height if
(a) the factored seismic forces are increased linearly by 2% per metre of height above 15 m, without exceeding forces corresponding to R_dR_o = 1.3;
(b) the height does not exceed 40 m when the specified short-period acceleration ratio ($I_EF_aS_a(0.2)$) is greater than 0.75 or the specified one-second spectral acceleration ratio ($I_EF_aS_a(1.0)$) is greater than 0.30;
(c) the height does not exceed 60 m when the specified short-period spectral acceleration ratio ($I_EF_aS_a(0.2)$) is greater than or equal to 0.35 but less than or equal to 0.75;
(d) the seismic forces and deformations are determined using the Dynamic Analysis Procedure described in the *NBCC*;
(e) the requirements of Clauses 27.1.3 to 27.1.8 are satisfied;
(f) all members of the seismic-force-resisting system are Class 1 or Class 2 sections;
(g) the width-to-thickness ratios of flat elements of member cross-sections satisfy the limits of the corresponding members in seismic-force-resisting systems qualifying for R_d of 2.0;

(h)　the columns are designed to resist in compression the effects of gravity loads combined with 1.30 times the member factored seismic forces, where the seismic induced axial loads for columns that are part of two or more intersecting seismic-force-resisting systems are obtained from analysis of the structure independently in any two orthogonal directions for 100% of the earthquake loads applied in one direction plus 30% of the earthquake loads in the perpendicular direction;

(i)　connections are designed to resist the effects of gravity loads combined with 1.30 times the member factored seismic forces, without exceeding the gross section strength of the members being joined, as determined using the probable yield stress $R_y F_y$;

(j)　connections are designed and detailed such that the governing failure mode is ductile when the member gross section strength does not control the connection design loads;

(k)　the factored seismic forces for diaphragms are determined for forces corresponding to $R_o R_d = 1.3$; and

(l)　members of the seismic-force-resisting system that intersect at an unbraced location are designed for an additional out-of-plane transverse force equal to 10% of the axial load carried by the compression members at that intersection point.

27.12　Special seismic construction

Other framing systems and frames that incorporate special bracing, ductile truss segments, seismic isolation, or other energy-dissipating devices shall be designed on the basis of published research results or design guides, observed performance in past earthquakes, or special investigation. A level of safety and seismic performance comparable to that required by Clause 27 shall be provided.

28　Shop and field fabrication and coating

28.1　Cambering, curving, and straightening

Cambering, curving, and straightening may be done by mechanical means, local application of heat, or both. The temperature of heated areas as measured by approved methods shall not exceed the limits specified in CSA W59.

28.2　Thermal cutting

Thermal cutting shall be performed by guided machine where practicable. Thermally cut edges shall meet the requirements of CSA W59. Re-entrant corners shall be free from notches and have the largest practicable radii, with a minimum radius of 14 mm.

28.3　Sheared or thermally cut edge finish

28.3.1

Planing or finishing of sheared or thermally cut edges of plates or shapes shall not be required unless noted on the drawings or included in a stipulated edge preparation for welding.

28.3.2

The use of sheared edges in the tension area shall be avoided in locations subject to plastic hinge rotation at factored loading. Sheared edges, if used, shall be finished smooth by grinding, chipping, or planing. The requirements of this Clause shall be noted on design drawings and on shop details where applicable.

28.3.3

Burrs shall be removed
(a)　as required in Clause 23.2;
(b)　when needed for proper fit-up for welding; and
(c)　when they create a hazard during or after construction.

28.4 Fastener holes

28.4.1 Drilled and punched holes

Unless otherwise shown on design documents or as specified in Clause 22.3.5, holes

(a) shall be made 2 mm larger than the nominal diameter of the fastener;

(b) may be punched when the thickness of the material is not greater than the nominal fastener diameter plus 4 mm;

(c) shall be either drilled from the solid or sub-punched or sub-drilled and reamed when the material is greater than the nominal fastener diameter plus 4 mm; and

(d) shall be drilled in CSA G40.21-700Q or ASTM A 514 steels more than 13 mm thick.

28.4.2 Holes at plastic hinges

In locations subject to plastic hinge rotation at factored loading, fastener holes in the tension area shall be either sub-punched and reamed or drilled full size. This requirement shall be noted on design drawings and shop details.

28.4.3 Thermally cut holes

Thermally cut holes produced by guided machine may be used in statically loaded structures if the actual hole size does not exceed the nominal hole size by more than 1 mm. Gouges not exceeding 1.5 mm deep may be permitted along edges of thermally cut slots. Manually cut fastener holes may be permitted only with the approval of the designer.

28.4.4 Alignment

Drifting done during assembly to align holes shall not distort the metal or enlarge holes. Holes in adjacent parts shall match well enough to permit easy entry of bolts. Holes, except oversize or slotted holes, may be enlarged to admit bolts by a moderate amount of reaming. However, gross mismatch of holes shall be cause for rejection.

28.5 Joints in contact bearing

Joints in compression that depend on contact bearing shall have the bearing surfaces prepared to a common plane by milling, sawing, or other suitable means. Surface roughness shall have a roughness height rating not exceeding 500 (12.5 μm), as specified in CSA B95, unless otherwise specified by the designer.

When shop assembled, such joints shall have at least 75% of the entire contact area in bearing. A separation not exceeding 0.5 mm shall be considered acceptable as bearing. The separation of any remaining portion shall not exceed 1 mm. A gap of up to 3 mm may be packed with non-tapered steel shims in order to meet the requirements of this Clause. Shims need not be other than mild steel, regardless of the grade of the main material.

28.6 Member tolerances

28.6.1

Structural members consisting primarily of a single rolled shape shall be straight within the tolerances allowed in CSA G40.20, except as specified in Clause 28.6.4.

28.6.2

Built-up bolted structural members shall be straight within the tolerances allowed for rolled wide-flange shapes in CSA G40.20, except as specified in Clause 28.6.4.

28.6.3

Dimensional tolerances of welded structural members shall be those specified in CSA W59, unless otherwise specified by the designer.

28.6.4
The out-of-straightness of fabricated compression members shall not exceed 0.001 of the axial length between points that are to be laterally supported.

28.6.5
Beams with bow within the straightness tolerance shall be fabricated so that, after erection, the bow due to rolling or fabrication shall be upward.

28.6.6
Completed members shall be free from twists, bends, and open joints. Sharp kinks or bends shall be cause for rejection.

28.6.7
A variation of 1 mm is permissible in the overall length of members with both ends finished for contact bearing.

28.6.8
Members without ends finished for contact bearing that are to be framed to other steel parts of the structure may have a variation from the detailed length not greater than 2 mm for members 10 m or less in length and not greater than 4 mm for members more than 10 m in length.

28.7 Cleaning, surface preparation, and shop coating

28.7.1 General
Steelwork need not be coated unless required by Clause 6.6 or otherwise specified by the designer.

28.7.2 Uncoated steel

28.7.2.1
Steelwork need not be cleaned of oil, grease, dirt, and other foreign matter unless encased in concrete or otherwise specified by the designer.

28.7.2.2
Steelwork to be encased in concrete need not be coated. Steelwork that is designed to act compositely with reinforced concrete and depends on natural bond for interconnection shall not be coated.

28.7.3 Coated steel

28.7.3.1 General
The requirements of the coating system, including surface preparation, minimum finished coating thickness, and coating or performance specifications, shall be specified to meet service conditions. The primer and subsequent coats shall be compatible. Coatings shall be applied thoroughly and evenly to dry, clean surfaces.

28.7.3.2 Surface preparation
Steelwork shall be cleaned of all loose mill scale, loose rust, weld slag and flux deposit, oil, grease, dirt, other foreign matter, and excessive weld spatter prior to application of the coating. When specified, special surface preparation prior to coating shall meet the requirements of SSPC SP 1; SSPC SP 2; SSPC SP 3; SSPC SP 5/NACE No. 1; SSPC SP 6/NACE No. 3; SSPC SP 7/NACE No. 4; SSPC SP 10/NACE No. 2; SSPC SP 11; SSPC SP 12; or SSPC SP 14, as applicable.

28.7.3.3 One-coat systems

Steelwork to be coated shall, at a minimum, be given a one-coat paint intended to withstand exposure to an essentially non-corrosive atmosphere for a period not exceeding six months in compliance with CISC/CPMA 1-73a, unless otherwise specified.

A one-coat shop primer intended to withstand exposure to an essentially non-corrosive atmosphere for a period not exceeding 12 months shall comply with to CISC/CPMA 2-75, unless otherwise specified by the designer.

28.7.3.4 Inaccessible surfaces

Surfaces that will be inaccessible after assembly shall be cleaned or cleaned and coated, as necessary, prior to assembly. Inside surfaces of enclosed spaces that will be entirely sealed off from any external source of oxygen need not be coated.

28.7.3.5 Field coating

Unless otherwise specified by the designer, the cleaning of steelwork in preparation for field coating, touch-up of shop coat, spot-coating of field fasteners, and general field coating shall not be considered part of the erection work.

28.7.4 Special surfaces

28.7.4.1

Coated faying surfaces in high-strength bolted slip-critical joints shall meet the requirements of Clause 23.3.

28.7.4.2

For members in compression, surfaces that are finished to bear shall be cleaned before assembly but shall not be coated unless otherwise specified by the designer.

28.7.4.3

Joints that are to be welded shall be kept free of all foreign matter, including paint, primer, or other coatings that could be detrimental to achieving a sound weldment. Welding procedures for welding over coatings shall be developed and accepted by the Canadian Welding Bureau in accordance with CSA W47.1. Such welding procedures shall include the paint/coating product identifier, manufacturer, and maximum coating thickness. Consideration for low hydrogen applications shall be made.

These welding procedures may apply to, e.g., joist shoes to supporting members, joist bridging, metal deck to supporting members, and shear connectors.

28.7.5 Metallic zinc coatings

28.7.5.1

Material to be hot-dip galvanized shall comply with CAN/CSA-G164.

28.7.5.2

Material to be zinc metallized shall comply with CSA G189.

29 Erection

29.1 Temporary conditions

29.1.1 General
Suitable provisions shall be made in accordance with this Standard to ensure that an adequate margin of safety exists in the uncompleted structure and members during erection. (See also Clause 4.3.4.)

29.1.2 Temporary loads
Suitable provisions shall be made to ensure that the loads incurred during steel erection can be safely sustained for their duration and without permanent deformation or other damage to any member of the steel frame and other building components supported thereby.

Temporary loads can include but are not limited to loads due to wind, equipment, equipment operation, and storage of construction materials.

29.1.3 Temporary bracing
Temporary bracing shall be employed whenever necessary to withstand all loads to which the structure may be subject during steel erection. Temporary bracing shall be left in place undisturbed as long as necessary for the safety and integrity of the structure.

29.1.4 Adequacy of temporary connections
As erection progresses, the work shall be securely bolted or welded to resist safely all dead, wind, and erection loads and to provide necessary structural integrity.

29.2 Alignment
Permanent welding or bolting shall not be performed until as much of the structure as will be stiffened thereby has been suitably aligned.

29.3 Erection tolerances

29.3.1 General
The steel framework shall be erected true and plumb within the specified tolerances. The tolerances specified in Clauses 29.3.2 to 29.3.11 are the maximum allowable tolerances for a given member. A member tolerance can be limited to less than the allowed tolerance due to a stricter tolerance controlling the member to which it is framed into or to a member that it supports.

29.3.2 Elevation of base plates
Column base plates shall be considered to be at their proper elevation if the following tolerances are not exceeded:
(a) for single- and multi-storey buildings designed as simple construction as specified in Clause 8.3: ±5 mm from the specified elevation; and
(b) for single- and multi-storey buildings designed as continuous construction as specified in Clause 8.2, or as partially restrained construction as specified in Clause 8.4: ±3 mm from the specified elevation.

29.3.3 Plumbness of columns

Unless otherwise specified by the designer, columns shall be considered plumb if their verticality does not exceed the following tolerances:

(a) for exterior columns of multi-storey buildings: 1/1000, but not more than 25 mm toward or 50 mm away from the building line in the first 20 storeys, plus 2 mm for each additional storey, up to a maximum of 50 mm toward or 75 mm away from the building line over the full height of the building;

(b) for columns adjacent to elevator shafts: 1/1000, but not more than 25 mm in the first 20 storeys, plus 1 mm for each additional storey, up to a maximum of 50 mm over the full height of the elevator shaft; and

(c) for all other columns: 1/500.

Column plumbness shall be measured from the actual column centreline at the base of the column to its centreline at the next adjacent storey. Deviation from straightness of the erected column shall meet the requirements of Clause 28.6.

29.3.4 Horizontal alignment of members

Unless otherwise specified by the designer, spandrel beams shall be considered aligned when the offset of one end relative to the other from the alignment shown on the drawings does not exceed $L/1000$. However, the offset need not be less than 3 mm and shall not exceed 6 mm.

Other members shall be considered aligned when the offset of one end relative to the other from the alignment shown on the drawings does not exceed $L/500$. However, the offset need not be less than 3 mm and shall not exceed 12 mm.

29.3.5 Elevations of members

The elevations of the ends of members shall be within 10 mm of the specified member elevation. Allowances shall be made for initial base elevation, column shortening, differential deflections, temperature effects, and other special conditions, but the maximum deviation from the specified slope shall not exceed $L/500$. The difference from the specified elevation between member ends that meet at a joint shall not exceed 6 mm.

29.3.6 Crane runway beams

Unless otherwise required by the operational characteristics of the crane, crane runway beams and monorail beams shall be erected within the following tolerances:

(a) The slope of a member shall not exceed $L/1000$. However, the difference in elevation of the ends need not be less than 3 mm and shall not exceed 6 mm. The difference in elevation of opposite points on two parallel runway beams shall not exceed 1/1000 of the distance between the runway beams and shall not exceed 6 mm.

(b) The offset of one end of the member relative to the other from the horizontal alignment shown on the drawings shall not exceed $L/500$. However, the offset need not be less than 3 mm and shall not exceed 8 mm.

(c) The distance between the ends of two parallel runway beams shall not deviate by more than 1/500 of the span of the runway beam. However, the difference in the distances between the runway beam ends need not be less than 3 mm and shall not exceed 10 mm.

29.3.7 Alignment of braced members

Members such as columns, beams, trusses, and open web steel joists that are braced between their supports shall be erected in such a way that the fabrication tolerances specified in this Standard are maintained.

29.3.8 Members with adjustable connections

Members with adjustable connections (e.g., shelf angles, sash angles, and lintels) shall be considered to be within tolerances when the following requirements are met:

(a) Each piece shall be level within $L/1000$; however, the difference in elevation of the ends need not be less than 3 mm and shall not exceed 6 mm.

(b) Adjoining ends of members shall be aligned vertically and horizontally within 2 mm.

(c) The location of the members both vertically and horizontally shall be within 10 mm of the location established by the dimensions on the drawings.

29.3.9 Column splices

Column splices and other compression joints that depend on contact bearing as part of the splice resistance shall, after alignment, have a maximum allowable separation of 6 mm. Any gap exceeding 1.5 mm shall be packed with non-tapered steel shims. Shims need not be other than mild steel, regardless of the grade of the main material.

29.3.10 Welded joint fit-up

The fit-up of joints that are to be field-welded shall be within the tolerances shown on the erection diagrams and shall not exceed the tolerances specified in CSA W59 when welding is completed.

29.3.11 Bolted joint fit-up

Bolted joint fit-up shall meet the requirements of Clause 28.4.4.

30 Inspection

30.1 General

Material and quality of work shall at all times be subject to inspection by qualified inspectors who represent and are responsible to the designer. The inspection shall cover shop work and field erection work to ensure compliance with this Standard.

30.2 Co-operation

Insofar as possible, all inspections shall be made in the fabricator's shop. The fabricator shall co-operate with the inspector and permit access for inspection to all places where work is being done. The inspector shall co-operate in avoiding undue delay in the fabrication or erection of the steelwork.

30.3 Rejection

Material or quality of work not meeting the requirements of this Standard may be rejected at any time during the progress of work once non-compliance is established.

30.4 Inspection of high-strength bolted joints

The inspection of high-strength bolted joints shall be performed in accordance with Clause 23.9.

30.5 Third-party welding inspection

When third-party welding inspection (visual and/or NDE) is specified by the owner, the welding inspection shall be performed by firms certified to CSA W178.1, except that visual inspection may also be performed by persons certified to Level 2 or 3 of CSA W178.2.

30.6 Identification of steel by marking

In the fabricator's plant, steel used for main components shall at all times be marked to identify its specification (and grade, if applicable). This shall be done by suitable markings or by recognized colour coding, except that cut pieces identified by piece mark and contract number need not continue to carry specification identification markings when it has been satisfactorily established that such cut pieces meet the required material specifications.

Table 1
Maximum width (or diameter)-to-thickness ratios: Elements in axial compression
(See Clauses 11.2, 13.3.1, 13.3.3.1, and 13.3.5.)

Description of elements	Limits
Elements supported along one edge	$\dfrac{b_{el}}{t} \leq \dfrac{200}{\sqrt{F_y}}$
Flanges of I-sections, T-sections, and channels	
Legs of angles	
Plate-girder stiffeners	
Stems of T-sections	$\dfrac{b_{el}}{t} \leq \dfrac{340}{\sqrt{F_y}}$
Flanges of rectangular hollow sections	$\dfrac{b_{el}}{t} \leq \dfrac{670}{\sqrt{F_y}}$
Flanges of box sections	
Flange cover plates and diaphragm plates between lines of fasteners or welds	
Webs supported on both edges	$\dfrac{h}{t} \leq \dfrac{670}{\sqrt{F_y}}$
Perforated cover plates	$\dfrac{b_{el}}{t} \leq \dfrac{840}{\sqrt{F_y}}$
Circular hollow sections	$\dfrac{D}{t} \leq \dfrac{23\,000}{F_y}$

Table 2
Maximum width (or diameter)-to-thickness ratios:
Elements in flexural compression
(See Clause 11.2.)

Description of elements	Section classification limits		
	Class 1	Class 2	Class 3
Flanges of I-sections or T-sections Plates projecting from compression elements Outstanding legs of pairs of angles in continuous contact with an axis of symmetry in the plane of loading	$\dfrac{b_{el}}{t} \le \dfrac{145}{\sqrt{F_y}}$	$\dfrac{b_{el}}{t} \le \dfrac{170}{\sqrt{F_y}}$	$\dfrac{b_{el}}{t} \le \dfrac{200}{\sqrt{F_y}}$
Stems of T-sections	$\dfrac{b_{el}}{t} \le \dfrac{145}{\sqrt{F_y}}$	$\dfrac{b_{el}}{t} \le \dfrac{170}{\sqrt{F_y}}$	$\dfrac{b_{el}}{t} \le \dfrac{340}{\sqrt{F_y}}$
Flanges of rectangular hollow sections	$\dfrac{b_{el}}{t} \le \dfrac{420}{\sqrt{F_y}}$	$\dfrac{b_{el}}{t} \le \dfrac{525}{\sqrt{F_y}}$	$\dfrac{b_{el}}{t} \le \dfrac{670}{\sqrt{F_y}}$
Flanges of box sections Flange cover plates and diaphragm plates between lines of fasteners or welds	$\dfrac{b_{el}}{t} \le \dfrac{525}{\sqrt{F_y}}$	$\dfrac{b_{el}}{t} \le \dfrac{525}{\sqrt{F_y}}$	$\dfrac{b_{el}}{t} \le \dfrac{670}{\sqrt{F_y}}$
Webs	$\dfrac{h}{w} \le \dfrac{1100}{\sqrt{F_y}}\left(1 - 0.39\dfrac{C_f}{\phi C_y}\right)$	$\dfrac{h}{w} \le \dfrac{1700}{\sqrt{F_y}}\left(1 - 0.61\dfrac{C_f}{\phi C_y}\right)$	$\dfrac{h}{w} \le \dfrac{1900}{\sqrt{F_y}}\left(1 - 0.65\dfrac{C_f}{\phi C_y}\right)$
Circular hollow sections	$\dfrac{D}{t} \le \dfrac{13\,000}{F_y}$	$\dfrac{D}{t} \le \dfrac{18\,000}{F_y}$	$\dfrac{D}{t} \le \dfrac{66\,000}{F_y}$

Note: *Elements with ratios exceeding Class 3 limits are Class 4 sections.*

Table 3
Values of k_s and c_1
(See Clauses 13.12.2.2 and 23.3.)

| | | | c_1 | | |
| | | | Turn-of-nut | | Other |
Class	Description	k_s	A 325 and A 325M bolts	A 490 and A 490M bolts	F 959, F1852, and F 2280
A	Clean mill scale or blast-cleaned with Class A coatings	0.33	0.82	0.78	0.72
B	Blast-cleaned or blast-cleaned with Class B coatings	0.50	0.90	0.85	0.78
C	Hot-dip galvanized with wire-brushed surfaces	0.40	0.90	0.85	0.78

Notes:
(1) Class A and Class B coatings are those coatings that provide a mean slip coefficient, k_s, of not less than 0.33 and 0.50, respectively.
(2) Values of c_1 for 5% probability of slip for values of k_s not specified in this Table are given as Slip Factor D in the RCSC's Guide to Design Criteria for Bolted and Riveted Joints.

Table 4
Matching electrode ultimate tensile strengths for CSA G40.21 steels
(See Clause 13.13.1.)

| Matching electrode ultimate tensile strength* MPa | G40.21 Grades, MPa | | | | | | |
	260	300	350	380	400	480	700
430	X	X†					
490	X	X	X‡	X			
550					X‡		
620						X	
820							X

*The electrode ultimate tensile strength is ten times the first two digits of the electrode classification in CSA W48.
†For HSS only.
‡For unpainted applications using "A" or "AT" steels where the deposited weld metal is to have atmospheric corrosion resistance or colour characteristics, or both, similar to the base metal, the requirements of Clauses 5.2.1.4 and 5.2.1.5 of CSA W59 shall apply.
Note: For matching conditions of ASTM steels, see Table 11-1 or 12-1 of CSA W59.

Table 5
Maximum intermediate transverse stiffener spacing
(See Clause 14.5.2.)

Web depth-to-thickness ratio, h/w	Maximum distance between stiffeners, a, in terms of clear web depth, h
≤ 150	$3h$
> 150	$\dfrac{67\,500\,h}{(h/w)^2}$

Table 6
Minimum edge distance for bolt holes, mm
(See Clauses 22.3.2 and 22.3.4.)

Bolt diameter		Minimum edge distance	
mm	in	At sheared edge	At rolled or sawn edges, or edges cut by gas†, plasma, laser, or water jet
—	5/8	28	22
16	—	28	22
—	3/4	32	25
20	—	34	26
—	7/8	38‡	28
22	—	38	28
24	—	42	30
—	1	44‡	32
27	—	48	34
—	1-1/8	51	38
30	—	52	38
—	1-1/4	57	41
36	—	64	46
Over 36	Over 1-1/4	1.75 × diameter	1.25 × diameter

†*Gas-cut edges shall be smooth and free from notches. The edge distance in this column may be decreased by* 3 mm *when the hole is at a point where calculated stress under factored loads is not more than 0.3 of the yield stress.*
‡*At the ends of beam-framing angles, this distance may be* 32 mm.

Table 7
Minimum bolt tension, kN
(See Clauses 23.8.1, 23.8.3, 23.8.4, 23.9.2, and I.1.)

Bolt diameter		Minimum bolt tension*	
mm	in	A 325, A 325M, and F 1852 bolts	A 490, A 490M, and F 2280 bolts
—	1/2	53	67
—	5/8	85	107
16	—	91	114
—	3/4	125	157
20	—	142	178
—	7/8	174	218
22	—	176	220
24	—	205	257
—	1	227	285
27	—	267	334
—	1-1/8	249	356
30	—	326	408
—	1-1/4	316	454
—	1-3/8	378	538
36	—	475	595
—	1-1/2	458	658

*Equal to 70% of the specified minimum tensile strength.

Table 8
Nut rotation from snug-tight condition*
(See Clauses 23.8.2 and I.1.)

Disposition of outer faces of bolted parts	Bolt length†	Turn
Both faces normal to bolt axis or one face normal to axis and other face sloped 1:20 max. (bevelled washers not used)‡	Up to and including 4 diameters	1/3
	Over 4 diameters and not exceeding 8 diameters or 200 mm	1/2
	Exceeding 8 diameters or 200 mm	2/3
Both faces sloped 1:20 max. from normal to bolt axis (bevelled washers not used)‡	All lengths of bolts	3/4

Nut rotation is rotation relative to a bolt regardless of whether the nut or bolt is turned. The tolerance on rotation is 30° over or under. This Table applies to coarse-thread heavy-hex structural bolts of all sizes and lengths used with heavy-hex semi-finished nuts.
†*Bolt length is measured from the underside of the head to the extreme end of point.*
‡*Bevelled washers are necessary when A 490, A 490M, or F 2280 bolts are used.*

Table 9
Detail categories for load-induced fatigue
(See Clauses 26.3.1 and 26.3.4.)

General condition	Situation	Detail category	Illustrative example (see Figure 2)
Plain members	Base metal		
	• with rolled or cleaned surfaces. Flame-cut edges with a surface roughness not exceeding 1000 (25 μm) as specified by CSA B95	A	1, 2
	• of unpainted weathering steel	B	
	• at re-entrant corners of geometric discontinuities such as copes, cuts, or block-outs	B	2a
	• at net section of eyebar heads and pin plates	E	
Built-up members	Base metal and weld metal in components, without attachments, connected by		3, 4, 5, 7
	• continuous full-penetration groove welds with backing bars removed, or	B	
	• continuous fillet welds parallel to the direction of applied stress	B	
	• continuous full-penetration groove welds with backing bars in place, or	B1	
	• continuous partial-penetration groove welds parallel to the direction of applied stress	B1	
	Base metal at ends of partial-length cover plates		
	• bolts in slip-critical connections	B	22
	• narrower than the flange, with or without end welds, or wider than the flange with end welds		
	• flange thickness ≤ 20 mm	E	7
	• flange thickness > 20 mm	E1	7
	• wider than the flange without end welds	E1	7
Groove-welded splice connections with weld soundness established by NDT and all required grinding in the direction of the applied stresses	Base metal and weld metal at full-penetration groove-welded splices		
	• of plates of similar cross-sections with welds ground flush	B	8, 9
	• with 600 mm radius transitions in width with welds ground flush	B	11
	• with transitions in width or thickness with welds ground to provide slopes not steeper than 1.0 to 2.5		10, 10a
	• G40.21-700Q and 700QT base metal	B1	
	• other base metal grades	B	

(Continued)

Table 9 (Continued)

General condition	Situation	Detail category	Illustrative example (see Figure 2)
	• with or without transitions having slopes not greater than 1.0 to 2.5, when weld reinforcement is not removed	C	8, 9, 10, 10a
	• at weld access holes		
	• of rolled members	C	
	• of built-up members	D	
Longitudinally loaded groove-welded attachments	Base metal at details attached by full- or partial-penetration groove welds		
	When the detail length in the direction of applied stress is		
	• less than 50 mm	C	6, 18
	• between 50 mm and 12 times the detail thickness, but less than 100 mm	D	18
	• greater than either 12 times the detail thickness or 100 mm		
	• detail thickness < 25 mm	E	18
	• detail thickness ≥ 25 mm	E1	18
	• with a transition radius, R, with the end welds ground smooth, regardless of detail length		12
	• $R \geq 600$ mm	B	
	• 600 mm $> R \geq 150$ mm	C	
	• 150 mm $> R \geq 50$ mm	D	
	• $R < 50$ mm	E	
	• with a transition radius, R, with the end welds not ground smooth	E	12
Transversely loaded groove-welded attachments with weld soundness established by NDT and all required grinding transverse to the direction of stress	Base metal at detail attached by full-penetration groove welds with a transition radius, R		12
	• to flange, with equal plate thickness and weld reinforcement removed		
	• $R \geq 600$ mm	B	
	• 600 mm $> R \geq 150$ mm	C	
	• 150 mm $> R \geq 50$ mm	D	
	• $R < 50$ mm	E	
	• to flange, with equal plate thickness and weld reinforcement not removed, or to web		
	• $R \geq 150$ mm	C	

(Continued)

Table 9 (Continued)

General condition	Situation	Detail category	Illustrative example (see Figure 2)
	• 150 mm > R ≥ 50 mm	D	
	• R < 50 mm	E	
	• to flange, with unequal plate thickness and weld reinforcement removed		
	• R ≥ 50 mm	D	
	• R < 50 mm	E	
	• to flange, for any transition radius with unequal plate thickness and weld reinforcement not removed	E	
Fillet-welded connections with welds normal to the direction of stress	Base metal		
	• at details other than transverse stiffener-to-flange or transverse stiffener-to-web connections	C*	19
	• at the toe of transverse stiffener-to-flange and transverse stiffener-to-web welds	C1	6
Fillet-welded connections with welds normal and/or parallel to the direction of stress	Shear stress on weld throat	E	16
Longitudinally loaded fillet-welded attachments	Base metal at details attached by fillet welds		
	• when the detail length in the direction of applied stress is		
	• less than 50 mm, and stud-type shear connectors	C	13, 14, 15, 18, 20
	• between 50 mm and 12 times the detail thickness, but less than 100 mm	D	14, 18, 20
	• greater than either 12 times the detail thickness or 100 mm		7, 14, 16, 18, 20
	• detail thickness < 25 mm	E	
	• detail thickness ≥ 25 mm	E1	
	• with a transition radius, R, with the end of welds ground smooth, regardless of detail length		12
	• R ≥ 50 mm	D	
	• R < 50 mm	E	
	• with a transition radius with the end of welds not ground smooth	E	12

(Continued)

Table 9 (Concluded)

General condition	Situation	Detail category	Illustrative example (see Figure 2)
Transversely loaded fillet-welded attachments with welds parallel to the direction of primary stress	Base metal at details attached by fillet welds		12
	• with a transition radius, R, with the end of welds ground smooth		
	• $R \geq 50$ mm	D	
	• $R < 50$ mm	E	
	• with any transition radius with end of welds not ground smooth	E	
Mechanically fastened connections	Base metal		17
	• at gross section of high-strength bolted slip-critical connections, except axially loaded joints in which out-of-plane bending is induced in connected materials	B	
	• at net section of high-strength bolted non-slip-critical connections	B	
	• at net section of non-pretensioned bolted connections	D	
	• at net section of riveted connections	D	
Anchor rods and threaded parts	Tensile stress range on the tensile stress area of the threaded part, including effects of bending	E	
Fillet-welded HSS to base plate	Shear stress on fillet weld	E1	21
A 325, A 325M, and F 1852 bolts in axial tension	Tensile stress on area A_b		
		See Clause 13.12.1.3	
A 490, A 490M, and F 2280 bolts in axial tension	Tensile stress on area A_b		

*The fatigue resistance of fillet welds transversely loaded is a function of the effective throat and plate thickness. See Frank and Fisher (1979).

$$F_{sr} = F_{sr}^C \left[\left(0.06 + 0.79 H/t_p \right) / \left(0.64 t_p^{1/6} \right) \right]$$

where

F_{sr}^C = fatigue resistance for Category C as determined in accordance with Clause 26.3.3. This assumes no penetration at the weld root

t_p = plate thickness

H = weld leg size

Table 10
Fatigue constants for detail categories
(See Clauses 26.3.3 and 26.3.4.)

Detail category	Fatigue life constant, γ	Constant amplitude threshold stress range, F_{srt}, MPa	nN'	Fatigue life constant, γ'
A	8190×10^9	165	1.82×10^6	223×10^{15}
B	3930×10^9	110	2.95×10^6	47.6×10^{15}
B1	2000×10^9	83	3.50×10^6	13.8×10^{15}
C	1440×10^9	69	4.38×10^6	6.86×10^{15}
C1	1440×10^9	83	2.52×10^6	9.92×10^{15}
D	721×10^9	48	6.52×10^6	1.66×10^{15}
E	361×10^9	31	12.1×10^6	0.347×10^{15}
E1	128×10^9	18	21.9×10^6	0.0415×10^{15}

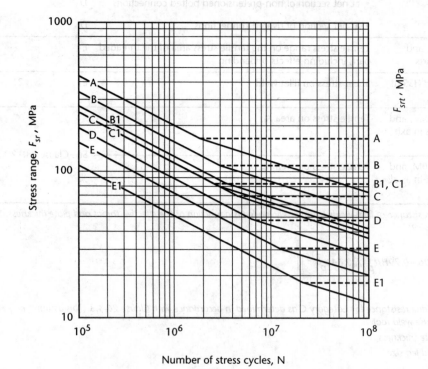

Figure 1
Fatigue constants for detail categories
(See Clauses 26.3.3 and 26.3.4.)

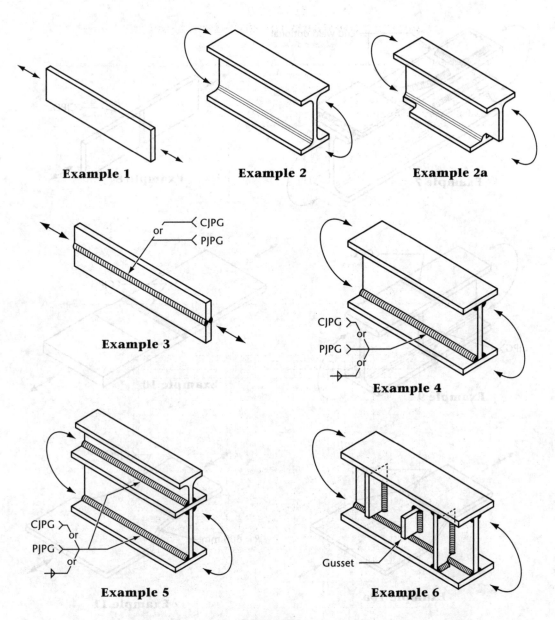

Figure 2
Illustrative examples of detail categories
(See Clause 26.3.4 and Table 9.)

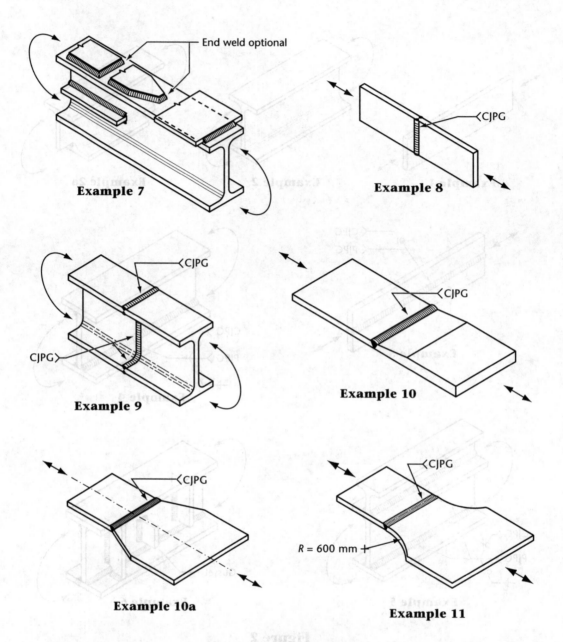

Figure 2 (Continued)

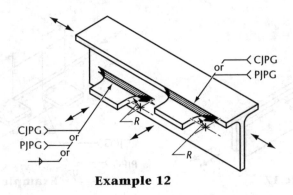

Example 12

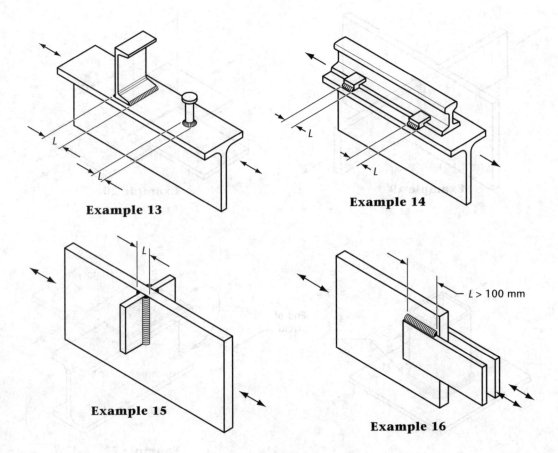

Example 13

Example 14

Example 15

Example 16

Figure 2 (Continued)

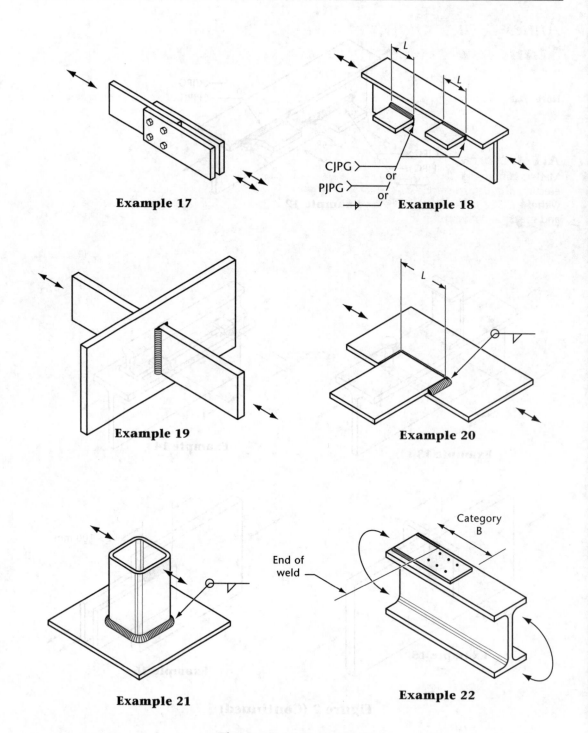

Example 17

Example 18

Example 19

Example 20

Example 21

Example 22

Figure 2 (Concluded)

Annex A (informative)
Standard practice for structural steel

Note: *This informative (nonmandatory) Annex has been written in normative (mandatory) language to facilitate adoption where users of the Standard or regulatory authorities wish to adopt it formally as additional requirements to this Standard.*

A.1 General

Matters concerning standard practice not covered by this Standard but pertinent to the fabrication and erection of structural steel (e.g., classification of material and contract documents) shall be in accordance with the CISC's *Code of Standard Practice for Structural Steel* unless otherwise clearly specified in the plans and specifications issued to the bidders.

Annex B (informative)
Margins of safety

Note: *This Annex is an informative (nonmandatory) part of this Standard.*

B.1

Code writers now use limit states design to provide a practical level of reliability over the lifetime of a structure. One of the advantages of limit states design is that by using load and resistance factors based on the statistical variation of the loads and resistances, a relatively uniform degree of reliability is obtained in the design of structures across a variety of configurations and load conditions. At the same time, economies accrue in limit states design since structures or portions of them are not designed for excessive safety, either due to the unrealistic load combinations or inaccurate modelling based on the assumed elastic behaviour of structural steel components used in the past. Moreover, by changing the reliability index in limit states design, greater or lesser safety can be assigned on a quantitative basis to entire structures or to components.

B.2

The load and resistance factors in limit states design, derived to give the desired reliability index, are related to the calculated probability of failure and are based on the statistical variations of the loads and resistances.

B.3

Limit states design was first introduced in the *NBCC, 1975,* where the reliability index for steel buildings as a whole was taken as 3.0. A greater reliability index was used for connectors so that the probability of the connector failing before the member as a whole was reduced and the more ductile mode of failure of the member was favoured. This was done to make the connections stronger than the members they joined. In the current NBCC and this edition of this Standard, the reliability index for steel buildings as a whole remains 3.0, and indices greater than this value are used for connections.

B.4

The development of member resistance factors used in the first limited states design standard, CSA S16.1-1974, is discussed in Kennedy and Gad Aly (1980) and others in Kennedy and Baker (1984). Since then, other resistance factors have been introduced based on statistical analyses of the resistances. That of 0.67 for welds was confirmed in the 1994 edition of CAN/CSA-S16.1, when the strength of transverse fillet welds was recognized to be 1.50 times that of longitudinal fillet welds (Lesik and Kennedy, 1990). Other resistance factors have been introduced for shear connectors, anchor rods, bearing of bolts on steel, and reinforcing bars, as well as $\phi_b = 0.80$ for high-strength bolts in shear and tension (Kennedy, 1999a) and $\phi_{bi} = 0.80$ and $\phi_{be} = 0.75$ for bearing on webs of interior loads and end reactions, respectively (Kennedy, et al., 1998; Kennedy, 1999b). Enhanced target reliability indices for calculating resistance factors of 4.5 were used for welds and bolts, and 3.5 for bearing on webs. In this edition of the Standard, a new resistance factor for the block shear, net section rupture, and bolt tear-out limit states, $\phi_u = 0.75$, has been introduced based on recent research by Driver et al. (2006) and Cai and Driver (2010). A review of resistance factors used in this Standard is presented by Schmidt and Bartlett (2002).

B.5

Cai, Q. and Driver, R.G. (2010). Prediction of bolted connection capacity for block shear failures along atypical paths. *AISC Engineering Journal* (in press).

Driver, R.G., Grondin, G.Y., and Kulak, G.L. (2006). Unified block shear equation for achieving consistent reliability. *Journal of Constructional Steel Research,* 62 (3), March, 210–222.

Kennedy, D.J.L. (1999a). *Bolts in bearing type connections, basis for increasing the resistance factor for high strength bolts to 0.80.* S16 Committee Communication.

Kennedy, D.J.L. (1999b). *Web crippling and yielding.* S16 Committee Communication.

Kennedy, D.J.L. and Baker, K.A. (1984). Resistance factors for steel highway bridges. *Canadian Journal of Civil Engineering,* 11 (2), June, 324–334.

Kennedy, D.J.L. and Gad Aly, M. (1980). Limit states design of steel structures — performance factors. *Canadian Journal of Civil Engineering,* 7 (1), March, 45–77.

Kennedy, S.J., Kennedy, D.J.L., and Medhekar, M.S. (1998). The bearing resistance of webs: Further studies of the post-buckling strength. *Proceedings of the Annual Conference, Structural Stability Research Council,* Atlanta, GA, September 21–23, 25–41.

Lesik, D.F. and Kennedy, D.J.L., (1990). Ultimate strength of fillet welded connections loaded in plane. *Canadian Journal of Civil Engineering,* 17 (1), February, 55–67.

Schmidt, B.J. and Bartlett, F.M. (2002). Review of resistance factor for steel: Resistance distributions and resistance factor calibration. *Canadian journal of Civil Engineering,* 29(1), February, 109-118.

Annex C (normative)
Crane-supporting structures

Note: *This Annex is a normative (mandatory) part of this Standard.*

C.1 General

Steel structures that support overhead cranes and hoists require special consideration in order to provide safe and serviceable structures. Electrically operated top-running overhead travelling cranes, underslung cranes, and monorails impose repetitive loads that can lead to the development and propagation of fatigue cracks in the crane-supporting structure. These loads shall be accounted for in the design and construction of the crane-supporting structure. Conditions that apply to these steel structures, where any component is subjected to fatigue loads as specified in Clause 26, are given in this Annex.

The requirements of this Standard for design for fatigue shall apply. The structural design shall take into account, among other factors, appropriate methods of analysis, rotational restraints at crane runway beam supports, crane load eccentricities, distortion leading to fatigue cracking, welded details, built-up column section details, bracing systems, deflections, and details related to crane rails. The construction specifications shall include (but not necessarily be limited to) requirements for materials, detailing, fabrication, erection, bearing and contact surfaces, dimensional tolerances, crane rail installation, and shop and field inspection.

The designer shall determine the loading parameters and the appropriate number of loading cycles at each level of load by analyzing the duty cycles for the design life of the structure, in addition to other crane details that are necessary to design the structure. This information shall be included in the structural design documents.

Note: *For design information and information to be shown on the structural design documents, see the CISC's Crane-Supporting Steel Structures: Design Guide.*

Annex D (informative)
Recommended maximum values for deflections for specified design live, snow, and wind loads

Note: *This Annex is an informative (nonmandatory) part of this Standard.*

D.1 General

Table D.1 provides deflection criteria for floor or roof members as a fraction of the span and for lateral drift as a fraction of the storey height. These criteria are related to the serviceability limit states. Although the criteria refer to specified live, snow, and wind loads, the designer should consider the inclusion of specified dead loads in some instances. For example, non-permanent partitions, which are classified by the *NBCC* as dead load, should be part of the loading considered under this Annex if they are likely to be applied to the structure after the completion of finishes susceptible to cracking.

D.2 Wind

Some building materials augment the rigidity provided by the steelwork; therefore, the deflections calculated for bare steel structures under wind loads can be somewhat reduced. The more common structural and non-structural elements that contribute to the stiffness of a building are masonry walls, certain types of curtain walls, masonry partitions, and concrete around steel members. Provided that the materials augmenting rigidity are accounted for in the analysis for wind loads, the deflections for comparison to the limits in Table D.1 can be reduced by a maximum of 15%. The deflections used for strength and stability calculations should not be reduced. In tall and slender structures (height greater than four times the width), the wind effects should be determined by means of dynamic analysis or wind tunnel tests.

Table D.1
Deflection criteria
(See Clauses D.1 and D.2.)

Building type	Deflection	Specified loading	Application	Maximum
Industrial	Vertical	Live, snow	Members supporting inelastic roof coverings	L/240
		Live, snow	Members supporting elastic roof coverings	L/180
		Live, snow	Members supporting floors	L/300
		Maximum wheel loads (no impact)	Crane runway girders for crane capacity of 225 kN and over	L/800
		Maximum wheel loads (no impact)	Crane runway girders for crane capacity under 225 kN	L/600
	Lateral	Crane lateral	Crane runway girders	L/600
		Crane lateral or wind	Storey drift*	h/400 to h/200
All others	Vertical	Live, snow	Members of floors and roofs supporting construction and finishes susceptible to cracking	L/360
		Live, snow	Members of floors and roofs supporting construction and finishes not susceptible to cracking	L/300
	Lateral	Wind	Building drift due to all effects	h/400
		Wind	Storey drift (relative horizontal movement of any two consecutive floors) in buildings in cladding and partitions without special provision to accommodate building frame deformation	h/500
		Wind	Storey drift, with special provision to accommodate building frame deformation	h/400

Legend:

h = storey height.

L = length or span.

The permissible drift of industrial buildings depends on such factors as wall construction, building height, and the effect of deflection on the operation of the crane. Where the operation of the crane is sensitive to lateral deflections, a lateral deflection of less than h/400 may be necessary.

Annex E (informative)
Floor vibrations

Note: *This informative (nonmandatory) Annex has been written in normative (mandatory) language to facilitate adoption where users of the Standard or regulatory authorities wish to adopt it formally as additional requirements to this Standard.*

E.1 General

The development of floors of lighter construction, longer spans, and less inherent damping can sometimes result in disturbing floor vibrations during normal human activity. The specific vibration characteristics of the floor should be evaluated by the building designer.

Such an evaluation shall, at a minimum, consider the following:

(a) the characteristics and nature of the forcing excitations, e.g., walking and rhythmic activities (see also the *NBCC*);

(b) acceptance criteria for human comfort (depending on the use and occupancy of the floor area);

(c) a determination of the natural frequency of the floor framing systems, including the effect of continuity;

(d) the modal damping ratio; and

(e) the effective floor weights.

For guidance, see Murray, et al. (1997) and Commentary I, *User's Guide — NBC 2010: Structural Commentaries (Part 4)*.

E.2 Light-framed construction

For guidance on vibrations due to walking on light-framed construction made of light steel members and wood deck, see Applied Technology Council (1999).

E.3 References

Applied Technology Council (1999). *Minimizing floor vibration*. ATC Design Guide 1, Applied Technology Council, Redwood City, California.

Murray, T.M., Allen, D.E. and Ungar, E.E. (1997). *Floor vibrations due to human activity*. Steel Design Guide Series 11. American Institute of Steel Construction, Chicago; Canadian Institute of Steel Construction, Toronto.

Annex F (informative)
Effective lengths of columns

Note: *This Annex is an informative (nonmandatory) part of this Standard.*

F.1

The slenderness ratio of a member whose failure mode involves buckling is defined as the ratio of the effective length to the applicable radius of gyration. The effective length, KL, may be thought of as the actual unbraced length, L, multiplied by a factor, K, so that the product, KL, is equal to the length of a pin-ended column of equal capacity to the actual member. The effective length factor, K, of a column of finite unbraced length therefore depends on the conditions of restraint afforded to the column at its braced locations.

F.2

A variation in K between 0.65 and 2.0 will apply to the majority of cases likely to be encountered in actual structures. Figure F.1 illustrates six idealized cases in which joint rotation and translation are either fully realized or non-existent.

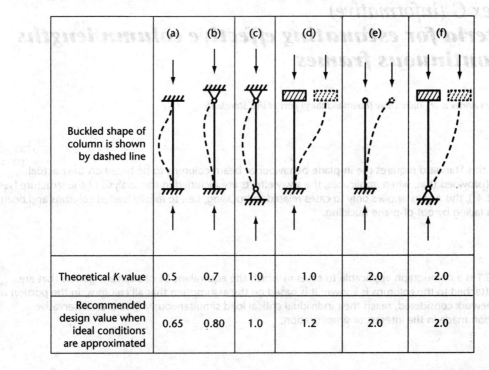

	(a)	(b)	(c)	(d)	(e)	(f)
Buckled shape of column is shown by dashed line						
Theoretical *K* value	0.5	0.7	1.0	1.0	2.0	2.0
Recommended design value when ideal conditions are approximated	0.65	0.80	1.0	1.2	2.0	2.0

End condition code		
		Rotation fixed, translation fixed
		Rotation free, translation fixed
		Rotation fixed, translation free
		Rotation free, translation free

Figure F.1
Effective lengths of columns
(See Clause F.2.)

Annex G (informative)
Criteria for estimating effective column lengths in continuous frames

Note: *This Annex is an informative (nonmandatory) part of this Standard.*

G.1

Because this Standard requires the in-plane behaviour of beam columns to be based on their actual lengths (provided that, when applicable, the sway effects are included in the analysis of the structure [see Clause 8.4]), this Annex applies only to cases related to buckling, i.e., to axially loaded columns and beam columns failing by out-of-plane buckling.

G.2

Figure G.1 is a nomograph applicable to cases in which the equivalent *I/L* of adjacent girders that are rigidly attached to the columns is known; it is based on the assumption that all columns, in the portion of the framework considered, reach their individual critical load simultaneously. This is a conservative assumption made in the interest of simplification.

G.3

The equation on which the nomograph is based is as follows:

$$\frac{G_U G_L}{4}(\pi/K)^2 + \frac{G_U + G_L}{2}\left(1 - \frac{\pi/K}{\tan\pi/K}\right) + 2\left[\frac{\tan\pi/2K}{\pi/K}\right] = 1$$

Subscripts *U* and *L* refer to the joints at the two ends of the column section being considered and

$$G = \frac{\Sigma I_c / L_c}{\Sigma I_g / L_g}$$

where

Σ = summation for all members rigidly connected to that joint and lying in the plane in which buckling of the column is being considered

I_c = moment of inertia of the column about the axes perpendicular to the plane of buckling

L_c = unsupported length of a column

I_g = moment of inertia of the girder about the axes perpendicular to the plane of buckling

L_g = unsupported length of a girder

G.4

For column ends supported by, but not rigidly connected to, a footing or foundation, *G* may be taken as 10 for practical designs. If the column end is rigidly attached to a properly designed footing, *G* may be taken as 1.0. Smaller values may be used if justified by analysis.

G.5

Refinements in girder I_g/L_g may be made when conditions at the far end of any particular girder are known definitely or when a conservative estimate can be made. For the case with no sidesway, multiply girder stiffnesses by the following factors:

(a) 1.5 if the far end of the girder is hinged; and

(b) 2.0 if the far end of the girder is fixed against rotation (i.e., rigidly attached to a support that is itself relatively rigid).

G.6

Having determined G_U and G_L for a column section, the effective length factor, K, is determined at the intersection of the straight line between the appropriate points on the scales for G_U and G_L with the scale for K.

G.7

The nomograph may be used to determine the effective length factors for the in-plane behaviour of compression members of trusses designed as axially loaded members even though the joints are rigid. In this case, there should be no in-plane eccentricities and all members of the truss meeting at the joint should not reach their ultimate load simultaneously. If it cannot be shown that all members at the joint do not reach their ultimate load simultaneously, the effective length factor of the compression members should be taken as 1.0.

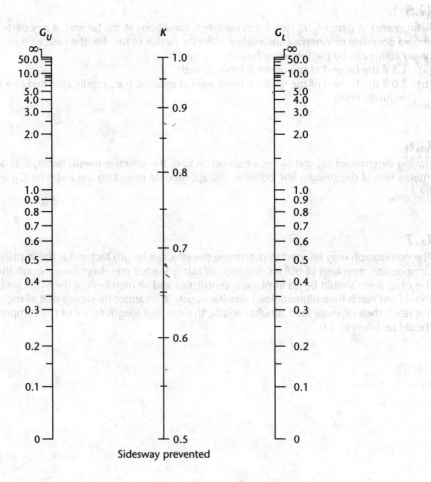

Sidesway prevented

Figure G.1
Nomograph for effective lengths column in continuous frames
(See Clause G.2.)

Annex H (informative)
Deflections of composite beams, joists, and trusses due to shrinkage of concrete

Note: *This Annex is an informative (nonmandatory) part of this Standard.*

H.1
Shrinkage-induced deflections result from the following process. Concrete decreases in volume as it cures, at first rapidly and then at a decreasing rate. When restrained, tensile strains and therefore tensile stresses can develop in the concrete. (It can even crack if the tensile strength is reached.)

A curing slab is restrained by the steel shape to which it is connected.

H.2
Figure H.1 shows the shrinkage strains that develop through the depth for a composite beam and the corresponding equilibrium conditions for unshored construction. It is evident that unshored composite members will deflect downward. (Shoring reduces the shrinkage deflection substantially, especially in the early stages when the rate of shrinkage is the greatest.)

H.3
Branson's (1964) method is used in this Standard to determine shrinkage deflections. As illustrated in Figure H.2(a), the first step in the method is to assume temporarily that the shrinkage of the concrete slab is not restrained by connection to the steel beam. The connection between the concrete slab and the beam is accounted for in two additional steps. First, a tensile force is applied to the centroid of the unrestrained slab so that the displacement of the slab under the force is equal to the unrestrained shrinkage displacement (see Figure H.2(b)). Compatibility is satisfied in this step. Second, equilibrium is satisfied by applying an equal and opposite force to the composite section (see Figure H.2(c)).

The method does not account for the cracking of concrete in tension, the non-linear stress-strain relationship of concrete, and other factors. To account for these factors and match theory with test results, the free shrinkage of the concrete is multiplied by an empirical coefficient.

The method gives reasonable results when an appropriate value is used for the empirical coefficient and suitable values are used for the free shrinkage and modular ratio.

H.4
The shrinkage deflection is directly proportional to the assumed free shrinkage strain. The free shrinkage strain depends on concrete properties such as the water/cement ratio, percentage of fines, entrained air, cement content, and curing conditions. A value of 583×10^{-6} may be used if other data are not available. This value was determined for composite beams supporting 75 mm concrete topping on 75 mm deck (150 mm total thickness) for inside conditions (see Ghali, et al. (2002), Annex A.2).

H.5
The modular ratio is calculated from the age-adjusted effective modulus of concrete, which in turn depends on the aging and creep coefficients. These coefficients may be taken as 0.73 and 2.7, respectively, if other data are not available. These coefficients were determined for the composite beams

described in Clause H.4, assuming the age at loading is 7 days (see Ghali, et al. (2002), Annexes A.7 and A.2, respectively). The shrinkage deflection is not sensitive to the modular ratio because both the transformed moment of inertia of the composite beam and the distance, y, vary with it.

H.6

The procedure in this Standard is used for determining the shrinkage deflections of simply supported composite beams, joists, and trusses. For many structural configurations, moments develop at the ends of beams, joists, and trusses as a result of partial or full continuity with adjacent members. It is often appropriate to account for continuity with adjacent members when determining shrinkage deflections.

H.7

Kennedy and Brattland (1992) propose an alternative method to determine shrinkage deflections. The method uses strain compatibility between steel and concrete, and a time-dependent modulus of elasticity of concrete in tension (see Shaker and Kennedy (1991)). It is iterative because the concrete response is non-linear. It is more difficult to use than the method specified in this Standard; however, the tensile stress-strain relationship of the concrete is satisfied.

H.8

Montgomery et al. (1983) give an example where the shrinkage deflections were excessive. Jent (1989) provides information on shrinkage effects on continuous composite beams.

H.9

Branson, D.E. (1964). Time-dependent effects on composite concrete beams. *Proceedings, American Concrete Institute Journal*, 61, 212–229.

Ghali, A., Favre, R. and Elbadry, M. (2002). *Concrete structures: Stresses and deformations*, 3rd ed. London: Spon Press.

Jent, K.A. (1989). Effects of shrinkage, creep and applied loads on continuous deck-slab composite beams. M.Sc. thesis, Queen's University, Kingston, Ontario.

Kennedy, D.J.L. and Brattland, A. (1992). Shrinkage tests of two full-scale composite trusses. *Canadian Journal of Civil Engineering*, 19 (2), 296–309.

Montgomery, C.J., Kulak, G.L. and Shwartsburd, G. (1983). Deflection of a composite floor system. *Canadian Journal of Civil Engineering*, 10 (2), 192–204.

Shaker, A.F. and Kennedy, D.J.L. (1991). *The effective modulus of elasticity of concrete in tension*. Structural Engineering Report 172, Department of Civil Engineering, University of Alberta, Edmonton.

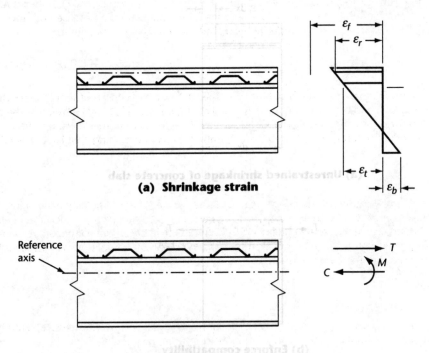

(a) Shrinkage strain

(b) Free-body diagram

Legend:

ε_f = free shrinkage strain of the concrete

ε_r = resulting restrained shrinkage strain

ε_t = compressive strain at top of steel beam

ε_b = tensile strain at bottom of steel beam

T = tensile force in concrete

C = compressive force in steel beam

M = moment in steel beam required for equilibrium about reference axis

Figure H.1
Composite beam subject to shrinkage forces
(See Clause H.2.)

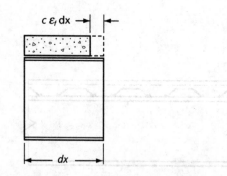

(a) Unrestrained shrinkage of concrete slab

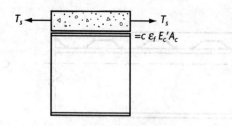

(b) Enforce compatibility

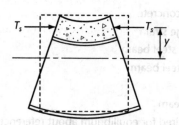

(c) Satisfy equilibrium

Legend:

c = empirical coefficient used to match theory with test results, which may be taken as 0.5

T_s = tensile force applied at centroid of unrestrained slab

A_c = effective area of concrete slab (for metal deck spanning perpendicular to the beam, the concrete area is taken above the flutes, and for metal deck parallel to the beam, the full concrete area is taken)

y = distance from centroid of effective area of concrete slab to the centroidal axis of the composite steel beam

E_c' = age-adjusted effective modulus of elasticity of concrete

E_f = unrestrained shrinkage strain of the concrete slab

Figure H.2
Composite beam subject to shrinkage forces
(See Clause H.3.)

Annex I (informative)
Arbitration procedure for pretensioning connections

Note: *This informative (nonmandatory) Annex has been written in normative (mandatory) language to facilitate adoption where users of the Standard or regulatory authorities wish to adopt it formally as additional requirements to this Standard.*

I.1 General

For pretensioned connections, when there is disagreement concerning the results of inspection of bolt pretensioning procedures, the following arbitration procedure shall be used unless an alternative has been specified:

(a) The inspector shall use a manual or power torque inspection wrench capable of indicating a selected torque value.

(b) Three bolts of the same grade and diameter as those under inspection and representative of the lengths and conditions of those in the structure shall be placed individually in a calibration device that indicates bolt tension. There shall be a washer under the part turned if washers are so used in the structure, or, if no washer is used, the material abutting the part turned shall be of the same specification and condition as that in the structure.

(c) When the inspection wrench is a manual wrench, each bolt specified in Item (b) shall be pretensioned in the calibration device by any convenient means to an initial tension of approximately 15% of the required bolt tension and then to the minimum tension specified for its size in Table 7. Tightening beyond the initial condition shall not produce greater nut rotation than that permitted by Table 8. The inspection wrench shall then be applied to the tightened bolt, and the torque necessary to turn the nut or head an additional 5° shall be determined. The average torque measured in the tests of three bolts shall be taken as the job inspection torque to be used in the manner specified in Item (e).

(d) When the inspection wrench is a power wrench, it shall first be applied to produce an initial tension of approximately 15% of the required fastener tension and then adjusted so that it will tighten each bolt specified in Item (b) to a tension of 5% to 10% greater than the minimum tension specified for its size in Table 7. This setting of the wrench shall be taken as the inspection torque to be used in the manner specified in Item (e). Tightening beyond the initial condition shall not produce greater nut rotation than that permitted by Table 8.

(e) Bolts represented by the sample prescribed in Item (b) that have been tightened in the structure shall be inspected by applying, in the tightening direction, the inspection wrench and its job inspection torque to 10% of the bolts, but not less than two bolts, selected at random in each connection. If no nut or bolt head is turned by this application of the job inspection torque, the connection shall be accepted as properly tightened. If any nut or bolt head is turned by the application of the job inspection torque, this torque shall be applied to all bolts in the connection and all bolts whose nut or head is turned by the job inspection torque shall be tightened and re-inspected. Alternatively, the fabricator or erector may choose to retighten all the bolts in the connection and then resubmit the connection for the specified inspection.

Annex J (informative)
Ductile moment-resisting connections

Note: *This informative (nonmandatory) Annex has been written in normative (mandatory) language to facilitate adoption where users of the Standard or regulatory authorities wish to adopt it formally as additional requirements to this Standard.*

J.1

Moment-resisting connections in moment-resisting frames and eccentrically braced frames are required by this Standard to deform in order that the frames can achieve specified interstorey drifts. Because analytical procedures alone cannot predict the performance, physical tests are required. This Annex provides guidance concerning the nature of such tests and references to test data.

J.2

The inelastic cyclic behaviour of a connection is influenced by size effects, bracing arrangements, welding details, and welding procedures. Test assemblies shall represent the size, detailing, and fabrication of the prototype. The test loading shall represent both the deformation magnitude and cyclic nature expected in a severe seismic event. Suitable testing protocols are given in publications by the U.S. Applied Technology Council (ATC, 1992), American Institute of Steel Construction (AISC, 2005), and U.S. Federal Emergency Management Agency (FEMA, 2000a).

J.3

Extensive testing, e.g., that undertaken by FEMA (2000a; 2006), has demonstrated the successful performance of several types of moment-resisting connection. These constitute prequalified connections and can be used if the prototype connection size lies within the range of those tested and if general restrictions and limitations are followed. CISC (2004) specifies design procedures, size, and other limitations for a number of prequalified moment-resisting connections.

J.4

AISC. (2005). ANSI/AISC 341-05, *Seismic provisions for structural steel buildings,* including Supplement No. 1 American Institute of Steel Construction (AISC), Chicago, Illinois.

ATC. (1992). *Guidelines for seismic testing of components of steel structures.* ATC-24. Redwood City, California.

CISC. (2004). *Moment connections for seismic applications.* Willowdale, Ontario.

FEMA. (2000a). *Recommended seismic design criteria for new steel moment-frame buildings.* Report FEMA350. Washington, D.C.

FEMA. (2000b). *State of art report on connection performance.* Report FEMA355D. Washington, D.C.

Annex K (normative)
Structural design for fire conditions

Note: *This Annex is a normative (mandatory) part of the Standard.*

K.1 General

K.1.1 Scope
This Annex specifies criteria for the design and evaluation of structural steel components, systems and frames for fire conditions. These criteria provide for the determination of the heat input, thermal expansion, and degradation in mechanical properties of materials that cause progressive decreases in strength and stiffness of structural components and systems at elevated temperatures.

K.1.2 Definitions
This Annex uses the following terms in addition to the terms defined in Clause 2.1:

Active fire protection — building materials and systems that are activated by a fire to mitigate adverse effects or to notify people to take some action to mitigate adverse effects.

Convective heat transfer — the transfer of thermal energy from a point of higher temperature to a point of lower temperature through the motion of an intervening medium.

Design-basis fire — a set of conditions that define the development of a fire and the spread of combustion products throughout a building or portion thereof.

Elevated temperatures — heating conditions experienced by building elements or structures as a result of fire, which are in excess of the anticipated ambient conditions.

Fire — destructive burning, as manifested by one or more of light, flame, heat, or smoke.

Fire endurance — a measure of the elapsed time during which a material or assembly continues to exhibit fire resistance.

Fire resistance — the property of assemblies that prevents or retards the passage of excessive heat, hot gases, or flames under conditions of use and enables them to continue to perform a stipulated function.

Fire resistance rating — the period of time a building element, component, or assembly maintains the ability to contain a fire, continues to perform a given structural function, or both, as determined by test or methods based on tests.

Fire separation — a construction assembly that acts as a barrier against the spread of fire and whose construction is formed of fire-resisting materials and tested in accordance with CAN/ULC-S101, or another approved standard fire resistance test, to demonstrate compliance with requirements prescribed by the regulatory authority.

Flashover — the rapid transition to a state of total surface involvement in a fire of combustible materials within an enclosure.

Heat flux — radiant energy per unit surface area.

Heat release rate — the rate at which thermal energy is generated by a burning material.

Passive fire protection — building materials and systems whose ability to resist the effects of fire does not rely on any outside activating condition or mechanism.

Performance-based design or **objective-based design** — an engineering approach to structural design that is based on agreed-upon performance goals and objectives, engineering analysis, and quantitative assessment of alternatives against the performance goals and objectives using accepted engineering tools, methodologies, and performance criteria.

Prescriptive design — design methods, e.g., specific technical requirements or deemed-acceptable solutions, that document specific compliance with general criteria established by the regulatory authority.

Restrained construction — floor and roof assemblies and individual beams in buildings where the surrounding or supporting structure is capable of resisting substantial thermal expansion throughout the range of anticipated elevated temperatures.

Unrestrained construction — floor and roof assemblies and individual beams in buildings that are assumed to be free to rotate and expand throughout the range of anticipated elevated temperatures.

K.1.3 Performance objectives

Structural components, members, and building frame systems shall be designed so as to maintain their load-bearing function during the design-basis fire and to satisfy other performance requirements specified for the building occupancy.

Deformation criteria shall be applied where the means of providing structural fire resistance or the design criteria for fire barriers require consideration of the deformation of the load-carrying structure.

Within the compartment of fire origin, forces and deformations from the design-basis fire shall not cause a breach of horizontal or vertical fire separation.

K.1.4 Design by engineering analysis

The analysis methods specified in Clause K.2 may be used to document the anticipated performance of steel framing when subjected to design-basis fire scenarios. These methods provide evidence of compliance with the performance objectives established in Clause K.1.3.

The analysis methods specified in Clause K.2 may be used to demonstrate an equivalency for an alternative material or method, as permitted by the regulatory authority.

K.1.5 Design by qualification testing

When required by the regulatory authority, the qualification testing methods specified in Clause K.3 may be used to document the fire resistance of steel framing subject to the standardized fire testing protocols.

K.1.6 Load combinations and required resistance

The required resistance of the structure and its elements shall be determined based on the following gravity load combination specified in *User's Guide – NBC 2010: Structural Commentaries (Part 4)* Commentary A, Paragraph 25 ("Load Combination for Determination of Fire Resistance"):

$$D + T_S + (\alpha L \text{ or } 0.25S)$$

where

D = specified dead load, as given in Clause 6.2.1

T_S = effects due to expansion, contraction, or deflection caused by temperature changes due to the design-basis fire specified in Clause K.2.2. T_S can be taken equal to zero for statically determinate structures or for structures that have sufficient ductility to allow the redistribution of temperature forces before collapse

α = 1.0 for storage areas, equipment areas, and service rooms, and 0.5 for other occupancies

L = specified occupancy live load, as given in Clause 6.2.1

S = specified variable load due to snow, as given in Clause 6.2.1

Notional lateral loads, in accordance with Clause 8.4.1, shall be applied in combination with this gravity load combination.

K.2 Structural design for fire conditions by analysis

K.2.1 General
Structural members, components, and building frames may be designed for elevated temperatures due to fire in accordance with this Clause.

K.2.2 Design-basis fire

K.2.2.1 General
A design-basis fire shall be identified to describe the heating conditions for the structure. These heating conditions shall relate to the fuel commodities and compartment characteristics present in the assumed fire area. The fuel load density based on the occupancy of the space shall be considered when determining the total fuel load. Heating conditions shall be specified in terms of a heat flux or temperature of the upper gas layer created by the fire. The variation of the heating conditions with time shall be determined for the duration of the fire.

When the analysis methods specified in Clause K.2 are used to demonstrate an equivalency as an alternative material or method as permitted by the regulatory authority, the design-basis fire shall be determined in accordance with CAN/ULC-S101.

K.2.2.2 Localized fire
Where the heat release rate from the fire is insufficient to cause flashover, a localized fire exposure shall be assumed. In such cases, the fuel composition, arrangement of the fuel array, and floor area occupied by the fuel shall be used to determine the radiant heat flux from the flame and smoke plume to the structure.

K.2.2.3 Post-flashover compartment fires
Where the heat release rate from the fire is sufficient to cause flashover, a post-flashover compartment fire shall be assumed. The determination of the temperature versus time profile resulting from the fire shall include fuel load, ventilation characteristics to the space (natural and mechanical), compartment dimensions, and thermal characteristics of the compartment boundary.

K.2.2.4 Exterior fires
The exposure of exterior structure to flames projecting from windows or other wall openings as a result of a post-flashover compartment fire shall be considered along with the radiation from the interior fire through the opening. The shape and length of the flame projection shall be used along with the distance between the flame and the exterior steelwork to determine the heat flux to the steel. The method specified in Clause K.2.2.3 shall be used for describing the characteristics of the interior compartment fire.

K.2.2.5 Fire duration
The fire duration in a particular area shall be determined by considering the total combustible mass, i.e., fuel load, available in the space. In the case of a localized fire or post-flashover compartment fire, the time duration shall be determined as the total combustible mass divided by the mass loss rate, except where determined from Clause K.2.2.3.

K.2.2.6 Active fire protection systems
The effects of active fire protection systems shall be considered when describing the design-basis fire.

Where automatic smoke and heat vents are installed in non-sprinklered spaces, the resulting smoke temperature shall be determined from calculation.

K.2.3 Temperatures in structural systems under fire conditions

Temperatures within structural members, components, and frames due to the heating conditions posed by the design-basis fire shall be determined by a heat transfer analysis.

K.2.4 Material properties at elevated temperatures

K.2.4.1 General

Material properties at elevated temperatures shall be determined from test data. In the absence of such data, the material properties specified in Clause K.2.4 may be used. These reduction factors shall not apply to steels with a yield strength in excess of 450 MPa or concretes with specified compression strength in excess of 55 MPa.

K.2.4.2 Thermal elongation

The following thermal elongation requirements shall apply:
(a) Thermal expansion of structural and reinforcing steels: for calculations at temperatures above 65 ×C, the coefficient of thermal expansion shall be $1.4 \times 10^{-5}/°C$.
(b) Thermal expansion of normal weight concrete (NWC): for calculations at temperatures above 65 °C, the coefficient of thermal expansion shall be $1.8 \times 10^{-5}/°C$.
(c) Thermal expansion of lightweight concrete (LWC): for calculations at temperatures above 65 °C, the coefficient of thermal expansion shall be $7.9 \times 10^{-6}/°C$.

K.2.4.3 Mechanical properties at elevated temperatures

The deterioration in strength and stiffness of structural members, components, and systems shall be taken into account in the structural analysis of the frame. The values F_{ym}, F_{pm}, F_{um}, E_m, f'_{cm}, E_{cm}, and ε_{cu} at elevated temperature to be used in structural analysis, expressed as the ratio with respect to the property at ambient temperature (assumed to be 20 °C), shall be as specified in Tables K.1 and K.2. Interpolation between these values may be used. Table K.1 specifies the reduction factors for the stress-strain relationship for steel at the elevated temperatures shown in Figure K.1.

K.2.5 Structural design

K.2.5.1 General structural integrity

The structural frame shall be capable of providing adequate strength and deformation capacity to withstand, as a system, the structural actions developed during the fire within the prescribed limits of deformation. The structural system shall be designed to sustain local damage, with the structural system as a whole remaining stable.

Continuous load paths shall be provided to transfer all forces from the exposed region to the final point of resistance. The foundation shall be designed to resist the forces and to accommodate the deformations developed during the design-basis fire.

K.2.5.2 Strength requirements and deformation limits

Conformance of the structural system to the requirements of this Annex shall be demonstrated by constructing a mathematical model of the structure based on principles of structural mechanics and evaluating this model for the internal forces and deformations in the members of the structure developed by the temperatures from the design-basis fire.

Individual members shall be provided with adequate strength to resist the shears, axial forces, and moments determined in accordance with this Annex.

Connections shall develop the strength of the connected members or the forces specified in this Clause. Where the means of providing fire resistance necessitates consideration of deformation criteria, the deformation of the structural system, or members thereof, under the design-basis fire shall not exceed the prescribed limits.

K.2.5.3 Methods of analysis

K.2.5.3.1 Advanced methods of analysis

The advanced methods of analysis may be used for the design of steel building structures for fire conditions. The design-basis fire exposure shall be that determined in accordance with Clause K.2.2. The analysis shall include both a thermal response and the mechanical response to the design-basis fire.

The thermal response shall produce a temperature field in each structural element as a result of the design-basis fire and shall incorporate temperature-dependent thermal properties of the structural elements and fire-resistive materials in accordance with Clause K.2.3.

The mechanical response results in forces and deflections in the structural system subjected to the thermal response calculated from the design-basis fire. The mechanical response shall explicitly take into account the deterioration in strength and stiffness with increasing temperature, the effects of thermal expansions, and large deformations. Boundary conditions and connection fixity shall represent the proposed structural design. The material properties shall be as specified in Clause K.2.4.

The resulting analysis shall consider all relevant limit states, e.g., excessive deflections, connection fractures, and overall or local buckling.

K.2.5.3.2 Simple methods of analysis

The simple methods of analysis specified in this Clause are applicable to the evaluation of the performance of individual members at elevated temperatures during exposure to fire.

The support and restraint conditions (forces, moments, and boundary conditions) applicable at normal temperatures may be assumed to remain unchanged throughout the fire exposure.

The thermal response may be modeled using a one-dimensional heat transfer equation with heat input as directed by the design-basis fire specified in Clause K.2.2. The maximum steel temperature, T, obtained from this analysis shall be assumed constant through the member cross-section and shall be used to determine the factored resistances of the members in Items (a) to (f) as follows:

(a) Tension members: the factored resistance of a tension member shall be determined as specified in Clause 13.2, using steel properties as specified in Clause K.2.4, with the temperature equal to the maximum steel temperature.

(b) Compression members: the factored resistance of a compression member shall be determined as specified in Clause 13.3 using steel properties as specified in Clause K.2.4; however, for steel temperatures equal to or greater than 200 °C, the factored compressive resistance for flexural buckling shall be determined as follows:

$$C_r(T) = (1 + \lambda(T)^{2dn})^{-1/dn} A F_y(T)$$

where

$C_r(T)$ = the factored compressive resistance at temperature, T

$$\lambda(T) = \frac{KL}{r} \sqrt{\frac{F_y(T)}{\pi^2 E(T)}} = \sqrt{\frac{F_y(T)}{F_e(T)}}$$

d = 0.6

n = as specified in Clause 13.3.1

(c) Flexural members: the factored shear and moment resistance of a flexural member shall be as specified in Clauses 13.4 to 13.6 using steel properties specified in Clause K.2.4; however, for steel temperatures equal to or greater than 200 °C, the bending strength for lateral-torsional buckling of laterally unsupported doubly-symmetric members shall be determined as follows:

$$M_r(T) = C_K M_p(T) + (1 - C_K) M_p(T) \left(1 - \left(\frac{C_K M_p(T)}{M_u(T)} \right)^{0.5} \right)^{C_z(T)}$$

where

C_K = 0.12

$M_p(T)$ = the plastic moment at elevated temperatures determined using $F_y(T)$

$M_u(T)$ = the elastic critical load at elevated temperatures, determined as follows:

$$M_u(T) = \frac{\omega_2 \pi}{L} \sqrt{E(T)I_y G(T)J + I_y C_w \left(\frac{\pi E(T)}{L}\right)^2}$$

where

ω_2 =   as defined in Clause 13.6.

$$C_z(T) = \frac{T + 800}{500} \le 2.4$$

(d) Combined axial force and flexure: the factored resistance of a member required to resist both bending moments and an axial tensile or compression forces shall be determined as specified in Clauses 13.8 and 13.9 using steel properties specified in Clause K.2.4 and flexural and axial strengths as specified in Items K.2.5.3.2 (a) to (c).

(e) Composite floor members: the thermal response of flexural elements supporting a concrete slab may be modeled using a one-dimensional heat transfer equation to calculate the maximum temperature of the bottom flange of the steel section. This temperature shall be taken as constant between the bottom flange to the mid-depth of the web and shall decrease linearly from the mid-depth of the web to the top flange of the steel beam by no more than 25% .

The factored resistance of a composite flexural member shall be determined as specified in Clause 17 using steel properties specified in Clause K.2.4.

(f) Other components and connections: the factored resistance of other components and connections shall be as specified in Clause 13. Factored resistances shall be calculated using steel properties specified in Clause K.2.4 at the maximum temperature determined by the design-basis fire.

K.3 Design by qualification testing

K.3.1 Qualification standards
Structural members and components in steel buildings shall be qualified for the rating period in accordance with CAN/ULC-S101, compliance with which may be demonstrated using ULC Subject C263(e).

K.3.2 Restrained construction
For floor and roof assemblies and individual beams in buildings, a restrained condition exists when the surrounding or supporting structure is capable of resisting actions caused by thermal expansion throughout the range of anticipated elevated temperatures.

Steel beams, girders, and frames supporting concrete slabs that are welded or bolted to integral framing members (i.e., columns and girders) shall be considered restrained construction.

K.3.3 Unrestrained construction
Steel beams, girders, and frames that do not support a concrete slab shall be considered unrestrained unless the members are bolted or welded to surrounding construction that has been designed and detailed to resist actions caused by thermal expansion.

A steel member bearing on a wall in a single span or at the end span of multiple spans shall be considered unrestrained unless the wall has been designed and detailed to resist effects of thermal expansion.

K.4 References

European Committee for Standardization

EN 1992-1-2:2004
Eurocode 2: Design of concrete structures — Part 1-2: General rules — Structural fire design

EN 1993-1-2:2005
Eurocode 3: Design of steel structures — Part 1-2: General rules — Structural fire design

EN 1994-1-2:2005
Eurocode 4: Design of composite steel and concrete structures — Part 1-2: General rules — Structural fire design

ULC (Underwriters Laboratories of Canada)

CAN/ULC-S101-07
Standard Methods of Fire Endurance Tests of Building Construction and Materials

Subject C263(e)-M1988
Criteria for Use in Extension of Data from Fire Endurance Tests

Other publications

Takagi, J., and Deierlein, G. 2009. *Proposed design equations for CAN/CSA S16* Annex K *provisions for steel members at high temperatures*. Report prepared for the Canadian Institute of Steel Construction, Markham, ON.

Table K.1
Reduction factors for stress-strain relationship of steel at elevated temperatures (Eurocode 3 and Eurocode 4)
(See Clause K.2.4.3.)

Steel temperature, T_{steel}, °C	Reduction factors at temperature, T_{steel}, relative to the value of F_y or E at 20 °C			
	Reduction factor (relative to E) for the slope of the linear elastic range, $k_E = E_m/E$	Reduction factor (relative to F_y) for proportional limit, $k_p = F_{pm}/F_y$	Reduction factor (relative to F_y) for effective yield strength, $k_y = F_{ym}/F_y$	Reduction factor (relative to F_y) for effective tensile strength, $k_u = F_{um}/F_y$
20	1.00	1.00	1.00	1.25
100	1.00	1.00	1.00	1.25
200	0.90	0.807	1.00	1.25
300	0.80	0.613	1.00	1.25
400	0.70	0.420	1.00	1.00
500	0.60	0.360	0.78	0.78
600	0.31	0.180	0.47	0.47
700	0.13	0.075	0.23	0.23
800	0.09	0.050	0.11	0.11
900	0.0675	0.0375	0.06	0.06
1000	0.0450	0.0250	0.04	0.04
1100	0.0225	0.0125	0.02	0.02
1200	0.00	0.00	0.00	0.00

Legend:

E = elastic modulus of steel (200 000 MPa assumed; earthquake loads and effects)

E_m = slope of the linear elastic range for steel at elevated temperature T_{steel}

F_{pm} = proportional limit for steel at elevated temperature T_{steel}

F_{um} = effective tensile strength of steel at elevated temperature T_{steel}

F_y = specified minimum yield stress, yield point, or yield strength

F_{ym} = effective yield strength of steel at elevated temperature T_{steel}

k_E = slope of linear elastic range, relative to slope at 20 °C

k_p = proportional limit, relative to yield strength at 20 °C

k_u = effective tensile strength, relative to yield strength at 20 °C

k_y = effective yield strength, relative to yield strength at 20 °C

Table K.2
Values for the main parameters of the stress-strain relationships of normal weight concrete (NWC) and lightweight concrete (LWC) at elevated temperatures (Eurocode 2 and Eurocode 4)

(See Clause K.2.4.3.)

Concrete temperature, $T_{concrete}$, °C	Reduction factor (relative to f'_c) for effective compressive strength, $k_c = f'_{cm}/f'_c$		E_{cm}/E_c	ε_{cu}, %
	NWC	LWC		NWC
20	1.00	1.00	1.00	0.25
100	1.00	1.00	0.92	0.40
200	0.95	1.00	0.75	0.55
300	0.85	1.00	0.59	0.70
400	0.75	0.88	0.43	1.00
500	0.60	0.76	0.26	1.50
600	0.45	0.64	0.10	2.50
700	0.30	0.52	0.083	2.50
800	0.15	0.40	0.067	2.50
900	0.08	0.28	0.050	2.50
1000	0.04	0.16	0.033	2.50
1100	0.01	0.04	0.017	2.50
1200	0.00	0.00	0.00	—

Legend:

E_c = elastic modulus of concrete

E_{cm} = tangent modulus of the stress-strain relationship of the concrete at elevated temperature $T_{concrete}$

f'_c = specified compressive strength of concrete at 28 days

f'_{cm} = effective value for the compressive strength of concrete at elevated temperature $T_{concrete}$

k_c = effective compressive strength relative to compressive strength at 20 °C

ε_{cu} = concrete strain corresponding to f'_{cm}

Note: *For LWC, values of ε_{cu} shall be obtained from tests.*

Strain range	Stress, σ	Tangent modulus
$\varepsilon \le \varepsilon_{pm}$	εE_m	E_m
$\varepsilon_{pm} < \varepsilon < \varepsilon_{ym}$	$F_{pm} - c + (b/a)\,[a^2 - (\varepsilon_{ym} - \varepsilon)^2\,]^{0.5}$	$\dfrac{b\left(\varepsilon_{ym} - \varepsilon\right)}{a\left[a^2 - \left(\varepsilon_{ym} - \varepsilon\right)^2\right]^{0.5}}$
$\varepsilon_{ym} \le \varepsilon \le \varepsilon_{tm}$	F_{ym}	0
$\varepsilon_{tm} \le \varepsilon \le \varepsilon_{um}$	$F_{ym}\,[1 - (\varepsilon - \varepsilon_{tm})/(\varepsilon_{um} - \varepsilon_{tm})]$	—
$\varepsilon = \varepsilon_{um}$	0.00	—

Notes:

(1) Parameters:
  (a) $\varepsilon_{pm} = F_{pm}/E_m$
  (b) $\varepsilon_{ym} = 0.02$
  (c) $\varepsilon_{tm} = 0.15$
  (d) $\varepsilon_{um} = 0.20$

(2) Functions:
  (a) $a^2 = \left(\varepsilon_{ym} - \varepsilon_{pm}\right)\left(\varepsilon_{ym} - \varepsilon_{pm} + c/E_m\right)$
  (b) $b^2 = c\left(\varepsilon_{ym} - \varepsilon_{pm}\right)E_m + c^2$
  (c) $c = \dfrac{\left(F_{ym} - F_{pm}\right)^2}{\left(\varepsilon_{ym} - \varepsilon_{pm}\right)E_m - 2\left(F_{ym} - F_{pm}\right)}$

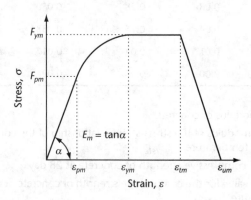

Legend:

E_m = slope of the linear elastic range
F_{pm} = proportional limit
F_{ym} = effective yield strength
ε_{pm} = strain at proportional limit
ε_{tm} = limiting strain for yield strength
ε_{um} = ultimate strain
ε_{ym} = yield strain

Figure K.1
Stress-strain relationship for steel at elevated temperatures (Eurocode 3)
(See Clause K.2.4.3.)

Annex L (informative)
Design to prevent brittle fracture

Note: *This Annex is an informative (nonmandatory) part of this Standard.*

L.1 General

Brittle fracture is a fracture mechanism accompanied by limited or no plastic deformation.

The design guidelines presented in this Annex are applicable to members and structural components subjected to tensile stresses arising from direct tension or bending when the rate of applied loading is high, e.g., dynamic or impact loading. Members and connections that contain notches, fabrication discontinuities, or other stress raisers need particular attention. Structures that are exposed to low temperatures are more susceptible to brittle fracture than those that are not. Although relatively uncommon, brittle fracture can also occur at normal temperatures, when fracture-sensitive details or metals (base or weld) with low notch toughness are subjected to dynamic tensile stresses.

The protected zones of seismically loaded structures should be designed to control brittle fracture.

When plates or heavy rolled sections are subjected to tensile stresses in the through-thickness direction, additional consideration needs to be given to the selection of the steel quality (see Clause L.3).

Statically loaded structures that are subjected to low temperature do not normally require the use of notch-tough steel. In these structures, brittle fracture can normally be avoided by following the design and fabrication criteria provided in this Standard and CSA W59. Attention should be paid to anchor rods (see ASTM F 1554) and details that give rise to stress concentrations.

Designers should be aware that the availability of notch-tough steel is somewhat limited (see Clause L.4).

L.2 Material Selection

The potential for brittle fracture depends mainly on the following factors (Barsom and Rolfe, 1999):

(a) steel strength;
(b) material thickness;
(c) loading rate;
(d) minimum service temperature;
(e) material toughness; and
(f) type of structural element.

These factors should be considered when selecting steel with appropriate notch toughness (Barsom, 1975; Barsom, 2002). Connection details and the presence of stress raisers also needs to be considered. Required notch toughness is expressed in terms of the test temperature at which the Charpy V-notch energy has a minimum value of 20 J or 27 J, as specified in CSA G40.21.

The approach presented in Tables L.1 to L.5 consists of defining the Charpy V-notch energy level and the testing temperature for four different service temperature ranges. Figure L.1 can be used to determine the minimum service temperature appropriate for structural steel exposed to outdoor conditions. The testing temperature can be significantly different from the service temperature to account for the difference in strain rate between the Charpy impact test and the strain rate applied to the structure.

Dynamic loading and impact loading are recognized in Tables L.1 to L.5. Dynamic loading is applicable to intermediate strain rates such as those occurring in structures subjected to seismic ground motions, wave loads, or wind-induced vibration. Impact loading is applicable to high strain rates that occur, e.g., in explosive or crash conditions.

When specifying steel for a specific application, the engineer should consider the probability of low temperature and extreme loading conditions occurring simultaneously.

The consequence of brittle fracture is recognized in the material selection. Fracture-critical members or joints are those for which local failure would cause complete structural collapse with serious consequences to life or very high cost. Primary tension members (tension and bending members or joints) are those for which failure would be restricted to localized areas not resulting in structural collapse. The fracture toughness of secondary framing members need not be considered.

The impact energy for the weld metal needs to be higher than for the base metal because welds usually have discontinuities, stress raisers, and high tensile residual stresses, which make weld metals more susceptible to brittle fracture. Given that the cost of weld metals is small relative to that of the structure, it is good practice to specify high-toughness filler metal to lower the risk of brittle fracture.

Table L.1
Recommended test temperatures and Charpy V-notch impact test values for primary tension members under dynamic loading
(See Clause L.2.)

CSA G40.21 Grade	Minimum average energy, J	Test temperature, °C, for minimum service temperature, T_s, °C			
		$T_s > 0$	$0 \geq T_s \geq -30$	$-30 \geq T_s > -60$	$T_s \leq -60$
260 WT	20	20	0	−20	−30
300 WT	20	20	0	−20	−30
350 WT and AT	27	20	0	−20	−30
CSA G40.21 Category	5	1	2	3	

Table L.2
Recommended test temperatures and Charpy V-notch impact test values for primary tension members under impact loading
(See Clause L.2.)

CSA G40.21 Grade	Minimum average energy, J	Test temperature, °C, for minimum service temperature, T_s, °C			
		$T_s > 0$	$0 \geq T_s > -30$	$-30 \geq T_s > -60$	$T_s \leq -60$
260 WT	20	0	−20	−45	−55
300 WT	20	0	−20	−45	−55
350 WT and AT	27	0	−20	−45	−55
CSA G40.21 Category	1	2	4	5	

Table L.3
Recommended test temperatures and Charpy V-notch impact test values for fracture critical members under dynamic loading
(See Clause L.2.)

CSA G40.21 Grade	Minimum average energy, J	Test temperature, °C, for minimum service temperature, T_s, °C			
		$T_s > 0$	$0 \geq T_s > -30$	$-30 \geq T_s > -60$	$T_s \leq -60$
260 WT	20	10	–10	–30	–50
300 WT	20	10	–10	–30	–50
350 WT and AT	27	10	–10	–30	–50
CSA G40.21 Category		1	2	3	5

Table L.4
Recommended test temperatures and Charpy V-notch impact test values for fracture critical members under impact loading
(See Clause L.2.)

CSA G40.21 Grade	Minimum average energy, J	Test temperature, °C, for minimum service temperature, T_s, °C			
		$T_s > 0$	$0 \geq T_s > -30$	$-30 \geq T_s > -60$	$T_s \leq -60$
260 WT	20	–10	–30	–55	–75
300 WT	20	–10	–30	–55	–75
350 WT and AT	27	–10	–30	–55	–75
CSA G40.21 Category		2	3	5	5

Table L.5
Recommended test temperatures and Charpy V-notch impact test values for weld metal
(See Clause L.2.)

Loading rate	Minimum average energy, J	Test temperature, °C, for minimum service temperature, T_s, °C	
		$T_s > -40$	$T_s \leq -40$
Dynamic	27	–30	–40
Impact	27	–50	–60

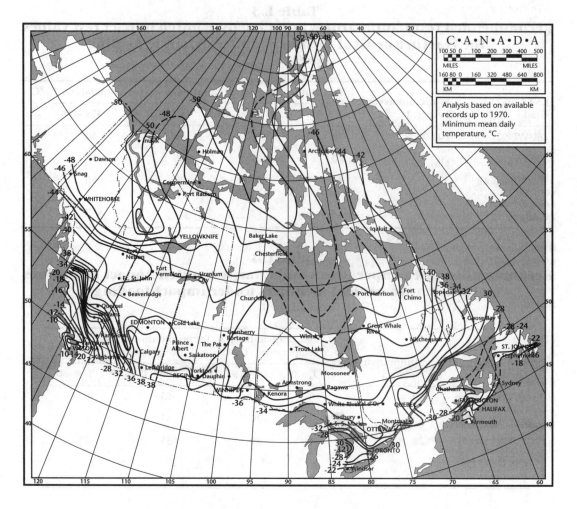

Figure L.1
Minimum mean daily temperatures in Canada
(See Clause L.2.)

L.3 Lamellar tearing

The material properties specified in Clause L.2 refer to the longitudinal and transverse directions. Where applied or residual through-thickness tensile stresses greater than 80% of the nominal strength exist, a fracture phenomenon known as lamellar tearing is possible. For this situation, steel with improved through-thickness tensile properties should be considered to reduce the risk of lamellar tearing (Barsom and Korvink, 1998).

The following aspects should be considered in the selection of steel assemblies or connections to control the risk of lamellar tearing:

(a) the criticality of the location in terms of applied tensile stress and the degree of redundancy;

(b) the strain in the through-thickness direction of the element to which the connection is made. This strain arises from the shrinkage of the weld metal as it cools. It can be greatly increased when free movement is restrained by other portions of the structure, e.g., in the connection of heavy truss web members to chords; and

(c) the nature of the joint detail, in particular welded cruciform, corner and T-joints. Lamellar tearing is most likely to arise if the strain in the joint acts through the thickness of the material, which occurs if the fusion face is roughly parallel to the surface of the material and the induced shrinkage strain is perpendicular to the direction of rolling of the material. The heavier the weld, the greater the susceptibility to lamellar tearing.

If tensile stresses are transferred in the through-thickness direction of the connected element, the connection detail, welding procedure, and sequence of welding needs to be designed to minimize constraints that can cause additional tensile stresses in the through-thickness direction from weld shrinkage.

To reduce the risk of lamellar tearing, it is important to select a base metal with improved through-thickness ductility and avoid weld orientation that place strains through the plate thickness. Also, welded joints need to be designed to minimize shrinkage restraint. Corner or T-joint welding details of rolled section or plates involving transfer of tensile forces in the through-thickness direction should be avoided whenever possible. Additional guidance on controlling lamellar tearing in welded structures can be found in Appendix Q of CSA W59.

L.4 Steel availability

Anyone selecting materials for structures at risk of brittle fracture should consult with suppliers regarding the availability of notch-tough materials. In general for Grade WT material, plates are more readily available than rolled shapes.

The inherent toughness of Grade W steel is often sufficient to prevent brittle fracture at low temperatures, although the necessary toughness is not guaranteed. CSA G40.21 Grade W steel may be substituted for CSA G40.21 Grade WT steel when the Charpy impact energy requirements are verified by the submission of test documentation.

L.5 Control of discontinuities

In addition to specifying materials with appropriate toughness, control of discontinuities is equally important for providing an acceptably low probability of brittle fracture.

Welded structures should meet the requirements of CSA W59 for acceptable size of discontinuities.

Connection details should be designed to minimize stress raisers, e.g., sharp corners and abrupt changes of stiffness resulting from changes in cross-section. Thick or high-strength materials are generally more susceptible to cold cracking in the heat-affected zones of welds and in areas of high residual stresses. In such cases, the choice of appropriate welding procedures is as important as the selection of the material.

When selecting construction details, the designer needs to account for the fact that some materials cannot be welded, or can be welded only under strict conditions. Prestressing steels, anchor rods, and high-strength bolts cannot be welded and high-carbon steels can be welded only under specific conditions.

Note: *For welding of reinforcing steel, see CAN/CSA-G30.18.*

L.6 References

CSA (Canadian Standards Association)
CAN/CSA-G30.18-M92 (R2007)
Billet-steel bars for concrete reinforcement

Other Publications
Barsom, J.M. (2002). Development of fracture toughness requirements for weld metals in seismic applications. *Journal of Materials in Civil Engineering*, 14 (7) 44–49.

Barsom, J.M. (1975). The development of AASHTO fracture-toughness requirements for bridge steels. Washington, D.C.: American Iron and Steel Institute.

Barsom, J.M., and Korvink, S.A. (1998). Through-thickness properties of structural steels. *Journal of Structural Engineering*, ASCE, 124 (7) 727–735.

Barsom, J.M., and Rolfe, S.T. (1999). *Fracture and fatigue control in structures: Applications of fracture mechanics*, 3rd. ed. West Conshohocken, Pennsylvania: ASTM.

PART TWO
CISC COMMENTARY ON CSA S16-09

Preface

This Commentary has been prepared by the Canadian Institute of Steel Construction in order to provide guidance on the intent of various provisions of CSA Standard S16-09, "Design of Steel Structures". This Commentary and the information contained in the references cited provide an extensive background to the development of the Standard and its technical requirements including the changes and new provisions introduced in the 2009 edition. The Preface to the Standard itself outlines the history of its development since the first edition in 1924.

CSA Standard S16-09 has been prepared by the Canadian Standards Association (CSA), an approved standards development organization of the Standards Council of Canada, according to the rules for development of consensus standards. The National Building Code of Canada 2010 has adopted CSA Standard S16-09 by reference.

The Institute gratefully acknowledges the efforts of the various members of the CSA Technical Committee on Steel Structures for their valuable contributions to the Commentary, especially, G. Grondin, R. Tremblay and R.G. Driver who helped to rewrite a significant portion of this edition. R.B. Vincent, the Committee Chair, M.I. Gilmor, the Committee Vice-Chair and former editor of the Commentary, D.J.L. Kennedy, the former Committee Chair and R.G. Redwood have provided valuable background information pertaining to many requirements introduced in previous editions of the Standard.

The information contained in the Commentary is provided by the Institute. It is not to be considered the opinion of the CSA Committee, nor does it detract from that Committee's responsibility and authority insofar as interpretation and revision of the Standard are concerned. For information on requesting interpretations, see Note (5) to the Preface of CSA S16-09.

The Institute provides this Commentary as a part of its commitment to the education of those interested in the use of steel in construction. The Institute assumes no responsibility for errors or oversights resulting from the use of the information contained herein. Anyone making use of the contents of this Commentary assumes all liability arising from such use. All suggestions for improvements of this Commentary will receive full consideration for future printings.

A.F. Wong
Editor

Introduction

Since the Canadian Standards Association introduced the first limit states design standard for structural steel, S16.1-1974 "Steel Structures for Buildings–Limit States Design" in 1974, the Standard has undergone a number of technical improvements, but its major requirements have remained virtually unchanged. However, with the introduction of the 1989 edition, a number of more significant changes were introduced, in part reflecting the maturing of the Standard but also the acquisition of more detailed information on behaviour of steel structures. Specific seismic design requirements for ductile behaviour were provided, and a new ductile system, eccentrically braced frame, was introduced. The 1994 edition continued this process with the refining of some requirements and the addition of a new lateral load-resisting system, the plate wall. The 2001 edition of the Standard was reorganized in a more logical order. In addition, the Standard underwent a number of technical improvements reflecting the incorporation of research results, including a significant expansion of Clause 27, Seismic Design Requirements.

When CSA S16-09 arrived, 35 years after the birth of its first limit states design version, S16.1-1974, 25 years after the official withdrawal of its last allowable stress design version, S16-1969, and 4 years after the release of the National Building Code of Canada 2005 that mandates limit states design for structures of all materials and for foundations, the title of the Standard was shortened to read "Design of Steel Structures". In this new edition, a new seismic-force-resisting system, buckling-restrained braced frame, has been introduced. The Standard stipulates additional requirements to permit the application of Conventional Construction in taller structures subjected to higher seismic hazard. Design provisions for openings through plate walls have been incorporated, and the design rules for use of built-up tubular link beam in eccentrically braced frames are provided. Research findings have also led to improvements in other areas, including the adoption of the unified block shear equation and the design procedure for single angle struts.

In the 2009 edition of CSA Standard S16, the traditional Appendices have been replaced by Annexes. Two Annexes have been added: Annex K, a normative annex that outlines the requirements for structural design for fire conditions and Annex L, an informative annex that provides information on design against brittle fracture.

Some specific changes introduced in CSA S16-09 are highlighted in the Preface of the Standard itself.

Background

To serve their intended purposes, all structures must meet the requirement that the occurrence of various types of collapse or unserviceability is limited to a sufficiently small value. Limit states are those conditions of the structure corresponding to the onset of the various types of collapse or unserviceability. The conditions associated with collapse are the ultimate limit states (ULS); those associated with unserviceability are the serviceability limit states (SLS), and that associated with fatigue is the fatigue limit state (FLS).

In limit states design, the capacity or performance of the structure or its components is checked against the various limit states at certain load levels. For the ultimate limit states of strength and stability, for example, the structure must retain its load-carrying capacity up to factored load levels, loads with only an acceptably small probability of being exceeded. For serviceability limit states, the performance of the structure at specified load levels must be satisfactory. (Specified loads are those prescribed by the Regulatory Authority. A factored load is the product of a specified load and its load factor.) Examples of the serviceability requirement include prevention of damage to non-structural elements, and restrictions on deflections, permanent deformations, slip in slip-critical connections, and acceleration under vibratory motion. For the fatigue limit state, the stress ranges for critical elements due to the loads applied to the structure over its useful life must not exceed the prescribed stress ranges.

The loads acting on a structure as well as the resistance of a member can only be defined statistically. When considering the ULS, a load factor (α) is applied to the specified load to take into account the fact that loads have a statistical distribution and loads higher than those anticipated may exist and also to take into account approximations in the analysis of the load effects. A resistance factor (ϕ) is applied to the nominal member (or component) strengths, or resistances (R), to take into account that the resistance of the member due to variability of the material properties, dimensions and workmanship may be different than anticipated, and also to take into account the type of failure and uncertainty in the prediction of the resistance. A major advantage, therefore, of limit states design is that the factors assigned to loads arising from different sources can be related to the uncertainty of their prediction, and the factors assigned to different members and components can be related to their reliability and to the different types of failure. Thus, a greater degree of consistency against failure can be obtained (Kennedy 1974; Allen 1975; Kennedy *et al.* 1976).

For the failure of structural steel members by yielding, the resistance factor is taken to be 0.90 (Kennedy and Gad Aly 1980). To maintain simplicity in design, the resistance formulas for buckling or other types of member failure have been adjusted so that a uniform resistance factor, $\phi = 0.90$, can be used and yet provide the necessary safety required in the definition of the resistance factor. The exceptions to a resistance factor, $\phi = 0.90$, are:

- Structural steel fracture across the net section, $\phi_u = 0.75$;

- Reinforcing steel bars (for composite construction), $\phi_r = 0.85$;

- Bolts in bearing-type connections and in tension connections, $\phi_b = 0.80$, this still ensures that the connectors will be stronger than the members being joined;

- Shear connectors (for composite construction), $\phi_{sc} = 0.80$;

- Beam web bearing, interior, $\phi_{bi} = 0.80$;

- Beam web bearing, end, $\phi_{be} = 0.75$;

- Bearing of bolts on steel, $\phi_{br} = 0.80$;

- Weld metal, to ensure that the weld is stronger than the member joined, $\phi_w = 0.67$;

- Anchor rods, $\phi_{ar} = 0.67$; and,

- Crushing resistance of concrete (for composite construction), $\phi_c = 0.65$, which is consistent with CAN/CSA-A23.3-04 and takes into account the greater strength variability and the brittle type of failure associated with concrete.

Probabilistic studies (Allen 1975) show that consistent probabilities of failure are determined for all dead-to-live load ratios when a dead load factor of 1.25 and a live load factor of 1.50 for use and occupancy loads are used. The 2005 NBCC gives load factors for environmental loads such as those due to snow and rain, wind, and earthquakes. As well, importance factors are applied to building structures depending on their use and occupancy (building importance category) with the highest factors applied to post-disaster structures. For certain types of structures, if there is a high degree of uncertainty in the loads, the designer may elect to use larger load factors. However, in situations where the dead load and the live loads are counteractive, it is important that α_D be taken as 0.9, or less, as appropriate, except when dead load counteracts earthquake effects α_D is taken as 1.0 or less.

Kennedy (1974) and Allen (1975) provide considerably more information on the type of probabilistic, calibration, and design studies that were performed while developing the limit states standard. The National Building Code of Canada (NBCC 2010) contains a more extensive discussion on limit states design. Kennedy and Gad Aly (1980) and Baker and Kennedy (1984) provide information on the statistical determination of the resistance factors (ϕ).

In the Commentary clauses that follow, the numbers and headings used refer to the relevant clause numbers and headings of Canadian Standards Association Standard S16-09. This will be referred to simply as S16-09 herein and after.

1. SCOPE AND APPLICATION

This Standard applies generally to steel structures, and structural steel components in other structures. The analysis, design, detailing, fabrication, and erection requirements contained in the Standard normally provide a satisfactory level of structural integrity for most steel structures.

Clause 1.2 states that requirements for some specific types of structures and members are given in other CSA Standards. Situations where additional requirements may be necessary are given in Clause 1.3. The Structural Commentaries to the National Building Code of Canada provide references to the technical literature on the topic of structural integrity.

Clause 1.3 describes types of structures that may need supplementary rules for design. Crane-supporting structures are included in this list.

Clause 1.4 prohibits the substitution of any other structural steel design standard (e.g. CSA S16-1969 or AISC) for S16-09. The treatment of a number of important technical issues relating to safety, such as notional loads, beam-columns, ductility of members and connections for earthquake loads, is either not covered or is treated in a manner inconsistent with the intent of S16-09 or the NBCC.

Clause 1.4 permits the designer (subject to approval from the Regulatory Authority) to supplement the formulas given in the Standard by a rational method of design. It is required, of course, that the structural reliability provided by the alternative (as measured by the reliability index, for example) be equal to, or greater, than those in the Standard. An example of such a rational method would be the design of stub-girders using the method set out by Chien and Ritchie (1984) based on tests (Bjorhovde and Zimmerman 1980; Kullman and Hosain 1985; Ahmad et al. 1990).

2. DEFINITIONS AND SYMBOLS

In Clauses 2.1 and 2.2, new definitions and symbols have been introduced.

2.3 Units

All coefficients appearing in equations and expressions in this Standard are consistent with forces measured in Newtons and lengths in millimetres. While most coefficients are themselves non-dimensional, in Clause 17.9.10, the coefficient 2.76 has units of megapascals.

3. REFERENCE PUBLICATIONS

The Standards listed are the latest editions at the time of printing. When reference is made to undated publications in specific clauses of this Standard, it is intended that the latest edition and revisions of these publications be used. Several new Standards have been added.

4. STRUCTURAL DOCUMENTS

4.1 General

The title "Structural Documents" reflects the fact that drawings are only part of a broadened range of structural documents that are currently used in the industry.

4.2 Structural Design Documents

4.2.1 Structural steel design documents, by themselves, should show all member designations, axis orientations, and dimensions needed to describe the complete steel structure. It should not be necessary, in order to ascertain information on structural steel components, to refer to documents produced for the use of other trades, as in some situations the fabricator may not be given, or have access to, the documents produced for other trades.

4.2.2 This list gives the minimum information to be included on the structural design documents in a logical order (much of it, no doubt, on Drawing S-1). By serving as a checklist, it will help insure that all the information the fabricator needs is provided and will help resolve disputes before they arise.

4.2.2(l) The development of adequate connections for structural members requires that the design engineer determine the shears, moments and axial forces resulting from the governing load combinations for which the connection must be designed. For complex combinations, a useful presentation of this information may be to list the maximum value of each (e.g. shear, moment, and axial force), along with the values of the others which coincide with that maximum. The principle is to provide coexistent sets of forces so that free body diagrams can be identified to ensure that governing forces are transmitted through connections and panels.

4.2.2(m) Structural stability, a fundamental consideration of design, extends to the behaviour of elements within a member as well as to the functioning of members in total. Stabilizing components are needed to achieve both the correct local behaviour and the correct overall behaviour anticipated by the design. Therefore, the design engineer must define bracing, stiffeners, and reinforcement that are required to prevent failure due to instability. An example is web reinforcement in moment connections to prevent local instability. It may actually be more economical to use a heavier section and avoid the need for stiffeners or reinforcing detail material. This option should best be considered at the design stage.

4.2.3 The importance of proper recording of revisions on design documents, whether electronic files or paper, is emphasized. Control of documents is addressed in Steel Fabrication Quality Systems Guideline (CISC 2002) and in the CISC Code of Standard Practice, Appendix J, in Part 7 of this Handbook.

4.2.4 Architectural, electrical and mechanical documents may be used for supplementary information, provided that the requirements in Clauses 4.2.1 and 4.2.2 for structural steel are shown on the structural documents.

4.3 Fabrication and Erection Documents

Although five types of documents are identified in the Standard, many structures which use pre-engineered connections from company or industry sources require only *shop details* and *erection diagrams*.

4.3.1 Connection Design Details

Connection design details, which often take the form of design brief sheets, typically show the configuration and details of nonstandard connections developed for specific situations. They are submitted to the design engineer for review to confirm that the structural intent has been understood and met, and they may be stamped by a professional engineer when appropriate. Drafting technicians use connection design details to prepare shop details.

4.3.2 Shop Details

Shop details frequently take the form of traditional shop drawings and are used to provide the fabrication shop with all the specific information required to produce the member. They are submitted to the design engineer for review to confirm that the structural intent has been understood and met. *Shop details* are not stamped by a professional engineer because they generally do not contain original engineering.

4.3.3 Erection Diagrams

Erection diagrams convey information about the permanent structure that is required by field personnel in order to assemble it. They are submitted to the design engineer for review, but are not stamped by a professional engineer because original engineering is generally not added by the fabricator.

4.3.4 Erection Procedures

Erection procedures outline methods and equipment, such as falsework and temporary guying cables, employed by the steel erector to assemble the structure safely. They may be submitted to the design engineer for review, and may be stamped by a professional engineer when appropriate.

4.3.5 Field Work Details

Field work details are drawings which describe modifications required to fabricated members. The work may be done either in the shop or at the job site depending on circumstances. When extra material is involved, *field work details* effectively become *shop details*. They are submitted to the design engineer for review.

5. MATERIALS – STANDARDS AND IDENTIFICATION

The design requirements have been developed on the assumption that the materials and products that will be used are those listed in Clause 5. These materials and products are all covered by standards prepared by the Canadian Standards Association (CSA) or the American Society for Testing and Materials (ASTM).

The standards listed provide controls over manufacture and delivery of the materials and products that are necessary to ensure that the materials and products will have the characteristics assumed when the design provisions of S16 were prepared. The use of materials and products other than those listed is permitted, provided that approval, based on published specifications, is obtained. In this case, the designer should assure himself that the materials and products have the characteristics required to perform satisfactorily in the structure. In particular, ductility is often as important as the strength of the material. Weldability and toughness may also be required in many structures.

The values for yield and tensile strength reported on mill test reports are not to be used for design. Only the specified minimum values published in product standards and specifications may be used. This requirement was implicit in earlier editions of the Standard by definition of the terms F_y and F_u but was made explicit in more recent editions. Furthermore, when tests are done to identify steel, the specified minimum values of the steel, once classified, shall be used as the basis for design.

When, however, sufficient representative tests are done on the steel of an existing structure to be statistically significant, those statistical data on the variation of the material and geometric properties may be combined with that for test/predicted ratios available in the literature to develop appropriate resistance factors. This is by no means equivalent, for example, to substituting a new mean yield stress for a specified minimum value as the new reference value, and the bias coefficient must be established. It could well be that, although a higher mean value of the yield stress is established, the bias coefficient, depending as it does on the reference value, would be less. It would be expected that the coefficient of variation for the material properties in particular, derived for the steel in a single structure, would be less than for steel in general.

In Clause 5.1.3, both CSA and ASTM are referenced standards for structural steel. Because W-shapes are no longer produced by Canadian mills, mill test certificates will more often refer to ASTM A572 Grade 50 or to ASTM A992. While ASTM A572 Grade 50 is comparable to G40.21 350W, ASTM A992 is a more restrictive version of A572 Grade 50 as it was developed specifically for seismic-resistant structures, but has become the most popular grade of wide-flange products available in North America.

In Clause 5.1.7, ASTM Standards for new bolting assemblies are referenced.

6. DESIGN REQUIREMENTS

This clause clearly distinguishes between those requirements that must be checked using specified loads (the fatigue and serviceability limit states) and those which must be checked using factored loads (the ultimate limit states). Many of the serviceability requirements (deflections, vibrations, etc.) are stipulated qualitatively and guidance, in quantitative form, is provided in Annexes. Thus, the designer is permitted to use the best information available to him in order to satisfy the serviceability requirements, but is also provided with information that the Technical Committee on Steel Structures considers to be generally suitable, when used with competent engineering judgement.

6.1 General

6.1.2 Structural Integrity

A clause on structural integrity acts as a reminder that measures may be necessary to guard against progressive collapse as a result of a local incident. Being inherently ductile, steel structures have generally had an excellent record of behaviour when subjected to unusual or unexpected loadings. However, connection details are particularly important in achieving this ductile behaviour. Details which rely solely on friction due to gravity to provide nominal lateral force resistance may have little or no resistance to unanticipated lateral loads if subjected to abnormal uplift conditions and should be carefully evaluated for such an eventuality or completely avoided.

6.2 Loads

Tables 11 and 12, introduced in S16S1-05, Supplement No. 1 to S16-01, are no longer included in the standard. These Tables essentially repeated information on Importance Factors provided in the NBCC.

Dead loads are to include the additional mass of construction materials that will be built into a structure as a result of deflections of supporting members, such as a concrete floor slab placed to a level plane but supported by members that were not cambered and that deflect under the weight of the concrete.

6.3 Requirements Under Specified Loads

6.3.1 Deflection

6.3.1.2 Even though deflections are checked under the actions of specified loads, additional loading may result from ponding of rain on roofs, or the ponding of finishes or concrete, while in the fluid state, on floors or roofs. Such additional loads are to be included in the design of the supporting members under ultimate limit states as required by Clause 7. More information on ponding is available in the National Building Code of Canada (NBCC 2010).

6.3.3 Dynamic Effect

6.3.3.2 Additional information on vibrations of floor systems may be found in Allen (1974), Murray (1975), Allen and Rainer (1976), Rainer (1980), Allen *et al.* (1985), Allen and Murray (1993), Murray *et al.* (1997).

6.7 Requirements Under Fire Conditions

Background information on S16-09 Annex K, Structural Design for Fire Conditions, is available on the CISC Fire Protection webpage:

www.cisc-icca.ca/content/technical/fp_coatings.aspx

6.8 Brittle Fracture

Annex L of S16-09 provides some design information to prevent failure of steel structures by brittle fracture. Clause 6.8 identifies the circumstances under which brittle fracture can occur and situations where brittle fracture should be considered as part of the design process. Annex L serves as a non-mandatory guide.

7. FACTORED LOADS AND SAFETY CRITERION

This clause sets forth the fundamental safety criterion (strength and stability) that must be met, namely:

Factored Resistance ≥ Effect of Factored Loads,

or

$$\phi R \geq \sum \alpha_i S_i$$

Table 13, introduced in S16S1-05, Supplement No. 1 to S16-01, is no longer included in this Standard. The Table essentially repeated information on load combinations for the ultimate limit states provided in the NBCC.

The factored resistance is given by the product ϕR where ϕ is the resistance factor and R is the nominal member strength, or resistance. The factored resistances of various types of members are given in Clause 13.1.

8. ANALYSIS OF STRUCTURE

Although the content of this clause has remained essentially the same as the 2001 edition, its content has been reorganized. Three types of construction are recognized in the 2009 Standard, namely, "rigidly connected and continuous", "simple", and "semi-rigid (or partially restrained)". While semi-rigid construction was developed in the 1930's and 1940's, both in the USA and in the UK, and was previously a successful practice, it is now not in common use in North America.

With semi-rigid connections, because the angles between connected parts change under applied bending moments, the joint behaviour is non-linear and the moment/rotation response must be established by test. Design of a semi-rigidly connected structure must take into account the effect of the "semi-rigid" connection stiffness on the stability of the structure. A second-order analysis is preferred because the non-linearities due to connection response and due to frame drift need to be assessed.

It is assumed that, if the connection has adequate capacity for inelastic rotation when subjected to the first application of factored gravity and lateral loading, under subsequent loading cycles the connection will behave elastically, although it will have a permanent inelastic deformation (Sourochnikoff 1950, Disque 1964). Such an assumption is valid except in joints where load fluctuation would create alternating plasticity in the connection (Popov and Pinkney 1969). With this form of construction, it is also important to consider the possibility of low-cycle, high-strain fatigue.

The use of open-web steel joists as connected members of these frames has been shown to be inadequate (Nixon 1981).

Clause 8 also permits the use of the two general methods of analysis – elastic and plastic analysis. Methods of elastic analysis are familiar to most designers.

8.3.2 Plastic Analysis

The use of plastic analyses at the factored load levels to determine the forces and moments throughout a structure implies that the structure achieves its limiting load capacity when sufficient plastic hinges have developed to transform the frame into a mechanism. As successive plastic hinges form, the load-carrying capacity of the structure increases above that corresponding to the formation of the initial plastic hinge until a mechanism develops. To achieve this, the members in which the hinges form before the mechanism develops must be sufficiently stocky (Class 1 sections) and well braced so that inelastic rotations can occur without loss of moment capacity.

Deflections at the specified load level are, of course, limited in accordance with Clause 6.2.1. Plastically designed structures are usually "elastic" at specified load levels i.e. no plastic hinges have formed. Therefore, the deflections would generally be computed on the basis of an elastic analysis.

8.3.2(a) Material

The plastic method relies on certain basic assumptions for its validity (ASCE 1971). Therefore, restrictions are imposed to preserve the applicability of the plastic theory. The basic restriction (Clause 8.3.2(a)) that the steel exhibits significant amounts of strain-hardening is required to ensure that satisfactory moment redistribution will occur (Adams and Galambos 1969). This behaviour should exist at the temperatures to which the structure will be subjected in service. Also, although not explicitly stated, plastically designed structures usually entail welded fabrication, and therefore the steel specified should also be weldable. At normal temperatures all the steels referred to in Clause 5.1.2 should be satisfactory except for CSA G40.21-M, 700 Q and 700 QT steels, for which $F_y > 0.85 F_u$.

A reassessment of the stress-strain data (Dexter and Genticore 1997, Dexter *et al*. 2002) showed that the requirement that the yield strength not exceed 0.80 of the ultimate strength could be relaxed to 0.85 of the latter.

8.3.2(b) Width-Thickness Ratios

In order to preclude premature local buckling, and thus ensure adequate hinge rotation, compression elements in regions of plastic moment must have width-thickness ratios no greater than those specified for Class 1 (plastic design) sections in Clause 11.2. Although both Class 1 and Class 2 sections can attain the fully plastic moment, only Class 1 sections will maintain this moment through the rotation necessary for redistribution of moments implicit in the plastic method of analysis.

8.3.2(c) Lateral Bracing

The lateral bracing requirements are considerably more severe than those for structures designed on the basis of an elastic moment distribution because of the rotation needed at the location of the plastic hinges. Such requirements, as are needed to ensure adequate behaviour in earthquakes, are the basis for these new requirements. These equations were derived for non-cyclic plastic rotations of 3 and 4 times the elastic rotation at first yield following the procedure proposed by Bansal (1971) and summarized in Chapter 10 (Figure 10.27) of Bruneau *et al*. (1998). For traditional plastic design, case (a) is applicable, and to provide for the ductility demands implied for the three types of seismic moment frame categories, cases (a) or (b) are applicable as indicated. Test results on inelastic beams under moment gradient are reported by Lay and Galambos (1967).

Because the final hinge in the failure mechanism does not require rotation capacity, the bracing spacing limitations of this clause do not apply, and the elastic bracing requirements of Clause 13.6(a) may be used.

Lateral bracing is required to prevent both lateral movement and twisting at a braced point. Lateral bracing is usually provided by floor beams or purlins which frame into the beam to be braced. These bracing members must have adequate axial strength and axial stiffness to resist the tendency to lateral deflection. These requirements are given in Clause 9.2. Further informa-

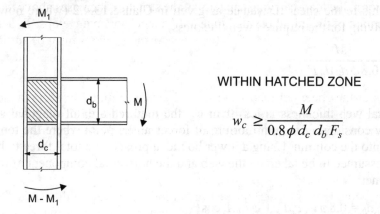

WITHIN HATCHED ZONE

$$w_c \geq \frac{M}{0.8 \phi d_c d_b F_s}$$

Figure 2-1
Web Thickness at Beam-to-Column Connections

tion on the design of bracing members is given in Lay and Galambos (1966). When the bracing member is connected to the compression flange of the braced member, the brace should possess bending stiffness to resist twisting of the braced member. Some information on the bending stiffness of braces is given in Essa and Kennedy (1995).

A concrete slab in which the compression flange is embedded or to which the compression flange is mechanically connected, as in composite construction, or metal decks welded to the top flange of the beam in the positive moment region, generally provide sufficient restraint to lateral and torsional displacements. When the lateral brace is connected to the tension flange, provision must be made for maintaining the shape of the cross-section and for preventing lateral movement of the compression flange. This can be accomplished with either diagonal struts to the compression flange or adequately designed web stiffeners.

8.3.2(d) Web Crippling

Web stiffeners are required on a member at a point of load application where a plastic hinge would form. Stiffeners are also required at beam-to-column connections where the forces developed in the beam flanges would either cripple the column web or, in the case of tension loads, distort the column flange with incipient weld fracture. The rules for stiffener design are given in Clause 21.3 (Kennedy *et al.* 1998). See ASCE (1971) for further details of stiffeners and Fisher *et al.* (1963) for special requirements pertaining to tapered and curved haunches.

When the shear force is excessive, additional stiffening may be required to limit shear deformations. The capacity of an unreinforced web to resist shear is taken to be that related to an average shear yield stress based on the Huber-Henckey-von Mises criterion of $F_y/\sqrt{3}$. For an effective depth of the web of a rolled shape of about 95% of the section depth, Clause 13.4.2 gives

$$V_r = 0.95 \phi w d F_y /\sqrt{3} = 0.55 \phi A_w F_y = 0.8 \phi A_w F_s$$

At beam-to-column connections, when the shear force exceeds that permitted above, the excess may be carried by providing doubler plates to increase the web thickness or by providing diagonal stiffeners (Figure 2-1). The force in the beam flange that is transferred into the web as a shear is approximately

$$V = M/d_b$$

Equating this to the shear resistance as given in Clause 13.4.2 (where now, $w = w_c$ and $d = d_c$), and solving for the required web thickness,

$$w_c \geq \frac{M}{0.8\phi\, d_c\, d_b\, F_s}$$

If the actual web thickness is less than w_c, the required area of diagonal stiffeners may be obtained by considering the equilibrium of forces at the point where the top flange of the beam frames into the column. Using a lower bound approach, the total force to be transmitted ($V = M/d_b$) is assumed to be taken by the web and the horizontal component of the force in the diagonal stiffener:

$$V = M/d_b = 0.8\phi\, w_c d_c F_s + \phi F_y A_s \cos\theta$$

where

A_s = cross-sectional area of diagonal stiffeners

$\theta = \tan^{-1}(d_b/d_c)$

The required stiffener area is therefore

$$A_s = \frac{1}{\cos\theta}\left(\frac{M}{\phi F_y d_b} - \frac{0.8\, w_c d_c F_s}{F_y}\right)$$

8.3.2(e) Splices

The bending moment diagram corresponding to the failure mechanism is the result of moment redistribution that occurred during the plastic hinging process. For example, points of inflection in the final bending moment distribution may have been required to resist significant moments to enable the failure mechanism to have developed (Hart and Milek 1965). To ensure that splices have sufficient capacity to enable the structure to reach its ultimate load capacity, a minimum connection requirement of $0.25\, M_p$ is specified in Clause 8.3.2(e). Also, at any splice location, the moments corresponding to various factored loading conditions must be increased by 10% above the computed value. The splice is then designed either for the larger of the moments so increased or for the minimum requirement of $0.25\, M_p$.

8.3.2(f) Impact and Fatigue

The use of moment redistribution to develop the strength of the structure corresponding to a failure mechanism implies ductile behaviour. Members that may be subjected repeatedly to heavy impact and members that may be subject to fatigue should not be designed on the basis of a plastic analysis because ductile behaviour cannot be anticipated under these conditions. Such members, at least for the present, are best proportioned on the basis of an elastic bending moment distribution.

8.3.2(g) Inelastic Deformations

For continuous beams, inelastic deformations may have a negligible effect on the strength of the structure. For other types of structures, in particular multi-storey frames, these secondary effects may have a significant influence on the strength of the structure (ASCE 1971).

In the structure shown inset in Figure 2-2, the secondary effects have reduced the lateral load carrying capacity (while maintaining the same vertical load) by approximately 25% (ASCE 1971; Adams 1974). The first plastic hinge formed at stage A in this structure while

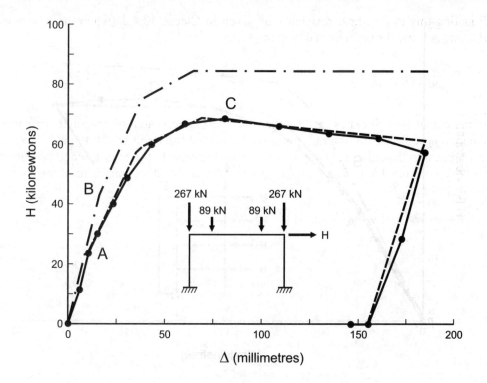

Figure 2-2
Observed and Predicted Load-Deflection Relationships

the ultimate strength (considering moment redistribution) was not attained until stage C. The inelastic deformations between these two stages have reduced the overall strength of the structure. Clause 8.4 requires that the sway effects produced by the vertical loads be accounted for in design. Therefore Clause 8.3.2(g) requires that, in a structure analyzed on the basis of a plastic moment distribution, the additional effects produced by inelastic sway deformations are accommodated. In most cases the actual strength of the structure can only be predicted by tracing the complete load-deflection relationship for the structure or for selected portions (Beedle *et al*. 1969). Methods are available to perform this type of design. For braced multi-storey frames, however, simpler techniques have also been developed (AISI 1968).

8.4 Stability Effects

Clause 8.4 recognizes that all building structures, whether unbraced or braced, are subjected to sway deformations. The vertical loads acting on the deformed structure produce secondary bending moments in the case of a moment-resisting frame, or additional forces in the vertical bracing system, in the case of a braced frame. These additional moments or forces (the stability effects) reduce the strength of the structure, as shown for a moment-resistant frame in Figure 2-2. In addition, bending moments and deflections, which exceed those predicted by a first order analysis, are produced at all stages of loading (Adams 1974). Similar effects are produced in structures containing a vertical bracing system, as shown in Figure 2-3 where the steel frame is linked to a shear wall (Adams 1974).

8.4.1 Within the context of elastic analysis, there are essentially two general categories of procedures used to assess the stability of frames, namely, effective length approaches and notional load approaches. In S16.1-M89, the effective length approach in use prior to that time was abandoned because of the complexity involved in getting the approach to yield an appropriate

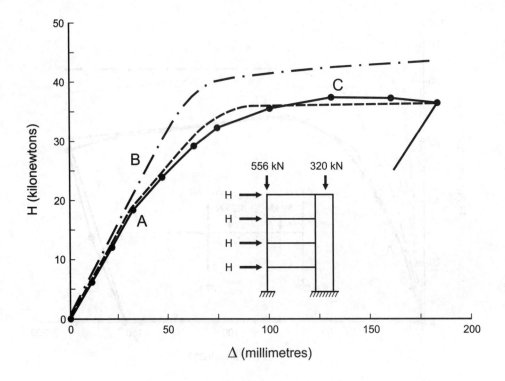

Figure 2-3
Load-Deflection Relationships

solution. The notional lateral load approach makes use of the actual column length ($K = 1.0$) and was adopted in 1989. It has been used for the design of beam-columns in Canada since then (MacPhedran and Grondin, 2007).

The concept of notional lateral loads is an internationally recognized technique for transforming a sway buckling problem into a bending strength problem. It accounts for the effect of initial out-of-plumb in the columns and for partial yielding at factored load levels. Following the recommendation of Kennedy (1995), the notional load is applied to all design load combinations. Thus, the factored lateral force to be used in establishing the value of Δ at the various levels of the building is the summation of the applied lateral force and the notional load and the horizontal reaction to prevent sway from gravity loads. Since the notional loads are applied for the only purpose of accounting fully for the P-Δ effects on the overturning moment without the necessity of incorporating the initial out-of-plumb and inelastic effects in the analysis of the structure, they do not need to be considered for shear design. These notional shear forces do not exist when equilibrium of the structure is considered on the structure in its deformed configuration.

The magnitude of the notional lateral load, applied at each storey, is taken as 0.005 times the sum of the factored gravity loads contributed by that storey. While there is variation in international standards regarding the magnitude of the notional load coefficient (Bridge *et al.*, 1997), Clarke and Bridge (1992, 1995) have shown that $0.005 \Sigma P$, established conservatively for a flagpole column (Kennedy *et al.*, 1990b), is an appropriate value that results in an adequate prediction of strengths in comparison with "exact" plastic zone analyses (Kanchanalai, 1977). There may be, as stated above, some conservatism in applying this magnitude of notional load to all load combinations in buildings where double-curvature bending of the columns predominates.

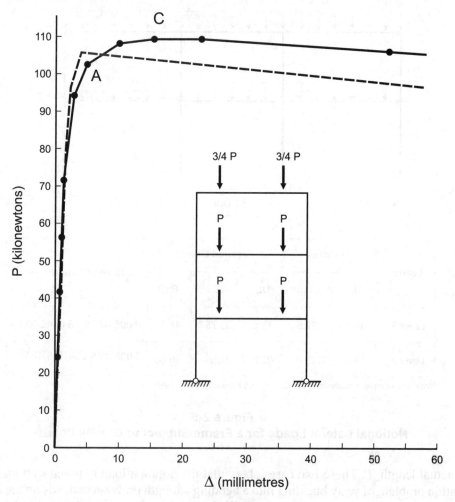

Figure 2-4
Load-Deflection Relationship – Vertical Load Only

The use of the notional lateral load fulfills several important functions. The applied notional loads transform a bifurcation problem of sway buckling into a bending strength problem. Second, because it accounts for the P-Δ moments directly, the use of effective length factors greater than 1.0 is obviated and its use allows effective lengths equal to the actual length to be used. At best the effective lengths used for sway buckling analyses are based on elastic analyses that are not appropriate for use with beam-column interaction equations that take into account inelastic material behaviour. Third, when equilibrium is formulated including the notional loads, the girders and beams restraining the columns are designed for the increased P-Δ moments that must exist in them for equilibrium just as the columns are. The use of effective lengths only accounts for increased moments in the columns and then only in an approximate manner with assumed elastic behaviour. Thus although there may be some slight conservatism in using a notional load of $0.005\Sigma P$ compared to a lesser value, this is more than offset by the three advantages enumerated above.

It is noted that the flagpole column is bent in single curvature whereas many columns in actual structures have some degree of double curvature. Consider now a sway column with complete fixity at both ends. It has very significant double curvature and an effective length of L. The sway buckling strength is now equal to the bending strength of a pin-ended column of the actual length with no notional lateral load because the effective length for buckling is equal

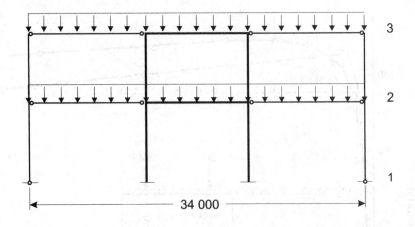

Loads	Specified		Factored Gravity			Notional Lateral Load
	DL	LL	DL	LL	Total	
Level 3	10.8	22.5	13.5	33.75	47.25	0.005(47.25 x 34) = 8.03 kN
Level 2	18.0	18.0	22.5	27.00	49.50	0.005(49.5 x 34) = 8.42 kN

Note: For complete analysis of this frame, see Kennedy, *et al*, 1990.

Figure 2-5
Notional Lateral Loads for a Frame Subject to Gravity Loads

to the actual length, L. These two cases show that the notional load required to transform the bifurcation problem of sway buckling into a bending strength problem depends on the end conditions in the actual structure and is greater when the degree of restraint is less. On the average, therefore, the notional load should be less than $0.005\,\Sigma P$ but Clarke and Bridge (1992, 1995) deem it to be the appropriate value.

The use of the notional lateral load remains of particular importance for structures subject to gravity loads only that may have insignificant lateral deflections and may only fail by elastic or inelastic sway buckling. Figure 2-4 shows a frame subject to vertical loads only. As the loads are increased, the effects of the vertical loads acting on the initial imperfections resulting from fabrication and erection, lead to failure through instability, much the same as for the combined load case shown in Figures 2-2 and 2-3. The notional lateral loads of 0.005 times the factored gravity loads acting at each storey, as required by clause 8.4.1, simulate this condition. Figure 2-5 shows, for a frame loaded with gravity loads only, the notional lateral loads that would be used to calculate the translational moments and forces for this load combination.

When either the gravity loads or the structure or both are asymmetric, horizontal reactions at floor levels are obtained when computing M_{fg}, defined as the first-order moment under factored gravity loads determined assuming that there is no lateral translation of the frame as shown in Figure 2-6. These horizontal reactions, when released by applying sway forces in the opposite direction, produce translational effects and must be considered for all valid load combinations, in addition to the notional lateral loads or the actual lateral loads as appropriate.

8.4.2 Since the introduction of S16.1-M89, the designer must account for the sway effects directly. This is done by (1) performing a second-order geometric elastic analysis for the moments and forces, or (2) accounting for these effects by amplifying the first order elastic trans-

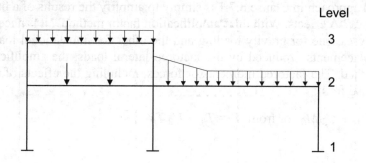

a) Asymmetrical frame with gravity loading

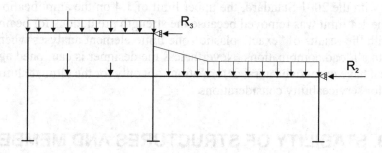

b) Computation of M_{fg}

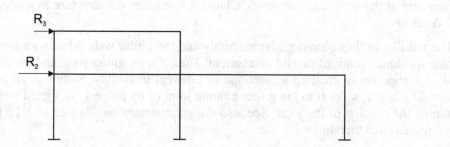

c) Computation of M_{ft} and Δ_f

Figure 2-6

lational moments by the factor U_2. The notional lateral loads (discussed in Clause 8.7.2) must be included in both of the above methods of analysis.

Computer programs are now commonly available to perform second-order elastic analyses based on equilibrium of the deformed structure. With these types of programs, the additional moments or forces generated by the vertical loads acting on the displaced structure (the so-called P-Δ effect) are taken into account directly and this method of analysis is the preferred method in Clause 8.7.1. In addition, most second-order programs also account for the change in column stiffness, caused by their axial loads (Galambos 1968).

The second approach in Clause 8.7.1 is simply to amplify the results of a first-order analysis to include the P-Δ effects. With this "amplification factor method", it is necessary to do two first-order analyses, one for gravity loading and the other for translational loading. From the horizontal displacements produced by the factored lateral loads, the amplification factor U_2 may be established. The factored moments or forces, including the effects of side-sway, may then be computed from:

$$M_f = M_{fg} + U_2\,M_{ft}\quad \text{or from}\quad T_f = T_{fg} + U_2\,T_{ft}$$

where $U_2 = \dfrac{1}{1 - \dfrac{\sum C_f \Delta_f}{\sum V_f h}}$

Starting with the 2001 Standard, the upper limit of 1.4 on the amplification factor U_2 was removed. The 1.4 limit was removed because the strength predictions for beam-columns compare well with the results of "exact" plastic zone finite element analyses when notional loads are applied to all load combinations. Nevertheless the designer is cautioned against designing structures that have excessive lateral deformations not only for the ultimate limit state of stability but also for serviceability considerations.

9. STABILITY OF STRUCTURES AND MEMBERS

9.1 Stability of Structures

Emphasis continues to be placed on the designer's responsibility to ensure stability of the structure and of the individual members. Clause 8.4 requires the structure as a whole to resist the P-Δ effects.

The stability of the column-girder assembly and the girder web, when a girder is continuous over a column, requires careful assessment. The column, girder web, and the girder flange are all in compression, creating a condition of inherent instability. Stability can be achieved by providing lateral support to the girder-column joint or by properly designed web stiffeners restraining the rotation of the joint. See also the commentary on Clauses 16.5.12.1, 13.6 and the references cited therein.

9.2 Stability of Members

This clause applies equally to columns, the compression chord of joists and trusses, and the compressed portion of beams. For the latter, it is only necessary to compute the maximum factored compressive force in that portion. The basic equation for the stiffness of the brace (Winter 1958) is derived on the premise that the brace or braces force the member to buckle into a series of half-sinewaves of length, L, the distance between bracing points, with nodes at the bracing points. For this to occur, the braces must provide both strength and stiffness.

Most bracing assemblies in buildings have inherent torsional resistance. Normally, header connections provide sufficient torsional restraint at supports, however, Cheng et al. (1988), Cheng and Yura (1988) and Yura (1995) note that beams with deep or extended copes should be given special consideration.

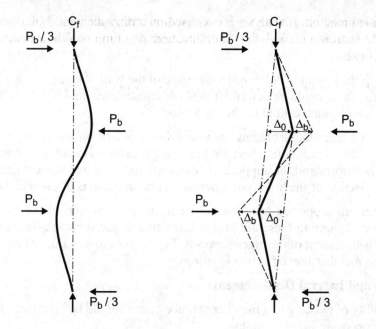

The solid line represents the initial misalignment. The dotted line represents the final displaced configuration due to all the forces acting on the system.

Figure 2-7
Δ_0 and Δ_b – Two Braces

Massey (1962) examined lateral bracing forces for beams while Zuk (1956) and Lay and Galambos (1966) considered requirements for structures analysed plastically. Ziemian (2010) summarized many of the design requirements for bracing assemblies.

For additional discussion on member bracing, refer to Ziemian (2010).

9.2.1 Initial Misalignment at Brace Point

Winter also showed that a critical parameter in designing the bracing is the initial out-of-straightness Δ_0 at the brace point. Based on S16 tolerances (Clause 29.3.7) a value for Δ_0 of no more than 0.002 times the distance between brace points may be used with Winter's model. A common construction technique used to reduce the initial misalignment is to pull the structure within tolerance at brace locations. Thus when the structure is pulled into alignment, one brace point at a time, the Δ_0 that results is the erection tolerance over a length of $2L$, i.e. $0.002L$ where L is the distance between brace points.

Figure 2-7 shows the critical values of Δ_0 when two brace points exist.

9.2.2 Displacement of Bracing Systems

Δ_b is the displacement of the member being braced at the brace point perpendicular to the member caused by the force P_b and any other external forces. This deflection may be the result of axial shortening or elongation of the bracing or its flexural displacement depending on whether the bracing resistance is provided axially or by bending. In addition to the brace deformation, the brace connection deformation and the brace support displacement must be included.

The Simplified method of analysis is premised on a displacement Δ_b not greater than Δ_0, and therefore Δ_b shall not exceed Δ_0. When justified, this limit may be exceeded in either of the detailed methods.

In the case of girts bracing columns in the plane of the wall, the girts are the bracing members that deform. There could be deformation in the connections, and the shear deformation of the cladding is the displacement at the brace support.

In the case of a brace angle bracing the lower flange of a beam and connected to the upper flange of a secondary flexural member; the brace angle deforms axially, the connection to the brace angle may deform and the supporting secondary member may deflect flexurally to contribute to the deflection of the brace point perpendicular to the axis of the member.

When braces are supported by a truss system, the deformation of the truss between its points of support (assuming these are on the same line as the support of the members being braced) is the displacement of the brace supports. Figure 2-7 shows values of the displacements Δ_0 and Δ_{0b} for a member braced at two locations.

9.2.4 Twisting and Lateral Displacements

The possibility of twisting of a member at brace points should be investigated and the bracing provided if necessary to prevent this.

The top (tension) flange at a cantilever, if not braced, can deflect more laterally than the bottom flange and therefore bracing of the cantilever end tension flange should be considered.

Torsional bracing can also increase the buckling load of cantilever beams.

The distortional buckling of steel beams in cantilever-suspended span construction was examined by Albert *et al.* (1992), and Essa and Kennedy (1995) investigated torsional restraint stiffness provided by open-web steel joists. In this type of construction it is essential to analyze potential lateral displacements at the tops of supporting columns because the beam web is also in vertical compression.

An inflection point cannot be considered a brace point (Ziemian 2010). Header connections normally provide sufficient torsional restraint at supports; however, Cheng *et al.* (1988), Cheng and Yura (1988) and Yura (1995) note that beams with deep or extended copes should be given special consideration.

Simply supported beams in single curvature typically require only lateral bracing at the compression flange.

9.2.5 Simplified Analysis

The simplified analysis permitting a brace to be designed conservatively for a force equal to $0.02C_f$ has been reintroduced but with the qualification that the resulting deflection Δ_b shall not exceed the initial misalignment Δ_0, which is consistent with Winter's original provisions. As the long history of successful use has shown, this provides a brace of such strength that both the stiffness and strength requirements are generally satisfied.

9.2.6 Detailed Analysis

9.2.6.1 Second-Order Method

To begin this solution manually, a deformed configuration is assumed and bracing forces determined by statics in terms of the deflections. With these calculated forces, the resulting bracing deflections are computed and compared to the deformations initially assumed. The process is repeated until satisfactory convergence is achieved. In checking a design, if the calculated deformations are less than the assumed deformed configuration, the conditions of strength and stiffness are satisfied and there is no need for further calculations, unless further optimization is desired. Alternatively, brace forces and deformations can be obtained from a computerized second-order analysis that accounts for P-Δ effects provided that the structure is modelled with the most critical initial misalignment condition.

Iterations to determine the forces and deflections are performed on the most critical deformed configuration. Typical deformed configurations to be investigated include those shown on Figure 2-7. When hinges are assumed in the braced member at the brace points, a slightly conservative solution is obtained.

The second-order method is useful in checking as-built conditions.

9.2.6.2 Direct Method

The design brace force is given directly in the expression for P_b where the factor β from Winter (1958) depends on the number of equally spaced braces by assuming that the displacement of the bracing system Δ_b is equal to the initial misalignment Δ_0. The required brace stiffness is $P_b/(\Delta_b + \Delta_0)$.

The initial assumption that Δ_b does not exceed Δ_0 must be confirmed.

By defining the maximum compressive force, C_f, as the maximum compression force in the segments bound by the brace points on either side of the brace point under consideration, the situation where a brace occurs near a point of contraflexure is accounted for. For trusses this applies when there is a significant change in the force in the chord at a panel point.

Consideration shall be made for cantilevered beams and beams bent in double curvature. Yura (1993) gives an amplification factor $C_d = [1 + (M_s/M_l)^2]$ where M_s and M_l refer to the smaller and larger moments respectively. This yields a maximum value of 2 when $M_s = M_l$.

For loads applied above the shear centre brace forces may be amplified. (Yura 1993) gives a factor $C_d = (1 + 1.2/n)$ where n is the number of braces. Braces counterbalance this effect.

Calibration of the bracing requirements with finite element analyses suggest that in some cases twisting of chords in trusses may result in brace forces 25% higher than those predicted by the direct method.

9.2.8 Accumulation of Forces

When an element in a structure must resist the bracing forces from more than one member, the average maximum out-of-straightness of the members should be used to compute the bracing forces. Provided that member misalignment is independent among members, it can be shown statistically that the average maximum out-of-straightness is a function of the maximum out-of-straightness of one member divided by the square root of the number of members (Kennedy and Neville 1986). The expression given in the standard is a conservative empirical equation that applies the statistical reduction to only 0.80 of the initial misalignment. In the design of such bracing systems it must be recognized that the (axial) displacement of the in-line brace increases from the location where the brace is affixed or restrained to the most remote member and the force in the in-line brace increases in the opposite direction. Beaulieu and Adams (1980) provide more guidance in selected cases.

In many cases two parallel frames or members are brought into alignment, and whatever misalignment remains is reflected in the initial position of the remaining members. The statistical reduction in the initial misalignment does not apply, and all members have essentially the same Δ_0.

9.2.9 Torsion

Because the shear centre of an asymmetric section does not coincide with the centroid, this section may be unintentionally loaded so as to produce torsion and biaxial bending. Both the connections and the members providing reactions should be checked.

10. DESIGN LENGTHS AND SLENDERNESS RATIOS

10.1 Simple Span Flexural Members

For design purposes, it is usually convenient to consider the length of a member as equal to the distance between centres of gravity of supporting members. In most instances the difference resulting from considering a member to be that length rather than its actual length, centre-to-centre of end connections, is small. In some cases, however, there is sufficient difference to merit computing the actual length. Regardless of the length used for design, the actual connection detail may cause an eccentric load, or moment, to act on the supporting member and this effect must be taken into account.

10.3 Members in Compression

10.3.1 General

The unbraced length and the effective length factors may be different for different axes of buckling. Information about effective lengths is given in Ziemian (2010) and Tall *et al.* (1974). Further guidance is provided in Annexes F and G of the Standard. The second-to-last sentence of Clause 10.3.1 introduces the concept that effective length factors depend on the potential failure mode – how the member would fail if the forces (and moments) were increased sufficiently – as discussed in subsequent clauses.

10.3.2 Failure Modes Involving Bending In-Plane

When the end moments and forces acting on a beam-column have been determined for the displaced configuration of the structure, that is to say, the sway effects have been included as required by Clause 8.4, the in-plane bending strength of the beam-column can be determined by analyzing a free-body of the member isolated from the remainder of the structure. In-plane displacements between the ends, which contribute to failure, arise from the end-moments and forces acting on the actual length. When the actual member length and the actual (or at least approximate) deflected shape are used, the analysis of the free-body will yield close to the correct member strength. Recourse to effective length factors is neither necessary nor appropriate.

When the actual member length is used together with the interaction expressions of Clause 13.8, the analysis is approximate and the in-plane member bending strength obtained will tend to be conservative. This simply arises because the value of the compressive resistance inherent in the interaction expression by using a length equal to the actual length (a K factor of 1.00) is that corresponding to single curvature buckling. For any other deflected shape, having accounted for sway effects, the compressive resistance is greater because the points of inflection of the deflected member shape are less than the member length apart. Under these circumstances, a better estimate of the strength, as is indeed permitted under Clause 1.4, can be obtained when the compressive resistance is based on the actual distance between points of inflection. Inelastic action of the member in the structure, however, may make this determination onerous. Therefore the relatively simple but sometimes conservative approach given in the Standard which obviates the use of effective length factors is presented as the usual procedure.

10.3.3 Failure Modes Involving Buckling

The compressive resistance of an axially loaded column depends on its end restraints as does the out-of-plane buckling resistance of a beam-column under uniaxial strong axis bending. The failure is a bifurcation mechanism.

10.4 Slenderness Ratios

The maximum slenderness ratio of 200 for compression members, stipulated as long ago as the 1974 Standard, has been retained in S16-09 for the reason that strength, or resistance, of a compression member becomes quite small as the slenderness ratio increases and the member becomes relatively inefficient.

For considerations of strength, no limiting slenderness ratio is required for a tension member and, indeed, none is applied to wire ropes and cables. However, a slenderness ratio limit of 300 is given with permission to waive this limit under specified conditions. The limit does assist in the handling of members and may help prevent flutter under oscillating loads such as those induced in wind bracing designed for tension loads only. Tension chords of trusses and joists have more stringent slenderness ratios (see commentary on Clauses 15 and 16).

Members whose design is governed by earthquake loadings may be subject to more stringent slenderness ratios depending on the ductility requirements of the lateral load-resisting system. See Commentary on Clause 27.

11. WIDTH (OR DIAMETER)-TO-THICKNESS RATIOS – ELEMENTS IN COMPRESSION

Clause 11 emphasises the distinction between elements in axial compression and elements in flexural compression by placing the maximum width-to-thickness ratios for these elements in Tables 1 and 2 respectively.

Clause 11.1.1 identifies four categories of cross-sections, Class 1 through Class 4, based upon the width-thickness ratios of the elements of the cross-section in compression that are needed to develop the desired flexural behaviour. With the ratios given in Table 2 of Clause 11 for Classes 1, 2, or 3, the respective ultimate limit states will be attained prior to local buckling of the plate elements. These ultimate limit states are: Class 1 – maintenance of the plastic moment capacity (beams), or the plastic moment capacity reduced for the presence of axial load (beam-columns), through sufficient rotation to fulfill the assumption of plastic analysis; Class 2 – attainment of the plastic moment capacity for beams, and the reduced plastic moment capacity for beam-columns, but with no requirement for rotational capacity; Class 3 – attainment of the yield moment for beams, or the yield moment reduced for the presence of axial load for beam-columns. Class 4 – have plate elements that buckle locally before the yield strength is reached.

Elements in Flexural Compression

The requirements given in Figure 2-8 for elements of Class 1, 2, and 3 sections in flexural compression, particularly those for W-shapes, are based on both experimental and theoretical studies. For example, the limits on flanges have both a theoretical basis (Kulak and Grondin 2002; ASCE 1971; Ziemian 2010) and an extensive experimental background (Haaijer and Thurlimann 1958; Lay 1965; Lukey and Adams 1969). For webs in flexural compression the limits $1100/\sqrt{F_y}$, $1700/\sqrt{F_y}$ and $1900/\sqrt{F_y}$ for Class 1, 2 and 3 respectively when $C_f/\phi C_y = 1.0$ come

Detail	Class 1	Class 2	Class 3
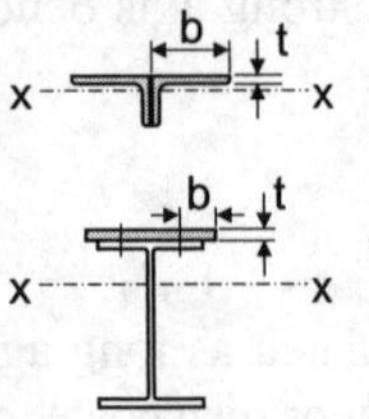 **L's connected continuously** (Flanges of I's or T's)	$\dfrac{b_{el}}{t} \le \dfrac{145}{\sqrt{F_y}}$ † † 2-L's or cover plates symmetric about plane of bending (x-x axis)	$\dfrac{b_{el}}{t} \le \dfrac{170}{\sqrt{F_y}}$ † † 2-L's or cover plates symmetric about plane of bending (x-x axis)	$\dfrac{b_{el}}{t} \le \dfrac{200}{\sqrt{F_y}}$
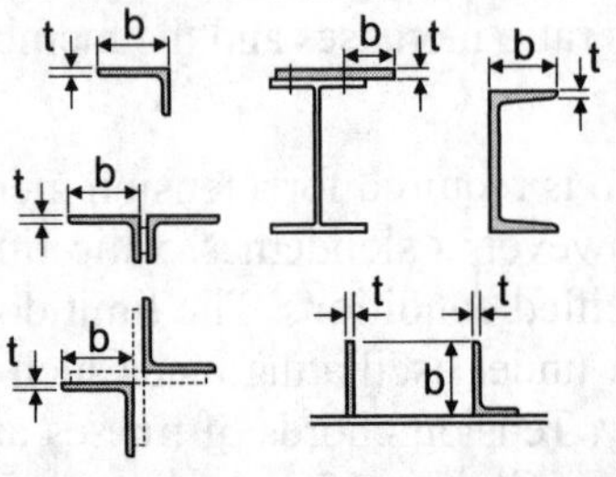	—	—	$\dfrac{b_{el}}{t} \le \dfrac{200}{\sqrt{F_y}}$ L's not continuously connected, flange of C's, asymmetric cover plates, plate girder stiffeners
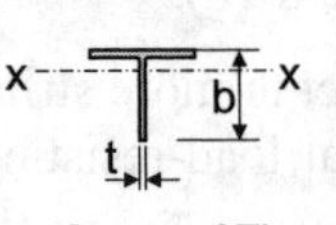 **Stems of T's** ‡ Symmetric about plane of bending or including asymmetry effects in analysis	$\dfrac{b_{el}}{t} \le \dfrac{145}{\sqrt{F_y}}$ ‡	$\dfrac{b_{el}}{t} \le \dfrac{170}{\sqrt{F_y}}$ ‡	$\dfrac{b_{el}}{t} \le \dfrac{340}{\sqrt{F_y}}$
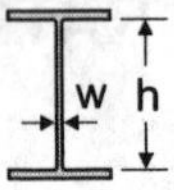 (web, w, h)	Bending only $\dfrac{h}{w} \le \dfrac{1100}{\sqrt{F_y}}$ Axial compression —	Bending only $\dfrac{h}{w} \le \dfrac{1700}{\sqrt{F_y}}$ Axial compression —	Bending only $\dfrac{h}{w} \le \dfrac{1900}{\sqrt{F_y}}$ Axial compression $\dfrac{h}{w} \le \dfrac{670}{\sqrt{F_y}}$
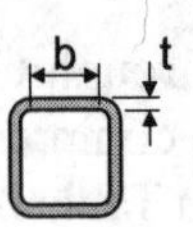 **HSS**	$\dfrac{b_{el}}{t} \le \dfrac{420}{\sqrt{F_y}}$	$\dfrac{b_{el}}{t} \le \dfrac{525}{\sqrt{F_y}}$	$\dfrac{b_{el}}{t} \le \dfrac{670}{\sqrt{F_y}}$
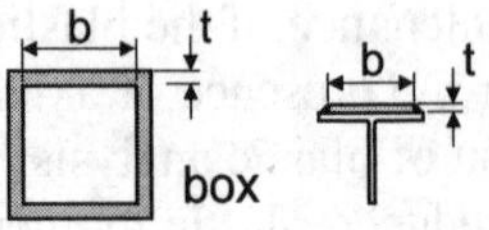 **box**	$\dfrac{b_{el}}{t} \le \dfrac{525}{\sqrt{F_y}}$	$\dfrac{b_{el}}{t} \le \dfrac{525}{\sqrt{F_y}}$	$\dfrac{b_{el}}{t} \le \dfrac{670}{\sqrt{F_y}}$
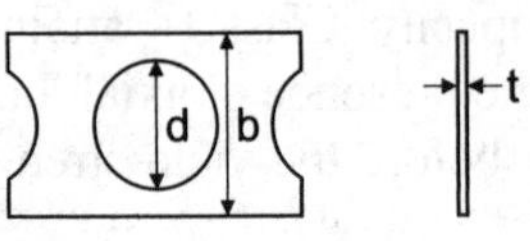 (d, b, t)	—	—	$\dfrac{b_{el}}{t} \le \dfrac{840}{\sqrt{F_y}}$
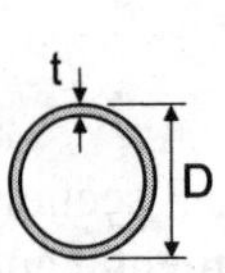 (D, t)	Bending only $\dfrac{D}{t} \le \dfrac{13\,000}{F_y}$ Axial compression —	Bending only $\dfrac{D}{t} \le \dfrac{18\,000}{F_y}$ Axial compression —	Bending only $\dfrac{D}{t} \le \dfrac{66\,000}{F_y}$ Axial compression $\dfrac{D}{t} \le \dfrac{23\,000}{F_y}$

Figure 2-8
Width-Thickness Ratios for Compression Elements

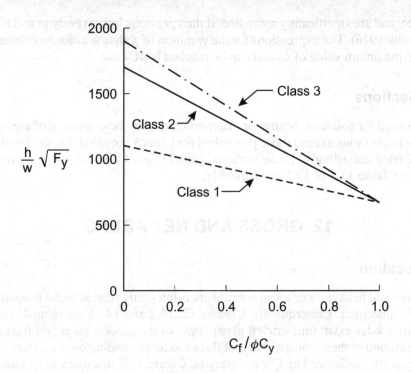

Figure 2-9
Width-Thickness Ratios for Webs

from both theory and tests on Class 1 sections (Haaijer and Thurlimann 1958) but mostly from test results for Class 2 and 3 sections (Holtz and Kulak 1973 and 1975).

For circular hollow sections in flexure, see Stelco (1973) for the requirements for Class 1 and Class 2 sections and Sherman and Tanavde (1984) for Class 3.

Elements in Axial Compression

The distinction between classes based on moment capacity does not apply to axially loaded members as the plate elements need only reach a strain sufficient for the plate elements to develop the yield stress. This strain is affected by the presence of residual stresses but there is no applied strain gradient across elements of the cross-section as there is for members subject to flexure. The width-thickness limits for the various plate elements are not dependent on the Class of the section and are only a function of the residual stress pattern and the edge conditions. Thus for webs, from Table 2 in the Standard for each of Classes 1, 2 and 3 when $C_f/\phi C_y = 1.0$, the limit on h/w is the same value of about $670/\sqrt{F_y}$ as given in Table 1. The width-thickness limit for the flanges of axially loaded columns, based on the same argument, is the same as for Class 3 beam flanges, i.e., $200/\sqrt{F_y}$ (Dawe and Kulak 1984). As well the limit on the D/t ratio of $23\,000/F_y$ (Winter 1970) for circular hollow sections in axial compression is the same irrespective of the Class.

Elements in Compression Due to Bending and Axial Load

In Figure 2-9, the requirements for webs in compression ranging from compression due to pure bending to that due to pure compression are plotted. Because all of the web is in compression for columns and only one-half for beams, the depth-to-thickness limits vary as a function of the amount of axial load. The results presented here reflect the research results of Dawe and

Kulak (1986), and are significantly more liberal than previous limits (Perlynn and Kulak 1974; Nash and Kulak 1976). The expressions for the variation of web h/w ratios have been corrected such that the maximum value of C_f that can be reached is ϕC_y.

Class 4 Sections

Sections used for columns, beams, or beam-columns may be composed of elements whose width-to-thickness ratios exceed those prescribed for Class 3 provided that the resistance equations are adjusted accordingly. These sections, called Class 4, are evaluated according to the rules given in Clause 13.3 or 13.5 as applicable.

12. GROSS AND NET AREAS

12.1 Application

The design and behaviour of tension members is integrally related to the proportioning and detailing of connections. Consequently, Clauses 12, 13.2 and 13.11 are related. Two possible overall failure modes exist: unrestricted plastic flow of the gross section and fracture of a net section. The second of these consists itself of three modes depending on the failure path and the degree of ductility available. The Commentary on Clause 13.2 discusses three specific tensile failure modes and that on Clause 13.11 treats combined tension and shear. Commentaries on failure areas are given here.

12.2 Gross Area

Yielding on the gross area from one end of the member to the other resulting in unrestricted plastic flow can occur before fracture on a net section. The gross area is obtained simply as the sum of the products of the thickness and gross widths of all cross-sectional elements.

12.3 Net Area

This clause defines areas used to determine tension member resistances. The requirements apply to both bolted and welded connections.

12.3.1 General

When each portion of the cross-section of a tension member is connected with sufficient fasteners to transmit the load attributable to that portion, the stress distribution at the connection is reasonably uniform, and the provisions of Clause 12.3.1 apply to the net area calculations. To establish the critical net area, all potential failure paths are examined. When the failure plane includes segments inclined to the applied force, an empirical term, $s^2 t/4g$, is added to the net area to correct for the presence of each inclined segment.

In determining the net area by summing the net area of each segment along the critical path, it is assumed, as has been demonstrated (Birkemoe and Gilmor 1978; Ricles and Yura 1983; Hardash and Bjorhovde, 1985), that all segments reach their full capacity simultaneously.

12.3.2 Allowance for Bolt Holes

The 2 mm allowance for bolt holes accounts for distortion or local material damage that may occur in forming the hole by punching. If it is not known at the design stage that the holes will be drilled or sub-punched and reamed, then punched holes should be assumed. The 2 mm allowance also is used with oversize or slotted holes.

12.3.3 Effective Net Area - Shear Lag

When the critical net section fracture path crosses unconnected cross-sectional elements, the directly connected elements tend to reach their ultimate strength before the complete net section strength is reached due to shear lag. When all cross-sectional elements are directly connected, shear lag does not occur and the effective net area is the total net area.

The loss in efficiency due to shear lag can be expressed as a reduction in the net area. Munse and Chesson (1963) suggested that this reduction could be taken as $1 - \bar{x}/L$ where $\bar{x}$ is the distance from the shear plane to the centroid of that portion of the cross-section being developed and L is the connected length.

Because the connected length is usually not known at the time of tension member design, reduction factors have been derived for specific cases, as given in Clause 12.3.3.2, based on an extensive examination of the results of over 1000 tests (Kulak *et al*. 1987). The reduction factor depends on the cross-sectional shape and the number of bolts (2, 3 or more) in the direction of the tensile load.

More severe reductions for shear lag are provided for angles connected by one leg based on work by Wu and Kulak (1993) who examined many test results on angles in tension connected with mechanical fasteners.

When block tear-out occurs in those elements that are directly connected, shear lag is not a factor. Shear lag need only be considered when the potential failure path under consideration crosses unconnected elements.

12.3.3.3 Similar reductions due to shear lag have been observed in welded connections (Kulak *et al*. 1987) when only welds parallel to the tensile load in the member are used. If the elements of the cross-section are connected by welds transverse to the tensile load, no reduction due to shear lag is necessary. For welded connections with matching electrodes and material of G40.21-300W grade steel, shear lag will be critical for cases where $A_{ne} \le 0.78 A_g$. For angles, this generally occurs when the length of weld along the toe exceeds the length of weld along the heel.

When the weld length is less than the distance between welds, it is likely that the weld is critical.

The direct use of the Munse and Chesson reduction factor, $1 - \bar{x}/L$, is permitted by this clause. Figure 2-10 gives examples of dimensions used in calculating this shear lag reduction factor.

12.4 Pin-Connected Tension Members

The net area increase across the pin hole is to allow for the significant non-uniform distribution of stress (Johnston 1939). The minimum net area within the 45° arc each side of the longitudinal axis is to avoid end splitting.

13. MEMBER AND CONNECTION RESISTANCE

13.1 Resistance Factors

The number of different resistance factors used in the Standard has continued to increase and now for convenience, all resistance factors are listed in Clause 13.1. The long-used basic value of ϕ of 0.90 for most resistances continues to provide consistent and adequate values of the reliability index when used with the load factors of Clause 7.2. (Kennedy and Gad Aly

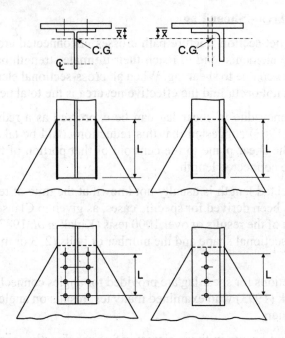

Figure 2-10
Dimensions Used for Shear Lag Calculations

1980, Baker and Kennedy 1984). In S16-09, the following new resistance factors have been added to the group:

$\phi_{br} = 0.80$ for the bearing of bolts on steel

$\phi_u = 0.75$ for rupture on the net sections

$\phi_c = 0.65$ for concrete

The resistance factor for bolt bearing on steel has been increased from 0.67, adopted in previous edition of the Standard, to 0.80. A recent reliability analysis demonstrated that a resistance factor of 0.80 provides an adequate margin of safety (Stankevicius *et al.* 2009). In earlier versions of S16, the resistance factor $\phi = 0.90$ was used in the equation for rupture of tension members at the net section. This resistance factor was multiplied by a factor of 0.85 to increase the safety index to about 4.0 to 4.5 for this ultimate limit state. S16-09 replaces 0.85ϕ by $\phi_u = 0.75$, which is just slightly lower than 0.85ϕ. The resistance factor ϕ_c was increased from 0.60 to 0.65 for consistency with the reinforced concrete design standard A23.3.

13.2 Axial Tension

The two overall potential failure modes for tension members and their connections are yielding of the gross section and fracture of a net section. Fracture of a net section further consists of three possible modes depending on how the elements of the cross-section are connected and how the net sections are loaded. Thus all possible failure modes described must be examined to establish the value that governs the factored tensile resistance. The resistances of two of the fracture modes chiefly involving tension on the net section are presented in Clause 13.2. The failure mode involving a combination of tension and shear, in which a block of material tears out, is referred to as block shear failure and is discussed in the commentary to Clause 13.11.

The appropriate areas to be used in each of the three modes are described in Clause 12.

The first of the three failure modes involves unrestricted plastic flow of the gross section when the yield deformations over the length of the member are excessive. This represents a limit state for which the failure is gradual. A reliability index β of 3.0 is considered acceptable for the tension member and thus the tensile resistance is

$$T_r = \phi A_g F_y; \ \text{(with } \phi = 0.90)$$

The second failure mode, involving a combination of tension and shear, in which a block of material tears out – block shear failure – is discussed in the commentary on Clause 13.11.

The third failure mode involves fracture of the member at the net section. The net section area can either be fully effective if all parts of the cross-section are connected, or it can be only partially effective if shear lag is present. Because this fracture occurs with little deformation and no reserve of strength exists beyond rupture, an increased value of β is appropriate for cases of fracture at the net section. In S16-09 the tensile resistance for this mode is written as:

$$T_r = \phi_u A_{ne} F_u$$

The resistance factor $\phi_u = 0.75$ used for this limit state results in an increased value of β of about 4.5. This philosophy is consistent with the reduced resistance factor used for connectors (bolts, welds, and shear connectors). The net effective area, A_{ne}, accounts for possible shear lag effect. If no shear lag is present, then $A_{ne} = A_n$.

The reduction factor of 0.75 for pin connections recognizes the greater non-uniformity of stress that occurs around a hole that is large relative to the material in which it is formed.

13.3 Axial Compression

Depending on the type of cross-section, the buckling load of an axially loaded compression member may be governed by flexural buckling, by torsional buckling or by flexural-torsional buckling.

13.3.1 Flexural Buckling of Doubly Symmetric Shapes

Axially loaded compression members with doubly-symmetric cross-sections, such as wide-flange shapes, I-shaped and HSS members that dominate in steel construction, normally reach their ultimate capacity either by yielding or by flexural buckling, the most common buckling mode.

Steel columns are conveniently classified as short, intermediate, or long members, and each category has an associated characteristic type of behaviour. A short column is one that can resist a load equal to the yield load ($C_y = A F_y$). A long column fails by elastic buckling. The maximum load depends only on the bending stiffness (EI) and length of the member. Columns in the intermediate range are most common in steel buildings. Failure is characterized by inelastic buckling and is greatly influenced by the magnitude and pattern of residual stresses that are present and the magnitude and shape of the initial imperfections or out-of-straightness. These effects are less severe for both shorter and longer columns. The expressions in this clause account for these effects that are dependent on the cross-section (Bjorhovde 1972).

Figure 2-11 indicates the variations in strengths for columns of three different values of the slenderness parameter, λ, and with the same out-of-straightness patterns and different residual stress patterns.

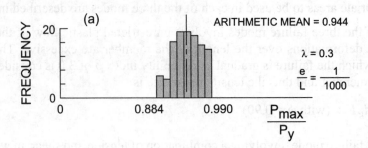

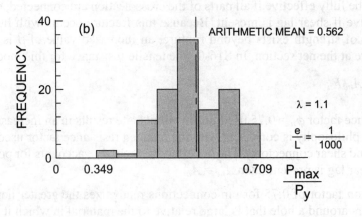

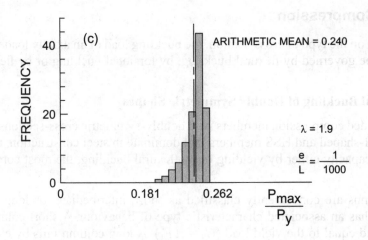

Figure 2-11
Typical Frequency Distribution Histograms for the Maximum Strength
of 112 Column Curves ($e/L = 1/1000$)

The compressive resistance expressions of Clause 13.3.1 are expressed in double exponential form (Loov 1996). With values of the parameter n of 1.34 and 2.24 for the cases shown in Clause 13.3.1, the expressions are always within 3% and generally within 1% of column Curves 2 and 1 of the Structural Stability Research Council (SSRC) (Ziemian 2010).

Steel shapes, unless explicitly stated, are assigned to SSRC Curve 2 ($n = 1.34$), which is therefore used for hot-rolled, fabricated structural sections, and based on Bjorhovde and Birkemoe (1979), cold-formed non-stress relieved, Class C, hollow structural sections, manufactured according to CSA Standard G40.20. HSS produced to ASTM A500 grades B and C are cold-formed non-stress relieved, and the use of $n = 1.34$ is therefore appropriate.

Because of a more favourable residual stress pattern and out-of-straightness, hot-formed or cold-formed stress relieved (Class H) hollow structural sections (Kennedy and Gad Aly, 1980) are assigned to SSRC Curve 1 or its equivalent curve here with a value of $n = 2.24$. For the same reasons, doubly-symmetric three-plate members with flange edges oxy-flame-cut are also assigned to the curve with $n = 2.24$ (Chernenko and Kennedy, 1991).

For heavy sections (W310x313 and heavier and W360x347 and heavier, referred to as Groups 4 and 5 sections in earlier versions of CSA Standard G40.20) made of ASTM A7 or A36 steel and welded sections fabricated from universal mill plate, a resistance less than that corresponding to $n = 1.34$ (SSRC Curve 2) is appropriate, and it is recommended that a value of $n = 0.93$, corresponding to Column Curve 3 (Ziemian 2010), be used.

Because column strengths are influenced by the magnitude and distribution of residual stresses, care should be exercised in the use of the expressions in this Standard. For example, adding material such as welded cover plates increases the area and may reduce the slenderness ratio of an existing column, but it may also increase the compressive residual stresses in fibres remote from the centroid of the member, thus detracting from the strength.

13.3.2 Flexural, Torsional or Flexural-Torsional Buckling

Two other modes of buckling, which may occur prior to flexural buckling, are torsional or flexural-torsional buckling.

Torsional buckling with twisting about the shear centre is a possible failure mode for point-symmetric sections, e.g., a cruciform section, and in some circumstances, for doubly-symmetric sections. Flexural-torsional buckling, a combination of torsion and flexure is a possible failure mode for open sections that are singly-symmetric or asymmetric such as T's and angles. Thus, for sections with coincident shear centre and centroid, three potential compressive buckling modes exist (two flexural and one torsional), while for singly symmetric sections two potential compressive buckling modes (one flexural and one flexural-torsional) exist and, for a non-symmetric section, only one mode (flexural-torsional) exists. Closed sections, strong torsionally, also do not fail by flexural-torsional buckling (See Ziemian 2010). For the theory of elastic flexural-torsional buckling see Goodier (1942), Timoshenko and Gere (1961), Vlasov (1959) and Galambos (1968). The equations given here are developed in the latter among others.

As the problem of inelastic flexural-torsional buckling is quite complex and is amenable generally only to inelastic finite element analyses, the approach given here is to compute the elastic buckling stress, F_e, from the equations given for doubly symmetric, singly symmetric or asymmetric sections and then calculate an equivalent slenderness ratio $\lambda = \sqrt{F_y/F_e}$ to be used in the equations of Clause 13.3. This comes from the fact that an elastic buckling curve, when non-dimensionalized by dividing by F_y can be written as $F_e/F_y = 1/\lambda^2$. When the inelastic equations of 13.3 are entered with the equivalent slenderness ratio, an inelastic compressive resistance results.

The equations given here are equivalent to those in CSA Standard S-136. There, however, for singly symmetric sections, the x-x axis is taken as the axis of symmetry because cold-formed channel sections are frequently used.

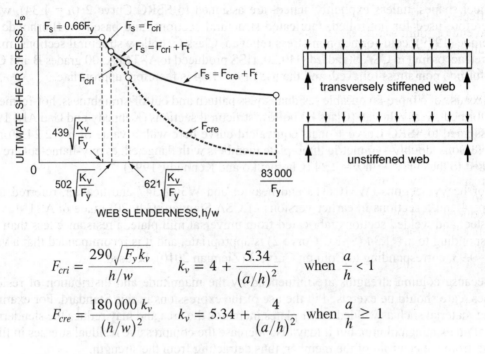

$$F_{cri} = \frac{290\sqrt{F_y k_v}}{h/w} \qquad k_v = 4 + \frac{5.34}{(a/h)^2} \qquad \text{when } \frac{a}{h} < 1$$

$$F_{cre} = \frac{180\,000\,k_v}{(h/w)^2} \qquad k_v = 5.34 + \frac{4}{(a/h)^2} \qquad \text{when } \frac{a}{h} \geq 1$$

F_t – See Clause 13.4.1.1(b) (iii) and (iv)

Figure 2-12
Ultimate Shear Stress – Webs of Flexural Members

13.3.3 Single-Angle Members in Compression

The design of single angles subjected to axial compression is addressed. The angle is connected by a single leg, which is attached to a gusset plate or the projecting leg of another member by welding or by a bolted connection (at least two bolts), and is not subjected to any transverse loading. The effect of end eccentricity and rotational end restraint, hence, any resulting flexure of the angle, is indirectly accounted for by incorporating the equivalent slenderness expressions provided in this Clause. These expressions have also been adopted by the AISC Specification (2005). They are essentially equivalent to those specified for equal-leg angles as web members in latticed transmission towers in ASCE 10-97 (ASCE, 2000). The slenderness expressions are considered valid for equal leg angles or unequal leg angles connected by the longer leg (ratio of long leg / short leg < 1.7). It is assumed that significant restraint about the y-axis, which is perpendicular to the connected leg (Note regarding convention: where the longer leg is connected, this axis is defined as the x-axis in the section properties tables for single angles in the CISC Handbook), exists due to the end connections. This causes the angle to flex and buckle primarily about the x-axis, hence, the use of the radius of gyration about the geometric axis parallel to the connected leg, r_x. The expressions for box trusses reflect greater rotational end restraint as compared to that provided by planar trusses. The slenderness expressions are not intended for use in the calculation of compression resistance of single angles used as diagonal braces in a braced frame. The procedure allows for the use of unequal-leg angles attached by the smaller leg provided that the equivalent slenderness is increased by an amount that is a function of the ratio of the longer to the shorter leg lengths. A minimum slenderness limit based on the slenderness about the minor principal axis must be met in all cases.

If the single-angle compression members cannot be evaluated using the equivalent slenderness expressions, then the provisions of Clause 13.3.2 shall be used for design accounting for the effect of end eccentricity and rotational end restraint. In evaluating C_r, the effective length due to end restraint should be considered. The procedure documented by Lutz (1992) to compute an effective radius of gyration for the angle can be implemented.

13.3.5 Members in Compression Subjected to Elastic Local Buckling

Two alternatives are available for approximating the factored compressive resistance of compression members that do not meet the local buckling requirements. The first is based on the notional removal of the width in excess of the limit for plate elements in axial compression to determine a reduced cross-sectional area. This area is used with the specified minimum yield strength and a slenderness based on the gross cross section to determine the factored compressive resistance by Clause 13.3.2 or 13.3.3. In the second alternative, the existing b/t ratio is used to establish the effective yield strength of a section just meeting the Class 3 limits. With this reduced yield strength and the gross cross section properties, Clause 13.3.2 or 13.3.3 establishes the factored resistance. Results by the two methods will not necessarily be the same. It is not necessary to refer to CSA S136 for members in axial compression that are subjected to elastic local buckling.

13.4 Shear

13.4.1.1 Elastic Analysis

The expressions for shear strength are given for unstiffened and stiffened plate girders. Unstiffened plate girders and rolled beams are simply special cases for which the shear buckling coefficient, $k_v = 5.34$.

The four ranges of resistance based on Basler (1961), correspond to the following modes of behaviour and are illustrated in Figure 2-12 for stiffened webs:

(a) Full yielding followed by strain-hardening and large deformation. The limiting stress of $0.66 F_y$ corresponds to shear deformation into the strain-hardening range and is higher than that derived from von Mises criterion ($0.577 F_y$), which forms the basis of Clause 13.4.2 for plastic analysis.

(b) A transition curve between strain-hardening and inelastic buckling at full shear yielding. ($F_s = 0.577 F_y$);

(c) Inelastic buckling, F_{cri}, accompanied by post-buckling strength, F_t, due to tension field action, if the web is stiffened; and,

(d) Elastic buckling, F_{cre}, accompanied by post-buckling strength, F_t, due to tension field action, if the web is stiffened.

In computing the shear resistance, it is assumed that the shear stress is distributed uniformly over the depth of the web. The web area (A_w) is the product of web thickness (w) and web depth (h) except for rolled shapes where it is customary to use the overall beam depth (d) in place of the web depth (h).

In panel zones and locations where strain-hardening develops quickly after the onset of shear yielding, the use of $0.66 F_y$ is valid.

13.4.2 Plastic Analysis

For structures analyzed plastically, high shears and moments may occur simultaneously at a hinge location. Yang and Beedle (1951) have shown that, when the maximum shear stress is limited to the von Mises value, the flexural resistance can be maintained at M_p. Taking the effective section depth as 95% of the nominal depth, this Clause gives an approximate shear resistance limited to the von Mises stress. (See Commentary to Clause 8.3.2(d)).

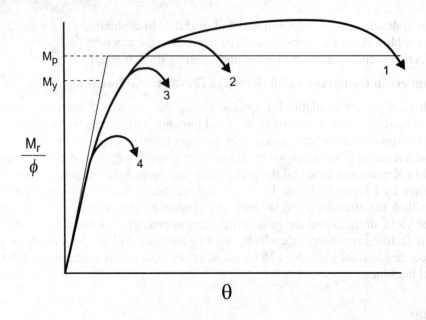

Figure 2-13
Moment-Rotation Curves

13.4.3 Webs of Flexural Members Not Having Two Flanges

When cross-sections do not have two flanges, the shear stress distribution can no longer be assumed to be uniform. For W-shapes with one flange coped, the elastic shear stress distribution may be determined from $\tau = VQ/It$. Limiting the maximum value to $0.66F_y$ is conservative as it does not allow for any plastification as shear yielding spreads from the most heavily stressed region. For W-shapes with two flanges coped, a parabolic shear stress distribution results from this procedure with a maximum shear stress equal to 1.5 times the average. The maximum shear stress can be based on strain-hardening provided shear buckling does not occur.

13.4.4 Pins

Additional information for pins in combined shear and moment is given in the Canadian Highway Bridge Design Code, CSA S6-06.

13.5 Bending: Laterally Supported Members

The factored moment resistances are consistent with the classification of cross-sections given in Clause 11, as illustrated by moment–rotation curves given in Figure 2-13.

The fully plastic moment, M_p, attained by Class 1 and 2 sections, implies that all fibres of the section are completely yielded. Any additional resistance that develops due to strain-hardening has been accounted for in the test/predicted ratio statistics used in developing resistance factors (Kennedy and Gad Aly 1980).

The stress distribution for Class 3 sections at the ultimate moment is assumed linear, with a maximum stress equal to the yield stress.

Class 4 sections reach their maximum moment resistance when a flange or web plate element buckles locally. Class 4 sections are divided into three categories.

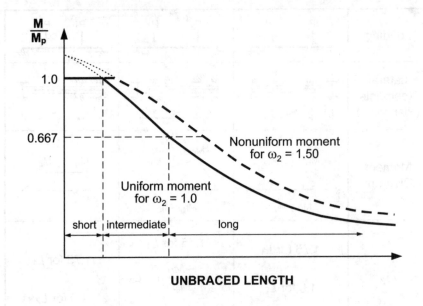

Figure 2-14
Variation of Uniform and Non-uniform Moment Resistances

The first consists of those sections with Class 4 flanges and webs. This type of section is designed to the requirements of CSA Standard S136 using the material properties appropriate to the structural steel specified.

The second category consists of those sections with Class 3 flanges and Class 4 webs. Clause 13.5(c)(ii) logically requires that these sections be designed in accordance with Clause 14.

The third category, with Class 4 flanges and Class 3 webs, a reduced, effective section modulus (Kalyanaraman *et al*. 1977) is used to compute the moment resistance. Alternatively, an effective yield stress established from Class 3 limits may be used to calculate the moment resistance.

13.6 Bending – Laterally Unsupported Members

Laterally unsupported beams may fail by lateral–torsional buckling at applied moments significantly less than the full cross-sectional strength (M_p or M_y). Even when the top flange is laterally supported, under some circumstances – for example, a roof beam subject to uplift – the laterally unsupported bottom flange may be in compression. General information on lateral–torsional buckling is summarized in Chen and Lui (1987).

Besides cross-sectional properties and aspects related to the loading itself, the lateral–torsional moment resistance depends on the unsupported (unbraced) length. Beams may be considered to be short, intermediate, or long depending on whether the moment resistance developed is the full cross-sectional strength, the inelastic lateral–torsional buckling strength, or the elastic lateral-torsional buckling strength, respectively, as shown in Figure 2-14 for Class 1 and 2 shapes capable of attaining M_p on the cross-section. The curve for Class 3 sections is similar, except that the maximum moment resistance is M_y, while for Class 4 sections, the maximum resistance is limited by local buckling.

The length, L, is generally taken as the distance between lateral supports. When beams are continuous through a series of lateral supports, interaction buckling (Trahair, 1968) occurs, and

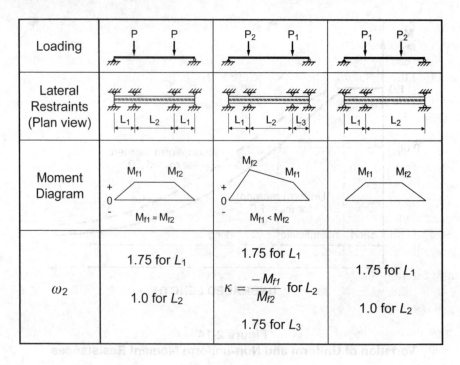

Figure 2-15
Various Cases of ω_2 for Linear Moment Gradients

the segment that tends to buckle laterally first is restrained by the adjoining segments. Nethercot and Trahair (1976a, 1976b), Kirby and Nethercot (1978) and Schmitke and Kennedy (1985) give methods of computing effective lengths under these circumstances. Points of contraflexure for bending about the major axis are not related to lateral-torsional buckling and therefore cannot be considered as points of lateral support (Schmitke and Kennedy 1985).

Without the equivalent moment factor, ω_2, the expression given for M_u is that for a doubly-symmetric beam subject to uniform moment. The factor ω_2 ranges from 1.0 to 2.5 and takes into account the fact that for lateral–torsional buckling a varying moment is less severe than a uniform moment. Also plotted in Figure 2-14 is the moment resistance for a beam for which $\omega_2 = 1.5$. It is seen that in the elastic region ($M_r \leq \frac{2}{3} M_p$) the full value of ω_2 is realized. In the inelastic region, however, the increase in M_r due to non-uniform moments gradually decreases to zero as the moment approaches M_p.

Wong and Driver (2010) and Driver and Wong (2007) demonstrate that the method for calculating ω_2 specified in previous editions of the Standard produces highly erroneous results in some common situations. To address this shortcoming, their general equation for determining ω_2 based on the moments at the quarter-points of the unbraced segment has been introduced into the Standard. This equation uses a similar method to that specified in the AISC Specification (AISC, 2005), except that it employs a square-root format that produces better results in cases where the ends of the unbraced segment experience moments that are close to those consistent with a rotationally fixed condition about the major axis. Wong and Driver (2010) provide a detailed discussion of aspects that affect the accuracy of equivalent moment factors and they compare numerous methods of determining this factor that have been proposed in the literature and that are being used in design standards around the world.

Due to its simplicity and familiarity to Canadian designers, the method from the previous edition of the Standard for determining ω_2 has been retained as an alternative approach for application only to cases where the moment gradient is linear between lateral supports, which is the scenario for which it was originally derived and therefore produces good results. Figure 2-15 illustrates several cases where the method of determining ω_2 based solely on the ratio of the moments at each end of the unbraced segment, κ, may still be used. The quarter-point moment method in the Standard also gives excellent results for linear moment gradients.

The expression for M_u assumes that the beam is loaded at the shear centre. A downward-acting load that is applied below the shear centre stabilizes the beam, whereas a downward-acting load applied above the shear centre destabilizes it. When a downward-acting load is applied to the beam above the shear centre, and the means of applying the load itself provides neither lateral nor rotational restraint to the beam (such as overslung suspended loads, loads from a column bearing on a transfer beam, etc.), there is a destabilizing effect that reduces the moment capacity of the beam. The Standard is now explicit that this deleterious effect must be taken into account. For top flange loading, a simple and conservative effective length approach is provided as an alternative to more accurate methods. For other positions of the load, unusual loading and other support conditions, Ziemian (2010) may be consulted.

Because laterally unsupported closed square and circular sections with $I_x = I_y$ show no tendency to buckle laterally, their moment of resistance is established using Clause 13.5 as emphasized in Clause 13.6(c).

For structural systems utilizing cantilever suspended-span construction (Gerber girders), see Albert et al. (1992) and Essa and Kennedy (1994(a), 1994(b), 1995).

For members bent about both principal axes, it should be remembered that M_{ry} is either M_{yy} or M_{yp} as a function of the class of the section, because there is no reduction for lateral–torsional buckling for weak axis buckling.

Clause 13.6(e) is new in this edition of the Standard, and it addresses beams that are generally I-shaped and are symmetric about the web's centreline, but which have flanges of unequal sizes, or only one flange (tee sections). In these sections, the shear centre is not coincident with the centroid of the section, and the smaller flange has higher stresses than the larger flange. The effects of these asymmetries are accounted for in the β_x term. The expression provided for β_x is an approximation of the complete expression,

$$\beta_x = \frac{1}{I_x}\int_A y(x^2 + y^2)dA - 2y_o$$

where x and y are coordinates on the cross-section based on an origin located at the geometric centroid, and y_o is the distance in the y-direction from the centroid to the shear centre. An approximate value for the warping torsional constant, C_w, is also provided in this clause. A more thorough treatment of monosymmetric beams can be found in Ziemian (2010).

Sections that have large differences in flange size may experience yielding of the smaller flange under service loads, if designed as Class 1 or Class 2 beams and the factored moment resistance is near ϕM_p. The maximum moment caused by the applied service loads must be less than the smaller M_y value to prevent permanent deformations from occurring during service conditions.

The method of strength determination generally follows the AISC (2005) methodology, with the exception that the elastic buckling capacity is determined considering the distribution of moments. This approach requires finding two lengths, L_{yr} and L_u, for beams that are in the inelastic buckling regime. L_{yr} is the length at which the elastic buckling moment, M_u, reaches M_{yr} and causes the initiation of yielding; i.e., the extreme fibre reaches $0.70\,F_y$, and yielding would occur in regions where residual stresses reach 30% of yield. The smaller value of S_x is used to determine M_{yr} (corresponding to yielding of the smaller flange). L_{yr} can be determined by any method, such as iterative approximations, but can be found via a direct solution with the following equation:

$$L_{yr} = \sqrt{\frac{(2P\beta_x + Q) + \sqrt{(2P\beta_x + Q)^2 + 4RP^2}}{2P^2}}$$

where $P = \dfrac{1.4F_y S_{x,min}}{\omega_3 \pi^2 EI_y}$, $Q = \dfrac{4GJ}{\pi^2 EI_y}$, and $R = \dfrac{4C_w}{I_y}$.

The other length, L_u, is the length at which the beam can carry its fully braced capacity, either M_p or M_y, depending on its local buckling classification. The value of:

$$1.1r_t\sqrt{E/F_y}$$

is based on work by White and Jung (2004). The term r_t is the radius of gyration of the tee-shaped area formed by the compression flange, and one-third of the portion of the web in compression as defined by the elastic neutral axis. Inelastic buckling capacity is determined by linear interpolation between M_{yr} and M_p (or M_y), based on the unbraced length of beam, L.

The value of ω_3 for tee sections must be less than or equal to 1.0. This is because reverse curvature in these beams is a worse condition than a uniform moment (Attard and Lawther, 1989), which is different from the case for doubly-symmetric sections. The warping torsional constant for tee sections should be taken as zero.

For monosymmetric sections other than those described above, a rational method must be used.

13.7 Lateral Bracing for Members in Structures Analyzed Plastically

See the Commentary on Clause 8.3.2(c). This clause is now consistent with seismic requirements.

13.8 Axial Compression and Bending

This Clause remains unchanged in the 2009 edition. Beam-column design is based on the assumption that the designer will first start by performing a second-order analysis.

(a) A distinction is made between braced and unbraced frames in that the design requirements for beam-columns are different for the two types of frames. Clause 13.8.1, based on Eurocode 3, states that a frame can be considered braced if it is five times as stiff as the same frame having moment-resisting connections instead of the bracing.

(b) Cross-sectional strength never governs for prismatic beam-columns in unbraced frames and need not be checked because it will never be smaller than the in-plane strength or the lateral-torsional buckling strength. Parenthetic statements in Clauses 13.8.2(a) and 13.8.3(a) waive this check.

(c) P-δ effects, related to the member deformation between the ends, have been found to be negligible for beam-columns in unbraced frames. This is because the maximum second-order elastic moment, including P-Δ (sway) effects, occurs at the ends of the beam-column. Therefore the factor U_1 is taken as 1.0 in the interaction equation for overall member strength of sway (unbraced) beam-columns in Clauses 13.8.2(b) and

(c) and 13.8.3.(b) and (c) (The P-δ effects continue to be considered for non-sway beam-columns).

(d) For weak-axis bending, the in-plane strength interaction equation introduced in Clause 13.8.2 with a factor β accounts more accurately for the effect of distributed plasticity on stability, by fitting the plastic-zone strength curves for different values of λ_y more closely. β increases from 0.6 when $\lambda_y = 0$ to 0.85 for values of λ_y greater than 0.625 where the distributed plasticity has a greater effect on the overall weak-axis stiffness.

For a general discussion of all aspects of Clause 13.8 and worked examples, see Essa and Kennedy (2000).

The value each term in the interaction equation takes is prescribed in the three sub-clauses (a), (b), and (c) depending on the particular mode of failure: cross-sectional strength, overall member strength, and lateral-torsional buckling strength, respectively. Clause 13.8.2 is applicable to Class 1 and Class 2 sections of I-shaped members while Clause 13.8.3 is applicable to all other classes of sections.

The interaction expressions account for the following:

- a laterally supported member fails when it reaches its in-plane moment capacity, reduced for the presence of axial load;
- a laterally unsupported member may fail by lateral-torsional buckling or a combination of weak-axis buckling and lateral buckling;
- a relatively short member can reach its full cross-sectional strength whether it is laterally supported or not;
- when subjected to axial load only, the axial compressive resistance, C_r, depends on the maximum slenderness ratio – below the yield load, the column fails by buckling. Column buckling is a bifurcation problem, not a bending strength problem;
- members bent about the weak axis, or with the same strength about both axes, do not exhibit out-of-plane behaviour,
- a constant moment has the most severe effect on in-plane behaviour. Other moment diagrams can be replaced by equivalent moment diagrams of reduced but uniform intensity;
- a constant moment has the most severe effect on the lateral-torsional buckling behaviour. (See commentary on Clause 13.6). This effect disappears if the member is short enough, in which case, cross-sectional strength controls; and
- moments may be amplified by axial loads increasing the deflections, the P-δ effect.

Four modes of failure, including local buckling of plate elements, are to be checked in design, as appropriate. They are addressed as follows:

1) Local buckling of an element

Before assessing the member failure modes, the element b/t ratios are checked to confirm the class of the section, the appropriate cross-sectional moment and axial compressive resistances, and to ensure local buckling does not occur prematurely.

2) Strength of the cross-section

The cross-sectional strength of a shape used as a beam-column is not to be exceeded. Clause 13.8.2(a) gives the cross-sectional strength requirements for Class 1 and Class 2 sections of I-shaped members and Clause 13.8. 3 (a) for all other classes of sections. The cross-sectional

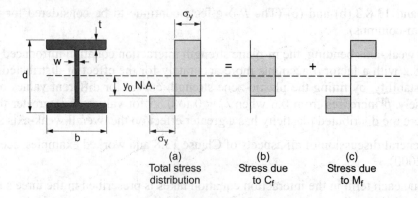

Figure 2-16
Idealized Stress Distribution in Plastified Section of Beam-Column

strength is also the limiting strength of short members. For prismatic beam-columns in un-braced frames, the cross-sectional strength never governs the design and need not be checked.

The cross-sectional strength of a Class 1 and Class 2 I-shaped section comprising relatively stocky plate elements is derived from the fully plastic stress distribution of the cross-section as shown in Figure 2-16. For uniaxial bending about the x-x axis and the y-y axis, expressions are respectively, using the limit states notation of this Standard:

$$M_{fx} = 1.18 \phi M_{px} \left(1 - \frac{C_f}{\phi A F_y} \right) \leq \phi M_{px}$$

$$M_{fy} = 1.67 \phi M_{py} \left(1 - \frac{C_f}{\phi A F_y} \right) \leq \phi M_{py}$$

Transposing the terms in the above expressions gives:

$$\frac{C_f}{\phi C_y} + 0.85 \frac{M_{fx}}{\phi M_{px}} \leq 1.0; \quad \frac{M_{fx}}{\phi M_{px}} \leq 1.0$$

$$\frac{C_f}{\phi C_y} + 0.6 \frac{M_{fy}}{\phi M_{py}} \leq 1.0; \quad \frac{M_{fy}}{\phi M_{py}} \leq 1.0$$

as shown in Figure 2-17. For biaxial bending it is conservative to combine these expressions linearly to give, using the limit states notation of this Standard:

$$\frac{C_f}{\phi C_y} + 0.85 \frac{M_{fx}}{\phi M_{px}} + 0.6 \frac{M_{fy}}{\phi M_{py}} \leq 1.0; \quad \frac{M_{fx}}{\phi M_{px}} + \frac{M_{fy}}{\phi M_{py}} \leq 1.0$$

This is identical to the two expressions in Clause 13.8.2 when, in the latter in accordance with Clause 13.8.2(a) for cross-sectional strength, U_{1x} and U_{1y} are set equal to 1.0, $C_r = \phi A F_y$ when $\lambda = 0$, $\beta = 0.6$ when $\lambda = 0$, and M_{rx} and M_{ry} are equal to ϕM_{px} and ϕM_{py}, respectively.

For uniaxial bending of sections other than Class 1 and Class 2 I-sections, the appropriate interaction expression is:

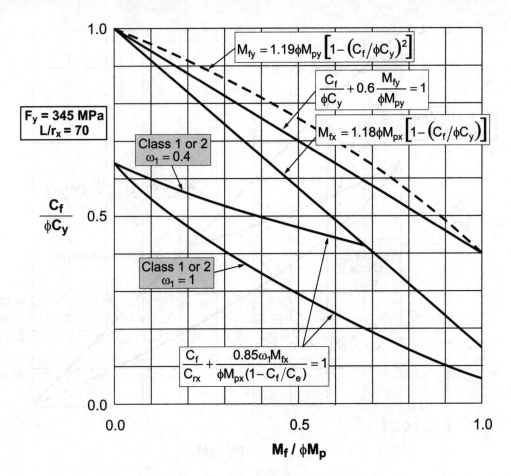

Figure 2-17
Interaction Expressions for Class 1 and Class 2 W-Shapes

$$\frac{C_f}{\phi\,C_y} + \frac{M_{fx}}{M_{rx}} \le 1.0$$

Extending this linear expression to biaxial bending gives:

$$\frac{C_f}{\phi\,C_y} + \frac{M_{fx}}{M_{rx}} + \frac{M_{fy}}{M_{ry}} \le 1.0$$

This agrees with Clause 13.8.3(a) when the appropriate values of the factored cross-sectional resistance quantities are used. Thus, for Class 3 sections the factored moment resistances are limited to ϕM_y and for Class 4 sections the resistances, C_r, M_{rx}, and M_{ry}, are based on local buckling.

3) Overall member strength

The overall strength (in-plane bending strength) of a member depends on its slenderness. As an actual beam-column has length, the axial compressive resistance, C_r, depends on its slenderness ratio and will be less than or equal to the yield load. For any particular beam-column, this fraction of the yield load can be established and is illustrated in Figure 2-17 for Class 1 or 2 sections, and in Figure 2-18 for Class 3 sections.

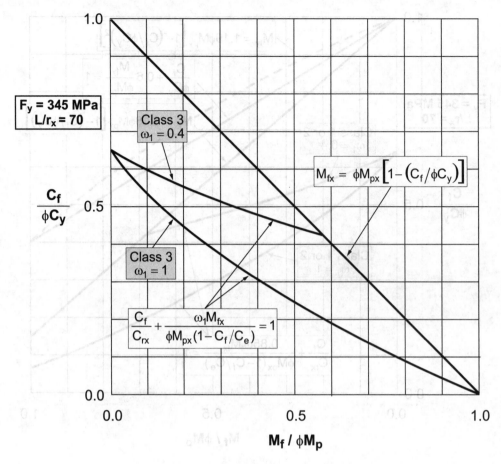

Figure 2-18
Interaction Expressions for Class 3 W-Shapes

In Figure 2-19 the variation in moment resistance in terms of M/M_p as a function of the slenderness L/r_x is plotted schematically as a solid line for a particular laterally supported Class 1 (or Class 2) section subject to a uniform moment about the x axis and carrying an axial load of $0.35C_y$. An appropriate interaction expression for the in-plane strength of such a Class 1 (or Class 2) I-section is

$$\frac{C_f}{\phi\, C_{rx}} + 0.85\, \frac{\omega_1 M_f}{\phi M_p \left(1 - \dfrac{C_f}{C_e}\right)} \leq 1.0$$

which can be deduced from Clause 13.8.2(b) when the terms in that expression are appropriately defined. Note that if the member is short the expression reduces to that for the cross-sectional strength. The compressive resistance, C_{rx}, is a function of the slenderness ratio L/r_x.

The term

$$\omega_1 = 0.6 - 0.4\,\kappa \geq 0.4$$

multiplied by the maximum non-uniform moment, M_f, gives an equivalent uniform moment, $\omega_1 M_f$, having the same effect on the in-plane member strength as the non-uniform moment (Ketter 1961).

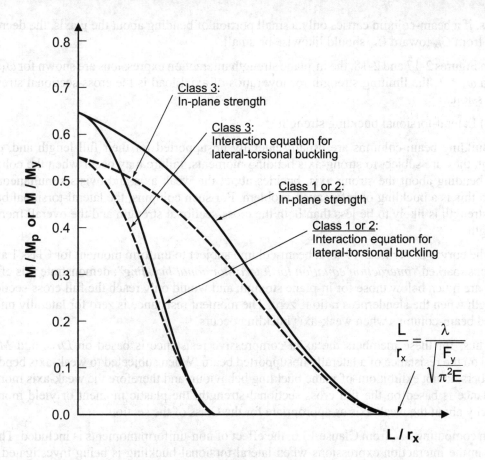

Figure 2-19
Variations of Moment Resistance with Slenderness Ratio

In order to account for the P-δ effects (the amplification of the moments caused by the axial loads acting on the deformed shape), the equivalent uniform moment, $\omega_1 M_f$, is amplified by the factor:

$$\frac{1}{1 - \dfrac{C_f}{C_e}} \quad \text{where: } C_e = \frac{\pi^2 EI}{L^2}$$

The in-plane strength of Class 1 or 2 sections is shown in Figure 2-17 for $F_y = 345$ MPa and $L/r_x = 70$. When $L/r_x = 0$ and $\omega_1 = 1$, the in-plane strength expressions 13.8.2(b) and 13.8.3(b) become the cross-sectional strength expressions 13.8.2(a) and 13.8.3(a), respectively. The curve for Class 3 sections is given in Figure 2-18.

In Figure 2-19, the curve of moment resistance versus slenderness ratio for the in-plane strength of a Class 3 section of equivalent cross-sectional strength to the Class 1 or 2 section is also given. It is similar to that for a Class 1 or 2 section except that, because the cross-sectional strength expression for Class 3 sections does not have the 0.85 factor that is appropriate for Class 1 or 2 and because the Class 3 section can only attain M_y, the curve for Class 3 for zero slenderness ratio reaches only about $0.55 M_p$ and not $0.65 M_p$ as for the Class 1 or 2 sections.

For biaxial bending, C_r is based conservatively on the maximum slenderness ratio. It could be argued that for biaxial bending the value used for C_r be interpolated between C_{rx} and C_{ry} on the basis of the proportion of the interaction fractions for bending about two axes. In other words, if a beam-column carries only a small portion of bending about the y-axis, the decrease in C_r from C_{rx} toward C_{ry} should likewise be small.

In Figures 2-17 and 2-18, the in-plane strength interaction expressions are shown for $\omega_1 = 1$. When $\omega_1 < 1$, the limiting strength for low ratios of axial load is the cross-sectional strength expression.

4) Lateral-torsional buckling strength

Building beam-columns are usually laterally unsupported for their full length and, even though they are subject to strong-axis bending moments, failure may occur when the column, after bending about the strong axis, buckles about the weak axis and twists simultaneously. Again this is a buckling or bifurcation problem. For such columns, the lateral-torsional buckling strength is likely to be less than both the cross-sectional strength and the overall member strength.

The curves in Figure 2-19 for a beam-column subject to uniform moment for Class 1 and 3 sections marked "*interaction equation for lateral-torsional buckling*", demonstrate this effect. They are much below those for in-plane strength and would only reach the full cross-sectional strength when the slenderness ratio is zero. The moment resistance is zero for laterally unsupported beam-columns when weak-axis buckling occurs.

Thus, for these members the axial compressive resistance is based on L/r_y, and M_{rx} is based on the resistance of a laterally unsupported beam. When subjected to weak-axis bending, members do not exhibit out-of-plane buckling behaviour, and therefore the weak-axis moment resistance is based on the full cross-sectional strength, the plastic moment or yield moment capacity about the weak axis as appropriate for the Class of the section.

In computing M_{rx} from Clause 13.6, the effect of non-uniform moments is included. Therefore, in the interaction expressions when lateral-torsional buckling is being investigated, the factored moment, M_{fx}, must also be a non-uniform moment, and not be replaced by an equivalent lesser moment. It is for this reason that the value of U_{1x} cannot be less than 1.0.

13.8.5 This clause gives generally conservative values of ω_1, the factor by which the maximum value of the non-uniform moment is multiplied to give an equivalent uniform moment having the same effect as the applied non-uniform moment on the overall strength of the member. For further discussion on ω_1, see Ziemian (2010) where it is called C_m. Figure 2-20 gives values of ω_1 for some special cases of transverse bending.

Figures 2-21 and 2-22 give additional guidance for the design of beam-columns subjected to various bending moment effects.

13.9 Axial Tension and Bending

The linear interaction expression of Clause 13.9(a) is a cross-sectional strength check. Conservatively, it does not take into account the fact that the bending resistance for Class 1 and 2 sections does not vary linearly with axial force, for which case a factor of 0.85 multiplying the moment term would appear to be appropriate (see Clause 13.8.2).

For members subjected predominantly to bending, i.e. when the tensile force is relatively small, failure may still occur by lateral-torsional buckling. The expressions of Clause 13.9(b) result from that of Clause 13.9(a) when a negative sign is assigned to the tension interaction component and when M_r is based on the overall member behaviour taking lateral-torsional buckling into account.

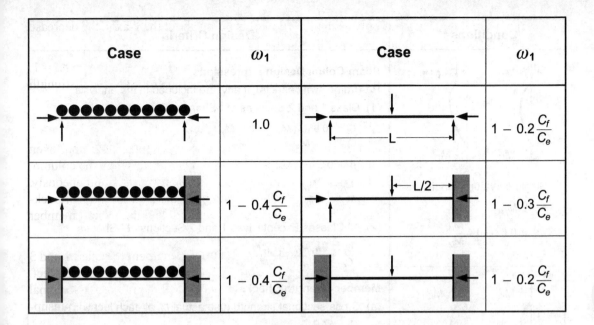

Case	ω_1	Case	ω_1
	1.0		$1 - 0.2\dfrac{C_f}{C_e}$
	$1 - 0.4\dfrac{C_f}{C_e}$		$1 - 0.3\dfrac{C_f}{C_e}$
	$1 - 0.4\dfrac{C_f}{C_e}$		$1 - 0.2\dfrac{C_f}{C_e}$

Figure 2-20
Values of ω_1 for Special Cases of Laterally Loaded Beam-Columns

13.10 Load Bearing

The bearing resistance given for accurately cut or fitted parts in contact, Clause 13.10.1(a), reflects the fact that a triaxial compressive stress state, restricting yielding of the parts in contact, generally exists. The value given is based on earlier working stress design standards, which have given satisfactory results.

For a cylindrical roller or rocker, Clause 13.10.1(b) recognizes that the roller or rocker may rest in a cylindrical groove in the supporting plate. This results in a supporting or contact area larger than that for the case of a flat supporting plate.

In the case of a cylindrical groove in the supporting plate, the maximum shearing stress developed due to a line load of q kN/mm, (Seeley and Smith, 1957) is,

$$\tau_{max} = 0.27\sqrt{\frac{qE}{2\pi(1-v^2)}\left(\frac{R_2-R_1}{R_2R_1}\right)}$$

where v is Poisson's ratio. From this, the unfactored bearing resistance, qL, is then

$$\frac{B_r}{\phi} = qL = \frac{2\pi L(1-v^2)\tau_{max}^2}{0.27^2 E}\left(\frac{R_1R_2}{R_2-R_1}\right)$$

Calibrating this resistance to that given in S16-1969 at $F_y = 300$ MPa gives $\tau_{max} = 0.77F_y$, and

$$\frac{B_r}{\phi} = 0.000\,26\left(\frac{R_1}{1-R_1/R_2}\right)LF_y^2$$

Conditions **	Design Criteria

<table>
<tr>
<td>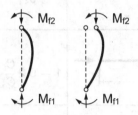
Single curvature bending

$M_{f2} \geq M_{f1}$

$\omega_1 = 0.6 + 0.4\dfrac{M_{f1}}{M_{f2}}$</td>
<td rowspan="3">

Beam-Colum Design Expressions

$P\Delta$ (frame sway effects), if any, are included in the analysis.

(1) Class 1 and 2 Sections of I-Shapes

$$\frac{C_f}{C_r} + \frac{0.85U_{1x}M_{fx}}{M_{rx}} + \frac{\beta U_{1y}M_{fy}}{M_{ry}} \leq 1.0$$

$$\beta = 0.6 + 0.4\lambda_y \leq 0.85$$

$$\frac{M_{fx}}{M_{rx}^*} + \frac{M_{fy}}{M_{ry}^*} \leq 1.0$$

(2) All Classes Except Class 1 and 2 Sections of I-Shapes

$$\frac{C_f}{C_r} + \frac{U_{1x}M_{fx}}{M_{rx}} + \frac{U_{1y}M_{fy}}{M_{ry}} \leq 1.0$$

Member Strength Checks

(a) Cross-sectional strength (use actual M_f at each location)

$C_r = \phi A F_y$

$M_r = \phi Z F_y$ = (for Class 1 and 2 sections)

$\quad = \phi S F_y$ = (for Class 3 sections)

$\quad$ = See S16-09 Clause 13.5(c) for Class 4 sections

M_{rx}^* and M_{ry}^* calculated according to Cl. 13.5 or 13.6 as appropriate

$U_1 = \omega_1/(1 - C_f/C_e) \geq 1.0$

(b) Overall member strength (use M_{f2} for M_f)

C_r = Factored compressive resistance (max. slenderness, K = 1),

$\quad$ Cl. 13.3, except C_r based on axis of bending for uniaxial bending

M_r = as given for M_r in (a) above

$U_1 = \omega_1/(1 - C_f/C_e)$, except for unbraced frames $U_1 = 1.0$

(c) Lateral-torsional buckling strength (use M_{f2} for M_f)

C_r = Factored compressive resistance (max. slenderness), Cl. 13.3

M_{rx} = value given by Clause 13.6

M_{ry} = as given for M_r in (a) above

For braced frames:

$\quad U_{1x} = \omega_{1x}/(1 - C_f/C_{ex}) \geq 1.0$

$\quad U_{1y} = \omega_{1y}/(1 - C_f/C_{ey})$

For unbraced frames:

$\quad U_{1x} = U_{1y} = 1.0$

</td>
</tr>
<tr>
<td>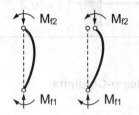
Single curvature bending

$M_{f1} = 0$

$\omega_1 = 0.6$</td>
</tr>
<tr>
<td>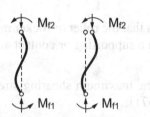
Double curvature bending

$M_{f2} \geq M_{f1}$

$\omega_1 = 0.6 - 0.4\dfrac{M_{f1}}{M_{f2}} \geq 0.4$</td>
</tr>
</table>

C_f = Factored compressive load	ω_1 = Coefficient used to determine equivalent uniform
C_r = Factored compressive resistance	column bending effect (x-x or -y-y)
M_f = Factored bending moment (x-x or y-y axis)	U_1 = Factor to account for moment gradient and mem-
M_r or M_r^* = Fact. moment resistance (x-x or y-y axis)	ber curvature second-order effects

** Moments M_{f1} and M_{f2} may be applied about one or both axes.

Figure 2-21
Prismatic Beam-Columns – Moments at Ends – No Transverse Loads

Conditions **	Design Criteria
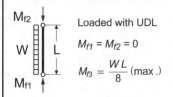 Loaded with UDL $M_{f1} = M_{f2} = 0$ $M_{f3} = \dfrac{WL}{8}$ (max.)	**Beam-Colum Design Expressions** $P\Delta$ (frame sway effects), if any, are included in the analysis. (1) Class 1 and 2 Sections of I-Shapes $$\frac{C_f}{C_r} + \frac{0.85 U_{1x} M_{fx}}{M_{rx}} + \frac{\beta U_{1y} M_{fy}}{M_{ry}} \le 1.0$$ $\beta = 0.6 + 0.4\lambda_y \le 0.85$ $$\frac{M_{fx}}{M_{rx}{}^*} + \frac{M_{fy}}{M_{ry}{}^*} \le 1.0$$
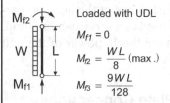 Loaded with UDL $M_{f1} = 0$ $M_{f2} = \dfrac{WL}{8}$ (max.) $M_{f3} = \dfrac{9WL}{128}$	(2) All Classes Except Class 1 and 2 Sections of I-Shapes $$\frac{C_f}{C_r} + \frac{U_{1x} M_{fx}}{M_{rx}} + \frac{U_{1y} M_{fy}}{M_{ry}} \le 1.0$$
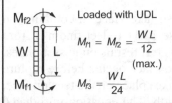 Loaded with UDL $M_{f1} = M_{f2} = \dfrac{WL}{12}$ (max.) $M_{f3} = \dfrac{WL}{24}$	**Member Strength Checks** (a) Cross-sectional strength (use actual M_f at each location) $C_r = \phi A F_y$ $M_r = \phi Z F_y$ = (for Class 1 and 2 sections) $= \phi S F_y$ = (for Class 3 sections) $= $ See S16-09 Clause 13.5(c) for Class 4 sections $M_{rx}{}^*$ and $M_{ry}{}^*$ calculated according to Cl. 13.5 or 13.6 as appropriate $U_1 = \omega_1/(1 - C_f/C_e) \ge 1.0$
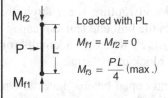 Loaded with PL $M_{f1} = M_{f2} = 0$ $M_{f3} = \dfrac{PL}{4}$ (max.)	(b) Overall member strength (use M_{max} for M_f) $C_r = $ Factored compressive resistance (max. slenderness, K = 1), $\quad\quad$ Cl. 13.3, except C_r based on axis of bending for uniaxial bending $M_r = $ as given for M_r in (a) above $U_1 = \omega_1/(1 - C_f/C_e)$, except for unbraced frames $U_1 = 1.0$
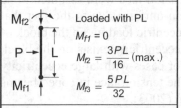 Loaded with PL $M_{f1} = 0$ $M_{f2} = \dfrac{3PL}{16}$ (max.) $M_{f3} = \dfrac{5PL}{32}$	(c) Lateral-torsional buckling strength (use M_{max} for M_f) $C_r = $ Factored compressive resistance (max. slenderness), Cl. 13.3 $M_{rx} = $ value given by Clause 13.6 $M_{ry} = $ as given for M_r in (a) above
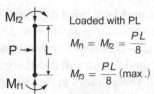 Loaded with PL $M_{f1} = M_{f2} = \dfrac{PL}{8}$ $M_{f3} = \dfrac{PL}{8}$ (max.)	For braced frames: $U_{1x} = \omega_{1x}/(1 - C_f/C_{ex}) \ge 1.0$ $U_{1y} = \omega_{1y}/(1 - C_f/C_{ey})$ For unbraced frames: $U_{1x} = U_{1y} = 1.0$

$C_f = $ Factored compressive load	$\omega_1 = $ Coefficient used to determine equivalent uniform
$C_r = $ Factored compressive resistance	$\quad\quad$ column bending effect (x-x or -y-y)
$M_f = $ Factored bending moment (x-x or y-y axis)	$U_1 = $ Factor to account for moment gradient and mem-
M_r or $M_r{}^* = $ Fact. moment resistance (x-x or y-y axis)	$\quad\quad$ ber curvature second-order effects

** Moments M_{f1} and M_{f2} may be applied about one or both axes.

Figure 2-22
Prismatic Beam-Columns with Transverse Loads

For a flat plate, the "Hertz" solution, as reported by Manniche and Ward-Hall (1975), gives the *allowable* load as

$$2.86 \, DL\frac{(2.7F_y)^2}{E} = 0.00020R_1LF_y^2$$

and indicates that the value of $0.00026 \, R_1$ obtained by calibration with the existing standard for a yield stress of about 300 MPa is somewhat conservative.

This is confirmed by Kennedy and Kennedy (1987) who reported that at this load no permanent deformation resulted and recommended that this value be used as a serviceability limit. They also reported that the rolling resistance of rollers varied as the fourth power of the unit normal load in kN/mm.

13.11 Block Shear – Tension Member, Beam, and Plate Connections

Tension fracture, which is discussed in Clause 13.2, can also take place in combination with shear. The new provisions for block shear failure in Clause 13.11 reflect findings from recent research (Driver *et al.* 2003). An examination of numerous test results on gusset plates, coped beams, angles and tees indicated that rupture on the tension face occurs before rupture on the shear face of the block of material. In fact, when rupture takes place on the tension face, the shear stress on the gross shear area exceeds the yield strength. The equation introduced in S16-09 uses a shear stress equal to the average of the yield and rupture shear strength, $0.6\left[(F_y+F_u)/2\right]$, on the gross shear area, A_{gv}. This term also gives the bolt end tear-out capacity (Cai and Driver, 2010). The tension component consists of $U_t A_n F_u$ where U_t accounts for the uniformity of the stress distribution on the tension face of the block of material.

Block shear tear out of angles, tees connected by the stem and coped beams have shown lower resistance than would be expected if the stress on the tension face were assumed to be uniform. In these cases the tensile stress is expected to be non-uniform due to the fact that only one shear face exists in all these cases, thus resulting in eccentric loading on the block of material. Values of U_t vary from 1.0 for cases where no load eccentricity exists on the block of material (e.g. block shear tear out of gusset plates) to 0.3 for cases with large eccentricity (coped beams with two lines of bolts). The low efficiency of the tension face in coped beams with two lines of bolts was noted in the work of Franchuk *et al.* (2003).

As illustrated in Figure 2-23, the block shear failure of structural tees can take various forms (Epstein and Stamberg, 2002) depending on whether the tee section is flange-connected or stem-connected. The first mode associated to flange-connected tees consists of tension and shear failure confined in the flange only. The other two block shear modes associated to flange-connected tees involve a tension plane in the flange (with or without shear planes in the flange) and a shear plane in the stem. The various possible modes should be investigated.

Recommended values of U_t for various connection details are given in Figure 2-24.

13.12 Bolts

13.12.1 Bolts in Bearing-Type Connections

13.12.1.2 Bolts in Bearing and Shear

In bearing-type connections (Clause 13.12.1.2(a)) excessive deformation in front of the loaded edge of the bolt hole may occur. Tests have shown (Munse 1959; Jones, 1958; de Back and de Jong 1968; Hirano 1970) that the ratio of the bearing stress (B_r/dt) to the ultimate tensile

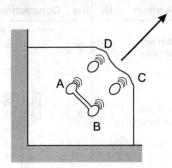

(a) Block Shear Failure of Gusset Plate

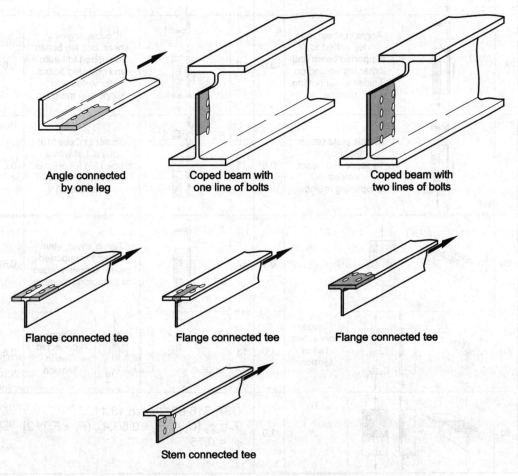

Angle connected
by one leg

Coped beam with
one line of bolts

Coped beam with
two lines of bolts

Flange connected tee

Flange connected tee

Flange connected tee

Stem connected tee

(b) Block Shear Failure of Angles, Coped Beams and Tees

Figure 2-23

strength of the plate (F_u) is in the same ratio as the end distance of the bolt (e) to its diameter (d). Thus,

$$\frac{B_r}{\phi d t} = \frac{e}{d} F_u$$

No.	Connections subject to block shear		U_t	No.	Connections subject to block shear		U_t
1	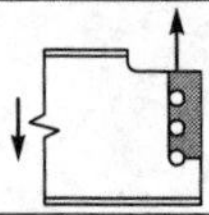	Coped beam with one row of bolts	0.9	7	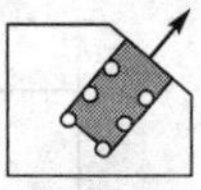	Gusset plate, symmetrical block and uniform tensile stresses	1.0
2	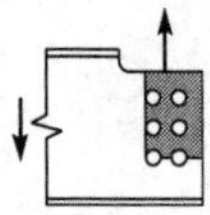	Coped beam with two rows of bolts	0.3	8	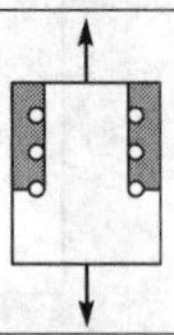	End plate welded to supported beam, bolted to supporting member	0.9
3	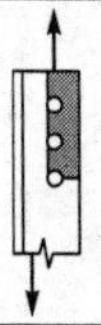	Angle in tension connected to one leg	0.6	9	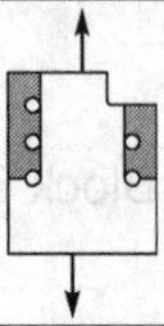	Similar to Case "8" above but with a clipped corner for erection safety	0.9
4	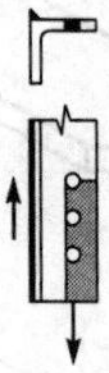	Angle in shear, one leg bolted to supported beam and other leg welded on 3 sides to supporting member	0.6	10	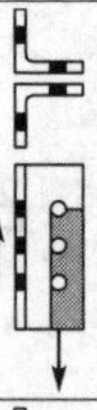	Double angles in shear, one leg bolted to supported beam and other leg bolted (or welded) to supporting member	0.6
5	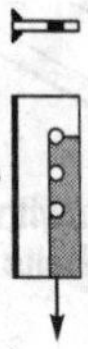	Single plate (shear tab) bolted to supported beam, welded to supporting member	0.6	11	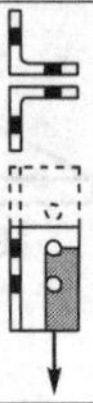	Similar to Case "10" above but with a clipped leg for erection safety (double-sided connection)	0.6
6a	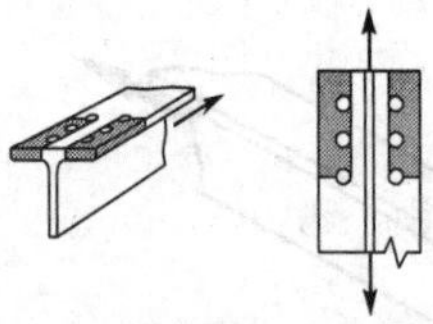	Flange-connected Tee in tension	0.9	12	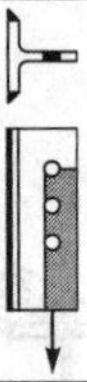	Tee in shear, stem bolted to supported beam, flanges welded to supporting member	0.6
6b	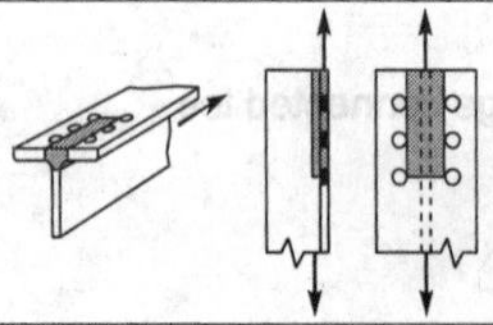	Flange-connected Tee in tension	1.0	13	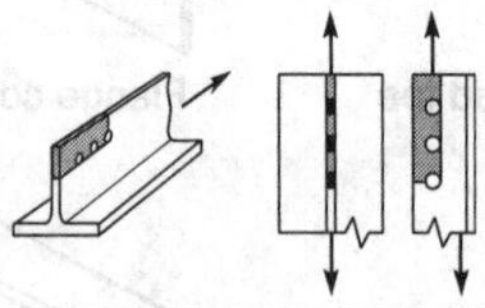	Stem-connected Tee in tension	0.6
6c	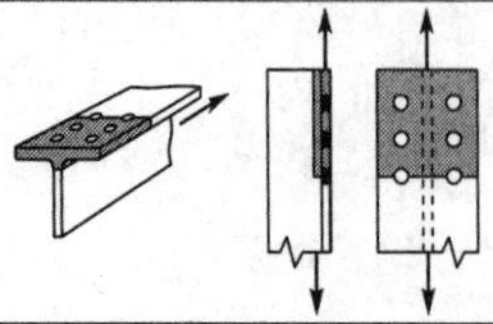	Flange-connected Tee in tension	1.0		CSA S16-09 Clause 13.11: $T_r = \phi_u\,[U_t\,A_n\,F_u + 0.60\,A_{gv}\,(F_y + F_u)\,/\,2]$ $\phi_u = 0.75$		

Figure 2-24
Values of U_t for Block Shear

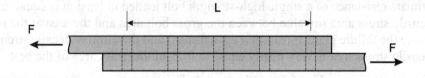

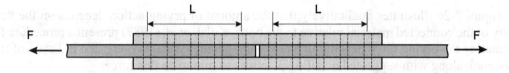

Figure 2-25
Lap Joint Length Definition for Lap and Butt Joints

or, for n fasteners, $B_r = \phi_{br} t n e F_u$

Because the test results do not provide data for e/d greater than 3, an upper limit of $e = 3d$ is imposed. That is,

$$B_r \leq 3\phi_{br} t d n F_u$$

For the bearing of bolts on steel, the value of ϕ_{br} in Clause 13.12.1.2 is to be taken as 0.80. For the bearing resistance perpendicular to long slotted holes, see Clause 13.12.1.2(b).

The note directs designers to Clause 13.11, to investigate any potential for block tear-out when the end distance, e, is small and to Clause 22.3.4 for minimum end distances.

Based on extensive testing, it has been established that the shear strength of high strength bolts is approximately 0.60 times the tensile strength of the bolt material. However, if threads are intercepted by a shear plane, there is less shear area available. The ratio of the area through the threads of a bolt to its shank area is about 0.70 for the usual structural sizes.

In the case of long joints, the load is not shared equally among the bolts with those fasteners towards the ends of the joint carrying the largest portion of the load. The step reduction in the 1994 Standard has been replaced by a linear reduction in bolt capacity when the joint length, exceeds $15d$. The reduction factor need not be less than 0.75. This approach is consistent with the European approach.

Note that the length L is that in which the load is transferred from one plate to another. For a lap joint with bolts in single shear, this is the total length between the centrelines of the end fasteners. For a butt joint with two lap plates and the bolts in double shear, it is the "half" length (see Figure 2-25).

In this context, "joint length" refers to an axially loaded connection, such as a lap splice, whose length is measured parallel to the direction of applied force. This clause does not apply to a shear connection at the end of a girder web where the load is distributed reasonably uniformly to the fasteners.

13.12.1.3 Bolts in Tension

The ultimate resistance of a single high-strength bolt loaded in tension is equal to the product of its tensile stress area (a value between the gross bolt area and the area at the root of the thread because the failure plane must intercept a thread) and the ultimate tensile strength of the bolt. The tensile stress area is very nearly equal to 0.75 of the gross area of the bolt.

In addition to the applied load, two other tensile forces – prying action and pretensioning – may act on the bolt and their effects have to be examined. The Standard states, in fact, that the factored tensile force is independent of the pretension but that the tensile prying force shall be added to the external load.

Figure 2-26 illustrates qualitatively that the amount of prying action depends on the flexibility of the connected material relative to the bolts. Kulak *et al.* (1987) present a procedure for calculating the prying force depending on the joint geometry that is presented in Part 3 of this Handbook along with suggested detailing practices to minimize this force.

The statement that the factored tensile force is independent of the pretension derives from Figure 2-27 where before any external load P is applied the bolt pretension is balanced by the plate pre-compression. When the external load is applied without distorting the connected material as shown, or equivalently when the connected material is "stiff", as the external force is increased, the bolt force remains almost constant at the bolt pretension while the contact pressure between the bolted plates decreases. Once the applied force is sufficiently large to separate the plates, the contact pressure goes to zero and the sum of the bolt forces becomes equal to the applied external force. The level of bolt pretension therefore affects the force at which the bolted plates will separate, but it has no effect on the joint tension capacity.

On the other hand, when the external load is applied through some thickness of material causing it to compress, more bolt elongation is required and there is some increase in the bolt tension. Measurements of actual bolt forces in connections of practical sizes have shown that the increase in the bolt force due to the flexibility of the connection is usually only about 5 to 10%. The Standard neglects this. Figure 2-28 depicts possible variations of the tension on a pretensioned bolt as it is loaded with an external load, P, as pretensions, T_0, decrease and in the presence of a prying force, F.

This Standard requires high-strength bolts subjected to tensile cyclic loading to be fully pretensioned and that the prying force not exceed 30% of the externally applied load. Two options are given to calculate the tensile stress range to compare to the permissible values. The first and most difficult takes into account the prying action, the pretension with possible relaxation due to joint deformations and the applied load. The second assumes the range is that due to the applied loads plus prying action. This is obviously conservative as the pretension reduces the applied load stress range.

13.12.1.4 Bolts in Combined Shear and Tension

The expression for the ultimate strength interaction between tension and shear applied to a fastener has been shown to model empirically the results of tests on single fasteners loaded simultaneously in shear and tension. The values of V_r and T_r are the full resistances in shear and tension respectively which would be used in the absence of the other loading. For small components of factored load relative to the resistance in one direction, the resistance in the other direction is reduced only a small amount; e.g., for a factored tension equal to 20 % of the full tensile resistance, the resistance available for shear is only reduced by 2 % of the full value which would be present in the absence of tension.

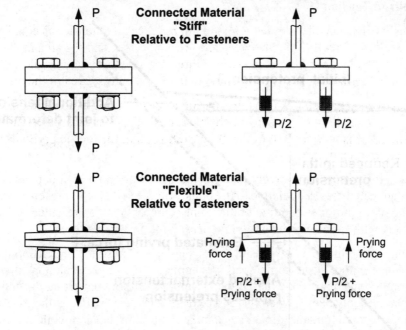

Figure 2-26
Effect of Prying Action on Bolt Tension

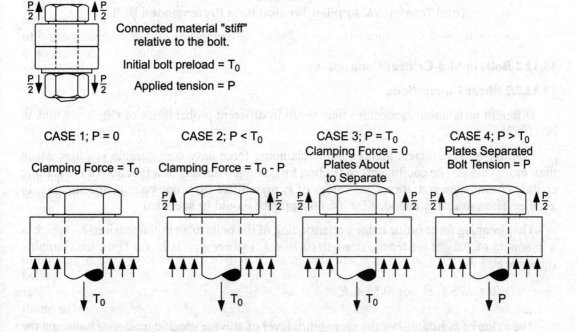

Connected material "stiff"
relative to the bolt.

Initial bolt preload = T_0

Applied tension = P

CASE 1; P = 0

Clamping Force = T_0

CASE 2; P < T_0

Clamping Force = T_0 - P

CASE 3; P = T_0
Clamping Force = 0
Plates About
to Separate

CASE 4; P > T_0
Plates Separated
Bolt Tension = P

Figure 2-27
Effect of Applied Tension on Tightened High-Strength Bolts

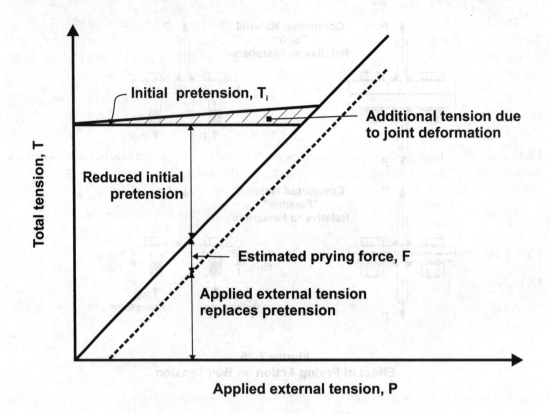

Figure 2-28
Total Tension vs. Applied Tension for a Pretensioned Bolt

13.12.2 Bolts in Slip-Critical Connections

13.12.2.2 Shear Connections

Different installation procedures may result in different probabilities of slip, see Kulak *et al.* (1987).

Both the slip coefficient and the initial clamping force have considerable variation about their mean values. The coefficients of friction for coatings can vary as a function of the specific coating constituents and, therefore, values of k_s may differ from one coating specification to another. The value of k_s intended for use on a project should be specified.

The clamping force is due to the pretensioning of the bolts to an initial tension, T_i, which is a minimum of 70% of the tensile strength $(0.70 A_s F_u)$ where $A_s = 0.75 A_b$. Thus, the clamping force per bolt is

$$0.70 \times 0.75 A_b F_u \quad \text{or} \quad 0.53 A_b F_u$$

The value of c_1 establishes the probability level of slip for specific grades of bolts and the installation method. Table 3 of S16-09 gives values of c_1 for bolts installed by turn-of-nut procedures and for a probability level of 5%. It also provides mean slip coefficients for the three most common cases of surface conditions. Values of k_s and c_1 for many other common situations are given by Kulak *et al.* (1987). For F959 washers and F1852 bolt assemblies, separate c_1 values are given as the clamping loads obtained are lower (but still above the minimum required of the Standard) than those obtained by turn-of-nut procedures.

The use of slip-critical connections should be the exception rather than the rule. They are the preferred solution only where cyclic loads or frequent load reversals are present, or where the use of the structure is such that the small one-time slips that may occur cannot be tolerated. See also Commentary Clause 22.2.2.

The slip resistance is reduced by a factor of 0.75 for slip-critical connections using long slotted holes to account for the reduced clamping force that otherwise would be present (Kulak et al. 1987).

13.12.2.3 The resistance to slip is reduced as tensile load is applied and reaches zero when the parts are on the verge of separation, as no clamping force then remains. The interaction relationship is linear.

The term $1.9/(nA_bF_u)$ is the reciprocal of the initial bolt tension, $0.53\,nA_bF_u$.

13.13 Welds

13.13.1 General

A resistance factor of $\phi_w = 0.67$ is used universally in this section, recognizing that a larger value of the reliability index is used for connector resistances.

When electrodes with ultimate strengths equal to or greater than that of the base metal are used, they are termed "matching electrodes" and, for G40.21 steels, are classified in Table 4. When atmospheric resisting steel grades are used in the uncoated condition, additional requirements for corrosion resistance or colour are also required for matching electrodes.

13.13.2 Shear

In general, the shear resistance of a weld is evaluated on the basis of both the resistance of the weld itself and of the base metal adjacent to the weld: the latter rarely governs. Thus, CJPG, PJPG, plug, and slot welds loaded in shear have resistances equal to the lesser of the weld throat or fusion face shear strength. Recent research involving over 150 tests on fillet welded splices by Ng et al. (2004a; 2004b), Deng et al. (2006), and Callele et al. (2009) showed that even when fillet welds failed at one of the fusion faces, capacities of welds oriented at 0°, 45°, and 90° to the line of action of the applied force that were calculated according to the weld metal capacity only gave test-to-predicted ratios that were always greater than 1.0. Therefore, for fillet welds oriented at an angle greater than about 45°, the base metal check effectively prevents the designer from taking advantage of the full capacity of the weld. Moreover, even when neglecting the base metal check, values of the reliability index of at least 4.5 were obtained. It was concluded by Callele et al. (2009) that the tensile strength of the base metal does not represent the actual tensile strength of the material at the fusion face, which is influenced by intermixing of the weld and base metals, and that unless over-matched electrodes are used the base metal check is not required for the design of fillet welds.

For fillet welds in shear, the resistance of the weld metal is given as a function of the angle between the axis of the weld and the line of action of the force. Callele et al. (2009) showed that when fillet welds with multiple orientations are contained within the same concentrically loaded joint, the lower ductility of the welds oriented closest to 90° prevents the more ductile welds from reaching their full capacity before failure of the joint takes place. The researchers proposed a simple means of accounting for this phenomenon conservatively by reducing the capacities of the more ductile weld segments by 0 to 15%. This method has been adopted into the Standard using the factor M_w.

Using the instantaneous shear centre concept, the resistance expression in 13.13.2.2 forms the basis of the eccentric load tables given in Part 3 of the CISC Handbook (Butler and Kulak

1971, Butler *et al.* 1972, Miazga and Kennedy 1989, Lesik and Kennedy 1990, Kennedy *et al.* 1990). This ultimate strength analysis, recognizing the true behaviour of the weldments, results in much more consistent strength predictions than the traditional approach (i.e., taking the quantity $1.00 + 0.50\sin^{1.5}\theta$ as 1.0).

In the expression for the shear strength of the weld, the factor 0.67 relates the shear strength of the weld to the electrode tensile strength, as given by the electrode classification number. Lesik and Kennedy (1990) give 0.75 for this factor, based on 126 tests reported in the literature. The coefficient 0.50 in the quantity $1.00 + 0.50\sin^{1.5}\theta$ is for tension-induced shear and is slightly more liberal than the average value of tension- and compression-induced shear of 1.42 reported by Lesik and Kennedy. In addition, the factor 1.50 is the correct value for Clause 13.13.3.3 in which tension is the critical case. The value of 0.50 has also been adopted by AWS and AISC.

Clause 13.13.2.3 provides users of the Standard with an expression to determine the factored resistance of flare bevel groove welds for open-web steel joists based on: observed data relating the face width to the effective throat thickness of flare bevel groove welds as reported by Skarborn and Daneff (1998), other data on welds in general from Lesik and Kennedy (1990), and the principles set forth in Galambos and Ravindra (1973). Thus, using $\phi_w = 0.67$ with the effective throat taken as 0.50 of the weld face as selected here leads to a reliability index of 4.25 as determined by Kennedy (2004).

13.13.3 Tension Normal to Axis of Weld

Gagnon and Kennedy (1989) established that the net area tensile resistance, i.e. on a unit area basis, transverse to the axis of a PJPG weld, is the same as for the base metal when matching electrodes are used. The previous conservative practice of assigning shear resistances to these welds was replaced in the 1989 edition with tensile resistances, consistent with the tensile resistance of complete penetration welds equalling the full tensile resistance of the member.

For T-type joints consisting of PJPG weld and a reinforcing fillet weld, Clause 13.13.3.3 provides a conservative estimate of the tensile resistance by taking the vector sum of the individual component resistances of the PJPG and fillet welds.

13.14 Welds and High-Strength Bolts in Combination

This new clause addresses the design of joints in which welds and high-strength bolts are placed in the same shear plane and are expected to share the applied shear force. The provisions are based on the work of Manuel and Kulak (1999) and Kulak and Grondin (2003). The capacity of each connector in this type of shear splice is reflected by its shear strength and shear deformation characteristics. When bolts and welds share the load, the fastener that possesses the least ductility (welds as opposed to bolts or transverse welds as opposed to longitudinal welds) is able to reach its full capacity before the full capacity of the more ductile fastener is fully developed. Therefore, the shear resistance of the joints consists of the full capacity of the least ductile fastener plus a fraction of the capacity of the more ductile fastener. The resistance of the joint is calculated based on the progression of failure from the least ductile fastener to the most ductile fastener. Consequently, the capacity of a typical joint that combines transverse and longitudinal welds and bolts could be limited by (i) the load at which the transverse weld fractures, (ii) the load at which the longitudinal welds fracture or (iii) the load at which the bolts fracture.

When considering case (i), tests by Manuel and Kulak have shown that the ductility of transverse welds is insufficient to mobilize a significant portion of the bolt shear strength, but sufficient to mobilize about 85% of the strength of the longitudinal welds. Case (ii) considers that the transverse weld, if present, has already fractured. In this case, the longitudinal welds are sufficiently ductile to mobilize a significant portion of the bolt shear strength. The work of Manuel and Kulak showed that the portion of the bolt shear strength that is mobilized by the time the longitudinal welds have fractured depends on the bolts bearing conditions at the time that the welds are added to the joint. They made a distinction between the case where the bolts are in full bearing in the direction of the applied load (positive bearing) and the case where the bolts are in bearing in the direction opposite to the applied load (negative bearing).

The results of later tests presented by Kulak and Grondin showed that joints where the bearing conditions are varied randomly could develop at least 50% of the shear strength of the bolts by the time the longitudinal welds fracture. Case (iii) considers the situation where both the transverse and longitudinal welds have fractured. At this point, only the bolts are able to resist the applied load. It should be noted that in cases (i) and (ii) a contribution from the slip resistance can be accounted for when the bolts have been pretensioned in accordance to Clause 23.8. However, in case (iii) no slip resistance is accounted for since the shear deformation in the bolts at the time that their full strength has been mobilized is sufficient to have released their pretension.

Equation (a) of Clause 13.14 considers case (i) described above. For this case only the welds contribute to the shear resistance, plus 25% of the slip resistance if the bolts are pretensioned. The strength of the welds is calculated using Clause 13.13.2.2 for $\theta = 90°$ for the transverse weld segment and $\theta = 0°$ for the longitudinal weld segment. Equation (b) considers case (ii) where the transverse weld has already fractured, and only the longitudinal welds and the bolts are left to carry the load. By the time the ductility of the longitudinal welds has been exhausted, 50% of the shear capacity of the bolts would be mobilized. Equation (c) considers case (iii) where only the bolts are left in the joint. At this stage the limit state is fracture of the bolts, and the strength of the joint is limited to the shear resistance of the bolts or the bearing resistance of the plates against the bolts.

It should be noted that in all the cases tested experimentally, the bolt resistance was always governed by bolt shear rather than plate bearing. Since the bearing resistance usually requires more deformation to develop than the shear resistance, it is possible that the contribution from the bolts may be less than 50% when plate bearing governs the bolt resistance. When bearing governs, the designer may want to use less than 50% of the bolt shear resistance. For typical examples of joint strength calculations, see Kulak and Grondin (2003).

14. BEAMS AND GIRDERS

14.1 Proportioning

Lilley and Carpenter (1940) have shown that reductions of flange area up to 15% can be disregarded in determining the effective moment of inertia, due to the limited inelastic behaviour near the holes.

14.2 Flanges

The theoretical cut-off point is the location where the moment resistance of the beam without cover plates equals the factored moment (Figure 2-29). The distance a' increases as shear lag becomes more significant, as is the case when the weld size is smaller, or when there is no weld across the end of the plate. Theoretical and experimental studies of girders with welded cover plates (ASCE 1967) show that the cover plate load can be developed within length a'. Clause 14.2.4 limits the length of a' for welded cover plates and may therefore necessitate an

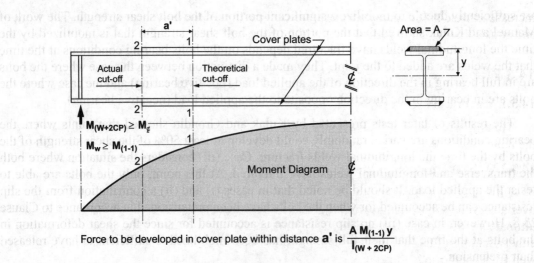

Force to be developed in cover plate within distance **a'** is $\dfrac{A\,M_{(1\text{-}1)}\,y}{I_{(W+2CP)}}$

Figure 2-29
Cover Plate Development

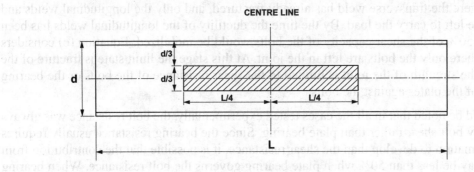

Unreinforced circular holes may be placed anywhere within the hatched zone
without affecting the strength of the beam for design purposes, provided:

1. Beam supports uniformly distributed load.
2. Beam section has an axis of symmetry in plane of bending.
3. Spacing of holes meets the requirements shown below.

SPACING OF HOLES

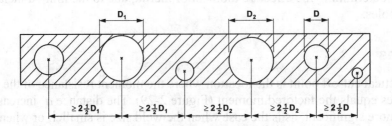

Figure 2-30
Unreinforced Circular Web Openings in Beams

increase in weld size or an extension of the cover plate so that the force at a distance a' from its end equals that which the terminal welds will support.

14.3 Webs

14.3.1 Maximum Slenderness

This limit prevents the web from buckling under the action of the vertical components of the flange force arising as a result of the curvature of the girder, (Kulak and Grondin 2009).

14.3.2 Web Crippling and Yielding

Unstiffened webs of beams and girders carrying loads or reactions concentrated normally over a short length of flange are resisted by compressive stresses in the plane of the web. The ultimate strength of the unstiffened web subjected to such edge loading may be governed by either yielding of the web or by crippling of the web (a localized out-of-plane buckling of the web adjacent to the loaded flange).

If the web is relatively stocky, yielding will occur prior to crippling and expressions 14.3.2(a)(i) and 14.3.2(b)(i) govern web resistances for interior loads and end reactions, respectively.

Relatively thin webs cripple before yielding, and the strength of the web is governed by expressions 14.3.2(a)(ii) and 14.3.2(b)(ii) for interior loads and end reactions, respectively.

The equations presented in the Standard are based on the work of Kennedy *et al.* (1998). These equations are much simplified relative to the 1994 Standard and correlate well with a set of 31 full-scale tests by Benichou (1994) and others at Carleton University. In the expression for web crippling, the contribution of the flange is neglected. It is argued that, at interior load points, the normal stress in the flanges of efficiently designed girders would approach the yield stress at factored loads. Consequently the flanges would not have significant plastic hinge capacity in developing a plastic hinge mechanism in the resistance of transverse loads.

For unstiffened portions of webs, when concentrated compressive loads are applied opposite one another to both flanges, the compressive resistance of the web acting as a column should also be investigated. (See also Clause 21.3)

Care should be taken in assessing the bearing length under yielding or deforming supports such as girders cantilevering over columns.

14.3.3 Openings

The conditions under which unreinforced circular openings may be used are based on Redwood and McCutcheon (1968) and are illustrated in Figure 2-30.

Elastic and plastic analysis to determine the effect of openings in a member are given in Bower *et al.* (1971) and Redwood (1971, 1972, 1973), respectively. See Part 5 of the Handbook for worked examples.

A combination of vertical and horizontal intersecting stiffeners (particularly on both sides of a web) is seldom justified and quite expensive to fabricate. Generally, horizontal stiffeners alone are adequate. When both vertical and horizontal stiffeners are necessary, the horizontal stiffeners should be on one side of the web, and vertical stiffeners on the other, in order to achieve economy.

14.3.4 Effect of Thin Webs on Moment Resistance

A plate girder with Class 3 flanges and Class 4 webs has a maximum moment resistance less than ϕM_y because the Class 4 web buckles prematurely due to the compressive bending stresses. The reduction in moment resistance is based on Basler and Thurlimann (1961). Figure

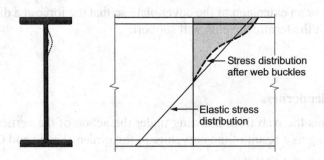

Figure 2-31
Approximate Stress Distribution in Girders with Buckeld Web

2-31 shows an approximate stress distribution in a girder with a buckled web. The reduction in moment resistance is generally small, as shown in Figure 2-32.

The limit of $1900/\sqrt{F_y}$ for the slenderness of a Class 3 web is replaced in this clause by $1900/\sqrt{M_y/(\phi S)}$ to account for the possibility that the factored moment may be less than $M_r = \phi S F_y$, thereby reducing the propensity for web buckling.

In some circumstances, a plate girder may be subjected to an axial compressive force in addition to the bending moment (e.g. rafters in a heavy industrial gable frame, beams in a braced frame). The constant 1900 is then multiplied by the factor $(1.0 - 0.65 C_f/\phi C_y)$ to account for the increased tendency for the web to buckle. The compressive stresses due to the axial load are additive to the compressive stress due to bending, thus increasing the depth of web in compression (see also commentary to Clause 11).

14.4 Bearing Stiffeners

The inclusion of a portion of the web in the column section resisting the direct load, and the assumption of an effective length of 0.75 times the stiffener length, are approximations to the behaviour of the web under edge loading that have proved satisfactory in many years of use.

14.5 Intermediate Transverse Stiffeners

14.5.1 Figure 2-33 illustrates the action of a thin girder web under load. Tension fields are developed in the interior panels but cannot develop in the unanchored end panels, for which the maximum shear stress is, therefore, either the elastic or inelastic critical plate buckling stress in shear.

14.5.2 The limits on stiffener spacing are based on practical considerations. When $a/h > 3$, the tension field contribution is reduced. When $h/w > 150$ the maximum stiffener spacing is reduced for ease in fabrication and handling.

14.5.3 Clause 14.5.3 requires that intermediate transverse stiffeners have both a minimum moment of inertia and a minimum area. The former provides the required stiffness when web panels are behaving in an elastic manner; the latter ensures that the stiffener can sustain the compression, to which it is subjected, when the web panel develops a tension field. Because stiffeners subject to compression act as columns, stiffeners placed only on one side of the web are loaded eccentrically and are less efficient. The stiffener factor (D) in the formula for stiffener area accounts for the lowered efficiency of stiffeners furnished singly, rather than in pairs.

$$\frac{M'_r}{M_r} = 1.0 - 0.0005 \frac{A_w}{A_f}\left[\frac{h}{w} - \frac{1900}{\sqrt{\frac{M_f}{\phi S}}}\right]$$

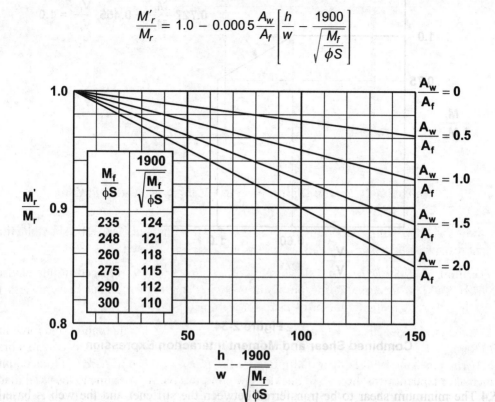

$\dfrac{M_f}{\phi S}$	$\dfrac{1900}{\sqrt{\dfrac{M_f}{\phi S}}}$
235	124
248	121
260	118
275	115
290	112
300	110

Figure 2-32
Reduced Moment Resistance in Girders with Thin Webs

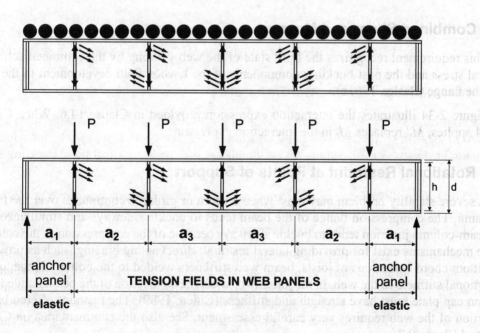

Figure 2-33
Action of a Thin-Web Plate Girder Under Load

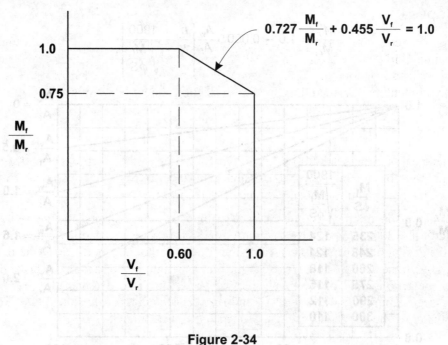

$$0.727 \frac{M_f}{M_r} + 0.455 \frac{V_f}{V_r} = 1.0$$

Figure 2-34
Combined Shear and Moment Interaction Expression

14.5.4 The minimum shear to be transferred between the stiffener and the web is based on Basler (1961c).

14.5.5 The requirement of attaching single intermediate stiffeners to the compression flange is to prevent tipping of the flange under loading.

14.6 Combined Shear and Moment

This requirement recognizes the limit state of the web yielding by the combined action of flexural stress and the post buckling components of the tension field development in the web near the flange (Basler, 1961b).

Figure 2-34 illustrates the interaction expression provided in Clause 14.6. When Clause 14.3.4 applies, M_r' replaces M_r in the interaction expression.

14.7 Rotational Restraint at Points of Support

A severe stability problem may exist when a beam or girder is continuous over the top of a column. The compression flange of the beam tends to buckle sideways and simultaneously, the beam-column junction tends to buckle sideways because of the compression in the column. Three mechanisms exist for providing lateral restraint: direct acting bracing, such as provided by bottom chord extensions of joists, beam web stiffeners welded to the bottom flange, or the distortional stiffness of the web. In the latter two cases, the connection of the beam flange to the column cap plate must have strength and stiffness (Chien, 1989). The restraint offered by the distortion of the web requires very careful assessment. See also the commentaries on Clause 13.6 and Clause 9.2.

14.8 Copes

Flanges are coped to permit beams to be connected to girder webs with simple connections while maintaining the tops of the flanges at the same elevation. Long copes may seriously affect the lateral-torsional buckling resistance of a beam (Cheng and Yura, 1986). The reduced shear and moment resistance at the coped cross-section should be examined.

14.10 Torsion

In many cases, beams are not subject to torsion because of the restraint provided by slabs, bracing or other framing members. The torsional resistance of open sections having two flanges consists of the St. Venant torsional resistance and the warping torsional resistance.

Information on moment–torque interaction diagrams for I-shaped members is given in Bremault *et al.* (2008) and Estabrooks and Grondin (2008). Serviceability criteria will often govern the design of a beam subject to torsion. Limiting the maximum stress due to bending and warping, at the specified load level, to the yield strength guards against inelastic deformation. For inelastic torsion of steel I-beams, see Yong Lin Pi and Trahair (1995). For elastic analyses, see Seaburg and Carter (1997), and Brockenbrough and Johnston (1974). For methods of predicting the angle of twist in a W-shape beam, see Englekirk (1994).

15. TRUSSES

15.1 Analysis

A "pure" truss is a triangulated system with pinned joints and with loads applied only at the joints. This being the case, the members of the truss are axially loaded "two-force" members acting either in tension or compression. Such trusses are now seldom made and the members meeting at a joint are likely welded or bolted together and not infrequently the chords are continuous through several joints. Under these circumstances, when the truss is loaded and the members change length, the geometry of the triangles, including the angles, change resulting in rotations of the joints and end moments develop in the members causing single or double in-plane curvatures. These deformation moments are called secondary moments as they are not due to the primary loading but solely due to the deformation of the truss with rigid joints. Moreover, because the truss members are much stiffer axially than they are flexurally, several researchers (Parcel and Murer 1934, Aziz 1972) have shown that, for steel trusses with rigid welded or bolted joints, after initial elastic behaviour the extreme fibres of the members begin to yield under the axial and bending strains. With further axial straining the moment that can coexist decreases and approaches zero as shown schematically in Figure 2-35, when all the strains in a member (though not uniform) are either in compression or tension. Thus the truss with sufficient ductility, even with rigid joints, behaves as though its members were pin-ended.

Primary moments are moments that can be induced in truss members due to loadings or due to connection geometry. Sometimes, for example, a top chord is used to support a roof deck directly and the transverse loads between joints bend the chord and induce end moments at the panel points which are distributed among the members meeting at a joint with some moments carried over to other joints. Thus, there are primary moments distributed throughout the truss. A common procedure is to analyze such a truss as a pin-jointed assemblage and to add to the forces so found the moments due to the transverse loadings.

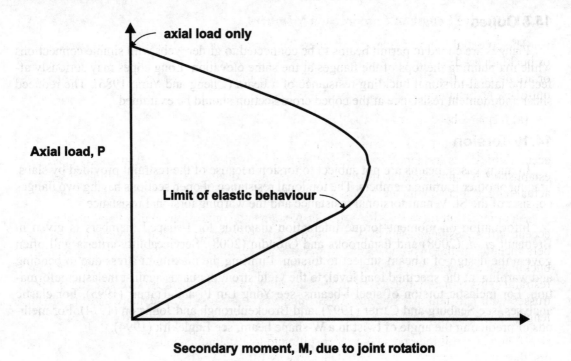

**Figure 2-35
Axial Load – Secondary Moment Interaction Diagram
for a Rigid-Jointed Ductile Steel Truss**

Primary moments are also induced when the centroidal axes of the members meeting at a joint do not intersect at a common point causing a rotation of the joint. These can be analyzed as for the other primary moments, taking the truss members as axially loaded members with the bending moments added. If the trusses with primary moments are analyzed using, say, an elastic plane frame analysis then the stress resultants found will include the axial forces in the members and both the primary and secondary moments. Because the secondary moments for ductile trusses are of little or no consequence, trusses proportioned on this basis will be stronger than they need be.

15.1.1 Simplified Method

The "Simplified Method" of analysis based on pin-connected truss members predicts closely the failure load of the tests even with large rigid connections, provided there is sufficient ductility at the connections so that redistribution of forces and moments may take place at the joints as the failure load is approached. Thus the sections must be at least Class 3. Bending effects of transverse loads applied between joints are simply treated as additional load actions to be carried. Out-of-plane buckling of compression members is conservatively not allowed. Alternatively, though not stated, the reduced strength of the truss because of this failure mode could be taken into account.

15.1.2 Detailed Method

This Clause lists the type of trusses for which the assumption of pin connections is not considered valid. Joint fixity must be considered, and the members must be designed for the combination of axial load and bending.

CISC Commentary on CSA S16-09

15.2.1 Effective Length of Compression Members

The potential failure modes of compression members in trusses are either in-plane bending or buckling modes. The effective length factors are, therefore, either taken to be equal to one or are based on the restraint at the ends. Thus, the following situations arise for in-plane and out-of-plane behaviour.

(a) In-plane behaviour

A compression member with bolted or welded end connections and with in-plane joint eccentricities acts in-plane as a beam-column with axial forces and end moments that can be established. It can be isolated from the structure and is designed as a beam-column based on its actual length, that is, with an effective length factor of 1.0.

A compression member with bolted or welded end connections and without in-plane joint eccentricities, designed as an axially loaded member, has end restraints provided that all members meeting at the two end joints do not reach their ultimate loads (yielding in tension or buckling in compression) simultaneously. The effective length factor depends on the degree of restraint. This typically occurs for trusses in which some members are oversize, for example, trusses with constant size chords. All members do not fail simultaneously and the effective length factors may be less than one.

If, however, all members reach their ultimate loads simultaneously and none restrain others, the effective length factor should be taken as 1.0.

(b) Out-of-plane behaviour

Unless members out-of-plane of the truss exist at the end joints under consideration, the restraint to out-of-plane buckling is small and should be neglected. Provided no out-of-plane displacement of the members' ends occurs, an effective length factor of 1.0 is therefore appropriate.

15.2.2 Joint Eccentricities

When the centroidal axes of the truss members do not intersect at a common point, the Standard requires that the bending moment due to the joint eccentricities be considered in the design.

15.2.3 Stability

Lateral bracing, which provides stability to the compression chords of trusses, must have stiffness and strength to satisfy the requirements of Clause 9.2. Braces must be properly attached to the member being braced and their ends must be fastened to rigid supports.

15.2.5 Web Members

It has been observed, on occasion, in tests of standardized trusses and joists that the first compression web member fails first even though the truss deformations may be quite significant. In these cases, certain chords and webs had been designed to S16 requirements to reach their factored loads more or less simultaneously. Because the tension chord, after yielding in the panel where the bending moment is a maximum, continues to carry load into the strain-hardening range, it overloads itself and the truss. The first compression web member with no such reserve then fails by buckling. By reducing the resistance factors for this member and its connections to 85%, more ductile modes of failure are encouraged at little extra cost. This requirement is also applied to joists in Clause 16.5.8.

In tests of trusses where the bottom chord bears on a reaction, severe bending deformations have been observed near the connections of the end compression diagonal because of the geometric distortion of the truss as deflections increase. The Standard requires that the stresses arising from these bending moments be included in the design of the end diagonal. Thus, the analysis of trusses with the bottom chord bearing must be carried out using the Detailed Method.

15.2.6 Compression Chord Supports

A frequently used rule to provide full support (Winter 1960) is for a brace to have a capacity in the order of 2% of the force in the main compression member.

15.2.7 Maximum Slenderness Ratio of Tension Chords

The slenderness ratio of tension chords is limited to 240 simply to facilitate handling during erection. The exceptions to this are noted in the clause.

16. OPEN-WEB STEEL JOISTS

16.1 Scope

Open-web steel joists (OWSJ or joists), as described in Clause 16.2, are generally proprietary products whose design, manufacture, transport, and erection are covered by the requirements of Clause 16. The Standard clarifies the information to be provided by the building designer (user-purchaser) and the joist manufacturer (joist designer-fabricator).

16.2 General

The distinction between standard and non-standard OWSJ no longer exists as OWSJs are designed specifically for each situation by the joist manufacturer. Those definitions related to joists that are still required are now found in Clause 2 of the Standard.

This clause lists functions that joists may fulfil other than the simple support systems for floors or roofs. These include continuous joists, cantilever joists, joists in lateral-load-resisting systems and support for bracing members.

16.3 Materials

The use of yield strength levels reported on mill test certificates for the purposes of design is prohibited here as throughout the Standard. This practice could significantly lower the margin of safety because any deviation from the specified value has already been accounted for statistically in the bias value – the ratio of the mean strength to the specified minimum value. Thus, all design rules have been, and are, based on the use of the specified minimum yield point or yield strength. For structural members cold-formed to shape, the increase in yield strength due to cold forming, as given in Clause 5.2 of CAN/CSA-S136, may be taken into account provided that the increase is based on the specified minimum values in the relevant structural steel material standard.

16.4 Design Documents

16.4.1 Building Structural Design Documents

The Standard recognizes that the building designer may not be the joist designer; therefore, the building structural design documents are required to provide specific information for the design of the joists. The information to be supplied includes a note that any drilling, cutting or welding has to be approved by the building designer.

Mark	Depth (mm)	Spacing (mm)	Specified Dead Load	Specified Live Load	Specified Snow Load	Specified Wind Load	Remarks
J1	600	1 300	4.0 kPa	2.4 kPa			$\Delta_{live} \leq \dfrac{span}{320}$ Suggested l_{eff} for vibration = _____
J2	700	2 000	8.9 kN 1.5 kN/m 3m ← 12 000 →		4.38 kN/m 10.2 kN/m 3m ← 12 000 →	0.6 kN/m ← 12 000 → -1.5 kN/m (uplift)	$\Delta_{live} \leq \dfrac{span}{240}$

Figure 2-36
Joist Schedule

Uplift and downward wind effects as well as balanced, unbalanced, non-uniform and concentrated loads, are to be shown by the building designer. Figure 2-36 shows a sample joist schedule that could be used to record all gravity loads on joists and any in-plane wind load acting normal to the top chord. Prior to the introduction of National Building Code of Canada 2005, the significance of downward wind effects on roof members depended primarily on the wind-to-snow load ratio. The adoption of load combinations in companion action format in NBCC 2005 eliminated the application of the combination (reduction) factor when wind acts in combination with variable gravity loads. This change resulted in the addition of downward wind effects to snow or live load regardless of wind-to-snow load ratios. The NBCC (2010) requires the internal suction in combination with any external downward wind pressure to be included in the total downward wind effect.

All heavy concentrated loads such as those resulting from partitions, large pipes, mechanical, and other equipment to be supported by OWSJ, should be shown on the structural design documents. Small concentrated loads may be allowed for in the uniform dead load.

The building designer should specify the building Importance Category as defined in the NBCC (2010). Alternatively, the NBCC Importance Factors, I_S, I_W and I_E, as appropriate, and the importance factor for live load (see Clause 6.2.2) when not equal to 1.0, should be specified.

Options, such as attachments for deck when used as a diaphragm, special camber and any other special requirements should also be provided. Where vibration of a floor system is a consideration, it is recommended that the building designer give a suggested effective composite moment of inertia, I_{eff} (Murray et al 1997). Because the depth of joists supplied among different joist manufacturers may vary slightly from nominal values, the depth, when it is critical, should be specified.

When sprayed fire protection is contemplated, reduce clearance by thickness of sprayed fire protection material.

Although steel joist manufacturers may indicate the maximum clear openings for ducts, etc. which can be accommodated through the web openings of each depth of their OWSJs, building designers should, in general, show on the building design drawings the size, location and elevation of openings required through the OWSJs (Figure 2-37). Large ducts may be accommodated by special design. Ducts which require open panels and corresponding rein-

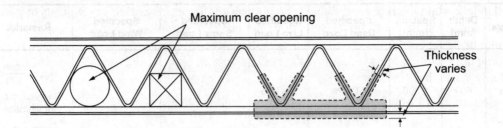

Figure 2-37
Sizes of Openings for Electrical and Mechanical Equipment

forcement of the joist should, where possible, be located within the middle half of the joist to minimize shear problems. This information is required prior to the time of tendering to permit appropriate costing.

Specific joist designations from a manufacturer's catalogue or from the AISC and Steel Joist Institute of the U.S.A. are not appropriate and should not be specified.

16.4.2 Joist Design Documents

The design information of a joist manufacturer may come in varying forms such as: design sheets, computer printout, and tables. Not all joist manufacturers make "traditional" detail drawings.

16.5.1 Loading for Open-Web Steel Joists

Maximum factored moments and shears are established either from the loading conditions in the design documents or from the loading conditions listed in Clause 16.5.1.

These loading conditions are consistent with Section 4.1 and Table 4.1.3.2.A of the National Building Code of Canada (2010). In particular, as required by the National Building Code of Canada, roofs and the joists supporting them may be subject to uplift loads due to wind.

16.5.2 Design Assumptions

The loads may be replaced by statically equivalent loads applied at the panel points for the purpose of determining axial forces in all members. It is assumed that any moments induced in the joist chord by direct loading do not influence the magnitude of the axial forces in the members. Tests on trusses (Aziz 1972) have shown that the secondary moments induced at rigid joints due to joint rotations do not affect the ultimate axial forces determined by a pin-jointed truss analysis.

16.5.3 Verification of Joist Manufacturer's Design

When there is difficulty in analyzing the effect of certain specific conditions, for example a particular web-chord connection, or a geometric configuration of a cold-formed chord, a joist manufacturer may elect to verify the design assumption by a test. In the numerical factor of 1.10 / 0.90, stipulated as a multiplier for the factored loads, the factor of 1.10 provides that the results of limited number of tests bear a similar statistical relationship to the entire series of joists that the average yield strength has to the specified minimum yield strength, F_y, and the 0.90 resistance factor in the divisor increases the test load as is appropriate.

16.5.6 Bottom Chord

A minimum radius of gyration is specified for bottom chord members, when in tension, to provide a minimum stiffness for handling and erection.

Under certain loading conditions, net compression forces may occur in segments of bottom chords and must be considered. Bracing of the chord, for compression, may be provided by regular bridging only if the bridging meets requirements of Clause 9.2. As a minimum, lines of bracing are specifically required near the ends of bottom chords in tension in order to enhance stability when the wind causes a net uplift.

Bottom chord bracing may be required for continuous and cantilever joists as shown in Figure 2-38.

In those cases, where the bottom chord has little or no net compression, bracing is not required for cantilever joists. However, it is generally considered good practice to install a line of bridging at the first bottom chord panel point as shown in Figure 2-38.

16.5.7 Top Chord

When the conditions set out in Clause 16.5.7.1 are fulfilled, only axial force need be considered when the panel length is less than 610 mm (Kennedy and Rowan 1964). In these cases, the stiffness of the floor or roof structure tends to help transfer loads to the panel points of the joist, thus offsetting the reduction in chord capacity due to local bending. When the panel length exceeds 610 mm, axial force and bending moment need to be considered. When calculating bending moments in the end panel, it is customary to assume the end of the chord to be pinned, even though the joist bearing is welded to its support. The stiffening effect of supported deck or of the web is to be neglected when determining the appropriate width-thickness ratio (Clause 16.5.5.1) of the compression top chord.

The requirement in Clause 16.5.7.5, that the flat width of the chord component be at least 5 mm larger than the nominal dimension of the weld, should be considered an absolute minimum. Increasing the dimension may improve workmanship. See Clauses 16.8.5.1 and 16.8.5.2 regarding workmanship requirements when laying and attaching deck to joists.

16.5.7.6

S16-09 stipulates this minimum thickness of joist top chord when the deck is connected to it by mechanical fasteners. Joist top chords that are too thin do not work well with pins or screws.

16.5.8 Webs

The length of web members for purposes of design are shown in Figure 2-39. With the exception of web members made of individual members, the effective length factor is always taken as 1.0. For individual members this factor is 0.9 for buckling in the plane of the web (see Clause G7 of Annex G), but is 1.0 for buckling perpendicular to the plane of the web.

It has been observed, on occasion, in the testing of joists that with critical chords and webs designed to reach their factored loads more or less simultaneously using the S16 requirements, that the first compression web member fails first even though the joist deformations may be quite significant. This appears to happen because the tension chord, after yielding in the panel where the joist bending moment is a maximum, continues to carry load into the strain-hardening range. It overloads itself and the joist. The first compression web member with no such reserve fails by buckling. By reducing the resistance factors for this member and its connections to 85%, more ductile modes of failure are encouraged at little extra cost. This requirement is also applied to trusses in Clause 15.2.4.

Vertical web members of modified Warren geometry are required to resist load applied at the panel point plus a bracing force to preclude in-plane buckling of the compression chord. A frequently used rule to provide full support (Winter 1960) is for a brace to have a capacity in the order of 2% of the force in the main compression member.

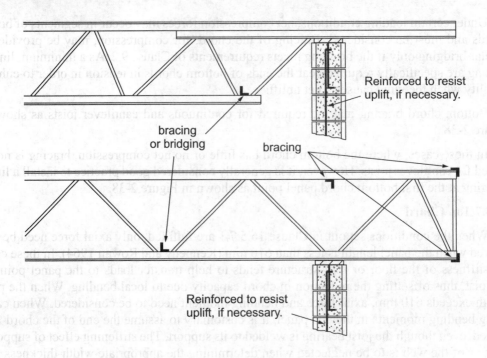

Reinforced to resist uplift, if necessary.

bracing or bridging

bracing

Reinforced to resist uplift, if necessary.

Figure 2-38
Bracing and Bridging of Cantilever Joists

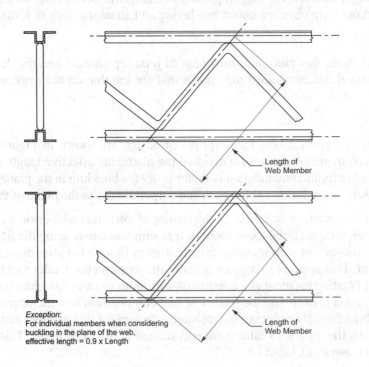

Length of Web Member

Length of Web Member

Exception:
For individual members when considering buckling in the plane of the web, effective length = 0.9 x Length

Length of Web Member

Figure 2-39
Length of Joist Web Members

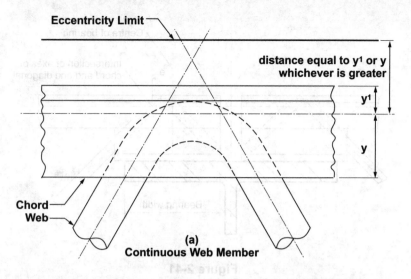

Eccentricity Limit

distance equal to y¹ or y whichever is greater

y^1

y

Chord
Web

**(a)
Continuous Web Member**

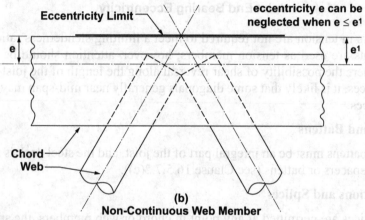

Eccentricity Limit

eccentricity e can be neglected when e ≤ e¹

e

e^1

Chord
Web

**(b)
Non-Continuous Web Member**

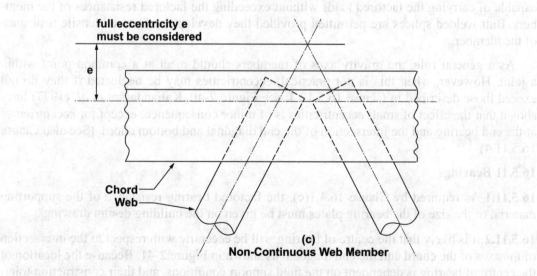

full eccentricity e must be considered

e

Chord
Web

**(c)
Non-Continuous Web Member**

**Figure 2-40
Eccentricity Limits at Panel Points of Joists**

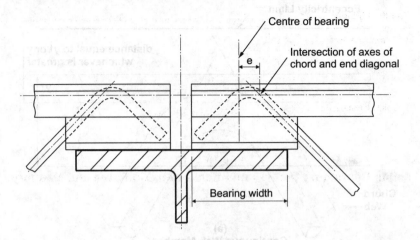

Figure 2-41
Joist End Bearing Eccentricity

Web members in tension are not required to meet a limiting slenderness ratio. This is significant when flats are used as tension members; however, attention should be paid to those loading cases where the possibility of shear reversal along the length of the joist exists. Under these circumstances, it is likely that some diagonals generally near mid-span may have to resist compression forces.

16.5.9 Spacers and Battens

Spacers and battens must be an integral part of the joist, and the steel deck is not to be considered to act as spacers or battens (see Clause 16.5.7.2(c)).

16.5.10 Connections and Splices

Although splices are permitted at any point in chord or web members, the splices must be capable of carrying the factored loads without exceeding the factored resistances of the members. Butt-welded splices are permitted provided they develop the factored tensile resistance of the member.

As a general rule, the gravity axes of members should meet at a common point within a joint. However, when this is not practical, eccentricities may be neglected if they do not exceed those described in Clause 16.5.10.4; see Figure 2-40. Kaliandasani *et al.* (1977) have shown that the effect of small eccentricities is of minor consequence, except for eccentricities at the end bearing and the intersection of the end diagonal and bottom chord. (See also Clause 16.5.11.4)

16.5.11 Bearings

16.5.11.1 As required by Clause 16.4.1(c), the factored bearing resistance of the supporting material or the size of the bearing plates must be given on the building design drawings.

16.5.11.2 It is likely that the centre of bearing will be eccentric with respect to the intersection of the axes of the chord and the end diagonal as shown in Figure 2-41. Because the location of the centre of bearing is dependent on the field support conditions, and their construction tolerances, it may be wise to assume a maximum eccentricity when designing the bearing detail. In lieu of specific information, a reasonable assumption is to use a minimum eccentricity of one half the minimum bearing on a steel support of 65 mm. When detailing joists, care must be taken to provide clearance between the end diagonal and the supporting member or wall.

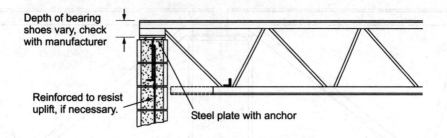

Figure 2-42
Joists Bearing on Steel Plate Anchored to Concrete and Masonry

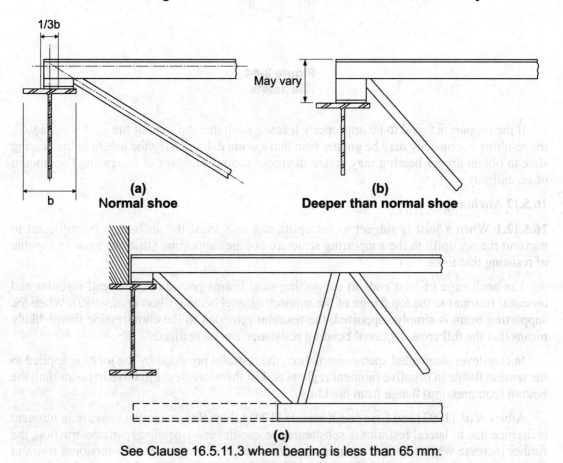

(a)
Normal shoe

(b)
Deeper than normal shoe

(c)
See Clause 16.5.11.3 when bearing is less than 65 mm.

Figure 2-43
Joists Bearing on Steel

See Figure 2-42. A maximum clearance of 25 mm is suggested to minimize eccentricities. One solution, to obtain proper bearing, is to increase the depth of the bearing shoe.

For spandrel beams and other beams on which joists frame from one side only, good practice suggests that the centre of the bearing shoe be located within the middle third of the flange of the supporting beam (Figure 2-43(a)). As the depth of bearing shoes vary, the building designer should check with the joist manufacturer in setting "top of steel" elevations. By using a deep shoe, interference between the support and the end diagonal will be avoided as shown in Figure 2-43(b).

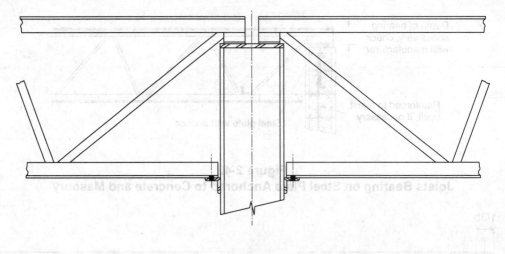

Figure 2-44
Tie Joists

If the support is found to be improperly located, such that the span of the joist is increased, the resulting eccentricity may be greater than that assumed. Increasing the length of the bearing shoe to obtain proper bearing may create the more serious problem of increasing the amount of eccentricity.

16.5.12 Anchorage

16.5.12.1 When a joist is subject to net uplift, not only must the anchorage be sufficient to transmit the net uplift to the supporting structure but the supporting structure must be capable of resisting that force.

The anchorage of joist ends to supporting steel beams provide both lateral restraint and torsional restraint to the top flange of the supporting steel beam (Albert *et al.* 1992). When the supporting beam is simply supported, the restraint provided to the compression flange likely means that the full cross-sectional bending resistance can be realized.

In cantilever-suspended span construction, the restraint provided by the joists is applied to the tension flange in negative moment regions and is, therefore, less effective in restraining the bottom (compression) flange from buckling.

Albert *et al.* (1992) and Essa and Kennedy (1993) show that, while the increase in moment resistance due to lateral restraint is substantial, in cantilever-suspended span construction, the further increase when torsional restraint is considered is even greater. The torsional restraint develops when the compression flange tends to buckle sideways distorting the web and twisting the top flange that is restrained by bending of the joists about the strong axis. The anchorage must therefore be capable of transmitting the moment that develops. For welds, a pair of 5 mm fillet welds 50 mm long coupled with the bearing of the joist seat would develop a factored moment resistance of about 1.8 kN·m

16.5.12.2 The function of tie joists is to assist in the erection and plumbing of the steel frame. Either the top or bottom chord is connected by bolting and, after plumbing the columns, the other chord is usually welded (Figure 2-44). In most buildings, tie joists remain as installed with both top and bottom chords connected; however, current practices vary throughout Canada with, in some cases, the bottom chord connections to the columns being made with slotted holes. Shrivastava *et al.* (1979) studied the behaviour of tie joist connections and concluded that they may be insufficient to carry lateral loads which could result from rigid bolting.

Table 2-1
Camber for Joists

Span	Camber (mm)		
	Nominal Camber	Minimum Camber	Maximum Camber
Up to 6 000	12 +	4	20
7 000	14	6	22
8 000	16	8	24
9 000	18	10	26
10 000	20	11	29
11 000	22	13	31
12 000	24	15	33
13 000	26	17	35
14 000	28	18	38
15 000	30	20	40
16 000	32	22	42

The designation tie joist is not intended to be used for joists participating in frame action.

16.5.12.3 When joists are used as part of a frame to brace columns, or to resist lateral forces on the finished structure, the appropriate moments and forces are to be shown on the building design drawings to enable the joists and the joist-to-column connections to be designed by the joist manufacturer.

In cantilever-suspended span roof framing, joists may also be used to provide stability for girders passing over columns. See also the commentary on Clauses 16.5.12.1 and 13.6.

16.5.13 Deflection

The method of computing deflections is based on truss action, taking into account the axial deformation of all components rather than the former approximate method of using a moment of inertia equal to that of the truss chords and adding an allowance for the "shear" deformation of the web members.

16.5.14 Camber

The nominal camber based on Clause 16.5.14 is taken to vary linearly with the span and is tabulated in Table 2-1, rounded to the nearest millimetre. Manufacturing tolerances are covered in Clause 16.10.9. The maximum difference in camber of 20 mm for joists of the same span, set to limit the difference between two adjacent joists, is reached at a span of 16 000 mm.

16.5.15 Vibration

Annex E of S16-09, Guide for Floor Vibrations, contains recommendations for floors supported on steel joists. By increasing the floor thickness (mass), both the frequency and the peak acceleration are reduced, thus reducing the annoyance more efficiently than by increasing the moment of inertia (I_x) of the joists. For this reason, the building designer should weigh, at the building design stage, the options in the Guide for Floor Vibrations to achieve the best performance.

16.5.16 Welding

Many welded joints used in joists are not prequalified under CSA W59, therefore the certified fabricator must have all these welded joints accepted by the Canadian Welding Bureau (CWB).

16.6 Stability During Construction

A distinction is made between bridging, put in to meet the slenderness ratio requirements for top and bottom chords, and the temporary support required by Clause 16.6 to hold joists against movement during construction. Permanent bridging, of course, can be used for both purposes.

16.7 Bridging

Figures 2-45, 2-46 and 2-47 provide illustrations of bridging and details of bridging connections.

16.7.7 Anchorage of Bridging

Ends of bridging lines may be anchored to the adjacent steel frame or adjacent concrete or masonry walls as shown in Figure 2-48.

Where attachment to the adjacent steel frame or walls is not practicable, diagonal and horizontal bridging shall be provided in combination between adjacent joists near the ends of bridging lines as shown in Figure 2-49. Joists bearing on the bottom chord will require bridging at the ends of the top chord.

16.7.9 Spacing of Bridging

Either horizontal or diagonal bridging is acceptable, although horizontal bridging is generally recommended for shorter spans, up to about 15 m, and is usually attached by welding. Diagonal bridging is recommended for longer spans and is usually attached by bolting. Bridging need not be attached at panel points and may be fastened at any point along the length of the joists. When horizontal bridging is used, bridging lines will not necessarily appear in pairs as the requirements for support of tension chords are not the same as those for compression chords. Because the ends of joists are anchored, the supports may be assumed to be equivalent to bridging lines.

16.8.1 Decking to Provide Lateral Support

When the decking complies with Clause 16.8 and is sufficiently rigid to provide lateral support to the top (compression) chord, the top chord bridging may be removed when it is no longer required. Bottom (tension) chord bridging is permanently required to limit the unsupported length of the chord to $240r$, as defined in Clause 16.7.9.

16.8.5 Installation of Steel Deck

16.8.5.1 Workmanship is of concern when decking is to be attached by arc-spot welding to top chords of joists. When the joist location is marked on the deck as the deck is positioned, the welders will be more likely to position the arc-spot welds correctly.

16.8.5.2 Arc-spot welds for attaching the deck to joists are structural welds and require proper welding procedures.

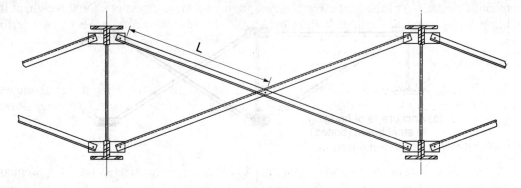

Figure 2-45
Diagonal Bridging of Joists

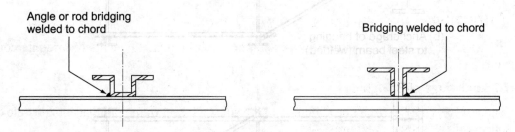

Angle or rod bridging
welded to chord

Bridging welded to chord

Figure 2-46
Horizontal Bridging Connections to the Joist's Top Chord

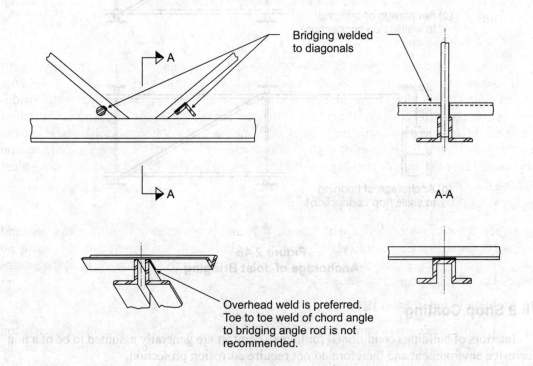

Bridging welded
to diagonals

A

A

A-A

Overhead weld is preferred.
Toe to toe weld of chord angle
to bridging angle rod is not
recommended.

Figure 2-47
Horizontal Bridging Connections to the Joist's Bottom Chord

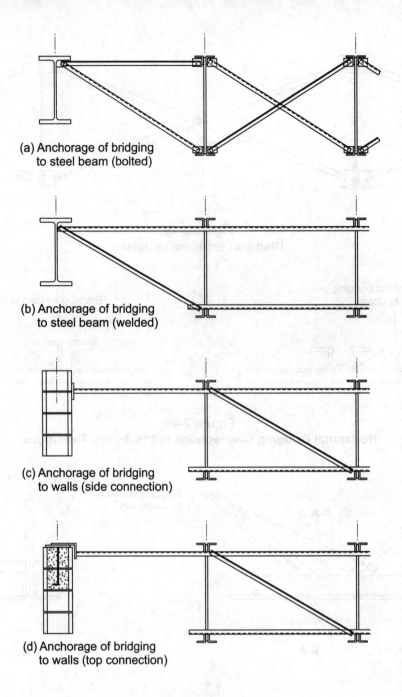

(a) Anchorage of bridging to steel beam (bolted)

(b) Anchorage of bridging to steel beam (welded)

(c) Anchorage of bridging to walls (side connection)

(d) Anchorage of bridging to walls (top connection)

Figure 2-48
Anchorage of Joist Bridging

16.9 Shop Coating

Interiors of buildings conditioned for human comfort are generally assumed to be of a non-corrosive environment and therefore do not require corrosion protection.

Joists normally receive one coat of paint suitable for a production line application, usually by dipping a bundle of joists into a tank. This paint is generally adequate for three months of exposure, which should be ample time to enclose, or paint, the joists.

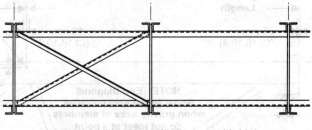

(a) diagonal bridging with horizontal bridging

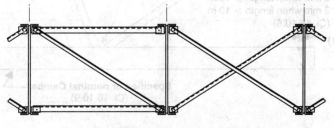

(b) horizontal bridging with diagonal bridging

Figure 2-49
Bracing of Joist Bridging

Special coatings and paints that require special surface preparations are expensive because these have to be applied individually to each joist by spraying or other means. For joists comprised of cold-formed members, surface preparations that were meant to remove mill scale from hot-rolled members are not appropriate.

16.10 Manufacturing Tolerances

Figure 2-50 illustrates many of the manufacturing tolerance requirements.

16.11 Inspection and Quality Control

16.11.3 Quality Control

When testing forms part of the manufacturer's normal quality control program, the test shall follow steps 1 to 4 of the loading procedure given in Part 5 of Steel Joist Facts (CISC 1980).

16.12 Handling and Erection

16.12.2 Erection Tolerances

Figure 2-51 illustrates many of the erection tolerance requirements. The provisions of Clause 16.12.2.5 aim to control the differential deflection between any three adjacent joists to smooth the supported deck's profile.

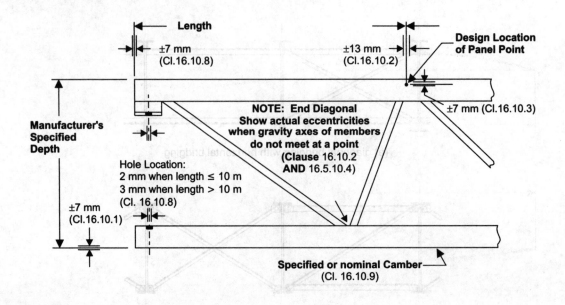

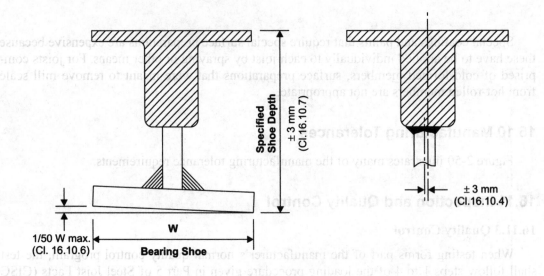

Figure 2-50
Joist Manufacturing Tolerances

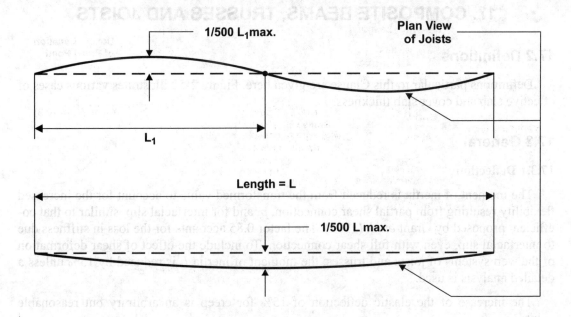

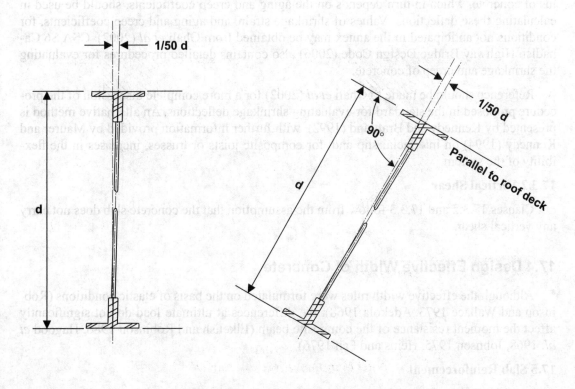

Figure 2-51
Joist Erection Tolerances

17. COMPOSITE BEAMS, TRUSSES AND JOISTS

17.2 Definitions

Definitions particular to this Clause are given here. Figure 2-52 illustrates various cases of effective slab and cover slab thickness.

17.3 General

17.3.1 Deflections

The moment of inertia is reduced from the transformed value to account for the increased flexibility resulting from partial shear connection, p, and for interfacial slip, similar to that co-efficient proposed by Grant *et al*. (1977). The factor 0.85 accounts for the loss in stiffness due to interfacial slip, even with full shear connection. To include the effect of shear deformation of the web systems of joists and trusses, the moment of inertia I_s is reduced by 15% unless a detailed analysis is used.

The increase of the elastic deflection of 15% for creep is an arbitrary but reasonable value.

Annex H of the Standard gives a detailed discussion of shrinkage deflections. There it is emphasized that appropriate values of the shrinkage strain and age-adjusted effective modulus of concrete, which in turn depends on the aging and creep coefficients, should be used in calculating these deflections. Values of shrinkage strain, and aging and creep coefficients, for conditions not anticipated in the annex may be obtained from Ghali *et al* (2002). CSA S6 Canadian Highway Bridge Design Code (2006) also contains detailed procedures for evaluating the shrinkage and creep of concrete.

Reference should be made to Ghali *et al* (2002) for a more complete discussion of the procedure proposed in the standard for evaluating shrinkage deflections. An alternative method is presented by Kennedy and Brattland (1992), with further information provided by Maurer and Kennedy (1994) on interfacial slip and, for composite joists or trusses, increases in the flexibility of the system.

17.3.2 Vertical Shear

Clauses 17.3.2 and 17.3.3 follow from the assumption that the concrete slab does not carry any vertical shear.

17.4 Design Effective Width of Concrete

Although the effective width rules were formulated on the basis of elastic conditions (Robinson and Wallace 1973, Adekola 1968), the differences at ultimate load do not significantly affect the moment resistance of the composite beam (Elkelish and Robinson 1986, Hagood *et al*. 1968, Johnson 1975, Heins and Fan 1976).

17.5 Slab Reinforcement

17.5.2 The effectiveness of the minimum requirement of two 15M bars at the ends of beams supporting ribbed slabs perpendicular to the beam proposed by Ritchie and Chien (1980) has been verified experimentally by Jent (1989).

17.5.3 The longitudinal shear forces generated by interconnecting solid concrete slabs to steel sections, trusses, or joists by means of shear connectors may cause longitudinal cracking of the slab directly over the steel. This effect is independent of any flexural cracking which may

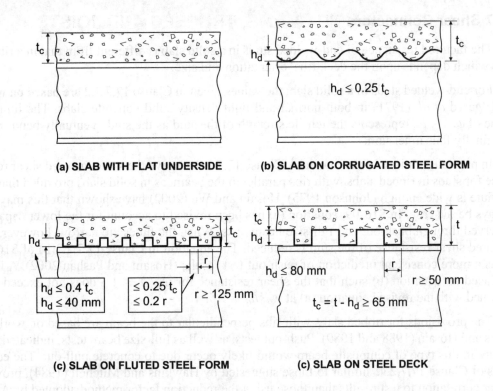

Figure 2-52
Effective Slab Thickness for Composite Beams

occur due to the slab spanning continuously over supports, although the two effects may combine. Longitudinal shear cracking is more apt to start from the underside of the solid slab, whereas flexural cracking is more apt to start at the top surface of the slab. Investigations by Johnson (1970), El-Ghazzi et al. (1976) and Davies (1969) have shown that a minimum area of transverse reinforcing steel is required to improve the longitudinal shear capacity of a solid slab composite beam. The minimum reinforcement ratio is the same as that specified in CSA Standard A23.3 (CSA 2004) for temperature and shrinkage reinforcement in reinforced concrete slabs.

17.5.4 For the reasons given in Clause 17.5.3, a minimum transverse reinforcement ratio of 0.002 is also specified for composite beams with ribbed slab when the ribs are parallel to the beam span. This ratio is reduced to 0.001 when the ribs are perpendicular to the beam span because the steel deck provides a measure of transverse reinforcement. Reinforcement of the cover slab may also be necessary for flexure, fire resistance, shrinkage, or temperature effects.

17.6 Interconnection

When unpainted sections, trusses, or joists are totally encased in concrete as specified, effective interconnection is obtained and no shear connectors are required.

The total sheet thickness and the total amount of zinc coating are limited in order to achieve sound welds.

Tests have shown that a shear connector is not fully effective if welded to a support which is too thin or flexible (Gobel 1968). For this reason the stud diameter is limited to 2.5 times the thickness of the part to which it is welded.

17.7 Shear Connectors

The factored resistance of end-welded studs in a solid slab is different from that in a ribbed slab which depends upon the deck ribs' orientation and size.

For end-welded studs in a solid slab, the values given in Clause 17.7.2.2 are based on work by Olgaard *et al.* (1971) in both normal and light-density solid concrete slabs. The limiting value of $\phi_{sc}A_{sc}F_u$ represents the tensile strength of the stud as the stud eventually bends over and finally fails in tension.

In previous editions of the Standard, Clause 17.7.2.3(a) gave the same factored shear resistance for studs in ribbed slabs, with ribs parallel to the beam, as in solid slabs provided that the rib flute is wide enough (Johnson 1975). Hosain and Wu (2002) have shown that this may not always be the case. In S16-09, equation (a) has been revised to account for the lower capacity observed through push-out and full-size beam tests. When the flutes are narrow, however, the factored shear resistance of the stud is reduced. The equation in Clause 17.7.2.3(b) of S16-09 gives a more consistent prediction of push-out test results (Hosain and Pashan 2002). A limit is placed on equation (b) such that the shear resistance for $w_d/h_d < 1.5$ does not exceed that obtained with the revised equation (a) at $w_d/h_d = 1.5$.

The provisions for ribbed slabs with ribs perpendicular to the beam are based on work by Jayas and Hosain (1988 and 1989). Push-out tests, as well as full-size beam tests, indicated that failure in this type of composite beam would likely occur due to concrete pull-out. The equations of Clause 17.7.2.4, similar to those suggested by Hawkins and Mitchell (1984), provide better correlation to test results than those using the reduction factor method adopted by AISC (1999). Figure 2-53 gives diagrams of the pullout surface area. Pullout areas for specific deck profiles and studs are given in Part 5 of the Handbook.

In order to minimize localized stresses in concrete, the lateral spacing centre-to-centre of studs used in pairs should be not less than four stud diameters. The minimum longitudinal spacing of connectors, in both solid slabs and ribbed slabs with ribs parallel to the beam, is based on Olgaard *et al.* (1971). The maximum spacing limits specified for mechanical ties in Clause 17.8 is applicable to headed studs, as they function in this capacity.

Further information on end-welded studs is found in Johnson (1970), Chien and Ritchie (1984), and Robinson (1988).

17.7.3 The shear value of channel connectors is based on Slutter and Driscoll (1965).

17.9 Design of Composite Beams with Shear Connectors

In order to minimize eccentricities before and after composite action, in composite joists and trusses, the web members should be positioned such that the lines of action intersect at a point halfway between the mid-depth of the cover slab and the centroid of the steel top chord.

17.9.1 A minimum flat width for the top chord of $1.4d + 20$ mm is stipulated to facilitate placement of the shear studs.

17.9.3 The factored moment resistance of a composite flexural member is based on the ultimate capacity of the cross-section (Robinson 1969, Vincent 1969, Hansell and Viest 1971, Robinson and Wallace 1973, Tall *et al.* 1974) where the following assumptions are made:

- concrete in tension is neglected;
- only the lower chord of a steel joist or truss is considered effective when computing the moment resistance;
- the internal couple consists of equal tension and compression forces;

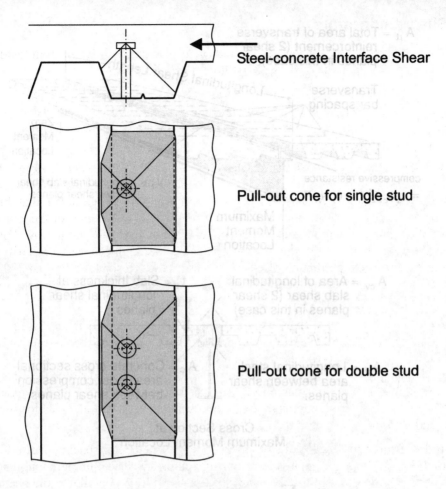

Steel-concrete Interface Shear

Pull-out cone for single stud

Pull-out cone for double stud

Figure 2-53
Pullout Surface Area with Ribbed Metal Deck

- the forces are obtained as the product of a limit states stress (ϕF_y for steel and $\alpha_1 \phi_c f'_c$ for concrete) times the respective effective areas; and,

- to take into account the greater variability of concrete elements strengths, the resistance factor is taken as 0.65 for concrete as compared to 0.90 for steel.

Three design cases are considered:

- Case 1 representing full shear connection with the plastic neutral axis in the slab;

- Case 2 representing full shear connection with the plastic neutral axis in the steel section; and,

- Case 3 representing partial shear connection for which the plastic neutral axis is always in the steel section.

Only Case 1 is permitted when joists or trusses are used to prevent buckling of top chord and overloading of the shear connectors. For Case 3, the depth of the concrete in compression is determined by the expression for "a" (Robinson 1969).

In S16-09, these assumptions have been modified somewhat such that the resistance factor for concrete and the ratio of average stress in the rectangular compression block to the specified concrete strength are consistent with the CSA Standard A23.3-04. Accordingly, $\phi_c = 0.65$

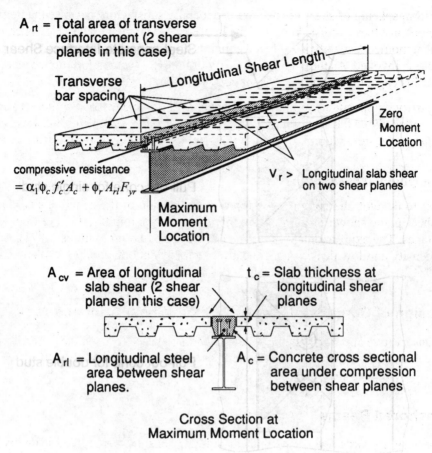

$$V_u = \sum q_r - \alpha_1 \phi_c f'_c A_c - \phi_r A_{rl} F_{yr}$$

$$V_r = (0.80 \phi_r A_{rt} F_{yr} + 2.76 \phi_c A_{cv}) \le 0.50 \phi_c f'_c A_{cv}$$

Figure 2-54
Potential Longitudinal Shear Planes

is used in place of 0.60, and $\alpha_1 \phi_c f'_c$ is given as the concrete strength in place of $0.85 \phi_c f'_c$. Reasoning for these changes to the concrete resistance factor and strength is described by Bartlett (2007).

17.9.4 Robinson (1988) and Jayas and Hosain (1989) show that a lower limit of 40% of full shear connection is acceptable for strength calculations. Below this value, the interfacial slip is such that integral composite action cannot be assured. A lower limit of 25% of full shear connection is used for deflection designs as deflections are computed at specified load levels. This latter provision is used where the flexural strength is based on the bare steel beam, but the increased stiffness due to the concrete is considered for deflection calculations. The concrete strength, $\alpha_1 \phi_c f'_c$, is used in place of $0.85 \phi_c f'_c$ (Bartlett, 2007).

17.9.5 Between the point of zero and maximum moment, a horizontal force associated with the internal resisting couple must be transmitted across the steel-concrete interface. The concrete strength, $\alpha_1 \phi_c f'_c$, is used in place of $0.85 \phi_c f'_c$ (Bartlett, 2007).

17.9.8 Uniform spacing of shear connectors is generally satisfactory because the flexibility of the connectors provides a redistribution of the interface shear among them. However, to ensure that sufficient moment capacity is achieved at points of concentrated load, the second provision of this clause is invoked. As the moment capacity of the steel section does not depend on shear connectors, this capacity is subtracted from both M_f and M_{fl}.

17.9.9 To justify composite action in the end panel of joists and trusses, sufficient shear studs must be provided above the seat or along a top chord extension, to transfer the horizontal shear from the slab to the steel section, otherwise the steel top chord acting alone must resist all the forces.

17.9.10 Longitudinal Shear

In order to develop the compressive force in the portion of the concrete slab outside the potential shear plane shown in Figure 2-54, net shear forces, totalling V_u, must be developed on these planes. The expressions for shear resistance are based on Mattock (1974). Values for semi-low density and low density concrete are given by Mattock et al. (1976) and Chien and Ritchie (1984).

17.10 Design of Composite Beams Without Shear Connectors

This conservative approach assumes that the composite section is about 10% stronger than the bare steel member, although the moment resistance computed according to Clause 17.10.2 typically gives a larger value.

17.11 Unshored Beams

This provision guards against permanent deformations under specified loads by limiting the total stress in the bottom fibre of the steel section. This limit has been shown (Kemp and Trinchero 1992) to be conservative. The ultimate strength of the composite beam, which exhibits ductile behaviour is not affected by the stress state at the specified load level.

18. COMPOSITE COLUMNS

This clause includes, in addition to the concrete-filled hollow structural sections, partially encased composite columns acting in compression in Clause 18.3, and rolled steel shapes encased in concrete in Clause 18.4. The latter parallels the requirements of CSA Standard A23.3 but using a column curve consistent with those used throughout this Standard. Thus the designer has in this Standard three types of steel-concrete columns from which to choose.

The design rules apply to specific research which should be consulted in conjunction with the requirements of this Clause.

18.1 Resistance Prior to Composite Action

For some of the systems described here the designer should be aware that the steel component may be designed to carry some of the loads before the concrete has gained strength.

18.2 Concrete-Filled Hollow Structural Sections

18.2.1 General

18.2.1.2 Axial Load on Concrete

Kennedy and MacGregor (1984) showed that direct bearing of the load on the concrete was not necessary for either axially loaded columns or beam-columns. When loads are applied to the steel shell, pinching between the steel and concrete quickly transfers loads to the concrete core. The Standard conservatively retains the requirement of direct bearing for the uppermost level but not for intermediate levels of multi-storey columns.

18.2.1.3 Composite Action in Bending

CIDECT (1970), Knowles and Park (1970), Wakabayashi (1977), Stelco (1981), and Budijgnto (1983) have demonstrated that the compression resistance of composite columns, consisting of hollow structural sections (HSS) completely filled with concrete, arises from both the steel and the concrete core. Obviously the full composite bending resistance at the ends of such members can only be realized when the connections are able to transfer the loads to the composite beam column.

18.2.2 Compressive Resistance

The expressions for compressive resistance introduced in S16-01 give a better fit to test results than those found in the preceding standard. The contributions of the concrete core and the hollow steel section are simply superposed. Both the steel and concrete contributions to the compressive resistances are decreased as a function of the slenderness parameter, λ, of the composite section that is considered in turn to depend on the elastic flexural stiffness of the steel section and a flexural stiffness of the concrete that is modified to account for creep under sustained loads. The same double exponential form of column curve, as used for other compressive resistances in the standard, is used for consistency. The value of the exponent "n" in the expression is taken as 1.80 to get the best fit with experimental results.

The triaxial load effect on the concrete due to the confining effect of the walls of circular HSS is based on work by Virdi & Dowling (1976). The triaxial effects increase the failure load of the concrete ($\tau' > 1.0$) and decrease the capacity of the steel section ($\tau < 1.0$) because the steel is in a biaxial stress state.

A $\phi_c = 0.65$ is now used in place of 0.60, and $\alpha_1 \phi_c f'_c$ is given as the concrete strength in place of $0.85 \phi_c f'_c$. Reasoning for these changes to the concrete resistance factor and strength is described by Bartlett (2007).

18.2.3 Bending Resistance

Lu and Kennedy (1994) show, for rectangular hollow sections with measured flange b/t ratios up to $700/\sqrt{F_y}$, that fully plastic stress blocks are developed in the steel and in the concrete. Their proposed model, based on such stress blocks with the steel stress level taken equal to the yield value, F_y, and the concrete stress level taken equal to the concrete strength, f'_c, at the time of testing, agreed excellently with test results. The two components support each other. The steel restrains or confines the concrete, increasing its compressive resistance to the full value rather than 0.85 of it, as used in reinforced concrete theory, while the concrete prevents inward buckling of the steel wall, thus increasing the steel strain at which local buckling occurs. Therefore, sections not even meeting the requirements of Class 3 sections in bending develop fully plastic stress blocks.

Geometric expressions are given to determine the factored compressive forces in the steel and concrete with rectangular stress blocks when equilibrium is for both rectangular and circular hollow structural sections.

A $\phi_c = 0.65$ is now used in place of 0.60, and $\alpha_1 \phi_c f'_c$ is given as the concrete strength in place of $0.85 \phi_c f'_c$. Reasoning for these changes to the concrete resistance factor and strength is described by Bartlett (2007).

18.2.4 Axial Compression and Bending

This clause is analogous to the expression in Clause 13.8.3 for I-shaped beam-columns. Extending the analogy, the cross-sectional resistance and in-plane strength should be checked and, if applicable, the lateral-torsional buckling strength should be checked for rectangular sections bent about their strong axis. Because of the very large torsional resistance of closed shapes, the latter is very unlikely to be a factor. With expressions introduced in S16-01 for circular hollow sections filled with concrete, the lower bound solution for such sections given in the preceding Standard is no longer required.

A $\phi_c = 0.65$ is now used in place of 0.60, and $\alpha_1 \phi_c f'_c$ is given as the concrete strength in place of $0.85 \phi_c f'_c$. Reasoning for these changes to the concrete resistance factor and strength is described by Bartlett (2007).

18.3 Partially Encased Composite Columns

As stated in the note to this Clause, these columns are a patented structural component. By CSA regulations, in the interests of promoting new technology, they are referenced in this Standard on the understanding with the patent holder that any patent rights will be made available either as a free license or on reasonable terms and conditions.

The basic concept is to provide a steel H-shape of relatively thin plates but with sufficient strength to carry gravity axial loads during construction until the concrete cast around the shape reaches sufficient strength to carry the remaining dead loads and all axial live and environmental loads while working compositely with the steel section. It is envisaged that the columns could be used in multi-storey applications with the concrete of the about-to-be encased steel shapes cast with the next higher floor that the columns are supporting. At this time the members are restricted to carrying axial loads. Figure 2-55 shows an elevation of the column. The steel straps between the column flanges restrain the flange tips from buckling and at the same time restrain the concrete between the two flanges.

18.3.1 General

The scope Clause lays out in detail the limits on geometry and strength of the component elements and materials – the steel section, the steel reinforcement and the concrete – that must be satisfied. These derive from the limits of the extensive series of tests, including full-scale tests, which were carried out at Lehigh University, University of Toronto, McGill University and École Polytechnique (Tremblay *et al.* 2000) to confirm and quantify the performance of the columns in all respects under axial loading. While extensive, the limits are sufficiently broad in scope to design columns of different cross-sections and slenderness limits to carry a wide range of loadings. Based on experimental and numerical research by Prickett and Driver (2006) and Begum *et al.*(2007) on partially encased composite columns with high-strength concrete, the upper limit on concrete strength has been increased from 40 MPa to 70 MPa. In S16-09, the method for determining the bending resistance is provided in Clauses 18.3.3 and the interaction expression for combined axial compression and bending in Clause 18.3.4.

18.3.2 Compressive Resistance

The expression for the compressive resistance (Tremblay *et al.* 2000) is of the same double exponential format used for both steel and other composite columns throughout this Standard. The exponent "n", 1.34, is the least value stipulated in the Standard. For both the steel section and the steel reinforcement, specified minimum yield strengths are used as the reference

Figure 2-55
Partially Encased Composite Columns

strengths and, for the concrete, $0.95 \, \alpha_1$ of the specified 28 day strength is used as this value gave a better fit to the test data than the 0.85 factor commonly used. The resistance factors for the three components are consistent with the remainder of the Standard. A $\phi_c = 0.65$ is now used in place of 0.60 (Bartlett 2007).

18.3.5 Special Reinforcement for Seismic Zones

Details are provided for longitudinal and transverse bars to be used where the specified one-second spectral acceleration ratio, $I_E F_v S_a(1.0)$, is greater than 0.30 in order to provide satisfactory performance compatible with that of reinforced concrete buildings designed for such seismic categories.

18.4 Encased Composite Columns

18.4.1 General

This Clause is provided because such columns may be found in a steel building structure. This Clause provides the designer with all the information needed to design this composite component as well as all other components in the building. The scope limits the doubly symmetric steel columns encased in concrete to which this clause applies to those given in CSA Standard A23.3.

18.4.2 Compressive Resistance

The factored compressive resistance is of the exact same form as that given in Clause 18.2 for concrete-filled hollow structural sections. In this regard, it differs in form from the resistance given in CSA Standard A23.3 but matches the factored compressive resistance of the latter closely for all slenderness ratios. The contributions of the concrete, structural steel shape and reinforcing steel to the strength are simply superposed. Both the steel and concrete contributions to the compressive resistances are decreased as a function of the slenderness parameter, λ, of the composite section that is considered in turn to depend on the elastic flexural stiffness of the steel section and a flexural stiffness of the concrete that is modified to account for creep under sustained loads. The same double exponential form of column curve as used for other compressive resistances in the standard is used for consistency. The value of the exponent "n" is taken as 1.80 to provide a close match of strengths with the resistance given in CSA Standard A23.3. A $\phi_c = 0.65$ is now used in place of 0.60, and $\alpha_1 \phi_c f'_c$ is given as the concrete strength in place of $0.85 \phi_c f'_c$. Reasoning for these changes to the concrete resistance factor and strength is described by Bartlett (2007).

18.4.4, 18.4.5 and 18.4.6 In the unusual case with multiple steel shapes enclosed in the concrete, the steel shapes are to meet the requirements of Clause 19 for built-up shapes until the concrete reaches $0.75 f'_c$. Alternatively, the load on the steel shapes could be limited to the sum of their independent resistances, having due regard as to how the loads are applied.

18.4.5 This clause emphasizes that there must be direct transfer of any load considered to be carried by the concrete to it.

To determine the bending resistance of encased composite columns, the designer is referred to Ziemian (2010). A $\phi_c = 0.65$ is now used in place of 0.60, and $\alpha_1 \phi_c f'_c$ is given as the concrete strength in place of $0.85 \phi_c f'_c$. Reasoning for these changes to the concrete resistance factor and strength is described by Bartlett (2007).

19. BUILT-UP MEMBERS

The term built-up member refers to any structural member assembled from two or more components. Such members may be used to resist compression, tension or bending, and the requirements for fastening together the various components vary accordingly.

The diagrams of Figures 2-56 and 2-57 illustrate the main provisions of Clause 19.

Many of the provisions are based on long-established practice and have proven satisfactory. In Clause 19.1.3, it is emphasized that the buckling could occur for outside components. In Clause 19.1.10, because it has been established that the tension diagonal of a crossed tension-compression pair supports the latter (see Commentary to Clause 27.5.3.1), the effective buckling length of the compression lacing can be taken as 0.50 of its total length.

Tension members are stitched together sufficiently to work in unison and to minimize vibration. For exposed members, components in contact should be fitted tightly together to minimize corrosion problems (Brockenbrough 1983).

When a built-up column buckles, shear is introduced in lacing bars (Clause 19.1.9) and battens and their connections (Clause 19.1.17), in addition to any transverse shears (Bleich, 1952).

Further discussion on columns with lacing and battens is given in Ziemian (2010).

For compression members composed of two or more rolled shapes connected at intervals, Clause 19.1.4 requires the use of an equivalent slenderness ratio, increased to take into account

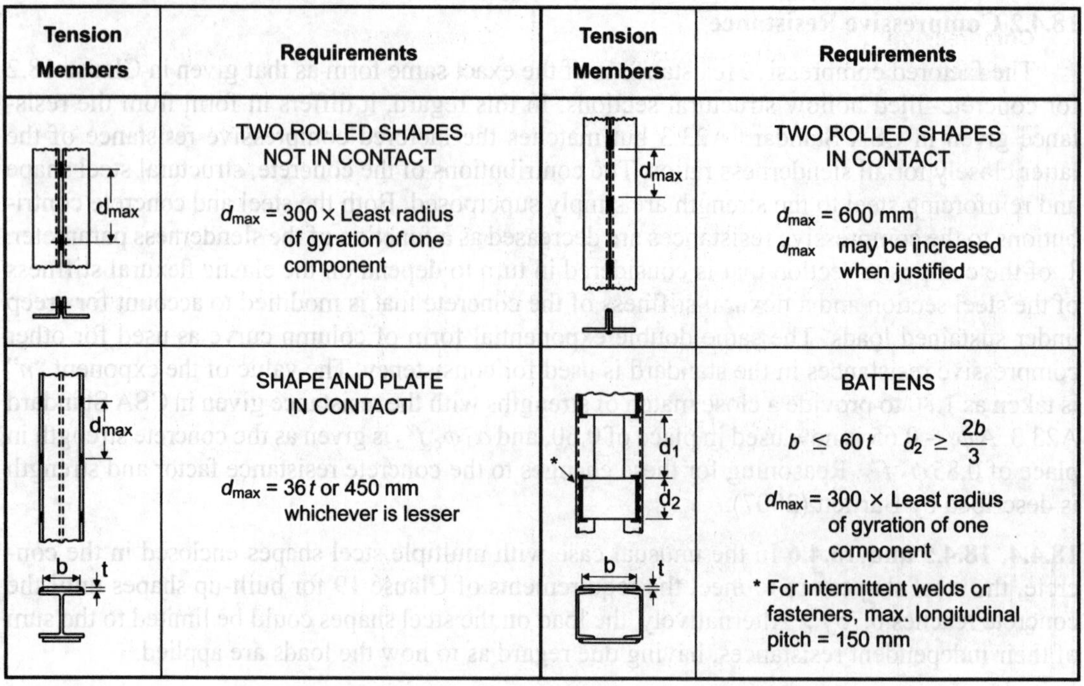

Tension Members	Requirements	Tension Members	Requirements
d_{max}	TWO ROLLED SHAPES NOT IN CONTACT d_{max} = 300 × Least radius of gyration of one component	d_{max}	TWO ROLLED SHAPES IN CONTACT d_{max} = 600 mm d_{max} may be increased when justified
d_{max} b t	SHAPE AND PLATE IN CONTACT d_{max} = 36 t or 450 mm whichever is lesser	d_1 d_2 * b t	BATTENS $b \leq 60\,t$ $d_2 \geq \dfrac{2b}{3}$ d_{max} = 300 × Least radius of gyration of one component * For intermittent welds or fasteners, max. longitudinal pitch = 150 mm

Figure 2-56
Built-up Tension Member Details

the flexibility of the interconnector. This increase is applied to the axis of buckling where the buckling mode of the member involves relative deformation that produces shear forces (see Clause 19.1.6) in the interconnectors between the individual shapes (Duan & Chen, 1988).

The requirements for starred angles are based on work by Temple *et al*. (1986), who showed that with fewer interconnectors the buckling strength was reduced.

20. PLATE WALLS

20.1 General

Early research at the University of Alberta (Kulak 1991, Driver *et al*. 1997, 1998(a), and 1998(b)) demonstrated that the plate wall system is an attractive alternative for resisting lateral wind and seismic loads. The system has the advantage that it is stiff enough to minimize displacements under extreme loading conditions, and has a high degree of redundancy. The system can be used for both new construction and the upgrading of existing structures.

Figure 2-58 shows a typical plate wall. The walls considered by Clause 20 imply thin, unstiffened infill plates. Under lateral loads, it is assumed that the buckling strength of the infill plate is negligible, but tension field action develops to resist lateral shears.

A brief overview of steel plate shear wall research, along with a comprehensive list of relevant references, can be found in Chapter 6 of Ziemian (2010).

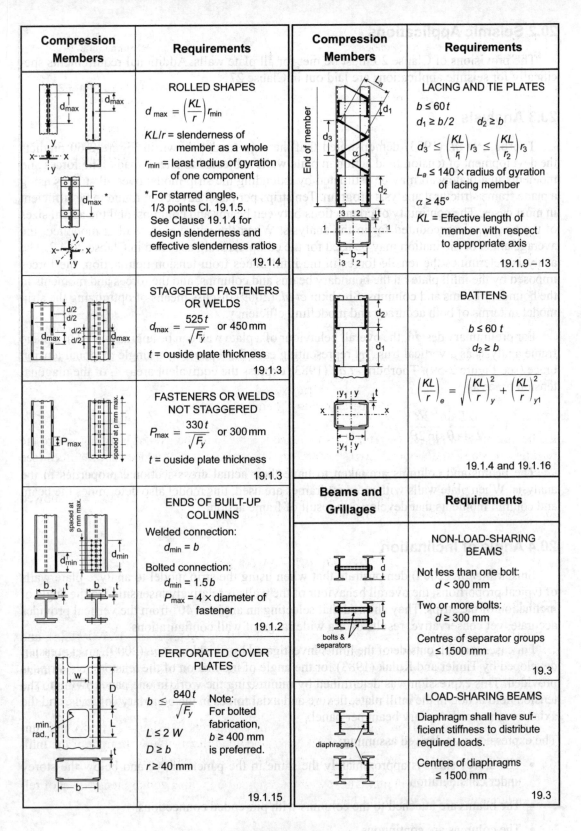

Figure 2-57
Built-up Compression Member Details

20.2 Seismic Applications

The provisions of Clause 20 must be met for all plate walls. Additional requirements specifically for seismic applications are laid out in Clause 27.

20.3 Analysis

Thorburn *et al.* (1983) demonstrated that the strip model shown in Figure 2-60 predicts the development of tension field action in plate walls subjected to lateral loads. The forces and moments in a plate wall may be estimated by extending the strip model over all storeys using a plane frame structural analysis program. Ten strips per panel have been found to be sufficient in most cases. The continuity of connections between beams and columns, and the actual sizes of the beams, are accounted for in the analysis. When the entire plate wall is modelled, the average angle of inclination may be used for the complete wall, as stated in Clause 20.4.2. The analysis determines the tensile forces in the infill plates from tension field action, the forces imposed by the infill plate on the boundary beams and columns, and the forces and moments in the boundary beams and columns. Shishkin *et al.* (2009) discuss means of optimizing the strip model in terms of both accuracy and modelling efficiency.

For preliminary design, the overall behaviour of a plate wall can be approximated in a plane frame analysis as a vertical truss by representing each infill panel by a single diagonal tension brace (see Figure 2-59). Thorburn *et al.* (1983) express the equivalent area, A, of the diagonal tension brace as

$$A = \frac{w L \sin^2 2\alpha}{2 \sin\theta \sin 2\theta}$$

The beams and columns are taken to have their actual cross-sectional properties in the analysis. When plate walls with moment frames are used, this model also determines the beam and column moments that develop as a result of frame action.

20.4 Angle of Inclination

Shishkin *et al.* (2009) demonstrate that when using the strip model to analyze plate walls of typical proportions, the overall behaviour of the walls is relatively insensitive to the angle of inclination of the strips. They showed that selecting an angle of 40° from the vertical provides accurate, yet conservative, results over a wide range of wall configurations.

For cases that fall outside of the limits investigated by Shishkin *et al.* (2009), an expression developed by Timler and Kulak (1983) for the angle of inclination of the tension field strips is provided. This expression was determined by minimizing the work in one panel owing to the tension field action in the infill plate, flexure and axial forces in the boundary columns, and the axial force in one boundary beam per panel.

The expression was derived assuming:

- The storey shear is approximately the same in the panels above and below the storey under consideration.

- The beams are attached to the columns with pin-ended connections.

- The columns are continuous.

- The storey heights are approximately equal.

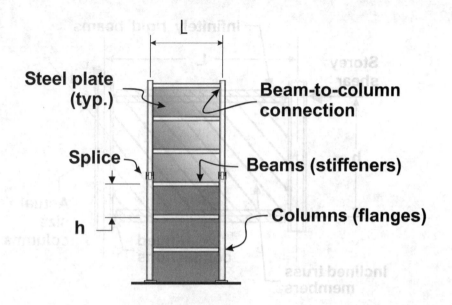

Steel plate
(typ.)

Beam-to-column
connection

Splice

Beams (stiffeners)

Columns (flanges)

h

Figure 2-58
Typical Plate Wall

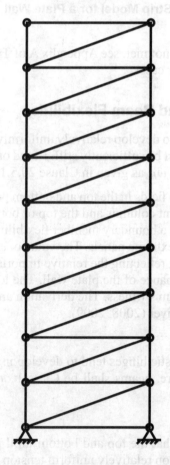

Figure 2-59
Plate Wall Diagonal Tension Brace Model

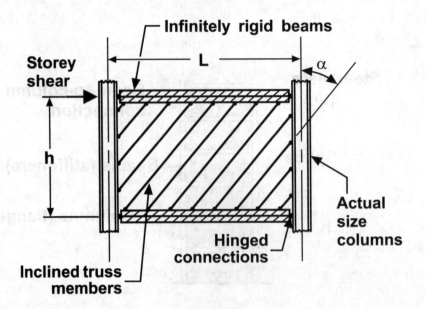

Figure 2-60
Strip Model for a Plate Wall

When these assumptions are not met, see Appendix A of Timler and Kulak (1983) to apply the least work derivation to other cases.

20.5 Limits on Column and Beam Flexibilities

In order for the tension field to develop relatively uniformly in the infill plate at each storey, the columns of the plate wall must be sufficiently stiff. Based on the word of Kuhn *et al.* (1952), the column flexibility parameter, ω_h, as given in Clause 20.5.1, shall not exceed 2.5.

The uniformity of the tension fields in the top and bottom panels of the plate wall depend on the stiffnesses of both the adjacent columns and the top or bottom beam, as appropriate. Dastfan and Driver (2008) developed a boundary member flexibility parameter, ω_L, to characterize the boundary stiffness for these extreme panels. The value of ω_L shall not exceed 2.5 at the top of the wall and 2.0 at the bottom, reflecting the relative importance of the behaviour of the bottom panel on the overall performance of the plate wall. The lower limit on ω_L of $0.84\,\omega_h$ is to prevent obtaining a negative beam stiffness. The derivation and application of both ω_L and ω_h are discussed by Dastfan and Driver (2008, 2009).

20.7 Beams and 20.8 Columns

Under high lateral loads, plastic hinges tend to develop in the beams and columns of plate walls. To avoid premature failure, beams shall be Class 1 or Class 2 sections, and columns Class 1 sections.

20.9 Anchorage of Infill Plates

These requirements ensure that the top and bottom infill plates are anchored to members that are sufficiently stiff to develop relatively uniform tension fields, and that the forces developed at the base of the wall are transferred properly into the substructure.

20.10 Infill Plate Connections

The infill plate is to be connected to the surrounding frame – and spliced, if required – to resist the factored ultimate tensile strength of the plate in order to ensure a ductile failure mode. These connections may be either welded or bolted.

21. CONNECTIONS

21.3 Restrained Members

When the compressive or tensile force transmitted by a beam flange to a column (approximated by the factored moment divided by the depth of the beam) exceeds the factored web bearing or flange tensile resistance of the column, stiffeners are required to develop the load in excess of the bearing or tensile resistance.

Taking the length of the column web resisting the compressive force as the thickness of the beam flange plus ten times the thickness of the column flange as in Clause 14.3.2(a)(i) results in the first equation given in Clause 21.3 for the bearing resistance of columns with Class 1 and 2 webs. For members with Class 3 and 4 webs, the bearing resistance of the web is limited by its buckling strength. The expression for the factored bearing resistance is conservatively based on the critical buckling stress of a plate with simply-supported edges:

$$\sigma_{cr} = k \frac{\pi^2 E}{12(1 - v^2)(h_c/w_c)^2} = \frac{723\,000}{(h_c/w_c)^2} \quad \text{when } k_{min} = 4$$

The number 640 000, given in Clause 21.3(a), reflects a further reduction for the effect of possible residual stresses.

Although not stated, the bearing resistance computed from the second equation should not exceed the first. In both expressions, if the compression flange is applied at the end of a column, the loaded length should be reduced to $t_b + 4t_c$ and the resistance factor should be reduced to ϕ_{be}.

Graham et al. (1959) also show, based on a yield line analysis, that the column flange bending resistance, when subject to a tensile load from the beam flange, can be taken conservatively to be $7t_c^2 F_{yc}$. Tests have shown that connections proportioned in accordance with this equation have carried the plastic moment of the beam satisfactorily.

When moment connections are made between beams and columns with relatively thick flanges (greater than about 50 mm) prudent fabrication practice suggests that the column flanges be inspected (such as radiographically) in the region surrounding the proposed weld locations to detect and thereby avoid any possible laminations that might be detrimental to the through-thickness behaviour of the column flange. Dexter and Melendrez (2000) reported on the results of recent studies on this topic.

Huang et al. (1973) demonstrated that beam-column connections designed such that the web was connected only for the shear force were capable of reaching the plastic capacity of the beam even though in some tests the webs were connected with bolts based on bearing-type connections in round or slotted holes. The slips that occurred were not detrimental to the static ultimate load capacity. For joints in zones of high seismicity, see Commentary on Clause 27.

Bolted extended end plate type connections are also commonly used for beam-to-column moment connections. Murray (2003) presents equations for the bearing and tensile resistances of the column flange opposite the flanges of the beam, for use with extended end plate type connections. AISC (2001) and Carter (1999) have adopted the design equations presented by Murray (2003). Note that the equation used in calculating the tensile resistance of the column flange is based on research using only ASTM A36 material. For this reason, if columns with higher yield strengths are used, it is recommended (conservatively) that the column yield strength be limited to 250 MPa (36 ksi) for calculating the tensile resistance of the column flange. Detailed design procedures for other limit states (other possible failure modes) for this type of connection are presented in Murray (1990) and AISC (2001). Prying action should also be checked on the end plate connection and the column flange opposite the tension flange of the beam. Clause 22.2.2(e) requires that bolts subject to tensile forces be pretensioned.

21.4 Connections of Tension or Compression Members

Obviously, the end connections must transmit the factored loads. In order to guard against providing a connection inconsistent with the member it connects, when the member size has been selected for some criterion other than strength, the designer may choose to provide a minimum connection with a capacity higher than the design load.

The requirement for a connection at least equal to 50% of the member's capacity was withdrawn in S16-01 as it was often misapplied, resulting in grossly oversized connections.

21.5 Bearing Joints In Compression Members

When determining the requirement for fasteners or welds to hold all parts securely in place, the stability of the structure shall be considered for all possible load conditions in accordance with the requirements of Clause 6.1.2.

21.6 Lamellar Tearing

In cases where shrinkage results as a consequence of welding under highly restrained conditions, very large tensile strains may be set up. If these are transferred across the through-thickness direction of rolled structural members or plates, lamellar tearing may result. Thornton (1973) and AISC (1973) give methods of minimizing lamellar tearing. Figure 2-61 illustrates one such case.

21.7 Placement of Fasteners and Welds

Gibson and Wake (1942) have shown that, except for cases of repeated loads, end welds on tension angles, and other similar members need not be placed so as to balance the forces about the neutral axis of the member.

21.8 Fillers

The intent of this clause is to ensure that the total load transferred through a connection will be transferred uniformly over the combined cross section of the filler plate and the connected material in order to avoid bending in the bolt shank. In order to do this, the filler plate should be connected for a load equivalent to the total load multiplied by the ratio of the filler plate thickness to the combined thickness of the filler plate and the connected material (see Figure 2-62). However, in slip-critical joints, tests with fillers up to 25 mm (1 inch) in thickness and with surface conditions comparable to other joint components show that the fillers act integrally with the remainder of the joint and they need not be developed before the splice material (Kulak *et al.* 2001).

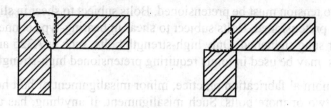

Figure 2-61
Details to Minimize Lamellar Tearing

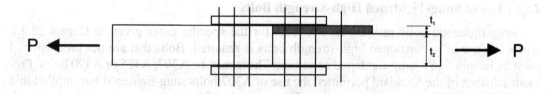

$$\text{Load on Filler} = P(w_1 t_1)/(w_1 t_1 + w_2 t_2)$$

Figure 2-62
Load on Filler Plate

21.10 Fasteners and Welds in Combination

21.10.1 Requirements for the design of joints that combine welds and high-strength bolts placed in the same shear plane are covered in a new clause, Clause 13.14.

21.11 High-Strength Bolts (in Slip-Critical Joints) and Rivets in Combination

The hot-driven rivets have a clamping force comparable to that of the pretensioned bolts, albeit somewhat more variable.

22. DESIGN AND DETAILING OF BOLTED CONNECTIONS

22.1 General

The behaviour of a joint depends both on how the bolts are loaded and installed. In the 1984 edition, for the first time, the use of snug-tightened high-strength bolts was permitted. Their use has proved successful. As there are four basic types of connections, three with bolts in shear and one with bolts in tension, it is absolutely essential that the drawings specify the type of connections used.

Kulak *et al.* (2001) shows that the ultimate shear and bearing resistance of a bolted connection are not dependent on the pretension in the bolt. As the number of situations (Clause 22.2.2) where pretensioning is required is limited, the norm for building construction is to use snug-tightened bearing-type connections. Departures from the norm are only to be made with due consideration. Few joints in building construction are subject to frequent load reversal nor are there many situations where a one-time slip into bearing cannot be tolerated.

Bolts subject to tension must be pretensioned. Bolts subject to shear in slip-critical connections must also be pretensioned. Bolts subject to shear in bearing-type connections may either be pretensioned or snug-tightened. Only high-strength bolts, such as A325 and A490 and their metric equivalents, may be used in joints requiring pretensioned high-strength bolts.

As a result of normal fabrication practice, minor misalignment of bolt holes may occur in connections with two or more bolts. Such misalignment, if anything, has a beneficial effect (Kulak *et al.* 2001) resulting in a stiffer joint, improved slip resistance and decreased rigid body motion.

Kulak *et al.* (2001) contains a comprehensive summary of bolt requirements.

22.2.1 Use of Snug-Tightened High-Strength Bolts

Snug-tightened bolts may be used, except for the specific cases given in Clause 22.2.2 where the use of pretensioned high-strength bolts is required. Bolts that are not pretensioned must be installed to a snug-tightened condition. These may be A307, A325 or A490 bolts. Previous editions of the Standard permitted the use of A307 bolts snug-tightened but implied that all A325 and A490 bolts were pretensioned. Because the ultimate limit states of shear through the bolt and bearing on the plate material are not significantly affected by the level of pretension (Kulak *et al.* 2001), it is only logical to permit bolts of higher strength than the A307 bolt to also be installed snug-tight in similar connections. This was recognized, in part, as early as the 1984 edition in Clause 22.7.1, which relaxed the inspection requirements of certain bearing-type joints.

22.2.2 Use of Pretensioned High-Strength Bolts

(a) Pretensioning of the bolts provides the clamping force in slip-critical connections and hence the slip resistance at the specified load level appropriate to the condition of the faying surfaces.

(b) Pretensioning of the bolts provides energy dissipation under cyclic earthquake loading in connections proportioned in accordance with the seismic requirements given in Clause 27, although these connections are proportioned as bearing-type connections for the ultimate limit state. The contact surfaces should be Class A or better for such joints.

(c) See (d).

(d) Pretensioning in both these connections ensures that the bolts don't work loose and, if necessary, ensures adequate fatigue behaviour.

(e) An example of such a connection is a tee-hanger connection. Pretensioning reduces the prying action and the stress range.

(f) In connections with oversize or slotted holes, pretensioning prevents gross movement within the joint. See also Clause 22.3.5.2 to determine for which cases slip-critical connections are required.

For the usual building structure, full wind loads and earthquake loads are too infrequent to warrant design for fatigue as the number of stress cycles are less than the 20 000 cycles given in Clause 26.3.5. Therefore, slip-critical connections are not normally required in buildings for wind or seismic load combinations. However, connections of a member subject to flutter where the number of cycles is likely higher is an exception. Popov and Stephen (1972) observed that the bolted web connections of welded-bolted moment connections slipped early in the cyclic process.

Slip-critical connections are required in connections involving oversized holes, certain slotted holes, fatigue loading, or crane runways and bridges. In assessing whether or not the joint slip is detrimental at service level loads, Popov and Stephen (1972) and Kulak *et al.* (2001) have shown that in joints with standard holes the average slip is much less than a millimetre. Bolts of joints in statically loaded structures are most likely in direct bearing after removal of the drift pins due to the self weight of the member and are thus incapable of further slip (RCSC 2004).

22.2.5 Fastener Components

A325M, A490M, A325 and A490 bolts are produced by quenching and tempering (ASTM 2009a, 2009b, 2009c, 2009d). A325 bolts are not as strong as A490 bolts but have greater ductility. For this reason and reasons of availability, the use of A490 bolts is subject to restrictions as discussed subsequently. ASTM F1852 and F2280 bolts, commonly known as 'tension control' or 'twist-off' bolts have mechanical and chemical properties equivalent to A325 and A490 bolts, respectively (ASTM 2008a, 2008b).

The normal bolt assembly consists of an A325, A490, F1852 or F2280 bolt, with a heavy hex head, restricted thread length, coarse threads, and a heavy hex nut. F1852 and F2280 bolt assemblies consist of a bolt with a splined end which typically has a button head. Alternatives to the normal bolt assemblies are available which differ in various aspects and, in some cases, may offer one or more advantages. Their use is permissible under the conditions set forth in Clause 22.2.5.3.

Designers are cautioned to ascertain the availability of A325M and A490M bolts before specifying their use. Alternatively, by basing the design on the bolt with the lower resistance, either the imperial series or the metric series bolt could be used depending upon availability.

Galvanized A325 bolts are permitted; however, metallic coated A490 bolts are not permitted (ASTM 2009c and 2009d) as they are especially susceptible to stress corrosion and hydrogen stress cracking (Kulak *et al.* 2001). The rotation requirement of this clause provides a means of testing the galvanized assembly for proper fit and for proper thread lubrication. Installation of F1852 and F2280 bolts is dependent upon consistent friction properties of the bolt threads and the nut. Therefore, these bolts should not be hot-dip galvanized or electroplated subsequent to purchase for use in pretensioned joints.

22.3.5 Bolt Holes

Details on the sizes and types of holes (standard, oversize, or slotted) permitted for bearing-type and slip-critical connections are given. While the Standard permits several hole-making methods, punching and drilling are the most common. Incremental punching is sometimes used in fabricating slotted holes, especially long slots. Thermal cutting of holes such as cutting the edges of a slot between two punched holes is acceptable within the requirements of Clause 28.4.3.

Clause 22.3.5.1 allows selected Imperial bolts in metric holes without restriction.

A hardened washer, when required, is intended to cover the hole (or bridge the slot) if it occurs in an outer ply.

The requirement of clause 23.5.2(d) for an 8 mm hardened washer for large diameter A490 bolts is to distribute the high clamping forces of these bolts. Where long slots are used it is an acceptable alternative to use 8 mm mild steel plate washers with a standard hardened washer under the head and the nut. The contract documents should specify any specific requirements.

23. INSTALLATION AND INSPECTION OF BOLTED JOINTS

Bolts required to be pretensioned must be tightened to tensions of at least 70% of their specified minimum tensile strength. All other bolts need only be snug-tightened.

Except when galvanized, A325 bolts may be reused once or twice, providing that proper control on the number of reuses can be established (Kulak *et al.* 2001; RCSC 2004). A490, F1852 and F2280 bolts should not be reused. The level of pretension attained in bolts of Grade A490 decreases significantly when the bolts are re-used. Once the spline end of twist-off F1852 and F2280 bolts has been broken off during the first installation, these bolts cannot be re-installed with a controlled pretension.

23.2 Connection Fit-up

The simple phrase "connections in firm contact when assembled" describes the snug-tightened condition.

23.3 Surface Conditions for Slip-Critical Connections

The treatment of the faying surfaces within the plies of slip-critical joints is to be consistent with the mean slip coefficient chosen for design (Clause 13.12). For clean mill scale, the surfaces must be free of substances which would reduce the slip coefficient. For other coatings, the surface preparation, coating application and curing should be similar to those used in the tests to obtain the slip coefficient. The Society for Protective Coatings (SSPC) provides specifications for cleaning and coating of steel structures. Kulak *et al.* (2001) provide information on slip for various surface conditions and coating types.

23.5 Use of Washers

Clauses 23.5.1 and 23.5.2 list the circumstances when ASTM F436 hardened washers are required under the turned element and with pretensioned bolts. It follows that these washers are not required in A325 bolt installations except for oversized or slotted holes in pretensioned connections.

The requirements for bevelled washers with ASTM A490 bolts are more stringent than for A325 bolts because of the somewhat reduced ductility of the former.

23.6 Storage of Fastener Components for Pretensioned Bolt Assemblies

It emphasizes that proper storage of fastener components is particularly critical for ASTM F1852 and F2280 bolts because the torque at which the splined end is sheared off the bolt shank is dependent on the friction characteristics between the bolt threads and the nut, which therefore must be maintained at the as-manufactured condition so that the relationship between the twist off torque and bolt pretension is what was intended, and is expected to be.

23.8 Pretensioned High-Strength Bolts

For all pretensioned high-strength bolt installations, it is critical that inspection for bolt pretension be done while the bolt tightening is in progress. Verification that the installation techniques described in this clause have been followed will provide adequate assurance that the required bolt tensions are being attained.

23.8.1 Installation Procedure

The pretensioning procedures included in this Standard have been proven (Kulak and Birkemoe 1993, Kulak and Undershute 1998) to provide bolt tensions required by this clause. Torque/tension relationships are highly variable and dependent upon many factors including, installation procedures, bolt finish, and bolt and nut thread conditions. For this reason, it is not possible to establish a standard bolt torque value that corresponds to the required bolt pretension values. Clause 23.9 describes the proper simple inspection procedures for bolted connections.

23.8.2 Turn-of-Nut Method

Any installation procedure used for pretensioning high strength bolts involves elongating the bolt to produce the desired tension. Although the shank of the bolt probably remains elastic, the threaded portion behaves plastically. Because the bolt as a whole is tightened into the inelastic range (the flat portion of the load-deformation curve) the exact location of "snug-tight" is not critical (Kulak *et al.* 2001). The turn-of-nut method is a strain or deformation control method and even a considerable change in deformation results in little change in load. Thus application of the specified amount of nut rotation results in pretensions that are not greatly variable. They are also greater than those prescribed in Table 7 that occur about where inelastic action begins. Although there is a reasonable margin against twist-off, the tolerance of ±30° or ±1/12 of a turn on nut rotation prescribed in the footnote to Table 8 is good practice, particularly when galvanized A325 bolts or black A490 bolts are used.

23.8.3 and 23.8.4 Use of F959, F1852 and F2280 Bolting Systems

The Standard permits the use of F1852, F2280 and F959 bolting systems. These systems are proprietary in nature, relying on a discernible physical change in a part of the bolt system that attempts to indicate that the minimum bolt tension has been achieved. Systems that rely on irreversible deformations or fracture of a part serve only to indicate that during installation, a force or torque sufficient to deform or fracture the part had been reached. Even with such a system, reliable results are dependent on strict adherence to the installation procedures for snugging of the joint and patterned tightening operations as given in Clause 23.8.1 and to the storage fastener requirements of Clause 23.6 for F1852 and F2280 bolts.

23.9 Inspection Procedures

Bolts, nuts and washers are normally received with a light residual coating of oil. This coating is not detrimental, in fact it is desirable, and should not be removed. This is especially important for F1852 and F2280 bolts since these bolts depend on the lubricant to achieve the desired level of pretension. Galvanized bolts and/or nuts may be coated with a special lubricant to facilitate tightening. Obviously, this should not be removed.

The inspection procedures used depend on whether the bolts are specified to be snug-tightened or pretensioned. In all cases, by Clause 23.9.1, the inspector shall observe that the procedure for the installation of the bolts conforms with the requirements of this Standard.

When snug-tightening is specified, the tightening is deemed satisfactory when all of the connected elements are in full contact. Galling of the turned element may be evident. Inadvertent pretensioning of snug-tightened bolts is normally not a cause for concern.

When pretensioning is specified, the tightening is deemed satisfactory when all of the elements are in full contact and observation of the sides of the turned elements shows that they have been slightly galled by the wrench. This is all that is required.

When bolts are tightened by the turn-of-nut method and when there is rotation of the part not turned by the wrench, the outer face of the nut may be match-marked with the bolt point before final tightening, thus affording the inspector visual means of noting nut rotation. Such marks may be made with crayon or paint by the wrench operator after the bolts have been snugged.

Should disagreement arise concerning the results of inspection of bolt tension of bolts specified to be pretensioned, arbitration procedures as given in Annex I are to be followed. The use of inspection torque values other than those established according to the requirements of Annex I is invalid because of the variability of the torque-tension relationship. The inspection procedure given in Annex I is the same as that recommended by the Research Council on Structural Connections (RCSC 2004) and places its emphasis on the need to observe the installation for the proper tightening procedures rather than using the arbitration procedures which in fact are less reliable.

Regardless of the installation procedure or the type of bolt-washer-nut assembly used, it is important to have all of the plies drawn up tight before starting the specific tightening procedure. This is particularly so for stiff joints that require pattern tightening.

24. WELDING

24.1 and 24.2 Arc and Resistance Welding

Consistent with CSA policy that the requirements of one standard are not repeated in another, the user of this Standard is referred to CSA Standards W59 and W55.3 for the requirements for arc and resistance welding, respectively, but only insofar as welding procedures and practice is concerned. The distinction is made that for arc welds the factored resistances for static loadings and the fatigue resistance for fatigue loadings are obtained from Clauses 13.13 and 26 of this Standard, respectively. (Much of the research into weld strengths and formulation of weld resistances has been done by members of this Standard committee.)

Designers' attention is drawn to the fact that in the U.S.A. cracking has been noted after welding of column web stiffener or of doubler plates on heavily rotarized W-shapes in the fillet regions. This is attributed to the loss of ductility due to cold working.

A minor difference between CSA Standard W59 and AWS D1.1 but of some importance, is that, when fatigue is a consideration, intermittent fillet welds are not prohibited in W59 if in the compression zone, whereas AWS D1.1 does not permit them even in the compression zone.

24.3 Fabricator and Erector Qualification

The intent of Clause 24.3 is simply that the responsibility for structural welding shall lie with the fabricators and erectors certified by the Canadian Welding Bureau as stated specifically in the clause. Such certification should ensure that the fabricators and erectors have the capability to make structural welds of the quality assumed by S16-09. Clause 24.3, as well as permitting work to be sublet to a Division 3 erector, reflects the requirements of CSA W47.1-09.

25. COLUMN BASES AND ANCHOR RODS

The clauses on column bases and anchor rods have been combined, as the two are likely found together as components of the same foundation unit. The designer is referred to appropriate clauses of CSA-A23.3 (CSA 2004) for the various resistances of the reinforced concrete elements. The compressive resistance of concrete is based on the stress block model as given in CSA A23.3.

In general, the use of base plates bearing directly on grout is preferred to the use of levelling plates interposed between the base plate and the grout. The latter condition may lead to uneven bearing.

The term anchor rods is used instead of anchor bolts because they are in fact threaded rods likely to be fabricated from a reinforcing bar or a plain bar of A36 or G40.21-300W steel, or other steel bar stock. The expressions for the tensile, shear, and combined shear and tensile resistance of anchor rods are similar to those for high-strength bolts. However, the tensile resistance is based directly on the tensile stress area, A_n, rather than 0.75 times the shank area as given in Clause 13.12. The basic elliptical interaction diagram is used for combined shear and tension. For tension and bending, the factored moment resistance is limited to the factored yield moment because the ductility of the steel used may be limited. For anchor rods in tension, the designer should specify a material with fracture toughness appropriate for the minimum service temperature. Pretensioning of anchor rods is usually not recommended, as there is a tendency for relaxation and a possibility of stress corrosion.

All anchor rod resistances, whether for tension, shear, bearing or moment or for use in interaction equations, are those given in this Clause.

26. FATIGUE

Clause 26 provides the requirements for the design of members and connections subject to fatigue. The fatigue limit state, which is the limiting case of the slow propagation of a crack within a structural element, can result from either live load effects directly or as the consequence of local distortion within the structure due indirectly to live load effects. These two cases are referred to as live load-induced fatigue and distortion-induced fatigue. The limit state of fatigue is checked at load levels expected to occur many times during the life of the structure – loads that are considered to be repetitive. In the event that more than 20 000 stress cycles take place, the loaded members, connections and fastening elements shall be proportioned so that the probability of fatigue failure is acceptably small. In such cases, the design shall be based on the best available information on the fatigue characteristics of the materials and components to be used. In the absence of more specific information, which is subject to the approval of the owner, the requirements of Clause 26 in its entirety provide guidance in proportioning members and parts. The fatigue design loads are taken to be the specified loads. In addition, Clause 26.1 requires, of course, that factored resistances be at least equal to the effect of factored static loads – load levels that occur very seldom, perhaps only a few times in the life of the structure, but which the structure must, nevertheless, be able to withstand in order to achieve the desired small probability against failure.

A substantial amount of experimental data, developed on steel beams since 1967 under the sponsorship of the National Co-operative Highway Research Program (NCHRP 1970, 1974; Fisher 1974) of the U.S.A., has shown that the most important factors governing fatigue resistance are the stress range, the type of detail and the number of cycles.

While fatigue is generally not a design consideration for buildings such as those for commercial or residential occupancies, industrial buildings may have many members, such as crane girders, for which fatigue is a concern. Other instances where fatigue is likely a consideration are amusement rides, wave guides, sign supports and beams supporting reciprocating machinery. When members and connections are subjected to fatigue loading, Clause 26 requires that they be designed, detailed and fabricated to minimize stress concentrations and abrupt changes in cross-section.

Fatigue crack growth is referred to either as load-induced or as distortion-induced. Load-induced stresses are those corresponding to the design loads normally considered by the designer. Distortion-induced stresses are those due to the relative movement of connected parts of an assemblage in such a way that large localized strains are produced. Because this phenomenon is not usually included in design calculations, distortion-induced fatigue is best avoided by using recognized details to obviate potential problems.

26.3 Live Load-Induced Fatigue

26.3.1 Calculation of Stress Range

The stress range is the algebraic difference between the maximum stress and the minimum stress at a given location due to the passage of the live load. For the usual structural details illustrated in Table 9 and in Figure 2 of the Standard, the stress range is established from nominal stresses calculated using a mechanics of materials approach. This simple representation of stress, without using stress concentration factors, is correct because stress concentrations and peak stresses are implicitly included in the resistances given in the Standard for the detail in question.

Because fatigue cracks grow only if there is a net tensile stress from the live load, it is not necessary to investigate fatigue at locations where the stress range due to live load is always in compression and at locations where the maximum tensile live load stress is less than the compressive dead load stress.

26.3.2 Design Criteria

The criteria expressed by the relationship $F_{sr} \geq f_{sr}$, simply states that the fatigue resistance (or allowable stress range) of a given detail must be equal to or exceed the calculated stress range due to the passage of the fatigue load. The fatigue resistance may be calculated from the equation $F_{sr} = (\gamma/nN)^{1/3} \geq F_{srt}$. Equations of this type for various detail categories are represented pictorially in Figure 1 of the Standard, by the series of parallel straight lines, the S–N (stress–number of cycles) curves, with slopes of 1/3. Each line has been established from a series of constant amplitude fatigue tests on details representative of the category at the mean minus two standard deviations on the fatigue life. The fatigue life constant, γ, for the appropriate detail is obtained from Table 10 of the Standard. Also shown in Table 10 is the constant amplitude threshold stress ranges F_{srt}, represented in Figure 1 of the Standard by the horizontal dashed lines. For a stress range both below F_{srt} and of constant amplitude, crack growth does not occur. The sloping lines are seen to continue below their intersections with the thresholds but at a slope of 1/5. This is discussed in the Commentary on Clause 26.3.3.

To calculate the fatigue resistance, the designer must estimate the number of applications (N) of the live load over the design life (usually 50 years) of the structure. The designer must also decide on the number of applications (n) of the stress range for each passage of the load. For example, a multi-wheeled crane may produce more than one stress cycle and perhaps of different amplitude each time the crane passes a specific location.

The design criteria in Clause 26.3.2 differs from both the highway bridge codes CSA S6-06 and AASHTO LRFD 1998 where the inequality $F_{sr} \geq F_{srt}/2$ is only one half of that in the S16-09. In the case of highway bridges, the calculated fatigue stress ranges are due to the passage of the "fatigue truck" weighing approximately half that of the "design truck" used for the strength evaluation. But vehicles using highways are not all equal in weight to the fatigue truck. Some are as heavy as the design truck or even heavier and many, many trucks – the bulk of the traffic – are lighter. Placed at the same position on the bridge as the fatigue truck, the design truck would produce about twice the stress range and can initiate crack growth even if the number of cycles is relatively few. The number and intensity of stress ranges due to the lighter trucks are difficult to assess and are generally unknown. To allow, at least approximately, for the occasional heavier trucks and all the lighter truck traffic causing many cycles of different stress ranges, the sloping lines with slopes of 1/3 are continued down to $F_{srt}/2$.

Clause 26.3.2, however, is orientated to the fatigue design of buildings, such as crane-supporting structures, rather than towards bridges. In these structures, dedicated to specific industrial uses, the variability in stress ranges due to the passages of loads can be expected to be much less than that for highway bridges catering to public traffic. As well, the rated capacity of the cranes, within limits, defines the maximum loads to be carried. Indeed, ladles, for example, cannot be overfilled significantly. (The number of cycles of loading is also related to the duty cycle of the operations.) Thus, the Standard allows for stress ranges below the F_{srt} where, as given in Eurocode 3, the sloping lines are continued at the lesser slope of 1/5 because of the slower rate of fatigue crack growth. This all implies that, barring the unlikely event that there is only one stress range, the number of cycles of different stress ranges will be assessed, and a cumulative fatigue damage rule applied such as given in Clause 26.3.3.

26.3.3 Cumulative Fatigue Damage

In reality, fatigue loading may be of variable stress amplitude that causes stress ranges of different magnitudes and of different numbers of cycles. The cumulative fatigue damage that results from the variable-amplitude loading is accounted for by the linear damage theory known as the Palmgren-Miner rule. Over the design life of the structure, the number of cycles for each identified stress range is estimated and divided by the fatigue life for that stress range as found from Table 10 or Figure 1 of the Standard. The sum of these fractions so determined, including those for the long-life region of behaviour where the slope of the S–N line is 1/5, shall not exceed 1 as given in this Clause. Kulak and Grondin (2009) provide more detailed information on fatigue.

26.3.4 Fatigue Constants and Detail Categories

Fatigue constants are given in Table 10. The detail categories (A to E1) were adopted decades ago, except that three additional illustrative examples were incorporated in Figure 2 of the Standard in its 2001 edition: re-entrant corners at copes, bolts in slip-critical connections at the ends of cover plates and weld access holes at groove-welded splices. Also added to Table 9 were high-strength bolts under tensile cyclic loading.

26.3.5 Limited Number of Cycles

This clause gives a limit on the number of cycles below which no special consideration other than good detailing is necessary for fatigue. The limit is the greater of 20 000 cycles and the fatigue life of the detail.

26.4 Distortion-Induced Fatigue

Secondary (uncalculated) stresses due to deformations and out-of-plane movements can also be a source of fatigue failures (Fisher 1978 and 1984). Crane girders, their attachments and supports require careful design and attention to details to minimize fatigue cracks (Griggs 1976).

If the web of a plate girder without longitudinal stiffeners is sufficiently slender, fatigue cracks may develop at the web-to-flange juncture due to a lateral bending of the web under repeated loads. To control this type of distortion-induced fatigue, the h/w ratio of plate girders used in fatigue conditions shall not exceed $3150/\sqrt{F_y}$ (Toprac and Natarajan 1971).

27. SEISMIC DESIGN

Specific seismic design requirements are given in this clause. While the requirements represent the best available knowledge, designers should be alert to new information leading to improved design procedures.

The NBCC assigns ductility-related force modification factors, R_d, and overstrength-related force modification factors, R_o, (i.e. load reduction factors) to various structural systems in relation to their capacity to dissipate energy by undergoing inelastic deformations and the minimum level of overstrength which can be counted on for each particular seismic-force-resisting system. The greater the ability of the structure to dissipate energy, the higher is the assigned value of R_d. Values of R_d greater than 1.0 can be justified only if the structure has the ability to undergo inelastic deformations without loss of resistance. The product of R_d and R_o is used as a divisor to reduce the magnitude of the seismic force.

The objective of Clause 27 is to provide details that will exhibit ductility consistent with the values of R_d and R_o assumed in the analysis. The Clause applies to all steel structures in Canada for which energy dissipation capability is required. This includes all structures for which $R_d \geq 2.0$. Structures for which $R_d = 1.5$ have been assumed in the past to have sufficient inherent energy dissipation capacity arising from traditional design and fabrication practices that no additional requirements were necessary. However, since energy dissipation properties can only be mobilized if brittle failure is avoided, minimum requirements are prescribed in Clause 27.11 to achieve this for structures subjected to higher seismic demand. In NBCC 2010, structures with $R_d = 1.5$ are permitted for buildings other than assembly occupancy that are taller than 15 m. Additional provisions have been introduced in Clause 27.11 for these structures.

In S16-09, the ductile buckling-restrained braced frame system was introduced. Bracing members in that system are specially designed and detailed to yield in both compression and tension without buckling. The system is expected to offer high ductility ($R_d = 4.0$) compared to concentrically braced frames in the Moderately Ductile ($R_d = 3.0$) and Limited Ductility ($R_d = 2.0$) categories, provided the inelastic performance of the bracing members is demonstrated through sub-assemblage and individual qualification cyclic testing. The seismic provisions for this system have been incorporated in Clause 27.8. Seismic design requirements for Type D and Type LD plate walls are provided in Clauses 27.9 and 27.10, respectively, while provisions for Conventional Construction are now stipulated in Clause 27.11.

Clause 27 thus defines the requirements for nine classes of frames with $R_d > 1.5$:

- ductile moment-resisting frames (Type D, with $R_d = 5.0$ and $R_o = 1.5$)
- moderately ductile moment-resisting frames (Type MD, with $R_d = 3.5$ and $R_o = 1.5$)
- moment-resisting frames with limited ductility (Type LD with $R_d = 2.0$ and $R_o = 1.3$)
- moderately ductile concentrically braced frames (Type MD, with $R_d = 3.0$ and $R_o = 1.3$)
- limited ductility concentrically braced frames (Type LD, with $R_d = 2.0$ and $R_o = 1.3$)
- ductile eccentrically braced frames (Type D, with $R_d = 4.0$ and $R_o = 1.5$)
- ductile buckling-restrained braced frames (Type D, with $R_d = 4.0$ and $R_o = 1.2$)
- ductile plate walls (Type D, with $R_d = 5.0$ and $R_o = 1.6$)
- limited ductility plate walls (Type LD, with $R_d = 2.0$ and $R_o = 1.5$).

In addition, other special framing systems are permitted under Clause 27.12.

In each structural system, certain structural elements are designed to dissipate energy by inelastic straining; other members and connections in the frame must be designed to respond elastically to the loads induced by the yielding elements. Generally, the dissipating elements in moment frames are the beams, in concentrically braced frames the braces, in eccentrically braced frames the links, and in plate walls the wall infill plates. Other elements may also contribute, but to a much lesser extent, for example the connection panel zone in moment-resisting frames, the gusset plates in concentrically braced frames, the outer beam segments in eccentrically braced frames and beams and columns in steel plate walls.

Properly detailed moment-resisting frames can exhibit very ductile behaviour. Three categories of moment-resisting frame are recognized: first, ductile moment-resisting, or Type D, frames, in which members and connections are selected and braced to ensure that severe inelastic straining can take place; second, moderately ductile moment-resisting frames, or Type MD, in which the member details can satisfy the lower inelastic straining demand in structures proportioned to resist the greater design loads, while at the same time, connections are adequate to accommodate the associated forces and deformations. For both systems connection details have to be demonstrated, by means of physical testing, as satisfying certain deformation criteria under the action of cyclic load. Results of previously tested connection assemblies may be used for this purpose subject to close similarity in size, material and geometry. Annex J contains information on connection designs and details to achieve the required behaviour. The third system, Type LD for limited ductility, undergoes still less inelastic demand consistent with the higher design loads, and can in general make use of traditional connection detailing, combined with special requirements associated with welding, etc.

Concentrically braced frames are those in which the centre-lines of diagonal braces, beams and columns are approximately concurrent with little or no joint eccentricity. Inelastic straining must take place in bracing members subjected principally to axial load. Compression members dissipate energy by inelastic bending after buckling, and in subsequent straightening after load reversal. Cyclic local buckling can lead to early fracture, and consequently width-to-thickness limits are restricted for braces. These frames usually have limited redundancy, and are prone to concentration of inelastic response in one or a few storeys where energy dissipation is localized. Emphasis in these categories is placed on the presence of braces with similar tensile strength in opposite directions such that the reduction in storey shear resistance is minimized in the event of brace buckling in a storey.

Two categories of concentrically braced frames are considered, those with moderate ductility (MD) and limited ductility (LD). Both permit several bracing configurations. Compared with past editions of the Standard, the provisions maintain strict limits on width-thickness ratios; overall slenderness limits of braces are relaxed, and changes have been made to the requirements for connection design forces. However, height limitations apply. In S16-09, bracing configurations with braces intersecting columns at one or more elevations between horizontal diaphragms are now permitted for Type LD braced frames, provided that the columns can accommodate the bending demand due to buckling and yielding of braces within the storey and that horizontal struts are introduced to ensure continuous load path between tension acting braces.

Ductile eccentrically braced frames are those in which diagonal braces, at least at one end, intersect the beam instead of the beam and column intersection or, in the case of chevron bracing, the two braces do not intersect the beam at a common point. These configurations create eccentric beam links that are designed to dissipate energy. The Standard gives provisions for frames with links in the beams. Beams can be W-shapes or built-up rectangular tubular sections. Lateral bracing at the link ends can be omitted when the latter is used.

In ductile buckling-restrained braced frames, the braces include a core element with reduced cross-section segment where yielding is expected to develop in both compression and tension. The core is prevented from buckling by means of a lateral restraining mechanism.

Typically, brace details vary depending on the suppliers, but the inelastic cyclic performance must be demonstrated by means of physical testing. The brace compressive and tensile resistances established in these tests must be used in the capacity design process.

Plate walls are formed by thin infill wall plates framed by beams and columns. These highly redundant and stiff systems dissipate energy by yielding of the infill plate and, often, yielding of the framing members. The good seismic performance anticipated is reflected in their respective applicable values of R_d and R_o. Two categories are defined, Types D and LD. In S16-09, new design requirements have been included for beams and columns of Type D plate walls. The Standard now permits the introduction of uniformly distributed circular perforations in the infill plates to avoid excessive lateral overstrength without resorting to using plates that are too thin for practical construction. Corner openings can also be introduced in the wall plates to facilitate the passage of electrical and mechanical equipment. In S16-09, the design and detailing requirements specified for Type D walls also apply to Type LD walls, except that beams and column need not be rigidly connected for Type LD walls.

In all systems, because the behaviour of connections will often be critical for good performance under severe earthquake loading, the engineer's responsibility for a seismically critical structure includes not only the provision of connection design loads but also the specification of connection type and details.

27.1 General

The expression "$I_E F_a S_a(0.2)$", adopted in the NBCC 2005, is referred to as the "specified short-period spectral acceleration ratio" in Clause 27, whereas the expression "$I_E F_v S_a(1.0)$" is referred to as the "specified one-second spectral acceleration ratio".

27.1.1 A distinction is made between the "seismic-force-resisting system" (SFRS) and the "vertical seismic-force-resisting system". The latter corresponds essentially to the vertical bracing, wall or frame system that takes the form of one or more of the systems described in Clause 27. The SFRS is the whole structural system resisting lateral loads, including the foundations, anchorage to foundations, the vertical seismic-force-resisting system, collector elements, and roof and floor diaphragms. In some cases, members specifically designed for gravity loading only may be relied upon for a contribution to a reserve lateral resistance following storey yielding, and in this case some provisions of Clause 27 apply also to these members (see Clause 27.5.5.2).

27.1.2 This Clause sets out the principles of capacity design and states that the ductile energy-dissipating elements must be clearly identified and detailed along the lateral load path, and that a proper strength hierarchy must be provided in the seismic-force-resisting system to constrain inelastic response to these ductile elements. The energy-dissipating elements must be designed to sustain several cycles of inelastic loading with minimum strength and stiffness deterioration. Other elements must be designed to remain essentially elastic for the duration of the seismic ground motion. Anchor rods must transfer the loads to the foundation.

The maximum anticipated seismic loads imposed on the non-dissipating elements can be determined by hand calculations, static incremental (push-over) analysis or nonlinear dynamic time-history analysis. The inelastic behaviour under cyclic loading of the dissipating elements, including yielding, strain hardening or strength degradation must be accounted for in the calculations and numerical models. Non-dissipative elements can be assumed to behave elastically in numerical models. A number of site-representative ground motions are necessary in nonlinear dynamic analysis, and maximum response loads in the members are to be determined. Such analyses may be of particular value for tall buildings, especially those beyond the height limits imposed by some other provisions of Clause 27. Other applications may be justified in cases where the requirements of capacity design are known to lead to conservative design loads (e.g. moment-resisting frames proportioned for stiffness and wind effects, plate walls or eccentrically braced frames with long links (Han 1998)).

In cases where the energy-dissipating elements have been oversized, a limit has been placed on the maximum forces that the non-dissipating elements must resist by setting the maximum anticipated seismic load equal to that corresponding to $R_d R_o = 1.3$. This maximum load corresponds to the elastic seismic load level determined using $R_d = 1.0$ while it is also recognized that the non-dissipating elements generally possess an overstrength level that justifies $R_o = 1.3$. Connections designed for seismic loads corresponding to $R_d R_o = 1.3$ must exhibit a ductile governing failure mode, such as yielding in tension or bolt bearing (Tremblay *et al.* 2009). Otherwise, the limit on seismic loads must be increased to loads corresponding to $R_d R_o = 1.0$. In computing the forces on the structure corresponding to $R_d R_o = 1.3$, the upper limit of V = $(2/3)S(0.2)I_E W/(R_d R_o)$ given in sentence 4.1.8.11(2) of NBCC 2005 applies provided that the seismic-force-resisting system has an R_d equal to or greater than 1.5. In this case, the upper limit becomes $(2/3)S(0.2)I_E W/1.3$. Also, where foundation "rocking" is accounted for in accordance with NBCC, design forces for the SFRS may be limited to values associated with maximum forces that can develop with foundation rocking (always larger than forces at $R_d R_o = 2$).

27.1.3 The vertical seismic force-resisting systems described in Clause 27 are expected to exhibit proper performance when non-structural elements such as walls or interior partitions are separated from the structural elements under earthquake deflections. If this cannot be achieved, the effects of the interaction must be accounted for in the analysis and the design.

27.1.4 Gravity load-carrying elements such as columns and beam-to-column connection elements must be able to support the companion gravity loads while undergoing the large deformations expected during earthquakes. For example, a simple beam end connection in the displaced configuration should resist shear due to the companion gravity loads.

Under a severe ground motion, columns in multi-storey structures will be subjected to shear forces and bending moments due to variations in storey drifts that will develop along the structure height. Splices in the columns that are not part of the seismic force-resisting systems must be designed to resist shear forces associated with this response. This provision applies in both orthogonal directions. Requirements for splices in columns that are part of the seismic-resisting systems are given in Clauses 27.2 to 27.11.

27.1.5 This Clause applies principally to the materials used in the yielding elements and connections of the seismic force-resisting system. Limits on the yield stress and the provisions of Clause 8.6(a) ensure adequate post-yield behaviour of the material. Use of other materials would require demonstration that the energy-dissipating elements can sustain the very high post-yield strains needed to achieve the performance assumed in design. Because of the dynamic loading, toughness requirements are now specified for buildings with specified short-period spectral acceleration ratios, $I_E F_a S_a(0.2)$, greater than 0.55 for thick plates and shapes in energy-dissipating elements, and in welded members anywhere in the seismic force-resisting system. Weld metal in primary connections is also subject to toughness requirements.

27.1.6 The requirements for bolted connections ensure that friction plays a role in load transfer, and too rapid slip into bearing is avoided.

If beam-to-column connections are demonstrated by means of physical testing to meet the various deformation requirements for different categories of moment-resisting frames and eccentrically braced frames, then the requirements of this clause can be waived.

27.1.7 In order to ensure the desired hierarchy of yielding, the relative strengths of dissipating and non-dissipating structural elements must be known. This requires knowledge of the actual, or probable, yield stresses. The specified minimum yield stress must be used when computing the resistance of the non-dissipating elements whereas the probable yield stress is used in estimating the loads arising from yielding elements. The probable yield stress may be obtained from coupon tests on the same heats of the materials used in the construction, or, since the material will not in general be available at the time of design, may be estimated by use of the factor R_y given in this clause. The imposed minimum value of 385 MPa implies a high R_y value for lower-yield steels in common use until quite recently, and is due in part to the use of multi-grade material in recent years and also to the uncertainty of the actual yields achieved in earlier grades.

For W shapes, similar ratios between expected and nominal yield strengths are observed for the flanges and the web and, hence, the same R_y value can be used for the entire cross section. Surveys by Schmidt and Bartlett (2002) and by Liu *et al.* (2007) showed that HSS exhibit higher characteristic-to-nominal yield strength ratios compared to W shapes. Furthermore, the ratio for HSS generally increases when the perimeter-to-wall thickness ratio is decreased, i.e. larger ratios for more compact sections such as those required for the energy-dissipating elements. A higher R_y value equal to 1.30 is therefore specified for HSS in CSA S16-09. This value corresponds to the ratio of the mean to nominal values of the product $A F_y$ based on the data collected by Schmidt and Bartlett (2002). CSA S16 does not provide any requirements for ASTM A53 pipes used as energy-dissipating elements such as bracing members. If this material is used, appropriate R_y values should be considered (see AISC 2005).

The error in using the minimum specified value rather than the probable value when calculating width-thickness limits is acceptably small. However, a minimum value of F_y is set at 350 MPa for use in this calculation due to the common use of multi-grade steels in recent years.

27.1.8 In the computation of second-order effects, a linear amplification is given following the procedure outlined in the Structural Commentaries to the National Building Code of Canada. This method differs from that given in Clause 8.6 since the displacements, under which this provision ensures that the prescribed lateral resistance can be developed, result from the anticipated inelastic seismic deformations. Notional loads and $P\Delta$ effects must be considered for the design of the energy-dissipating elements. They need not be considered for the design of the non-dissipating elements (e.g. beams and columns in concentrically braced steel frames) as the lateral load effects on these elements are limited by the capacity of the dissipating elements. In case the dissipating elements are overstrong and the seismic loads corresponding to the $R_d R_o = 1.3$ (or 1.0, as applicable) are used to size the non-dissipating elements, notional loads and $P\Delta$ effects must be included in the analysis.

27.1.9 Regions where large inelastic strains are expected to occur in the SFRS are designated as protected zones. Protected zones include plastic hinging regions in moment frames, links of ductile eccentrically braced frames, braces in concentrically braced steel frames, etc. They are defined in the Clauses applicable to the designated system. Within these zones, discontinuity, rapid change in cross-section or material embrittlement caused by welding, cutting or penetration at the fabrication plant or the construction site may lead to premature fracture under cyclic inelastic response. Hence, unless engineered or part of test assemblies satisfying the specified performance, welded, bolted, screwed or shot-in attachments for perimeter edge angles, exterior facades, partitions, ductwork, piping or other construction shall not be placed within protected zones. For instance, welded shear studs and decking attachments that penetrate the beam flange shall not be placed on the beam flanges within the protected zone, unless approved by the Designer. Decking arc-spot welds required to secure decking are, however, permitted. Fabrication or erection operations that cause discontinuities are also prohibited in protected zones. Discontinuities accidentally created within protected zones, such as tack welds, erection aids, air-arc gouging and thermal cutting shall be repaired as required by the Designer. Guidance on acceptable repair methods can be found in CSA-W59.

The extent of the protected zones must be identified on the design documents. The information can be conveyed to the construction site by means of coating and labels on both faces with large lettering pertaining to the restriction on attachments and penetrations. Where the protected zones are subsequently covered by fire protection material, provision for visible labels after the application of fire protection should be considered.

27.2 Type D (Ductile) Moment-Resisting Frames, R_d = 5.0, R_o = 1.5

27.2.1 General

27.2.1.1 Type D moment-resisting steel frames have traditionally been designed to develop inelastic deformations at beam-to-column joints, either by plastic hinging in the beams or columns, or by inelastic shear deformations in the panel zone of H-shaped columns (bent about the strong axis). However, numerous welded moment frames have suffered connection fractures as a result of the 1994 Northridge and 1995 Kobe earthquakes, calling for a comprehensive review of that design practice. Extensive revisions to Clause 27.2 were introduced in the 2001 edition of S16 based on the research findings and engineering consensus reached following these two earthquakes (FEMA 1995, 1997, 2000). No major changes have been made in S16-09, except for the addition of the provision for protected zones in Clause 27.2.8.

The current design philosophy requires that plastic hinges develop at predetermined locations within the frame, such as in beams away from the face of the columns. This is possible either by locally strengthening the beams near the columns (by haunches, cover plates or other methods), by locally weakening the beams at selected plastic hinge locations some distance from the columns or by using special detailing that ensures ductile response. Annex J references documents giving specific details that will achieve the necessary ductility. Other systems are permissible if demonstrated by physical tests to be capable of providing the performance specified in later Clauses.

Whenever column bases are designed to have a flexural resistance, plastic hinges are necessary to permit development of the preferred plastic collapse mechanism (see Figure 2-63 – Desirable beam-sway collapse mechanism, and undesirable column-sway mechanism). Column hinging is otherwise undesirable as it may lead to formation of a storey plastic mechanism with undue ductility demands compared to other storeys. An exception is made for single-storey buildings, for which this risk of localized damage is not an issue. This waiver is not extended to two-storey (or taller) buildings; given that the same column section is likely to be used over the two storeys, this could force concentration of plastic deformations at the first storey, resulting in greater local ductility demands than assumed by the design process.

Although the panel zone provides excellent ability to absorb energy by means of cyclic plastic shearing deformations (Popov *et al.* 1986), large inelastic deformations there result in large curvatures in the column flanges. For joints in which the beams are welded to the columns, these curvatures may precipitate cracking of the beam weld at that location. Panel zone yielding without considerable concurrent beam yielding is generally not desirable for these connections, and the current provisions limit this behaviour except when using a connection detail for which panel zone yielding has been found appropriate by testing. Note that optimization of panel zone and beam yielding is difficult given the inherent statistical variability in the steel strength of beams and columns.

27.2.1.3 In evaluating the relative strengths of the structural components at the joint, an estimate should be made of the contribution of the slab. Clause 27.2.8 specifies that studs are not permitted in beam plastic hinge regions. Thus the contribution of the slab can be neglected if specific construction details are provided that prevent the slab bearing on the columns. In the

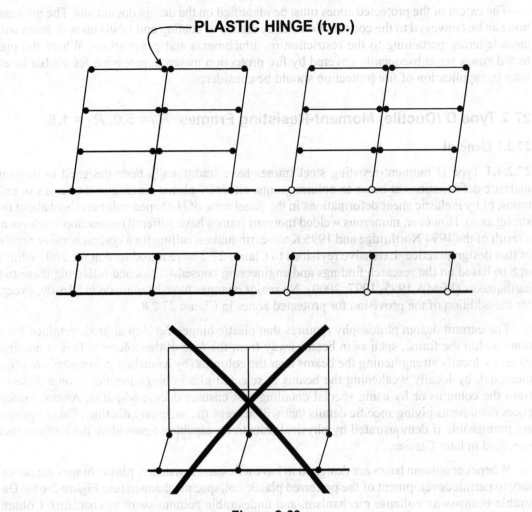

Figure 2-63
Desirable Beam-Sway Collapse Mechanism
and Undesirable Column-Sway Mechanism

absence of such details, under positive bending moment, the ultimate compressive resistance of the concrete can reach values of $1.3f'_c$.

27.2.2 Beams

27.2.2.1 In moment frames, beams are nearly always bent in reverse curvature between columns unless one end is pinned. The lateral bracing requirements here assume that the seismic moment at one end of the beam is M_p, and that zero seismic moment exists at the other end; to these the gravity load moments must be added.

Lateral bracing of beams near the plastic hinge location should be according to the configuration, strength, and stiffness considered in the tests referenced in the commentary on Clause 27.2.5. Attachments in the area of anticipated plastic behaviour are in general proscribed (see Clause 27.2.8).

27.2.3 Columns (Including Beam-Columns)

27.2.3.1 The width-thickness requirements for columns that develop plastic hinging follow from Clause 27.2.1.2. The axial load in the column is also restricted because the rapid deterioration of beam-column flexural strength when high axial loads are acting limits the ductility.

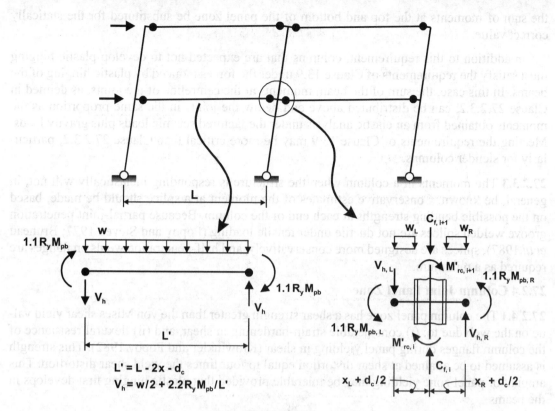

Figure 2-64
Type D Moment-Resisting Frame – Free-Body Diagram

When columns are expected to develop plastic hinging, structural elements adjacent to the column plastic hinges must be able to resist the full plastic moment of the columns. For example, at the base of a column, the intended performance would not be achieved if anchor rods yield instead of the column itself. Due to anchor rod elongation, column base fixity would be lost after a few cycles, resulting in a considerable reduction in base shear resistance and the ensuing risk of an undesirable localized storey-collapse mechanism at the first level.

27.2.3.2 Columns may accumulate forces from several yielding elements, and these must be considered.

The equation presented in this clause is intended to minimize plastic hinging in columns and promote plastic hinging of beams. Hence, it does not apply to columns in single-storey buildings where plastic hinging is expected near the top of the columns. This equation cannot ensure that individual columns will not yield at some time during earthquake response, due to the shifting of column inflection points during dynamic response (Bondy 1996), but the extent of this yielding should not be detrimental. This requirement is in addition to the requirements of Clause 13.9.

For the equation presented to be statically correct, equilibrium requires that the moment at the intersection of the beam and column centrelines should be determined by projecting the sum of the nominal column plastic moment from the top and bottom of the beam moment connection (Figure 2-64 – Free-body diagrams to calculate V_p at the plastic hinge location, and moment at face and centre of column). However, this may be conservative for connections having deep panel zones and/or haunches, and current North American practice permits that the sum of moments at the top and bottom of the panel zone be substituted for the statically correct value.

In addition to this requirement, columns that are expected not to develop plastic hinging must satisfy the requirements of Clause 13.9 under the forces induced by plastic hinging of the beams. In this case, the sum of the beam moments at the centreline of the joints, as defined in Clause 27.2.3.2, can be distributed above and below the joints in the same proportion as the moments obtained from an elastic analysis under the factored seismic loads plus gravity loads. Meeting the requirements of Clause 13.9 may be more critical than Clause 27.2.3.2, particularly for slender columns.

27.2.3.3 The moments in a column when the structure is responding inelastically will not, in general, be known. Conservative estimates of the moment at a splice should be made, based on the possible bending strengths at each end of the column. Because partial-joint penetration groove welded splices are not ductile under tensile loading (Popov and Steven 1977; Bruneau et al.1987), splices are designed more conservatively, and half-penetration welds on flanges are required as a minimum.

27.2.4 Column Joint Panel Zone

27.2.4.1 The column panel zone has a shear strength greater than the von Mises shear yield value on the web due to: (i) considerable strain-hardening in shear, and (ii) flexural resistance of the column flanges during panel yielding in shear (Krawinkler and Popov 1982). This strength is assumed to be attained at shear distortion equal to four times the yield shear distortion. This amount of panel zone yielding may be tolerable provided that plastic hinging first develops in the beams

Yielding in the panel zone is perceived by some as beneficial since it reduces the inelastic demand on the beams and provides sharing of energy dissipation. However, some concerns remain for beam welded connections because of the impact of plastic shear distortions and localized column flange bending on the integrity of the beam flange welds. A consensus opinion has not yet been reached. An upper limit of 0.2 is placed on the term $3b_c t_c^2/d_c d_b w'$ to ensure that the panel zone strength is not reached prior to development of the plastic moment enhanced by strain-hardening in the adjacent beams.

27.2.4.2 These requirements ensure that the panel zone can undergo cyclic plastic straining. All four sides of the doubler plates must be welded to contiguous elements, unless the doubler plate extends beyond the stiffeners. Lateral bracing to the column flange may be provided through transverse beams connected to the column web.

Stronger panel zones can usually be provided at low cost, and the Von Mises equation ($0.58F_y$ on the entire web of the column) is proposed as an alternative to the panel zone strength equation of Clause 27.2.4.1. In this case, the panel zone remains elastic and special detailing of the panel zone described in the first part of this clause is not warranted. Note that the 0.55 in the shear strength equations is obtained by taking the depth of column web equal to $0.95d_c$.

27.2.4.3 The details given in this clause are necessary to ensure strength and ductility of the panel zone and its reinforcement.

27.2.5 Beam-to-Column Joints and Connections

27.2.5.1 Extensive research was initiated following the Northridge earthquake to identify the reasons that led to the numerous observed beam-to-column connection fractures, and to formulate new connection design requirements. The result of this large research endeavour is a database of connection types that have been experimentally proven able to provide satisfactory seismic performance, with specific information regarding configurations, details, quality control, and other requirements. Reference to this material includes CISC (2009), Ricles *et al.* (2004) and the references given in Annex J.

The designer must either:

(a) use connections conforming to size, material, detail dimension and other limitations, configurations, quality controls and welding types and procedures of those already proven satisfactory by tests, or

(b) conduct tests to demonstrate that under a number of cycles of loading the required total drift specified in this clause can be reached. A protocol for such testing is referenced in Annex J.

27.2.5.2 The beam web connection shall have a resistance adequate to carry shears induced by yielding at the beam-to-column joint.

27.2.6 Bracing

Bracing of both top and bottom beam flanges as well as column flanges shall be considered. If no transverse beams exist at a level, the column must be designed to provide restraint to yielding beam flanges in the manner indicated in (d).

27.2.7 Fasteners

Consideration should be given to the fact that plastic hinge locations will not be predicted by an elastic analysis of the frame. A few welded wide-flange column shapes, with webs thicker than 20 mm, do not have complete penetration welds between their web and flanges. These are identified in the tables of properties and dimensions, Part 6.

27.2.8 Protected Zones

In S16-01, Clause 27.2.2 prohibited abrupt changes in beam flange cross-section where plastic hinging was expected (unless a reduced beam section was used), and limitations on attachments that could detrimentally affect the inelastic performance of plastic hinges were prescribed in Clause 27.2.8. In S16-09, these two clauses have been replaced by a new Clause 27.2.8 to address the zones that must be protected in moment-resisting frames. This new clause should be applied in conjunction with Clause 27.1.9 where limitations applicable to protected zones are defined. In moment-resisting frames, protected zones include segments along the beams and columns where plastic hinges are expected to occur. Limitations on cross-section changes in beam plastic hinges are also specified.

27.3 Type MD (Moderately Ductile) Moment-Resisting Frames, R_d = 3.5, R_o = 1.5

The ductility-related force modification factor of 3.5 is sufficiently large for Type MD moment-resisting frames to develop large cyclic inelastic deformations during earthquakes. For that reason, and because larger structural members will result from the larger design forces considered, most requirements of Clause 27.2 are applicable. However, beam-to-column joints need only be able to develop a minimum drift angle rotation of 0.03 radians (compared with 0.04 for comparably designed Type D moment-resisting frames). This reduced deformation requirement may be useful when a tested connection fails to reach the 0.04 requirement. A greater advantage of this clause may, however, consist in adopting the relaxed provisions of 27.3(a) and (b) in combination with the higher design load. Practical applications of this system include moment frames in moderate seismicity regions where added frame stiffness is required to satisfy $U_2 \leq 1.4$ (Clause 27.1.8) or wind effects.

27.4 Type LD (Limited Ductility) Moment-Resisting Frames, $R_d = 2.0$, $R_o = 1.3$

This system can accept limited yielding in beams, columns or joints. Panel zone design follows Clause 27.2.4.2, and thus only limited yielding is expected. These frames are subject to restrictions on height and seismic demand level. They are restricted to 60 metres and 30 metres in height for regions of moderate and high seismicity, respectively. In addition, the strong-column/weak-beam design concept applies to buildings with specified short-period spectral acceleration ratios ($I_E F_a S_a(0.2)$) greater than 0.55 and any buildings taller than 60 metres (permitted in low seismicity regions only). However, nominal plastic beam moments are considered in the strong-column design because of limited beam yielding in this system as compared to that in the more ductile categories. To accommodate yielding, sections must be Class 2 or better. It is anticipated that in many cases joint details will conform to traditional forms of construction used for moment-resisting frames. If welded joints are used, Clause 27.4.4.3 reduces the tensile resistance to a normal load on the column flange to 60% of the value given in Clause 21.3 to account for the highly non-uniform stresses in a beam flange when welded to an unstiffened column flange. Also for welded joints, Clause 27.4.4.4 specifies detailed requirements for removal of steel backing bars and run-off tabs used for welding the bottom flange, and the repair of potential notches.

Connections that can accommodate an interstorey drift angle of 0.02 radians, following tests as discussed in Annex J, may alternatively be used.

Practical applications of this system include moment-resisting frames in moderate seismicity regions where added frame stiffness is required to satisfy drift limits, $U_2 \leq 1.4$ (Clause 27.1.8) or wind effects and certain low-rise buildings in higher seismicity areas.

27.5 Type MD (Moderately Ductile) Concentrically Braced Frames, $R_d = 3.0$, $R_o = 1.3$

27.5.1 General

Type MD concentrically braced frames are designed to dissipate energy essentially by yielding of the bracing members. Energy dissipation occurs under brace elongation, inelastic buckling of the braces and inelastic bending when the braces are subsequently straightened. In low-rise V-brace or chevron-brace frames, energy can also be dissipated through limited bending of the beams at the brace intersection point.

27.5.2 Bracing Systems

27.5.2.1

Three bracing configurations are explicitly provided for in the braced frame category, and a maximum building height is specified for each. Multi-storey concentrically braced frames have limited capability of distributing vertically the inelastic demand after buckling and yielding of the braces have developed at a given level. Lateral overstrength resulting from the inherent difference in capacity between tension and compression braces acting in pairs serves to prevent the concentration of inelastic demand (Lacerte and Tremblay 2006). The continuity of the columns which, when provided as specified in Clause 27.5.5.2, provides sufficient reserve strength and stiffness, also helps mitigate the formation of a weak storey response and dynamic instability under severe earthquakes (MacRae et al. 2004, Chen et al. 2008).

The tendency to instability is more pronounced in tall frames in which the inelastic demand tends to concentrate in the bottom floors, which are the first affected by the ground motion, or in the upper levels due to higher mode effects. Thus, a maximum height is specified for each of the three concentric bracing configurations explicitly provided for in Clauses 27.5 and 27.6.

The provisions of Clauses 27.5 and 27.6 are based on the results of frame behavioural studies using inelastic time-history analysis (Tremblay 2000, Tremblay and Robert 2001, Marino and Nakashima 2006). The buildings studied were regular in form with uniform storey height varying between 3.5 and 4 m. Frames with heights up to 80% of the height limits as specified in NBCC can be expected to perform satisfactorily with no further inelastic analysis being needed. Those within the height range of 80% to 100% of the NBCC limits are required to be designed for additional seismic forces as stipulated in Clauses 27.5.2 and 27.6.2 for each respective braced frame configuration. Taller buildings, those with significantly greater storey heights or other systems (e.g. bracing combined with moment-resisting beam-to-column connections), may require further study, and such systems can be investigated using inelastic time-history analysis; alternatively, it would be necessary to demonstrate that each storey possesses a reserve of strength and stiffness, at the drifts expected under the inelastic response, to prevent a concentration of inelastic actions.

Judgement must also be exercised when the geometry of the frame deviates significantly from the uniform configuration considered in the referenced studies. For instance, industrial buildings or hangars in which the bracing system in any one level includes a stack of two or more bracing panels may be prone to concentration of the inelastic demand in a few bracing members. Such configuration is only permitted for Type LD braced steel frames, and special requirements apply, as described in Clause 27.6.6.

Knee bracing and K-bracing are excluded from the Type MD braced frame category because plastic hinging that will develop within the clear length of the columns may lead to their instability. Braced frames consisting of more than one X-bracing panel are permitted for Type LD braced frames, as described in the subsequent section.

27.5.2.2 Proportioning

In order to achieve symmetric inelastic response, the storey shear resistance in opposite directions should remain equal or nearly the same under the design earthquake. Because the capacity of a concentrically braced frame after buckling of the braces is mainly governed by its tension braces, the requirement is based on the storey shear resistance provided by the tension-acting braces in each direction. In order to avoid excessive torsional response in the inelastic response, this requirement must be met in each vertical plane of braces and in both orthogonal directions.

27.5.2.3 Tension-Compression Bracing

In tension-compression bracing systems, braces in each vertical plane are designed to resist their share of factored tensile and compressive forces based on the analysis. These braces typically act in pairs as is the case in single-storey X-bracing, two-storey (split) X-bracing, chevron bracing or V-bracing configuration. Tension-compression bracing also includes configurations consisting of an odd number of braces provided that they satisfy Clause 27.5.2.2 in every plane of bracing at every level. Compared with the tension-only system, the stockier braces in this system provide greater post-buckling capacity and stiffness. This, combined with the stiffness provided by continuous columns, has been shown to provide stability in frames up to about 32 metres in height (Tremblay 2000, Tremblay and Poncet 2007, Izvernari et al. 2007). Therefore, Moderately Ductile tension-compression frames that are within 40 metres in height, as permitted in NBCC, but exceed 32 metres, should be designed for higher forces as required in this clause.

27.5.2.4 Chevron Bracing

The commentary to Clause 27.5.2.3 also applies to this Clause. Chevron bracing, in which the braces (which may be either both above the beam or both below it) meet within the central region of the beam, is permitted in the Type MD concentrically braced frame category provided that the beams in the bracing bents remain essentially elastic after buckling of the bracing members has occurred. Braces in frames with such strong beams can develop their full yield capacity in tension, and the structure exhibits a more stable hysteretic response than when weaker beams are employed. Frames with weaker beams typically experience rapid and significant deterioration of their storey shear resistance and stiffness after buckling of the braces (Remennikov and Walpole 1998a; Tremblay and Robert 2000, 2001). When the tension brace yields in tension, the compression brace at the same level only develops its post-buckling resistance, C'_u, as defined in Clause 27.5.3.4. This case is illustrated in Figure 2-66. When braces are connected to the beam from above, the expected brace compression resistance of the brace, C_u, must also be considered; this condition may be more critical when there is an extremely high gravity load and the beam plastic bending produces a downward displacement at the plastic hinge. For both cases the beams must be checked as beam-columns resisting the bending moments and axial forces due to the gravity loading and these brace loads without the vertical support provided by the braces. Beam-to-column connections must be sized for the same loading conditions.

Limited yielding in the beams does not adversely affect the response of low-rise chevron braced frames, and the brace tension load to be used in the design of the beams in frames up to 4 storeys has been reduced for such frames (Tremblay and Robert 2000, 2001). In such a case, plastic hinging will likely develop in the beams, and the beam connections should then be designed for shear forces associated with the probable bending resistance of the beams.

In both designs, the beams must be adequately laterally restrained at the brace connection point to resist out-of-plane components of the axial load acting in the beams and the braces.

27.5.2.5 Tension-Only Bracing

Designing the braces to resist, in tension, 100% of the lateral loads acting in each direction can lead to a more economical design when the lateral loads are low or moderate or when long braces are used. Tension-only bracing is not permitted in V-or chevron bracing. Although the contribution of these braces when acting in compression is ignored in resisting design lateral loads, the braces must meet the slenderness limit and detailing requirements in Clause 27.5.3, and the compression loads they can deliver must be accounted for in the design of the connections, beams and columns (see Clauses 27.5.4 and 27.5.5). Because the braces are generally less stocky as compared to tension-compression braces, this system exhibits less energy dissipation capacity, and larger inelastic deformations are therefore expected. Every column in the building is required to be fully continuous in order to resist in bending the concentration of inelastic demand in a single storey. It has been shown that frames up to about 16 metres in height perform satisfactorily (Tremblay 2000). Moderately Ductile tension-only braced frames that are within 20 metres in height, as permitted in NBCC, but exceed 16 metres, should be designed for higher forces as required in this clause. However, other bracing systems may prove to be more economical for frames taller than 3 storeys in height because erection safety usually dictates field splices for column tiers spanning more than 3 storeys.

27.5.3 Diagonal Bracing Members

In most cases, including tension-only systems, the post-buckling capacity of braces is necessary to contribute to stability and therefore in all these systems, the slenderness limits specified in this clause apply to braces in all Type MD concentrically braced frames, including tension-only systems.

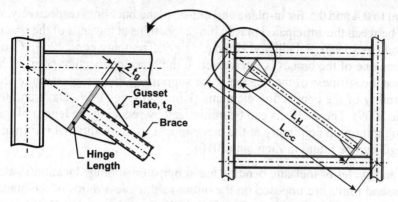

(a) Single Brace

(b) X-bracing

Figure 2-65
Out-of-Plane Buckling of a Brace with Gusset Plates
Detailed to Accommodate End Inelastic Rotation

27.5.3.1 The energy dissipation capacity of bracing members under cyclic inelastic loading increases when the effective slenderness ratio, KL/r, is decreased (Jain *et al*. 1980, Popov and Black 1980, Tremblay *et al*. 2003, Lee and Bruneau 2005), and maximum brace slenderness has traditionally been specified to control the dynamic response of braced frames. Bracing systems with slender braces designed to act both in tension and compression have, however, significant lateral overstrength due to the difference that exists between the compressive and tensile capacities of the braces. This overstrength permits the maintenance of a stable inelastic response under severe earthquakes, and that is why it is possible to allow a brace slenderness limit of 200 for Type MD frames. This limit still provides a minimum energy dissipation capacity that allows the use of tension-only braces in low-rise structures. Past test programs showed that rectangular and circular HSS bracing members with low slenderness ratios can develop premature fracture at the plastic hinge region (Fell *et al* 2009, Tang and Goel 1989, Tremblay *et al*. 2002, Tremblay *et al*. 2008); a minimum effective slenderness ratio is specified to preclude this undesirable failure mode.

When determining the brace slenderness, the actual support conditions of the braces must be accounted for in determining KL. As discussed later (see Clause 27.5.4.3), the brace end connection detail with a single gusset plate and free hinge zone in the gusset shown in Figure 2-65(a) has gained wide acceptance in practice. When using this detail, the brace effective length KL for out-of-plane buckling can be taken equal to the length between the hinge locations, L_H. Tests on double-angle braces using that detail showed that a K factor of 0.5 can be applied to evaluate the brace slenderness for in-plane buckling (Astaneh-Asl and Goel 1984). For X-bracing, when the brace end connections are detailed with single vertical gussets, K can be taken equal to 0.4 and 0.5 for in-plane and out-of-plane buckling, respectively, with L taken as the length between the anticipated plastic hinge locations at the ends of the bracing members (El-Tayem and Goel 1986, Sabelli and Hohbach 1999, Tremblay *et al.* 2003). Caution must be exercised when one of the braces is interrupted at the brace connection point of X-bracing, as this can reduce the stiffness of the tension brace supporting the compression brace and/or lead to local instability of the connecting elements (Kim and Goel 1996, Davaran 2001, Doravan and Hoveidae 2009). These effects can be minimized by reducing the length of the connection or by ensuring minimum continuity at the brace intersection. Additional information on brace effective length can be found in Ziemian (2010).

27.5.3.2 Several cycles of inelastic bending are anticipated at hinge location(s) along the bracing members, and limits are imposed on the width-to-thickness ratios of the braces to prevent premature fracture of these members. Physical testing has shown that HSS bracing members exhibit limited fracture life, and relatively more stringent limits are specified for these sections (Fell *et al.* 1989, Lee and Goel 1987, Liu 1987, Sherman 1996, Tang and Goel 1989). Relaxation of width-to-thickness limits is permitted when lower inelastic demand is expected in the braces such as when slender bracing members are used (buckling becomes essentially elastic) or when the structure is located in a region of low seismicity (Tremblay 2001). The inelastic demand is also less critical in the vertical legs of double-angle bracing members buckling about their plane of symmetry, and less stringent requirements are specified for this case.

27.5.3.3 Buckling of the individual elements of built-up bracing members under earthquake loading may result in high localized inelastic deformations which can lead to premature fracture of the braces (Aslani and Goel 1991). Individual buckling is therefore precluded by limiting the slenderness of the individual components. When buckling of the braces induces shear in the stitch fasteners, these fasteners are expected to transfer in shear the full yield capacity of the smaller brace component upon subsequent straightening of the braces, and the stitch connections must be designed accordingly (Astaneh-Asl and Goel 1985).

Braces with bolt holes at the location of the plastic hinges have exhibited early fracture at the net section, and bolted stitches must be avoided in these regions (Astaneh-Asl and Goel 1984). In determining the governing overall slenderness of the bracing members and the location of plastic hinges, attention must be paid to the actual end fixity and support conditions of the bracing members (see also Clause 27.5.3.1). Plastic hinges in the bracing members will develop approximately at half the distance between supports, i.e., at one quarter and three quarters of the brace length in X-bracing, as well as near the brace end connections if such connections do not permit rotation to develop upon buckling.

27.5.3.4 Probable Brace Resistances

In previous editions of CSA S16, brace expected strength values to be used in capacity design were specified in Clauses related to brace connection design. Recognizing that brace capacities are also used for the design of beams, columns, connections other than brace connections, etc., a separate clause has been introduced in S16-09 to define clearly the expected strength values of braces in tension and compression. A realistic estimate of the expected compressive strength of a brace, C_u, is obtained by multiplying its compressive resistance by 1.2. In this calculation, the probable yield stress of the steel should be used, and the resistance factor does not apply. In tension, the maximum anticipated brace force T_u corresponds to the probable yield tensile strength. The compressive resistance of a brace reduces when the brace is subjected to cyclic inelastic axial loading (Lee and Bruneau 2005), and this post-buckling brace compression resistance can lead to more critical loading conditions for members or connections, such as beams of chevron bracing or interior columns. Figure 2-66(a) shows examples where compression acting braces in the buckled state (C'_u) produce maximum axial compression in the beam of an X-bracing and maximum bending moment in the beam of a chevron bracing.

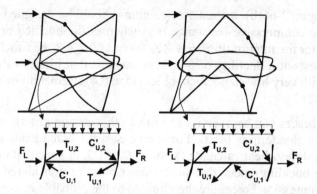

(a) Beams in X-Bracing and Chevron Bracing

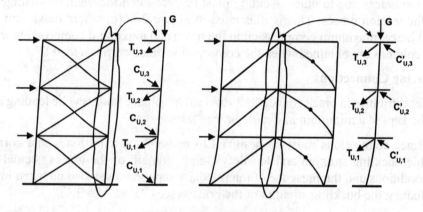

(b) Exterior and Interior Columns

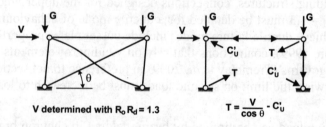

V determined with $R_o R_d = 1.3$

$$T = \frac{V}{\cos \theta} - C'_U$$

(c) Tension Brace Connection – Beam and Column Forces at $R_d R_o = 1.3$

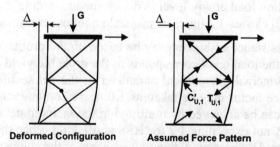

Deformed Configuration   Assumed Force Pattern

(d) Columns and Struts When Braces Meet Columns Between Floors

Figure 2-66
Brace Axial Loads for the Design of Members and Connections

For the frame in Figure 2-66(b), the exterior columns should be designed for the condition at the brace's probable compressive resistance (C_u) whereas the buckled brace condition (C'_u) should be assumed for the interior. In S16, C'_u is taken as $0.2\,A\,R_y\,F_y$ which corresponds to the value observed in tests at a ductility of 3.0. Tests suggest that higher values can be used for bracing members with very low slenderness (λ less than 0.4) (Remennikov and Walpole 1998b, Tremblay et al. 2002).

In some cases, braces can be oversized to meet other design criteria such as drift, width-to-thickness ratio, or slenderness limits. For such cases, the brace loads need not exceed the forces induced by a storey shear calculated with $R_d R_o = 1.3$, as specified in Clause 27.1.2. The possibility of brace buckling under that storey shear must be considered in the calculations: the forces in the compression braces are then limited to the probable buckling or post-buckling strength, whichever is more critical, and the load redistribution from the compression braces to the tension braces due to brace buckling must be accounted for when evaluating the forces acting in the tension braces. This is illustrated in Figure 2-66(c) where maximum tension in the tension brace, maximum compression in the beam and maximum compression in the right-hand-side columns are obtained when the compression brace carries a load C'_u.

27.5.4 Bracing Connections

27.5.4.1 Eccentricities in brace connections can lead to damage under cyclic loading and should therefore be kept to a minimum in ductile braced frames.

27.5.4.2 Brace connections must be designed to resist brace axial loads that correspond to the probable buckling strength and tensile yielding strength of the braces. Actual brace end restraint conditions and the presence of intermediate supports must also be taken into account when evaluating the buckling strength of the braces (see Clause 27.5.3.1).

In view of the uncertainty associated with the amplitude of the seismic ground motions and their effects on building structures, connections designed for the upper brace force limit corresponding to $R_d R_o = 1.3$ must be detailed for a ductile mode of behaviour. Details that may be considered to achieve ductile failure modes include gusset plates proportioned for ductility (Cheng and Grondin, 1999), connections that rely on yielding of elements or in which bearing failure of bolts governs (Tremblay et al. 2009) in preference to net section fracture or bolt shear failure. Otherwise, the limit on seismic loads must be increased to loads corresponding to $R_d R_o = 1.0$.

The brace tension load can be limited by beam yielding in chevron bracing in which the beams are not designed to carry the full tensile yield load of the braces. In such a case, the brace tension connection load at any level is determined assuming the beam yields while the compression brace still carries 1.2 times its probable nominal compressive strength.

The net section resistance of braces may be based on the probable tensile strength of the brace material, since the load level corresponds to the probable yield stress of the brace. Furthermore, since the principal geometrical parameter of the net section and gross section are identical, the resistance factor may be taken as 1.0. Based on coupon test data assembled by Schmidt (2000), this can be achieved by multiplying the factored net section resistance of the brace by R_y/ϕ with R_y not exceeding 1.2 for HSS and 1.1 for other shapes. This factor cannot be applied to the factored resistance of other components of the connections such as net section reinforcement plates, gusset plates, bolts or welds. Information on net section reinforcement for slotted HSS members can be found in Yang and Mahin (2005) and Haddad and Tremblay (2006). Alternative solutions have recently been proposed for HSS brace connections including the modified hidden gap connection by Martinez-Saucedo et al. (2008) and structural cast connectors (de Oliveira et al. 2008).

27.5.4.3 Buckling of the braces will induce a rotational demand at the brace ends, and the connections must be detailed to avoid any premature fracture at this location. Proper detailing must be provided to allow this rotation to develop in the brace connections or through controlled plastic hinging in the bracing members, away from the connections. Note that this ductile rotational behaviour must be allowed for, either in or out of the plane of the frame, depending on the governing effective brace slenderness. If a single gusset plate connection is used, the former case can be achieved by leaving a clear distance equal to two times the thickness of the gusset at the end of the bracing member (or the connecting elements), as illustrated in Figure 2-65, in order to have a hinge forming in the gusset plate along a line perpendicular to the brace member's longitudinal axis (Astaneh-Asl and Goel 1985). Tearing of the gusset plate will rapidly develop if this geometry is not carefully met. If a plastic hinge is to develop in the bracing member, the connection must have a factored flexural resistance about the anticipated buckling axis equal to $1.1R_y M_p$ of the bracing member. The Commentary to Clause 27.5.4.2 concerning the factor R_y/ϕ applies also here, except that R_y is not limited to 1.1 when both load and resistance are directly related to the yield stress.

27.5.5 Columns, Beams, and Connections Other than Brace Connections

This clause provides specific requirements for columns, beams and connections other than brace connections. For brace connection requirements, refer to Clause 27.5.4 and this commentary.

27.5.5.1 Columns, beams, and other connections in the lateral-load-resisting system must be designed to carry the gravity loads together with the effects due to the brace forces that are expected to develop under the design earthquake. Member forces under this condition can be obtained by replacing the bracing members by the brace forces specified in Clause 27.5.3.4. As illustrated in Figure 2-66, in a given storey, it should be assumed that yielding in the tension braces develops simultaneously with either the probable compressive or post-buckling strength of the compression braces, depending upon which case produces the more critical condition for the element being designed. For tension-only systems the compressive resistance of the braces should not be ignored. In any case the brace forces need not exceed those associated with a storey shear corresponding to $R_d R_o = 1.3$ (including load redistribution due to brace buckling).

In multi-storey structures, the likelihood of having all the bracing members develop their full capacity at the same time diminishes as the number of storeys above the level under consideration becomes large. In X-bracing (or split-X bracing), this can be accounted for in determining axial forces in columns by using statistical combinations of the brace-induced loads that have been proposed in the literature (Redwood and Channagiri 1991, Lacerte and Tremblay 2006, Richards 2009). When the axial force in a column is due to brace buckling only, as in chevron bracing with the braces framing below the beams, this reduction is less important, and all braces must be considered as buckling simultaneously (Tremblay and Robert 2001).

When calculating axial load in beams, attention should be paid to the lateral load path at the level under consideration.

27.5.5.2 Columns in multi-storey structures are most often continuous over two or more storeys, and the flexural stiffness and strength of these columns contribute to reduce the concentration of inelastic demand in a given storey along the height of the building. This behaviour is now explicitly accounted for in this clause, and the columns must therefore be made continuous to prevent a soft-storey formation unless another system is provided (Tremblay 2000, Tremblay 2003). It should be noted that all columns in the frame, and not only those in the vertical bracing system, are to be treated in this way. In addition, the bending moments that are expected to develop in the columns must be accounted for in design. Non-linear dynamic analyses have shown that these moments reach approximately 20% of the plastic moment of the columns, both for gravity columns and columns in bracing bents. It is permitted to splice columns for axial and shear forces only. In order to maintain structural integrity, every splice in the building must be designed for a shear force assuming double curvature in the columns.

Gravity columns possess some reserve capacity due to the reduced factored gravity loads assumed to be present during the design earthquake, and the bending moments are therefore ignored in their design. Class 3 sections are specified, however, to avoid brittle failure in case inelastic rotation develops over a short period of time during the earthquake. More stringent provisions are prescribed for columns in braced bays in view of their primary role in resisting lateral loads and the large axial forces they must sustain due to seismic loading. Class 1 or 2 sections are required, and columns must be designed as beam-columns assuming a moment equal to 0.20 times their plastic moment. In this check, columns must be assumed to be bent in single curvature ($\kappa = -1.0$).

27.5.5.3 See Commentary to Clause 27.2.3.3

27.5.6 Protected Zones

Bracing members are considered as protected zones over their full length because yielding in tension is expected to develop at any location along the braces. Brace connections are designated as protected zones as they are likely to sustain high strain and inelastic rotational demands upon brace buckling and under large storey drifts.

27.6 Type LD (Limited Ductility) Concentrically Braced Frames, $R_d = 2.0$, $R_o = 1.3$

27.6.1 General

Braced frames of this category are designed with an R_d factor of 2.0 and are thus expected to undergo lower inelastic response than Type MD braced frames. However, inelastic response is still restricted to bracing members and beams of low-rise chevron braced frames. The frames must therefore be designed according to Clause 27.5 except that some relaxation is permitted in view of the lower anticipated ductility demand.

27.6.2 Bracing Systems

Frames provided with higher lateral resistance are less prone to soft-storey response, and taller buildings are permitted in this frame category. Frames with heights up to 80% of the height limits specified in NBCC can be expected to perform satisfactorily with no further inelastic analysis needed. Those within the height range of 80% to 100% of the NBCC limits are required to be designed for additional forces stipulated in this clause.

27.6.2.1 Tension-Compression Bracing

This clause applies to all tension-compression bracing configurations, including Chevron bracing systems. Bracing configurations, consisting of pairs of compression and tension braces meeting a column on one side at one or more elevations between horizontal diaphragms, may be used in limited-ductility frames provided that the specific requirements of Clause 27.6.6 are satisfied.

27.6.2.2 Chevron Bracing

Chevron bracing with no special beam capacity requirements is permitted up to 20 m in this category. During an earthquake, the beams in such frames lose the vertical support provided by the braces and must then be capable of supporting their tributary gravity loads without the help of the braces. Significant plastic hinging is expected in these beams, and beam-to-column connections must be designed to sustain the forces that develop when the probable nominal flexural resistance of the beams is reached (Tremblay and Robert 2000). Chevron braced frames so proportioned exhibit severe deterioration of their storey shear resistance after brace buckling and cannot be used in structures taller than 20 m without risk of soft-storey response. Chevron bracing with a strong-beam design as specified in Clause 27.5.2.4 should be used for these taller structures.

27.6.2.3 Tension-Only Bracing

Compared with Type MD tension-only braced frames, columns in this system are required to be fully continuous and have a constant cross-section over only two storeys.

27.6.3 Diagonal Bracing Members

27.6.3.1 Single- and two-storey braced frames with slender braces, including rods, bars, etc. having KL/r greater than 200 are permitted in this frame category. Other requirements for ductile braced frames, including minimum brace connection resistance, still apply, however.

27.6.3.2 Very limited inelastic compressive strains are expected in braces with KL/r greater than 200, as permitted in Clause 27.6.3.1. Therefore, stringent width-to-thickness ratios do not apply for these braces. The inelastic demand anticipated in frames with specified short-period spectral acceleration ratios ($I_E F_a S_a(0.2)$) less than 0.45 is also small, and Class 2 sections are permitted in these locations.

27.6.4 Bracing Connections

Clause 27.5.4.3 need not apply for slender braces in frames located in lower seismic hazard categories as low rotational demand is expected at the ends of such braces.

27.6.5 Columns, Beams and Other Connections

Abrupt changes in the inter-storey drift angle from one storey to another is not expected in frames of this category when located in low seismicity regions. For such frames, column splice connections as currently fabricated and built in practice should provide sufficient shear capacity to ensure integrity of the gravity columns, and no minimum shear force is prescribed for splices in these columns.

27.6.6 Columns with Braces Intersecting Between Floors

In tall single-storey steel buildings such as airplane hangars or industrial facilities, bracing configurations consisting of multi-tier X-bracing panels are quite common. When subjected to strong shaking, nonlinear time-history analysis shows that brace buckling and yielding tend to concentrate in the bracing panel where inelastic response is triggered first. As the panel loses significant horizontal shear resistance due to buckling of the braces, it acts as a fuse protecting the remaining panels. This may occur even if all panels have identical geometry and braces, as brace buckling will likely initiate at one location due to unavoidable differences present in the structure. As a result, inelastic deformations will concentrate in just one pair of braces, with potential premature brace fracture, and significant flexural demand will be imposed on the columns, which can impair their integrity (Figure 2-66(d)).

This bracing configuration is permitted only in Type LD braced frames, as the system is expected to sustain a limited degree of inelastic response. Horizontal struts must be provided between the columns at each brace intersection level such that the tensile capacity of the braces can be mobilized after brace buckling without imposing excessive unbalanced horizontal loads on the columns at brace-to-column intersections (Figure 2-66(d)). The capacity of the columns must then be verified when subjected to the gravity loads together with the axial loads and bending moments that are induced when the design storey drift, i.e. $R_d R_o$ times the elastic roof lateral displacement, is reached at the roof level assuming that brace yielding in tension develops in only one panel. The struts must also be designed to carry the axial loads that will develop under that condition. Member forces can be determined through nonlinear incremental static

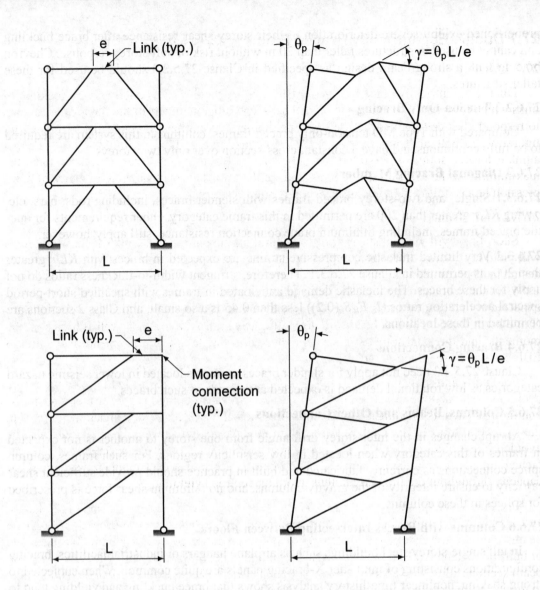

Figure 2-67
Common Configurations of Eccentrically Braced Frames

analysis of the frame in which the horizontal load applied at roof level is gradually increased until the lateral roof displacement reaches the design drift. Gravity loads must be applied at the beginning of the analysis, and brace yielding and buckling must be considered in this calculation. In place of such an analysis, a linear elastic analysis may be used. In this elastic model the tension and compression braces in the panel where inelastic response is likely to initiate are replaced by forces representing their expected tensile and post-buckling resistances, respectively (see Figure 2-66(d)). The lateral load at the roof level is increased until the design roof displacement is attained. In the process, compression braces in the other panels are replaced by forces equal to their post-buckling strength C'_u if the computed compression loads exceed their resistance C_u. Out-of-plane forces and deformations may develop upon brace buckling, and an out-of-plane force equal to 10% of the member compression loads must be considered in the analysis at brace-to-column intersections.

CISC Commentary on CSA S16-09

27.7 Ductile Eccentrically Braced Frames, R_d = 4.0, R_o = 1.5

27.7.1 General

Ductile eccentrically braced frames (EBF) are designed to dissipate energy by yielding of links which form part of the beam in braced bays, and other members of the frame are designed to respond elastically while the links are yielding and strain-hardening. Some common configurations of EBF are shown in Figure 2-67. The load in each brace is limited by the fact that a link is located at one or possibly both ends. The brace is designed to remain elastic under the maximum load the link can develop, and hence the uncertain load-carrying capacity of compression braces following yield or buckling is not a concern.

27.7.2 Link Beams

Short links will yield in shear prior to flexural hinging at the link ends whereas long links will yield in flexure before shear. Either mode is acceptable, although short links are easier to design and have somewhat more stable and predictable post-yield behaviour (Kasai and Popov 1986, Engelhardt and Popov 1992). Long links must be Class 1 sections as flexural hinging is expected at link ends whereas short links may have Class 2 flanges provided the web is Class 1 (Engelhardt, 2005). The link beam will normally carry high axial forces as well as high bending moments, and the axial forces cannot be neglected in the design. For a general discussion of EBF behaviour, see Popov *et al.* (1989).

For short- and moderate-length links in particular, the web is expected to undergo severe cyclic inelastic action with straining well into the strain-hardening range. For this reason discontinuities such as openings, splices, and stress raisers such as welded attachments (except the stiffeners) must be avoided. Splices within the link are not acceptable and should also be avoided in the outer parts of the link beam near the link ends (with the exception of links attached directly to columns). The webs should be of uniform depth to maintain the same shear capacity throughout the link length, thus avoiding confined yielding.

In earlier research and past applications of the system, link beams were made of W shapes, and design and detailing rules in previous editions of CSA S16 had been developed for W-shape beams. Berman and Bruneau (2008a) recently proposed design procedures for link beams made of built-up rectangular hollow sections and experimentally validated them. The use of built-up beam sections allow the links to be sized to match closely the design force demand and, hence, to minimize the capacity design force demand requirement. Furthermore, when properly sized, tubular links do not require lateral bracing. This option offers an attractive solution in situations where lateral bracing is impossible or impractical, for example in a braced bent along an exterior column line, next to an elevator or stairway shaft. Provisions for the design and detailing of EBFs with built-up rectangular tubular links have therefore been introduced in CSA S16-09. Specific requirements are typically presented in parallel for links with wide-flange cross-sections and with built-up tubular cross-sections. No reference to link cross-sections is made, however, when requirements equally apply to EBFs of either type.

27.7.3 Link Resistance

The nominal resistances of the link are defined taking into account the axial force, but this may be neglected if it is low. The interaction between bending moment and shearing force has been found to be negligible and is in fact neglected. The factored values of these resistances (nominal resistance times ϕ) are used when proportioning beams for the factored load effects. Nominal values are used to determine capacity design forces applied on other frame members (see Clauses 27.7.9, 27.7.10 and 27.7.12).

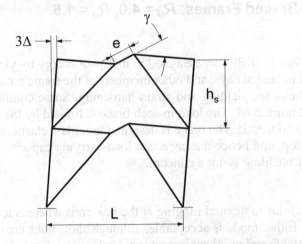

Inelastic link rotation:

$$\gamma = (L / e)\, \theta_p$$

where:

$$\theta_p = 3\Delta / h_s$$

Figure 2-68
Inelastic Drift Angle vs Link Rotation in an Eccentrically Braced Frame
(Rigid Plastic Mechanism Shown)

27.7.4 Link Length

Very short links are proscribed since they will tend to undergo very high shearing deformations, and develop very high and unpredictable forces.

Upper limits on the length are needed when the link is subjected to axial force. These are based on Engelhardt and Popov (1989).

27.7.5 Link Rotation

The inelastic link rotation must be limited as specified in this Clause to ensure that the ductile capacity of the link is not exceeded. The limits in CSA S16 were based on earlier test programs on links made of ASTM A36 steel with $F_y = 248$ MPa. Recent tests by Okazaki *et al.* (2005) and Okazaki and Engelhardt (2007) showed that the limits also apply to links made of the higher strength steel ASTM A992 ($F_y = 345$ MPa). The inelastic link rotation is computed for each storey in the following way:

- elastic interstorey deflections are obtained from an elastic analysis of the structure under lateral loads corresponding to the NBCC base shear distributed according to NBCC for the purpose of calculating deflections (either based on the static method or the distribution obtained from modal analysis).

- these deflections are multiplied by 3 to give an estimate of the maximum inelastic deflections expected under severe shaking.

- assuming the frame undergoes an interstorey drift corresponding to the calculated inelastic deflections as a rigid plastic mechanism, with deformations confined to the link, the link rotation angle (i.e. the angle between the link and the link beam outside the link) is obtained. As illustrated in Figure 2-68, γ is determined as a function of the inelastic interstorey drift corresponding to the calculated inelastic deflections.

Figure 2-67 shows rigid plastic mechanisms for two common EBF configurations. This procedure gives reasonable results for frames having relatively low height-to-width aspect ratios, such as those shown in Figures 2-67 and 2-68. However, axial deformation of columns due to overturning effect (chord drift) contributes significantly to interstorey drifts in upper storeys for frames with higher aspect ratios but does not affect the link rotations. This chord drift effect can be eliminated by making the columns axially rigid (i.e. modelled with very large cross-sectional areas) in the elastic analysis described above.

27.7.6 Link Stiffeners

27.7.6.1 Links with Wide-Flange Cross-Sections

Full-depth stiffeners on both sides of the web are required to clearly define the end of the link and to transfer the high shearing forces over the full web depth. Requirements for intermediate web stiffeners are based on physical test results and are needed to ensure the ductile performance of the link. For short links, stiffeners control shear buckling of the yielding web, while for long links, stiffeners required near the ends control flange buckling.

Flange-to-stiffener welds of the link end stiffeners are required to develop the full stiffener yield capacity because of the very high forces that must be transferred between the brace and link at a point where high shear and bending loads occur.

27.7.6.2 Links with Built-Up Tubular Cross-Sections

As is the case for wide-flange links, full-depth stiffeners are required at the ends of links. These stiffeners are provided on one side of each link web at the diagonal brace connection.

Full-depth intermediate stiffeners are also needed for shear-yielding built-up tubular links ($e \leq 1.6\ M_p/V_p$). As for wide-flange links, the required stiffener spacing depends on the magnitude of the link rotation angle. In CSA S16, only the equation for the spacing needed to develop a link rotation angle of 0.08 radian ($20w - (d - 2t)/8$) by Berman and Bruneau (2005) is given, as experimental and analytical data is only available to support this closer stiffener spacing. A similar expression ($37w - (d - 2t)/8$) has been proposed for a 0.02 radian rotation, but the more restrictive stiffener spacing is required for all links until other data become available. The presence of intermediate web stiffeners was shown to be significant for shear-yielding built-up box links with h/w greater than $0.64\sqrt{E/F_y}$ and less than or equal to $1.67\sqrt{E/F_y}$ (Berman and Bruneau 2008a). For shear links with h/w less than or equal to $0.64\sqrt{E/F_y}$, flange buckling is the controlling limit state, and intermediate stiffeners have no effect.

For links with lengths exceeding $1.6\ M_p/V_p$, compression local buckling of both webs and flanges (resulting from compressive stresses associated with the development of the plastic moment) dominates link strength degradation. This buckling resistance is unaffected by the presence of intermediate web stiffeners. As a result, intermediate web stiffeners are not required for long links provided that the webs and flanges have a width-to-thickness ratio not exceeding $0.64\sqrt{E/F_y}$ as they are both subjected to large compressive stresses.

The built-up box beams tested and simulated numerically by Berman and Bruneau (2008a) had intermediate stiffeners welded to both webs and flanges. A typical cross-section is shown in Figure 2-69. However, the presence of stiffeners did not influence flange buckling. Whereas web stiffeners in wide-flange links may also provide stability to the flanges (Malley and Popov 1983), this is not the case with built-up box cross-sections. Therefore, for built-up box section links, weld attachment of intermediate flange stiffeners is not required. In particular, intermediate stiffeners may be welded to the inside faces, enhancing architectural appeal and improving resistance to corrosion and reducing the risk of debris accumulation between stiffeners in exposed applications.

27.7.7 Lateral Support for Link

The required capacity of lateral bracing for wide-flange links is much greater than is usually the case for beams because of the anticipated large inelastic deformations and accompanying forces amplified by strain-hardening. No lateral bracing is required for links with rectangular built-up tubular cross-sections, provided that the moment of inertia of the links about the

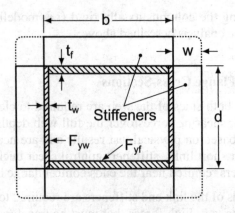

Figure 2-69
Built-Up Tubular Link Cross-Section with Intermediate Stiffener

vertical axis in the plane of the EBF is not less than 0.67 times the moment of inertia about the axis perpendicular to the plane of the EBF, as specified in Clause 27.7.2.5.

27.7.8 Link Beam-to-Column Connection

Links are often connected directly to the column face in order to accommodate doorways adjacent to columns. This configuration causes severe straining of the link, connection welds and column flanges as the link deforms. Tests by Okazaki *et al.* (2006) on link-to-column connections designed and fabricated using pre-Northridge practices showed poor performance. Test specimens with improved welding details alone did not develop the level of inelastic rotation intended in design. Until joint details that can exhibit satisfactory inelastic behaviour are developed, link connections must be demonstrated to meet the performance criteria defined in this clause. As for moment-resisting frames, this demonstration can be provided by cyclic tests of full-scale prototypes of the link and column assemblage, following the procedures given in AISC (2005).

If the connection region is reinforced so that a short length of beam adjacent to the column remains elastic under the action of strain-hardened link forces, such demonstration may not be necessary. For this to be acceptable the link must be short, thus limiting the flange forces, and have full-depth stiffeners at the end of the elastic region. In this case, the link ends at the stiffeners.

Link beam-to-column connections can be avoided by adopting a chevron bracing configuration, thereby locating the links away from the columns.

27.7.9 Beam Outside the Link

Forces due to strain-hardening of a wide-flange link are taken as $1.3 R_y$ times the nominal strength of the link, as defined in Clause 27.7.9.2. The 1.3 factor accounts for the increase above the yield value due to strain-hardening, and R_y accounts for the probable yield stress exceeding the minimum specified value. The forces developed in the outer beam segment (and the brace, see Clause 27.7.9.2) due to these strain-hardened link forces must be calculated; if reinforcement of the outer beam segment is to be avoided, it will often be necessary to provide a moment-resisting connection between brace and link beam so that the brace can relieve the outer beam segment of some of the resulting bending moment. It should be noted that this part of the beam will normally also carry a high axial force. Because the beam segment considered in this clause will be part of the same member as the link, (i) its resistance can be increased by the factor R_y thus, in this case, nullifying any effect of an enhanced yield stress, and (ii) the nominal, rather than factored, resistance is used since most of the uncertainties associated with the resistance factor, ϕ, affect both load and resistance identically.

The strain-hardening factor of 1.3 is the same for all link lengths, i.e. whether yield is related to shear or bending moment. That this factor exceeds the strain-hardening factor used for beams in moment-resisting frames is due to the shorter span-to-depth ratio of the link, leading to greater inelastic strains. The outer beam segment is subject to bending and axial loads, and must be adequately laterally braced. If a plastic hinge is expected at the link end of this segment, bracing must conform to Clause 13.7(a), which requires bracing within a specified distance of the hinge. While a floor slab will often be present to provide support to the top flange, the bottom flange at this location must also be braced (or torsional restraint provided). The likelihood of a plastic hinge at the link end of the outer beam segment can be determined by examining the distribution of the link end moment between beam and brace according to their relative elastic stiffnesses.

For links with a built-up tubular cross-section, Berman and Bruneau (2008a) reported a higher strain-hardening response than for wide-flange links. Built-up rectangular box links can develop a maximum strength which is typically 11% larger than for wide-flange links. The forces to consider for designing the braces and columns are therefore increased accordingly.

27.7.10 Diagonal Braces

The forces used for the design of braces and their connections are consistent with those specified for the outer beam segment in Clause 27.7.9. Although expected to respond elastically, the brace section is restricted to Classes 1 or 2 because of the uncertain stress distribution in the brace-to-beam connection and the possibility of excessive strains in part of the brace cross-section.

27.7.12 Columns

Column design can be based on lower strain-hardening factors than braces and beams since, except for the top several storeys, the cumulative effect of a number of yielding links will be less than the sum of their maximum possible developed forces. A recent study on axial loads in EBF columns is presented in Richards (2009).

Column moments under gravity and lateral loads induced by eccentric shears and moment-resisting beam connections can be calculated. Those arising from variations in inelastic drifts between adjacent storeys cannot be predicted unless an inelastic dynamic analysis is performed. Columns serve an important role by providing an alternative means of resisting storey shear due especially to link yield. Under these conditions, columns can be effective in preventing soft-storey deformations. Column continuity is therefore desirable, and design of the connections should consider the shear and bending that may develop. On the basis of numerical studies of the dynamic response of a variety of EBF structures (Kasai and Han (1997), Han (1998), Koboevic (2000)), inelastic dynamic analysis may be avoided if the additional end bending moments specified in CSA S16 are combined with the bending moments acting in the plane of the frame obtained from a linear elastic analysis.

The requirements for column splices containing partial-joint-penetration groove welds follow those for ductile moment frames.

27.7.13 Protected Zone

Links in EBFs are designated as protected zones and shall satisfy the requirements of Clause 27.1.9.

27.8 Ductile Buckling Restrained Braced Frames, R_d = 4.0, R_o = 1.2

27.8.1 General

Buckling-restrained braced frames are essentially concentrically braced steel frames that are constructed with bracing members specifically designed and detailed so as not to buckle. A typical buckling-restrained brace is illustrated in Figure 2-70. The brace has a steel core. A segment of this core is fabricated with a reduced cross-section where axial yielding is expected to develop in both compression and tension. The core is prevented from buckling by means of a restraining system. In the example shown in Figure 2-70, a steel tube filled with mortar is used for this purpose. Unbonding material is placed at the interface between the core and the mortar so that axial loads are resisted by the core only. In a severe earthquake, energy dissipation is therefore provided by yielding of the brace core in compression and tension. Several alternative designs and systems of buckling-restrained bracing have been developed. More information on the system can be found in Sabelli (2004) and López and Sabelli (2004).

27.8.2 Bracing Systems

When loaded well into the inelastic range, the brace's compression capacity typically exceeds its tension capacity significantly. For this reason, bracing configurations consisting of braces intersecting columns from one side only should intersect the columns at roof and floor elevations.

Buckling-restrained bracing (BRB) members exhibit very stable hysteretic response with large energy dissipation capacity. However, S16 restricts the application of BRB to frames not exceeding 40 metres in height except where the specified short-period spectral acceleration ratio is less than 0.35. Concentration of inelastic demand and soft-storey response of taller frames, without beam-to-column rigid connections, have been observed in analytical studies. For these taller structures, use of this system is permitted only when inelastic dynamic stability is demonstrated. Alternative design solutions for tall frame stability have been reported in the literature (Merzouq and Tremblay 2006, Tremblay 2003, Tremblay and Poncet 2007).

27.8.3 Bracing Members

27.8.3.1 Foreign researchers have reported satifactory buckling-restrained bracing designs of variety (e.g. Uang and Nakashima 2004, Xie 2005). In the U.S., proprietary BRB products are distributed by specialty suppliers. In Canadian applications, BRB members made of mortar-filled tubes have been fabricated and installed by steel fabricators (Tremblay *et al.* 1999, 2006). Provisions in CSA S16-09 focus on general performance based design requirements together with qualification testing requirements for the bracing members. Specific bracing design and detailing required to achieve the specified performance are not given in CSA S16-09. Typically, BRB manufacturers supply their products in compliance with S16 requirements and project-specific requirements as specified by the structural engineer for the project, such as dimensions and other geometric details, strength and deformation capacities, etc.

In CSA S16, the compression and tension resistances of a BRB member are assumed equal in magnitude. Hence the same expression is used to determine the factored axial resistances in tension and compression. Contrary to other structural steel elements, the factored resistance of BRB members can be determined using the yield stress value obtained from coupon testing. This explains the relatively low value of the overstrength-related seismic force modification factor, R_o specified in NBCC for the system – 1.2 versus 1.3 or greater for the other seismic force resisting systems. Minimum ductility requirements are specified for the brace core material to prevent premature fracture under inelastic cyclic loading.

Results from nonlinear time history analyses have shown that axial deformations of buckling restrained members can exceed significantly the values corresponding to the anticipated

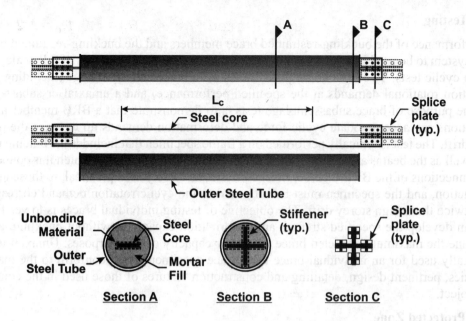

Figure 2-70
Buckling-Restrained Bracing Member (Typical)

total deflections (including inelastic response), as defined in NBCC. Therefore, 2.0 times the NBCC value is required.

Strain hardening is expected to develop following yielding of the core of BRB members. In compression, friction between the core and the restraining mechanism and Poisson's effects are expected to enhance the brace resistance at large deformations. These factors must be considered when determining probable brace resistances for capacity design purposes. These effects vary depending on the type of BRB system and will typically be more important as the cyclic brace deformation increases. Therefore, they must be determined based on qualification tests specified in CSA S16 for the bracing system and deformation demands applicable to the project.

27.8.4 Brace Connections

Brace connections must be designed and detailed to resist brace forces corresponding to the attainment of probable brace resistances. The steel core projections at the ends of BRB members and connection elements must also be capable of resisting the local force demand and accommodating local deformations that accompany large lateral frame deformations (Tsai and Hsiao 2008, Mahin *et al.* 2004). Information on BRB connections can be found in Berman and Bruneau (2009), Fahnestock *et al.* (2007), and Tremblay *et al.* (2006).

27.8.5 Beams, Columns, and Connections Other Than Brace Connections

As in concentrically braced frames, beams, columns, and other connections should resist the effects of gravity loads, if any, together with forces corresponding to the tensile and compressive brace resistances determined in Clause 27.8.3. Differences in compressive and tensile brace resistances must be accounted for in the calculations.

Columns in multi-storey BRB frames serve to distribute vertically the inelastic demand in the structure. They must therefore be designed to account for the effects due to the redistribution of loads when bracing members develop their probable tensile and compressive resistances.

27.8.6 Testing

Performance of the buckling-restrained brace members and the buckling-restrained braced frame system to be used in a construction project must be verified by means of full-scale qualification cyclic tests. Two tests are required: a test of a brace subassemblage (including brace connection rotational demands at the specified performance) and a uniaxial or subassembly test. The purpose of brace subassemblage tests is to demonstrate that a BRB member and its connections can accommodate cyclic force and deformation demands up to twice the design storey drift. The test is typically performed on a frame specimen that includes the bracing member as well as the beams and columns (or parts of beams and columns) to which it is connected. End connections of the BRB member must conform, as closely as is practical, to those used in construction, and the specimen must be subjected to the cyclic rotation demand corresponding to twice the design storey drift. The objective of testing individual braces is to verify that they can develop the specified strength and deformation capacities, without buckling, and to determine the maximum expected brace forces for capacity design purposes. Uniaxial testing is typically used for an individual brace test. Brace specimens must conform to the material properties, pertinent design, detailing and construction features of those used in the construction project.

27.8.7 Protected Zone

The steel core of buckling restrained braces as well as the elements used to connect the brace core to beams and columns are protected zones and must comply with the requirements of Clause 27.1.9.

27.9 Type D (Ductile) Plate Walls, R_d = 5.0, R_o = 1.6

27.9.1 General

Plate walls are built of relatively thin infill plates connected at every level to the surrounding beam and column framing members. The infill plates provide for the resistance to storey shear forces whereas the overturning moment is resisted by the columns. Shear buckling of the infill plates can be controlled by means of stiffeners (Alinia and Dastfan 2007, Chusilp and Usami 2002, Chen et al. 2006, Sabouri-Ghomi et al. 2008) or by encasing them into concrete walls or panels (Zhao and Astaneh 2004). Although this leads to higher initial stiffness and shear capacity being delivered by the infill plates, recent research and practice in North America have shown that unstiffened plate walls can represent an effective design strategy for resisting lateral wind and seismic loads. Provisions in Clause 27 of S16 have therefore been developed for unstiffened plate wall systems.

Stable hysteretic behaviour under cyclic lateral loading has been demonstrated in several past experimental studies (Tromposch and Kulak 1987, Kulak 1991, Driver et al. 1997, 1998a, 1998b, Lubell et al. 2000, Berman and Bruneau 2003, 2005b, Qu et al. 2008, Vian et al. 2009). Much of the cyclic energy imparted to a wall is dissipated by the yielding of infill plates in tension along inclined lines. Upon load reversal, the tension field forces reduce, then the plate buckles under low compressive load and a new tension field develops in a manner consistent with the shear force in the opposite direction. Significant advantages of plate walls are their high lateral strength and stiffness, which make them very suitable for high seismic applications.

If the beams of a plate wall are attached to the columns using standard simple shear connections, the hysteretic behaviour is pinched. The behaviour can be improved if moment connections are provided between the beams and columns surrounding the infill plate panels. This Standard distinguishes between Type D (ductile) plate walls, in which rigid frame action contributes to the overall lateral load resistance, and Type LD (limited-ductility) plate walls, in which rigid connections are optional. Type LD walls must satisfy all requirements for Type D walls except as indicated in Clause 27.10.

For ductile framed plate walls, energy is dissipated during earthquakes by tensile yielding of the infill plates and the development of plastic flexural hinges at the ends of the beams and at the column bases. The provisions in Clause 27 aim at achieving this behaviour. Additional design guidance for the system can be found in Sabelli and Bruneau (2007).

27.9.2 Infill Plates

The infill plate at every level is designed to resist 100% of the factored storey shear force. The equation for the factored shear resistance is based on the shear yielding capacity of the infill plate, assuming full tension field response is developed (Berman and Bruneau 2003, Sabouri-Ghomi and Roberts 1991):

$$V_y = 0.5\, F_y\, w\, L \sin 2\alpha$$

where α is the angle of inclination of the tension field with respect to the vertical. This angle is determined in accordance with Clause 20.4. Of particular interest is the fact that the shear strength of plate walls designed according to this standard has been found not to be sensitive to the inclination of the tension field and that using a single value of 40° throughout the wall height can give accurate predictions of the shear strength of the plates (Shishkin $et\ al.$ 2005). The resistance V_y corresponds to the full yield capacity of the infill plates. Tension stresses in infill plates are not uniformly distributed, and yielding develops progressively upon increasing lateral loads. The capacity V_y is reached only at large lateral deformations under lateral loads equal to 1.1 to 1.5 times the lateral loads initiating yielding in the plates (Berman and Bruneau 2003). In NBCC and S16, the factored resistance of seismic force-resisting systems is typically based on the lateral strength at onset of yielding of the system, the difference between the fully developed lateral capacity and the factored lateral resistance being taken into account by the overstrength-related force modification factor, R_o (Mitchell $et\ al.$ 2003). To make the design consistent with these code assumptions, the factor 0.5 in the equation for V_y is reduced to 0.4 in the equation used to determined V_r in Clause 27.9.2.1.

In capacity design, beams, columns and connections in plate walls must be designed to resist tensile yielding forces that will develop in the infill plates at large deformations ($R_y F_y w$, shown as ω in Figure 2-71. Also see comments below on Clauses 27.9.3 and 27.9.4). These capacity design forces need not exceed forces corresponding to $R_o R_d = 1.3$ (see Clause 27.1.2).

Engineers and fabricators often select a minimum infill plate thickness to ease workmanship and handling or to maintain reasonable flatness. This practice may lead to capacity design forces that significantly exceed the seismic force demand when the design storey shear is low compared to the factored resistance (upper levels, wall width dictated by architectural layout, etc.). When reasons other than structural requirements dictate the minimum plate thickness, design forces can be reduced by using low yield stress steel for the infill plates (Vian and Bruneau 2004). In that case, the probable yield stress should be taken as an average yield stress, obtained in accordance with CSA G40.20 (see Clause 27.1.7), and the availability of the steel must be verified. Alternatively, circular perforations may be introduced in the infill plate to reduce its capacity. As illustrated in Figure 2-72(a), the perforations must be uniformly distributed and aligned such that diagonal tension strips can form upon buckling of the plates. Clause 27.9.2.3 provides an equation for calculating the factored shear resistance of such perforated infill plates. Minimum detailing requirements are also specified in the Clause.

Infill plates made of thin sheet steel (0.91 mm) have been successfully used and their adequate inelastic seismic performance has been demonstrated by Berman and Bruneau (2005b).

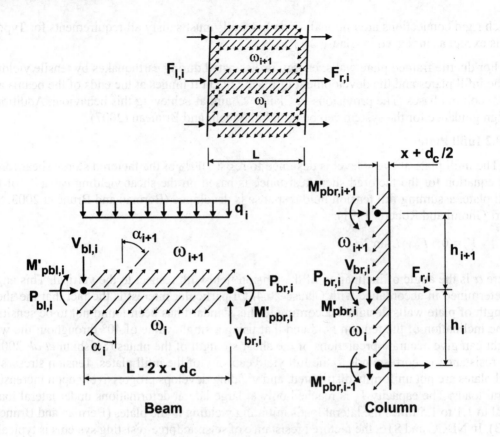

Figure 2-71
Forces Due to Tension Yielding of the Infill Plate
and Plastic Hinging at the Beam Ends

S16 does not include any provision for this application. If this innovative approach is contemplated, caution must be exercised to ensure that the sheet steel used meets the minimum ductility requirements specified in Clause 27.1.5, the fabrication and installation are consistent with methodologies used in supporting research, reliable welds are consistently provided, etc.

The stiffness of regularly perforated infill plates can be estimated using an effective plate thickness, w_{eff}, given by:

$$w_{eff} = \frac{1 - \dfrac{\pi}{4}\left(\dfrac{D}{S_{diag}}\right)}{1 - \dfrac{\pi}{4}\left(\dfrac{D}{S_{diag}}\right)\left(1 - \dfrac{N_r D \sin\theta}{H_c}\right)} w$$

where N_r is the number of perforations along the strips (4 in Figure 2-72(a)), θ is the inclination of the strips, and H_C is the infill plate clear height. Other parameters are defined in Figure 2-72(a). Additional design information and supporting analytical and experimental evidences on the behaviour of plate walls with perforated infill plates can be found in Roberts and Sabouri-Ghomi (1992), Purba and Bruneau (2009), and Vian *et al.* (2009). It is noted that the perforations allow the passage of mechanical and electrical ducts and pipes.

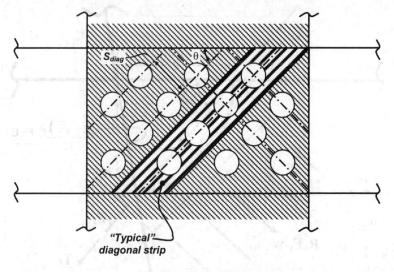

(a) Perforated Infill Plate

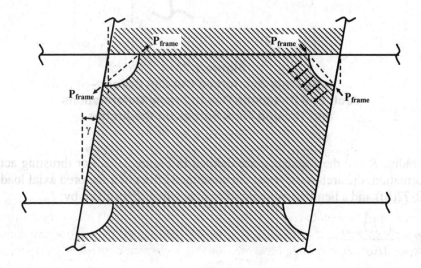

(b) Infill Plate with Cut-Out Corner

Figure 2-72

An alternative solution for the passage of utilities in infill plates is to utilize quarter-circle cut-outs in the plate corners, as permitted in Clause 27.9.2.4 and illustrated in Figure 2-72(b). In that case, the original shear strength and stiffness of the infill plates are preserved provided that the cut-outs are suitably reinforced with arching plates and meet geometrical requirements. Forces acting in the reinforcing arch are a combination of effects due to arching action under tension forces due to infill plate yielding in tension and thrusting action due to change of angle at the corner of the frame. The factored tensile force T_f induced in the arch by tension field action in the infill plate can be taken equal to:

$$T_f = \frac{R_y F_y w R^2}{4e}$$

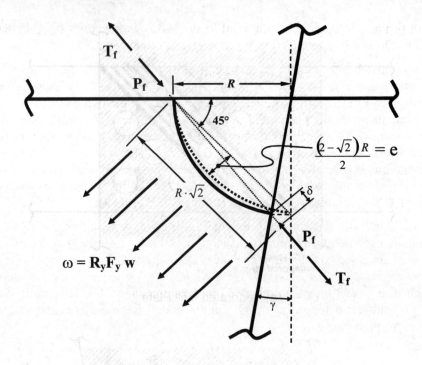

Figure 2-73
Infill Plate Reinforced Cut-Out Corner –
Arch End Reactions Due to Frame Deformations
and Tension Field Forces on the Arches

where the radius R and the distance e are defined in Figure 2-73. For thrusting action due to frame deformation, the arch must resist the combined effect of a factored axial load P_f (P_{frame} in Figure 2-72(b)) and a bending moment $M_f = P_f e$, where P_f is given by:

$$P_f = \frac{15EI_y}{16e^2}\frac{\Delta}{h_s}$$

In the expression for P_f, I_y is the moment of inertia of the reinforcement, Δ is the design storey drift, and h_s is the storey height. It is noted that the arch plate width is irrelevant in that calculation, and it is instead conservatively obtained by considering the strength required to resist the axial component of force in the arch due to the panel forces at the closing corner. The design for the two loading cases, i.e., T_f and P_f & M_f, can be done independently because the components of arch forces due to tension field action (T_f) forces are opposing those due to frame corner opening (P_f) (see Figures 2-72(b) and 2-73). Beams and columns must resist the tension and compression forces acting at the ends of the arching reinforcement. Further details are given in Vian *et al.* (2009) and Purba and Bruneau (2007, 2009).

27.9.3 Beams

Beams are expected to develop plastic hinges at their ends. Past tests have shown that lateral resistance and energy dissipation capacity under cyclic loading is essentially supplied by moment-resisting frame response once the infill plate has been stretched in larger cycles. To achieve minimum frame response, CSA S16 requires the boundary moment-resisting frame to be designed for a factored storey shear resistance, $V_{r, MRF} = 25\%$ of the design seismic storey shear. This factored resistance is taken as $V_{r, MRF} = 2\,M_{rb}/h_s$, where M_{rb} is the beam factored resistance in bending in the absence of axial loads, and h_s is the storey height (Berman and Bruneau 2003, Qu and Bruneau, 2009).

Beams must also be designed to resist the combined effects of axial loads, shear forces and bending moments due to gravity loads together with infill plate yielding in tension and plastic hinging at the ends of the beams, as depicted in Figure 2-71. Beam axial loads are due to the horizontal components of the plate yield loads acting both along the beams and the columns (Berman and Bruneau 2008b). When calculating the plastic hinge resistance of the beams, the axial load effects should be taken into account. Beam and column forces can be determined by manual calculations. Alternatively, a static incremental (push-over) analysis can be performed using the infill plate strip model by Thorburn *et al.* (1983) with inelastic response assigned to the strips, beams, and columns (Berman and Bruneau 2003, 2008b).

In Clause 27.9.2, the shear resistance of the infill plates is based on the assumption that full tension field response can eventually develop in the plates. For this to occur, the horizontal boundary members at the base and top of plate walls should meet the minimum flexural stiffness requirement, as specified in Clause 20.9. Alternatively, the plate panel at the wall base can be attached to a steel member embedded in the foundations. For long walls, Sabelli and Bruneau (2007) suggest that vertical struts could be added at the center of the wall to provide a vertical support to the top beam.

27.9.4 Columns

Columns must be designed to remain essentially elastic once yielding develops in the infill plates and the beams. Axial loads, shear forces and bending moments arising from yielding of the infill plate and beams, as illustrated in Figure 2-71, must therefore be added to the effects of gravity loads on the columns (Sabelli and Bruneau 2007, Berman and Bruneau 2008b). Plastic hinges in columns are permitted only at the column bases.

Bending moments and shear forces induced by infill plate forces can be significant. Column shear yielding must be considered. Li *et al.* (2009) recently proposed and verified through testing the use of struts between floors to reduce shear and bending moment demands on columns. Composite columns inherently possess high axial and flexural strength and stiffness, and can therefore represent an effective design solution (Astaneh-Asl 2001, Deng *et al.* 2008).

Columns must satisfy the minimum flexural stiffness requirement of Clause 20.7.9 to ensure adequate infill plate tension field response.

When plastic hinging is expected at the column bases, the columns must be detailed such that plastic rotation develops above the base plate or the foundation beam. Premature local buckling in the plastic hinge region must also be prevented (Driver *et al.* 1997).

27.9.6 Beam-to-Column Joints and Connections

Beam-to-column connections must be designed to resist forces anticipated in the infill plates, beams and columns. Plate walls inherently possess high lateral stiffness, and the anticipated storey drifts are less than anticipated in ductile moment-resisting frames; this is reflected in the limited rotation capacity requirement for the beam-to-column joint (0.02 rad).

Reduced beam section (RBS) beam-to-column connections have been used in past cyclic test programs (e.g., Vian *et al.* 2009, Qu *et al.* 2008). Well proportioned RBS connections exhibit good plastic rotation capacity and help to minimize shear forces in beams, and flexural and axial load demands on columns.

27.9.7 Protected Zones

Components of the plate walls that are expected to develop large inelastic deformations, such as infill plates, hinges in beams and columns, and their connections, are designated as protected zones and must satisfy the requirements of Clause 27.1.9.

27.10 Type LD (Limited-Ductility) Plate Walls, R_d = 2.0, R_o = 1.5

For plate walls with limited ductility, seismic energy input is expected to be dissipated primarily by yielding of the infill plate panels. Rigid frame connections are not necessary. However, capacity design requirements for beams, columns and connections apply.

27.11 Conventional Construction, R_d = 1.5, R_o = 1.3

In its 2001 edition, the standard introduced provisions for structures of Conventional Construction. The provisions were considered necessary because it was recognized that Conventional Construction would be used for many low-rise structures subjected to considerable seismic hazard, and that most steel structure failures in seismic events are associated with brittle connection details. Provisions related to connections and diaphragms were introduced to prevent brittle failure either by providing ductile connection details, or increasing the design loads. These provisions still apply for seismic-force-resisting systems with specified short-period spectral acceleration ratios ($I_E F_a S_a(0.2)$) greater than 0.45.

Connections of primary framing members forming the seismic-force-resisting system are typically beam-to-column connections in the moment-resisting frame or braced frame, including member splices subjected to seismic forces in tension, shear or both, and connections to the foundations. In braced frames, they also include brace-to-beam, brace-to-column and brace-to-brace connections. Beams acting as collectors, chords and struts in diaphragms are also primary framing members.

Connections that may be considered ductile if appropriately proportioned include extended-end-plate moment connections, flange-plate moment connections, gusset plates proportioned for ductility (Cheng and Grondin 1999) and bolted connections in which the governing failure mode corresponds to bolt bearing failure. Recent tests (Tremblay *et al.* 2009) showed that welded connections comprising fillet welds may not possess sufficient ductility to prevent fracture, regardless of load direction. They should also be designed for the amplified loads.

The failure of steel deck diaphragms is typically controlled by failure of the connections between the individual deck sheets and between the deck sheets and the supporting structure. Diaphragms designed and constructed using connections that have been shown by testing to be ductile can be designed using the factored forces calculated for conventional construction while those diaphragms with connections that have not been shown to be ductile should be designed using forces calculated using $R_d R_o$ = 1.3. Button-punched side lap connections or arc-spot welded connections commonly used for steel decks have not shown adequate ductile behaviour under cyclic loading. Research investigation into diaphragm designs for more ductile response is underway. Test results reported by Essa *et al.* (2003), Tremblay *et al.* (2004) and Hilti (2007) suggest that diaphragms made of thin steel deck sheets (0.76 mm and 0.91 mm) with power-actuated frame fasteners and screwed sidelaps can accommodate some inelastic deformations through screw tilting and bearing and tearing of the steel deck sheets at frame fasteners. Welded connections with washers, when properly fabricated, can also sustain inelastic deformation demand (Peuler *et al.* 2002) although this approach is generally less appealing from a practical standpoint.

Cantilever column structures composed of single or multiple beam-columns fixed at the base and pin-connected or free at their upper ends can be designated as Conventional Construction, provided that they are proportioned to satisfy the specific requirements in this clause.

In NBCC 2005, the use of Conventional Construction for steel buildings, subject to moderate and high seismicities, was restricted to buildings not exceeding 15 metres in height. This restriction was intended to retain the traditional 3-storey height limit stipulated in previous editions of the NBCC. However, this height limit was not intended for single-storey steel structures such as steel mills and aircraft hangers that may well exceed 15 metres in height. This has been clarified in the User's Guide – NBCC 2005, and Conventional Construction may be used for this type of structure. Structures such as stadia, large exhibition halls, arenas, convention centres and other similar structures must satisfy the 15 m height restrictions.

In anticipation of a new provision in NBCC 2010 that extends the use of Conventional Construction for steel buildings that are subjected to moderate and high seismicities and are taller than 15 m, several special requirements and height restrictions have been introduced in S16-09 to ensure proper response and prevent premature failure and non-ductile behaviour. Amplified design seismic loads are specified to compensate for the greater uncertainty in the prediction of the force demand in taller structures. Response spectrum or time history dynamic analysis must be used to determine force and deformations. Minimum ductility requirements for steel material and notch-toughness for thick plates, heavy shapes and weld metal apply to these structures and more stringent cross-section stockiness requirements are prescribed to delay local buckling. Amplified design forces are specified for columns in view of the consequences of column buckling. Higher design loads for columns should encourage yielding in adjacent members such as beams, braces, etc. A special requirement is given to prevent overloading of columns that serve as part of two or more systems intersecting on plan. To avoid premature connection failure, a member's end connections should resist the lesser of its gross cross-section probable capacity and the amplified connection design forces, given in this Clause. In addition, unless yielding is expected to develop in the adjoining members, connections must also be designed and detailed for a minimum inelastic deformation capacity. This could be achieved through plate yielding or bolt bearing. Higher seismic design loads are also specified for diaphragms such that they remain essentially elastic and can maintain their capacity to distribute seismic forces among the vertical elements of the seismic force resisting system. Lastly, a minimum out-of-plane force is specified at unbraced member intersections to prevent excessive out-of-plane deformations and/or instability.

27.12 Special Seismic Construction

Many different types of alternative structural systems have been developed to dissipate seismic energy in a ductile and stable manner. One such system, the Special Truss Moment Frames (Goel and Itani 1994, Goel et al. 1998), can sustain significant inelastic deformations within a specially designed and detailed segment of the truss. The AISC Seismic Provisions (AISC 2005) provide design and detailing guidance for this system. Design provisions for seismically isolated structures are available (BSSC 2003). In these cases the provisions could be modified as appropriate to provide a level safety and seismic performance comparable to that implied by the S16 requirements.

28. SHOP AND FIELD FABRICATION AND COATING

This clause and the clauses on erection and inspection serve to show that design cannot be considered in isolation, but is part of the design and construction sequence. The resistance factors used in this Standard and the methods of analysis are related to tolerances and good practices in fabrication, erection and inspection procedures. See also CISC (2002). The NBCC requires steel building systems to be manufactured by companies certified to the requirements of CAN/CSA-A660-M. This requirement is no longer repeated in S16-09 (provided under Clause 28.7 in S16-01).

28.1 Cambering, Curving, and Straightening

CSA Standard W59 specifies that the temperature of the heated areas shall not exceed 650°C in general and not more than 590°C for QT plate.

28.3 Sheared or Thermally Cut Edge Finish

28.3.2 The use of sheared edges is restricted because the micro-cracking induced may reduce the ductility.

28.4 Fastener Holes

28.4.1 The thickness of 700Q steels that can be punched is restricted because of the excessive damage that occurs at the edge of the hole. The maximum plate thickness for thermally cut holes, as allowed in Clause 28.4.3, is dependent upon the thermal cutting process and equipment used.

28.4.2 The restriction of this clause is similar to that of Clause 28.3.2.

28.4.3 Thermally cut holes are now allowed for static load applications when subject to the restrictions of this Clause. Iwankiw and Schlafly (1982) found no significant difference in connection strength of double lap joints with holes made by punching, drilling and flame cutting.

28.5 Joints in Contact Bearing

Milling techniques will realistically result in some measurable deviation. Tests by Popov and Stephen (1977a) on columns with intentionally introduced gaps at milled splice joints indicated that the compressive resistance of spliced columns is similar to unspliced columns. Local yielding reduces the gap. While in these tests column splice gaps of 1.6 mm were left unshimmed, the Standard is more restrictive and defines full contact as a separation not exceeding 0.5 mm. Because shims will be subjected to either biaxial or triaxial stress fields, mild steel shims may be used regardless of the grade of the main material.

28.6 Member Tolerances

The resistance factors given in this Standard, particularly for compression members, are consistent with the distribution of out-of-straightness of members produced to the straightness tolerances given here (Kennedy and Gad Aly 1980, Chernenko and Kennedy 1991).

28.7 Cleaning, Surface Preparation, and Shop Coating

Throughout this section the word "painting" has been replaced by "coating" to accommodate coating systems other than paint.

There are five instances where steelwork need not be or should not be coated:

- steelwork concealed by an interior building finish or in a limited corrosive environment;

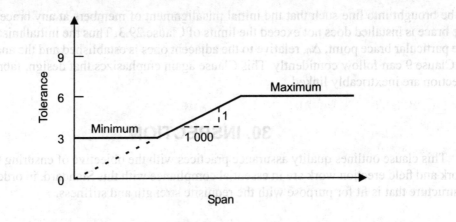

Figure 2-74
Horizontal Alignment Tolerances of Spandrel Beams

- steelwork encased in concrete;
- faying surfaces of slip-critical joints, except as permitted by Clause 23;
- surfaces finished to bear unless otherwise specified;
- steelwork where any coating could be detrimental to achieving a sound weldment; and,
- surfaces in an enclosed space entirely sealed off from external source of oxygen.

Specific requirements are provided in Clause 28.7.4.3 for a limited number of applications where welding over coating is permitted.

28.7.5 Metallic Zinc Coatings

These represent coatings other than paint and include hot-dip galvanizing and zinc metallized coatings both of which are to comply with the relevant CSA Standards.

29. ERECTION

29.3 Erection Tolerances

This entire clause provides helpful definitions of tolerances for the location of the ends of members with respect to their theoretical locations. Tolerances are given for column base plates, for alignment and elevations of horizontal or sloping members. For column splice tolerances, also see Commentary on Clause 28.5.

Clauses 29.3.4, 29.3.5, 29.3.6 and 29.3.8 are written in a parallel manner, in that the offset of one end relative to the other, or the elevation of one end relative to the other, both with respect to their theoretical locations shown on the drawings, e.g. the member is not plumb or not level, is expressed as a function of the length but with upper and lower limits. The lower limit represents a realistic assessment of adequate positioning, and the upper limit is a maximum not to be exceeded by the largest members, as illustrated in Figure 2-74 for horizontal alignment of spandrel beams.

29.3.7 Alignment of Braced Members

This clause is an outgrowth of the extensive work on restructuring Clause 9 on Stability of Structures and Members during the preparation of S16-01. Clause 9.2.1 requires the structure to be brought into line such that the initial misalignment of members at any brace point when the brace is installed does not exceed the limits of Clause 29.3. Thus the initial misalignment at the particular brace point, Δ_0, relative to the adjacent ones is established and the analyses given in Clause 9 can follow confidently. This Clause again emphasizes that design, fabrication, and erection are inextricably linked.

30. INSPECTION

This clause outlines quality assurance practices with the objective of ensuring that all shop work and field erection work are in essential compliance with this Standard, in order to provide a structure that is fit for purpose with the requisite strength and stiffness.

30.5 Third-Party Welding Inspection

Third-party welding inspection, just as for any other inspection procedures, is to ensure, insofar as possible by visual inspection, that the welds are fit for purpose, that is, they have the requisite strength and stiffness. The first distinction the inspector should make is to determine from the design engineer whether any components of the structure are subject to fatigue loading, in which case visible weld defects can have a significant effect on the fatigue life.

In cases where an engineering assessment of welds in existing structures is required due to defects, such as porosity, poor profile, lack of fusion, undercut, blow holes, lack of penetration, and craters, that exceed the limits given in CSA W59, the underlying question is, for statically loaded structures, how much have the defects reduced the weld strength. Kennedy (1967, 1968) suggests for statically loaded welds that weld strengths are reduced in the proportion of the defect area to the effective throat area.

REFERENCES

AASHTO. 2007 (R2009). LRFD bridge design specifications, SI Units, 4th Edition. American Association of State Highway and Transportation Officials, Washington, DC.

Adams, P. F. 1974. The design of steel beam-columns. Canadian Steel Industries Construction Council, Willowdale, Ont.

Adams, P. F., and Galambos, T. V. 1969. Material considerations in plastic design. International Association for Bridge and Structural Engineering, 29-II.

Adekola, A. O. 1968. Effective widths of composite beams of steel and concrete. The Structural Engineer, 46(9): 285-289.

Ahmad, M., Chien, E. Y. L., and Hosain, M. U. 1990. Modified stub-girder floor system: full-scale tests. ASCE Structures Congress. Baltimore, MA.

AISC. 1973. Commentary on highly restrained welded connections. Engineering Journal, American Institute of Steel Construction, Third Quarter.

— 2005. Specification for structural steel buildings, ANSI/AISC 360-05. American Institute of Steel Construction. Chicago, IL.

— 2005. Steel construction manual. 13th Edition. American Institute of Steel Construction. Chicago, IL.

— 2005. Seismic design manual. American Institute of Steel Construction, Chicago, IL.

AISI. 1968. Plastic design of braced multi-storey steel frames. American Iron and Steel Institute, Washington, DC.

Albert, C., Essa, H.S., and Kennedy, D.J.L., 1992. Distortional buckling of steel beams in cantilever-suspended span construction. Canadian Journal of Civil Engineering, 19(5): 767-780.

Alinia, M.M., and Dastfan, M. 2007. Cyclic behaviour, deformability and rigidity of stiffened steel shear panels. Journal of Constructional Steel Research, 63, 554–563

Allen, D. L. 1974. Vibrational behaviour of long-span floor slabs. Canadian Journal of Civil Engineering, 1(1).

— 1975. Limit states design – A probabilistic study. Canadian Journal of Civil Engineering, 2(1).

Allen, D. E., and Murray, T.M. 1993. Design criterion for vibrations due to walking. Engineering Journal, American Institute of Steel Construction, 30(4): 117-129.

Allen, D. E., and Rainer, J. H. 1976. Vibration criteria for long-span floors. Canadian Journal of Civil Engineering, 3(2).

Allen, D. E., Rainer, J. H., and Pernica, G. 1985. Vibration criteria for assembly occupancies. Canadian Journal of Civil Engineering, 12(3).

ASCE. 1967. Commentary on welded cover-plated beams. Subcommittee on Cover Plates, Task Committee on Flexural Members, ASCE, J. of the Structural Division, 93(ST4).

— 1971. Commentary on plastic design in steel. Manual of Engineering Practice, No. 41, American Society of Civil Engineers.

— 2000. Design of latticed steel transmission structures, ASCE 10-97. American Society of Civil Engineers, Reston, VA.

Aslani, F., and Goel, S.C. 1991. Stitch spacing and local buckling in seismic-resistant double-angle bracing, J. of Struct. Eng., ASCE, 2442-2463.

Astaneh-Asl, A. 2001. Seismic behavior and design of steel shear walls. Steel Tips, Structural Steel Educational Council, Moraga, CA.

Astaneh-Asl, A., and Goel, S.C. 1984. Cyclic in-plane buckling of double-angle bracing. J. of Struct. Eng., ASCE, 110(ST9): 2036-2055.

— 1985. Cyclic out-of-plane buckling of double-angle bracing. J. of Struct. Eng., ASCE, 111(ST5): 1135-1153.

Astaneh, A., Goel, S.C., and Hanson, R.D. 1986. Earthquake-resistant design of double-angle bracings. Engineering Journal, AISC, 23(4): 133-147.

ASTM. 2008a. Standard specification for "Twist Off" type tension control structural bolt/nut/washer assemblies, steel, heat treated, 120/105 ksi minimum tensile strength. Standard F1852-08, American Society for Testing and Material.

— 2008b. Standard specification for "Twist Off" type tension control structural bolt/nut/washer assemblies, steel, heat treated, 150 ksi minimum tensile strength. Standard F2280-08, American Society for Testing and Material.

— 2009a. Standard specification for high-strength bolts for structural steel joints [metric]. Standard A325M-09, American Society for Testing and Material.

— 2009b. Standard specification for high-strength steel bolts, Class 10.9 and 10.9.3, for structural steel joints [metric]. Standard A490M-09, American Society for Testing and Material.

— 2009c. Standard specification for structural bolts, steel, heat-treated, 120/105 ksi minimum tensile strength. Standard A325-09, American Society for Testing and Material.

— 2009d. Standard specification for heat-treated, steel structural bolts, 150 ksi minimum tensile strength. Standard A490-09, American Society for Testing and Material.

Attard, M.M. and Lawther, R. 1989. Effect of secondary warping on lateral buckling, Engineering Structures, Vol 11, April 1989, pp 112-118.

Aziz, T.S.A. 1972. Inelastic nonlinear behaviour of steel triangulated planar frames. M. Eng. Thesis, Carleton University, Ottawa, Ont.

Baker, K. A. and Kennedy, D.J.L. 1984. Resistance factors for laterally unsupported steel beams and biaxially loaded steel beam-columns. Canadian Journal of Civil Engineering, 11(4): 1008-1019.

Bansal, J.P. 1971. The lateral instability of continuous steel beams. Ph.D. Department, University of Texas, Austin.

Bartlett, F.M. 2007. Canadian Standards Association standard A23.3-04 resistance factor for concrete in compression, Canadian Journal of Civil Engineering, 34, 1029-1037.

Basler, K. 1961a. New provisions for plate girder design. Proceedings, AISC National Engineering Conference.

— 1961b. Strength of plate girders under combined bending and shear. ASCE Journal of the Structural Division, 87(ST7).

— 1961c. Strength of plate girders in shear. ASCE Journal of the Structural Division, 87(ST7).

Basler, K., and Thurlimann, B. 1961. Strength of plate girders in bending. ASCE Journal of the Structural Division, 87(ST6).

Beaulieu, D., and Adams, P. F. 1980. Significance of structural out-of-plumb forces and recommendations for design. Canadian Journal of Civil Engineering, 7(1).

Beedle, L. S., Lu, L. W., and Lim, L. C. 1969. Recent developments in plastic design practice. ASCE Journal of the Structural Division, 95(ST9).

Begum, M., Driver, R.G., and Elwi, A.E. 2007. Numerical simulations of the behaviour of partially encased composite columns. Structural Engineering Report No. 269, July, Department of Civil and Environmental Engineering, Univ. of Alberta, Edmonton, Canada. 251 pp.

Benichou, N. 1994. Behaviour of webs of rolled steel beams subjected to concentrated loads. Ph.D. Thesis, Dept. of Civ. and Env. Eng., Carleton University, Ottawa, Sept, 219 pages.

Berman, J.W., and Bruneau, M. 2003. Plastic analysis and design of steel plate shear walls. J. Struct. Eng., ASCE, 129, 11, 1448-1456.

— 2005a. Approaches for the seismic retrofit of braced steel bridge piers and proof-of-concept testing of a laterally stable eccentrically braced frame. Technical Report MCEER-05-0004, Multidisciplinary Center for Earthquake Engineering Research, Buffalo, NY.

— 2005b. Experimental investigation of light-gauge steel plate shear walls. J. Struct. Eng., ASCE, 131, 2, 259–267.

— 2008a. Tubular links for eccentrically braced frames I: Finite element parametric study & II: Experimental verification. J. Struct. Eng., ASCE, 134, 5, 692-712.

— 2008b. Capacity design of vertical boundary elements in steel plate shear walls. Eng. J., AISC, 45, 3, 57-71.

— 2009. Cyclic testing of a buckling restrained braced frame with unconstrained gusset connections. J. Struct. Eng., ASCE, 135, 12, 1499-1510.

Birkemoe, P. C., and Gilmor, M. I. 1978. Behaviour of bearing critical, double-angle beam connections. Engineering Journal, AISC, Fourth Quarter.

Bjorhovde, R. A. 1972. A probabilistic approach to maximum column strength. Proceedings, ASCE Conference on Safety and Reliability of Metal Structures.

Bjorhovde, R., and Birkemoe, P. C. 1979. Limit states design of HSS columns. Canadian Journal of Civil Engineering, 6(2).

Bjorhovde, R., and Zimmerman, T. J. 1980. Some aspects of stub-girder design. Proceedings of the Canadian Structural Engineering Conference. Canadian Steel Construction Council. Willowdale, Ont.

Bleich, F. 1952. Buckling strength of metal structures. McGraw-Hill. New York., NY.

Bondy, K.D., 1996. A more rational approach to capacity design of seismic moment frame columns. Earthquake Spectra. Vol.12, No.3: 395-406.

Bower, J. E., et al. 1971. Suggested design guide for beams with web holes. Journal of the Structural Division, American Society of Civil Engineers, 97(ST11).

Bremault, D., Driver, R., and Grondin, G. 2008. Limit states design approach for rolled wide flange beams subject to combined torsion and flexure. Structural engineering report 279, Department of Civil and Environmental Engineering, University of Alberta, Edmonton, Canada.

Bridge, R.O., Clarke, M.J., Leon, R.T., Lui, E.M., Sheikh, T.M., White, D.W. and Hajjar, J.F. 1997. Effective length and notional load approaches for assessing frame stability: Implications for American steel design. American Society of Civil Engineers, New York, N.Y.

Brockenbrough, R. L. 1983. Considerations in the design of bolted steel joints for weathering steel. Engineering Journal, American Institute of Steel Construction 20(1).

Brockenbrough, R. L., and Johnston, B. G. 1974. Steel design manual. United States Steel Corp., Pittsburgh, PA.

Bruneau, M., Mahin, S., and Popov, E.P. 1987. Ultimate behavior of butt welded splices in heavy rolled steel sections. Report No. UCB/EERC-87/10 Earthquake Engineering Research Center, Berkeley, CA.

Bruneau, M., Uang, C.M. and Whittaker, A. 1998. Ductile Design of Steel Structures. McGraw-Hill, New York, NY. 485 pp.

BSSC. 2003. NEHRP Recommended provisions for seismic regulations for new buildings and other structures. FEMA 450, Building Seismic Safety Council, Washington, D.C.

Budijgnto, P. 1983. Design methods for composite columns. Project Report G83-6, Department of Civil Engineering, McGill University.

Butler, L.J. and Kulak, G.L. 1971. Strength of fillet welds as a function of direction of load. Welding Research Supplement, Welding Journal. Welding Research Council, 36(5): 2315-2345.

Butler, L.J., Pal, S. and Kulak, G.L. 1972. Eccentrically loaded welded connections. Journal of the Structural Division, American Society of Civil Engineers 98(ST5): 989-1005.

Cai, Q. and Driver, R.G. 2010. Prediction of bolted connection capacity for block shear failures along atypical paths. Engineering Journal, American Institute of Steel Construction, vol. 47, 4th Quarter.

Callele, L.J., Driver, R.G., and Grondin, G.Y. 2009. Design and behavior of multi-orientation fillet weld connections. Engineering Journal, American Institute of Steel Construction, vol. 46, no. 4, pp. 257-272.

Carter, C. J. 1999. Stiffening of wide flange columns at moment connections: wind and seismic applications. American Institute of Steel Construction, Chicago IL

Chen, C.-H., Lai, J.-W., and Mahin, S. 2008. Numerical modelling and performance assessment of concentrically braced steel frames. Proc. ASCE Struct. Congress Crossing Borders, Vancouver, BC, 314, 260.

Chen, W. F., and Lui, E.M. 1987. Structural stability, theory and implementation. Elsevier. New York, NY.

Chen, Z., Ge, H., and Usami, T. 2006. Hysteretic model of stiffened shear panel dampers. J. Struct. Eng., ASCE, 132, 3, 478-483.

Cheng, J.J.R. and Grondin, G.Y. 1999. Recent developments in the behavior of cyclically loaded gusset plate connections. Proc. North American Steel Construction Conference, AISC. pp. 8-1 to 8-22.

Cheng, J.J.R., and Yura, J. A. 1986. Local web buckling of coped beams. Journal of Structural Engineering, American Society of Civil Engineers, 112(10).

— 1988. Lateral buckling tests on coped steel beams. Journal of Structural Engineering, American Society of Civil Engineers, 114(1): 16-30.

Cheng, J.J.R., Yura, J.A., and Johnson, C.P. 1988. Lateral buckling of coped steel beams. Journal of Structural Engineering, American Society of Civil Engineers, 114(1): 1-15.

Chernenko, D.E. and Kennedy, D.J.L. 1991. An analysis of the performance of welded wide flange columns. Canadian Journal of Civil Engineering, 18(4).

Chien, E.Y.L. 1989. Roof framing with cantilever (Gerber) girders & open-web steel joists. Canadian Institute of Steel Construction, Willowdale, Ont.

Chien, E.Y.L., and Ritchie, J. K. 1984. Design and construction of composite floor systems. Canadian Institute of Steel Construction, Willowdale, Ont.

Chusilp, P., and Usami, T. 2002. New elastic stability formulas for multiple-stiffened shear panels. J. Struct. Eng., ASCE, 128, 6, 833-836.

CIDECT. 1970. Concrete filled hollow section steel columns design manual. Monograph No. 1, International Committee for the Study and Development of Tubular Structures. Whitefriars Press Ltd., London.

CISC. 1980. Steel Joist Facts, 2nd Edition. Canadian Institute of Steel Construction, Willowdale, Ont.

— 2002. Steel Fabrication Quality Systems Guideline. Canadian Institute of Steel Construction, Willowdale, Ont.

— 2009. Moment Connections for Seismic Applications. Canadian Institute of Steel Construction, Markham, Ontario.

Clarke, M.J. and Bridge, R.Q. 1992. The inclusion of imperfections in the design of beam-columns, Proc. 1992 Annual Tech. Session, Structural Stability Research Council, Bethlehem: 327-346.

— 1995. The notional load approach to the design of frames, Res. Rep. No. R718 , School of Civil and Mining Eng., University of Sydney, Australia, Dec.

CSA. 1969. Steel structures for buildings. CSA Standard S16-1969, Canadian Standards Association, Toronto, Ont.

— 2004. Design of concrete structures. CSA Standard A23.3-04, Canadian Standards Association, Mississauga, Ont.

— 2006 Canadian highway bridge design code. CSA Standard S6-06. Canadian Standards Association, Mississauga, Ont.

— 2007. North American specification for the design of cold-formed steel structural members. CSA Standard S136-07. Canadian Standards Association, Mississauga, Ont.

— 2010. Certification of manufacturers of steel building systems, CSA Standard A660-10, Canadian Standards Association, Mississauga, Ont.

Dastfan, M. and Driver, R.G. 2008. Flexural stiffness limits for frame members of steel plate shear wall systems. Proc., Annual Stability Conference, Structural Stability Research Council, April 2-5, Nashville, TN, USA.

— 2009. Investigations on the effect of frame member connection rigidity on the behavior of steel plate shear wall systems. Proc., STESSA 2009 Behaviour of Steel Structures in Seismic Areas, August, Philadelphia, PA, USA.

Davaran, A. 2001. Effective length factor for discontinuous X-bracing systems. J. Struct. Eng., ASCE, 127, 2, 106-112.

Davaran, A. and Hoveidae, N. 2009. Effect of mid-connection detail on the behavior of X-bracing systems. J. Constr. Steel Research, 65, 2, 290-298.

Davies, C. 1969. Tests on half-scale steel concrete composite beams with welded stud connectors. The Structural Engineer, 47(1): 29-40.

Dawe, J. L., and Kulak, G. L. 1984. Local buckling of W shape columns and beams. Journal of Structural Engineering, American Society of Civil Engineers, 110(6).

— 1986. Local buckling behavior of beam-columns. Journal of Structural Engineering, American Society of Civil Engineers, 112(11).

de Back, J., and de Jong, A. 1968. Measurement on connections with high strength bolts, particularly in view of the permissible arithmetical bearing stress. Report 6-68-3, Stevin Laboratory, Delft University of Technology, Netherlands.

de Oliveira, J.C., Packer, J.A., Christopoulos, C. 2008. Cast steel connectors for circular hollow section braces under inelastic cyclic loading. J. Struct. Eng., ASCE, 134, 3, 374-383.

Deng, K., Grondin, G.Y., and Driver, R.G. 2006. Effect of loading angle on the behavior of fillet welds. Engineering Journal, American Institute of Steel Construction, vol. 43, no. 1, pp. 9-23.

Deng, X., Dastfan, M., and Driver, R.G. 2008. Behaviour of steel plate shear walls with composite columns. Proc., Structures Congress 2008 Crossing Borders, ASCE, 314, Vancouver, BC, Canada.

Dexter, R.J., Altstadt, S.A., and Gardner, C.A. 2002. Strength and Ductility of HPS70W Tension Members and Tension Flanges with Holes, Final Report to American Iron and Steel Institute, University of Minnesota, March.

Dexter, R.J., and Gentilcore, M.L. 1997. Evaluation of Ductile Fracture Models for Ship Structural Details, Report SSC-393, Ship Structure Committee, Washington, DC.

Dexter, R.J., and Melendrez, M.I. 2000. Through-thickness properties of column flanges in welded moment connections. Journal of Structural Engineering, American Society of Civil Engineers, 126(1): 24-31.

Disque, R. O. 1964. Wind connections with simple framing. Engineering Journal, AISC, July.

Driver, R. G., Grondin, G. Y., and Kulak, G. L. 2006. Unified block shear equation for achieving consistent reliability, Journal of Constructional Steel Research, Vol. 62, pp. 210-222.

Driver, R. G., and Kennedy, D. J. L. 1989. Combined flexure and torsion of I-shaped steel beams. Canadian Journal of Civil Engineering, 16(2).

Driver, R.G., et al. 1997. Seismic behaviour of steel plate shear walls, Structural Engineering Report No. 215, Department of Civil and Environmental Engineering, University of Alberta.

— 1998(a). FE and simplified modelling of a steel plate shear wall, Journal of Structural Engineering, American Society of Civil Engineers, 124(2): 121-130.

— 1998(b). Cyclic test of a four storey steel plate shear wall, Journal of Structural Engineering, American Society of Civil Engineers, 124(2): 112-120.

Driver, R.G. and Wong, E. 2007. Critical evaluation of the CSA S16-01 equivalent moment factor for laterally unsupported beams. Proc., Canadian Society for Civil Engineering Annual Conference, June 6–9, Yellowknife, Canada.

Duan, L. and Chen, W-F. 1988. Design rules of built-up members in Load and Resistance Factor design. Journal of Structural Engineering, American Society of Civil Engineers, 114(11): 2544-2554.

El-Ghazzi, M. N., Robinson, H., and Elkholy, I.A.S. 1976. Longitudinal shear capacity of slabs of composite beams. Canadian Journal of Civil Engineering, 3(4).

Elkelish, S., and Robinson, H. 1986. Effective widths of composite beams with ribbed metal deck. Canadian Journal of Civil Engineering, 13(5): 575-582.

El-Tayem, A.A., and Goel, S.C. 1986. Effective length factor for the design of X-bracing systems. Engineering Journal, AISC, 24: 41-45.

Englehardt, M.D., and Popov, E.P. 1989. Behaviour of long links in eccentrically braced frames. EERC Report 89-01, University of California, Berkeley, CA.

— 1992. Experimental performance of long links in eccentrically braced frames. ASCE Journal of Structural Engineering, 118(11): 3067-3088.

Englekirk, R. 1994. Steel structures – Controlling behavior through design. John Wiley & Sons. New York, NY.

Epstein, H. I., and Stamberg, H. 2002. Block shear and net section capacities of structural Tees in tension: test results and code implications. AISC Engineering Journal, Vol. 39, Fourth quarter, pp. 228-239.

Essa, H.S. and Kennedy, D.J.L. 1994a, Station Square revisited: distortional buckling collapse. Canadian Journal of Civil Engineering, 21(3): 377-381.

— 1994b, Design of cantilever beams: a refined approach. Journal of Structural Engineering, American Society of Civil Engineers. 120 (ST9): 2623-2636.

— 1995, Design of steel beams in cantilever-suspended span construction. Journal of Structural Engineering, American Society of Civil Engineers. 121(ST11): 1667-1673.

— 2000. Proposed provisions for the design of steel beam-columns in S16-2001. Canadian Journal of Civil Engineering, 27(4): 610-619.

Essa, H.S., Tremblay, R., and Rogers, C. 2003. Behavior of roof deck diaphragms under quasi-static cyclic loading. Journal of Structural Engineering, ASCE, 129(12): 1658-1666.

Estabrooks, B., and Grondin, G. 2008. Combined bending and torsion of steel I-shaped beams. Structural Engineering report 276, Department of Civil and Environmental Engineering, University of Alberta, *www.engineering.ualberta.ca/structures/reports.cfm.*

EUROCODE No. 4. 1987. Common unified rules for composite steel and concrete structures. Report EUR 9886 EN, Commission of the European Communities, Luxembourg.

Fahnestock, L. A., Ricles, J.M., and Sause, R. 2007. Experimental evaluation of a large-scale buckling-restrained braced frame, J. Struct. Eng., ASCE, 133, 9, 1205–1214.

Fell, B.V., Kanwinde, A.M., Deierlein, G.G., and Myers, A.T. 2009. Experimental investigation of inelastic cyclic buckling and fracture of steel braces, J. Struct. Eng., ASCE, 135, 1, 1-19.

FEMA. 1995. FEMA 267 (SAC 95-02) Interim guidelines: Evaluation, repair, modification and design of steel moment frames. Federal Emergency Management Agency. Washington, DC.

— 1997. FEMA 267A (SAC 96-03) Interim guidelines advisory no. 1 – Supplement to FEMA 267. Federal Emergency Management Agency. Washington, DC.

— 2000. Recommended seismic design criteria for new steel moment-frame buildings. Report FEMA 350. Federal Emergency Management Agency, Washington, D.C.

Fisher, J. W. 1974. Guide to 1974 AASHTO fatigue specifications. AISC, Chicago, IL.

— 1978. Fatigue cracking in bridges from out-of-plane displacements. Canadian Journal of Civil Engineering, 5(4).

— 1984. Fatigue and fracture in steel bridges – Case studies. John Wiley & Sons.

Fisher, J, W., Lee, G. C, Yura, J. A., and Driscoll, G. C. 1963. Plastic analysis and tests of haunched corner connections. Bulletin No. 91, Welding Research Council.

Franchuk, C.R., Driver, R.G., and Grondin, G.Y. 2003. Experimental investigation of block shear failure in coped steel beams. Canadian Journal of Civil Engineering, 30: 871-881.

Frank, K. H. 1980. Fatigue strength of anchor bolts. Journal of the Structural Division, American Society of Civil Engineers, 106(ST6).

Gagnon, D. G., and Kennedy, D. J. L. 1989. Behaviour and ultimate tensile strength of partial joint penetration groove welds. Canadian Journal of Civil Engineering, 16(3).

Galambos, T. V. 1968. Structural members and frames. Prentice-Hall Inc., Englewood Cliffs, NJ.

— 1998. Guide to stability design criteria for metal structures (5th ed.). Structural Stability Research Council, John Wiley & Sons, Inc., New York, NY.

Ghali, A., Favre, R., and Elbadry, M. 2002. Concrete structures: Stresses and deformations, 3rd ed. London: Spon Press.

Ghobarah, A., Korol, R.M., and Osman, A. 1992. Cyclic behaviour of extended end plate joints. ASCE. Journal of Structural Engineering, 118(ST5)

Gibson, G. T., and Wake, B. T. 1942. An investigation of welded connections for angle tension members. Welding Journal, American Welding Society.

Gobel, G. 1968. Shear strength of thin flange composite specimens. Engineering Journal, AISC, April.

Goel, S.C., and Itani, A. 1994. Seismic resistant special truss moment frames. ASCE Journal of Structural Engineering. 120(6).

Goel, S.C., Rai, D.C., and Hisham, S. 1998. Special truss moment resisting frames – Design guide. Research Report UMCEE 98-44. Dept. of Civ. Eng., Univ. of Michigan, Ann Arbor, MI.

Goodier, J.N., 1942, Flexural-torsional buckling of bars of open section. Cornell University Engineering Experiment Station Bulletin No. 28, January.

Graham, J. D., Sherbourne, A. N., Khabbaz, R. N., and Jensen, C. D. 1959. Welded interior beam-to-column connections. American Institute of Steel Construction.

Grant, J. A., Fisher, J. W., and Slutter, R. G. 1977. Composite beams with formed steel deck. Engineering Journal, AISC, First Quarter.

Griggs, P. H. 1976. Mill building structures. Proceedings, Canadian Structural Engineering Conference, Canadian Steel Construction Council, Willowdale, Ont.

Haaijer, G., and Thurlimann, B. 1958. On inelastic buckling in steel. ASCE Journal of the Engineering Mechanics Division, April.

Haddad, M., and Tremblay, R. 2006. Influence of connection design on the inelastic seismic response of HSS steel bracing members. In Tubular Structures XI: Proc. 11th Int. Symp. and IIW Int. Conf. on Tubular Structures, Québec, QC, 639-646.

Hagood, T. A., Jr., Guthrie, L., and Hoadley, G. 1968. An investigation of the effective concrete slab width for composite construction. Engineering Journal, AISC, 5(1): 20-25.

Han, X.M., 1998. Design and behaviour of eccentrically braced frames in moderate seismic zones, M.Eng. thesis, Department of Civil Engineering and Applied Mechanics, McGill University, Montreal.

Hansell, W. C., and Viest, I. M. 1971. Load factor design for steel highway bridges. Engineering Journal, AISC, 8(4).

Hardash, S., and Bjorhovde, R. 1985. New design criteria for gusset plates in tension. Engineering Journal, AISC, 21(2): 77-94.

Hart, W. H., and Milek, W. A. 1965. Splices in plastically designed continuous structures. Engineering Journal, AISC, April.

Hawkins, N. M., and Mitchell, D. 1984. Seismic response of composite shear connections. ASCE Journal of Structural Engineering, 110(9): 2120-2136.

Heins, C. P., and Fan, H. M. 1976. Effective composite beam width at ultimate load. ASCE Journal of the Structural Division, 102(ST11).

Hirano, N. 1970. Bearing stresses in bolted joints. Society of Steel Construction of Japan Tokyo, 6(58).

Holtz, N. M., and Kulak, G. L. 1970. High strength bolts and welds in load-sharing systems. Studies in Structural Engineering, No. 8, Technical University of Nova Scotia.

— 1973. Web slenderness limits for compact beams. SER 43, Department of Civil Engineering, University of Alberta.

— 1975. Web slenderness limits for non-compact beams. SER 51, Department of Civil Engineering, University of Alberta.

Hosain, M.U., and Pashan, A. 2002. Research in Canada on steel-concrete composite floor systems: an update. Proceedings of ICASS'02 -Third International Conference on Advances in Steel Structures, Hong Kong, 9-11 December, Volume 1: 527-534, Elsevier, Oxford, UK.

Hosain, M.U., and Wu. H. 2002. Composite beams with parallel wide ribbed metal deck: push-out and full size beam tests, Composite Construction in Steel and Concrete IV, Special Monograph of the Structural Engineering Institute, ASCE, 415-425.

Huang, J.S., Chen, W.F., and Beedle, L.S. 1973. Behaviour and design of steel beam-to-column moment connections. Welding Research Council Bulletin, 188: 1-23.

Iwankiw, N., and Schlafly, T. 1982. Effect of hole-making on the strength of double lap joints, Engineering Journal, AISC, 19(3): 170-178.

Izvernari, C., Lacerte, M., and Tremblay, R. 2007. Seismic performance of multi-storey concentrically braced steel frames designed according to the 2005 Canadian seismic provisions. Proc. 9th Canadian Conference on Earthquake Engineering, Ottawa, ON. Paper No. 1419.

Jain, A.K., Goel, S.C., and Hanson, R.D. 1980. Hysteretic cycles of axially loaded steel members. J. of the Struct. Div., ASCE, 106: 1777-1795.

Jayas, B. S., and Hosain, M. U. 1988. Behaviour of headed studs in composite beams: push-out tests. Canadian Journal of Civil Engineering, 15(2), 240-253.

— 1989. Behaviour of headed studs in composite beams: full-size tests. Canadian Journal of Civil Engineering, 16(5), 712-724.

Jent, K. A. 1989. Effects of shrinkage, creep and applied loads on continuous deck-slab composite beams. M.Sc. thesis, Queen's University, Kingston, Ont.

Ji, X., Kato, M., Wang, M., Hitaka, T., and Nakashima, M. 2009. Effect of gravity columns on mitigation of drift concentration for braced frames. Journal of Constructional Steel Research, 65, 12, 2148-2156.

Johnson, R. P. 1970. Longitudinal shear strength of composite beams. ACI Journal Proceedings, 67.

— 1975. Composite structures of steel and concrete. Volume 1: beams, columns, frames and applications in buildings. Crosby Lookwood Staples, London, England : 210.

Johnston, B. G. 1939. Pin connected plate links. Transactions, American Society of Civil Engineers.

Jones, J. 1958. Bearing-ratio effect on strength of riveted joints. Transactions, American Society of Civil Engineers, 123: 964-972.

Kaliandasani, R. A., Simmonds, S. H., and Murray, D. W. 1977. Behaviour of open web steel joists. Report No. 62, Department of Civil Engineering, University of Alberta.

Kalyanaraman, V., Pekoz, T., and Winter, G. 1977. Unstiffened compression elements. ASCE. Journal of the Structural Division, 103(ST9).

Kanchanalai, T. 1977. The design and behavior of beam-columns in unbraced steel frames. CESRL Report No. 77-2, AISI Project No. 189 – Column design in unbraced frames, Report No. 2, Structures Research Laboratory, The University of Texas at Austin.

Kasai, K., and Han, X. 1997. New EBF design method and application: redesign and analysis of US-Japan EBF. STESSA Conference, Tokyo.

Kasai, K., and Popov, E.P. 1986. General behavior of WF steel shear link beams. ASCE Journal of Structural Engineering, 112(ST2): 362-382.

Kemp, A.R., and Trinchero, P. 1992. Serviceability stress limits for composite beams. Composite Construction and Engineering Foundation Conference, June 15-19, Potosi, MO.

Kennedy, D.J.L. 1967, Evaluation of structural weld defects. Canadian Welding Society Annual Meeting, Montreal, May.

— 1968. Evaluation of structural weld defects. Canadian Welder and Fabricator: 10-14.

— 1974. Limit states design – An innovation in design standards for steel structures. Canadian Journal of Civil Engineering, 1(1).

— 1995. Limit states design of beam-columns in CSA S16.1-94. Proc. Int. Conf. on Struct. Stability and Des., G.J.Hancock and M.A.Bradford, eds., Oct 30-Nov 1, Balkerna, Rotterdam, 461-465.

— 2004. Analysis of strength of flare bevel groove welds in open web steel joists. Committee communication.

Kennedy, D.J.L., Allen, D. E., Adams, P. F., Kulak, G. L., Turner, D. K., and Tarlton, D. L. 1976. Limit states design. Proceedings of the Canadian Structural Engineering Conference, Canadian Steel Industries Construction Council, Willowdale, Ont.

Kennedy, D.J.L., and Brattland, A. 1992. Shrinkage tests of two full-scale composite trusses. Canadian Journal of Civil Engineering, 19(2).

Kennedy, D.J.L., and Gad Aly, M. 1980. Limit states design of steel structures – Performance factors. Canadian Journal of Civil Engineering, 7(1).

Kennedy, D.J.L., Kulak, G.L., and Driver, R.G. 1994, Discussion to postbuckling behavior of steel-plate shear walls, by Elgaaly, M., Caccese, V., and Du., C. Journal of Structural Engineering, ASCE, 120(7): 2250-2251.

Kennedy, D.J.L., Miazga, G.S., and Lesik, D.F. 1990. Discussion of evaluation of fillet weld shear strength of FCAW electrodes by McClellan, R.W. Welding Journal, August 1989, Welding Journal Reference, 44-46.

Kennedy, D.J.L., Picard, A., and Beaulieu, D. 1990. New Canadian provisions for the design of steel beam-columns. Canadian Journal of Civil Engineering, 17(6).

Kennedy, D.J.L., and Rowan, W.H.D. 1964. Behaviour of compression chords of open web steel joists. Canadian Institute of Steel Construction, Willowdale, ON.

Kennedy, J.B., and Neville, A.M. 1986, Basic statistical methods for engineers and scientists. Third edition, Harper and Row, New York, NY.

Kennedy, S. J., and Kennedy, D. J. L. 1987. The performance and strength of hardened steel test roller assemblies. Proceedings, CSCE Centennial Conference, May 19-22. Montreal, QC: 513-531.

Kennedy, S. J. Kennedy, D. J. L., and Medhekar, M.S. 1998. The bearing resistance of webs: further studies of the post buckling strength. Proc. Annual Meeting, Structural Stability Research Council, Atlanta, Sept. 21 -23

Kennedy, S.J., and MacGregor, J.G. 1984. End connection effects on the strength of concrete filled HSS beam-columns. Structural Engineering Report 115, Department of Civil Engineering, University of Alberta, Edmonton, Alberta.

Ketter, R. L. 1961. Further studies of the strength of beam-columns. ASCE, Journal of the Structural Division, 87(ST6): 135-152.

Kirby, P. A., and Nethercot, D. A. 1978. Design for structural stability. Granada. London, England.

Knowles, R. B., and Park, R. 1970. Axial load design for concrete filled steel tubes. ASCE, Journal of the Structural Division, 96(ST10).

Koboevic, S., 2000. An approach to seismic design of eccentrically braced frames. Ph.D. Thesis, Department of Civil Engineering and Applied Mechanics, McGill University, Montreal.

Krawinkler, H., and Popov, E.P. 1982. Seismic behaviour of moment connections and joints. ASCE, Journal of the Structural Division, 108(ST2), 373-391.

Kuhn, P., Peterson, J. P., and Levin, L. R. 1952, A summary of diagonal tension, Part I – Methods of analysis, Technical Note 2661, National Advisory Committee for Aeronautics, Langley Aeronautical Laboratory, Langely Field, VA.

Kulak, G.L. 1985. Behaviour of steel plate shear walls, Proceedings, The 1985 International Engineering Symposium on Structural Steel, Chicago.

— 1986. Unstiffened steel plate shear walls: static and seismic behaviour, in steel structures, Recent Research Advances and Their Applications to Design, Edited by M.N. Pavlovic, Elsevier Applied Science Publishers, London.

— 1991. Unstiffened steel plate shear walls. Structures subjected to repeated loading: Stability and strength, R. Narayanan and T.M. Roberts, eds., Elsevier Applied Science, New York, N.Y.

Kulak, G.L., and Birkemoe, P.C. 1993. Field studies of bolt pretension. Journal of Constructional Steel Research, No. 25: 95-106.

Kulak, G. L., and Dawe, J. L. 1991. Discussion of design interaction equations for steel members. Sohal, I. S., Duan, L., and Chen W-F. ASCE, Journal of Structural Engineering, 117(ST7): 2191-2193.

Kulak, G. L., Fisher, J. W., and Struik, J.H.A. 2001. Guide to design criteria for bolted and riveted joints, Second edition. Research Council on Structural Connections. (Original copyright 1987 by John Wiley & Sons, Inc. transferred to RCSC). *www.boltcouncil.org/files/2ndEditionGuide.pdf*

Kulak, G. L., and Grondin, G.Y., 2000. Block shear failure in steel members – A review of design practice. Proceedings of the Fourth International Workshop on Connections in Steel Structures IV: Steel Connections in the New Millennium. Roanoke, VA., AISC, Chicago.

— 2003. Strength of joints that combine bolts and welds. AISC Engineering Journal, Second quarter, pp. 89-98.

— 2009. Limit states design in structural steel, 8th Edition. Canadian Institute of Steel Construction, Markham, ON.

Kulak, G.L., Kennedy, D.J.L., and Driver, R.G. 1994. Discussion to experimental study of thin steel-plate shear walls under cyclic load, by Caccese, V., Elgaaly, M., and Chen, R. Journal of Structural Engineering, ASCE, Vol 120, No.10, pp. 3072-3073.

Kulak, G.L., Kennedy, D.J.L., Driver, R.G., and Medhekar, M. 1999. Behavior of steel plate shear walls. Proceedings, 1999 North American Steel Construction Conference, Toronto.

Kulak, G.L., and Smith, I.F.C. 1993. Analysis and design of fabricated steel structures for fatigue: A primer for civil engineers. Dept. of Civil Eng. SER 190. University of Alberta, Edmonton. AB.

Kulak, G.L., and Undershute, S.T. 1998. Tension control bolts: Strength and installation. Journal of Bridge Engineering, ASCE, 3(1).

Kullman R. B., and Hosain, M. U. 1985. Shear capacity of stub-girders: full-scale tests. ASCE, Journal of Structural Engineering, 111(ST1): 56-75.

Lacerte, M., and Tremblay, R. 2006. Making use of brace overstrength to improve the seismic response of multi-storey split-X concentrically braced steel frames. Can. J. of Civ. Eng., 33, 8, 1005-1021.

Lay, M. G. 1965. Flange local buckling in wide-flange shapes. ASCE Journal of the Structural Division, 91(ST6).

Lay, M. G., and Galambos, T. V. 1966. Bracing requirements for inelastic steel beams. ASCE Journal of the Structural Division, 92(ST2).

— 1967. Inelastic beams under moment gradient. ASCE Journal of the Structural Division, 93(ST1).

Lee, K., and Bruneau, M. 2005. Energy dissipation of compression members in concentrically braced frames: Review of experimental data. J. Struct. Eng., ASCE, 131, 4, 552–559.

Lee, S., and Goel, S.C. 1987. Seismic behavior of hollow and concrete-filled square tubular bracing members. Research Report UMCE 87-11, Dept. of Civ. Eng., Univ. of Michigan, Ann Arbor, Mich.

Lesik, D.F., and Kennedy, D.J.L. 1990. Ultimate strength of fillet welded connections loaded in plane. Canadian Journal of Civil Engineering 17(1), 55-67.

Li, C.-H., Tsai, K.-C., Lin, C.-H., and Chen, P.-C. 2009. Cyclic tests of four two-storey narrow steel plate shear walls. Part 1: Analytical studies and specimen design & Part 2: Experimental results and design implications. Earthquake Eng. and Struct. Dyn. Published Online: 26 Nov 2009.

Lilley, S. B., and Carpenter, S. T. 1940. Effective moment of inertia of a riveted plate girder. Transactions, American Society of Civil Engineers.

Liu, J., Sabelli, R., Brockenbrough, R.L., and Fraser, T.P. 2007. Expected yield stress and tensile strength ratios for determination of expected member capacity in the 2005 AISC seismic provisions. AISC Eng. J., 44, 1, 15-25.

Liu, Z. 1987. Investigation of concrete-filled steel tubes under cyclic bending and buckling. Ph.D. Thesis, Dept. of Civ. Eng., Univ. of Michigan, Ann Arbor, Michigan.

Liu, Z., and Goel, S.C. 1988. Cyclic load behavior of concrete-filled tubular braces. ASCE Journal of Structural Engineering, 114(ST7):1488-1506.

Loov, R. 1996. A simple equation for axially loaded steel column design curves. Canadian Journal of Civil Engineering. 23(1): 272-276.

López, W.A., and Sabelli, R. 2004. Seismic design of buckling-restrained braced frames, Steel Tips, Structural Steel Education Council, Moraga, CA.

Lu, Y.Q., and Kennedy, D.J.L. 1994. The flexural behaviour of concrete-filled hollow structural sections. Canadian Journal of Civil Engineering, 21(1), 111-130.

Lubell, A.S., Prion, H.G.L., Ventura, C.E., and Rezai, M. 2000. Unstiffened steel plate shear wall performance under cyclic loading. J. Struct. Eng., ASCE, 126, 4, 453-460.

Lukey, A. F., and Adams, P. F. 1969. Rotation capacity of beams under moment gradient. ASCE Journal of the Structural Division, 95(ST6).

Lutz, L.A. 1992. Critical slenderness of compression members with effective lengths about non-principal axes. Proceedings of the Annual Technical Session and Meeting of the Structural Stability Research Council, Bethlehem, PA, 107-116.

MacPhedran, I.J., and Grondin, G.Y. 2006. A brief history of beam-column design. 1st International Structural Specialty Conference, Calgary, Alberta, May 23-26.

MacRae, G.A., Kimura, Y., and Roeder, C. 2004. Effect of column stiffness on braced frame seismic behavior, ASCE J. Struct. Eng., Vol. 130, No. 3, 381–391.

Mahin, S., Uriz, P., Aiken, I., Field, C., and Ko, E. 2004. Seismic performance of buckling restrained braced frame systems. Proc. 13th World Conf. on Earthquake Eng., Vancouver, B.C., Canada, Paper No. 1681.

Malley, J.O., and Popov. E.P. 1983. Design considerations for shear links in eccentrically braced steel frames. EERC Report No. UCB/EERC-83/24, Univ. of California, Berkeley, CA.

Manniche, K., and Ward-Hall, G. 1975. Mission bridge – Design and construction of the steel box girder. Canadian Journal of Civil Engineering, 2(2).

Manuel, T.J., and Kulak, G.L. 1998. Strength of joints that combine bolts and welds. Dept. of Civil Eng. SER 222. University of Alberta, Edmonton, AB.

— 2000. Strength of joints that combine bolts and welds. ASCE Journal of Structural Engineering, 126(3): 279-287.

Marino, E.M., and Nakashima, M. 2006. Seismic performance and new design procedure for chevron-braced frames. Earthquake Eng. and Struct. Dyn., Vol. 35, No. 4, 433-452.

Martinez-Saucedo, G., Packer, J.A., and Christopoulos, C. 2008. Gusset plate connections to circular hollow section braces under inelastic cyclic loading. J. Struct. Eng. 134, 7, 1252-1258.

Massey, C. 1962. Lateral bracing forces of steel I-beams. ASCE Engineering Mechanics Division, 88(EM6).

Mattock, A. H. 1974. Shear transfer on concrete having reinforcement at an angle to the shear plane. Special Publication 42, Shear in Reinforced Concrete, American Concrete Institute: 17-42.

Mattock, A. H., Li, W. K., and Wang, T.C. 1976, Shear transfer in lightweight reinforced concrete. PCI Journal, 21(1): 20-39.

Maurer, M.B. and Kennedy D.J.L. 1994. Shrinkage and flexural tests of a full-scale composite truss. Structural Engineering Report 206, Department of Civil Engineering, University of Alberta.

Merzouq, S., and Tremblay, R. 2006. Seismic design of dual concentrically braced steel frames for stable seismic performance for multi-storey buildings. Proc. 8th U.S. National Conference on Earthquake Eng., San Francisco, CA, Paper 1909.

Miazga, G.S., and Kennedy, D.J.L. 1989. Behaviour of fillet welds as a function of the angle of loading. Canadian Journal of Civil Engineering 16: 583-599.

Munse, W. H. 1959. The effect of bearing pressure on the static strength of riveted connections. Bulletin No. 454, Engineering Experimental Station, University of Illinois, Urbana, IL.

Munse, W. H., and Chesson, E. 1963. Riveted and bolted joints: net section design. ASCE. Journal of the Structural Division, 89(ST1), Part 1.

Murray, T. M. 1975. Design to prevent floor vibrations. Engineering Journal, AISC, third quarter, pp. 83-87.

— 2003. Extended end plate connections – Seismic and wind applications. Steel Design Guide 4, American Institute of Steel Construction, Chicago.

Murray, T.M., Allen, D.E., and Ungar, E.E. 1997. Floor vibrations due to human activity. Steel Design Guide Series 11. American Institute of Steel Construction, Chicago; Canadian Institute of Steel Construction, Toronto.

Nash, D. S., and Kulak, G. L. 1976. Web slenderness limits for non-compact beam-columns. Report No. 53, Department of Civil Engineering, University of Alberta.

NBCC. 2005. National Building Code of Canada. National Research Council of Canada, Ottawa, Ont.

— 2010. National Building Code of Canada. National Research Council of Canada, Ottawa, Ont.

NCHRP. 1970. Effect of weldments on the fatigue strength of steel beams. Report 102, National Cooperative Highway Research Program, Transportation Research Board, National Academy of Sciences, Washington, DC.

— 1974. Fatigue strength of steel beams with welded stiffeners and attachments. Report 147, National Cooperative Highway Research Program, Transportation Research Board, National Academy of Sciences, Washington, DC.

Nethercot, D. A., and Trahair, N. S. 1976a. Inelastic lateral buckling of determinate beams. ASCE Journal of the Structural Division, 102(ST4):701-717.

— 1976b. Lateral buckling approximations for elastic beams. ISE. The Structural Engineer. 54(6): 197-204.

Ng, A.K.F., Deng, K., Grondin, G.Y., and Driver, R.G. 2004a. Behavior of transverse fillet welds: experimental program. Engineering Journal, American Institute of Steel Construction, vol. 41, no. 2, pp. 39-54.

Ng, A.K.F., Driver, R.G., and Grondin, G.Y. 2004b. Behavior of transverse fillet welds: parametric and reliability analyses. Engineering Journal, American Institute of Steel Construction, vol. 41, no. 2, pp. 55-67.

Nixon, D. 1981. The use of frame action to resist lateral loads in simple construction. Canadian Journal of Civil Engineering, 8(4).

Okazaki, T., Arce, G., Ryu, C., and Engelhardt, M.D. 2005. Experimental study of local buckling, overstrength, and fracture of links in eccentrically braced frames. J. Struct. Eng., ASCE, 131, 10, 1526-1535.

Okazaki,T., Engelhardt, M.D., Nakashima, M., and Suita, K. 2006. Experimental performance of link-to-column connections in eccentrically braced frames. Journal of Structural Engineering, ASCE, 132, 8, 1201–1211.

Okazaki, T., and Engelhardt, M.D. 2007. Cyclic loading behavior of EBF links constructed of ASTM A992 steel. J. Constr. Steel Research, 63, 6, 751-765.

Olgaard, J. G., Slutter, R. G., and Fisher, J. W. 1971. Shear strength of stud connectors in light-weight and normal-weight concrete. Engineering Journal, AISC, April.

Parcel, J.I., and Murer, E.B. 1934. The effect of secondary stresses upon ultimate strength, Proceedings (with discussions in Transactions) American Society of Civil Engineers, Reston, Virginia, Vol. 60: 55p.

Perlynn, M. J., and Kulak, G. L. 1974. Web slenderness limits for compact beam-columns. Structural Engineering Report 50, Department of Civil Engineering, University of Alberta.

Popov, E.P., Amin, N.R., Louie, J.J.C., and Stephen, R.M. 1986. Cyclic behaviour of large beam-column assemblies. Engineering Journal, AISC, 23(1): 9-23.

Popov, E.P., and Black, R.G. 1980. Steel struts under severe cyclic loading. J. of the Struct. Div., ASCE, 107(ST9): 1587-1881.

Popov, E.P., Englehardt, M.D., and Ricles, J.M. 1989. Eccentrically braced frames: U.S. practice. AISC Engineering Journal, 36(2): 66-80.

Popov, E. P., and Pinkney, R. B. 1969. Cyclic yield reversal in steel building connections. ASCE Journal of the Structural Division, 95(ST3).

Popov, E. P., and Stephen, R. M. 1972. Cyclic loading of full-size steel connections. Steel Research for Construction, Bulletin No.21, AISI.

— 1977a. Capacity of columns with splice imperfections. Engineering Journal, AISC, 14(1).

— 1977b. Tensile capacity of partial penetration groove welds. ASCE. Journal of the Structural Division, 103(ST9).

Prickett, B.S., and Driver, R.G. 2006. Behaviour of partially encased composite columns made with high performance concrete. Structural Engineering Report No. 262, January, Department of Civil and Environmental Engineering, University of Alberta, Edmonton, Canada.

Purba, R., Bruneau, M., 2007. Design recommendations for perforated steel plate shear walls. Technical Report MCEER-07-0011, MCEER, University at Buffalo, Buffalo, NY.

— 2009. Finite-element investigation and design recommendations for perforated steel plate shear walls. J. Struct. Eng., ASCE, 135, 11, 1367-1376.

Qu, B., and Bruneau, M. 2009. Design of steel plate shear walls considering boundary frame moment resisting action. J. Struct. Eng., ASCE, 135, 12, 1511-1521.

Qu, B., Bruneau, M., Lin, C.H., Tsai, K.C. 2008. Testing of full scale two-story steel plate shear walls, with RBS connections and composite floor. J. Struct. Eng., ASCE, 134, 3, 364-373.

Rainer, J. H. 1980. Dynamic tests on a steel-joist concrete-slab floor. Canadian Journal of Civil Engineering, 7(2).

RCSC. 2004. Specification for structural joints using ASTM A325 or A490 bolts. Research Council on Structural Connections. *www.boltcouncil.org/files/2004RCSCSpecification.pdf*

Redwood, R. G. 1971. Simplified plastic analysis for reinforced web holes. Eng. J., AISC, 8(4).

— 1972. Tables for plastic design of beams with rectangular holes. Engineering Journal, AISC, 9(1).

— 1973. Design of beams with web holes. Canadian Steel Industries Construction Council, Willowdale, Ont.

Redwood, R. G., and Channagiri, V.S. 1991. Earthquake resistant design of concentricity braced steel frames. Canadian Journal of Civil Engineering, 18(5).

Redwood, R. G., Feng Lu, Bouchard, G., and Paultre, P. 1991. Seismic response of concentrically braced steel frames. Canadian Journal of Civil Engineering, 18(6).

Redwood, R., and McCutcheon, J. 1968. Beam tests with unreinforced web openings. ASCE Journal of the Structural Division, 94(ST1).

Remennikov, A.M., and Walpole, W.R. 1998a. Seismic behavior and deterministic design procedures for steel V-braced frames. Earthquake Spectra, Vol. 14, No. 2, 335-355.

— 1998b. A note on compression strength reduction factor for a buckled strut in seismic-resisting braced system. Eng. Struct., 20, 8, 779–782.

Richards, P.W. 2009. Seismic column demands in ductile braced frames. J. Struct. Eng., ASCE, 135, 1, 33–41.

Ricles, J.M., and Yura, J.A. 1983. Strength of double-row bolted web connections. Journal of Structural Engineering, ASCE, 109(ST1): 126-142.

Ricles, J.M., Zhang, X., Lu, L.-W. and Fisher, J. 2004. Development of seismic guidelines for deep-column steel moment connections. ATLSS Report No. 04-13, Lehigh University, Bethlehem, PA.

Ritchie, J.K., and Chien, E.Y.L. 1980. Composite structural systems – Design, construction and cost considerations. Proceedings, Canadian Structural Engineering Conference, CISC.

Roberts, T., and Sabouri-Ghomi, S. 1992. Hysteretic characteristics of unstiffened perforated steel plate shear panels. Thin-Walled Struct., 14, 139–151.

Robinson, H. 1969. Composite beam incorporating cellular steel decking. ASCE Journal of the Structural Division, 95(ST3).

— 1988. Multiple stud shear connections in deep ribbed metal deck. Canadian Journal of Civil Engineering, 15(4).

Robinson, H., and Wallace, I. W. 1973. Composite beams with 1½ inch metal deck and partial and full shear connection. Transactions, Canadian Society for Civil Engineering, 16(A-8), published in the Engineering Journal, Engineering Institute of Canada.

Sabelli, R. 2004, Recommended provisions for buckling-restrained braced frames, AISC Eng. J., Vol. 41, No. 4, pp. 155-175.

Sabelli, R., and Bruneau, M. 2007. Steel plate shear walls. Steel Design Guide 20, AISC, Chicago, IL.

Sabelli, R. and Hohbach, D. 1999. Design of cross-braced frames for predictable buckling behavior. J. of Struct. Eng., ASCE, 125(ST2): 163-168.

Sabelli, R., Mahin, S., and Chang, C. 2003. Seismic demands on steel braced frame buildings with buckling restrained braces. Engineering Struct., 25, 5, 656-666.

Sabouri-Ghomi, S., Kharrazi M.H.K., Mam-Azizi, S.-E-D., and Sajadi, R.A. 2008. Buckling behavior improvement of steel plate shear wall systems. The Structural Design of Tall and Special Buildings, 17, 4, 823-837.

Sabouri-Ghomi, S., and Roberts, T.M. 1991. Nonlinear dynamic analysis of thin steel plate shear walls. Computers & Structures, 39, 1-2, 121-127.

Schmidt, B.J. 2000. Review of the resistance factor for steel. M.Sc. thesis, Department of Civil and Environmental Engineering, University of Western Ontario, London, Ontario.

Schmidt B.J., and Bartlett, F.M. 2002. Review of resistance factor for steel: data collection. Can. J. Civ. Eng., 29, 1, 98–108.

Schmitke, C.D., and Kennedy, D.J.L. 1985. Effective lengths of laterally continuous, laterally unsupported steel beams. Canadian Journal of Civil Engineering. 12(3): 603-616.

Schumacher, A. S., Grondin, G. Y., and Kulak, G. L. 1999. Connection of infill panels in steel plate shear walls. Canadian Journal of Civil Engineering, 26(5): 549-563.

Seaburg, P.A., and Carter, C.J. 1997. Torsional analysis of structural steel members, Steel design guide series 9, AISC, Chicago, IL.

Seeley, F. B., and Smith, J. O. 1957. Advanced mechanics of materials (2nd ed.). John Wiley & Sons, Inc., New York, NY. pp. 365-367.

Shaker, A.F., and Kennedy, D.J.L. 1991, The effective modulus of elasticity of concrete in tension. Structural Engineering Report 172, Department of Civil Engineering, University of Alberta, Edmonton, Alberta.

Sherman, D.R. 1996. Designing with Structural Tubing. Engineering Journal, AISC, 33: 101-109.

Sherman, D. R., and Tanavde, A. S. 1984. Comparative study of flexural capacity of pipes. Department of Civil Engineering, University of Wisconsin-Milwaukee.

Shishkin, J.J., Driver, R.G., and Grondin, G.Y. 2005. Analysis of steel plate shear walls using the modified strip model. Structural Engineering Report No. 261, Dept. of Civ. and Env. Eng., Univ. of Alberta, Edmonton, AB.

— 2009. Analysis of steel plate shear walls using the modified strip model. Journal of Structural Engineering, American Society of Civil Engineers, vol. 135, no. 11, pp. 1357-1366.

Shrivastava, S. C., Redwood, R. G., Harris, P. J., and Ettehadieh, A. A. 1979. End moments in open web steel tie joists. McGill University, June.

Skarborn, S., and Daneff G. 1998. Shear resistance of flare bevel and puddle welds in open-web steel joist applications. Canadian Society for Civil Engineering, Annual Conference, Halifax NS, 10 pp.

Slutter, R. G., and Driscoll, G. C. 1965. Flexural strength of steel concrete composite beams. ASCE Journal of the Structural Division, 95(ST2).

Sourochnikoff, B. 1950. Wind-stresses in semi-rigid connections of steel framework. Transactions, American Society of Civil Engineers.

SSPC. Good Painting Practice, SSPC Painting Manual, Vol. 1, Fourth Edition, Society for Protective Coatings, Pittsburgh, PA.

— Systems and Specifications, SSPC Painting Manual, Vol. 2, Eighth Edition, Society for Protective Coatings, Pittsburgh, PA.

Stankevicius, J., Josi, G., Grondin, G.Y., and Kulak, G.L. 2009. Measurement of slip coefficient for grade ASTM A588 steel. Structural Engineering Report 268, Department of Civil and Environmental Engineering, University of Alberta. *www.engineering.ualberta.ca/structures/reports.cfm*

STELCO. 1973. Hollow structural sections – Design manual for columns and beams. The Steel Company of Canada Limited, Hamilton, Ont.

— 1981. Hollow structural sections – Design manual for concrete-filled HSS columns. The Steel Company of Canada Limited, Hamilton, Ont.

Tall, L., *et al*. 1974. Structural steel design (2nd ed.). The Ronald Press Company, New York, NY.

Tang, X. and Goel, S.C. 1989. Brace fractures and analysis of phase I structure. J. of Struct. Engrg., ASCE, 115, 1960-1976.

Temple, M.C., Schepers, J.A., and Kennedy, D.J.L. 1986. Interconnection of starred angle compression members. Canadian Journal of Civil Engineering, 13(6).

Thorburn, L. J., Kulak, G. L., and Montgomery, C. J. 1983. Analysis of steel plate shear walls. Structural Engineering. Report No. 107, Department of Civil Engineering, Univ. of Alberta, Edmonton, Alberta.

Thornton, C. H. 1973. Quality control in design and supervision can eliminate lamellar tearing. Engineering Journal, AISC, Fourth Quarter.

Timler, P. A., and Kulak, G. L. 1983. Experimental study of steel plate shear walls. Structural Engrg. Report No. 114, Department of Civil Engineering, Univ. of Alberta, Edmonton, Alberta.

Timoshenko, S.P., and Gere, J.M. 1961. Theory of elastic stability, Second edition, McGraw-Hill, New York, NY .

Toprac, A., and Natarajan, M. 1971. Fatigue strength of hybrid plate girders. ASCE Journal of the Structural Division, 97(ST4).

Trahair, N.S. 1968. Interaction buckling of narrow rectangular continuous beams. Civil Engineering Trans. Inst. of Eng. Australia.

Tremblay, R. 1997. Seismic performance of RBS connections for steel moment resisting frames: Influence of loading rate and floor slab. Proceedings of Second International Conference on Behaviour of Steel Structures in Seismic Areas, Kyoto, Japan.

— 1998. Conception des cadres rigides en acier – Développements survenus suite aux séismes de Northridge et de Kobe. Calcul parasismique des charpentes d'acier/Earthquake resistant design of steel structures, Seminar notes.

— 2000. Influence of brace slenderness on the seismic response of concentrically braced steel frames. Behaviour of steel structures in seismic areas. Proceedings of the Third STESSA Conference 2000, Montreal, A.A. Balkema, Rotterdam: 527-534.

— 2001. Seismic behaviour and design of concentrically braced steel frames. AISC Eng. J., 38 (3): 148-166.

— 2002. Inelastic seismic response of bracing members. J. of Const. Steel Research. 58: 665-701

— 2003. Achieving a stable inelastic seismic response for concentrically braced steel frames. Eng. J., AISC, 40(2): 111-129.

Tremblay, R., Archambault, M.-H., and Filiatrault, A. 2003. Seismic response of concentrically braced steel frames made with rectangular hollow bracing members. Journal of Structural Engineering, ASCE, 129(12): 1626-1636.

Tremblay, R., Bolduc. P., Neville, R., and DeVall, R. 2006. Seismic testing and performance of buckling restrained bracing systems, Can. J. of Civ. Eng., 33, 2, 183-198.

Tremblay, R., Bruneau, M., Nakashima, M., Prion, H.G.L., Filiatrault, A. and DeVall, R. 1996. Seismic design of steel buildings: Lessons from the 1995 Hyogoken-Nanbu earthquake. Can. J. of Civ. Engrg., 23: 727-756.

Tremblay, R., Castonguay, P.X., Guilini-Charette, K., and Koboevic, S. 2009. Seismic performance of conventional construction braced steel frames designed according to Canadian seismic provisions. Proc. 2009 ASCE Structures Congress, Austin, TX, 341, 87.

Tremblay, R., Chicoine, T., and Massicotte, B. 2000. Design equation for the axial capacity of partially encased non-compact columns. Proceedings Composite Construction in Steel and Concrete IV, Banff, Canada, June, United Engineering Foundation, ASCE, Reston, VA: 506-517.

Tremblay, R., Degrange, G., and Blouin, J. 1999. Seismic rehabilitation of a four-storey building with a stiffened bracing system. Proc. 8th Can. Conf. on Earthquake Eng., Vancouver, B.C., 549-554.

Tremblay, R., Haddad, M., Martinez, G., Richard, J., and Moffatt, K. 2008. Inelastic cyclic testing of large size steel bracing members. Proc. 14WCEE, Beijing, China, Paper No. 05-05-0071.

Tremblay, R., Massicotte, B., Filion, I., and Maranda, R. 1998. Experimental study on the behaviour of partially encased composite columns made of light welded H steel shapes under compressive axial loads. Proc. Annual Meeting, Structural Stability Research Council, Atlanta, Sept. 21-23: 195-204.

Tremblay, R., and Poncet, L. 2007. Improving the seismic stability of concentrically braced steel frames. Eng. J., AISC, 44, 2, 103-116.

Tremblay, R., and Robert, N. 2000. Design of low- and medium-rise chevron braced steel frames. Can. J. of Civ. Eng., 27(6): 1192-1206.

— 2001. Seismic performance of low- and medium-rise chevron braced steel frames. Can. J. of Civ. Eng. 28(4): 699-714.

Tremblay, R., Rogers, C., Martin, É., and Yang, W. 2004. Analysis, testing and design of steel roof deck diaphragms for ductile earthquake resistance. Journal of Earthquake Engineering, Imperial College Press, 8(5): 775-816.

Tremblay, R., Timler, P., Bruneau, M., and Filiatrault, A. 1995. Performance of steel structures during the January 17, 1994 Northridge earthquake. Can. J. of Civ. Eng., 22, 338-360.

Tromposch, E. W., and Kulak, G. L. 1987. Cyclic and static behaviour of thin panel steel plate shear walls. Structural Engineering Report No. 145, Department of Civil Engineering, University of Alberta.

Tsai, K.C., and Hsiao, P.-C. 2008. Pseudo-dynamic test of a full-scale CFT/BRB frame – Part II: Seismic performance of buckling-restrained braces and connections. Earthquake Eng. and Struct. Dyn., 37, 7 1099–1115.

Uang, C.-M., and Nakashima, M. 2004. Steel buckling-restrained braced frames. In Earthquake Engineering – From Engineering Seismology to Performance-Based Engineering (ed. Y. Bozorgnia and V. V. Bertero), Chapter 16, CRC Press, Boca Raton.

Vian, D., and Bruneau, M. 2004. Testing of special LYS steel plate shear walls. Proc. 13th World Conf. on Earthquake Eng., Vancouver, Canada, Paper No. 978.

Vian, D., Bruneau, M., Tsai, K.-C., and Lin, U.C. 2009. Special perforated steel plate shear walls with reduced beam section anchor beams. I: Experimental investigation, & II: Analysis and design recommendations, J. of Struct. Eng., ASCE, 135, 3, 211-228.

Vincent, G. S. 1969. Tentative criteria for load factor design of steel highway bridges. Steel Research Construction Bulletin No. 15, AISI, Washington, DC.

Virdi, K. S., and Dowling, P. J. 1976. A unified design method for composite columns. Memoires, IAB-SE, No. 36-11.

Wakabayashi, M. 1977 A new design method of long composite beam-columns. Proceedings, ASCE International Colloquium on Stability of Structures under Static and Dynamic Loads, Washington, DC., May.

White, D.W., and Jung, S.-K. 2004. Unified flexural resistance equations for stability design of steel I-section members – uniform bending tests. Structural Engineering, Mechanics and Materials Report No. 04-28. Georgia Institute of Technology.

Winter, G. 1958. Lateral bracing of columns and beams. ASCE Journal of the Structural Division, 84(ST2).

— 1970. Commentary on the 1968 edition of the specification for the design of cold-formed steel structural members. American Iron and Steel Institute, Washington, DC.

Wong, E., and Driver, R.G. 2010. Critical evaluation of equivalent moment factor procedures for laterally unsupported beams. Engineering Journal, American Institute of Steel Construction, vol. 47, no. 1.

Wu, Y., and Kulak, G. L. 1993. Shear lag in bolted single and double angle tension members. Structural Engineering Report, Department of Civil Engineering, University of Alberta, SER 187.

Yang, C.H., and Beedle, L.S. 1951. Behavior of I and WF beams in shear. Fritz Engineering Lab. Report No. 205B21, Lehigh Univ., Bethlehem, Pa.

Yang, F., and Mahin, S. 2005. Limiting net section fracture in slotted tube braces. Steel Tips, Technical Information and Product Service, Structural Steel Educational Council, Moraga, CA.

Yong Lin Pi and Trahair, N.S. 1995. Inelastic torsion of steel I-beams. ASCE Journal of Structural Engineering, 121(ST4).

Yura, J.A. 1993. Fundamentals of Beam Bracing. Proceedings, Structural Stability Research Council Conference "Is Your Structure Suitably Braced?", Milwaukee, WI, April.

— 1995. Bracing for Stability – State-of-the-Art. Proceedings, Structures Congress XIII, American Society of Civil Engineers, Boston, MA, April: 88-103.

Yura, J.A., Birkemoe, P.C., and Ricles, J.M. 1982. Web shear connections: an experimental study. American Society of Civil Engineers. Journal of the Structural Division, 108(ST2).

Zhao, Q., and Astaneh-Asl, A. 2004. Cyclic behavior of traditional and innovative composite shear walls. J. Struct. Eng., ASCE, 130, 2, 271–284.

Ziemian, R.D. (Editor). 2010. Guide to stability design criteria for metal structures, 6th Edition. John Wiley & Sons, Inc., Hoboken, NJ.

Zuk, W. 1956. Lateral bracing forces on beams and columns. Engineering Mechanics Division, American Society of Civil Engineers, 82(EM3).

Notes

PART THREE
CONNECTIONS AND TENSION MEMBERS

GENERAL INFORMATION

Part Three contains tables, examples, dimensions and general information of assistance to designers, detailers and others concerned with the design and detailing of connections and tension members according to the requirements of Clauses 12, 13.2, 13.12.1.2(a), 13.11, 13.12, 13.13, 21, 22 and 23 of CSA-S16-09. Information is included for both metric series and Imperial series bolts, although all design data is given in SI units. While the basic steel grade for W shapes is CSA-G40.21 350W, detail material (angles and plates) is still G40.21 300W.

For convenience, Part Three is divided into seven main sections:

Bolt Data

Pages 3-5 to 3-37 contain information on diameter, area and strength of bolts, including bolt resistances and unit resistances, for evaluating bolts in bearing-type connections, slip-critical connections, and bolts subjected to tension and prying action. Tables are also included for evaluating eccentric loads on various bolt groups.

Weld Data

Pages 3-38 to 3-55 contain information on the factored resistance of welds, including values for various sizes of fillet welds with a comparison between Imperial and metric fillet weld sizes. Tables are included for evaluating eccentric loads on various weld groups and configurations.

Framed Beam Shear Connections

Pages 3-56 to 3-73 contain information on common types of beam shear connections traditionally considered standard in the industry. Included are double-angle beam connections, simple end-plate connections, single-angle beam connections, shear tab beam connections and tee-type beam connections.

Seated Beam Shear Connections

Pages 3-74 to 3-79 contain information on unstiffened and stiffened seated beam shear connections of a type commonly used in practice, where direct framing of the supported beam is either not desirable or possible.

Moment Connections

Pages 3-80 to 3-88 contain examples of welded and welded/bolted moment connections, and information for the design of stiffeners on supporting columns.

Hollow Structural Section Connections

Pages 3-89 to 3-98 contain information regarding the connecting of HSS sections.

Tension Members

Pages 3-99 to 3-105 contain tables and examples for calculating net effective areas and for evaluating the tensile resistance of bolted and welded tension members.

CONNECTION LOADS

Connections are designed and detailed for the member reactions and loads given on the structural steel design drawings by the designer. Most connections are designed for factored loads; however, specified loads are used for calculating the slip resistance of slip-critical connections, such as those subjected to dynamic loadings.

In evaluating member loads and forces, it is preferable to keep different types of load separate to facilitate application of the different load factors and load combination factors specified in Clause 7.2 of CAN/CSA S16-09 and other governing codes. However, this may not always be convenient, and Fig. 3-1 is included to permit an approximate evaluation of either the total specified load or the total factored load when either one is known, and the ratio of the specified dead load to specified live load is known, or the unit specified dead load and unit specified live load are both known. The curve is based on load factors α given in Clause 7.2.3 and makes no allowance for possible live load reductions permitted by the applicable building codes.

Example

Given:

The total factored dead and live load reaction at the end of a beam to be designed as a slip-critical connection is 235 kN, and the specified unit dead and live loads are 4.35 kPa and 2.16 kPa, respectively. What is the reaction under specified load?

Solution:

Ratio $D/L = 4.35/2.16 = 2.0$

From Fig. 3-1, for $D/L = 2.0$, $(L+D)/(\alpha_L L + \alpha_D D) = 0.75$

Therefore the specified load reaction is $0.75 \times 235 = 176$ kN

Figure 3-1

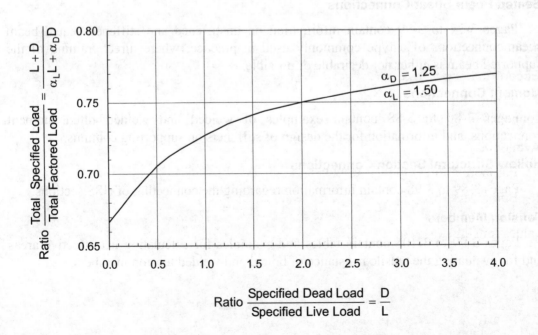

BOLT DATA

General

Tables in this section include information for both metric series and Imperial series bolts. Data for the metric series bolts is based on ASTM Specifications A325M and A490M, and for the Imperial series bolts on ASTM Specifications A325, A490 and A307. Values are tabulated in ascending order of nominal cross-sectional area A_b (mm^2) to facilitate comparison between metric and Imperial sizes. Bold type is used for metric series bolts when both metric sizes and Imperial sizes appear on the same table.

A significant change affecting the resistance of bolts in bearing-type connections was introduced in CSA S16-09, as the resistance factor for the bearing of bolts on steel, ϕ_{br}, increased from 0.67 to 0.80. In the previous edition (CSA S16-01) the resistance factor for bolts, ϕ_b, had also increased from 0.67 to 0.80.

This section includes the following:

Bolt Data Metric and Imperial Series

Table 3-1 on page 3-6 lists the size, nominal diameter (mm), nominal area (mm^2) and values of $A_b F_u$ for bolt sizes from M16 to M36 and ½ inch to 1½ inch diameter.

Bolts in Bearing-Type Connections

Tables 3-2 to 3-7 on pages 3-7 to 3-11 list values of bearing and bolt resistances computed in accordance with Clause 13.12.1. Tables 3-8 and 3-9 on page 3-13 assist in evaluating combined shear and tension on bolts.

Bolts in Slip-Critical Connections

Tables 3-10 and 3-11 on page 3-15 list resistances for use with bolts in slip-critical connections, computed in accordance with Clause 13.12.2.

Bolts in Tension and Prying Action

Tables and design aids on pages 3-19 to 3-25 assist in evaluating the effects of prying action on bolts loaded in tension.

Eccentric Loads on Bolt Groups

Tables for evaluating eccentric loads on bolts in bearing-type and slip-critical connections for various bolt group configurations are given on pages 3-29 to 3-37.

Availability

For more information on the range of commonly used fasteners, refer to Part 6.

Before specifying metric bolts, the designer should check on their current availability in the quantities required. To facilitate substitution, use the lower of the metric or Imperial values for similar sizes.

BOLT DATA
Metric and Imperial Series

Table 3-1

Bolt Size		Nominal Diameter of Bolt (mm)	Nominal Area, A_b (mm²)	$A_b F_u$ ** (kN)				
Metric *	Imperial			A325M	A490M	A325	A490	A307
	½	12.70	127			104	131	
	⅝	15.88	198			163	205	81.9
M16		**16.00**	**201**	**167**	**209**			
	¾	19.05	285			235	295	118
M20		**20.00**	**314**	**261**	**327**			
M22		**22.00**	**380**	**316**	**395**			
	⅞	22.23	388			320	402	161
M24		**24.00**	**452**	**375**	**470**			
	1	25.40	507			418	524	
M27		**27.00**	**573**	**475**	**595**			
	1⅛	28.58	641			465	664	
M30		**30.00**	**707**	**587**	**735**			
	1¼	31.75	792			574	819	
M36		**36.00**	**1018**	**845**	**1060**			
	1½	38.10	1140			827	1180	

* The number following the letter M is the nominal bolt diameter in millimetres.

** See Table 3-3 page 3-8 for specified minimum tensile strengths, F_u.

BOLTS IN BEARING-TYPE CONNECTIONS

General

Connections are generally detailed as bearing-type, unless the designer has specified that the connection is "slip-critical". Bearing-type connections are designed for factored loads, and Tables 3-2 to 3-9 on the following pages assist in evaluating the requirements of Clause 13.12.1 of CSA S16-09. Clause 22.3.5.2 lists the size and type of holes permitted with bearing type connections.

Table 3-2 summarizes the requirements of Clause 13.12.1.2 for bolts in shear and Clause 13.12.1.3 for bolts in tension, and lists expressions for factored resistance and unit factored resistance of bolts in bearing-type connections.

Table 3-3 lists values of the specified minimum tensile strength F_u and unit factored shear resistances, $0.48 F_u$ and $0.34 F_u$, and values of unit factored tensile resistances, $0.60 F_u$, for A325M, A490M, A325, A490 and A307 bolts.

Table 3-4 lists factored shear and tensile resistances in kN/bolt for both metric series and Imperial series bolts.

Table 3-5 lists values of the specified minimum tensile strength F_u for common grades of structural steel, and values of unit factored bearing resistances, $0.80 F_u$ and $3 \phi_{br} F_u$.

Tables 3-6 and 3-7 list factored bearing resistance in kN/bolt for five different values of F_u for the connected material. Bearing resistances in these tables are given in terms of the material thickness t, grade and bolt size.

The tearing out of material beyond a bolt or group of bolts is governed by Clause 13.11 (Block Shear). Other examples of "block shear" failure modes in bolted connections are illustrated in Tension Members starting on page 3-99.

Tables 3-8 and 3-9 on page 3-13 assist in evaluating bolts in combined shear and tension according to Clause 13.12.1.4.

Table 3-2

CSA S16-09 SUMMARY
Bearing-Type Connections

Bolt Situation In Joint	Factored Resistance	Unit Factored Resistance ($n = m = A_b = 1$, $\phi_b = 0.80$)	Clause Reference
BOLTS IN SHEAR			13.12.1.2
Shear on bolts with threads excluded from shear plane	$V_r = 0.60 \phi_b n m A_b F_u$	$V_r = 0.48 F_u$	13.12.1.2(c)
Shear on bolts with threads intercepted by shear plane	$V_r = 0.42 \phi_b n m A_b F_u$	$V_r = 0.34 F_u$	
For joints longer than 15 d	$(1.075 - 0.005 L / d) V_r$ $\geq 0.75 V_r$		13.12.1.2(c)
Bearing on main material (standard holes)	$B_r = 3 \phi_{br} t d n F_u$	$B_r = 2.4 t d F_u$ ($\phi_{br} = 0.80$)	13.12.1.2(a)
BOLTS IN TENSION	$T_r = 0.75 \phi_b n A_b F_u$	$T_r = 0.60 F_u$	13.12.1.3

Note: See Clause 22.3.5.2 of CSA S16-09 regarding the use of oversize or slotted bolt holes.

UNIT FACTORED SHEAR AND TENSILE RESISTANCES**

Table 3-3

$\phi_b = 0.80$

Bolt Grade	Specified Minimum Tensile Strength F_u	Unit Factored Shear Resistance		Unit Factored Tensile Resistance
		Threads Excluded $0.6\,\phi_b\,F_u = 0.48\,F_u$	Threads Intercepted $0.7 \times 0.6\,\phi_b\,F_u = 0.34\,F_u$	$0.75\,\phi_b\,F_u = 0.60\,F_u$
	MPa	MPa	MPa	MPa
A325M	**830**	**398**	**279**	**498**
A490M	**1040**	**499**	**349**	**624**
A325 (d ≤ 1")	825	396	277	495
A325 (d ≥ 1⅛")	725	348	244	435
A490	1035	497	348	621
A307*	414	199	139	248

* Use of A307 bolts in connections is covered in CSA S16-09 Clause 23.1.
** Values for Imperial series bolts are based on ASTM Specifications A325 and A490 soft-converted to SI units.

FACTORED SHEAR AND TENSILE RESISTANCES

Table 3-4

kN per bolt

$\phi_b = 0.80$

Bolt Size		Nominal Area	Factored Shear Resistance [†] – Single Shear **						Factored Tensile Resistance		
			Threads Excluded			Threads Intercepted [††]					
Metric*	Imperial	A_b	A325 A325M	A490 A490M	A307	A325 A325M	A490 A490M	A307	A325 A325M	A490 A490M	A307
		mm²	kN	kN	kN	kN	kN	kN	kN	kN	kN
	½	127	50.3	63.1		35.2	44.2		62.9	78.9	
	⅝	198	78.4	98.4	39.3	54.9	68.9	27.5	98.0	123	49.2
M16		**201**	**80.1**	**100**		**56.1**	**70.2**		**100**	**125**	
	¾	285	113	142	56.6	79.0	99.1	39.6	141	177	70.8
M20		**314**	**125**	**157**		**87.6**	**110**		**156**	**196**	
M22		**380**	**151**	**190**		**106**	**133**		**189**	**237**	
	⅞	388	154	193	77.1	108	135	54.0	192	241	96.4
M24		**452**	**180**	**226**		**126**	**158**		**225**	**282**	
	1	507	201	252		141	176		251	315	
M27		**573**	**228**	**286**		**160**	**200**		**285**	**358**	
	1⅛	641	223	318		156	223		279	398	
M30		**707**	**282**	**353**		**197**	**247**		**352**	**441**	
	1¼	792	276	393		193	275		345	492	
M36		**1018**	**406**	**508**		**284**	**356**		**507**	**635**	
	1½	1140	397	566		278	396		496	708	

* The number following the letter M is the nominal bolt diameter in millimetres.
** For double shear, multiply tabulated values by 2.
† For long lap splices, see CSA S16-09 Clause 13.12.1.2.
†† Threads are intercepted if thin material next to the nut is combined with detailing for minimum bolt stick-through (the nut).

Table 3-5 — UNIT FACTORED BEARING RESISTANCE

$\phi_{br} = 0.80$

	Material Standard and Grade		Specified Minimum Tensile Strength, F_u	$0.80\,F_u$	$3\,\phi_{br}\,F_u$
			MPa	MPa	MPa
CSA-G40.21	260W, 260WT		410	328	984
	300W for HSS only		410	328	984
	300W, 350W, 300WT		450	360	1080
	350G, 350WT, 350R, 350A, 350AT		480	384	1152
	380W and 380WT for HSS only		480	384	1152
	400W, 400WT, 400A, 400AT		520	416	1248
	480W, 480WT, 480A, 480AT		590	472	1416
	550W, 550WT, 550A, 550AT		620	496	1488
ASTM	A36		400	320	960
	A572	Grade 42 (290)	415	332	996
		Grade 50 (345)	450	360	1080
	A588	F_y = 42 ksi (290 MPa)	435	348	1044
		F_y = 46 ksi (315 MPa)	460	368	1104
		F_y = 50 ksi (345 MPa)	485	388	1164
	A992		450	360	1080

Table 3-6 — FACTORED BEARING RESISTANCE, B_r* (kN / bolt)

CSA G40.21 300W, 350W, 300WT (F_u = 450 MPa)

t (mm)	1/2	5/8	M16	3/4	M20	M22	7/8	M24	1	M27	1 1/8	M30	1 1/4	M36	1 1/2
4	54.9	68.6	69.1	82.3	86.4	95.0	96.0	104	110	117	123	130	137	156	165
4.5	61.7	77.2	77.8	92.6	97.2	107	108	117	123	131	139	146	154	175	185
5	68.6	85.7	86.4	103	108	119	120	130	137	146	154	162	171	194	206
6	82.3	103	104	123	130	143	144	156	165	175	185	194	206	233	247
7	96.0	120	121	144	151	166	168	181	192	204	216	227	240	272	288
8	110	137	138	165	173	190	192	207	219	233	247	259	274	311	329
9	123	154	156	185	194	214	216	233	247	262	278	292	309	350	370
10	137	171	173	206	216	238	240	259	274	292	309	324	343	389	411
11		189	190	226	238	261	264	285	302	321	339	356	377	428	453
12		206	207	247	259	285	288	311	329	350	370	389	411	467	494
13				267	281	309	312	337	357	379	401	421	446	505	535
14				288	302	333	336	363	384	408	432	454	480	544	576
15					324	356	360	389	411	437	463	486	514	583	617
16						380	384	415	439	467	494	518	549	622	658
17							408	441	466	496	525	551	583	661	700
18								467	494	525	555	583	617	700	741
19									521	554	586	616	652	739	782
20										583	617	648	686	778	823
21											648	680	720	816	864
22												713	754	855	905
23													789	894	946
24														933	988
25														972	1029
26														1011	1070
27														1050	1111

* $B_r = 3\,\phi_{br}\,t\,d\,F_u$ for one bolt, where $\phi_{br} = 0.80$. For joints with long slotted holes, see S16-09 Clause 13.12.1.2(b). Shear resistance of the bolt or block tear-out of the plate material may govern.

ASTM A36 (F_u = 400 MPa)

t (mm)	½	⅝	M16	¾	M20	M22	⅞	M24	1	M27	1⅛	M30	1¼	M36	1½
4	48.8	61.0	61.4	73.2	76.8	84.5	85.3	92.2	97.5	104	110	115	122	138	146
4.5	54.9	68.6	69.1	82.3	86.4	95.0	96.0	104	110	117	123	130	137	156	165
5	61.0	76.2	76.8	91.4	96.0	106	107	115	122	130	137	144	152	173	183
6	73.2	91.4	92.2	110	115	127	128	138	146	156	165	173	183	207	219
7	85.3	107	108	128	134	148	149	161	171	181	192	202	213	242	256
8	97.5	122	123	146	154	169	171	184	195	207	219	230	244	276	293
9	110	137	138	165	173	190	192	207	219	233	247	259	274	311	329
10	122	152	154	183	192	211	213	230	244	259	274	288	305	346	366
11	134	168	169	201	211	232	235	253	268	285	302	317	335	380	402
12		183	184	219	230	253	256	276	293	311	329	346	366	415	439
13		198	200	238	250	275	277	300	317	337	357	374	396	449	475
14			215	256	269	296	299	323	341	363	384	403	427	484	512
15				274	288	317	320	346	366	389	411	432	457	518	549
16				293	307	338	341	369	390	415	439	461	488	553	585
17					326	359	363	392	415	441	466	490	518	588	622
18						380	384	415	439	467	494	518	549	622	658
19							405	438	463	492	521	547	579	657	695
20								461	488	518	549	576	610	691	732
21									512	544	576	605	640	726	768
22										570	604	634	671	760	805
23										596	631	662	701	795	841
24											658	691	732	829	878
25												720	762	864	914
26													792	899	951

CSA G40.21 260W, 260WT (F_u = 410 MPa)

t (mm)	½	⅝	M16	¾	M20	M22	⅞	M24	1	M27	1⅛	M30	1¼	M36	1½
4	50.0	62.5	63.0	75.0	78.7	86.6	87.5	94.5	100	106	112	118	125	142	150
4.5	56.2	70.3	70.8	84.4	88.6	97.4	98.4	106	112	120	127	133	141	159	169
5	62.5	78.1	78.7	93.7	98.4	108	109	118	125	133	141	148	156	177	187
6	75.0	93.7	94.5	112	118	130	131	142	150	159	169	177	187	213	225
7	87.5	109	110	131	138	152	153	165	175	186	197	207	219	248	262
8	100	125	126	150	157	173	175	189	200	213	225	236	250	283	300
9	112	141	142	169	177	195	197	213	225	239	253	266	281	319	337
10	125	156	157	187	197	216	219	236	250	266	281	295	312	354	375
11	137	172	173	206	216	238	241	260	275	292	309	325	344	390	412
12		187	189	225	236	260	262	283	300	319	337	354	375	425	450
13		203	205	244	256	281	284	307	325	345	366	384	406	461	487
14				262	276	303	306	331	350	372	394	413	437	496	525
15				281	295	325	328	354	375	399	422	443	469	531	562
16				300	315	346	350	378	400	425	450	472	500	567	600
17						368	372	401	425	452	478	502	531	602	637
18						390	394	425	450	478	506	531	562	638	675
19								449	475	505	534	561	594	673	712
20								472	500	531	562	590	625	708	750
21									525	558	590	620	656	744	787
22										584	619	649	687	779	825
23											647	679	719	815	862
24												708	750	850	900
25													781	886	937
26													812	921	975

* $B_r = 3 \phi_{br} t d F_u$ for one bolt, where ϕ_{br} = 0.80. For joints with long slotted holes, see S16-09 Clause 13.12.1.2(b).
Shear resistance of the bolt or block tear-out of the plate material may govern.

Table 3-7   FACTORED BEARING RESISTANCE, B$_r$* (kN / bolt)

CSA G40.21 350G, 350WT, 350R, 350A, 380W, 380WT (F$_u$ = 480 MPa)

t (mm)	½	⅝	M16	¾	M20	M22	⅞	M24	1	M27	1⅛	M30	1¼	M36	1½
4	58.5	73.2	73.7	87.8	92.2	101	102	111	117	124	132	138	146	166	176
4.5	65.8	82.3	82.9	98.8	104	114	115	124	132	140	148	156	165	187	198
5	73.2	91.4	92.2	110	115	127	128	138	146	156	165	173	183	207	219
6	87.8	110	111	132	138	152	154	166	176	187	198	207	219	249	263
7	102	128	129	154	161	177	179	194	205	218	230	242	256	290	307
8	117	146	147	176	184	203	205	221	234	249	263	276	293	332	351
9	132	165	166	198	207	228	230	249	263	280	296	311	329	373	395
10		183	184	219	230	253	256	276	293	311	329	346	366	415	439
11		201	203	241	253	279	282	304	322	342	362	380	402	456	483
12				263	276	304	307	332	351	373	395	415	439	498	527
13				285	300	329	333	359	380	404	428	449	475	539	571
14					323	355	358	387	410	435	461	484	512	581	614
15						380	384	415	439	467	494	518	549	622	658
16							410	442	468	498	527	553	585	664	702
17								470	497	529	560	588	622	705	746
18									527	560	593	622	658	746	790
19										591	625	657	695	788	834
20											658	691	732	829	878
21												726	768	871	922
22													805	912	966
23														954	1009
24														995	1053
25														1037	1097
26															1141

CSA G40.21 400W, 400WT, 400A, 400AT (F$_u$ = 520 MPa)

t (mm)	½	⅝	M16	¾	M20	M22	⅞	M24	1	M27	1⅛	M30	1¼	M36	1½
4	63.4	79.2	79.9	95.1	100	110	111	120	127	135	143	150	158	180	190
4.5	71.3	89.2	89.9	107	112	124	125	135	143	152	160	168	178	202	214
5	79.2	99.1	100	119	125	137	139	150	158	168	178	187	198	225	238
6	95.1	119	120	143	150	165	166	180	190	202	214	225	238	270	285
7	111	139	140	166	175	192	194	210	222	236	250	262	277	314	333
8	127	158	160	190	200	220	222	240	254	270	285	300	317	359	380
9		178	180	214	225	247	250	270	285	303	321	337	357	404	428
10		198	200	238	250	275	277	300	317	337	357	374	396	449	475
11			220	262	275	302	305	329	349	371	392	412	436	494	523
12				285	300	329	333	359	380	404	428	449	475	539	571
13					324	357	361	389	412	438	464	487	515	584	618
14						384	388	419	444	472	499	524	555	629	666
15								449	475	505	535	562	594	674	713
16								479	507	539	571	599	634	719	761
17										573	606	636	674	764	808
18											642	674	713	809	856
19												711	753	854	903
20													792	899	951
21														943	999
22														988	1046
23														1033	1094
24															1141

* B$_r$ = 3 ϕ_{br} t d F$_u$ for one bolt, where ϕ_{br} = 0.80. For joints with long slotted holes, see S16-09 Clause 13.12.1.2(b). Shear resistance of the bolt or block tear-out of the plate material may govern.

Bolts in Combined Shear and Tension (Bearing-Type Connections)

Clause 13.12.1.4 of CSA S16-09 requires that bolts subjected to shear and tension satisfy

the expression $\left(\dfrac{V_f}{V_r}\right)^2 + \left(\dfrac{T_f}{T_r}\right)^2 \leq 1$, where V_f is the factored shear load on the bolt and T_f is

the factored tensile load including prying effects. If the shear-tension ratio V_f/T_f is X, solving

for V_f and T_f gives $V_f = X\,T_f$, and $T_f = \left(\dfrac{V_r^2\,T_r^2}{X^2\,T_r^2 + V_r^2}\right)^{1/2}$.

Combined shear and tension usually occurs for the threads-excluded case, since a plate or flange thin enough to include threads in the shear plane (about 10 mm) has little capacity to transmit tension. Table 3-8 gives values of V_f and T_f for various shear-tension ratios X for ¾, M20, M22, ⅞, M24 and 1-inch A325M or A325 bolts, with threads excluded from the shear plane. Table 3-9 gives values for A490M or A490 bolts.

Example

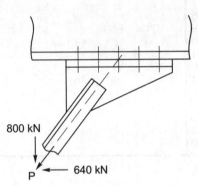

Given: A bracing connection for an inclined factored load P, with a tension component T_f of 800 kN and a shear component V_f of 640 kN, uses a tee section cut from a W410x74. Check the number of M20, A325M bolts required, assuming G40.21 350W steel with a 90 mm gauge on the tee flange and a 90 mm bolt pitch.

800 kN

P ← 640 kN

Solution:

Shear-tension ratio is $X = 640/800 = 0.80$.

From Table 3-8, permitted $V_f = 88.8$ kN and permitted $T_f = 111$ kN per bolt.

Therefore, number of bolts required $= 640/88.8$ or $800/111 = 7.21 \approx 8$.

Although only 8 bolts are required, try 10 bolts because of prying action. Check the effects of prying action on the bolt tension, and the connection capacity (see page 3-19).

Applied factored tensile load per bolt is $800/10 = 80$ kN $= P_f$.

For W410x74, $t = 16.0$ mm, $w = 9.7$ mm, and flange width = 180 mm.

$b = (90 - 9.7)/2 = 40.2$; $b' = 40.2 - 10 = 30.2$ mm; $1.25\,b = 50.3$

$a = (180 - 90)/2 = 45.0 < 1.25\,b$; $a' = 45.0 + 10 = 55.0$

$$K = (4 \times 30.2 \times 10^3)/(0.9 \times 90 \times 350) = 4.26 \qquad \text{(Eqn. 1)}$$

$$\delta = 1 - 22/90 = 0.756 \qquad \text{(Eqn. 2)}$$

In Eqn. 4, use bolt load at failure, $T_f = 111$ kN rather than T_r.

$$\alpha = \left(\frac{4.26 \times 111}{16.0^2} - 1\right) \times \frac{55.0}{0.756\,(55.0 + 30.2)} = 0.723 \quad \delta\alpha = 0.547 \qquad \text{(Eqn. 4)}$$

Connection capacity $= (16.0^2/4.26)(1.547)10 = 930$ kN > 800 — OK (Eqn. 5)

To find actual bolt load (including prying):

$$\alpha = \left(\frac{4.26 \times 80}{16.0^2} - 1\right) \times \frac{1}{0.756} = 0.438 \text{ (for applied load)}: \quad \delta\alpha = 0.331 \qquad \text{(Eqn. 6)}$$

$$T_f \approx 80\left[1 + \left(\frac{30.2}{55.0} \times \frac{0.331}{1.331}\right)\right] = 90.9 \text{ kN} < 111 \text{ kN} \quad - \text{OK} \qquad \text{(Eqn. 7)}$$

Table 3-8

Bearing-Type Connections

A325M and A325 Bolts (Threads Excluded, $\phi_b = 0.80$)

Shear-Tension Ratio		3/4		M20		M22		7/8		M24		1	
X = V_f / T_f													
X	1/X	V_f	T_f	V_f	T_f	V_f	T_f	V_f	T_f	V_f	T_f	V_f	T_f
0	T_r	0	141	0	156	0	189	0	192	0	225	0	251
0.10	10.00	14.0	140	15.5	155	18.8	188	19.1	191	22.4	224	24.9	249
0.20	5.00	27.4	137	30.4	152	36.8	184	37.2	186	43.8	219	48.6	243
0.30	3.33	39.6	132	43.8	146	53.1	177	54.0	180	63.3	211	70.5	235
0.40	2.50	50.4	126	56.0	140	67.6	169	68.8	172	80.8	202	89.6	224
0.50	2.00	60.0	120	66.5	133	80.5	161	81.5	163	95.5	191	107	213
0.60	1.67	67.8	113	75.0	125	90.6	151	92.4	154	108	180	121	201
0.70	1.43	74.2	106	82.6	118	99.4	142	102	145	119	170	132	189
0.80	1.25	80.0	100	88.8	111	107	134	109	136	127	159	142	177
0.90	1.11	84.3	93.7	93.6	104	113	126	115	128	135	150	150	167
1.00	1.00	88.1	88.1	97.7	97.7	118	118	120	120	141	141	157	157
1.11	0.90	91.6	82.4	102	91.4	123	111	124	112	147	132	163	147
1.25	0.80	95.1	76.1	105	84.3	128	102	130	104	151	121	169	135
1.43	0.70	98.4	68.9	109	76.4	132	92.5	134	93.8	157	110	176	123
1.67	0.60	102	61.1	113	67.7	137	81.9	139	83.1	163	97.5	182	109
2.00	0.50	105	52.4	116	58.1	141	70.3	143	71.3	167	83.7	186	93.2
2.50	0.40	108	43.0	119	47.7	144	57.7	146	58.5	172	68.7	191	76.4
3.33	0.30	110	32.9	122	36.5	147	44.2	149	44.8	175	52.6	195	58.5
5.00	0.20	112	22.3	124	24.7	150	29.9	152	30.3	178	35.6	198	39.6
10.00	0.10	113	11.3	125	12.5	151	15.1	153	15.3	180	18.0	200	20.0
V_r	0	113	0	125	0	151	0	154	0	180	0	201	0

Table 3-9

A490M and A490 Bolts (Threads Excluded, $\phi_b = 0.80$)

Shear-Tension Ratio		3/4		M20		M22		7/8		M24		1	
X = V_f / T_f													
X	1/X	V_f	T_f	V_f	T_f	V_f	T_f	V_f	T_f	V_f	T_f	V_f	T_f
0	T_r	0	177	0	196	0	237	0	241	0	282	0	315
0.10	10.00	17.6	176	19.5	195	23.5	235	23.9	239	28.0	280	31.2	312
0.20	5.00	34.4	172	38.0	190	46.0	230	46.8	234	54.8	274	61.0	305
0.30	3.33	49.8	166	55.2	184	66.6	222	67.8	226	79.2	264	88.5	295
0.40	2.50	63.2	158	70.0	175	84.8	212	86.0	215	101	252	112	281
0.50	2.00	75.0	150	83.0	166	101	201	102	204	120	239	134	267
0.60	1.67	85.2	142	94.2	157	114	190	116	193	136	226	151	252
0.70	1.43	93.1	133	104	148	125	179	127	181	148	212	166	237
0.80	1.25	100	125	111	139	134	168	136	170	160	200	178	223
0.90	1.11	106	118	117	130	142	158	144	160	169	188	188	209
1.00	1.00	111	111	122	122	148	148	150	150	176	176	197	197
1.11	0.90	114	103	128	115	154	139	157	141	183	165	204	184
1.25	0.80	119	95.4	133	106	160	128	163	130	190	152	213	170
1.43	0.70	124	86.5	137	95.8	166	116	169	118	197	138	220	154
1.67	0.60	128	76.6	141	84.8	172	103	173	104	203	122	227	136
2.00	0.50	131	65.7	146	72.8	176	88.1	179	89.5	210	105	234	117
2.50	0.40	135	53.9	149	59.7	181	72.3	184	73.4	215	86.0	240	95.9
3.33	0.30	138	41.3	152	45.7	185	55.4	187	56.2	220	65.9	245	73.4
5.00	0.20	140	28.0	155	31.0	188	37.5	191	38.1	223	44.6	249	49.7
10.00	0.10	141	14.1	156	15.6	189	18.9	192	19.2	225	22.5	251	25.1
V_r	0	142	0	157	0	190	0	193	0	226	0	252	0

BOLTS IN SLIP-CRITICAL CONNECTIONS

General

The name slip-critical emphasizes that this type of connection is required only when the consequences of slip are critical to the performance of the structure. Clause 22.2.2(a) of CSA S16-09 requires slip-critical connections where slippage into bearing cannot be tolerated, such as structures sensitive to deflection, or subject to fatigue or frequent load reversals. Slip-critical shear joints transfer the specified loads by the slip resistance (friction) of the clamped faying surfaces in accordance with Clause 13.12.2.

In addition to the slip resistance, the strength (factored resistance) of the joint under factored loads must also be checked.

Tables

Tables 3-10 and 3-11 are based on Clause 13.12.2.2 of S16-09 for bolts in slip-critical connections.

Table 3-10 lists values c_1 for a 5% probability of slip, and values of unit slip resistance $(0.53\, c_1\, k_s\, F_u)$ for A325M, A490M, A325 and A490 bolts for the contact surfaces (Class A, Class B and Class C) given in Table 3 of S16-09.

Table 3-11 lists slip resistance values $(V_s = 0.53\, c_1\, k_s\, m\, n\, A_b\, F_u)$ for bolted joints with a single faying surface ($m = 1$) for Class A and Class B contact surfaces for M16 to M36 A325M and A490M bolts, and ½ to 1½ inch A325 and A490 bolts.

Example

Given:

A single shear connection is subject to 370 kN at the specified load level and 550 kN at the factored load level. Select the number of M20 A325M bolts required for a slip-critical connection. Steel is G40.21-350W, 6 mm thick, and the surface is clean mill scale (Class A). Assume 80 mm bolt pitch and 30 mm bolt end distance.

Solution:

(a) For specified loads:

From Table 3-11, V_s = 37.4 kN (M20 A325M bolt for clean mill scale). Number of bolts required is $370/37.4 = 9.9$. Use 10 (say 2 lines of 5, parallel to the force).

(b) Confirm connection at factored loads. This includes checking bolts for shear resistance, checking material for bolt bearing, and checking material for block shear.

From Table 3-4 (page 3-8), V_r = 87.6 kN (M20 A325M, threads intercepted). Factored shear resistance of bolts is $10 \times 87.6 = 876$ kN > 550 kN

From Table 3-6 (page 3-9), the factored bearing resistance at one M20 bolt in 6 mm thick 350W material is 130 kN. 10 bolts give a resistance of $130 \times 10 = 1300$ kN > 550 kN

From S16-09, Clause 13.11: $A_n = (80 - 24)\,6 = 336$ mm^2, $A_{gv} = (8 \times 80 + 2 \times 30)\,6 = 4200$ mm^2
Factored block shear resistance:
$$T_r = \phi_u [U_t A_n F_u + 0.60 A_{gv}(F_y + F_u)/2]$$
$$= 0.75\,[1.0 \times 336 \times 450 + 0.6 \times 4200\,(350 + 450)/2] = 869 \text{ kN} > 550 \text{ kN}$$

Note: the efficiency factor, U_t, was taken as 1.0 in this example. Depending on the connection details, a lower value may apply (see Clause 13.11).

Table 3-10
UNIT SLIP RESISTANCE, $0.53\, c_1\, k_s\, F_u$
For 5% Probability of Slip

Contact Surface of Bolted Parts	Class	A	B	C
	Description	Clean mill scale, or blast-cleaned with Class A coatings $k_s = 0.33$	Blast-cleaned, or blast-cleaned with Class B coatings $k_s = 0.50$	Hot-dip galvanized with wire-brushed surfaces $k_s = 0.40$
A325M $F_u = 830$ MPa	c_1	0.82	0.90	0.90
	$0.53\, c_1\, k_s\, F_u$ (MPa)	119	198	158
A490M $F_u = 1040$ MPa	c_1	0.78	0.85	0.85
	$0.53\, c_1\, k_s\, F_u$ (MPa)	142	234	187
A325 (d ≤ 1") $F_u = 825$ MPa	c_1	0.82	0.90	0.90
	$0.53\, c_1\, k_s\, F_u$ (MPa)	118	197	157
A325 (d ≥ 1⅛") $F_u = 725$ MPa	c_1	0.82	0.90	0.90
	$0.53\, c_1\, k_s\, F_u$ (MPa)	104	173	138
A490 $F_u = 1035$ MPa	c_1	0.78	0.85	0.85
	$0.53\, c_1\, k_s\, F_u$ (MPa)	141	233	187

See CSA S16-09 Clause 13.12.2.2 for values of c_1 and k_s.

Table 3-11
SLIP RESISTANCE, V_s
For Single Shear ** (m = 1)

Bolt Size		Nominal Area	Class A Surfaces		Class B Surfaces	
Metric +	Imperial	A_b	A325M, A325	A490M, A490	A325M, A325	A490M, A490
		mm²	kN per bolt	kN per bolt	kN per bolt	kN per bolt
	½	127	15.0	17.9	25.0	29.6
	⅝	198	23.4	28.0	39.0	46.2
M16		201	23.9	28.5	39.8	47.1
	¾	285	33.7	40.2	56.1	66.4
M20		314	37.4	44.5	62.2	73.6
M22		380	45.2	53.9	75.2	89.0
	⅞	388	45.9	54.8	76.3	90.5
M24		452	53.8	64.1	89.5	106
	1	507	60.0	71.6	99.8	118
M27		573	68.2	81.3	113	134
	1⅛	641	66.6	90.5	111	149
M30		707	84.2	100	140	166
	1¼	792	82.4	112	137	185
M36		1018	121	144	202	238
	1½	1140	119	161	197	266

These resistances are for use with specified loads in accordance with Clause 13.12 of CSA S16-09.
** For double shear (m = 2) multiply tabulated values by 2.
+ The number following the letter M is the nominal bolt diameter in millimetres.

Bolts in Combined Shear and Tension — Slip-Critical Connections

Clause 13.12.2.3 of CSA S16-09 requires that bolts subjected to both shear and tension in a slip-critical connection satisfy the following relationship for specified loads:

$$\frac{V}{V_s} + 1.9\frac{T}{n\,A_b\,F_u} \leq 1.0$$

The above relationship can conservatively be expressed (see Commentary on Clause 13.12.2 in Part 2 of this Handbook) as:

$$\frac{V}{V_s} + \frac{T}{T_i} \leq 1.0$$

where T_i is the specified installed tension.

If the shear-tension ratio V/T on the bolts is X, solving for V and T gives $V = XT$, and $T = V_s/(X + V_s/T_i)$.

Table 3-12 lists values of V and T for various shear-tension ratios X for Class A contact surfaces (clean mill scale or blast cleaned with Class A coatings, $k_s = 0.33$) using A325M or A325 bolts in single shear. This table can be used to establish directly the number of bolts required to satisfy the interaction equation for slip-critical connections subjected to a combination of shear and tension.

Example

Given:

Find the number of M20 A325M bolts required in a slip-critical connection to resist a specified tension force of 320 kN and a specified shear force of 400 kN. The single faying surface consists of clean mill scale.

Solution:

Prying is not a factor when making the specified shear vs. specified tension interaction check. Within permitted loadings, prying is only a redistribution of the contact forces between the material surfaces, having no significant affect upon resistance to slipping.

Shear-tension ratio is $400/320 = 1.25$

From Table 3-12, for M20 bolts and $V/T = 1.25$,

permitted V and T are 30.9 kN and 24.7 kN, respectively, per bolt.

Therefore, number of bolts required is $400/30.9$ or $320/24.7 = 12.9$

Try 14 bolts.

The connection also has to be confirmed for strength, including bolt prying and flange bending, as a bearing-type connection at factored loads.

Table 3-12
$c_1 = 0.82$
$k_s = 0.33$

SPECIFIED SHEAR AND TENSION (kN/BOLT)
Slip-Critical Connections, Class A Surfaces
A325M and A325 Bolts

Shear/Tension Ratio X = V/T		¾		M20		M22		⅞		M24		1	
X	1/X	V	T	V	T	V	T	V	T	V	T	V	T
0.5		21.9	43.7	24.2	48.4	29.3	58.6	29.7	59.4	34.9	69.7	38.8	77.6
0.6		23.2	38.7	25.7	42.9	31.1	51.9	31.6	52.6	37.0	61.7	41.2	68.7
0.7		24.3	34.7	27.0	38.5	32.6	46.5	33.0	47.2	38.8	55.4	43.1	61.6
0.8		25.1	31.4	27.9	34.9	33.8	42.2	34.2	42.8	40.2	50.2	44.7	55.9
0.9		25.9	28.8	28.7	31.9	34.7	38.6	35.2	39.1	41.3	45.9	46.0	51.1
1.0	1.0	26.5	26.5	29.4	29.4	35.6	35.6	36.1	36.1	42.3	42.3	47.1	47.1
1.11	0.9	27.1	24.4	30.0	27.0	36.3	32.7	36.9	33.2	43.2	38.9	48.1	43.3
1.25	0.8	27.8	22.2	30.8	24.6	37.1	29.7	37.6	30.1	44.3	35.4	49.3	39.4
1.43	0.7	28.3	19.8	31.4	22.0	38.0	26.6	38.6	27.0	45.3	31.7	50.3	35.2
1.67	0.6	29.0	17.4	32.2	19.3	38.8	23.3	39.5	23.7	46.3	27.8	51.5	30.9
2.00	0.5	29.6	14.8	33.0	16.5	39.8	19.9	40.4	20.2	47.4	23.7	52.8	26.4
2.50	0.4	30.5	12.2	33.8	13.5	40.8	16.3	41.5	16.6	48.5	19.4	54.0	21.6
3.33	0.3	31.3	9.4	34.7	10.4	41.7	12.5	42.3	12.7	49.7	14.9	55.3	16.6
5.00	0.2	32.0	6.4	35.5	7.1	43.0	8.6	43.5	8.7	51.0	10.2	57.0	11.4
10.00	0.1	33.0	3.3	36.0	3.6	44.0	4.4	45.0	4.5	52.0	5.2	58.0	5.8
V_s	0	33.7	0	37.4	0	45.2	0	45.9	0	53.9	0	60.0	0

$$V = XT, \quad T = \frac{V_s}{X + V_s/T_i}$$

NOTES

BOLTS IN TENSION AND PRYING ACTION

General

Connections with fasteners loaded in tension occur in many common situations, such as hanger and bracing connections with tee-type gussets, and end-plate moment connections. Clause 13.12.1.3 of CSA S16-09 requires that when bolts are loaded in direct tension, the effects of prying action be taken into account in proportioning the bolts and connected parts. This clause also requires that the connection be arranged to minimize prying forces when subjected to tensile cyclic loading.

The actual stress distribution in the flange of a tee-type connection is extremely complex as it depends upon the bolt size and arrangement, and upon the strength and dimensions of the connecting flange. Consequently, various design methods have been proposed in the technical literature for proportioning such connections. The procedures given in this section are based on the recommendations contained on page 285 *of Guide to Design Criteria for Bolted and Riveted Joints,* second edition, by Kulak, Fisher and Struik.

The procedures include a set of seven equations for selecting a trial section and for evaluating the bolt forces and flange capacity. Equilibrium Eqn. 4 uses the full tensile resistance T_r of the bolts to determine α for use in the connection capacity Eqn. 5. This provides a value for the maximum capacity of the connection. Similarly, Eqn. 6 uses the applied factored tensile load per bolt P_f to determine α for use in the amplified bolt force Eqn. 7. This provides a value for the factored load per bolt (including prying) T_f of the bolts.

Based on these equations, Table 3-13 on page 3-24 and Figure 3-2 on page 3-25 provide aids for preliminary design and checking purposes. They demonstrate the effect of applied factored tensile load per bolt and flange geometry upon flange thicknesses for various bolt sizes, assuming static loads.

In general, prying effects can be minimized by dimensioning for minimum practical gauge distance and for maximum permissible edge distance. For repeated loading the flange must be made thick enough and stiff enough so that deformation of the flange is virtually eliminated. In addition, special attention must be paid to bolt installation to ensure that the bolts are properly pretensioned to provide the required clamping force.

The expressions for prying effects are based on tests carried out on tees. For angles, assuming the distribution of moment shown, the moment equilibrium equation can be derived from statics as:

$$P_f b = Q a \quad \text{Therefore} \quad Q/P_f = b/a$$

References

DOUTY, R. T., and McGUIRE, W. 1965. High strength bolted moment connections. ASCE Journal of the Structural Division, April.

KULAK, G.L., FISHER, J.W., and STRUIK, J.H.A. 1987. Guide to design criteria for bolted and riveted joints, 2nd edition. John Wiley & Sons, New York, N.Y.

NAIR, R. S., BIRKEMOE, P. C., and MUNSE, W. H. 1969. High strength bolts subject to tension and prying. Structural Research Series 353, September, Department of Civil Engineering, U. of Ill., Urbana.

Equations

$$K = 4b'10^3 / (\phi\, p\, F_y) \qquad (1)$$

$$\delta = 1 - d'/p \qquad (2)$$

$$\text{Range of } t = \left(\frac{K P_f}{(1 + \delta\alpha)}\right)^{1/2} \qquad (3)$$

t_{min} when $\alpha = 1.0$, t_{max} when $\alpha = 0.0$

$$\alpha = \left(\frac{K T_r}{t^2} - 1\right) \times \frac{a'}{\delta(a' + b')}, \quad 0 \le \alpha \le 1.0 \qquad (4)$$

$$\text{Connection capacity} = (t^2 / K)(1 + \delta\alpha)n \qquad (5)$$

$$\alpha = \left(\frac{K P_f}{t^2} - 1\right) \times \frac{1}{\delta} \quad \text{(for use in Eqn. 7)} \qquad (6)$$

$$T_f \approx P_f\left[1 + \left(\frac{b'}{a'} \times \frac{\delta\alpha}{1 + \delta\alpha}\right)\right] \le T_r \qquad (7)$$

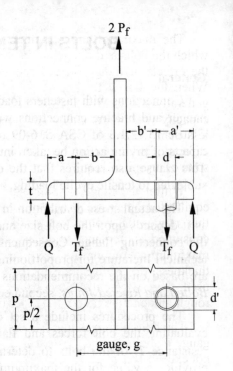

Nomenclature

K = Parameter as defined in Eqn. 1
P_f = Applied factored tensile load per bolt, (kN)
Q = Prying force per bolt at factored load, $Q = T_f - P_f$, (kN)
T_f = Factored load per bolt including prying (amplified bolt force), (kN)
T_r = Factored tensile resistance of bolts, $\phi_b\, 0.75\, A_b F_u$, (kN)
F_y = Yield strength of flange material, (MPa)
a = Distance from bolt line to edge of tee flange, not more than $1.25\, b$, (mm)
a' = $a + d/2$, (mm)
b = Distance from bolt line (gauge line) to face of tee stem, (mm)
b' = $b - d/2$, (mm)
d = Bolt diameter, (mm)
d' = Nominal hole diameter, (mm)
n = Number of flange bolts in tension
p = Length of flange tributary to each bolt, or bolt pitch, (mm)
t = Thickness of flange, (mm)
α = Ratio of sagging moment at bolt line to hogging moment at stem of tee
δ = Ratio of net to gross flange area along a longitudinal line of bolts (see Eqn. 2)
ϕ = Resistance factor for the tee material, (0.9)

Preliminary Design Tables

Table 3-13 on page 3-24 lists the maximum and minimum values of flange thickness t calculated with Eqn. 3 using $\alpha = 0.0$ and $\alpha = 1.0$ for a range of values of P_f. Results are tabulated for various flange bolt patterns and bolt sizes.

The maximum and minimum values of t indicate a range of flange thickness within which the bolts and flange are in equilibrium for the particular flange geometry, and in which the effects of flange flexure and prying reduce the effective tension capacity of the bolts. When the flange thickness is greater than the larger value of t, ($\alpha = 0.0$), the flange is generally sufficiently thick and stiff to virtually eliminate prying action, and the connection capacity will be limited by the tensile resistance of the bolts. When the flange thickness is less than the smaller value of t, ($\alpha = 1.0$), the flange thickness will govern the connection capacity, and the bolts will usually have excess capacity to resist the applied tension load in spite of prying effects.

Within the range of flange thickness for $0.0 < \alpha < 1.0$, with the bolts and flange in equilibrium, the ratio T_f/P_f will increase from unity for t_{max} to a maximum value for t_{min}. In this range, the bolts control the capacity with the flange strength being increasingly consumed as the flange thickness decreases. (It can be helpful to note that the typical ratio of maximum to minimum flange thickness is about 1.33, and that at the mimimum flange thickness, the prying ratio T_f/P_f is about the same. When the maximum flange thickness is used, there is essentially no prying and the ratios $t_{max}/t_{req'd}$ and T_f/P_f are both 1.0. Thus, a rough guide to the ratio $t_{max}/t_{req'd}$ is the available prying ratio T_r/P_f of the desired bolt size.)

The bolt pitch p should be approximately 4 to 5 times the bolt size ($4\,d \leq p \leq 5\,d$) and the gauge g should be kept as small as practicable. Also, dimension a for design purposes must not exceed $1.25\,b$.

Figure 3-2 on page 3-25 graphs the amplified bolt force T_f for various applied loads P_f, flange thicknesses t, and four different values of b (40 mm, 45 mm, 50 mm and 55 mm) with M20, M22 and M24 A325M bolts. These graphs can be used to evaluate the effects of flange thickness, gauge distance and bolt size on the amplified bolt force, and to establish reasonable trial connection parameters.

Design Procedure

Trial Section

1) Select an intended number and size of bolts as a function of the applied factored tensile load per bolt P_f and the anticipated prying ratio.

2) With P_f, the bolt size, and trial values of b' and p, use Eqns. 1, 2 and 3 (with $\alpha = 0.0$ and $\alpha = 1.0$) to identify a range of acceptable flange thicknesses. (Alternatively, use Table 3-13 on page 3-24.)

3) Identify an intended flange thickness.

Figure 3-2 (page 3-25) may also be used to identify an intended bolt size and flange geometry based on the amplified bolt force being less than the bolt tensile resistance.

Design Check

1) Recalculate K, if necessary, and use Eqn. 4 to determine α for use in Eqn. 5.

2) Calculate the connection capacity with Eqn. 5. (If α from Eqn. 4 < 0.0, use $\alpha = 0.0$, and if $\alpha > 1.0$, use $\alpha = 1.0$.)

3) Equations 6 and 7 can be used if desired to determine the total bolt tension, including prying (amplified bolt force), that results from the applied load.

Note:

CSA S16-09, Clause 22.2.2(e) requires that all bolts subject to tensile loadings be pretensioned when installed, and Clause 13.12.1.3 requires that connections with tensile cyclic loads on bolts be arranged to minimize prying forces.

Example 1

Given:

Design a tension tee connection with 4 ASTM A325M bolts in tension for a factored static load of 560 kN assuming the bolts are on a 100 mm gauge, at a pitch of 110 mm, with the tee connected to rigid supports. Use G40.21 350W steel.

Solution:

Trial Section

Applied load per bolt = $560 / 4 = 140$ kN $= P_f$

Assume M22 bolts, 24 mm hole diameter, 15 mm web. $T_r = 189$ kN

Available prying ratio T_r / P_f is $189 / 140 = 1.35$ OK for near-minimum flange

$b = (100 - 15) / 2 = 42.5$ mm $b' = 42.5 - 22 / 2 = 31.5$ mm

$K = 4 \times 31.5 \times 10^3 / (0.9 \times 110 \times 350) = 3.64$ (Eqn. 1)

$\delta = 1 - (24 / 110) = 0.782$ (Eqn. 2)

$$t_{min} = \left(\frac{3.64 \times 140}{1.782}\right)^{1/2} = 16.9 \text{ mm}; \quad t_{max} = \left(\frac{3.64 \times 140}{1.0}\right)^{1/2} = 22.6 \text{ mm} \qquad \text{(Eqn. 3)}$$

(Alternatively, the range of t, by rough interpolation from Table 3-13 on page 3-24, could be seen to be about 17 to 23 mm.)

One possible solution is W410x85 *(t = 18.2 mm)*. Usual gauges are given on page 6-168. The final choice is determined by the maximum available prying ratio T_r / P_f for the bolt size finally selected.

Design Check

Try W410x85 with M22 bolts: $d = 22$ mm, $d' = 24$ mm

$t = 18.2$ mm, $w = 10.9$ mm, flange width $= 181$ mm

$b = (100 - 10.9)/2 = 44.6$ mm; $b' = 44.6 - 22/2 = 33.6$ mm; $1.25\, b = 55.8$ mm

$a = (181 - 100)/2 = 40.5 < 1.25\, b;\ a' = 40.5 + 22/2 = 51.5;\ a' + b' = 85.1$

$K = 4 \times 33.6 \times 10^3 / (0.9 \times 110 \times 350) = 3.88$ (Eqn. 1)

$\delta = 0.782$ (as above) (Eqn. 2)

$$\alpha = \left(\frac{3.88 \times 189}{18.2^2} - 1\right) \times \frac{51.5}{0.782 \times 85.1} = 0.939, \quad 0 \le \alpha \le 1.0 \qquad \text{(Eqn. 4)}$$

$\delta\alpha = 0.782 \times 0.939 = 0.734$

Connection capacity $= (18.2^2 / 3.88)(1.734)\, 4 = 592$ kN > 560 kN (Eqn. 5)

To find actual bolt load (including prying), if desired:

$$\alpha = \left(\frac{3.88 \times 140}{18.2^2} - 1\right) \times \frac{1}{0.782} = 0.818 \qquad \text{(Eqn. 6)}$$

$\delta\alpha = 0.782 \times 0.818 = 0.640$

$$T_f = 140\left[1 + \left(\frac{33.6}{51.5} \times \frac{0.640}{1 + 0.640}\right)\right] = 176 \text{ kN} < 189 \text{ kN} \qquad \text{(Eqn. 7)}$$

Tee stem capacity is $0.9\,(2 \times 110)\,10.9 \times 350 = 755$ kN > 560 kN

Example 2

Given:

Use Table 3-13 and Figure 3-2 to select the bolt size and trial dimensions for a tee cut from a W410x85 section (G40.21 350W). The factored tensile load is 480 kN and a bolt gauge of 100 mm is preferred. Confirm the trial design.

Solution:

Since Table 3-13 and Figure 3-2 are intended only for the selection of a trial section that must be checked with Eqns. 1, 2, 4 and 5 on page 3-20 (illustrated in the previous example), precise interpolation is not necessary. As discussed on page 3-21, a comparison of the available ratio T_r/P_f (for the bolts chosen) to the ratio t_{max}/t for a trial flange thickness (for the value of t_{max} selected from Table 3-13) will indicate whether a combination of bolt size, flange thickness and geometry is suitable.

For W410x85: $t = 18.2$ mm, $w = 10.9$ mm, flange width $= 181$ mm

For $g = 100$ mm, $b = (100 - 10.9)/2 = 44.6$ mm (Use $b = 45$ in Table 3-13)

With 4 bolts, $P_f = 480/4 = 120$ kN, and $T_r/P_f = 156/120 = 1.30$ for M20 bolts.

Table 3-13, with $b = 45$, M20 bolts and $P_f = 120$ kN, $p \approx 100$ mm gives $t_{max} = 23.1$ mm

$$t_{max}/t = 23.1/18.2 = 1.27 < T_r/P_f = 1.30$$

Alternatively, Figure 3-2 can be used to select the bolt size based on the flange thickness and the amplified bolt force.

Use graph for $b = 45$ mm *(b = 44.6 mm, see above)*

Enter graph at applied load per bolt of 120 kN and flange thickness $t = 18$ mm

With M20 bolts, amplified bolt force, $T_f \approx 150$ kN $< T_r = 156$ kN

Proceed with the design check using M20 bolts; $p = 5d = 100$ mm.

$b = 44.6$ mm; $b' = 44.6 - 20/2 = 34.6$ mm; $1.25 b = 55.8$ mm

$a = (181 - 100)/2 = 40.5$ mm $< 1.25 b = 55.8$ mm

$a' = 40.5 + 20/2 = 50.5$ mm; $a' + b' = 50.5 + 34.6 = 85.1$ mm

$K = 4 \times 34.6 \times 10^3/(0.9 \times 100 \times 350) = 4.39$ (Eqn. 1)

$\delta = 1 - (22/100) = 0.780$ (Eqn. 2)

$$\alpha = \left(\frac{4.39 \times 156}{18.2^2} - 1\right) \times \frac{50.5}{0.780 \times 85.1} = 0.812, \quad 0 \le \alpha \le 1.0 \quad \delta\alpha = 0.633 \qquad \text{(Eqn. 4)}$$

Connection capacity $= (18.2^2/4.39)(1.633)\,4 = 493$ kN > 480 kN   (Eqn. 5)

Check total bolt load (amplified bolt force):

$$\alpha = \left(\frac{4.39 \times 120}{18.2^2} - 1\right) \times \frac{1}{0.780} = 0.757 \quad \delta\alpha = 0.590 \qquad \text{(Eqn. 6)}$$

$$T_f = 120 \left[1 + \left(\frac{34.6}{50.5} \times \frac{0.590}{1 + 0.590}\right)\right] = 151 \text{ kN} < 156 \text{ kN} \qquad \text{(Eqn. 7)}$$

RANGE OF t

$$t = \sqrt{\dfrac{K P_f}{(1 + \delta\alpha)}}$$

Table 3-13

t_{min} when $\alpha = 1.0$, t_{max} when $\alpha = 0.0$

b (mm)	Bolt size	$P_f = 80$ kN pitch p (mm) 80	90	100	$P_f = 100$ kN pitch p (mm) 80	90	100	$P_f = 120$ kN pitch p (mm) 80	90	100	$P_f = 140$ kN pitch p (mm) 80	90	100
35	3/4	13.6	12.8	12.0	15.3	14.3	13.4	16.7	15.6	14.7	18.1	16.9	15.9
		18.0	17.0	16.1	20.1	19.0	18.0	22.0	20.8	19.7	23.8	22.4	21.3
	M20	13.6	12.7	11.9	15.2	14.2	13.4	16.6	15.5	14.6	17.9	16.8	15.8
		17.8	16.8	15.9	19.9	18.8	17.8	21.8	20.6	19.5	23.6	22.2	21.1
40	3/4	14.9	14.0	13.2	16.7	15.6	14.7	18.3	17.1	16.1	19.7	18.5	17.4
		19.7	18.5	17.6	22.0	20.7	19.7	24.1	22.7	21.5	26.0	24.5	23.3
	M20	14.9	13.9	13.1	16.6	15.5	14.6	18.2	17.0	16.0	19.7	18.4	17.3
		19.5	18.4	17.5	21.8	20.6	19.5	23.9	22.5	21.4	25.8	24.3	23.1
45	3/4	16.1	15.1	14.2	18.0	16.8	15.9	19.7	18.4	17.4	21.3	19.9	18.8
		21.2	20.0	19.0	23.7	22.4	21.2	26.0	24.5	23.3	28.1	26.5	25.1
	M20	16.1	15.0	14.1	17.9	16.8	15.8	19.7	18.4	17.3	21.2	19.8	18.7
		21.1	19.9	18.9	23.6	22.2	21.1	25.8	24.3	23.1	27.9	26.3	24.9
50	3/4	17.2	16.1	15.2	19.2	18.0	16.9	21.1	19.7	18.6	22.8	21.3	20.1
		22.7	21.4	20.3	25.3	23.9	22.7	27.8	26.2	24.8	30.0	28.3	26.8
	M20	17.2	16.0	15.1	19.2	17.9	16.9	21.0	19.6	18.5	22.7	21.2	20.0
		22.5	21.2	20.2	25.2	23.8	22.5	27.6	26.0	24.7	29.8	28.1	26.7
55	3/4	18.2	17.0	16.1	20.4	19.1	18.0	22.3	20.9	19.7	24.1	22.6	21.3
		24.0	22.7	21.5	26.9	25.3	24.0	29.4	27.7	26.3	31.8	30.0	28.4
	M20	18.2	17.0	16.0	20.3	19.0	17.9	22.3	20.8	19.6	24.1	22.5	21.2
		23.9	22.5	21.4	26.7	25.2	23.9	29.3	27.6	26.2	31.6	29.8	28.3

b (mm)	Bolt size	$P_f = 120$ kN pitch p (mm) 90	100	110	$P_f = 140$ kN pitch p (mm) 90	100	110	$P_f = 160$ kN pitch p (mm) 90	100	110	$P_f = 180$ kN pitch p (mm) 90	100	110
40	M22	16.8	15.8	15.0	18.2	17.1	16.2	19.4	18.3	17.3	20.6	19.4	18.4
		22.2	21.0	20.0	23.9	22.7	21.6	25.6	24.3	23.1	27.1	25.7	24.5
	7/8	16.8	15.8	15.0	18.2	17.1	16.2	19.4	18.3	17.3	20.6	19.4	18.4
		22.1	21.0	20.0	23.9	22.7	21.6	25.5	24.2	23.1	27.1	25.7	24.5
45	M22	18.2	17.2	16.3	19.7	18.5	17.6	21.0	19.8	18.8	22.3	21.0	19.9
		24.0	22.8	21.7	25.9	24.6	23.4	27.7	26.3	25.1	29.4	27.9	26.6
	7/8	18.2	17.1	16.2	19.7	18.5	17.5	21.0	19.8	18.8	22.3	21.0	19.9
		24.0	22.7	21.7	25.9	24.5	23.4	27.7	26.2	25.0	29.3	27.8	26.5
50	M22	19.5	18.4	17.4	21.1	19.8	18.8	22.5	21.2	20.1	23.9	22.5	21.3
		25.7	24.4	23.2	27.8	26.3	25.1	29.7	28.1	26.8	31.5	29.9	28.5
	7/8	19.5	18.4	17.4	21.1	19.8	18.8	22.5	21.2	20.1	23.9	22.5	21.3
		25.7	24.3	23.2	27.7	26.3	25.1	29.6	28.1	26.8	31.4	29.8	28.4
55	M22	20.7	19.5	18.5	22.4	21.1	20.0	23.9	22.5	21.4	25.4	23.9	22.7
		27.3	25.9	24.7	29.5	28.0	26.7	31.5	29.9	28.5	33.4	31.7	30.2
	7/8	20.7	19.5	18.5	22.4	21.1	20.0	23.9	22.5	21.3	25.4	23.9	22.6
		27.3	25.9	24.7	29.4	27.9	26.6	31.5	29.9	28.5	33.4	31.7	30.2

b (mm)	Bolt size	$P_f = 160$ kN pitch p (mm) 100	110	120	$P_f = 180$ kN pitch p (mm) 100	110	120	$P_f = 200$ kN pitch p (mm) 100	110	120	$P_f = 220$ kN pitch p (mm) 100	110	120
40	M24	18.1	17.1	16.3	19.2	18.2	17.3	20.2	19.1	18.2	21.2	20.1	19.1
		23.9	22.7	21.8	25.3	24.1	23.1	26.7	25.4	24.3	28.0	26.7	25.5
	1	17.9	17.0	16.2	19.0	18.0	17.1	20.0	19.0	18.1	21.0	19.9	18.9
		23.6	22.5	21.5	25.0	23.8	22.8	26.3	25.1	24.0	27.6	26.3	25.2
45	M24	19.6	18.6	17.7	20.8	19.7	18.8	21.9	20.8	19.8	23.0	21.8	20.8
		25.9	24.7	23.6	27.5	26.2	25.1	28.9	27.6	26.4	30.4	28.9	27.7
	1	19.5	18.5	17.6	20.7	19.6	18.6	21.8	20.6	19.6	22.9	21.6	20.6
		25.6	24.4	23.4	27.2	25.9	24.8	28.6	27.3	26.1	30.0	28.6	27.4
50	M24	21.1	19.9	19.0	22.3	21.2	20.1	23.6	22.3	21.2	24.7	23.4	22.3
		27.8	26.5	25.4	29.5	28.1	26.9	31.1	29.6	28.4	32.6	31.1	29.7
	1	21.0	19.8	18.9	22.2	21.0	20.0	23.4	22.2	21.1	24.6	23.3	22.1
		27.5	26.2	25.1	29.2	27.8	26.7	30.8	29.3	28.1	32.3	30.8	29.5
55	M24	22.4	21.2	20.2	23.8	22.5	21.4	25.1	23.7	22.6	26.3	24.9	23.7
		29.6	28.2	27.0	31.4	29.9	28.6	33.0	31.5	30.2	34.7	33.0	31.6
	1	22.3	21.1	20.1	23.7	22.4	21.3	24.9	23.6	22.5	26.2	24.8	23.6
		29.3	28.0	26.8	31.1	29.6	28.4	32.8	31.3	29.9	34.4	32.8	31.4

$K = 4\,b'\,10^3 / (\phi\,p\,F_y)$ where $\phi = 0.90$ and $F_y = 350$ MPa

Figure 3-2

AMPLIFIED BOLT FORCE, T_f (kN)

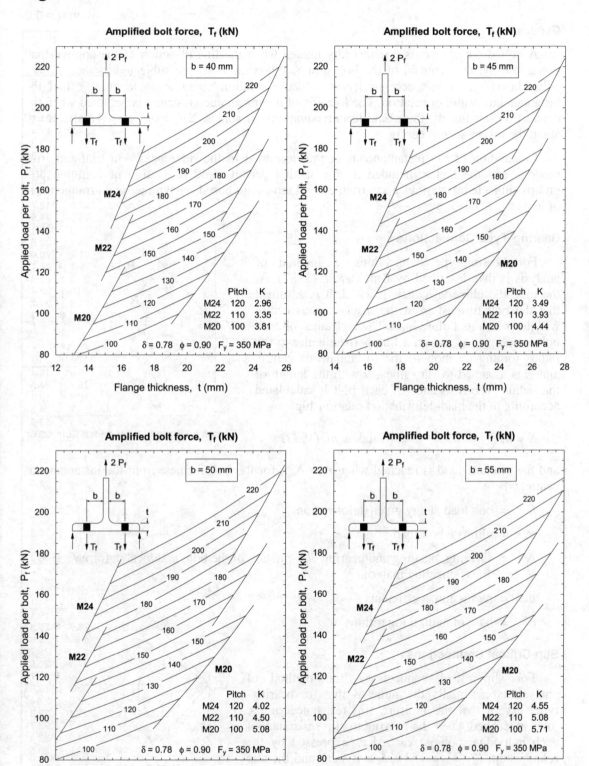

ECCENTRIC LOADS ON BOLT GROUPS

General

A bolted connection is eccentrically loaded when the line of action of the applied load passes outside the centroid of the bolt group. When the bolts are subjected to shear forces only, the effect of this eccentricity is to cause rotation about a single point called the instantaneous centre of rotation. The location of the instantaneous centre is obtained when the connection satisfies the three equilibrium equations for statics, $\Sigma F_x = 0$, $\Sigma F_y = 0$ and $\Sigma M = 0$ about the instantaneous centre.

Calculation of the instantaneous centre described in the references is a trial-and-error process, and the tables included in this section permit rapid evaluation of common bolt groups subjected to various eccentricities. All tables are based on symmetrical arrangements of bolts.

Bearing-Type Connections

For bearing-type connections, a method of analysis is that described by Kulak *et al.* (1987). At the time the ultimate load is reached, it is assumed that the bolt furthest from the instantaneous centre will just reach its failure load. The resistance of each bolt is assumed to act on a line perpendicular to the radius joining the bolt to the instantaneous centre, and Δ is assumed to vary linearly with the length of the radius. The resistance of each bolt is calculated according to the load-deformation relationship:

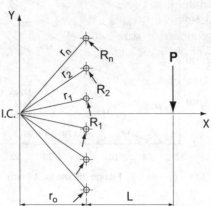

$$R = R_u (1 - e^{-\mu \Delta})^\lambda \quad \text{........ Kulak } et \ al. \text{ (1987)}$$

Forces on Eccentrically Loaded Connection

and the ultimate load is reached when $\Delta = \Delta_{max}$ for the bolt furthest from the instantaneous centre, where

R = bolt load at any given deformation

R_u = ultimate bolt load

Δ = shearing, bending and bearing deformation of the bolt, and local deformation of the connecting material

μ, λ = regression coefficients

e = base of natural logarithms

Slip-Critical Connections

For slip-critical connections, the method of analysis is essentially the same as that for bearing-type, except that the limiting slip resistance of the joint is reached when the maximum slip resistance of each individual bolt is reached as expressed by the relationship, $R = V_s = 0.53 \, c_1 \, k_s \, m \, n \, A_b \, F_u$ and the slip resistance of each bolt is assumed to be equal.

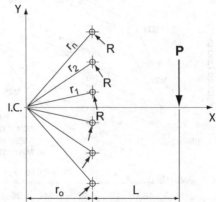

Forces on Eccentrically Loaded
Slip-Critical Connection

Tables

Tables 3-14 to 3-20 have been developed using the method described for bearing-type connections. Values tabulated are non-dimensional coefficients C and may be used for bolts of any diameter. In determining the coefficients C, the following values were used: R_u = 74 kips (329 kN), μ = 10.0, λ = 0.55, Δ_{max} = 0.34 inches (8.64 mm). These values were obtained experimentally for ¾ inch diameter A325 bolts and are reported by Crawford and Kulak (1971).

The ultimate load P for each bolt group and eccentricity was computed and then divided by the maximum value of R (when $\Delta = \Delta_{max}$) to obtain the values of C.

The tables may thus be used to obtain the factored resistance, expressed as a vertical load P, of a connection by multiplying the coefficient C, for any particular bolt group and eccentricity, by the factored shear resistance of a single bolt. i.e. $P_f = C V_r$.

Coefficients were developed in a similar way for slip-critical connections, except that the individual bolt resistances for all bolts in the group were assumed to be equal. The coefficients calculated in this way were from 5% to 10% higher than those for bearing-type connections. Thus only one set of tables, based on the bearing-type connections, is provided for use with both bearing-type and slip-critical connections.

Use of Tables

Bearing-Type Connections

1) To obtain the coefficient C required for a given geometry of bolts and eccentricity of load, divide the factored load P_f by the factored shear resistance V_r of a single bolt for the appropriate shear condition, i.e. $C = P_f/V_r$.

2) To determine the capacity of a given connection, multiply the coefficient C for the bolt group and eccentricity by the appropriate bolt shear resistance value V_r of a single bolt, i.e. $P_f = C V_r$.

V_r is the factored shear resistance of the bolt from Table 3-4. Used in this way these tables provide a margin of safety which is consistent with bolts in joints less than 1300 mm long and subjected to shear produced by concentric loads only.

Slip-Critical Connections

Although developed using the method for bearing-type connections, these tables can also be used for slip-resistant connections using the *specified* load P and the appropriate slip resistance value V_s for the bolt size and condition of the faying surface.

1) Required $C = P/V_s$

2) Capacity $P = C V_s$

V_s is the slip resistance determined from Tables 3-10 and 3-11.

References

CRAWFORD, S.F., and KULAK, G.L. 1971. Eccentrically loaded bolted connections. ASCE Journal of the Structural Division, **97**(ST3), March.

KULAK, G.L. 1975. Eccentrically loaded slip resistant connections. AISC Engineering Journal, **12**(2), Second Quarter.

KULAK, G.L., and GRONDIN, G.Y. 2006. Limit states design in structural steel, CISC.

KULAK, G.L., FISHER, J.W., and STRUIK, J.H.A. 1987. Guide to design criteria for bolted and riveted joints (2nd Ed.). John Wiley and Sons.

SHERMER, C.L. 1971. Plastic behaviour of eccentrically loaded connections. AISC Engineering Journal, **8**(2), April.

Example

1. Given:

A double column bracket must be designed to support a factored load of 700 kN at an eccentricity of 400 mm. Find the number of ¾ inch A325 bolts per flange required for a gauge dimension of 120 mm and a pitch of 80 mm assuming a bearing-type connection.

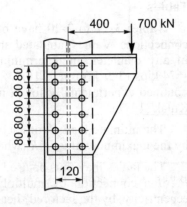

Solution:

$P_f = 700/2 = 350$ kN $\qquad L = 400$ mm

$V_r = 113$ kN (Table 3-4 page 3-8, single shear, threads excluded)

Required $C = 350/113 = 3.10$

From Tables 3-15 and 3-16, for 2 lines of bolts

6 rows at 80 mm gauge, $C = 3.49$

at 320 mm gauge, $C = 4.77$

Interpolating for 120 mm gauge $C = 3.49 + (4.77 - 3.49) \times 40/240 = 3.70$

Use 6 rows of bolts (total 12 bolts)

Capacity is $3.70 \times 113 = 418$ kN per side

The connected material should be thick enough to provide bearing capacity for the 113 kN resistance of the bolts in accordance with CSA S16-09, Clause 13.12.1.2. Minimum edge distances must conform with Clause 22.3.2.

Note: In double-angle beam connections, the eccentricity may be neglected in the web-framing leg when connected with a single row of bolts (see p. 3-58).

2. Given:

Find the number of ⅞ inch bolts required for a similar bracket assuming a slip-critical connection with clean mill scale and a specified load of 500 kN.

Solution:

$P = 500/2 = 250$ kN $\qquad L = 400$ mm

$V_s = 45.9$ kN (Table 3-11, page 3-15) $\qquad$ Required $C = 250/45.9 = 5.45$

From Tables 3-15 and 3-16, for 2 lines of bolts:

8 rows at 80 mm gauge, $C = 5.89$

at 320 mm gauge, $C = 7.17$

Interpolating for 120 mm gauge, $C = 5.89 + (7.17 - 5.89) \times 40/240 = 6.10$

Use 8 rows of bolts (total 16 bolts)

Capacity is $6.10 \times 45.9 = 280$ kN per side

The ultimate strength of the joint would also be checked in bearing and shear for factored loads.

$$C = \frac{P_f}{V_r}, \text{ or } \frac{P}{V_s}$$

Moment Arm, L, mm												Number of Bolts	Pitch b mm
75	100	125	150	175	200	225	250	300	400	500	600		
0.94	0.74	0.61	0.51	0.44	0.39	0.35	0.32	0.26	0.20	0.16	0.13	2	
1.87	1.50	1.24	1.05	0.90	0.79	0.71	0.64	0.53	0.40	0.32	0.27	3	
2.96	2.51	2.14	1.86	1.63	1.45	1.30	1.18	0.99	0.75	0.61	0.51	4	
4.06	3.58	3.14	2.76	2.45	2.19	1.98	1.80	1.52	1.15	0.92	0.77	5	
5.16	4.68	4.20	3.76	3.38	3.06	2.78	2.54	2.16	1.66	1.34	1.12	6	
6.25	5.78	5.29	4.82	4.39	4.00	3.66	3.37	2.89	2.23	1.80	1.51	7	80
7.32	6.88	6.40	5.91	5.44	5.01	4.62	4.28	3.70	2.88	2.34	1.97	8	
8.38	7.97	7.50	7.01	6.53	6.06	5.64	5.24	4.57	3.59	2.93	2.47	9	
9.43	9.04	8.60	8.11	7.62	7.14	6.68	6.26	5.50	4.37	3.59	3.03	10	
10.5	10.1	9.68	9.22	8.73	8.24	7.76	7.30	6.48	5.20	4.30	3.64	11	
11.5	11.2	10.8	10.3	9.83	9.34	8.85	8.38	7.50	6.08	5.05	4.30	12	
1.03	0.82	0.68	0.57	0.50	0.44	0.39	0.35	0.30	0.22	0.18	0.15	2	
2.01	1.65	1.37	1.17	1.01	0.89	0.79	0.72	0.60	0.45	0.36	0.30	3	
3.12	2.70	2.34	2.04	1.80	1.61	1.45	1.32	1.11	0.84	0.68	0.57	4	
4.22	3.79	3.38	3.00	2.69	2.42	2.19	2.00	1.69	1.29	1.04	0.87	5	
5.31	4.90	4.46	4.05	3.67	3.34	3.06	2.81	2.40	1.85	1.50	1.26	6	
6.39	5.99	5.57	5.13	4.72	4.34	4.00	3.70	3.19	2.48	2.02	1.69	7	90
7.45	7.08	6.67	6.23	5.80	5.39	5.01	4.66	4.07	3.19	2.61	2.20	8	
8.50	8.16	7.76	7.34	6.90	6.47	6.06	5.68	5.00	3.98	3.27	2.76	9	
9.54	9.22	8.85	8.44	8.01	7.57	7.14	6.73	5.99	4.82	3.99	3.38	10	
10.6	10.3	9.93	9.53	9.11	8.67	8.24	7.81	7.02	5.72	4.76	4.06	11	
11.6	11.3	11.0	10.6	10.2	9.77	9.34	8.90	8.07	6.66	5.59	4.78	12	
1.11	0.89	0.74	0.63	0.55	0.48	0.43	0.39	0.33	0.25	0.20	0.17	2	
2.13	1.78	1.50	1.28	1.12	0.98	0.88	0.79	0.66	0.50	0.40	0.33	3	
3.25	2.86	2.51	2.21	1.96	1.76	1.59	1.45	1.23	0.93	0.75	0.63	4	
4.35	3.96	3.58	3.22	2.90	2.63	2.39	2.19	1.86	1.43	1.15	0.96	5	
5.43	5.07	4.68	4.29	3.93	3.60	3.31	3.06	2.63	2.04	1.66	1.39	6	
6.49	6.16	5.78	5.39	5.01	4.64	4.31	4.00	3.48	2.73	2.23	1.87	7	100
7.54	7.24	6.88	6.50	6.10	5.72	5.35	5.01	4.41	3.50	2.88	2.43	8	
8.59	8.30	7.97	7.60	7.21	6.81	6.43	6.06	5.39	4.34	3.59	3.05	9	
9.62	9.36	9.04	8.69	8.31	7.92	7.52	7.14	6.42	5.24	4.37	3.72	10	
10.6	10.4	10.1	9.77	9.41	9.02	8.63	8.24	7.48	6.19	5.20	4.45	11	
11.7	11.4	11.2	10.8	10.5	10.1	9.73	9.34	8.56	7.18	6.08	5.24	12	
1.25	1.03	0.86	0.74	0.65	0.57	0.51	0.47	0.39	0.30	0.24	0.20	2	
2.33	2.01	1.73	1.50	1.32	1.17	1.05	0.95	0.79	0.60	0.48	0.40	3	
3.44	3.12	2.80	2.51	2.26	2.04	1.86	1.70	1.45	1.11	0.90	0.75	4	
4.52	4.22	3.90	3.58	3.28	3.00	2.76	2.55	2.19	1.69	1.37	1.15	5	
5.59	5.31	5.00	4.68	4.36	4.05	3.76	3.50	3.06	2.40	1.96	1.66	6	
6.64	6.39	6.10	5.78	5.46	5.13	4.82	4.53	4.00	3.19	2.63	2.23	7	120
7.67	7.45	7.18	6.88	6.56	6.23	5.91	5.60	5.01	4.07	3.38	2.88	8	
8.70	8.50	8.25	7.97	7.66	7.34	7.01	6.69	6.06	5.00	4.20	3.59	9	
9.73	9.54	9.31	9.04	8.75	8.44	8.11	7.79	7.14	5.99	5.08	4.37	10	
10.7	10.6	10.4	10.1	9.83	9.53	9.22	8.89	8.24	7.02	6.01	5.20	11	
11.8	11.6	11.4	11.2	10.9	10.6	10.3	9.99	9.34	8.07	6.98	6.08	12	
1.46	1.25	1.08	0.94	0.83	0.74	0.67	0.61	0.51	0.39	0.32	0.26	2	
2.57	2.33	2.09	1.87	1.67	1.50	1.36	1.24	1.05	0.79	0.64	0.53	3	
3.66	3.44	3.20	2.96	2.72	2.51	2.32	2.14	1.86	1.45	1.18	0.99	4	
4.71	4.52	4.30	4.06	3.82	3.58	3.35	3.14	2.76	2.19	1.80	1.52	5	
5.75	5.59	5.39	5.16	4.92	4.68	4.44	4.20	3.76	3.06	2.54	2.16	6	
6.78	6.64	6.45	6.25	6.02	5.78	5.54	5.29	4.82	4.00	3.37	2.89	7	160
7.81	7.67	7.51	7.32	7.11	6.88	6.64	6.40	5.91	5.01	4.28	3.70	8	
8.82	8.70	8.55	8.38	8.18	7.97	7.74	7.50	7.01	6.06	5.24	4.57	9	
9.84	9.73	9.59	9.43	9.25	9.04	8.83	8.60	8.11	7.14	6.26	5.50	10	
10.8	10.7	10.6	10.5	10.3	10.1	9.90	9.68	9.21	8.24	7.31	6.48	11	
11.9	11.8	11.6	11.5	11.3	11.2	11.0	10.8	10.3	9.34	8.38	7.50	12	

See page 3-26 for more details regarding these tables.

ECCENTRIC LOADS ON BOLT GROUPS
Coefficients C

$$C = \frac{P_f}{V_r}, \text{ or } \frac{P}{V_s}$$

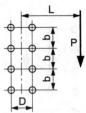

Table 3-15

Pitch b mm	Bolts per Vertical Row	D = 80 mm											
		Moment Arm, L, mm											
		75	100	125	150	175	200	225	250	300	400	500	600
	1	0.70	0.57	0.48	0.42	0.37	0.33	0.30	0.28	0.23	0.18	0.15	0.12
	2	2.15	1.78	1.52	1.31	1.16	1.03	0.93	0.85	0.72	0.55	0.44	0.37
	3	3.88	3.25	2.77	2.41	2.13	1.91	1.73	1.58	1.34	1.03	0.83	0.70
	4	5.93	5.13	4.47	3.93	3.50	3.14	2.85	2.60	2.22	1.70	1.38	1.15
	5	8.08	7.18	6.36	5.66	5.06	4.57	4.15	3.80	3.24	2.50	2.03	1.71
	6	10.3	9.33	8.42	7.60	6.87	6.25	5.71	5.25	4.51	3.49	2.84	2.39
80	7	12.4	11.5	10.6	9.66	8.83	8.09	7.44	6.87	5.92	4.61	3.75	3.17
	8	14.6	13.7	12.7	11.8	10.9	10.1	9.31	8.64	7.51	5.89	4.82	4.07
	9	16.7	15.9	14.9	14.0	13.0	12.1	11.3	10.5	9.23	7.30	5.99	5.07
	10	18.8	18.0	17.1	16.2	15.2	14.3	13.4	12.5	11.1	8.83	7.29	6.18
	11	20.9	20.1	19.3	18.4	17.4	16.4	15.5	14.6	13.0	10.5	8.69	7.39
	12	23.0	22.3	21.4	20.5	19.6	18.6	17.7	16.7	15.0	12.2	10.2	8.69
	2	2.26	1.89	1.61	1.39	1.23	1.10	0.99	0.90	0.76	0.58	0.47	0.39
	3	4.10	3.47	2.97	2.59	2.29	2.05	1.86	1.69	1.44	1.11	0.90	0.75
	4	6.22	5.45	4.79	4.24	3.79	3.41	3.10	2.84	2.42	1.86	1.51	1.26
	5	8.39	7.57	6.79	6.09	5.49	4.97	4.53	4.15	3.55	2.74	2.23	1.88
	6	10.6	9.74	8.91	8.12	7.41	6.77	6.22	5.74	4.95	3.85	3.14	2.64
90	7	12.7	11.9	11.1	10.2	9.46	8.73	8.07	7.48	6.49	5.08	4.15	3.50
	8	14.8	14.1	13.3	12.4	11.6	10.8	10.1	9.38	8.21	6.50	5.33	4.51
	9	16.9	16.3	15.5	14.6	13.8	12.9	12.1	11.4	10.1	8.03	6.63	5.62
	10	19.0	18.4	17.6	16.8	16.0	15.1	14.3	13.5	12.0	9.70	8.05	6.85
	11	21.1	20.5	19.8	19.0	18.2	17.3	16.4	15.6	14.0	11.5	9.59	8.19
	12	23.2	22.6	21.9	21.2	20.3	19.5	18.6	17.8	16.1	13.3	11.2	9.62
	2	2.37	1.99	1.70	1.48	1.30	1.17	1.05	0.96	0.81	0.62	0.50	0.42
	3	4.30	3.68	3.17	2.77	2.45	2.20	1.99	1.82	1.55	1.19	0.97	0.81
	4	6.46	5.74	5.09	4.53	4.07	3.67	3.34	3.06	2.62	2.02	1.64	1.38
	5	8.64	7.90	7.16	6.48	5.88	5.35	4.90	4.50	3.86	2.99	2.43	2.05
	6	10.8	10.1	9.32	8.58	7.89	7.26	6.70	6.20	5.37	4.20	3.43	2.89
100	7	12.9	12.3	11.5	10.7	10.0	9.30	8.64	8.05	7.04	5.55	4.55	3.85
	8	15.0	14.4	13.7	12.9	12.2	11.4	10.7	10.0	8.87	7.08	5.84	4.95
	9	17.1	16.5	15.9	15.1	14.4	13.6	12.8	12.1	10.8	8.74	7.25	6.17
	10	19.2	18.7	18.0	17.3	16.6	15.8	15.0	14.3	12.8	10.5	8.79	7.51
	11	21.3	20.8	20.2	19.5	18.7	18.0	17.2	16.4	14.9	12.4	10.4	8.96
	12	23.3	22.8	22.3	21.6	20.9	20.2	19.4	18.6	17.1	14.4	12.2	10.5
	2	2.58	2.19	1.88	1.64	1.46	1.30	1.18	1.07	0.91	0.70	0.56	0.47
	3	4.64	4.06	3.55	3.12	2.78	2.49	2.26	2.06	1.76	1.36	1.10	0.93
	4	6.83	6.21	5.61	5.06	4.58	4.17	3.82	3.51	3.02	2.34	1.90	1.60
	5	8.99	8.40	7.77	7.15	6.57	6.05	5.58	5.16	4.46	3.48	2.84	2.39
	6	11.1	10.6	9.96	9.32	8.70	8.10	7.55	7.04	6.17	4.88	4.01	3.39
120	7	13.2	12.7	12.1	11.5	10.9	10.2	9.64	9.06	8.03	6.45	5.33	4.52
	8	15.3	14.8	14.3	13.7	13.1	12.4	11.8	11.2	10.0	8.17	6.81	5.81
	9	17.4	17.0	16.4	15.9	15.3	14.6	14.0	13.3	12.1	10.0	8.43	7.23
	10	19.4	19.0	18.6	18.0	17.4	16.8	16.2	15.5	14.3	12.0	10.2	8.78
	11	21.5	21.1	20.7	20.2	19.6	19.0	18.4	17.7	16.4	14.0	12.0	10.4
	12	23.5	23.2	22.8	22.3	21.8	21.2	20.6	19.9	18.6	16.1	14.0	12.2
	2	2.92	2.54	2.22	1.97	1.75	1.58	1.43	1.31	1.12	0.86	0.70	0.58
	3	5.10	4.64	4.18	3.76	3.39	3.07	2.80	2.57	2.19	1.69	1.38	1.16
	4	7.28	6.84	6.37	5.90	5.45	5.04	4.67	4.33	3.77	2.97	2.43	2.05
	5	9.40	9.01	8.56	8.09	7.61	7.14	6.70	6.28	5.55	4.42	3.64	3.09
	6	11.5	11.1	10.7	10.3	9.81	9.33	8.85	8.39	7.53	6.14	5.12	4.37
160	7	13.5	13.2	12.9	12.5	12.0	11.5	11.0	10.6	9.63	8.01	6.76	5.81
	8	15.6	15.3	15.0	14.6	14.2	13.7	13.2	12.8	11.8	10.0	8.56	7.41
	9	17.6	17.4	17.1	16.7	16.3	15.9	15.4	15.0	14.0	12.1	10.5	9.16
	10	19.7	19.4	19.2	18.8	18.5	18.0	17.6	17.2	16.2	14.3	12.5	11.0
	11	21.7	21.5	21.2	20.9	20.6	20.2	19.8	19.3	18.4	16.4	14.6	13.0
	12	23.7	23.5	23.3	23.0	22.7	22.3	21.9	21.5	20.6	18.6	16.7	15.0

See page 3-26 for more details regarding these tables.

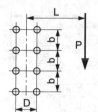

$$C = \frac{P_f}{V_r}, \text{ or } \frac{P}{V_s}$$

D = 320 mm												Bolts per Vertical Row	Pitch b mm
Moment Arm, L, mm													
75	100	125	150	175	200	225	250	300	400	500	600		
1.36	1.23	1.12	1.03	0.95	0.89	0.83	0.78	0.69	0.57	0.48	0.42	1	
2.89	2.63	2.41	2.22	2.06	1.91	1.79	1.68	1.50	1.22	1.04	0.90	2	
4.56	4.16	3.82	3.53	3.27	3.04	2.85	2.67	2.38	1.95	1.65	1.43	3	
6.37	5.86	5.40	5.00	4.65	4.34	4.07	3.82	3.41	2.79	2.36	2.04	4	
8.30	7.69	7.12	6.62	6.17	5.76	5.40	5.08	4.53	3.72	3.15	2.73	5	
10.3	9.62	8.97	8.37	7.82	7.33	6.89	6.49	5.80	4.77	4.04	3.50	6	
12.4	11.6	10.9	10.2	9.59	9.01	8.49	8.01	7.17	5.91	5.01	4.34	7	80
14.4	13.7	12.9	12.2	11.5	10.8	10.2	9.65	8.67	7.17	6.08	5.27	8	
16.5	15.8	15.0	14.2	13.4	12.7	12.0	11.4	10.3	8.52	7.24	6.28	9	
18.6	17.9	17.1	16.3	15.4	14.7	13.9	13.2	12.0	9.97	8.50	7.38	10	
20.7	20.0	19.2	18.4	17.5	16.7	15.9	15.1	13.8	11.5	9.84	8.55	11	
22.8	22.1	21.3	20.5	19.6	18.8	17.9	17.1	15.6	13.2	11.3	9.81	12	
2.92	2.66	2.44	2.25	2.08	1.94	1.82	1.70	1.52	1.24	1.05	0.91	2	
4.63	4.24	3.90	3.60	3.34	3.11	2.91	2.74	2.44	2.00	1.69	1.47	3	
6.50	6.00	5.55	5.15	4.79	4.48	4.20	3.95	3.52	2.89	2.44	2.11	4	
8.48	7.89	7.34	6.84	6.38	5.97	5.61	5.28	4.71	3.87	3.28	2.84	5	
10.5	9.88	9.25	8.66	8.12	7.63	7.18	6.77	6.07	5.00	4.23	3.66	6	
12.6	11.9	11.3	10.6	9.98	9.40	8.87	8.39	7.53	6.22	5.28	4.57	7	90
14.7	14.0	13.3	12.6	11.9	11.3	10.7	10.1	9.13	7.58	6.44	5.59	8	
16.8	16.1	15.4	14.7	14.0	13.3	12.6	12.0	10.8	9.03	7.69	6.68	9	
18.9	18.2	17.5	16.8	16.0	15.3	14.6	13.9	12.7	10.6	9.06	7.88	10	
20.9	20.3	19.6	18.9	18.1	17.4	16.6	15.9	14.6	12.3	10.5	9.16	11	
23.0	22.4	21.8	21.0	20.3	19.5	18.7	18.0	16.5	14.0	12.1	10.5	12	
2.95	2.69	2.47	2.28	2.11	1.97	1.84	1.73	1.54	1.26	1.06	0.92	2	
4.71	4.32	3.98	3.68	3.41	3.18	2.98	2.80	2.49	2.05	1.73	1.50	3	
6.63	6.14	5.69	5.29	4.93	4.61	4.32	4.07	3.63	2.98	2.52	2.18	4	
8.65	8.08	7.55	7.05	6.60	6.18	5.81	5.47	4.90	4.03	3.41	2.96	5	
10.7	10.1	9.52	8.95	8.41	7.92	7.46	7.05	6.33	5.23	4.43	3.84	6	
12.8	12.2	11.6	10.9	10.3	9.78	9.25	8.76	7.89	6.53	5.55	4.81	7	100
14.9	14.3	13.7	13.0	12.4	11.7	11.1	10.6	9.59	7.99	6.80	5.91	8	
17.0	16.4	15.8	15.1	14.4	13.8	13.1	12.5	11.4	9.55	8.15	7.09	9	
19.1	18.5	17.9	17.2	16.5	15.9	15.2	14.5	13.3	11.2	9.62	8.39	10	
21.1	20.6	20.0	19.4	18.7	18.0	17.3	16.6	15.3	13.0	11.2	9.78	11	
23.2	22.7	22.1	21.5	20.8	20.1	19.4	18.7	17.3	14.9	12.9	11.3	12	
3.02	2.76	2.54	2.34	2.17	2.03	1.90	1.78	1.59	1.30	1.10	0.95	2	
4.86	4.48	4.14	3.84	3.57	3.33	3.12	2.93	2.61	2.14	1.82	1.57	3	
6.86	6.40	5.96	5.57	5.20	4.88	4.59	4.32	3.87	3.18	2.69	2.33	4	
8.93	8.43	7.93	7.45	7.01	6.59	6.21	5.87	5.26	4.34	3.68	3.19	5	
11.0	10.5	9.99	9.46	8.95	8.47	8.02	7.60	6.85	5.69	4.84	4.19	6	
13.1	12.6	12.1	11.5	11.0	10.5	9.94	9.46	8.58	7.16	6.10	5.30	7	120
15.2	14.7	14.2	13.7	13.1	12.5	12.0	11.4	10.4	8.79	7.53	6.56	8	
17.3	16.8	16.3	15.8	15.2	14.6	14.1	13.5	12.4	10.5	9.07	7.91	9	
19.3	18.9	18.4	17.9	17.4	16.8	16.2	15.6	14.4	12.4	10.7	9.40	10	
21.4	21.0	20.5	20.0	19.5	18.9	18.3	17.7	16.5	14.3	12.5	11.0	11	
23.4	23.1	22.6	22.2	21.6	21.1	20.5	19.9	18.7	16.3	14.3	12.7	12	
3.15	2.90	2.67	2.48	2.30	2.15	2.02	1.90	1.69	1.38	1.17	1.01	2	
5.13	4.78	4.45	4.15	3.88	3.63	3.40	3.20	2.86	2.35	1.99	1.73	3	
7.21	6.83	6.45	6.07	5.72	5.40	5.09	4.82	4.34	3.59	3.04	2.64	4	
9.31	8.93	8.53	8.12	7.72	7.33	6.96	6.61	5.99	4.98	4.24	3.68	5	
11.4	11.0	10.7	10.2	9.81	9.39	8.98	8.58	7.83	6.60	5.65	4.93	6	
13.5	13.1	12.8	12.4	11.9	11.5	11.1	10.6	9.81	8.36	7.21	6.30	7	160
15.5	15.2	14.9	14.5	14.1	13.7	13.2	12.8	11.9	10.3	8.93	7.84	8	
17.6	17.3	17.0	16.6	16.2	15.8	15.4	14.9	14.0	12.3	10.8	9.51	9	
19.6	19.4	19.1	18.7	18.4	17.9	17.5	17.1	16.2	14.3	12.7	11.3	10	
21.6	21.4	21.1	20.8	20.5	20.1	19.7	19.2	18.3	16.5	14.7	13.2	11	
23.6	23.4	23.2	22.9	22.6	22.2	21.8	21.4	20.5	18.6	16.8	15.1	12	

See page 3-26 for more details regarding these tables.

ECCENTRIC LOADS ON BOLT GROUPS
Coefficients C

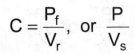

$$C = \frac{P_f}{V_r}, \ \text{or} \ \frac{P}{V_s}$$

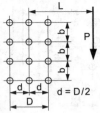

Table 3-17

Pitch b mm	Bolts per Vertical Row	D = 160 mm											
		Moment Arm, L, mm											
		75	100	125	150	175	200	225	250	300	400	500	600
	1	1.49	1.28	1.11	0.98	0.87	0.77	0.69	0.63	0.53	0.40	0.32	0.27
	2	3.57	3.06	2.67	2.35	2.10	1.89	1.72	1.57	1.34	1.03	0.83	0.70
	3	6.06	5.24	4.60	4.09	3.67	3.32	3.03	2.78	2.38	1.83	1.49	1.25
	4	8.98	7.92	7.02	6.27	5.65	5.13	4.69	4.31	3.70	2.87	2.34	1.97
	5	12.1	10.9	9.73	8.76	7.93	7.22	6.62	6.11	5.28	4.11	3.36	2.83
	6	15.3	14.0	12.7	11.6	10.5	9.66	8.90	8.23	7.13	5.59	4.57	3.86
80	7	18.5	17.2	15.9	14.6	13.4	12.3	11.4	10.6	9.20	7.26	5.96	5.04
	8	21.7	20.4	19.1	17.7	16.4	15.2	14.1	13.2	11.5	9.15	7.54	6.39
	9	24.9	23.7	22.3	20.9	19.6	18.3	17.1	16.0	14.1	11.2	9.27	7.88
	10	28.1	26.9	25.6	24.2	22.8	21.4	20.1	18.9	16.8	13.5	11.2	9.53
	11	31.2	30.1	28.8	27.4	26.0	24.6	23.3	22.0	19.6	15.9	13.3	11.3
	12	34.3	33.3	32.1	30.7	29.3	27.9	26.5	25.1	22.6	18.5	15.5	13.3
	2	3.68	3.17	2.76	2.44	2.18	1.96	1.78	1.63	1.39	1.07	0.87	0.73
	3	6.31	5.49	4.83	4.29	3.86	3.50	3.19	2.93	2.51	1.94	1.58	1.32
	4	9.35	8.31	7.41	6.65	6.01	5.47	5.00	4.61	3.96	3.08	2.51	2.12
	5	12.5	11.4	10.3	9.32	8.47	7.73	7.10	6.56	5.68	4.45	3.64	3.07
	6	15.8	14.6	13.4	12.3	11.3	10.4	9.57	8.87	7.71	6.07	4.98	4.21
90	7	19.0	17.8	16.6	15.4	14.3	13.2	12.3	11.4	9.98	7.90	6.51	5.52
	8	22.2	21.1	19.8	18.6	17.4	16.2	15.2	14.2	12.5	9.99	8.26	7.01
	9	25.3	24.3	23.1	21.9	20.6	19.4	18.2	17.1	15.2	12.3	10.2	8.66
	10	28.4	27.5	26.3	25.1	23.9	22.6	21.4	20.2	18.1	14.7	12.3	10.5
	11	31.6	30.7	29.6	28.4	27.1	25.9	24.6	23.4	21.1	17.3	14.6	12.5
	12	34.7	33.8	32.8	31.6	30.4	29.2	27.9	26.6	24.2	20.1	17.0	14.6
	2	3.80	3.28	2.86	2.53	2.26	2.04	1.86	1.70	1.45	1.12	0.91	0.76
	3	6.55	5.73	5.05	4.50	4.05	3.68	3.36	3.09	2.65	2.06	1.67	1.40
	4	9.67	8.68	7.79	7.01	6.36	5.80	5.32	4.90	4.23	3.30	2.69	2.27
	5	12.9	11.8	10.8	9.83	8.98	8.24	7.58	7.01	6.08	4.78	3.92	3.31
	6	16.1	15.1	14.0	12.9	11.9	11.0	10.2	9.49	8.29	6.55	5.39	4.57
100	7	19.3	18.3	17.2	16.1	15.0	14.0	13.1	12.2	10.7	8.55	7.06	6.00
	8	22.5	21.5	20.5	19.3	18.2	17.1	16.1	15.1	13.4	10.8	8.97	7.64
	9	25.6	24.7	23.7	22.6	21.5	20.4	19.3	18.2	16.3	13.3	11.1	9.44
	10	28.7	27.9	26.9	25.9	24.8	23.6	22.5	21.4	19.3	15.9	13.3	11.4
	11	31.8	31.1	30.1	29.1	28.0	26.9	25.7	24.6	22.4	18.7	15.8	13.6
	12	34.9	34.2	33.3	32.4	31.3	30.2	29.0	27.9	25.6	21.6	18.4	15.9
	2	4.02	3.49	3.07	2.72	2.44	2.20	2.01	1.84	1.58	1.22	0.99	0.83
	3	6.98	6.19	5.50	4.91	4.43	4.03	3.70	3.41	2.94	2.29	1.86	1.57
	4	10.2	9.31	8.47	7.70	7.03	6.44	5.94	5.49	4.76	3.73	3.05	2.58
	5	13.4	12.5	11.6	10.7	9.92	9.17	8.50	7.90	6.89	5.44	4.48	3.80
	6	16.6	15.8	14.9	14.0	13.0	12.2	11.4	10.7	9.39	7.50	6.21	5.27
120	7	19.8	19.0	18.1	17.2	16.3	15.4	14.5	13.6	12.1	9.80	8.15	6.95
	8	22.9	22.2	21.4	20.5	19.5	18.6	17.7	16.8	15.1	12.4	10.4	8.86
	9	26.0	25.4	24.6	23.7	22.8	21.9	20.9	20.0	18.2	15.1	12.8	11.0
	10	29.1	28.5	27.8	27.0	26.1	25.2	24.2	23.2	21.4	18.0	15.3	13.3
	11	32.1	31.6	30.9	30.2	29.3	28.4	27.5	26.5	24.6	21.0	18.1	15.7
	12	35.2	34.7	34.1	33.4	32.6	31.7	30.8	29.8	27.9	24.2	21.0	18.3
	2	4.42	3.91	3.47	3.11	2.80	2.54	2.33	2.14	1.84	1.43	1.16	0.98
	3	7.61	6.95	6.31	5.72	5.20	4.75	4.37	4.04	3.50	2.75	2.25	1.90
	4	10.9	10.2	9.52	8.84	8.20	7.61	7.08	6.60	5.79	4.59	3.79	3.21
	5	14.0	13.5	12.8	12.1	11.4	10.7	10.1	9.47	8.39	6.75	5.59	4.76
	6	17.2	16.6	16.0	15.4	14.7	14.0	13.3	12.6	11.3	9.29	7.78	6.66
160	7	20.3	19.8	19.2	18.6	17.9	17.2	16.5	15.8	14.4	12.1	10.2	8.80
	8	23.3	22.9	22.4	21.8	21.2	20.5	19.8	19.1	17.7	15.0	12.9	11.2
	9	26.4	26.0	25.6	25.0	24.4	23.8	23.1	22.4	20.9	18.2	15.8	13.8
	10	29.4	29.1	28.7	28.2	27.6	27.0	26.4	25.7	24.2	21.4	18.8	16.5
	11	32.5	32.2	31.8	31.3	30.8	30.2	29.6	28.9	27.5	24.6	21.9	19.5
	12	35.5	35.2	34.9	34.4	33.9	33.4	32.8	32.2	30.8	27.9	25.1	22.5

See page 3-26 for more details regarding these tables.

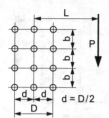

$$C = \frac{P_f}{V_r}, \text{ or } \frac{P}{V_s}$$

D = 320 mm												Bolts per Vertical Row	Pitch b mm
Moment Arm, L, mm													
75	100	125	150	175	200	225	250	300	400	500	600		
1.98	1.79	1.63	1.49	1.38	1.28	1.19	1.11	0.98	0.77	0.63	0.53	1	
4.21	3.81	3.47	3.18	2.93	2.71	2.52	2.35	2.07	1.65	1.36	1.15	2	
6.67	6.05	5.52	5.06	4.68	4.34	4.04	3.77	3.32	2.66	2.20	1.87	3	
9.39	8.57	7.85	7.23	6.68	6.20	5.78	5.41	4.77	3.84	3.19	2.72	4	
12.3	11.3	10.4	9.61	8.90	8.28	7.74	7.25	6.42	5.18	4.32	3.69	5	
15.3	14.2	13.2	12.2	11.4	10.6	9.93	9.32	8.27	6.70	5.60	4.79	6	
18.4	17.3	16.1	15.0	14.0	13.1	12.3	11.6	10.3	8.39	7.03	6.03	7	80
21.6	20.4	19.2	18.0	16.9	15.9	14.9	14.0	12.5	10.3	8.61	7.40	8	
24.8	23.6	22.3	21.1	19.9	18.7	17.7	16.7	14.9	12.3	10.3	8.90	9	
27.9	26.7	25.5	24.2	22.9	21.7	20.6	19.5	17.5	14.5	12.2	10.5	10	
31.0	29.9	28.7	27.4	26.1	24.8	23.6	22.4	20.2	16.8	14.2	12.3	11	
34.2	33.1	31.9	30.6	29.3	27.9	26.6	25.4	23.1	19.3	16.4	14.2	12	
4.26	3.86	3.51	3.22	2.97	2.75	2.55	2.38	2.10	1.67	1.38	1.17	2	
6.80	6.17	5.64	5.18	4.79	4.44	4.14	3.87	3.41	2.74	2.27	1.93	3	
9.61	8.80	8.09	7.46	6.90	6.42	5.98	5.60	4.95	3.99	3.32	2.83	4	
12.6	11.7	10.8	9.98	9.26	8.62	8.06	7.56	6.71	5.43	4.53	3.88	5	
15.7	14.7	13.7	12.7	11.9	11.1	10.4	9.78	8.70	7.07	5.92	5.07	6	
18.8	17.8	16.7	15.7	14.7	13.8	13.0	12.2	10.9	8.90	7.48	6.42	7	90
22.0	21.0	19.8	18.7	17.7	16.6	15.7	14.8	13.3	10.9	9.20	7.92	8	
25.2	24.1	23.0	21.9	20.7	19.6	18.6	17.6	15.9	13.1	11.1	9.56	9	
28.3	27.3	26.2	25.1	23.9	22.7	21.6	20.6	18.6	15.5	13.1	11.4	10	
31.4	30.5	29.4	28.3	27.1	25.9	24.7	23.6	21.5	18.0	15.3	13.3	11	
34.5	33.6	32.6	31.5	30.3	29.1	27.9	26.7	24.5	20.7	17.7	15.4	12	
4.31	3.91	3.56	3.27	3.01	2.79	2.59	2.42	2.13	1.70	1.40	1.19	2	
6.93	6.31	5.76	5.30	4.90	4.55	4.24	3.97	3.50	2.81	2.34	1.99	3	
9.82	9.03	8.32	7.69	7.13	6.63	6.19	5.80	5.13	4.14	3.45	2.95	4	
12.9	12.0	11.1	10.3	9.61	8.97	8.39	7.87	7.00	5.68	4.75	4.07	5	
16.0	15.1	14.1	13.2	12.4	11.6	10.9	10.2	9.13	7.44	6.25	5.36	6	
19.2	18.2	17.2	16.2	15.3	14.4	13.6	12.8	11.5	9.40	7.92	6.82	7	100
22.3	21.4	20.4	19.4	18.4	17.4	16.4	15.6	14.0	11.6	9.79	8.44	8	
25.5	24.6	23.6	22.6	21.5	20.5	19.5	18.5	16.8	13.9	11.8	10.2	9	
28.6	27.7	26.8	25.8	24.7	23.6	22.6	21.6	19.7	16.5	14.0	12.2	10	
31.7	30.9	30.0	29.0	27.9	26.9	25.8	24.7	22.7	19.2	16.4	14.3	11	
34.8	34.0	33.2	32.2	31.2	30.1	29.0	27.9	25.8	22.0	18.9	16.5	12	
4.42	4.01	3.66	3.36	3.10	2.87	2.67	2.49	2.20	1.76	1.45	1.23	2	
7.18	6.57	6.02	5.55	5.13	4.77	4.45	4.17	3.69	2.98	2.48	2.11	3	
10.2	9.47	8.78	8.15	7.58	7.07	6.61	6.21	5.51	4.46	3.73	3.19	4	
13.3	12.5	11.8	11.0	10.3	9.64	9.05	8.51	7.59	6.20	5.20	4.47	5	
16.5	15.7	14.9	14.0	13.2	12.5	11.8	11.1	9.98	8.19	6.91	5.95	6	
19.6	18.9	18.1	17.2	16.3	15.5	14.7	14.0	12.6	10.4	8.82	7.62	7	120
22.8	22.1	21.3	20.4	19.5	18.6	17.8	17.0	15.4	12.9	11.0	9.49	8	
25.9	25.2	24.5	23.6	22.7	21.8	20.9	20.1	18.4	15.5	13.3	11.5	9	
29.0	28.4	27.6	26.8	26.0	25.1	24.2	23.3	21.5	18.3	15.8	13.8	10	
32.0	31.5	30.8	30.0	29.2	28.3	27.4	26.5	24.7	21.3	18.4	16.2	11	
35.1	34.6	34.0	33.2	32.4	31.6	30.7	29.7	27.9	24.3	21.2	18.7	12	
4.64	4.23	3.88	3.57	3.30	3.07	2.86	2.67	2.35	1.89	1.57	1.34	2	
7.63	7.07	6.54	6.06	5.63	5.24	4.90	4.60	4.09	3.32	2.78	2.38	3	
10.8	10.2	9.57	8.99	8.43	7.92	7.45	7.02	6.27	5.13	4.31	3.70	4	
13.9	13.4	12.7	12.1	11.5	10.9	10.3	9.74	8.76	7.22	6.11	5.28	5	
17.1	16.6	16.0	15.3	14.6	14.0	13.3	12.7	11.6	9.67	8.23	7.13	6	
20.2	19.7	19.1	18.5	17.9	17.2	16.5	15.8	14.6	12.3	10.6	9.20	7	160
23.3	22.8	22.3	21.7	21.1	20.4	19.8	19.1	17.7	15.2	13.2	11.5	8	
26.3	25.9	25.5	24.9	24.3	23.7	23.0	22.3	20.9	18.3	16.0	14.1	9	
29.4	29.0	28.6	28.1	27.5	26.9	26.3	25.6	24.2	21.4	18.9	16.8	10	
32.4	32.1	31.7	31.2	30.7	30.1	29.5	28.8	27.4	24.6	22.0	19.6	11	
35.5	35.2	34.8	34.3	33.8	33.3	32.7	32.1	30.7	27.9	25.1	22.6	12	

See page 3-26 for more details regarding these tables.

$$C = \frac{P_f}{V_r}, \text{ or } \frac{P}{V_s}$$

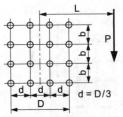

Table 3-19

Pitch b mm	Bolts per Vertical Row	D = 240 mm											
		Moment Arm, L, mm											
		75	100	125	150	175	200	225	250	300	400	500	600
80	1	2.33	2.04	1.79	1.58	1.41	1.27	1.15	1.05	0.90	0.70	0.57	0.48
	2	5.14	4.52	4.00	3.58	3.22	2.92	2.67	2.46	2.11	1.64	1.34	1.13
	3	8.40	7.43	6.65	5.98	5.42	4.94	4.53	4.17	3.59	2.80	2.28	1.93
	4	12.1	10.9	9.77	8.84	8.05	7.37	6.78	6.27	5.43	4.25	3.48	2.94
	5	16.2	14.6	13.3	12.1	11.0	10.2	9.38	8.70	7.57	5.96	4.89	4.14
	6	20.3	18.7	17.1	15.7	14.4	13.3	12.3	11.5	10.0	7.94	6.54	5.54
	7	24.6	22.9	21.2	19.6	18.1	16.8	15.6	14.5	12.8	10.2	8.41	7.14
	8	28.9	27.2	25.4	23.7	22.0	20.5	19.2	17.9	15.8	12.7	10.5	8.94
	9	33.1	31.5	29.7	27.9	26.1	24.5	23.0	21.6	19.1	15.4	12.8	10.9
	10	37.3	35.7	34.0	32.2	30.4	28.6	26.9	25.4	22.6	18.4	15.4	13.1
	11	41.5	40.0	38.3	36.5	34.6	32.8	31.1	29.4	26.4	21.6	18.1	15.5
	12	45.7	44.2	42.6	40.8	39.0	37.1	35.3	33.5	30.3	25.0	21.0	18.1
90	2	5.24	4.61	4.09	3.66	3.31	3.00	2.75	2.53	2.17	1.69	1.38	1.16
	3	8.65	7.67	6.87	6.20	5.63	5.14	4.72	4.35	3.76	2.93	2.39	2.02
	4	12.5	11.3	10.2	9.26	8.45	7.75	7.14	6.61	5.74	4.51	3.70	3.13
	5	16.7	15.2	13.9	12.7	11.6	10.7	9.93	9.23	8.05	6.36	5.23	4.43
	6	20.9	19.4	17.9	16.5	15.3	14.1	13.1	12.2	10.7	8.54	7.05	5.98
	7	25.2	23.7	22.1	20.6	19.1	17.8	16.6	15.5	13.7	11.0	9.10	7.74
	8	29.4	28.0	26.4	24.8	23.2	21.8	20.4	19.2	17.0	13.7	11.4	9.73
	9	33.6	32.2	30.7	29.1	27.5	25.9	24.4	23.0	20.5	16.7	13.9	11.9
	10	37.8	36.5	35.0	33.4	31.8	30.1	28.6	27.0	24.3	19.9	16.7	14.3
	11	42.0	40.7	39.3	37.7	36.1	34.4	32.8	31.2	28.3	23.4	19.7	17.0
	12	46.1	45.0	43.6	42.1	40.4	38.8	37.1	35.5	32.3	27.0	22.9	19.8
100	2	5.35	4.71	4.19	3.76	3.39	3.08	2.82	2.60	2.24	1.74	1.42	1.20
	3	8.89	7.92	7.11	6.43	5.85	5.35	4.92	4.54	3.92	3.06	2.50	2.11
	4	12.9	11.7	10.6	9.66	8.84	8.13	7.50	6.96	6.05	4.77	3.92	3.31
	5	17.1	15.8	14.5	13.3	12.2	11.3	10.5	9.75	8.54	6.78	5.58	4.73
	6	21.4	20.0	18.6	17.3	16.0	14.9	13.9	13.0	11.4	9.13	7.55	6.42
	7	25.6	24.3	22.9	21.5	20.1	18.8	17.6	16.5	14.6	11.8	9.79	8.35
	8	29.9	28.6	27.2	25.7	24.3	22.9	21.6	20.3	18.1	14.7	12.3	10.5
	9	34.0	32.9	31.5	30.1	28.6	27.1	25.7	24.3	21.9	17.9	15.1	12.9
	10	38.2	37.1	35.8	34.4	32.9	31.4	30.0	28.5	25.8	21.4	18.1	15.5
	11	42.3	41.3	40.1	38.7	37.3	35.8	34.3	32.8	29.9	25.1	21.3	18.4
	12	46.4	45.5	44.3	43.0	41.6	40.1	38.6	37.1	34.2	28.9	24.7	21.4
120	2	5.56	4.93	4.40	3.95	3.58	3.26	2.99	2.76	2.38	1.86	1.52	1.28
	3	9.36	8.41	7.58	6.87	6.27	5.76	5.31	4.92	4.26	3.34	2.74	2.31
	4	13.5	12.4	11.4	10.4	9.61	8.87	8.22	7.65	6.68	5.30	4.36	3.70
	5	17.8	16.7	15.5	14.4	13.4	12.4	11.6	10.8	9.49	7.60	6.29	5.34
	6	22.1	21.0	19.8	18.6	17.4	16.3	15.3	14.4	12.8	10.3	8.57	7.31
	7	26.3	25.3	24.1	22.9	21.7	20.5	19.3	18.3	16.3	13.3	11.1	9.55
	8	30.4	29.5	28.4	27.2	26.0	24.8	23.6	22.4	20.2	16.7	14.0	12.1
	9	34.6	33.7	32.7	31.6	30.4	29.1	27.9	26.6	24.3	20.3	17.2	14.8
	10	38.7	37.9	36.9	35.9	34.7	33.5	32.2	30.9	28.5	24.1	20.6	17.9
	11	42.8	42.1	41.2	40.1	39.0	37.8	36.6	35.3	32.8	28.1	24.2	21.1
	12	46.9	46.2	45.4	44.4	43.3	42.2	40.9	39.7	37.1	32.2	28.0	24.6
160	2	5.98	5.36	4.82	4.36	3.97	3.63	3.34	3.09	2.68	2.10	1.72	1.46
	3	10.1	9.28	8.49	7.76	7.12	6.57	6.08	5.66	4.95	3.92	3.22	2.73
	4	14.4	13.6	12.7	11.8	11.0	10.3	9.58	8.97	7.92	6.35	5.27	4.49
	5	18.6	17.9	17.0	16.1	15.2	14.3	13.5	12.7	11.3	9.19	7.68	6.57
	6	22.8	22.1	21.3	20.4	19.5	18.6	17.7	16.8	15.2	12.5	10.6	9.07
	7	27.0	26.3	25.6	24.8	23.9	22.9	22.0	21.1	19.3	16.2	13.7	11.9
	8	31.1	30.5	29.8	29.0	28.2	27.3	26.4	25.4	23.5	20.1	17.3	15.0
	9	35.2	34.6	34.0	33.3	32.5	31.6	30.7	29.8	27.9	24.2	21.1	18.5
	10	39.2	38.8	38.2	37.5	36.8	35.9	35.1	34.1	32.2	28.5	25.0	22.1
	11	43.3	42.8	42.3	41.7	41.0	40.2	39.4	38.5	36.6	32.8	29.2	26.0
	12	47.3	46.9	46.4	45.8	45.2	44.5	43.7	42.8	41.0	37.2	33.4	30.0

See page 3-26 for more details regarding these tables.

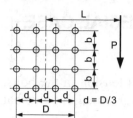

$$C = \frac{P_f}{V_r}, \text{ or } \frac{P}{V_s}$$

D = 480 mm												Bolts per Vertical Row	Pitch b mm
Moment Arm, L, mm													
75	100	125	150	175	200	225	250	300	400	500	600		
2.91	2.70	2.50	2.33	2.18	2.04	1.91	1.79	1.58	1.27	1.05	0.90	1	
6.01	5.56	5.16	4.81	4.49	4.20	3.94	3.70	3.29	2.66	2.22	1.90	2	
9.31	8.61	8.01	7.48	6.99	6.56	6.16	5.80	5.17	4.20	3.52	3.01	3	
12.8	11.9	11.1	10.4	9.73	9.13	8.59	8.10	7.25	5.93	4.98	4.27	4	
16.6	15.5	14.4	13.5	12.7	11.9	11.3	10.6	9.54	7.84	6.60	5.68	5	
20.5	19.2	18.0	16.9	15.9	15.0	14.2	13.4	12.1	9.95	8.41	7.25	6	
24.5	23.2	21.8	20.5	19.4	18.3	17.3	16.4	14.8	12.3	10.4	8.98	7	80
28.7	27.2	25.7	24.3	23.0	21.8	20.6	19.6	17.7	14.8	12.5	10.9	8	
32.8	31.3	29.8	28.3	26.8	25.5	24.2	23.0	20.8	17.4	14.9	12.9	9	
37.0	35.5	33.9	32.3	30.8	29.3	27.9	26.6	24.2	20.3	17.4	15.1	10	
41.2	39.7	38.1	36.5	34.9	33.3	31.8	30.3	27.7	23.4	20.1	17.5	11	
45.3	43.9	42.3	40.7	39.0	37.4	35.8	34.2	31.4	26.6	22.9	20.0	12	
6.05	5.60	5.20	4.84	4.52	4.23	3.97	3.73	3.32	2.69	2.25	1.92	2	
9.42	8.72	8.12	7.58	7.09	6.65	6.25	5.89	5.26	4.28	3.59	3.07	3	
13.1	12.1	11.3	10.6	9.94	9.34	8.79	8.30	7.43	6.09	5.12	4.41	4	
16.9	15.8	14.8	13.9	13.0	12.3	11.6	11.0	9.85	8.12	6.85	5.90	5	
20.9	19.7	18.5	17.4	16.4	15.5	14.7	13.9	12.5	10.4	8.78	7.58	6	
25.0	23.7	22.4	21.2	20.0	18.9	17.9	17.0	15.4	12.8	10.9	9.44	7	90
29.2	27.8	26.5	25.1	23.8	22.6	21.5	20.4	18.5	15.5	13.2	11.5	8	
33.4	32.0	30.6	29.2	27.8	26.5	25.2	24.0	21.9	18.4	15.7	13.7	9	
37.5	36.2	34.8	33.4	31.9	30.5	29.1	27.8	25.4	21.5	18.5	16.1	10	
41.7	40.4	39.0	37.6	36.1	34.6	33.2	31.8	29.1	24.7	21.3	18.7	11	
45.8	44.6	43.3	41.8	40.3	38.8	37.3	35.8	33.0	28.2	24.4	21.4	12	
6.09	5.64	5.24	4.88	4.56	4.27	4.00	3.77	3.35	2.72	2.27	1.95	2	
9.53	8.84	8.22	7.68	7.20	6.75	6.36	5.99	5.35	4.37	3.66	3.14	3	
13.3	12.4	11.6	10.8	10.1	9.55	9.00	8.50	7.62	6.26	5.28	4.54	4	
17.2	16.1	15.1	14.2	13.4	12.6	11.9	11.3	10.2	8.40	7.11	6.13	5	
21.3	20.1	19.0	17.9	16.9	16.0	15.1	14.4	13.0	10.8	9.16	7.92	6	
25.4	24.2	23.0	21.8	20.7	19.6	18.6	17.7	16.0	13.4	11.4	9.91	7	100
29.6	28.4	27.1	25.9	24.6	23.5	22.3	21.3	19.4	16.3	13.9	12.1	8	
33.8	32.6	31.3	30.0	28.7	27.4	26.2	25.0	22.9	19.3	16.6	14.5	9	
37.9	36.8	35.6	34.2	32.9	31.6	30.3	29.0	26.6	22.6	19.5	17.1	10	
42.1	41.0	39.8	38.5	37.1	35.8	34.4	33.1	30.5	26.1	22.6	19.8	11	
46.2	45.2	44.0	42.7	41.4	40.0	38.6	37.2	34.5	29.8	25.9	22.8	12	
6.18	5.72	5.32	4.96	4.63	4.34	4.08	3.84	3.42	2.78	2.33	2.00	2	
9.76	9.08	8.46	7.92	7.42	6.97	6.57	6.20	5.55	4.55	3.82	3.28	3	
13.6	12.8	12.0	11.3	10.6	9.98	9.42	8.91	8.02	6.62	5.59	4.83	4	
17.7	16.8	15.8	14.9	14.1	13.3	12.6	11.9	10.8	8.98	7.63	6.60	5	
21.9	20.9	19.9	18.9	17.9	17.0	16.1	15.3	13.9	11.6	9.93	8.62	6	
26.1	25.1	24.0	22.9	21.9	20.9	19.9	19.0	17.3	14.6	12.5	10.9	7	120
30.2	29.3	28.2	27.1	26.0	24.9	23.9	22.8	20.9	17.7	15.3	13.4	8	
34.4	33.5	32.5	31.4	30.2	29.1	28.0	26.9	24.8	21.2	18.3	16.1	9	
38.5	37.7	36.7	35.6	34.5	33.4	32.2	31.0	28.8	24.8	21.6	19.0	10	
42.6	41.8	40.9	39.9	38.8	37.6	36.5	35.3	32.9	28.6	25.1	22.1	11	
46.7	46.0	45.1	44.1	43.1	41.9	40.7	39.6	37.2	32.6	28.7	25.4	12	
6.36	5.91	5.51	5.14	4.81	4.52	4.25	4.00	3.58	2.92	2.46	2.11	2	
10.2	9.56	8.95	8.39	7.89	7.44	7.02	6.65	5.98	4.94	4.17	3.59	3	
14.3	13.6	12.8	12.1	11.5	10.9	10.3	9.78	8.84	7.37	6.27	5.43	4	
18.5	17.7	17.0	16.2	15.4	14.6	13.9	13.3	12.1	10.2	8.69	7.57	5	
22.7	22.0	21.2	20.3	19.5	18.7	17.9	17.1	15.7	13.3	11.5	10.0	6	
26.8	26.2	25.4	24.6	23.7	22.9	22.0	21.2	19.6	16.8	14.5	12.8	7	160
30.9	30.3	29.6	28.9	28.0	27.2	26.3	25.4	23.7	20.5	17.9	15.8	8	
35.0	34.5	33.8	33.1	32.3	31.4	30.6	29.7	27.9	24.5	21.6	19.1	9	
39.1	38.6	38.0	37.3	36.6	35.7	34.9	34.0	32.2	28.6	25.4	22.6	10	
43.2	42.7	42.1	41.5	40.8	40.0	39.2	38.3	36.5	32.8	29.4	26.4	11	
47.2	46.8	46.3	45.7	45.0	44.2	43.4	42.6	40.8	37.1	33.5	30.3	12	

See page 3-26 for more details regarding these tables.

ECCENTRIC LOAD ON BOLT GROUPS — SPECIAL CASE

High-Strength Bolts

For connections where the eccentric load causes both shear and tension in the bolts, the following design method may be used when the fasteners are high-strength bolts that have been tightened to the specified minimum initial tension.

A bracket connected by means of bolts with an initial tension T_i is shown below. Both simple and unwieldy methods are available for determining tension that is applied to the upper bolts by the load on the bracket. Generally, the simpler solutions are considerably more conservative than the more accurate but unwieldy ones. The solution presented here is easy to use and conservative.

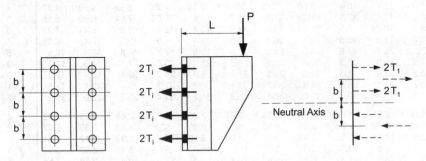

A neutral axis is assumed through the centre of gravity of the bolt group. Those bolts above the axis are said to carry the tension while those below are considered to be in "compression", so that the applied moment is resisted by a couple applied at the resultants of the upper and the lower bolts. The upper bolts are all taken to be equally loaded; this plastic stress distribution is justified by results that are still conservative compared to more precise methods.

Bolt tension from the applied moment is therefore:

$$T_1 = \frac{PL}{n' d_m}$$

n' = number of bolts above the neutral axis

d_m = moment arm between resultants of the tensile and compressive forces.

Bolt shear from the applied load is:

$$V = \frac{P}{n}$$

Fasteners in the top half of the connection are subjected to tension, from both the applied moment and from prying (if any), and shear. Bolts in the bottom half are subjected to shear only, with top and bottom bolts participating equally.

The connection should be proportioned so that the bolt tension T_1 due to the moment PL (plus bolt tension due to prying), when combined with the bolt shear, meets the requirements of CSA S16-09 for bolts subjected to combined shear and tension. The relevant clauses are 13.12.1.4 for bearing-type connections and 13.12.2.3 for slip-critical connections.

Example 1

Given:

Check the adequacy of eight M20, A325M bolts (2 rows of 4, at 80 mm pitch) for the connection shown on page 3-36 for a factored load P of 300 kN at an eccentricity L of 150 mm. Assume the material thickness is adequate so that prying action on the bolts is not significant.

Solution:

Factored tension in one bolt:

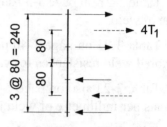

$$T_1 = \frac{P_f L}{n' d_m} = \frac{300 \times 150}{4(2 \times 80)} = 70.3 \text{ kN}$$

$$< 156 \text{ kN} \quad (\text{Table 3-4})$$

Factored shear in one bolt:

$$V_f = \frac{P_f}{n} = \frac{300}{8} = 37.5 \text{ kN} \quad < 125 \text{ kN} \quad (\text{Table 3-4})$$

Check combined shear and tension for $V_f / T_f = 37.5 / 70.3 = 0.53$

From Table 3-8 on page 3-13, for bearing-type connections,

permissible $V_f = 69.0$ kN (by interpolation) > 37.5 kN

and permissible $T_f = 131$ kN (by interpolation) > 70.3 kN

Example 2

Given:

Determine the number of M20, A325M bolts required to design the connection in Example 1 as a slip-critical connection for a specified load of 200 kN. Assume clean mill scale faying surfaces.

Solution:

Try 10 bolts (2 rows of 5, at 80 mm pitch)

Specified tension in one bolt:

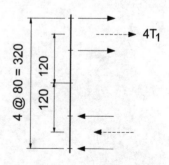

$$T_1 = \frac{P L}{n' d_m} = \frac{200 \times 150}{4(2 \times 120)} = 31.3 \text{ kN}$$

$$T_f = 1.5 \times 31.3 = 47.0 \text{ kN} \quad < 156 \text{ kN} \quad (\text{Table 3-4})$$

Specified shear in one bolt:

$$V = \frac{P}{n} = \frac{200}{10} = 20.0 \text{ kN} \quad < 37.4 \text{ kN} \quad (\text{Table 3-11})$$

Check combined shear and tension for $V/T = 20.0/31.3 = 0.64$

From Table 3-12 on page 3-17,

for V/T of 0.60, permissible $V = 26.0$ kN > 20.0 kN

and for V/T of 0.70, permissible $T = 38.8$ kN > 31.3 kN

WELD DATA

General

Tables in this section are based on CSA S16-09. Information on weld resistances and electrode designations in CSA Standard W48 may be found in Table 3-22 on page 3-40.

Tables

Table 3-21 on page 3-39 summarizes weld resistances as a function of type of load and type of weld.

Table 3-22 on page 3-40 provides information on matching electrodes and gives unit factored weld resistances for various electrodes.

Table 3-23 also on page 3-40 gives factored shear resistances for a range of effective throats per millimetre of weld length, for various electrodes.

Table 3-24 on page 3-41 lists factored shear resistances of a range of fillet weld sizes per millimetre of weld length, for various electrodes.

Table 3-25 also on page 3-41 shows fillet weld resistances as a function of the angle between the axis of the weld and the direction of the load.

Tables 3-26 to 3-33 on pages 3-44 to 3-51 present the resistance of various weld configurations when they are loaded eccentrically in the plane of the welds.

Table 3-34 on page 3-55 presents weld resistances when the eccentric load is in a plane perpendicular to the plane of the welds.

Type of Load	Type of Weld	Factored Resistance
Shear (including tension or compression-induced shear in fillet welds)	Complete and partial joint penetration groove welds, and plug and slot welds	Lesser of: base metal, $V_r = 0.67\,\phi_w A_m F_u$ weld metal, $V_r = 0.67\,\phi_w A_w X_u$
	Fillet welds	Lesser of: base metal, $V_r = 0.67\,\phi_w A_m F_u$ weld metal, $V_r = 0.67\,\phi_w A_w X_u\,(1.00 + 0.50 \sin^{1.5}\theta)\,M_w$ [1]
Tension (normal to axis of load)	Complete joint penetration groove weld (made with matching electrodes) [2]	Same as the base metal
	Partial joint penetration groove weld (made with matching electrodes) [2]	$T_r = \phi_w A_n F_u \leq \phi A_g F_y$ [3]
	Partial joint penetration groove weld combined with a fillet weld (made with matching electrodes) [2]	$T_r = \phi_w \sqrt{(A_n F_u)^2 + (A_w X_u)^2} \leq \phi A_g F_y$
Compression (normal to axis of load)	Complete joint penetration groove weld (made with matching electrodes) [2]	Same as the base metal
	Partial joint penetration groove weld (made with matching electrodes) [2]	Same as the base metal, for the nominal area of the fusion face normal to the compression plus the area of the base metal fitted in contact bearing. [4]

* The detail design of welded joints is to conform to the requirements of CSA Standard W59.

A_m = shear area of effective fusion face.

A_w = area of effective weld throat, plug or slot.

A_n = nominal area of fusion face normal to the tensile force.

θ = angle of axis of weld with the line of action of force (0° for a longitudinal weld and 90° for a transverse weld).

[1] M_w is the strength reduction factor for multi-orientation fillet welds. See CSA S16-09 Clause 13.13.2.2.

[2] Summary information on matching electrodes is included in Table 3-22.

[3] When overall ductile behaviour is desired (member yielding before weld fracture) $A_n F_u > A_g F_y$.

[4] See CSA-S16-09, Clause 28.5.

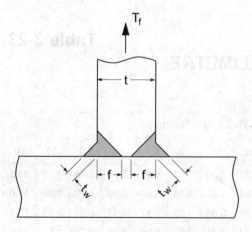

f :   to be used for A_n (see CSA Standard W59 for effective fusion face)

t_w :   to be used for A_w (see CSA Standard W59 for effective weld throat)

t :   to be used for A_g

Application of expression $T_r = \phi_w \sqrt{(A_n F_u)^2 + (A_w X_u)^2} \leq \phi A_g F_y$

ELECTRODE CLASSIFICATION[1]
AND UNIT FACTORED WELD RESISTANCE[2]

$\phi_w = 0.67$

WELD METAL				BASE METAL			
Metric Electrode Classification Number	Electrode Ultimate Tensile Strength	Unit Factored Resistance on Weld Metal		Specified Minimum Tensile Strength of Base Metal F_u	Base Metal Specification and Grade CSA G40.21 or ASTM	F_y	Unit Factored Resistance on Base Metal $0.67 \phi_w F_u$
		Shear on Effective Throat, A_w $0.67 \phi_w X_u$	Shear per Millimetre of Fillet Weld Size, $0.67 \phi_w X_u / \sqrt{2}$				
	MPa	MPa	MPa	MPa		MPa	MPa
E43XX	430	193	136	410	260W, 260WT	260	184
				400	A36	250	180
E49XX	490	220	156	450[3]	300W, 300WT	300	202
				450	350W	350	202
				480	350WT 350R, 350A	350	215
				480	380W	380	215
				415	A572 Gr 42	290	186
				450	A572 Gr 50	345	202
				435	A588 F_y = 42	290	195
				460	A588 F_y = 46	315	206
				485	A588 F_y = 50	345	218
E55XX	550	247	175	520	400W, 400WT 400A, 400AT	400	233
E62XX	620	278	197	590	480W 480A, 480AT	480	265
				620	550W 550A, 550AT	550	278
E82XX	820	368	260	800	700Q, 700QT	700	359

1. For complete information concerning electrode classification and strength matching of base metals, refer to CSA W59.
2. Factored weld resistance (kN) = tabulated unit resistances x (A_w or A_m) / 10^3.
3. F_u = 410 MPa for 300W HSS.

FACTORED SHEAR RESISTANCE
ON EFFECTIVE THROAT PER MILLIMETRE
OF WELD LENGTH (kN / mm)

Electrode Classification	Unit Shear Resist. (MPa)	Effective Throat Thickness (mm)												
		5	6	7	8	10	12	16	20	25	30	35	40	50
E43XX	193	0.965	1.16	1.35	1.54	1.93	2.32	3.09	3.86	4.83	5.79	6.76	7.72	9.65
E49XX	220	1.10	1.32	1.54	1.76	2.20	2.64	3.52	4.40	5.50	6.60	7.70	8.80	11.0
E55XX	247	1.23	1.48	1.73	1.98	2.47	2.96	3.95	4.94	6.17	7.41	8.64	9.88	12.3
E62XX	278	1.39	1.67	1.95	2.23	2.78	3.34	4.45	5.57	6.96	8.35	9.74	11.1	13.9
E82XX	368	1.84	2.21	2.58	2.94	3.68	4.42	5.89	7.36	9.20	11.0	12.9	14.7	18.4

Table 3-24

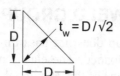

$t_w = D/\sqrt{2}$

FACTORED SHEAR RESISTANCE OF FILLET WELDS PER MILLIMETRE OF WELD LENGTH WHEN ANGLE $\theta^* = 0°$

Matching Electrode Applications

Metric Size Fillet Welds					Imperial Size Fillet Welds				
Fillet Weld Size, D	Electrode Classification				Fillet Weld Size, D	Electrode Classification			
	E43XX	E49XX	E55XX	E62XX		E43XX	E49XX	E55XX	E62XX
mm	kN/mm				in.	kN/mm			
5	0.682	0.778	0.873	0.984	3/16	0.650	0.741	0.831	0.937
6	0.819	0.933	1.05	1.18	1/4	0.867	0.988	1.11	1.25
8	1.09	1.24	1.40	1.57	5/16	1.08	1.23	1.39	1.56
10	1.36	1.56	1.75	1.97	3/8	1.30	1.48	1.66	1.87
12	1.64	1.87	2.09	2.36	7/16	1.52	1.73	1.94	2.19
14	1.91	2.18	2.44	2.76	1/2	1.73	1.98	2.22	2.50
16	2.18	2.49	2.79	3.15	5/8	2.17	2.47	2.77	3.12
18	2.46	2.80	3.14	3.54	3/4	2.60	2.96	3.33	3.75
20	2.73	3.11	3.49	3.94					

Tabulated resistances for both metric and imperial-size fillet welds are based on X_u for the metric electrode classification.

* CSA S16-09 Clause 13.13.2.2: $V_r = 0.67\,\phi_w\,A_w\,X_u\,(1.0 + 0.5\sin^{1.5}\theta)\,M_w$

Table 3-25

FACTORED SHEAR RESISTANCE OF FILLET WELDS PER MILLIMETRE OF WELD LENGTH, FOR ANGLE θ^*

E49XX Electrodes

Weld Size	Angle θ between weld axis and force direction						Weld Size	Angle θ between weld axis and force direction					
	0°	15°	30°	45°	60°	90°		0°	15°	30°	45°	60°	90°
mm	kN/mm						in.	kN/mm					
5	0.778	0.829	0.915	1.01	1.09	1.17	3/16	0.741	0.790	0.872	0.961	1.04	1.11
6	0.933	0.995	1.10	1.21	1.31	1.40	1/4	0.988	1.05	1.16	1.28	1.39	1.48
8	1.24	1.33	1.46	1.61	1.75	1.87	5/16	1.23	1.32	1.45	1.60	1.73	1.85
10	1.56	1.66	1.83	2.02	2.18	2.33	3/8	1.48	1.58	1.74	1.92	2.08	2.22
12	1.87	1.99	2.20	2.42	2.62	2.80	7/16	1.73	1.84	2.03	2.24	2.42	2.59
14	2.18	2.32	2.56	2.82	3.05	3.27	1/2	1.98	2.11	2.32	2.56	2.77	2.96
16	2.49	2.65	2.93	3.23	3.49	3.73	5/8	2.47	2.63	2.91	3.20	3.46	3.70
18	2.80	2.98	3.29	3.63	3.93	4.20	3/4	2.96	3.16	3.49	3.84	4.16	4.44
20	3.11	3.32	3.66	4.04	4.36	4.67							

Only single weld orientations are considered ($M_w = 1$). For loads on specific weld patterns, see Tables 3-26 to 3-33.

* When over-matched electrodes are used, the base metal capacity should also be checked (S16-09 Clause 13.13.2.2).

ECCENTRIC LOADS ON WELD GROUPS

When the line of action of a load on a weld group does not pass through the centre of gravity of the group, the connection is eccentrically loaded. The elastic method of analysis was the traditional approach used in the first two editions of this Handbook.

The third edition incorporated the work of Butler *et al.* (1972), which showed that the margins of safety for eccentrically loaded weld groups analysed elastically were both high and variable. They suggested a method of analysis based on the load-deformation characteristics of the weld and the instantaneous centre of rotation analogy similar to that for eccentrically loaded bolt groups. For this method of analysis, the weld group is considered to be divided into a discrete number of finite weld elements. The resistance of the weld group to the external eccentric load is provided by the combined resistances of the weld elements.

The resistance of each weld element is assumed to act on a line perpendicular to the radius extending from the instantaneous centre of rotation to the centroid of the weld element, as shown on the accompanying figure, where θ is the angle between the axis of the weld and the direction of the weld resistance, R_n. The ultimate load is obtained when the ultimate strength and deformation of some weld element is reached. The resistance of the remaining weld elements is then computed by assuming that deformations vary linearly with the distance from the instantaneous centre. The correct location of the instantaneous centre is assured when the connection is in equilibrium, that is, when the three equations of statics, $\Sigma F_x = 0$, $\Sigma F_y = 0$ and $\Sigma M = 0$ are simultaneously satisfied.

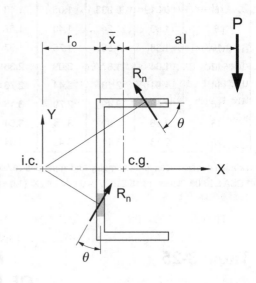

In the ninth edition of this Handbook, design tables for the factored resistances of eccentrically loaded weld groups were calculated using the work of Lesik and Kennedy (1990). This method of analysis was also based on the instantaneous centre of rotation method and featured refined load-deformation characteristics. Notably, the shear strength of a fillet weld, V_θ, at an angle θ from the line of action of the applied load was expressed by:

$$\frac{V_\theta}{V_o} = (1 + 0.5\sin^{1.5}\theta)$$

where V_o is the shear strength of a longitudinal weld.

In the tenth edition, factored resistances for eccentrically loaded weld groups (Tables 3-26 to 3-33 on the following pages) were based on the method of Lesik and Kennedy (1990) but modified by the strength reduction factor for multi-orientation fillet welds, M_w, in accordance with CSA S16-09 Clause 13.13.2.2. See also the work of Callele *et al.* (2005).

Tables

1. Use of Tables

The coefficients C listed in Tables 3-26 to 3-33 are based on an electrode ultimate strength, $X_u = 490$ MPa (E49XX), a base metal tensile strength, $F_u = 450$ MPa, and a resistance factor for welded connections, $\phi_w = 0.67$.

(a) To determine the capacity P of the eccentrically loaded weld group in kN, multiply the appropriate coefficient C by the number of millimetres of weld size D and the length of the weld L, in millimetres.

(b) To determine the required number of millimetres of weld size D, divide the factored load P, in kN, by the appropriate coefficient C and the length of the weld L, in mm.

2. Other Weld Configurations

For situations not covered by the tables of Eccentric Loads on Weld Groups, the method of analysis in which the vector sum of the factored longitudinal and transverse shear loads does not exceed the factored resistances of the weld is recommended as being convenient to use as it can readily be computed. Alternatively, interpolating between weld configurations in the tables which "bracket" the situation being evaluated will often be sufficient to confirm adequacy.

Example

For an example on the use of these tables, see page 3-52.

References:

BUTLER, L.J., PAL, S., and KULAK, G.L. 1972. Eccentrically loaded welded connections. ASCE Journal of the Structural Division, **98**(ST5), May.

CALLELE, L.J., GRONDIN, G.Y. and DRIVER, R.G. 2005. Strength and behaviour of multi-orientation fillet weld connections. Structural Engineering Report No. 255, March, University of Alberta.

KULAK, G.L., and TIMLER, P.A. 1984. Tests on eccentrically loaded fillet welds. Structural Engineering Report No. 124, December, University of Alberta.

LESIK, D.F., and KENNEDY, D.J.L. 1990. Ultimate strength of fillet welded connections loaded in plane. Canadian Journal of Civil Engineering, **17**(1), February.

SWANNELL, P., and SKEWES, I.C. 1977. Design of welded brackets loaded in-plane: general theoretical ultimate load techniques and experimental programme. Australian WRA, RC #46, December, University of Queensland.

Coefficients C

Electrode: E49XX

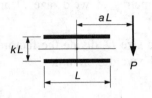

P = Factored eccentric load, kN
L = Length of each weld, mm
D = Size of fillet weld, mm
C = Coefficients tabulated below
$$P = CDL$$

Required Minimum $C = \dfrac{P}{DL}$

Required Minimum $D = \dfrac{P}{CL}$

Required Minimum $L = \dfrac{P}{CD}$

a	\multicolumn{16}{c}{k}
	0.0	0.1	0.2	0.3	0.4	0.5	0.6	0.7	0.8	0.9	1.0	1.2	1.4	1.6	1.8	2.0
0.00	.467	.467	.467	.467	.467	.467	.467	.467	.467	.467	.467	.467	.467	.467	.467	.467
0.05	.395	.400	.410	.422	.432	.440	.446	.451	.454	.456	.457	.460	.461	.462	.462	.463
0.10	.355	.359	.369	.383	.396	.409	.420	.429	.436	.441	.445	.451	.454	.457	.458	.459
0.15	.321	.324	.334	.346	.362	.377	.391	.403	.413	.422	.428	.438	.445	.449	.452	.455
0.20	.290	.294	.303	.315	.330	.346	.362	.376	.389	.400	.409	.423	.433	.440	.445	.448
0.25	.264	.267	.276	.288	.302	.318	.335	.351	.365	.378	.389	.407	.419	.429	.436	.441
0.30	.241	.244	.253	.265	.278	.293	.310	.326	.342	.356	.368	.389	.405	.416	.425	.432
0.35	.221	.224	.232	.243	.256	.271	.287	.304	.320	.334	.349	.371	.389	.403	.414	.423
0.40	.204	.207	.215	.225	.238	.252	.267	.283	.299	.314	.329	.354	.374	.390	.402	.412
0.45	.189	.192	.199	.209	.221	.234	.249	.264	.280	.296	.311	.336	.358	.376	.390	.401
0.50	.175	.178	.185	.195	.206	.219	.232	.247	.263	.278	.293	.321	.343	.362	.378	.390
0.60	.153	.156	.162	.171	.181	.193	.206	.219	.233	.247	.262	.290	.314	.335	.353	.368
0.70	.136	.138	.144	.152	.161	.172	.184	.196	.209	.222	.235	.263	.288	.310	.329	.346
0.80	.121	.124	.129	.136	.145	.155	.166	.177	.188	.201	.213	.239	.264	.287	.306	.324
0.90	.110	.112	.117	.124	.131	.141	.150	.161	.172	.183	.195	.219	.243	.265	.286	.304
1.00	.100	.102	.106	.113	.120	.129	.138	.148	.158	.168	.179	.201	.224	.246	.267	.285
1.20	.085	.086	.090	.096	.102	.110	.118	.126	.135	.144	.153	.173	.193	.214	.233	.251
1.40	.074	.075	.079	.083	.089	.096	.103	.110	.118	.126	.134	.152	.169	.187	.206	.224
1.60	.065	.066	.070	.074	.079	.084	.091	.097	.105	.111	.119	.135	.151	.167	.184	.200
1.80	.058	.059	.062	.066	.070	.076	.081	.087	.094	.100	.107	.121	.135	.150	.165	.180
2.00	.053	.054	.056	.060	.064	.069	.074	.079	.085	.091	.097	.110	.123	.136	.150	.164
2.20	.048	.049	.051	.054	.058	.063	.067	.073	.078	.083	.089	.100	.112	.125	.137	.150
2.40	.044	.045	.047	.050	.054	.058	.062	.067	.071	.077	.082	.093	.103	.115	.127	.138
2.60	.041	.042	.044	.046	.050	.053	.057	.062	.066	.071	.076	.086	.096	.107	.117	.128
2.80	.038	.039	.041	.043	.046	.050	.054	.058	.062	.066	.071	.080	.089	.099	.109	.120
3.00	.036	.036	.038	.040	.043	.046	.050	.054	.058	.062	.066	.075	.084	.093	.102	.112

When over-matched electrodes are used, the base metal capacity should also be checked (S16-09 Clause 13.13.2.2).

Table 3-27

ECCENTRIC LOADS ON WELD GROUPS

Electrode: E49XX

Coefficients C

P = Factored eccentric load, kN
L = Length of each weld, mm
D = Size of fillet weld, mm
C = Coefficients tabulated below

$$P = CDL$$

Required Minimum $C = \dfrac{P}{DL}$

Required Minimum $D = \dfrac{P}{CL}$

Required Minimum $L = \dfrac{P}{CD}$

a	k															
	0.0	0.1	0.2	0.3	0.4	0.5	0.6	0.7	0.8	0.9	1.0	1.2	1.4	1.6	1.8	2.0
0.00	.311	.311	.311	.311	.311	.311	.311	.311	.311	.311	.311	.311	.311	.311	.311	.311
0.05	.311	.311	.311	.311	.311	.311	.311	.309	.308	.307	.306	.305	.303	.302	.302	.301
0.10	.311	.311	.311	.311	.309	.307	.305	.303	.301	.300	.299	.297	.295	.295	.294	.294
0.15	.309	.307	.305	.302	.299	.297	.295	.293	.292	.290	.289	.288	.287	.286	.286	.286
0.20	.296	.294	.291	.288	.286	.284	.282	.281	.280	.279	.279	.278	.278	.278	.278	.279
0.25	.278	.276	.274	.272	.271	.269	.268	.268	.267	.267	.267	.268	.268	.269	.270	.271
0.30	.259	.257	.256	.255	.255	.254	.254	.254	.255	.255	.256	.257	.259	.260	.262	.263
0.35	.240	.239	.238	.238	.238	.239	.240	.241	.242	.243	.244	.247	.249	.252	.254	.256
0.40	.222	.221	.222	.222	.223	.225	.227	.228	.230	.232	.234	.237	.240	.243	.246	.248
0.45	.205	.205	.206	.208	.210	.212	.214	.216	.218	.221	.223	.227	.231	.235	.238	.241
0.50	.191	.191	.192	.194	.197	.200	.202	.205	.208	.211	.214	.219	.223	.227	.231	.234
0.60	.165	.166	.168	.171	.175	.178	.182	.186	.189	.192	.195	.202	.208	.213	.217	.221
0.70	.145	.146	.148	.152	.156	.160	.165	.169	.173	.176	.180	.187	.194	.200	.205	.209
0.80	.129	.130	.133	.137	.141	.145	.150	.155	.159	.163	.167	.174	.181	.187	.193	.198
0.90	.116	.117	.120	.124	.128	.133	.138	.142	.147	.151	.155	.163	.170	.177	.183	.188
1.00	.105	.106	.109	.113	.118	.122	.127	.132	.137	.141	.145	.153	.160	.168	.174	.179
1.20	.089	.090	.092	.096	.101	.105	.110	.115	.119	.124	.128	.136	.144	.151	.158	.163
1.40	.076	.077	.080	.084	.088	.093	.097	.101	.106	.110	.114	.122	.130	.137	.144	.149
1.60	.067	.068	.070	.074	.078	.082	.086	.091	.095	.099	.103	.111	.119	.126	.133	.138
1.80	.060	.061	.063	.066	.070	.074	.078	.082	.086	.090	.094	.102	.109	.116	.123	.128
2.00	.054	.055	.057	.060	.064	.067	.071	.075	.079	.083	.087	.094	.101	.107	.114	.119
2.20	.049	.050	.052	.055	.058	.062	.065	.069	.073	.076	.080	.087	.094	.100	.106	.112
2.40	.045	.046	.048	.050	.053	.057	.060	.064	.067	.071	.074	.081	.087	.094	.100	.106
2.60	.042	.042	.044	.047	.049	.053	.056	.059	.063	.066	.069	.076	.082	.088	.094	.100
2.80	.039	.039	.041	.043	.046	.049	.052	.055	.059	.062	.065	.071	.077	.083	.089	.094
3.00	.036	.037	.038	.041	.043	.046	.049	.052	.055	.058	.061	.067	.073	.079	.084	.089

When over-matched electrodes are used, the base metal capacity should also be checked (S16-09 Clause 13.13.2.2).

Table 3-28

ECCENTRIC LOADS ON WELD GROUPS

Coefficients C

Electrode: E49XX

$P = CDL$

P = Factored eccentric load, kN
L = Length of weld parallel to load, mm
D = Size of fillet weld, mm
C = Coefficients tabulated below
xL = Distance from vertical weld to centre of gravity of weld group

Required Minimum $C = \dfrac{P}{DL}$

Required Minimum $D = \dfrac{P}{CL}$

Required Minimum $L = \dfrac{P}{CD}$

a	k															
	0.0	0.1	0.2	0.3	0.4	0.5	0.6	0.7	0.8	0.9	1.0	1.2	1.4	1.6	1.8	2.0
0.00	.156	.179	.226	.272	.319	.366	.412	.459	.505	.552	.599	.692	.785	.879	.972	1.065
0.05	.156	.179	.226	.272	.319	.366	.412	.459	.505	.552	.599	.692	.785	.879	.972	1.065
0.10	.156	.179	.226	.272	.319	.366	.412	.459	.505	.552	.599	.692	.785	.877	.967	1.058
0.15	.155	.179	.226	.272	.319	.364	.408	.452	.496	.540	.584	.672	.760	.848	.936	1.025
0.20	.148	.179	.223	.264	.305	.347	.388	.430	.473	.515	.557	.643	.728	.814	.900	.986
0.25	.139	.173	.210	.248	.287	.327	.366	.407	.447	.488	.529	.611	.694	.778	.862	.947
0.30	.129	.162	.196	.232	.269	.306	.344	.383	.421	.460	.500	.580	.660	.743	.825	.909
0.35	.120	.150	.182	.216	.251	.286	.322	.359	.396	.433	.472	.549	.628	.708	.790	.872
0.40	.111	.139	.170	.201	.234	.267	.301	.336	.372	.408	.445	.521	.598	.676	.755	.836
0.45	.103	.130	.158	.187	.218	.249	.282	.316	.350	.385	.420	.493	.569	.646	.724	.804
0.50	.095	.121	.147	.175	.204	.234	.264	.297	.330	.363	.398	.468	.542	.617	.693	.773
0.60	.083	.105	.128	.153	.179	.206	.234	.263	.293	.324	.356	.424	.492	.566	.639	.716
0.70	.073	.093	.113	.136	.159	.183	.209	.235	.264	.292	.323	.386	.452	.521	.591	.665
0.80	.065	.083	.101	.121	.142	.165	.188	.213	.238	.265	.293	.352	.416	.482	.550	.620
0.90	.058	.074	.091	.109	.129	.149	.171	.194	.217	.243	.269	.325	.384	.446	.514	.581
1.00	.053	.067	.083	.100	.117	.136	.156	.177	.200	.223	.248	.301	.358	.416	.478	.544
1.20	.044	.057	.070	.084	.099	.115	.133	.152	.171	.192	.214	.262	.312	.365	.422	.482
1.40	.038	.049	.060	.073	.086	.101	.116	.133	.150	.169	.189	.230	.276	.324	.375	.431
1.60	.034	.043	.053	.064	.076	.089	.103	.117	.133	.150	.168	.205	.247	.291	.338	.387
1.80	.030	.038	.048	.057	.068	.079	.092	.105	.119	.134	.151	.185	.223	.263	.306	.353
2.00	.027	.035	.043	.052	.062	.072	.083	.095	.108	.122	.137	.168	.202	.240	.280	.323
2.20	.025	.032	.039	.047	.056	.066	.076	.087	.099	.112	.125	.154	.185	.221	.257	.297
2.40	.022	.029	.036	.043	.052	.060	.070	.080	.091	.103	.116	.142	.172	.203	.238	.275
2.60	.021	.027	.033	.040	.047	.056	.065	.074	.084	.095	.107	.132	.159	.189	.221	.256
2.80	.019	.025	.031	.037	.044	.052	.060	.069	.079	.089	.099	.123	.148	.176	.207	.239
3.00	.018	.023	.029	.035	.042	.048	.056	.065	.074	.083	.093	.115	.139	.166	.194	.225
x	0	.008	.029	.056	.089	.125	.164	.204	.246	.289	.333	.424	.516	.610	.704	.800

When over-matched electrodes are used, the base metal capacity should also be checked (S16-09 Clause 13.13.2.2).

Table 3-29

ECCENTRIC LOADS
ON WELD GROUPS

Electrode: E49XX

Coefficients C

P = Factored eccentric load, kN
L = Length of weld parallel to load, mm
D = Size of fillet weld, mm
C = Coefficients tabulated below
xL = Distance from vertical weld to centre of gravity of weld group

$$P = CDL$$

$$\text{Required Minimum } C = \frac{P}{DL}$$

$$\text{Required Minimum } D = \frac{P}{CL}$$

$$\text{Required Minimum } L = \frac{P}{CD}$$

| a | \multicolumn{16}{c}{k} |
	0.0	0.1	0.2	0.3	0.4	0.5	0.6	0.7	0.8	0.9	1.0	1.2	1.4	1.6	1.8	2.0
0.00	.156	.179	.226	.272	.319	.366	.412	.459	.505	.552	.599	.692	.785	.879	.972	1.065
0.05	.156	.179	.226	.272	.319	.366	.412	.459	.505	.552	.599	.686	.772	.857	.943	1.029
0.10	.156	.179	.226	.272	.319	.366	.412	.454	.496	.537	.579	.663	.746	.829	.912	.996
0.15	.155	.179	.226	.272	.314	.354	.395	.435	.475	.516	.556	.636	.717	.799	.880	.962
0.20	.148	.179	.221	.260	.299	.337	.376	.414	.453	.492	.531	.609	.688	.767	.847	.928
0.25	.139	.173	.209	.245	.282	.319	.355	.393	.430	.468	.505	.581	.658	.736	.815	.894
0.30	.129	.162	.195	.230	.264	.300	.335	.371	.407	.443	.480	.554	.629	.705	.783	.861
0.35	.120	.151	.182	.214	.248	.281	.316	.350	.385	.420	.455	.527	.601	.675	.752	.829
0.40	.111	.140	.170	.200	.232	.264	.296	.330	.363	.397	.432	.502	.574	.647	.721	.797
0.45	.103	.130	.158	.187	.217	.247	.279	.311	.343	.376	.410	.478	.548	.620	.693	.768
0.50	.095	.121	.147	.174	.203	.232	.263	.293	.324	.356	.388	.456	.524	.595	.667	.740
0.60	.083	.105	.129	.153	.179	.206	.233	.262	.291	.321	.352	.415	.480	.547	.617	.688
0.70	.073	.093	.114	.136	.160	.184	.210	.237	.264	.291	.320	.380	.442	.506	.574	.642
0.80	.065	.083	.102	.122	.144	.167	.190	.215	.240	.266	.294	.350	.408	.471	.535	.601
0.90	.058	.075	.092	.111	.131	.152	.173	.196	.220	.245	.270	.323	.380	.439	.500	.564
1.00	.053	.068	.084	.101	.119	.139	.160	.181	.203	.227	.251	.301	.355	.410	.468	.530
1.20	.044	.057	.071	.085	.101	.118	.137	.156	.176	.197	.218	.263	.311	.363	.416	.472
1.40	.038	.049	.061	.074	.088	.103	.119	.136	.154	.173	.192	.233	.276	.324	.373	.425
1.60	.034	.043	.054	.065	.077	.091	.105	.120	.137	.154	.171	.209	.249	.292	.337	.385
1.80	.030	.039	.048	.058	.069	.081	.094	.108	.123	.138	.155	.189	.226	.265	.307	.352
2.00	.027	.035	.043	.052	.062	.073	.085	.097	.111	.125	.141	.172	.206	.243	.281	.323
2.20	.025	.032	.039	.048	.057	.067	.077	.089	.101	.114	.128	.158	.190	.224	.260	.299
2.40	.022	.029	.036	.044	.052	.061	.071	.081	.093	.105	.118	.146	.176	.208	.242	.278
2.60	.021	.027	.033	.040	.048	.057	.066	.075	.086	.097	.109	.135	.163	.193	.225	.259
2.80	.019	.025	.031	.037	.045	.053	.061	.070	.080	.090	.102	.126	.153	.181	.211	.243
3.00	.018	.023	.029	.035	.042	.050	.057	.066	.075	.084	.095	.118	.143	.170	.198	.229
x	0	.008	.029	.056	.089	.125	.164	.204	.246	.289	.333	.424	.516	.610	.704	.800

When over-matched electrodes are used, the base metal capacity should also be checked (S16-09 Clause 13.13.2.2).

Coefficients C

Electrode: E49XX

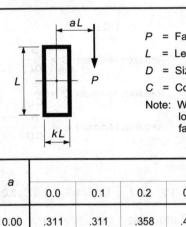

P = Factored eccentric load, kN
L = Length of longer welds, mm
D = Size of fillet weld, mm
C = Coefficients tabulated below
Note: When load P is perpendicular to longer side L, use table on facing page.

$$P = CDL$$

$$\text{Required Minimum } C = \frac{P}{DL}$$

$$\text{Required Minimum } D = \frac{P}{CL}$$

$$\text{Required Minimum } L = \frac{P}{CD}$$

a	\multicolumn{11}{c}{k}
	0.0	0.1	0.2	0.3	0.4	0.5	0.6	0.7	0.8	0.9	1.0
0.00	.311	.311	.358	.404	.451	.498	.544	.591	.638	.684	.731
0.05	.311	.311	.358	.404	.451	.498	.544	.591	.638	.684	.731
0.10	.311	.311	.358	.404	.451	.498	.544	.591	.638	.684	.731
0.15	.309	.311	.358	.404	.451	.498	.544	.587	.628	.670	.711
0.20	.296	.311	.358	.403	.441	.480	.519	.559	.599	.639	.680
0.25	.278	.311	.345	.380	.416	.454	.492	.530	.569	.608	.648
0.30	.259	.290	.323	.356	.392	.427	.464	.501	.539	.577	.615
0.35	.240	.270	.301	.333	.367	.402	.438	.473	.510	.547	.584
0.40	.222	.250	.280	.312	.344	.378	.412	.447	.483	.519	.555
0.45	.206	.233	.261	.291	.322	.355	.388	.422	.457	.492	.529
0.50	.191	.217	.244	.273	.303	.335	.366	.400	.434	.468	.503
0.60	.166	.189	.214	.240	.268	.297	.328	.360	.392	.425	.459
0.70	.145	.167	.189	.214	.240	.268	.296	.325	.356	.387	.420
0.80	.129	.148	.169	.192	.217	.243	.270	.298	.326	.356	.386
0.90	.116	.133	.153	.174	.198	.221	.246	.273	.299	.327	.357
1.00	.105	.121	.139	.159	.180	.203	.226	.251	.277	.303	.331
1.20	.089	.102	.118	.136	.154	.174	.196	.218	.241	.265	.288
1.40	.076	.088	.102	.118	.134	.152	.171	.191	.211	.233	.255
1.60	.067	.078	.090	.104	.119	.135	.152	.170	.189	.208	.228
1.80	.060	.069	.080	.093	.107	.121	.137	.153	.170	.188	.206
2.00	.054	.062	.072	.084	.097	.110	.124	.139	.154	.171	.188
2.20	.049	.057	.066	.077	.088	.100	.113	.127	.142	.157	.173
2.40	.045	.052	.061	.070	.081	.092	.105	.117	.131	.145	.160
2.60	.042	.048	.056	.065	.075	.086	.097	.109	.121	.134	.148
2.80	.039	.045	.052	.061	.070	.080	.090	.101	.113	.125	.138
3.00	.036	.042	.049	.057	.065	.074	.084	.095	.106	.117	.129

When over-matched electrodes are used, the base metal capacity should also be checked (S16-09 Clause 13.13.2.2).

Table 3-31

ECCENTRIC LOADS ON WELD GROUPS

Electrode: E49XX

Coefficients C

$$P = CDL$$

P = Factored eccentric load, kN
L = Length of longer welds, mm
D = Size of fillet weld, mm
C = Coefficients tabulated below
Note: When load P is parallel to longer side L, use table on facing page.

Required Minimum $C = \dfrac{P}{DL}$

Required Minimum $D = \dfrac{P}{CL}$

Required Minimum $L = \dfrac{P}{CD}$

a	k										
	0.0	0.1	0.2	0.3	0.4	0.5	0.6	0.7	0.8	0.9	1.0
0.00	.467	.493	.519	.546	.572	.599	.625	.652	.678	.705	.731
0.05	.395	.430	.469	.508	.548	.587	.624	.652	.678	.705	.731
0.10	.355	.389	.425	.465	.506	.547	.588	.627	.666	.704	.731
0.15	.321	.353	.389	.427	.467	.509	.550	.591	.632	.672	.711
0.20	.290	.322	.357	.395	.432	.473	.514	.556	.598	.639	.680
0.25	.264	.295	.328	.365	.403	.441	.482	.523	.564	.606	.648
0.30	.241	.270	.303	.338	.375	.412	.451	.491	.532	.574	.615
0.35	.221	.249	.280	.314	.350	.386	.423	.462	.503	.543	.584
0.40	.204	.230	.260	.292	.328	.362	.398	.436	.475	.515	.555
0.45	.189	.214	.242	.274	.306	.341	.375	.412	.451	.489	.529
0.50	.175	.199	.227	.256	.288	.322	.356	.390	.428	.465	.503
0.60	.153	.175	.200	.227	.256	.287	.320	.353	.387	.421	.459
0.70	.136	.155	.178	.203	.230	.259	.289	.320	.353	.386	.420
0.80	.121	.139	.160	.184	.208	.235	.263	.292	.323	.354	.386
0.90	.110	.127	.146	.167	.191	.215	.241	.269	.296	.326	.357
1.00	.100	.115	.133	.153	.175	.197	.222	.248	.275	.303	.331
1.20	.085	.098	.114	.131	.150	.170	.191	.214	.238	.263	.288
1.40	.074	.085	.099	.114	.131	.149	.168	.188	.209	.232	.255
1.60	.065	.075	.088	.101	.116	.133	.150	.168	.187	.207	.228
1.80	.058	.068	.078	.091	.104	.119	.135	.151	.169	.187	.206
2.00	.053	.061	.071	.083	.095	.108	.122	.137	.153	.170	.188
2.20	.048	.056	.065	.075	.087	.099	.112	.126	.141	.156	.173
2.40	.044	.051	.060	.069	.080	.091	.103	.116	.130	.145	.160
2.60	.041	.047	.055	.064	.074	.085	.096	.108	.121	.134	.148
2.80	.038	.044	.051	.060	.069	.079	.089	.100	.113	.125	.138
3.00	.036	.041	.048	.056	.065	.074	.084	.094	.105	.117	.129

When over-matched electrodes are used, the base metal capacity should also be checked (S16-09 Clause 13.13.2.2).

Coefficients C

Electrode: E49XX

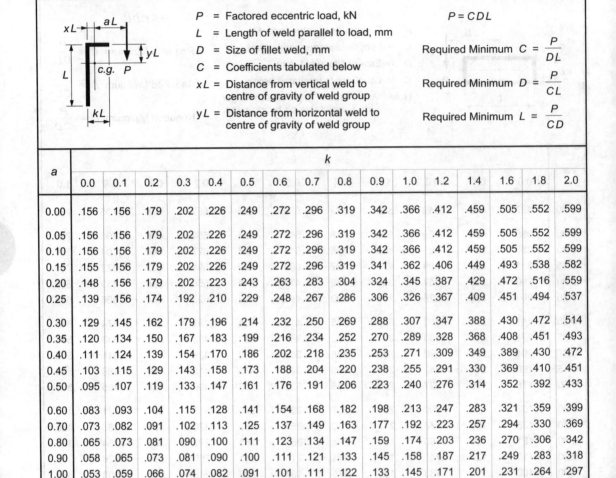

P	= Factored eccentric load, kN	$P = CDL$
L	= Length of weld parallel to load, mm	Required Minimum $C = \dfrac{P}{DL}$
D	= Size of fillet weld, mm	
C	= Coefficients tabulated below	Required Minimum $D = \dfrac{P}{CL}$
xL	= Distance from vertical weld to centre of gravity of weld group	
yL	= Distance from horizontal weld to centre of gravity of weld group	Required Minimum $L = \dfrac{P}{CD}$

a	k															
	0.0	0.1	0.2	0.3	0.4	0.5	0.6	0.7	0.8	0.9	1.0	1.2	1.4	1.6	1.8	2.0
0.00	.156	.156	.179	.202	.226	.249	.272	.296	.319	.342	.366	.412	.459	.505	.552	.599
0.05	.156	.156	.179	.202	.226	.249	.272	.296	.319	.342	.366	.412	.459	.505	.552	.599
0.10	.156	.156	.179	.202	.226	.249	.272	.296	.319	.342	.366	.412	.459	.505	.552	.599
0.15	.155	.156	.179	.202	.226	.249	.272	.296	.319	.341	.362	.406	.449	.493	.538	.582
0.20	.148	.156	.179	.202	.223	.243	.263	.283	.304	.324	.345	.387	.429	.472	.516	.559
0.25	.139	.156	.174	.192	.210	.229	.248	.267	.286	.306	.326	.367	.409	.451	.494	.537
0.30	.129	.145	.162	.179	.196	.214	.232	.250	.269	.288	.307	.347	.388	.430	.472	.514
0.35	.120	.134	.150	.167	.183	.199	.216	.234	.252	.270	.289	.328	.368	.408	.451	.493
0.40	.111	.124	.139	.154	.170	.186	.202	.218	.235	.253	.271	.309	.349	.389	.430	.472
0.45	.103	.115	.129	.143	.158	.173	.188	.204	.220	.238	.255	.291	.330	.369	.410	.451
0.50	.095	.107	.119	.133	.147	.161	.176	.191	.206	.223	.240	.276	.314	.352	.392	.433
0.60	.083	.093	.104	.115	.128	.141	.154	.168	.182	.198	.213	.247	.283	.321	.359	.399
0.70	.073	.082	.091	.102	.113	.125	.137	.149	.163	.177	.192	.223	.257	.294	.330	.369
0.80	.065	.073	.081	.090	.100	.111	.123	.134	.147	.159	.174	.203	.236	.270	.306	.342
0.90	.058	.065	.073	.081	.090	.100	.111	.121	.133	.145	.158	.187	.217	.249	.283	.318
1.00	.053	.059	.066	.074	.082	.091	.101	.111	.122	.133	.145	.171	.201	.231	.264	.297
1.20	.044	.050	.056	.062	.069	.077	.086	.095	.104	.114	.125	.149	.174	.202	.231	.263
1.40	.038	.043	.048	.054	.060	.067	.074	.082	.090	.099	.109	.130	.153	.178	.205	.234
1.60	.034	.038	.042	.047	.052	.059	.066	.073	.080	.088	.097	.115	.137	.159	.184	.210
1.80	.030	.034	.038	.042	.047	.052	.059	.065	.072	.079	.087	.104	.123	.144	.167	.191
2.00	.027	.030	.034	.038	.042	.047	.053	.059	.065	.071	.079	.095	.112	.131	.152	.174
2.20	.025	.028	.031	.035	.038	.043	.048	.054	.059	.065	.072	.086	.102	.121	.140	.160
2.40	.022	.025	.028	.032	.035	.040	.044	.049	.055	.060	.066	.080	.095	.111	.129	.149
2.60	.021	.024	.026	.029	.033	.036	.041	.046	.050	.056	.061	.074	.088	.103	.120	.138
2.80	.019	.022	.024	.027	.030	.034	.038	.042	.047	.052	.057	.069	.082	.096	.112	.129
3.00	.018	.020	.023	.025	.029	.032	.036	.040	.044	.048	.053	.064	.077	.090	.105	.121
x	0	.005	.017	.035	.057	.083	.113	.144	.178	.213	.250	.327	.408	.492	.579	.667
y	.500	.455	.417	.385	.357	.333	.313	.294	.278	.263	.250	.227	.208	.192	.179	.167

When over-matched electrodes are used, the base metal capacity should also be checked (S16-09 Clause 13.13.2.2).

Table 3-33

ECCENTRIC LOADS ON WELD GROUPS

Electrode: E49XX

Coefficients C

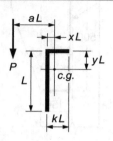

P = Factored eccentric load, kN
L = Length of weld parallel to load, mm
D = Size of fillet weld, mm
C = Coefficients tabulated below
xL = Distance from vertical weld to centre of gravity of weld group
yL = Distance from horizontal weld to centre of gravity of weld group

$$P = CDL$$

Required Minimum $C = \dfrac{P}{DL}$

Required Minimum $D = \dfrac{P}{CL}$

Required Minimum $L = \dfrac{P}{CD}$

| a | \multicolumn{16}{c}{k} | | | | | | | | | | | | | | | |
	0.0	0.1	0.2	0.3	0.4	0.5	0.6	0.7	0.8	0.9	1.0	1.2	1.4	1.6	1.8	2.0
0.00	.156	.156	.179	.202	.226	.249	.272	.296	.319	.342	.366	.412	.459	.505	.552	.599
0.05	.156	.156	.179	.202	.226	.249	.272	.296	.319	.342	.366	.404	.441	.479	.518	.557
0.10	.156	.156	.179	.202	.226	.249	.272	.295	.313	.330	.348	.384	.420	.458	.496	.535
0.15	.155	.156	.179	.202	.226	.245	.262	.279	.296	.312	.329	.364	.400	.437	.475	.514
0.20	.148	.156	.179	.198	.214	.230	.246	.261	.277	.294	.310	.344	.380	.417	.455	.494
0.25	.139	.155	.170	.185	.200	.215	.229	.245	.260	.276	.293	.326	.362	.399	.436	.475
0.30	.129	.144	.158	.172	.186	.200	.214	.229	.244	.259	.276	.310	.345	.381	.419	.457
0.35	.120	.134	.147	.160	.173	.186	.200	.214	.229	.244	.260	.294	.328	.365	.403	.440
0.40	.111	.124	.136	.148	.161	.173	.187	.201	.215	.230	.247	.279	.314	.350	.386	.425
0.45	.103	.115	.126	.138	.150	.162	.175	.189	.203	.218	.233	.266	.299	.335	.372	.410
0.50	.095	.107	.117	.128	.140	.152	.164	.178	.191	.206	.221	.253	.286	.321	.357	.395
0.60	.083	.093	.102	.113	.123	.134	.146	.159	.171	.185	.200	.230	.263	.296	.331	.367
0.70	.073	.082	.090	.099	.109	.120	.131	.142	.155	.168	.182	.211	.242	.274	.308	.343
0.80	.065	.073	.081	.089	.098	.108	.118	.129	.141	.153	.166	.194	.224	.254	.287	.320
0.90	.058	.065	.073	.080	.089	.098	.107	.118	.129	.140	.153	.179	.207	.237	.268	.301
1.00	.053	.059	.066	.073	.081	.089	.098	.108	.118	.129	.141	.166	.193	.222	.251	.283
1.20	.044	.050	.056	.062	.069	.076	.084	.092	.102	.111	.122	.145	.169	.195	.223	.252
1.40	.038	.043	.048	.053	.059	.066	.073	.081	.089	.098	.107	.128	.150	.174	.200	.227
1.60	.034	.038	.042	.047	.052	.058	.065	.071	.079	.087	.096	.114	.135	.157	.181	.205
1.80	.030	.034	.038	.042	.047	.052	.058	.064	.071	.078	.086	.103	.122	.142	.164	.188
2.00	.027	.030	.034	.038	.042	.047	.052	.058	.064	.071	.078	.094	.111	.130	.150	.172
2.20	.025	.028	.031	.034	.038	.043	.048	.053	.059	.065	.072	.086	.102	.120	.139	.159
2.40	.022	.025	.028	.032	.035	.039	.044	.049	.054	.060	.066	.080	.095	.111	.129	.148
2.60	.021	.023	.026	.029	.033	.036	.041	.045	.050	.055	.061	.074	.088	.104	.120	.138
2.80	.019	.022	.024	.027	.030	.034	.038	.042	.047	.052	.057	.069	.082	.097	.112	.130
3.00	.018	.020	.023	.025	.028	.032	.035	.039	.044	.048	.053	.065	.077	.091	.106	.122
x	0	.005	.017	.035	.057	.083	.113	.144	.178	.213	.250	.327	.408	.492	.579	.667
y	.500	.455	.417	.385	.357	.333	.313	.294	.278	.263	.250	.227	.208	.192	.179	.167

When over-matched electrodes are used, the base metal capacity should also be checked (S16-09 Clause 13.13.2.2).

Example

Given:

A column bracket of G40.21-350W steel supports a factored load of 650 kN. The width of the bracket is 300 mm. Welds are made using E49XX electrodes. For the weld configuration shown, find the required weld size.

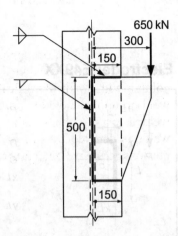

Solution:

Referring to Table 3-28, page 3-46,

$$D = \frac{P}{C L}$$

= number of millimetres of fillet weld leg size

$k = 150 / 500 = 0.3$

From the bottom line of Table 3-28, for $k = 0.3$ $x = 0.056$

Referring to the figure in Table 3-28, $aL + xL = 300$

For $L = 500$, $500\,a + 0.056\,(500) = 300$, $a = 0.544$

For $a = 0.544$ and $k = 0.3$, $C = 0.165$ by interpolation

Therefore, $D = \dfrac{650}{0.165 \times 500} = 7.88$ say 8 mm

Notes:

1. The final choice of the fillet weld size to be used in an actual connection will also depend on the minimum and maximum sizes required by a) the physical thickness of the parts joined and b) the requirements of Standard CSA W59.

2. The strength of an actual connection will also depend on the resistances of the connected parts.

ECCENTRIC LOADS ON WELD GROUPS
SHEAR AND MOMENT

Two configurations involving a vertical load applied out-of-plane with respect to the fillet weld group are shown in Figure 3-3. In Figure 3-3(a), a plate is welded to the flange of a column with a pair of vertical fillet welds. The eccentricity of the load, P, with respect to the weld group is denoted by aL, where L is the weld length. In Figure 3-3(b), a stiffened seat is welded to the column using a tee-shaped weld configuration. The length of the horizontal welds is denoted by kL. In both types of connections, the eccentric load causes the lower portions of the welded parts to bear against each other.

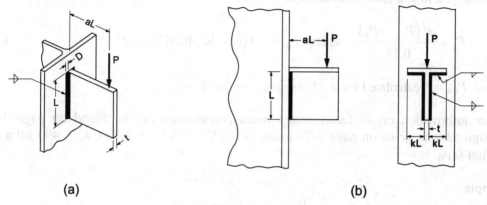

(a)   (b)

Figure 3-3

The closed-form solutions given below for the welded connections shown in Figures 3.3(a) and (b) were developed by Kwan *et al.* (2010) and Picard and Beaulieu (1991), respectively.

1. Pair of vertical welds ($k = 0$), Figure 3-3(a)

(a) For $a/Q > 0.53$, the factored load resistance (based on weld failure) is given by:

$$P_r = \frac{0.711\phi_w F_y t L}{a(Q+1.421)} \quad \text{where} \quad a = \text{eccentricity ratio (Fig. 3.3), and} \quad Q = \frac{F_y t}{X_u D} \tag{1a}$$

(b) For $a/Q \leq 0.53$, the factored load resistance (based on weld failure) is given by:

$$P_r = P_{ro}[1 - 1.89(a/Q)] + 1.89(a/Q)P_{r53} \quad \text{where} \quad P_{ro} = 2(0.67)\phi_w 0.7071 X_u D L \tag{1b}$$

and P_{r53} is obtained using equation (1a) for an eccentricity a that yields a value of a/Q of 0.53 for the applicable value of Q.

(c) For all values of a/Q, the factored load resistance based on failure in the plate (due to material yield only – instability is not considered) is given by:

$$P_r = \frac{2\phi_w V_p\left(\sqrt{a^2L^2V_p^2 + 3M_p^2} - aLV_p\right)}{3M_p}, \quad \text{where} \quad M_p = \frac{tL^2F_u}{4}, \quad \text{and} \quad V_p = \frac{tLF_u}{2} \tag{1c}$$

A design table is given on page 3-55 for $\phi_w = 0.67$, $X_u = 490$ MPa, $F_y = 300$ MPa and $F_u = 450$ MPa. The tabulated coefficients are given by: $C' = P/L$

2. Tee-shaped configuration with horizontal and vertical welds ($k = 0.2$), Figure 3-3(b)

(a) For $a \geq 0.40$ and plate thickness $t \leq 40$ mm, the factored load resistance is given by:

$$P = \frac{0.5\,\phi_w\,D\,L\,X_u}{a}\left(\frac{1.4Q - 0.08}{Q + 2}\right), \text{ where } Q = \frac{F_y\,t}{X_u\,D} \tag{2a}$$

(b) For $a < 0.40$ and plate thickness $t \leq 40$ mm:

$$P = P_0 + \frac{a^2(P_{0.4} - P_0)}{0.16}, \text{ where } P_0 = 2.4(0.67)\phi_w\,0.7071\,X_u\,D\,L \tag{2b}$$

and $P_{0.4} = P$ calculated for $a = 0.4$ using case (a) above.

Further information on stiffened seated beam connections can be found on page 3-78. A design table is given on page 3-79 for $\phi_w = 0.67$, $k = 0.2$, $t = 1.7\,D$, $X_u = 490$ MPa and $F_y = 300$ MPa.

Example

Given:

A 12 mm plate carrying a 275 kN factored load is welded to a column with a pair of fillet welds 250 mm long. Find the fillet weld size required if the 275 kN load acts at an eccentricity of 130 mm.

Solution:

$L = 250$ mm, $aL = 130$ mm; therefore, $a = 130/250 = 0.52$

C' required is $P/L = 275/250 = 1.1$ Try $D = 6$ mm fillet weld

From Table 3-34, for $t = 12$ mm and 6 mm weld size:

$C' = 1.20$ for $a = 0.50$, and 1.06 for $a = 0.60$

Therefore, for $a = 0.52$, $C' = 1.17$ (by interpolation) > 1.1

The minimum weld size based on the thickness of the materials joined and the resistance of the connected parts must also be checked.

References:

DAWE, J.L., and KULAK, G.L. 1974. Welded connections under combined shear and moment. ASCE Journal of the Structural Division, **100**(ST4), April.

KWAN, Y.K., GOMEZ, I.R., GRONDIN, G.Y. and KANVINDE, A.M. 2010. Strength of welded joints under combined shear and out-of-plane bending. Canadian Journal of Civil Engineering, 37(2): 250-261.

PICARD, A., and BEAULIEU, D. 1991. Calcul des charpentes d'acier. Canadian Institute of Steel Construction, Willowdale, Ontario (in French).

Table 3-34   ECCENTRIC LOADS ON WELD GROUPS
Coefficients C'

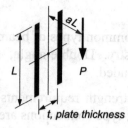

P = Factored eccentric load, kN $P = C'L$
L = Length of each weld, mm   Required Minimum $C' = P/L$
C' = Coefficients tabulated below   Required Minimum $L = P/C'$

t, plate thickness

Plate Thickness, t	8 mm	10 mm		12 mm			16 mm		
Weld Size, D	5	5	6	5	6	8	6	8	10
0.0	1.39	1.56	1.74	1.56	1.87	2.09	1.87	2.49	2.79
0.1	1.24	1.44	1.55	1.45	1.73	1.86	1.75	2.31	2.48
0.2	1.11	1.33	1.38	1.35	1.60	1.66	1.63	2.13	2.22
0.3	0.991	1.22	1.24	1.25	1.46	1.49	1.52	1.95	1.98
0.4	0.891	1.11	1.11	1.15	1.33	1.34	1.40	1.77	1.78
0.5	0.804	0.997	1.01	1.05	1.20	1.21	1.29	1.60	1.61
0.6	0.729	0.886	0.912	0.943	1.06	1.09	1.17	1.42	1.46
0.7	0.665	0.772	0.831	0.841	0.926	0.997	1.06	1.23	1.33
0.8	0.595	0.675	0.732	0.742	0.810	0.914	0.939	1.08	1.19
0.9	0.529	0.600	0.650	0.659	0.720	0.815	0.832	0.960	1.06
1.0 (a)	0.476	0.540	0.585	0.593	0.648	0.733	0.749	0.864	0.953
1.2	0.397	0.450	0.488	0.494	0.540	0.611	0.624	0.720	0.794
1.4	0.340	0.386	0.418	0.424	0.463	0.524	0.535	0.617	0.680
1.6	0.298	0.338	0.366	0.371	0.405	0.458	0.468	0.540	0.595
1.8	0.265	0.300	0.325	0.330	0.360	0.407	0.416	0.480	0.529
2.0	0.238	0.270	0.293	0.297	0.324	0.367	0.374	0.432	0.476
2.2	0.216	0.246	0.266	0.270	0.295	0.333	0.340	0.393	0.433
2.4	0.198	0.225	0.244	0.247	0.270	0.305	0.312	0.360	0.397
2.6	0.183	0.208	0.225	0.228	0.249	0.282	0.288	0.332	0.366
2.8	0.170	0.193	0.209	0.212	0.232	0.262	0.267	0.309	0.340
3.0	0.159	0.180	0.195	0.198	0.216	0.244	0.250	0.288	0.318

Plate Thickness, t	20 mm			25 mm				40 mm			
Weld Size, D	8	10	12	8	10	12	14	10	12	14	16
0.0	2.49	3.11	3.48	2.49	3.11	3.73	4.35	3.11	3.73	4.35	4.98
0.1	2.33	2.89	3.10	2.35	2.91	3.47	3.88	2.96	3.53	4.09	4.66
0.2	2.17	2.66	2.77	2.21	2.71	3.21	3.46	2.81	3.32	3.83	4.34
0.3	2.01	2.44	2.48	2.06	2.51	2.94	3.10	2.65	3.12	3.57	4.02
0.4	1.85	2.22	2.23	1.92	2.31	2.68	2.78	2.50	2.92	3.31	3.70
0.5	1.69	1.99	2.01	1.78	2.11	2.42	2.51	2.35	2.71	3.05	3.38
0.6	1.53	1.77	1.82	1.64	1.91	2.16	2.28	2.20	2.51	2.79	3.06
0.7	1.37	1.54	1.66	1.50	1.71	1.89	2.03	2.05	2.30	2.53	2.74
0.8	1.21	1.35	1.46	1.36	1.51	1.66	1.78	1.89	2.10	2.27	2.42
0.9	1.08	1.20	1.30	1.22	1.34	1.47	1.58	1.74	1.89	2.01	2.15
1.0 (a)	0.968	1.08	1.17	1.07	1.21	1.32	1.42	1.59	1.69	1.80	1.94
1.2	0.807	0.900	0.976	0.893	1.01	1.10	1.18	1.28	1.38	1.50	1.61
1.4	0.692	0.772	0.836	0.765	0.865	0.946	1.01	1.06	1.18	1.29	1.38
1.6	0.605	0.675	0.732	0.670	0.757	0.828	0.888	0.923	1.03	1.13	1.21
1.8	0.538	0.600	0.650	0.595	0.672	0.736	0.789	0.821	0.917	1.00	1.08
2.0	0.484	0.540	0.585	0.536	0.605	0.662	0.710	0.739	0.826	0.902	0.968
2.2	0.440	0.491	0.532	0.487	0.550	0.602	0.646	0.671	0.751	0.820	0.880
2.4	0.403	0.450	0.488	0.446	0.504	0.552	0.592	0.615	0.688	0.751	0.807
2.6	0.372	0.416	0.450	0.412	0.466	0.510	0.547	0.568	0.635	0.694	0.745
2.8	0.346	0.386	0.418	0.383	0.432	0.473	0.507	0.528	0.590	0.644	0.692
3.0	0.323	0.360	0.390	0.357	0.403	0.442	0.474	0.492	0.550	0.601	0.646

Electrode: E49XX   Base metal: F_y = 300 MPa, F_u = 450 MPa   See page 3-53 for more information.

FRAMED BEAM SHEAR CONNECTIONS

General

This section of Part Three contains information on five common types of beam shear connections traditionally considered standard in the industry. Double-angle, simple end-plate, single-angle, shear tab, and tee connections are included.

Connections of these types are generally designed for strength requirements under factored loads. The capacities of welds and of bolts in bearing-type connections are based on their factored resistances.

Tabulated bolt capacities for bearing-type connections are based on threads intercepted by the shear planes (unless noted otherwise) and have been calculated according to CSA S16-09, Clause 13.12.1.2. Starting with the 1989 edition, S16 no longer implies that threads are excluded from the shear plane when the material thickness adjacent to the nut is equal to 10 mm. Without special precautions, such a thickness may allow threads to be intercepted. For practical reasons, it is suggested that bearing-type shear connections be designed on the assumption of intercepted threads when combinations of thin material and detailing for minimum bolt stick-through (the nuts) are expected.

Slip-critical bolt capacities are included for double-angle and end-plate connections for use with connections such as those subjected to fatigue or frequent load reversal. Values are based on Class A (clean mill scale or blast-cleaned with Class A coatings) contact surfaces $(k_s = 0.33)$. The capacities are to be used with *specified loads only*.

Tables of bolt and weld capacities are based on M20 and M22 A325M bolts and 3/4 and 7/8-inch diameter A325 bolts, and on E49XX electrodes. They assume the use of angles and detail material with a specified minimum yield strength $F_y = 300$ MPa and a specified minimum tensile strength $F_u = 450$ MPa. For the supported and supporting members, $F_y = 345$ MPa and $F_u = 450$ MPa are assumed.

Although based on specific arrangements of bolts and welds, the tables are general in nature and are intended to facilitate the design of any shear connection without precluding types not shown. These tables can be used by steel fabricators to prepare drawing office and shop standards, by design authorities to check fabricator standards, and by educational institutions to teach structural steel design and detailing.

The standard connections of individual fabricators will depend upon fabrication methods and material sources. They may differ from those shown in the tables regarding length and size of angles and other detail material, as well as gauge and pitch of bolts.

Minimum Material Thickness

Together with the tabulated capacities of welds and bolts in bearing-type connections, information is provided concerning the minimum required thickness of supporting and supported material to develop the full connector capacities. These minimum thicknesses were generally determined in the following manner.

For welded connections, for each weld size the weld shear resistance was equated to the shear resistance of the supported beam web, and the equation solved for the web material thickness t. The weld resistance is based on S16-09 Clause 13.13.2.2, and the web resistance (Clause 13.4.1.1) is $V_r = \phi A_w F_s$, with $F_s = 0.66 F_y$ and A_w = web area.

For bolts in bearing-type connections, the minimum material thickness was derived by equating the bearing capacity of the material to the shear capacity of the bolts while assuming that supported beams are not coped. For webs of beams (both supporting and supported) and for webs and flanges of (supporting) columns, the factored bearing resistance has been calculated according to Clause 13.12.1.2(a).

Block shear failure was also considered in calculating the minimum required material thickness for bolted connections. This mode of failure was evaluated according to Clause 13.11, taking into account the various possible failure patterns, as illustrated below.

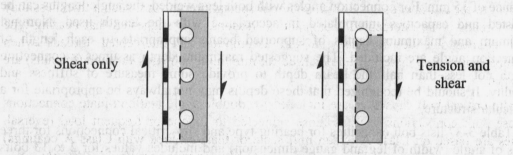

Block Shear Failure
S16-09 Clause 13.11

DOUBLE-ANGLE BEAM CONNECTIONS

Tables 3-37 and 3-38 on pages 3-64 and 3-65, respectively, list capacities of bolted and welded double-angle beam connections. At the bottom of each table are values for minimum material thickness required to develop the connector capacities listed in the corresponding columns. For material thicknesses less than those listed, the corresponding connector capacities must be reduced by the ratio of the thickness of material supplied to the thickness of material listed. Any combination of welded or bolted legs can be selected from the tables.

Bolt capacities are based on concentric loading as tests have shown that eccentricity does not influence the ultimate strength of the bolts in connections using a single line of bolts in the web-framing leg. Weld capacities include the effect of eccentricity for connection angles.

The connection angle length L is based on a bolt pitch of 80 mm assuming an end distance of 35 mm. For connection angles with both legs welded, the angle lengths can be adjusted and capacities interpolated in accordance with the length used. Nominal minimum and maximum depths of supported beams appropriate to each length of connection angle are included. The suggested maximum depth assumes a connection length not less than half the beam depth to provide some measure of stiffness and stability. It should be recognized that these depths may not always be appropriate for a particular structure.

Table 3-37 lists bolt capacities for bearing-type and slip-critical connections for three sizes of angle (width of leg and gauge dimension) and includes values for 2 to 13 bolts per vertical line based on a bolt pitch of 80 mm. For web-framing legs, bolt capacities are based on the "double shear" condition and for outstanding legs on the "single shear" condition. Thus two vertical lines of bolts in the outstanding legs (one line in each angle leg) have the same capacity as one vertical line in the web-framing leg. When beams are connected to both sides of the supporting material, the total bolt capacity in the outstanding legs is double that listed, provided the thickness of the supporting material is equal to or greater than that listed for the web of the supported beam.

For connection angles, the minimum required thickness to develop the bolt capacities is listed in the table. To ensure connection flexibility the angle thickness selected should not be greater than necessary, with a minimum thickness of 6 mm for practical reasons. Bolt capacities are provided separately for both conditions of threads included (intercepted) and threads excluded. See Clause 13.12.1.2 of CSA S16-09.

Table 3-38 lists weld capacities for web-framing legs and for outstanding legs. Values are tabulated for four sizes of fillet weld and are based on the length (L) and size (angle width W) of connection angles listed. For the web-framing leg welds, capacities were calculated using the instantaneous centre of rotation method (see pages 3-42 and 3-46). For the outstanding leg welds, the out-of-plane eccentricity between weld lines and the vertical beam reaction was taken into account. For both the web-framing and outstanding legs, the effect of eccentricity is included for angles up to 310 mm in length; for longer connections, the weld capacity is not reduced by the effect of eccentricity. The minimum angle thickness is equal to the weld size plus 2 mm.

Design of bearing-type connections for types and sizes of bolts other than those shown in Table 3-37 will be facilitated by the resistance tables on pages 3-7 to 3-11, and for slip-critical connections by the tables on page 3-15.

Encroachment by Framing Angles On Beam Fillets

The maximum length of framing angles needs to be compatible with the clear distance T between the flange fillets of a beam. In compact situations, it is customary to tolerate a modest amount of encroachment by the angles onto the toes of the fillets. Encroachments that create a gap not greater than 1 mm under the end of an angle are listed, as a function of the fillet radius, in Table 3-35 on page 3-60.

Supported Beams with Copes.

When copes are required at the ends of supported beams to avoid interference with the supporting material, the capacity of the beam in the vicinity of the connection and/or the capacity of the connection may be reduced. When selecting the beam size, the designer should consider the effect of copes on the load-carrying capacity of the beam, and the detailer should be aware that copes often reduce the capacity of connections on beams with thin webs.

With reference to the beam, the *Steel Construction Manual* (AISC 2005) provides guidance for a variety of situations that include shear at the reduced section, flexural yielding of the coped section due to bending, and web buckling in the vicinity of the cope due to shear and bending. The shear resistance of the web is calculated according to S16-09 Clause 13.4.3.

With reference to the connection, tension and shear block failure, or "block shear" is generally the failure mode when copes govern. See S16-09 Clause 13.11. Block shear takes a different pattern when connection material is bolted to the supported beam than it does when connection material is welded to the beam. In the former case, the pattern is usually a tension tear along a horizontal line from the end of the beam to the bottom bolt hole of the connection combined with a vertical shearing through the line of bolts to the cope. For welded connection angles, there are corresponding tension and shear lines, but along the toes of the welds. The vertical shearing extends all the way to the cope, with the result that the weld across the top of the angles does not participate in the connection resistance.

A detailing aid for evaluating the block shear resistance of a bolted connection on a coped beam is presented in Table 3-36 on page 3-61. The two coefficients C_1 and C_2 were calculated based on S16-09 Clause 13.11 for combined tension and shear failure. Coefficient C_1 is a function of the horizontal and vertical edge distances L_h and L_v to the beam end and the cope, respectively. Coefficient C_2 is a function of the bolt diameter and the number of bolts. The sum of the coefficients multiplied by the web thickness gives the block shear resistance in kN.

Tests cited by Yura *et al.* (1980) have shown that the capacity of single-line bolted connections computed assuming failure along the "block tear-out" line are conservative, but when two lines of bolts are used in the web-framing leg, the effects of eccentricity should be taken into account.

References

AISC. 2005. Steel Construction Manual, 13th Edition, American Institute of Steel Construction.

BIRKEMOE, P.C. and GILMOR, M.I. 1978. Behaviour of bearing-critical double-angle beam connections. Engineering Journal, Fourth Quarter, AISC.

YURA, J.A., BIRKEMOE, P.E. and RICLES, J.M. 1980. Beam web shear connections –an experimental study. Beam-to-Column Building Connections: State of the Art, Preprint 80-179, April, ASCE.

Fillet Encroachment   Table 3-35

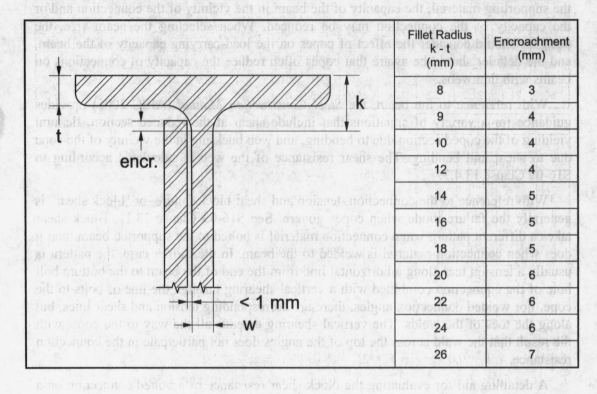

Fillet Radius k - t (mm)	Encroachment (mm)
8	3
9	4
10	4
12	4
14	5
16	5
18	5
20	6
22	6
24	6
26	7

Table 3-36

COEFFICIENTS FOR BLOCK SHEAR
Based on bolt pitch of 80 mm and standard holes*
CSA G40.21-350W, ASTM A992, A572 grade 50

Coefficient C_1

L_v (mm)	L_h (mm)												
	25	26	28	30	32	34	38	45	52	59	66	73	80
25	12.1	12.4	13.0	13.6	14.2	14.8	16.0	18.1	20.3	22.4	24.5	26.6	28.8
26	12.2	12.5	13.2	13.8	14.4	15.0	16.2	18.3	20.4	22.6	24.7	26.8	29.0
28	12.6	12.9	13.5	14.1	14.7	15.3	16.6	18.7	20.8	22.9	25.1	27.2	29.3
30	13.0	13.3	13.9	14.5	15.1	15.7	16.9	19.0	21.2	23.3	25.4	27.5	29.7
32	13.3	13.6	14.2	14.8	15.4	16.1	17.3	19.4	21.5	23.6	25.8	27.9	30.0
34	13.7	14.0	14.6	15.2	15.8	16.4	17.6	19.8	21.9	24.0	26.1	28.3	30.4
38	14.4	14.7	15.3	15.9	16.5	17.1	18.3	20.5	22.6	24.7	26.8	29.0	31.1
45	15.6	15.9	16.6	17.2	17.8	18.4	19.6	21.7	23.8	26.0	28.1	30.2	32.3
52	16.9	17.2	17.8	18.4	19.0	19.6	20.8	23.0	25.1	27.2	29.3	31.5	33.6
59	18.1	18.5	19.1	19.7	20.3	20.9	22.1	24.2	26.3	28.5	30.6	32.7	34.9
66	19.4	19.7	20.3	20.9	21.5	22.1	23.3	25.5	27.6	29.7	31.9	34.0	36.1
73	20.7	21.0	21.6	22.2	22.8	23.4	24.6	26.7	28.9	31.0	33.1	35.2	37.4
80	21.9	22.2	22.8	23.4	24.0	24.6	25.9	28.0	30.1	32.2	34.4	36.5	38.6

Coefficient C_2

n	Bolt		
	¾ in.	M20	1 in.
2	10.8	10.7	9.9
3	25.1	25.0	24.2
4	39.4	39.3	38.5
5	53.7	53.6	52.8
6	68.1	67.9	67.1
7	82.4	82.2	81.5
8	96.7	96.5	95.8
9	111.0	110.8	110.1
10	125.3	125.1	124.4

$\phi_u = 0.75$ $U_t = 0.9$ $F_y = 345$ MPa $F_u = 450$ MPa

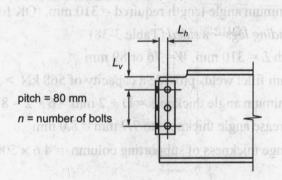

pitch = 80 mm
n = number of bolts

Block shear

$T_r = \phi_u [U_t A_n F_u + 0.6 A_{gv}(F_y + F_u)/2]$ (S16-09 Clause 13.11)

$T_r = (C_1 + C_2) w$ (using coefficients in Table 3-36)

Design example

W460x89 beam using four ¾ in. bolts with: $L_v = 45$ mm, $L_h = 38$ mm and $w = 10.5$ mm

From Table 3-36: $C_1 = 19.6$ $C_2 = 39.4$

$T_r = (C_1 + C_2) w = (19.6 + 39.4) 10.5 = 620$ kN

where

T_r	= factored resistance for block shear		L_h	= distance, centre of hole to beam end
w	= thickness of the beam web		L_v	= distance, center of hole to cope
A_n	= net area in tension		n	= number of bolts
A_{gv}	= gross area in shear		d_h	= design allowance for hole diameter *

* The design allowance for punched holes is 2 mm larger than the hole diameter (S16-09, Clause 12.3.2). Coefficient C_2 was calculated using $d_h = 23$ mm for ¾ in. bolts, 24 mm for M20 bolts and 29 mm for 1 in. bolts.

Example 1

Bolted to beam web, bearing-type, welded to column flange.

Given:

W530x92 beam connected to flange of W250x73 column,
both ASTM A992 steel.

Reaction due to factored loads = 500 kN

Beam web thickness = 10.2 mm; column flange thickness = 14.2 mm.

Detail material G40.21-300W steel, M20 A325M bolts, E49XX electrodes.

Solution:

Web-framing legs – bolted (Table 3-37)

Vertical line with four bolts (threads included) provides a capacity of:

701 kN > 500 kN OK

Web thickness, based on bearing, required for steels with F_u = 450 MPa

= 8.1 × 500 / 701 = 5.8 mm < 10.2 mm OK

Angle thickness required:

= 7.7 × 500 / 701 = 5.5 mm. Try 6.4 mm.

Minimum angle length required = 310 mm. (OK for 4 bolts and 530 mm beam depth)

Outstanding legs – welded (Table 3-38)

With L = 310 mm, W = 76 or 89 mm

6 mm fillet welds provide a capacity of 568 kN > 500 kN OK

Minimum angle thickness = D + 2 mm = 6 + 2 = 8 mm

Increase angle thickness to 7.9 mm ≈ 8.0 mm

Flange thickness of supporting column = 4.6 × 500 / 568 = 4.0 mm < 14.2 mm OK

Use:

76x76x7.9 connection angles 310 mm long, four M20 A325M bolts in web-framing
legs and 6 mm fillet welds on outstanding legs.

Example 2

Welded to beam web, bolted to column flange, bearing-type.

Given:

Same as example 1

Solution:

Web-framing legs – welded (Table 3-38)

6 mm fillet welds provide a capacity of 808 kN with angle length $L = 310$ mm and $W = 76$ mm

Web thickness required for 6 mm fillet welds, $L = 310$ mm

$$= 9.1 \times 500 / 808 = 5.6 \text{ mm} < 10.2 \text{ mm} \quad \text{OK}$$

Outstanding legs – bolted (Table 3-37)

Try 7.9 mm angle thickness.

For $L = 310$ mm, $W = 76$ or 89 mm, four bolts (threads included) per vertical line, bolt shear capacity is 701 kN > 500 kN OK

Angle thickness required $= 7.7 \times 500 / 701 = 5.5 \text{ mm} < 7.9 \text{ mm}$ OK

The required flange thickness of the supporting column, with a beam framing from one side, is one half the required thickness of the supported beam web:

$$14.2 \text{ mm} > 8.1 / 2 = 4.1 \text{ mm} \quad \text{OK}$$

Use:

89x76x7.9 connection angles, 310 mm long, 89 mm outstanding legs, g = 130 mm with eight M20 A325M bolts (2 rows of 4) and 6 mm fillet welds.

Example 3

Bolted to beam web and bolted to both sides of supporting member, supported beams not coped, bearing-type.

Given:

W530x92 beam of ASTM A992 steel, factored reaction 500 kN, framing from both sides of 11.0 mm web of WWF800x161 girder of G40.21 350W steel.

Detail material – G40.21 300W steel, M20 A325M bolts.

Solution:

Web framing legs – same as example 1

Outstanding legs – bolted to both sides of supporting member (Table 3-37)

Total reaction on girder web is $2 \times 500 = 1000$ kN

For beams connected to both sides of supporting member, the bolt capacity is double that listed in the table:

$$2 \times 701 = 1400 \text{ kN} > 1000 \text{ kN}$$

Required web thickness of supporting member, based on bearing, is the same as that given for web thickness of supported beam. For angle $L = 310$ mm, $W = 76$ or 89 mm, four M20 A325M bolts per vertical line (threads included), the girder web thickness is:

$$11.0 \text{ mm} > 8.1 \text{ mm} \quad \text{OK}$$

Use:

89x89x7.9 connection angles, 310 mm long, four M20 A325M bolts per vertical line in both web-framing and outstanding legs.

BOLTED DOUBLE ANGLE[1] BEAM CONNECTIONS

Table 3-37

M20, M22 A325M Bolts
3/4, 7/8 A325 Bolts

BOLT CAPACITY - EITHER LEG WITH BOLTS

Web-Framing Leg   Outstanding Legs

Angle Width and Gauge		
W	g	g₁
102	140	65
89	130	60
76	100	45

Nominal depth of supported beam (mm)		Conn. Angle Length L (mm)	Bolts per Vertical Line	BEARING-TYPE CONNECTIONS Factored Load Resistance (kN) Threads Included				BEARING-TYPE CONNECTIONS Factored Load Resistance (kN) Threads Excluded			
				Bolt Size				Bolt Size			
min.	max.			3/4	M20	M22	7/8	3/4	M20	M22	7/8
200	310	150	2	316	350	424	430	451	501	606	615
310	460	230	3	474	526	636	645	677	751	909	922
380	610	310	4	632	701	848	860	903	1000	1210	1230
460	760	390	5	790	876	1060	1080	1130	1250	1510	1540
530	920	470	6	948	1050	1270	1290	1350	1500	1820	1840
610	1100	550	7	1110	1230	1480	1510	1580	1750	2120	2150
690	1200	630	8	1260	1400	1700	1720	1810	2000	2420	2460
800		710	9	1420	1580	1910	1940	2030	2250	2730	2770
900		790	10	1580	1750	2120	2150	2260	2500	3030	3070
920		870	11	1740	1930	2330	2370	2480	2750	3330	3380
1100		950	12	1900	2100	2540	2580	2710	3000	3630	3690
1200		1030	13	2050	2280	2760	2800	2930	3250	3940	3990

				SLIP-CRITICAL CONNECTIONS[2] Specified Load Resistance (kN)							
200	310	150	2	135	150	181	184	Tabulated values are based on the following angle leg widths:			
310	460	230	3	202	224	271	275				
380	610	310	4	270	299	362	367				
460	760	390	5	337	374	452	459	For 3/4 and M20 bolts, W = 76 mm or 89 mm			
530	920	470	6	405	449	543	551				
610	1100	550	7	472	524	633	643	For M22 and 7/8 bolts, W = 89 mm or 102 mm			
690	1200	630	8	540	598	724	734				
800		710	9	607	673	814	826				
900		790	10	674	748	905	918	Resistance factors:			
920		870	11	742	823	995	1010	φ = 0.90, φ_u = 0.75			
1100		950	12	809	898	1090	1100	φ_b = 0.80, φ_br = 0.80			
1200		1030	13	877	972	1180	1190				

Specified Minimum Tensile Strength (MPa)			Minimum Required Web Thickness of Supported Beam[3,4] (mm)				Minimum Required Web Thickness of Supported Beam[3,4] (mm)			
F_u = 450			7.7	8.1	8.9	9.0	11.0	11.6	12.7	12.8
Specified Minimum Yield and Tensile Strengths (MPa)			Minimum Required Thickness of Framing Angles (mm)				Minimum Required Thickness of Framing Angles (mm)			
F_y = 300, F_u = 450			6.9	7.7	9.4	9.5	9.9	11.0	13.4	13.6

1. Connection angles are assumed to be material with F_y = 300 MPa.
2. Tabulated values for slip-critical connections assume Class A contact surfaces with k_s = 0.33.
3. For supporting material with beams framing from both sides, minimum required thickness is equal to tabulated values for web thickness of supported beam. For supporting material with beams framing from one side, minimum required thickness is one-half the tabulated values.
4. Coped beams may have additional requirements. See page 3-59.

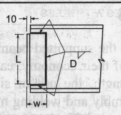 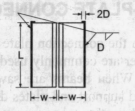

Web-Framing Leg with Welds	Outstanding Leg with Welds	WELDED DOUBLE ANGLE BEAM CONNECTIONS[1] Table 3-38

WELDED DOUBLE ANGLE BEAM CONNECTIONS[1]
Table 3-38

E49XX Fillet Welds

WELD CAPACITY Factored Load Resistance (kN)				WELD CAPACITY Factored Load Resistance (kN)				Conn. Angle Length L (mm)	Nominal Depth of Supported Beam (mm)	
Fillet Size D (mm)				Fillet Size D (mm)						
5	6	8	10	5	6	8	10		min.	max.
Angle Width W = 76 mm				Angle Width W = 89 mm						
369	443	590	738	135	157	202	246	150	200	310
538	646	861	1080	303	356	460	563	230	310	460
674	808	1080	1350	473	568	754	933	310	380	610
782	939	1250	1560	596	715	953	1190	390	460	760
888	1070	1420	1780	718	861	1150	1440	470	530	920
994	1190	1590	1990	840	1010	1340	1680	550	610	1100
1100	1320	1760	2200	962	1150	1540	1920	630	690	1200
1210	1450	1930	2410	1080	1300	1740	2170	710	800	
1310	1570	2100	2620	1210	1450	1930	2410	790	900	
1420	1700	2270	2830	1330	1600	2130	2660	870	920	
1520	1830	2440	3050	1450	1740	2320	2900	950	1100	
1630	1950	2610	3260	1570	1890	2520	3150	1030	1200	
Angle Width W = 64 mm				Angle Width W = 76 mm						
355	425	567	709	146	170	218	265	150	200	310
515	618	824	1030	322	380	491	602	230	310	460
628	754	1000	1260	473	568	758	947	310	380	610
734	881	1170	1470	596	715	953	1190	390	460	760
840	1010	1340	1680	718	861	1150	1440	470	530	920
945	1130	1510	1890	840	1010	1340	1680	550	610	1100
1050	1260	1680	2100	962	1150	1540	1920	630	690	1200
1160	1390	1850	2310	1080	1300	1740	2170	710	800	
1260	1520	2020	2530	1210	1450	1930	2410	790	900	
1370	1640	2190	2740	1330	1600	2130	2660	870	920	
1480	1770	2360	2960	1450	1740	2320	2900	950	1100	
1600	1920	2560	3200	1570	1890	2520	3150	1030	1200	

Minimum Required Web Thickness of Supported Beam [2] (mm)				Minimum Thickness of Supporting Material with Beam Framing on One Side [3]				Specified Minimum Yield Strength of Material (MPa)		
7.6	9.1	12.1	15.2	3.8	4.6	6.1	7.6	$F_y = 345$		

1. Connection angles are assumed to be material with $F_y = 300$ MPa.

2. Coped beams may have additional requirements. See page 3-59.

3. For supporting material with beams framing from both sides, use double the tabulated value.

END-PLATE CONNECTIONS

End-plate connections with the connection plate welded to the supported beam and bolted to the supporting member are commonly used because of their economy, ease of fabrication, and performance. When beams are saw-cut to length, the use of simple jigging procedures to locate and support end plates during assembly and welding makes it possible to meet the tighter fabrication tolerances required without difficulty.

Research on simple end-plate shear connections has shown that their strength and flexibility compare favourably with double-angle shear connections for similar material thickness, depth of connection, and arrangement of bolts (gauge and pitch). For practical reasons it is suggested that the minimum thickness of the end-plate be 6 mm, and for adequate flexibility, that the maximum thickness be limited to 10 mm. The gauge dimension g should preferably be between 100 mm and 150 mm for plates up to 10 mm thick, but may be as low as 80 mm for minimum thickness plates with F_y not greater than 300 MPa.

Table 3-39 lists the capacities of bolts and welds for typical end-plate connections with 2 to 8 bolts per vertical line, together with the minimum thickness of the end plate, supporting, and supported members to develop the full capacity of the bolts and welds, respectively. End-plate thicknesses are based on minimum edge distances in S16-09 Table 6.

For added safety during erection, clipped end plates with one upper corner of the end plate removed may be used. Tests at Queen's University demonstrated that clipped end-plate connections have similar moment-rotation characteristics to unclipped end-plate connections; therefore, weld capacities in Table 3-39 may be used directly for design, but tabulated bolt values must be reduced by the value of a single bolt.

Table 3-39 also includes bolt capacities for slip-critical joints for those situations where bearing-type connections are not suitable.

References

VAN DALEN, K., and MACINTYRE, J.R. 1988. The rotational behaviour of clipped end-plate connections. Canadian Journal of Civil Engineering, **15**(1), February.

Example

Given:

W410x60 beam of ASTM A992 steel framing into web of WWF700x152 girder of G40.21-350W steel. The factored reaction is 325 kN.

Beam web thickness = 7.7 mm, girder web thickness =11.0 mm. G40.21 grade 300W steel plate detail material, M20 A325M bolts, and E49XX electrodes

Solution:

Try 3 bolts per vertical line (threads included).

Factored resistance = 526 kN > 325 kN OK

For 230 mm-long end plate, weld capacity for 5 mm fillet welds is 342 kN > 325 kN

Required end-plate thickness = 7.4 × 325 / 526 = 4.6 mm. Use 6 mm minimum.

Minimum thickness of supported beam web = 7.6 × 325 / 342 = 7.2 mm < 7.7 mm

Minimum thickness of supporting girder web (beams framing from one side)
= 4.1 × 325 / 526 = 2.5 mm < 11.0 mm OK

If beams were framing from both sides, the required web thickness of the girder would be twice the listed value, pro-rated for the actual factored load:

2 × 4.1 × 325 / 526 = 5.1 mm < 11.0 mm OK

Use: End plate 160x6x230 mm connected to web of the supported beam with 5 mm E49XX fillet welds, and six M20 A325 bolts (2 rows of 3 at 100 mm gauge).

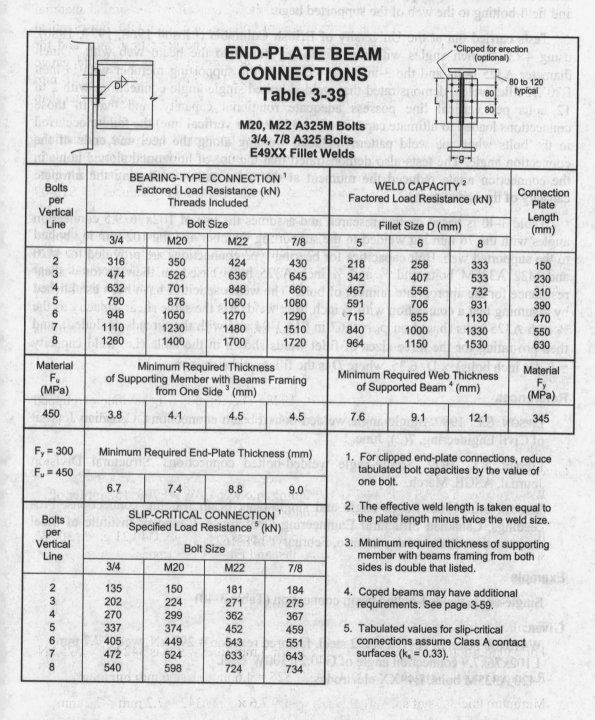

END-PLATE BEAM CONNECTIONS
Table 3-39

M20, M22 A325M Bolts
3/4, 7/8 A325 Bolts
E49XX Fillet Welds

*Clipped for erection (optional)

80 to 120 typical

Bolts per Vertical Line	BEARING-TYPE CONNECTION [1] Factored Load Resistance (kN) Threads Included				WELD CAPACITY [2] Factored Load Resistance (kN)			Connection Plate Length (mm)
	Bolt Size				Fillet Size D (mm)			
	3/4	M20	M22	7/8	5	6	8	
2	316	350	424	430	218	258	333	150
3	474	526	636	645	342	407	533	230
4	632	701	848	860	467	556	732	310
5	790	876	1060	1080	591	706	931	390
6	948	1050	1270	1290	715	855	1130	470
7	1110	1230	1480	1510	840	1000	1330	550
8	1260	1400	1700	1720	964	1150	1530	630

Material F_u (MPa)	Minimum Required Thickness of Supporting Member with Beams Framing from One Side [3] (mm)				Minimum Required Web Thickness of Supported Beam [4] (mm)			Material F_y (MPa)
450	3.8	4.1	4.5	4.5	7.6	9.1	12.1	345

F_y = 300 F_u = 450	Minimum Required End-Plate Thickness (mm)			
	6.7	7.4	8.8	9.0

Bolts per Vertical Line	SLIP-CRITICAL CONNECTION [1] Specified Load Resistance [5] (kN)			
	Bolt Size			
	3/4	M20	M22	7/8
2	135	150	181	184
3	202	224	271	275
4	270	299	362	367
5	337	374	452	459
6	405	449	543	551
7	472	524	633	643
8	540	598	724	734

1. For clipped end-plate connections, reduce tabulated bolt capacities by the value of one bolt.

2. The effective weld length is taken equal to the plate length minus twice the weld size.

3. Minimum required thickness of supporting member with beams framing from both sides is double that listed.

4. Coped beams may have additional requirements. See page 3-59.

5. Tabulated values for slip-critical connections assume Class A contact surfaces (k_s = 0.33).

SINGLE-ANGLE BEAM CONNECTIONS

For some applications, single-angle connections provide a satisfactory alternative to double-angle or end-plate connections. They are particularly suitable where limited access prevents the erection of beams with double-angle or end-plate connections, and where speed of erection is a primary consideration.

The connection angle may be either bolted or welded to the supporting and supported members; however, usual practice involves shop fillet-welding to the supporting member and field-bolting to the web of the supported beam.

Tests carried out at the University of British Columbia (Lipson 1968, 1977, 1980), using 4×3×⅜ inch angles with the 4-inch leg bolted to the beam web with ¾ inch diameter A325 bolts and the 3-inch leg welded to the supporting member with ¼ inch E70XX fillet welds, demonstrated that welded-bolted single-angle connections with 2 to 12 bolts per vertical line possess adequate rotational capacity, and that in those connections loaded to ultimate capacity (2 to 8 bolts per vertical line) the failure occurred in the bolts when the weld pattern included welding along the heel and ends of the connection angle. The tests also demonstrated that the use of horizontal slotted holes in the connection angle reduced the moment at the bolts without affecting the ultimate capacity of the connection.

Table 3-40 is based on this research and assumes the use of 102x76x9.5 connection angles with the 76 mm leg welded to the supporting member and the 102 mm leg bolted to the supported web. Bolt capacities for bearing-type connections are provided for M20 and M22 A325M bolts and ¾ and ⅞ inch A325 bolts based on their factored shear resistance for the appropriate number of bolts. The weld capacities have been established by assuming that a connection with ¼ inch fillet welds has the same shear capacity as the ¾ inch A325 bolts (based on $\phi_b = 0.67$ in S16.1-94 and with the threads excluded), and then pro-rating for the three sizes of fillet welds shown in the table (i.e. weld capacity $= V_r$ {¾ inch bolts} $\times D / 6.35$, where D is the fillet weld size in mm).

References

LIPSON, S.L. 1980. Single-angle welded-bolted beam connections. Canadian Journal of Civil Engineering, **7**(2), June.

LIPSON, S.L. 1977. Single-angle welded-bolted connections. Structural Division Journal, ASCE, March.

LIPSON, S.L. 1968. Single-angle and single-plate beam framing connections. Proceedings, Canadian Structural Engineering Conference, Canadian Institute of Steel Construction, Willowdale, Ontario, February: 141–162.

Example

Single-angle welded-bolted beam connection (Table 3-40)

Given:

W410x60 beam of ASTM A992 steel, factored reaction = 290 kN, web = 7.7 mm
L102x76x7.9 connection angle of G40.21 300W steel.
M20 A325M bolts, E49XX electrodes.

Solution:

With threads included in the shear plane, bolt capacity with four M20 A325M bolts is 350 kN > 290 kN OK

Web thickness required is $4.1 \times 290 / 350 = 3.4$ mm < 7.7 mm OK

Angle thickness required is $7.2 \times 290 / 350 = 6.0$ mm < 7.9 mm OK

Angle length required for 4 bolts is 310 mm, and weld capacity using 5 mm E49XX fillet welds is 298 kN > 290 kN OK

Use:

L102x76x7.9 connection angle, 310 mm long, 76 mm leg welded to supporting member with 5 mm E49XX fillet welds; 102 mm leg bolted to web of supported beam with four M20 A325M bolts.

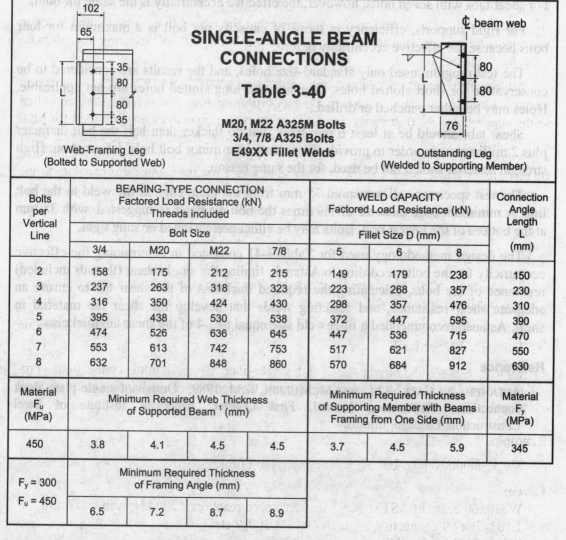

SINGLE-ANGLE BEAM CONNECTIONS
Table 3-40

M20, M22 A325M Bolts
3/4, 7/8 A325 Bolts
E49XX Fillet Welds

Web-Framing Leg
(Bolted to Supported Web)

Outstanding Leg
(Welded to Supporting Member)

Bolts per Vertical Line	BEARING-TYPE CONNECTION Factored Load Resistance (kN) Threads included				WELD CAPACITY Factored Load Resistance (kN)			Connection Angle Length L (mm)
	Bolt Size				Fillet Size D (mm)			
	3/4	M20	M22	7/8	5	6	8	
2	158	175	212	215	149	179	238	150
3	237	263	318	323	223	268	357	230
4	316	350	424	430	298	357	476	310
5	395	438	530	538	372	447	595	390
6	474	526	636	645	447	536	715	470
7	553	613	742	753	517	621	827	550
8	632	701	848	860	570	684	912	630

Material F_u (MPa)	Minimum Required Web Thickness of Supported Beam [1] (mm)				Minimum Required Thickness of Supporting Member with Beams Framing from One Side (mm)			Material F_y (MPa)
450	3.8	4.1	4.5	4.5	3.7	4.5	5.9	345

$F_y = 300$ $F_u = 450$	Minimum Required Thickness of Framing Angle (mm)			
	6.5	7.2	8.7	8.9

1. Coped beams may have additional requirements. See page 3-59.

SHEAR TAB BEAM CONNECTIONS

When the loading does not require the strength of bolts in double shear, a simple and economical connection is a single plate welded vertically onto a supporting member with the supported member bolted to the plate. Shear tabs – as they are commonly known – were studied by Astaneh *et al* (1989) in an experimental program to define a suitable design method for proportioning and rating them. Table 3-41 was prepared by following recommendations in that paper.

Astaneh identified that the strength of shear tabs is a function of several variables. The first is the stiffness of the supporting member. A shear tab on a column flange is restrained from following the end rotation of the supported member, whereas a shear tab on one side of a supporting beam is more free to rotate in its own plane. This results in different effective eccentricities upon the bolts. The eccentricities are also a function of the number of bolts in the connection. Generally, shear tabs on flexible supports have larger bolt eccentricities, and therefore lower resistances, than do those on rigid supports. For shear tabs with seven bolts, however, the effective eccentricity is the same for both.

For rigid supports, efficiency in terms of capacity per bolt is a maximum for four bolts because the effective eccentricity is zero.

The test program used only standard-size holes, and the results are considered to be conservative for short slotted holes. Oversize and long slotted holes are not applicable. Holes may be either punched or drilled.

Shear tabs should be at least 6 mm thick, but no thicker than half the bolt diameter plus 2 millimetres in order to provide the potential for minor bolt hole deformation. High strength material should not be used, for the same reason.

The test specimens all measured 75 mm from the plate edge at the weld to the bolt line. A minimum edge distance of 1½ times the bolt diameter is suggested, with 35 mm at the bottom of the lowest bolt. Bolts may be either pretensioned or snug tight.

The design methodology used for Table 3-41 consisted in determining the effective eccentricity for the bolts according to Astaneh, finding the single shear (threads included) resistance of the bolts, calculating the required thickness of the shear tab to ensure an adequate shear resistance, and selecting welds that develop the shear tab material in shear. Astaneh recommended a fillet weld size equal to 3/4 of the shear tab thickness.

Reference

ASTANEH, A., CALL, S.M., and MCMULLIN, K.M. 1989. Design of single plate shear connections. Engineering Journal, First Quarter, American Institute of Steel Construction, Chicago, Illinois.

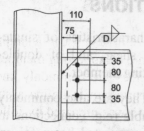

SHEAR TAB BEAM CONNECTIONS
Table 3-41

BEARING-TYPE CONNECTIONS
Factored Load Resistance (kN)
M20, M22 A325M and 3/4, 7/8 A325 Bolts
G40.21 300W Steel, E49XX Fillet Welds

RIGID SUPPORT

Number of Bolts	Connection Plate Length (mm)	3/4 Bolts			M20 Bolts		
		Resistance (kN)	Plate Thickness (mm)	Weld Size D (mm)	Resistance (kN)	Plate Thickness (mm)	Weld Size D (mm)
2	150	79.3	6	5	88.2	6	5
3	230	173	6	5	193	6	5
4	310	264	6	5	294	8	6
5	390	310	6	5	345	8	6
6	470	360	6	6	401	8	6
7	550	413	8	6	459	8	6

Number of Bolts	Connection Plate Length (mm)	M22 Bolts			7/8 Bolts		
		Resistance (kN)	Plate Thickness (mm)	Weld Size D (mm)	Resistance (kN)	Plate Thickness (mm)	Weld Size D (mm)
2	150	107	6	5	108	6	5
3	230	233	8	6	236	8	6
4	310	356	10	8	360	10	8
5	390	417	10	8	422	10	8
6	470	485	10	8	491	10	8
7	550	556	10	8	563	10	8

FLEXIBLE SUPPORT

Number of Bolts	Connection Plate Length (mm)	3/4 Bolts			M20 Bolts		
		Resistance (kN)	Plate Thickness (mm)	Weld Size D (mm)	Resistance (kN)	Plate Thickness (mm)	Weld Size D (mm)
2	150	62.1	6	5	69.1	6	5
3	230	123	6	5	137	6	5
4	310	195	6	5	217	6	5
5	390	269	6	5	299	6	5
6	470	342	8	6	380	8	6
7	550	413	8	6	459	8	6

Number of Bolts	Connection Plate Length (mm)	M22 Bolts			7/8 Bolts		
		Resistance (kN)	Plate Thickness (mm)	Weld Size D (mm)	Resistance (kN)	Plate Thickness (mm)	Weld Size D (mm)
2	150	83.6	6	5	84.6	6	5
3	230	165	6	5	167	6	5
4	310	262	8	6	266	8	6
5	390	362	8	6	366	8	6
6	470	460	8	6	465	8	6
7	550	556	8	6	563	8	6

Note: Bolt capacities are calculated assuming that threads intercept the shear plane.

TEE-TYPE BEAM CONNECTIONS

Tee-type beam connections combine some of the characteristics of single-angle connections with the web-framing leg bolted in single shear, and of double-angle connections with the outstanding legs welded to the supporting member.

Their main advantage is speed and ease of erection. They are also commonly used where hole making in the supporting member is undesirable (e.g. connections to HSS columns), and to avoid coping the bottom flange of the supported beam for erection purposes.

Costs are generally higher than for other types of simple beam connections because of the higher costs of fabricating the tee-sections.

Table 3-42 lists bolt capacities for bearing-type web-framing connections, and weld capacities for connections of outstanding legs. Bolt shear capacities were calculated based on the vertical reaction alone (i.e. without eccentricity), assuming that threads intercept the shear plane. Weld shear capacities were calculated by taking into account the out-of-plane eccentricity between the face of the support and the bolt line. These values are the same as those listed in Table 3-38 for the outstanding legs of welded double-angle connections. To ensure adequate connection flexibility, the flange thickness of the tees should be held to a minimum.

Example

Tee-type welded/bolted beam connections (Table 3-42)

Given:

W460x74 beam of ASTM A992 steel, Factored reaction = 375 kN
Column – HSS 254x254x13 of G40.21-350W steel
Beam web thickness = 9.0 mm

M20 A325M bolts, E49XX electrodes.

Solution:

Try a tee cut from W200x59 beam (ASTM A992); web thickness = 9.1 mm.

These thicknesses of beam web and tee web (stem) will result in threads intercepting the shear plane.

Five bolts per vertical line provide a capacity of 438 kN > 375 kN OK

Beam web thickness required for F_u of 450 MPa is

$$4.1 \times 375 / 438 = 3.5 \text{ mm} < 9.0 \text{ mm} \text{OK}$$

Tee stem (web) thickness required is $6.8 \times 375 / 438 = 5.8$ mm < 9.1 mm OK

Length of tee required for 5 bolts is 390 mm, and weld capacity for 5 mm fillet welds is 596 kN > 375 kN OK

Clear depth of beam web between fillets, T = 395 mm > 390 mm   OK

Use:

Tee cut from W200x59, 390 mm long, five M20 A325M bolts connecting webs of beam and tee, and 5 mm E49XX fillet welds to supporting material.

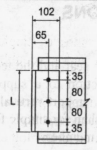

TEE-TYPE BEAM CONNECTIONS
Table 3-42

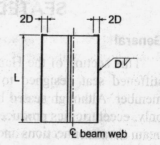

M20, M22 A325M Bolts
3/4, 7/8 A325 Bolts
E49XX Fillet Welds

Web-Framing Leg
(Bolted to Supported Web)

Outstanding Leg
(Welded to Supporting Member)

℄ beam web

Bolts per Vertical Line	BEARING-TYPE CONNECTIONS Factored Load Resistance (kN) Threads Included				WELD CAPACITY Factored Load Resistance (kN)			Connection Tee Length L (mm)
	Bolt Size				Fillet Size D (mm)			
	3/4	M20	M22	7/8	5	6	8	
2	158	175	212	215	135	157	202	150
3	237	263	318	323	303	356	460	230
4	316	350	424	430	473	568	754	310
5	395	438	530	538	596	715	953	390
6	474	526	636	645	718	861	1150	470
7	553	613	742	753	840	1010	1340	550
8	632	701	848	860	962	1150	1540	630
Material F_u (MPa)	Minimum Required Web Thickness of Supported Beam [1] (mm)				Minimum Required Thickness of Supporting Member with Beams Framing from One Side (mm)			Material F_y (MPa)
450	3.8	4.1	4.5	4.5	3.8	4.6	6.1	345
Material (MPa) $F_y = 345$ $F_u = 450$	Minimum Thickness of Tee Stem (mm)							
	6.1	6.8	8.3	8.5				

1. Coped beams may have additional requirements. See page 3-59.

SEATED BEAM SHEAR CONNECTIONS

General

This section of the Handbook deals with the unstiffened angle seat and the tee-type stiffened seat designed to provide a simple beam shear connection to a supporting member. Although seated beam shear connections are designed to support vertical loads only, eccentricities produced by these connections may be greater than for simple framed beam shear connections and can influence the design of supporting members.

Seated beam shear connections are most commonly used at beam-to-column supports. If used at beam-to-girder supports, the girder web must be checked for adequate local stability and resistance. Economy with seated beam shear connections results from simple shop fabrication, together with ease and speed of field erection.

The unstiffened angle seat consists of a relatively thick angle either shop-welded or bolted to the supporting member. When the supporting member is a column web, access for welding may be restricted. Load capacity of an unstiffened angle seat is limited by the angle thickness. This capacity can be increased by stiffening the angle; however, stiffened angle seats are more expensive to fabricate, and stiffened seats using tee-stubs built up from plate are usually more economical. Stiffened seats designed for large loads are generally referred to as brackets and are beyond the scope of this section.

A seated beam must be stabilized laterally with a flexible clip angle attached either to the top flange of the beam or to the beam web near the top of the beam. The clip angle must be thin enough to permit end rotation of the beam. Either welds or bolts can be used to connect the clip angle to the beam and supporting member. When welds are used, the fillet welds should be located along the toes of the angle.

Unstiffened Angle Seats

The capacity of unstiffened angle seats depends on the bending capacity of the seat angle, and is governed by the web thickness and effective bearing length of the supported beam. When the vertical leg of the seat angle is welded to the supporting member, the top of the angle is restrained by the welds, so that the capacity of the angle seat is assumed to be limited by the bending capacity of the outstanding leg. When the vertical leg is bolted to the supporting member, the top of the angle is not restrained by the bolts; therefore, it is assumed that bending in the vertical leg, rather than the outstanding leg, controls the bending capacity of the angle seat.

Tables 3-43 and 3-44 list capacities for welded and bolted unstiffened angle seats of various thicknesses for seat lengths of 180 mm and 230 mm, assuming beams of ASTM A992 steel $(F_y = 345$ MPa$)$, seat angles of G40.21-300W steel $(F_y = 300$ MPa$)$ and welds made with E49XX electrodes. Capacities are based on the design models illustrated in the tables, with no allowance made for possible restraint provided by any connection between the seat and the bottom flange of the supported beam.

Tabulated values assume a seat angle fillet radius of 10 mm. For detailing purposes, the gap between the end of the supported beam and the face of the supporting member is taken equal to 10 mm, although calculations are based on a gap of 20 mm.

Beam web bearing capacities in Tables 3-43 and 3-44 are based on web yielding and crippling according to Clauses 14.3.2(b)(i) and (ii) of CSA S16-09.

Vertical Leg Welded to Supporting Member

Table 3-43 lists the beam web bearing resistance for welded seats with various angle thicknesses and beam web thicknesses, and the vertical leg weld resistance for various weld sizes and angle vertical leg lengths. The beam web bearing resistance was calculated according to Clause 14.3.2(b), with the bearing length obtained by equating the value from Clause 14.3.2(b)(i) to the plastic bending resistance of the angle outstanding leg. The bottom flange thickness of the supported beam was approximated by $t_f \approx 1.8\,w - 3$, where w is the beam web thickness. The vertical weld capacity was determined with the model illustrated at the bottom of the table. The welds are assumed to carry the vertical load and a tension force computed from the conservative eccentricities listed near the bottom of the table. Angle thicknesses in the top row apply throughout the table. Compression from the eccentric moment is carried by contact at the lower middle of the angle. Vertical bending resistance of the angle is also checked.

Vertical Leg Bolted to Supporting Member

Table 3-44 lists the beam web bearing resistance for bolted seats and the seat angle bending resistance based on the model illustrated at the top of the table. Bolt capacities are given for four sizes of bolt, two or four bolts per seat angle, for threads excluded and threads intercepted. These bolt capacities are based on assumptions thought to be conservative.

Example

Given: W530x92 beam of ASTM A992 steel, factored reaction = 200 kN
Beam web thickness = 10.2 mm, flange width = 209 mm.

Solution:

(a) *Unstiffened angle seat welded to supporting member*

Seat angle thickness and beam web bearing capacity:

From Table 3-43, a beam web thickness of 10 mm with $L = 230$ mm (to permit the 209 mm flange to be welded to the seat) and a 12.7 mm-thick angle provide a beam web bearing capacity of 226 kN > 200 kN. The 10.2 mm web is therefore adequate.

Vertical leg connection:

For an angle thickness of 12.7 mm with a vertical leg of 152 mm and a conservatively assumed eccentricity of 50 mm, 8 mm fillet welds provide connection capacity of 228 kN > 200 kN OK

Use 152x102x12.7 seat angle 230 mm long with 152 mm leg welded to supporting member with 8 mm E49XX fillet welds on each side of the vertical leg.

(b) *Unstiffened angle seat bolted to supporting member*

Seat angle thickness and beam web bearing capacity:

From Table 3-44, a 15.9 mm seat angle 230 mm long provides a capacity of:

$$196 + 0.2\,(223 - 196) = 201 \text{ kN} > 200 \text{ kN}$$

The 10.2 mm web is adequate. Four M20 bolts will provide a capacity of 265 kN (threads excluded). Bolt bearing does not govern in this case (not shown).

Use a 152x102x15.9 seat angle 230 mm long with 152 mm leg bolted to supporting member with 4 - M20 A325M bolts.

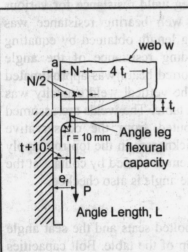

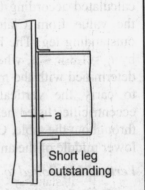

Beam – G40.21-350W or ASTM A992
Angle – G40.21-300W
E49XX Fillet Welds

Web bearing resistance (yielding)

$$P = \phi_{be}\, w(N + 4t_f)F_{yw}$$

Angle leg flexural resistance

$$P = \frac{(Lt^2/4)\phi F_{ya}}{N/2 + a - t - r}$$

The above expressions were equated and solved for N, which was used to calculate P for top half of table.

Short leg outstanding

For detailing purposes, gap $a = 10$ mm, but calculations are based on $a = 20$ mm.

$r = 10$ mm   Estimated $t_f \approx 1.8w - 3$

		Angle t (mm)	7.9		9.5		12.7		15.9		19.1	
		Angle L (mm)	180	230	180	230	180	230	180	230	180	230
Beam web factored bearing resistance (yielding and crippling, kN)	Beam w (mm)	5	58.9	64.5	70.2	76.9	92.7	93.4	93,4	93.4	93.4	93.4
		6	73.8	79.7	86.3	93.4	111	121	135	135	135	135
		7	91.9	97.8	105	113	133	143	160	173	183	183
		8		119	128	135	157	167	187	200	217	233
		9			154	161	185	195	217	230	248	265
		10			184	191	216	226	249	263	283	300
		11				224	251	261	286	299	322	338
		12				261	290	300	326	339	363	380
		13					332	342	370	383	409	425
		14					379	388	418	430	458	474
		Fillet Weld D (mm)	6		6		8		8		10	
		Angle L (mm)	180	230	180	230	180	230	180	230	180	230
Seat vertical leg factored weld resistance (kN)	Seat Angle	89x76	93.0	73.4	87.5	86.7	104	104				
		102x76	113	95.7	107	107	128	128	117	117		
		127x89	153	149	146	146	177	177	163	163	188	188
		152x102	194	194	186	186	228	228	211	211	246	246
		203x152					339	339	318	318	374	374
		Eccentricity e_f	35		40		50		60		70	

Tensile resistance of welds:

$$T_r = 2[0.67\phi_w(l-c)DX_u/\sqrt{2}] = 2Pe_f/l$$

Shear resistance of welds:

$$V_r = 2[0.67\phi_w\, c\, D X_u/\sqrt{2}] = P$$

Above expressions were solved for P by eliminating c to obtain:

$$P = \frac{0.948\phi_w D X_u l^2}{2e_f + l}$$

But P cannot exceed the vertical bending resistance of total angle, taken as: $P = 4\phi S_x F_y / L$

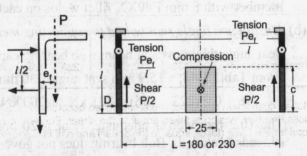

Table 3-44

BOLTED UNSTIFFENED ANGLE SEATS
Factored Resistances

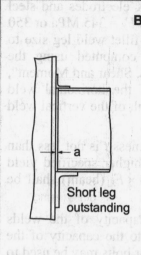

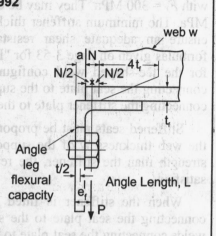

Beam – G40.21-350W or ASTM A992
Angle – G40.21-300W
M20, M22 A325M Bolts
3/4, 7/8 A325 Bolts

Web bearing resistance (yielding)

$$P = \phi_{be}\, w(N + 4t_f) F_{yw}$$

Angle leg flexural resistance

$$P = \frac{(Lt^2/4)\phi F_{ya}}{N/2 + a - t/2}$$

The above expressions were equated and solved for N, which was used to calculate P for top half of table.

For detailing purposes, gap a = 10 mm, but calculations are based on a = 20 mm.

Estimated $t_f \approx 1.8\, w - 3$

Short leg outstanding

Angle leg flexural capacity

Angle Length, L

Factored Resistance – Beam Web Bearing or Seat Angle Bending (kN)								
Angle t (mm)		9.5		12.7		15.9		19.1
Angle L (mm)		180	230	180	230	180	230	180	230
Beam web thickness w (mm)	5	49.2	56.2	69.1	78.4	89.1	93.4	93.4	93.4
	6		66.5	81.1	91.3	103	116	126	135
	7			94.9	106	119	133	144	160
	8				123	137	152	163	181
	9					158	173	186	204
	10					181	196	210	229
	11						223	238	257
	12							269	288
	13								322
	14								360

Factored Bolt Capacity (kN)								
Bolt Size	3/4		M20		M22		7/8	
No. of Bolts	2	4	2	4	2	4	2	4
Threads excluded	176	239	195	265	236	321	240	326
Threads included	138	210	153	233	185	282	188	286

Angle length, L

60 min.

	L	180	230
	g	100	130

Bolted connection capacities were calculated according to CSA S16-09 Clause 13.12.1.4. For a single row of bolts, the bolt tension is taken equal to the shear. For two rows of bolts, the top row is assumed to resist the total tensile force (taken equal to the shear) and half the total shear.

Single row of bolts (n = 2): $V_f = \dfrac{2 T_r V_r}{\sqrt{T_r^2 + V_r^2}}$ Two rows of bolts (n = 4): $V_f = \dfrac{4 T_r V_r}{\sqrt{T_r^2 + 4 V_r^2}}$

STIFFENED SEATED BEAM CONNECTIONS

Table 3-45 lists factored resistances of stiffened seats for the tee-shaped weld configuration shown. Capacities are based on the use of E490XX electrodes and steel with $F_y = 300$ MPa. They may be used conservatively for steel with $F_y = 345$ MPa or 350 MPa. The minimum stiffener thickness t is equal to 1.7 times the fillet weld leg size to ensure an adequate shear resistance. Factored resistances are computed using the formulas given on page 3-53 for "Eccentric Loads on Weld Groups, Shear and Moment", for the tee-shaped weld configuration, with the total length of the horizontal weld connecting the seat plate to the support equal to 0.4 times the length of the vertical weld connecting the stiffener plate to the support.

Stiffened seats must be proportioned so that the stiffener thickness t is not less than the web thickness w of the supported beam. If the beam has a higher specified yield strength than the stiffener, the relationship, $t \times F_y$ (stiffener) $= w \times F_y$ (beam) shall be satisfied.

When the stiffener is fitted to bear against the seat, the capacity of the welds connecting the seat plate to the stiffener shall be at least equal to the capacity of the welds connecting the seat plate to the supporting member. Welds or bolts may be used to connect the supported beam to the seat and for attachment of the clip angle required to stabilize the beam. See the figures in Table 3-45 for the general arrangement.

When stiffened seats are in line on opposite sides of a column web, the size of the vertical fillet welds (for E49XX electrodes) shall not exceed $F_y / 524$ times the thickness of the column web, so as not to exceed the shear resistance of the column web. As an alternative to limiting the weld size, a longer stiffener may be used to reduce the shear stresses in the column web.

Example

Given:

W530x101 beam with a factored reaction of 450 kN
Web thickness = 10.9 mm, flange width = 210 mm, flange thickness = 17.4 mm
Connected to web of W310x97 column, web thickness = 9.9 mm
Design stiffened welded seat for beams connected to both sides of column web
ASTM A992 steel for the beam and column, G40.21-300W steel for the stiffener
E49XX electrodes

Solution:

(a) *Vertical stiffener*

Required length of bearing: $B_r = \phi_{be} w(N + 4t) F_y$ Clause 14.3.2(b)(i)

$N = B_r/(\phi_{be} w F_y) - 4t = 450 \times 10^3 / (0.75 \times 10.9 \times 345) - 4 \times 17.4 = 90$ mm

For $g = 10$ mm clearance, minimum stiffener width, $W = N + g = 90 + 10 = 100$ mm

Eccentricity, $e = aL = W - 0.5N = 100 - 0.5 \times 90 = 55$ mm

For stiffeners on both sides of column web, maximum effective weld size so that shear resistance of column web is not exceeded is:

$9.9 \times 345 / 524 = 6.5$ mm. Try $D = 6$ mm fillet welds.

Minimum stiffener thickness for shear is $1.7 \times 6 = 10.2$ mm. Try 12 mm stiffener.

From Table 3-45, with $e = 55$ mm, 6 mm fillet welds and $L = 250$ mm, capacity provided is 473 kN (by interpolation) > 450 kN OK

Check $b/t = 100/12 = 8.3 < 200/\sqrt{300} = 11.5$ OK   (S16-09, Table 1)

Use 12x100 stiffener, 250 mm long, welded to column web with 6 mm fillet welds.

(b) *Horizontal Seat Plate*

Try 12 mm plate and 6 mm fillet welds (same as vertical stiffener)

Minimum length of weld required to attach seat plate to column web:

$0.4L = 0.4 \times 250 = 100$ mm

Minimum length of seat plate, including clearances for horizontal stiffener welds:

$100 + (2 \times 6) + 12 = 124$ mm

Minimum length of seat plate assuming beam is bolted to seat:

beam flange width = 210 mm

Minimum length of seat plate assuming beam is welded to seat:

$210 + 2(2 \times 6) = 234$ mm

Use 12x100 seat plate, 210 mm long, welded to column web with 6 mm fillet welds on underside of seat, and bolted to bottom flange of the beam with two M20 A325M bolts.

(c) *Weld between stiffener and seat plate*

Minimum length of weld required = 100 mm (same as between seat plate and column web) for 6 mm fillets

Length available is 2×100 mm = 200 mm > 100 mm OK

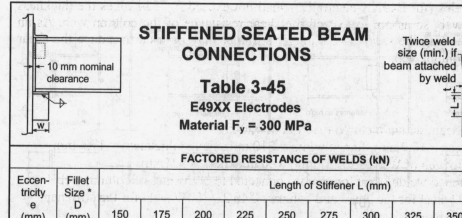

STIFFENED SEATED BEAM CONNECTIONS

Table 3-45

E49XX Electrodes

Material F_y = 300 MPa

10 mm nominal clearance

Twice weld size (min.) if beam attached by weld

Normal location clip angle

Optional location clip angle

		FACTORED RESISTANCE OF WELDS (kN)										
Eccen-tricity e (mm)	Fillet Size * D (mm)	Length of Stiffener L (mm)										
		150	175	200	225	250	275	300	325	350	400	450
e = 50	6	219	292	360	426	490	552	613	674	734	852	969
	8	292	389	480	568	653	736	818	898	978	1140	1290
	10	365	486	600	710	816	920	1020	1120	1220	1420	1610
	12	438	583	720	852	979	1100	1230	1350	1470	1700	1940
e = 70	6	143	195	276	351	422	491	557	622	685	810	931
	8	191	260	368	468	563	654	743	829	914	1080	1240
	10	239	325	460	585	704	818	929	1040	1140	1350	1550
	12	287	390	551	702	844	981	1110	1240	1370	1620	1860
e = 90	6	112	152	198	251	332	409	482	553	621	754	881
	8	149	202	264	335	443	545	643	737	828	1000	1180
	10	186	253	330	418	554	681	804	921	1040	1260	1470
	12	223	304	396	502	664	818	964	1110	1240	1510	1760
e = 110	6	91	124	162	205	253	307	388	466	541	683	819
	8	122	166	216	274	338	409	518	622	721	911	1090
	10	152	207	270	342	422	511	647	777	902	1140	1360
	12	182	248	324	411	507	613	777	932	1080	1370	1640

* Minimum plate thickness, t = 1.7 D

See page 3-53 for more information.

MOMENT CONNECTIONS

General

Continuous construction requires moment-resisting beam-to-column connections that will maintain, virtually unchanged, the original angles between intersecting members at specified loads. Rigid moment connections can be provided by using welds, bolts or combinations of welds and bolts. Numerous configurations and details are possible; Figure 3-4 shows four possible arrangements.

The connections illustrated below apply to moment frames subject to gravity and wind loads. They may be used to resist seismic forces corresponding to $R_d = 1.5$ in frames of "Conventional Construction". Where the building height is within 15 m, Clause 27.11.1 of CSA S16-09 requires that factored seismic forces be increased for buildings with specified short-period spectral acceleration ratios, $I_E F_a S_a(0.2)$, greater than 0.45, unless connections are designed so that the expected failure mode is ductile (See Commentary). Where $I_E F_a S_a(0.2)$ exceeds 0.35 and the building height exceeds 15 m, Clause 27.11.3 provides specific connection design requirements for Conventional Construction. See Clause 27.11.3 and Commentary. For moment connections in Type D, Type MD and Type LD moment-resisting frames, ductile eccentrically braced frames and Type-D plate walls, see the pertinent provisions for each respective system in S16-09 Clause 27 and Annex J.

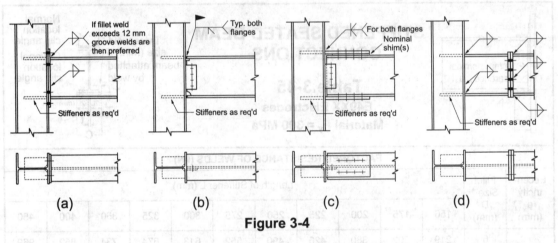

Figure 3-4

Figure 3-4 (a) illustrates a heavy plate shop-welded to the end of the beam and field-bolted to the column. The end plate distributes flange forces over a greater length of column web than does a fully welded joint, but prying action must be considered.

Figure 3-4 (b) illustrates beam flanges field-welded directly to the column with groove welds. Shear capacity is developed by a seat angle, web framing angle or plate, or by welding the beam web directly to the column. Backing bars and run-off tabs for the welds may be required.

Figure 3-4 (c) illustrates the use of moment plates shop-welded to the column with groove or fillet welds and fillet-welded, or preferably bolted, to the flanges of the beam. The moment plates are spaced to accommodate rolling tolerances for beam depth and flange tilt, and nominal shims are provided to fill any significant gap. Minor gaps are closed by the action of bolting. Shear capacity is usually provided by a web plate welded to the column and field-bolted to the beam.

Figure 3-4 (d) illustrates the use of short beam sections shop-welded to the column, and field-bolted to the beam near a point of contraflexure. An end-plate connection is shown but lapping splice plates for the flanges and web may be more economical depending on the forces to be transmitted and the relative ease of achieving field fit-up.

To ensure that the connection provided is consistent with the design assumptions used to proportion members of a structure, it is important that the designer provide the fabricator with governing maximum and coincident moments, shears and axial forces to be developed at the connection. See Clause 4 in S16-09 and the Commentary. In addition, the "type" of seismic moment-resisting frame should be specified.

Column Stiffeners

Where rigid connections are required, the resistance of a column section to local deformation is important. With relatively small beams connected to heavy columns, the columns will provide the degree of fixity assumed in the design of beams. With large beams, however, the columns will usually have to be strengthened locally by means of stiffeners, doubler plates or both.

Column stiffeners are provided opposite tension flanges of the connected beams to minimize curling of the column flanges with resultant overstressing of the central portion of the weld connecting the beam flange (or moment plate) to the column. Opposite the compression flanges of the beams, column stiffeners are provided to prevent buckling of the column web. The most commonly used stiffeners are horizontal plates. When beams of different depths frame into opposite flanges of the column, either inclined stiffeners or horizontal plate stiffeners opposite the flange of each beam may be used. If shear generated in the column web at the moment connection exceeds the column shear capacity, "doubler" plates or diagonal plate stiffeners are used to increase the column web shear capacity locally. Clause 21.3 of S16-09 specifies requirements for web stiffeners on H-type columns when a beam is rigidly framed to the column flange.

References

The following references contain more detailed information on the design of moment connections. Some refer to allowable stress rules and must be interpreted for limit states applications.

ASCE. 1971. Commentary on plastic design in steel. American Society of Civil Engineers, New York, N.Y.

BLODGETT, O.W. 1966. Design of welded structures. The James F. Lincoln Arc Welding Foundation, Cleveland, Ohio.

CHEN, W.F., and LUI, E.M. 1988. Static flange moment connections. Journal of Constructional Steel Research, Elsevier Science Publishers, New York, N.Y., Vol. 10: 65-66.

CHEN, HUANG and BEEDLE. 1974. Recent results on connection research at Lehigh. Regional Conference on Tall Buildings, Bangkok, Thailand, pages 799-813.

CISC. 2004. Moment Connections for Seismic Applications. Canadian Institute of Steel Construction, Willowdale, Ontario.

FEMA. 2000. Recommended Seismic Design Criteria for New Steel Moment-Frame Buildings. Report FEMA-350, Federal Emergency Management Agency, Washington, DC.

GOEL, S.C., STOJADINOVIC, B. and LEE, K-H. 1997. Truss analogy for steel moment connections. Engineering Journal, American Institute of Steel Construction, 34(2).

GRAHAM, SHERBOURNE and KHABBAZ. 1959. Welded interior beam-to-column connections. The American Institute of Steel Construction, Chicago, Illinois.

HUANG, CHEN and BEEDLE. 1973. Behavior and design of steel beam-to-column moment connections. Welding Research Council Bulletin, October.

KRISHNAMURTHY, N. 1978. A fresh look at bolted end plate behavior and design. Engineering Journal, American Institute of Steel Construction, 15(2).

MODULAR LEARNING SYSTEM. 1996. Principles of welding design, module 32 — moment connections. Gooderham Centre for Industrial Learning (a division of the Canadian Welding Bureau), Mississauga, Ontario.

PACKER, J.A. 1977. A limit state design method for the tension region of bolted beam-column connections. The Structural Engineer, 5(10), October.

REGEC, HUANG and CHEN. 1973. Test of a fully-welded beam-to-column connection. Welding Research Council Bulletin, October.

TALL L. (editor). 1964. Structural steel design (2nd. ed.). The Ronald Press Company, New York, N.Y.

Examples

Note: In the following examples, the solution chosen in each case is intended to illustrate only one of several satisfactory solutions that could be used. In any given situation, the design will be influenced by the individual fabricator's experience, fabrication methods and erection procedures.

Example 1

Given:

Design an interior beam-to-column connection for the following coincident forces and moments due to factored loads.

Factored beam moments = 240 kN·m and 310 kN·m

Factored beam shears = 110 kN and 130 kN

Steel: ASTM A992 (W shapes), CSA G40.21-300W (plates), E49XX electrodes

W310x86 Column   W410x60 Beam

t_c = 16.3 mm	t = 12.8 mm
w_c = 9.1 mm	w = 7.7 mm
b = 254 mm	d = 407 mm
d = 310 mm	b = 178 mm
k_1 = 23 mm	Class 1 in bending
T = 238 mm	

Solution:

(a) Web Connection

The design of the connection between the beam web and the column flange need only account for the vertical shear, neglecting eccentricity. (Design for 130 kN shear.)

3-82

Two alternatives are shown to illustrate a field-welded and a field-bolted condition.

Alternative 1

Single plate field-welded to beam web, shop-welded to column flange, holes for 2 - M20 erection bolts

To resist the factored shear, try 5 mm fillet on 6 mm plate.

Required weld length is $130/0.778 = 167$ mm   (Table 3-24, page 3-41)

Use 230 mm length of plate, for a 410 mm beam   (Table 3-38, page 3-65)

Check plate for factored shear capacity.   (Clause 13.11, S16-09)

Gross plate area: $A_{gv} = 230 \times 6 = 1380$ mm^2

$$T_r = \phi_u 0.6 A_{gv} (F_y + F_u)/2 = 0.75 \times 0.6 \times 1380 (300 + 450)/2 = 233 \text{ kN}$$

> 130 kN   Use $6 \times 75 \times 230$ plate with 5 mm E49XX fillet weld.

Alternative 2

Single plate shop-welded to column flange, field-bolted to beam web with M20 A325M bolts

From Table 3-4, page 3-8, factored shear resistance, single shear, threads intercepted, for M20 A325M bolts = 87.6 kN

For 2 bolts, $V_r = 2 \times 87.6 = 175$ kN > 130 kN

Check factored bearing resistance on beam web, $w = 7.7$ mm

From Table 3-6 on page 3-9, B_r for $t = 7$ mm is 151 kN per bolt > 87.6 kN

Try 6 mm plate, 230 mm long, 2 bolts at 160 mm pitch:

Bearing resistance for 6 mm, Table 3-6, $B_r = 130$ kN > 87.6 kN

Required thickness of plate (based on shear resistance, Clause 13.11) is:

$$130 \times 10^3 / [0.75 \times 0.6 \times 230 (300 + 450)/2] = 3.3 \text{ mm} < 6 \text{ mm}$$

Block shear resistance (tension + shear, Clause 13.11) is adequate (not shown).

Use 6 x 80 x 230 plate and two M20 A325M bolts at 160 mm pitch.

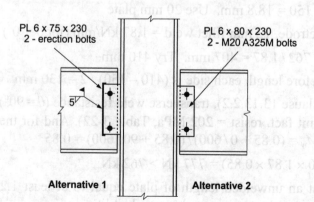

PL 6 x 75 x 230
2 - erection bolts

PL 6 x 80 x 230
2 - M20 A325M bolts

Alternative 1   Alternative 2

Alternative 2 replaces the two erection bolts with permanent high-strength bolts, and eliminates vertical field welding (likely a better solution).

(b) Flange Connection

Two alternatives are shown to illustrate field-bolted and field-welded conditions.

Alternative 1

Top and bottom moment plates shop-welded to column, field-bolted to beam flanges with A325M bolts

Flange force due to factored loads is $310 \times 1000 / 407 = 762$ kN

From Table 3-4, page 3-8, required number of M20 A325M bolts (threads excl.) is:

$762 / 125 = 6.1$ Use 8 bolts   (2 rows of 4)   Shear per bolt $= 762 / 8 = 95.3$ kN

Check factored bearing resistance on beam flange, $t = 12.8$ mm

From Table 3-6, page 3-9, for $t = 12$ mm, $B_r = 259$ kN > 95.3 kN

From S16-09, Clause 13.2(a), gross area of required plate is

$762 \times 10^3 / (0.9 \times 300) = 2\ 820$ mm^2

and required net effective area is: $762 \times 10^3 / (0.75 \times 450) = 2\ 260$ mm^2

Try 200x16 plate, and check areas.

Gross area is $200 \times 16 = 3\ 200$ mm$^2 > 2\ 820$ mm^2

Net area is $(200 - 48)16 = 2\ 430$ mm$^2 > 2\ 260$ mm^2

Assuming 80 mm pitch, 40 mm end distance, 130 mm clear to column flange, plate length required is: $(3 \times 80) + 40 + 130 = 410$ mm

Alternative 2

Moment plate field-welded to column flange and top flange of beam, bottom flange of beam welded directly to column flange with groove weld

As in alternative 1, the moment plate is designed to transmit the factored beam flange force of 762 kN.

Plate area required (gross) is $762 \times 10^3 / (0.9 \times 300) = 2\ 820$ mm^2

Select plate width narrower than beam flange width to permit downhand welding.

Try 150 mm plate. Maximum weld size would be $(178 - 4 - 150)/2 = 12$ mm.

Plate thickness required is $2\ 820 / 150 = 18.8$ mm. Use 20 mm plate

From Table 3-24, for E49XX electrode, 12 mm fillet weld $= 1.87$ kN/mm (for $\theta = 0°$)

Approx. weld length required is: $762 / 1.87 = 407$ mm. Try 410 mm.

End weld length is 150 mm, therefore length each side is $(410 - 150) / 2 = 130$ mm

For the multi-orientation weld (Clause 13.13.2.2), transverse weld resistance ($\theta = 90°$) is governed by the base metal (unit fact. resist $= 202$ MPa, Table 3-22). And for the two longitudinal welds, $\theta_1 = 0°$, $M_w = (0.85 + 0/600)/(0.85 + 90/600) = 0.85$

$V_r = 12 \times 150 \times 0.202 + 2(130 \times 1.87 \times 0.85) = 777$ kN > 762 kN

It is generally recommended that an unwelded length of plate equal to at least 1.2 times the plate width be provided, in order to ensure adequate ductility.

Therefore minimum plate length is $130 + (1.2 \times 150) = 310$ mm.

Use 20 x 150 x 310 plate welded to column flange with full penetration groove weld and welded to top flange of beam with 410 mm of 12 mm fillet welds.

If the flange plate is also subject to compression, the axial compressive resistance should be checked.

A possible third alternative would be to field-weld the top and bottom flanges of the beam directly to the column flange with full penetration groove welds using backing bars fitted against the column flange.

(c) Column Shear Capacity

The column will be subject to a shear force due to the unbalanced moment. S16-09, Clause 21.3 requires stiffening of the column web if this shear exceeds

$$V_r = 0.8 \, \phi \, A_w \, F_s \quad \text{(Clause 13.4.2)}$$

where F_s is calculated according to Clause 13.4.1.1

$$h/w = (310 - 2 \times 16.3)/9.1 = 30.5 < 1014/\sqrt{F_y} = 54.6$$

$$F_s = 0.66 \, F_y = 0.66 \times 345 = 228 \text{ MPa}$$

$$V_r = 0.8 \times 0.9 \times 9.1 \times 310 \times 228 = 463 \text{ kN}$$

Shear force is $(310 - 240) \times 1000 / 407 = 172$ kN < 463 kN   OK

Thus, no reinforcing of the web is required for shear. (Shear forces from the column, above and below the moment connections, are ignored for simplicity.)

(d) Column Stiffeners

Design the column stiffeners to S16-09, Clause 21.3.

Clause 21.3(a): $B_r = 0.80 \times 9.1 \, (12.8 + (10 \times 16.3)) \, 0.345 = 442$ kN < 762 kN

Therefore, stiffeners are required opposite the compression flange for capacity of $762 - 442 = 320$ kN

Clause 21.3(b): $T_r = 7 \times 0.9 \times 16.3^2 \times 0.345 = 577$ kN < 762 kN

Stiffeners are also required opposite the tension flange for a capacity of $762 - 577 = 185$ kN

Total stiffener area required at compression flange is:

$$320 / (0.9 \times 0.300) = 1\,190 \text{ mm}^2$$

Maximum b/t ratio is $145/\sqrt{300} = 8.37$ (to match the Class 1 beam)

Try 90 mm wide stiffener each side of column web (beam flange is 178 mm wide).

Minimum $t = 90 / 8.37 = 10.8$ mm   Try 12 mm

Effective stiffener width to clear column k_1 distance is $(178/2) - 23 = 66$ mm

Effective stiffener area is $2 \times 66 \times 12 = 1\,580$ mm^2 $> 1\,190$ mm^2 OK

Use 12x90 stiffener each side of column web opposite compression flange.

Use same stiffeners opposite tension flange.

(e) Stiffener Welds

Welds connecting stiffeners to column flange must be sufficient to develop a total force in the two stiffeners of 320 kN.

For double fillet welds at stiffener ends (length 66 mm), weld resistance required is

$$320 / (2 \times 66) = 2.42 \text{ kN/mm}$$

From Table 3-24, page 3-41, 10 mm E49XX fillet welds provide

$$2 \times 1.56 = 3.12 \text{ kN/mm} \quad \text{OK}$$

Welds connecting stiffeners to column web must transfer shear forces due to unbalanced beam moment of $172 / 2 = 86.0$ kN per side.

Approximate weld length available is T distance of 238 mm. Assume 230 mm.

Weld resistance required is $86.0 / 230 = 0.374$ kN/mm (one-sided weld will do). Use single 5 mm fillet weld on each stiffener for 0.778 kN/mm. (Table 3-24)

Example 2

Given:

Design an exterior beam-to-column connection for an elastically analyzed frame, in which the column size is the same as example 1, and the beam is a W460x74 having a factored end moment of 310 kN·m and a factored end shear of 130 kN.

W310x86 column	W460x74 beam
See example 1	t = 14.5 mm
for dimensions	w = 9.0 mm
	d = 457 mm
	b = 190 mm
	Class 1 (in bending)

130 kN   310 kN·m

Solution

This example is basically an extension of Example 1, and the solutions given are intended only to provide information on other possibilities.

(a) Web Connection

Use an unstiffened seat angle shop-welded to the column to carry the beam shear and to support the beam during erection.

From Table 3-43, page 3-76, for a beam web of 9 mm and a seat length of 230 mm, a 9.5 mm thick angle will provide a beam web bearing capacity of 161 kN > 130 kN. Also a vertical leg of 127 mm with 6 mm fillet welds provides a vertical leg connection capacity of 146 kN > 130 kN.

Use 127x89x9.5 angle x 230 mm long with 127 mm leg vertical, welded to column flange with 6 mm E49XX fillet welds.

(b) Flange Connection

Assume field-welded connection with full penetration groove welds connecting top and bottom flanges of the beam directly to the column flange (suggested alternative 3 in Example 1). The seat angle would serve as backing for the bottom flange weld.

(c) Column Shear Capacity

Shear force is $310 \times 1\ 000 / 457 = 678$ kN (shears from column ignored)

Diagonal stiffeners will be used to carry shear in excess of the 463 kN shear capacity of the column web (see Example 1).

Horizontal component of stiffener force is $678 - 463 = 215$ kN

If θ is the angle between stiffener and horizontal plane,

$$\cos \theta = 310 / (310^2 + 457^2)^{1/2} = 0.561$$

Force in stiffener is $215 / \cos \theta = 215 / 0.561 = 383$ kN

Total stiffener area required is $383 / (0.9 \times 0.300) = 1\ 420$ mm^2

For 90 mm wide stiffener, effective width is 66 mm (as in Example 1).

Stiffener thickness required is $1\ 420 / (2 \times 66) = 10.8$ mm   Try 12 mm.

b/t is $90/12 = 7.5 < 8.37$ maximum   OK   (see Example 1)

Use one 12x90 diagonal stiffener each side of column web.

(d) Horizontal Column Web Stiffeners

$B_r = 0.80 \times 9.1 (14.5 + (10 \times 16.3)) 0.345 = 446$ kN < 678 kN   Clause 21.3(a)

Stiffeners are required opposite the compression flange for: $678 - 446 = 232$ kN

$T_r = 7 \times 0.9 \times 16.3^2 \times 0.345 = 577$ kN < 678 kN   Clause 21.3(b)

Stiffeners are also required opposite the tension flange for: $678 - 577 = 101$ kN

Design stiffeners for 232 kN; area required is: $232 / (0.9 \times 0.300) = 859$ mm^2

Use two 12x90 stiffeners (see Example 1).

(e) Stiffener Welds

Diagonal Stiffeners

Welds connecting the stiffeners to the column flanges must be sufficient to develop a total force in the two stiffeners of 383 kN (see above).

For double fillet welds at ends of stiffeners (length = 66 mm), weld resistance required is $383 / (2 \times 66) = 2.90$ kN/mm

From Table 3-24, 10 mm E49XX fillet welds provide $2 \times 1.56 = 3.12$ kN/mm

Use 10 mm E49XX fillet welds top and bottom at each end of stiffeners, and nominal 5 mm stitch welds between stiffener and column web.

Horizontal Stiffeners

The end welds must develop total forces in the stiffeners of 232 kN, for which double 8 mm fillet welds are OK.

Welds connecting the horizontal stiffeners to the column web need transfer only a portion of the stiffener load to the column web, as most of that load proceeds down the diagonal stiffeners. However, it is conservative to size these welds to transfer the total load in the stiffeners. For an approximate weld length of 230 mm (see Example 1), weld resistance required is:

$$232 / (2 \times 230) = 0.504 \text{ kN/mm}$$

for which a single 5 mm weld on each stiffener provides 0.778 kN/mm.

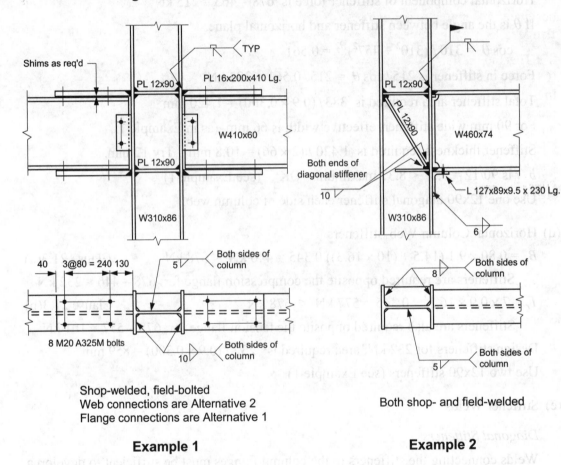

Shims as req'd

PL 12x90
PL 16x200x410 Lg.
W410x60
PL 12x90
W310x86

TYP

PL 12x90
PL 12x90
W460x74
Both ends of diagonal stiffener
L 127x89x9.5 x 230 Lg.
W310x86

40   3@80 = 240   130
Both sides of column
8 M20 A325M bolts
Both sides of column

Both sides of column
Both sides of column

Shop-welded, field-bolted
Web connections are Alternative 2
Flange connections are Alternative 1

Both shop- and field-welded

Example 1

Example 2

Note: The angles formed by the diagonal stiffener with the column flange and the horizontal stiffener often are not suitable for fillet welds ($60° \leq \theta \leq 120°$). However, by providing the size of a fillet weld, the designer indicates the required weld resistance. Shop detail drawings used by the fabricator must show an appropriate configuration of fillet and groove welds that will develop that resistance.

HOLLOW STRUCTURAL SECTION CONNECTIONS

General

Hollow structural sections are frequently used for columns, trusses and space structures due to aesthetics, reduced weight for compression members and other reasons. This section of the Handbook presents sketches of some commonly used connections (Figures 3-5 to 3-9), and information for HSS welds (Figure 3-10, and Tables 3-46 and 3-47). Since the behaviour and resistance of welded HSS connections are not always intuitive, their detail design should be undertaken only by engineers who are familiar with current literature on the subject.

The connections illustrated in Figures 3-5 and 3-6 are simple shear connections designed in a conventional manner. The recommended width-to-thickness ratio of the tee flange is 13 or more in order to ensure suitable rotational flexibility.

The International Committee for the Study and Development of Tubular Structures (CIDECT) has played a major role in sponsoring international research that has resulted in the International Institute of Welding (IIW) making comprehensive design recommendations for HSS connections. Subsequently, a series of "state-of-the-art" design guides edited by CIDECT has been produced (see references). Based on this research, CISC has published *Hollow Structural Section Connections and Trusses—a Design Guide, 2nd Edition* (1997), which is presented as a practical and comprehensive 464-page book dedicated to the Canadian market with design examples that generally meet the requirements of CAN/CSA-S16.1-94.

Basic Considerations for Welded HSS Connections

A prime application of HSS members is in architecturally exposed areas where careful attention must be given to aesthetics of the connections. Simple welded connections without the use of reinforcing material often present the most pleasing and economical solutions. The following fundamentals should be kept in mind.

1. HSS members should not be selected on the basis of minimum mass. That implies that the members will need to be connected for their full capacity, which often is not possible without detail reinforcing material.

2. The force that can be transmitted from one HSS member to another is known as the "connection resistance" and is a function of the relative dimensions and wall thicknesses of the members. It is frequently less than the capacity of the connected member. Therefore, it is necessary to establish that the contemplated members have sufficient connection resistance before the member sizes can be confirmed.

3. Furthermore, design documents that specify "connect for member capacity" often have the effect of causing HSS connections to be reinforced, even if that was not the intent.

4. Square and rectangular HSS are much easier to fabricate than are round HSS because of the complexities of the connection profiles.

5. Try to avoid connections whose members are the same width. Welding is simpler and less expensive if fillet welds can be used along the sides of the connected member. On the other hand, connection resistance increases as the width of branch members approaches the width of main members, and is a maximum when the widths are the same. Therefore, to obtain optimum strength and economy with a square or rectangular HSS connection, the branch member should be as wide as possible, but not wider than the main member minus about five or six times the wall thickness of the main member (since the outer corner radius is generally between two and three times the wall thickness).

6. Connection resistance is improved when branch members have thin walls relative to the main member. A smaller-size main member with a thicker wall may not be much heavier than a larger one with a thinner wall.

7. Full-penetration welds are seldom justified (other than for member splices). They are not advantageous where connection resistance is less than the member capacity. In addition, they are not prequalified for HSS, and the certification for welders is more difficult. Inspection is much more difficult.

8. Ultrasonic inspection has limited application to HSS connections, and radiographic inspection is often only applicable to full-strength splicing of members.

Additional Considerations for HSS Trusses

1. Optimum economy can often be achieved by reducing the number of different size members that are used in a truss. It is less expensive to procure and handle a relatively large amount each of just of few sizes than a small amount each of many sizes.

2. Simple gap connections are usually the most economical when connecting pairs of web members to a truss chord. Overlap connections require additional profiling of members, more precise fitting, and sometimes interrupted fitting to perform concealed welding. Reinforced connections are generally the most expensive.

3. If fatigue is a design consideration, careful attention should be paid to the connection details. It is suggested that overlap connections of at least 50% be used for trusses subjected to fatigue loading.

4. Primary bending moments due to eccentricity e (Figure 3-7) may be ignored, with regard to *connection* design, provided the intersection of the centre lines of the web members lies within the following range measured from the centre line of the chord: 25% of the chord depth towards the outside of the truss, and 55% of the chord depth towards the inside of the truss.

5. Secondary bending moments (due to local connection deformations) may be neglected provided dimensional parameters of the connected members fall within ranges presented in Packer and Henderson (1997).

6. Since the effectiveness of load transfer from one HSS section to another is more a function of dimensional parameters of the members connected than it is of the amount of welding, Packer and Henderson (1997) outline methods to calculate connection efficiency and weld effectiveness.

7. Research by Frater and Packer (1992a, 1992b) and by Packer and Cassidy (1995) has established that welding for HSS truss connections can be related to the type of connection and loading. When web members of gap K or N connections are inclined at 60° or more to the chord, welds along the heel of the web members should be considered ineffective; when the webs are inclined at 50° or less, welds on all four faces of the webs are effective. When web members of T, Y and X connections are inclined at 60° or more to the chord, welds along both the toe and heel of the web members should be considered ineffective; when the webs are inclined at 50° or less, welds along the toes of the web members should be considered ineffective. These weld effective length provisions have also been adopted by AWS D1.1 (2002).

8. Profiling of round members is generally required when they are joined to other members. If aesthetics allow the web members to have the ends flattened instead of profiled, cost savings may be achieved.

E49XX electrodes are normally used for HSS supplied from 350W material with 450 MPa minimum ultimate stress. Table 3-46 on page 3-97 gives the size of fillet welds necessary to develop the strength of the parent material in either shear or tension in accordance with Clause 13.13.2 of S16-09.

In HSS connections, members are usually welded all around. Table 3-47 on page 3-98 gives the length of welds for square and rectangular web members connected to chord members at various angles θ, calculated in accordance with Clause 10.8.5.1 of AWS D1.1 (1990).

References

AWS. 1990. Structural welding code – steel, 12th ed. ANSI/AWS D1.1-90. American Welding Society, Miami, Florida, U.S.A.

AWS. 2002. Structural welding code – steel, 18th ed. ANSI/AWS D1.1/D1.1M:2002. American Welding Society, Miami, Florida, U.S.A.

FRATER, G.S., and PACKER, J.A. 1992a. Weldment design for RHS truss connections. I: Applications. Journal of Structural Engineering, American Society of Civil Engineers, 118(10), pp. 2784-2803.

FRATER, G.S., and PACKER, J.A. 1992b. Weldment design for RHS truss connections. II: Experimentation. Journal of Structural Engineering, American Society of Civil Engineers, 118(10), pp. 2804-2820.

PACKER, J.A., and CASSIDY, C.E. 1995. Effective weld lengths for HSS T, Y and X connections. Journal of Structural Engineering, American Society of Civil Engineers, 121(10).

PACKER, J.A., and HENDERSON, J.E. 1997. Hollow structural section connections and trusses—a design guide, 2nd edition. Canadian Institute of Steel Construction, Willowdale, Ontario.

WARDENIER, J., KUROBANE, Y., PACKER, J.A., DUTTA, D., and YEOMANS, N. 1991. Design guide for circular hollow section (CHS) joints under predominantly static loading. CIDECT (ed.) and Verlag TÜV Rheinland GmbH, Köln, Germany.

PACKER, J.A., WARDENIER, J., KUROBANE, Y., DUTTA, D., and YEOMANS, N. 1992. Design guide for rectangular hollow section (RHS) joints under predominantly static loading. CIDECT (ed.) and Verlag TÜV Rheinland GmbH, Köln, Germany.

Figure 3-5

BEAM TO HSS COLUMN CONNECTIONS

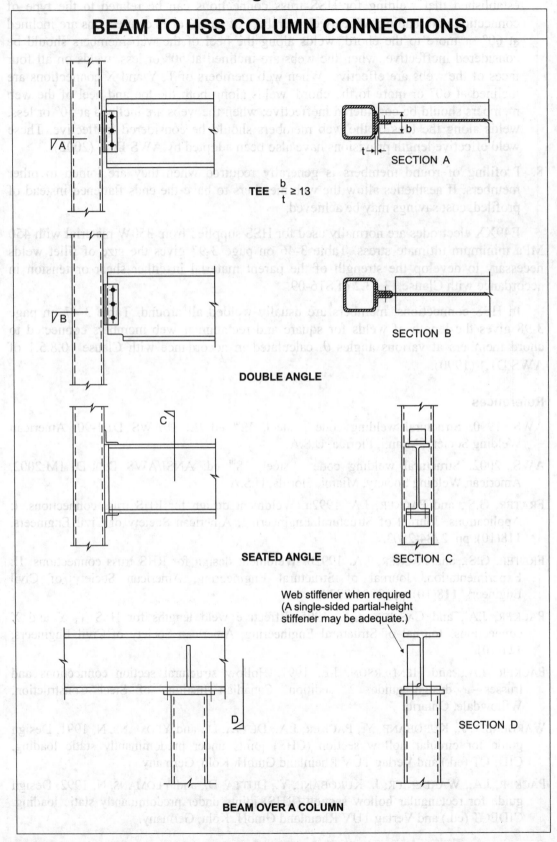

SECTION A

TEE $\dfrac{b}{t} \geq 13$

SECTION B

DOUBLE ANGLE

SEATED ANGLE

SECTION C

Web stiffener when required
(A single-sided partial-height
stiffener may be adequate.)

SECTION D

BEAM OVER A COLUMN

Figure 3-6

TRUSS TO COLUMN AND GIRDER CONNECTIONS

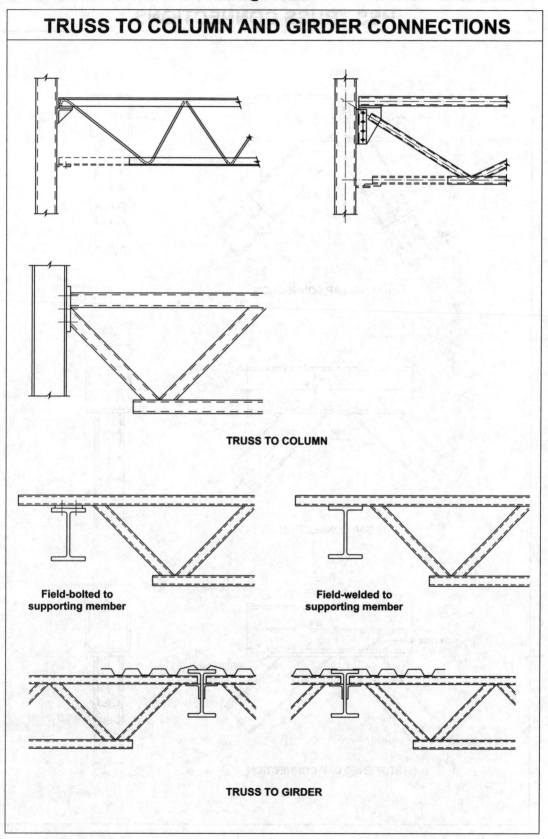

TRUSS TO COLUMN

Field-bolted to supporting member

Field-welded to supporting member

TRUSS TO GIRDER

Figure 3-7

HSS TRUSS CONNECTIONS

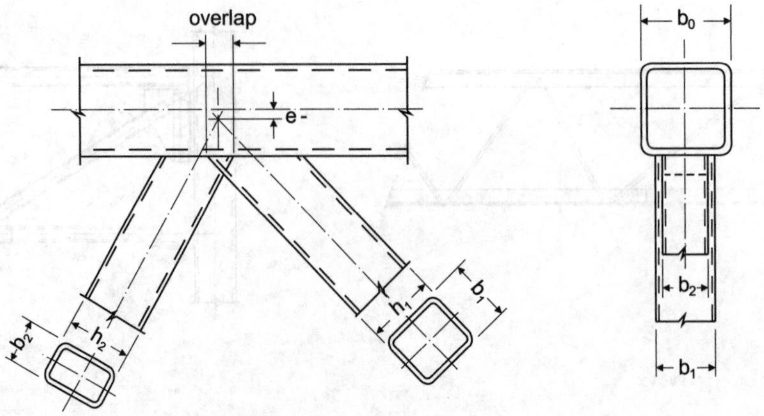

(a) OVERLAP CONNECTION

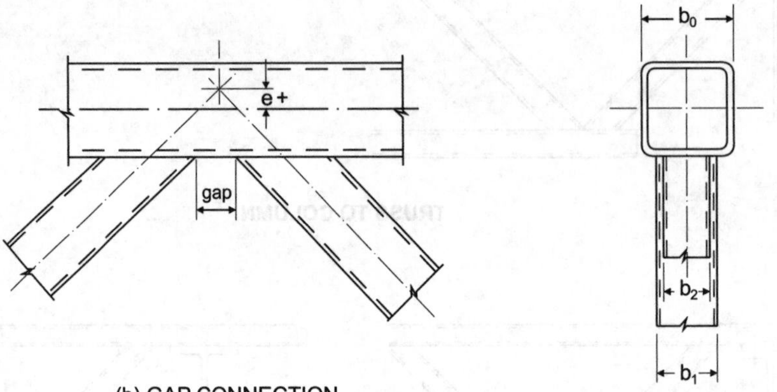

(b) GAP CONNECTION

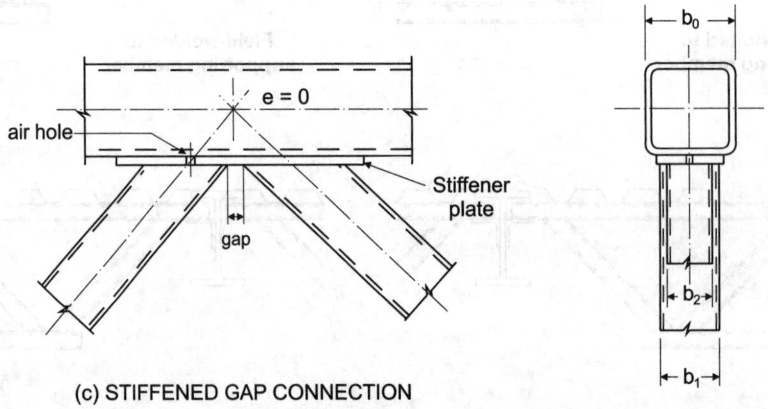

(c) STIFFENED GAP CONNECTION

Figure 3-8

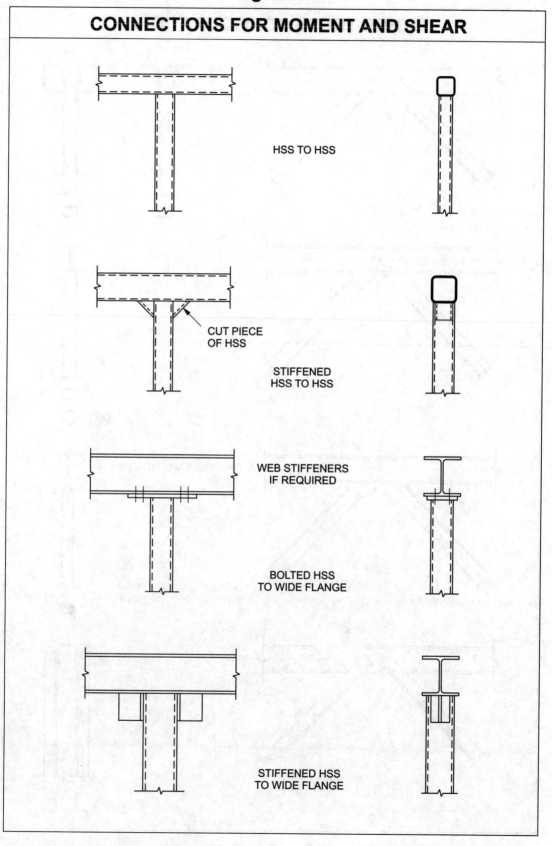

CONNECTIONS FOR MOMENT AND SHEAR

HSS TO HSS

CUT PIECE
OF HSS

STIFFENED
HSS TO HSS

WEB STIFFENERS
IF REQUIRED

BOLTED HSS
TO WIDE FLANGE

STIFFENED HSS
TO WIDE FLANGE

Figure 3-9

OTHER TRUSS CONFIGURATIONS

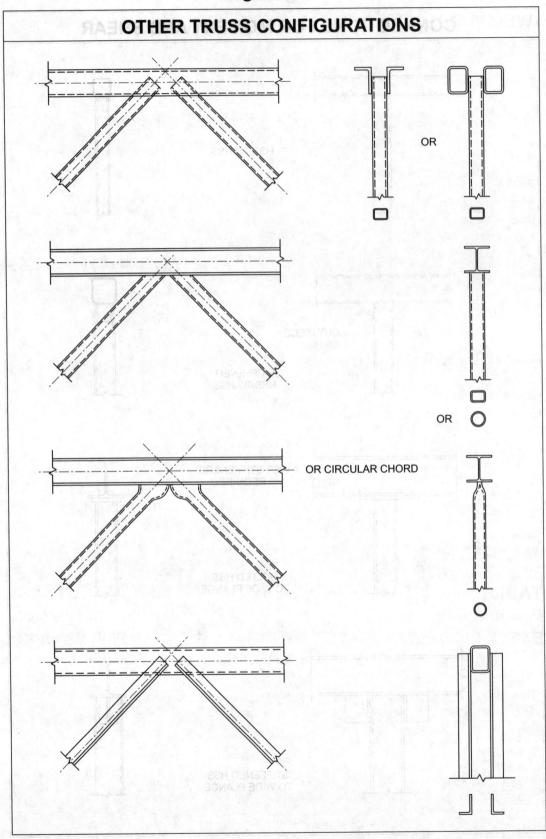

Figure 3-10

WELDING DETAILS FOR HOLLOW STRUCTURAL SECTIONS

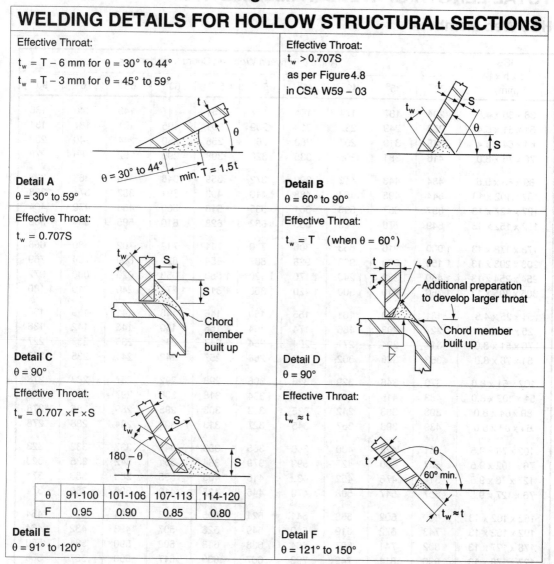

Detail A
θ = 30° to 59°

Effective Throat:
$t_w = T - 6$ mm for θ = 30° to 44°
$t_w = T - 3$ mm for θ = 45° to 59°

θ = 30° to 44°   min. T = 1.5t

Detail B
θ = 60° to 90°

Effective Throat:
$t_w > 0.707S$
as per Figure 4.8
in CSA W59 – 03

Detail C
θ = 90°

Effective Throat:
$t_w = 0.707S$

Chord member built up

Detail D
θ = 90°

Effective Throat:
$t_w = T$ (when θ = 60°)

Additional preparation to develop larger throat

Chord member built up

Detail E
θ = 91° to 120°

Effective Throat:
$t_w = 0.707 \times F \times S$

180 − θ

θ	91-100	101-106	107-113	114-120
F	0.95	0.90	0.85	0.80

Detail F
θ = 121° to 150°

Effective Throat:
$t_w \approx t$

60° min.
$t_w \approx t$

TABLE 3-46
F_u = 450 MPa
E49XX Electrodes

HSS CONNECTIONS
90° Fillet Size to Develop
Wall Strength

Wall Thickness (mm)	Fillet Leg Size (mm)						
	Wall in Shear	Wall in Tension: angle between weld axis and direction of force*					
		0°	15°	30°	45°	50°	90°
3.81	6	8	8	8	8	6	6
4.78	8	10	10	10	8	8	8
6.35	10	14	14	12	10	10	10
7.95	12	18	16	14	14	14	14
9.53	14	20	20	18	16	16	16
11.13	16	24	22	20	18	18	18
12.70	18	26	26	22	20	20	20

* See CSA S16-09, Clause 13.13.2.2. M_w = 1.0 for single-orientation welds.

HSS Web Members

HSS b x h x t (mm)	Angle θ Between Web and Chord Member									
	30°	35°	40°	45°	50°	55°	60°	65°	70°	90°
38 x 38 x 4.8	204	187	174	164	157	151	147	143	140	136
51 x 51 x 6.4	272	249	232	219	209	201	195	191	187	181
64 x 64 x 6.4	348	319	297	280	268	258	250	244	240	232
76 x 76 x 8.0	416	381	355	335	320	308	299	292	286	278
89 x 89 x 9.5	484	443	413	390	372	359	348	340	333	323
102 x 102 x 13	544	498	464	438	418	403	391	382	374	363
127 x 127 x 13	697	637	593	561	535	516	500	488	479	464
152 x 152 x 13	849	776	723	683	652	628	610	595	584	566
178 x 178 x 13	1 000	916	853	806	770	741	719	702	689	668
203 x 203 x 13	1 150	1 060	983	928	887	854	829	809	794	769
254 x 254 x 13	1 460	1 330	1 240	1 170	1 120	1 080	1 050	1 020	1 000	972
305 x 305 x 13	1 760	1 610	1 500	1 420	1 360	1 310	1 270	1 240	1 210	1 180
51 x 25 x 4.8	181	170	161	155	150	146	143	141	139	136
25 x 51 x 4.8	227	203	186	174	164	156	150	145	142	136
76 x 51 x 8.0	317	294	277	264	254	247	241	236	233	227
51 x 76 x 8.0	363	328	302	283	268	257	248	241	235	227
102 x 51 x 8.0	370	346	329	316	306	298	292	287	283	278
51 x 102 x 8.0	463	415	380	354	334	318	306	297	289	278
89 x 64 x 8.0	393	363	342	325	313	303	295	289	285	278
64 x 89 x 8.0	439	398	367	345	327	313	303	294	288	278
102 x 76 x 9.5	461	426	400	380	365	353	344	337	332	323
76 x 102 x 9.5	507	460	425	399	379	364	351	342	335	323
127 x 76 x 9.5	514	478	452	432	416	405	395	388	383	374
76 x 127 x 9.5	607	547	503	470	445	425	410	398	389	374
152 x 102 x 13	650	602	568	541	521	505	493	484	476	464
102 x 152 x 13	743	672	619	580	549	526	507	493	482	464
178 x 127 x 13	802	741	697	664	638	618	602	590	581	566
127 x 178 x 13	896	811	749	703	667	639	617	600	587	566
203 x 102 x 13	755	706	671	644	624	608	595	585	578	566
102 x 203 x 13	943	847	776	722	681	649	624	605	590	566
203 x 152 x 13	954	880	827	786	755	731	712	697	686	668
152 x 203 x 13	1 050	951	880	826	784	752	727	707	692	668
254 x 152 x 13	1 060	984	929	889	857	833	814	799	788	769
152 x 254 x 13	1 250	1 130	1 040	968	916	875	844	819	800	769
305 x 203 x 13	1 360	1 260	1 190	1 130	1 090	1 060	1 030	1 010	997	972
203 x 305 x 13	1 560	1 410	1 300	1 210	1 150	1 100	1 060	1 030	1 010	972

Notes:

1. Outside corner radius assumed equal to $2t$.
2. Perimeters shown in table are for the thickest wall HSS of each size; therefore, perimeters are conservative for smaller wall thicknesses.
3. Perimeters calculated by: $K_a [4\pi t + 2(b - 4t) + 2(h - 4t)]$, where $K_a = [(h/\sin\theta) + b]/(h + b)]$

TENSION MEMBERS

General

Members subject to axial tension (i.e. when the resultant tensile load on the member is coincident with the longitudinal centroidal axis of the member) can be proportioned assuming a uniform stress distribution. The factored tensile resistance is calculated on the basis of yielding on the gross area and fracture on the net area (or effective net area reduced for shear lag) as per Clause 13.2 of CSA S16-09. Net area and effective net area reduced for shear lag are defined in Clause 12.3.

Net Area

Tables 3-48 to 3-51 are intended to simplify the calculation of net area according to the requirements of Clause 12.3.

Hole Diameters for Net Area

Table 3-48 on page 3-104 lists the specified hole diameter for various bolt sizes according to Clause 22.3.5.2, and the diameter of holes for calculating net area according to Clause 12.3.2.

Reduction of Area for Holes

Table 3-49 on page 3-104 lists values for the reduction of area for holes of different diameter in material of various thicknesses.

Staggered Holes in Tension Members

Table 3-50 on page 3-105 lists values of $s^2/4g$ required to calculate the net width of any diagonal or zig-zag line of holes according to the requirements of Clause 12.3.1(b) for various pitches from 25 to 240 mm and for various gauges from 25 to 320 mm. Values of $s^2/4g$ for pitches and gauges between those listed can be interpolated.

Effective Net Area – Reduced for Shear Lag

Clause 12.3.3 of S16-09 contains provisions for determining the loss of efficiency due to shear lag when tension members are not connected by all their elements.

Shear Lag Values of $1 - \bar{x}/L$

Table 3-51 on page 3-105 lists values of $1 - \bar{x}/L$ as a function of $\bar{x}$ and L for use with Clause 12.3.3.3(c) when computing the effective net area reduced for shear lag of section elements projecting from a welded connection.

Design Example - Shear Lag

Given:

An HSS152x152x6.4 of 350W material carries a factored load of 480 kN in tension and is connected by a single plate welded into slots in the HSS walls as shown. The plate will be bolted between a pair of splice plates. Design the plate using 300W steel.

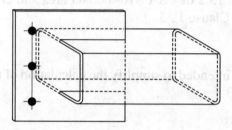

Solution:

Try a 12×240 mm plate

Tensile gross-area yield

$$T_r = \phi\, A_g F_y \qquad \text{S16-09, Clause 13.2(a)(i)}$$

$$= 0.9 \times 12 \times 240 \times 300$$

$$= 778 \text{ kN} > 480 \text{ kN}$$

Tensile net-area rupture (through the bolt line)

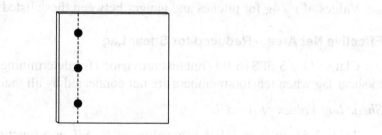

Try three M22 A325M bolts; use 45 mm edge and end distances.

Note: If holes are known to be drilled rather than punched, the specified hole diameter can be used for the net section.   Clause 12.3.2

$$A_{ne} = [240 - (3 \times 24)]\,12$$

$$= 2020 \text{ mm}^2$$

$$T_r = \phi_u A_{ne} F_u \qquad \text{Clause 13.2(a)(ii)}$$

$$= 0.75 \times 2020 \times 450$$

$$= 682 \text{ kN} > 480 \text{ kN}$$

Block shear failure

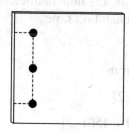

Bolt gauge $= (240 - 2 \times 45)/2 = 75$ mm

Net area in tension:

$$A_n = (2 \times 75 - 2 \times 24)\,12 = 1220 \text{ mm}^2$$

Gross area in shear:

$$A_{gv} = 2 \times 45 \times 12 = 1080 \text{ mm}^2$$

$$T_r = \phi_u\,[U_t A_n F_u + 0.60\,A_{gv}(F_y + F_u)/2] \qquad \text{Clause 13.11}$$

$$= 0.75\,[1.0 \times 1220 \times 450 + 0.60 \times 1080(300 + 450)/2]$$

$$= 594 \text{ kN} > 480 \text{ kN}$$

Bolt shear

Bolt: $V_r = 106$ kN (Table 3-4, page 3-8, threads intercepted)

Connection bolts:

$$V_r = 3 \times 2 \times 106$$

$$= 636 \text{ kN} > 480 \text{ kN}$$

Bearing resistance at bolt holes

$$B_r = 3\,\phi_{br}\,n\,t\,d\,F_u \qquad \text{Clause 13.12.1.2(a)}$$

$$= 3 \times 0.80 \times 3 \times 12 \times 22 \times 450$$

$$= 855 \text{ kN} > 480 \text{ kN}$$

Plate shear failure (by bolts pulling out the end of the plate)

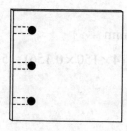

End distance (from centre of bolt hole): $e = 45$ mm

According to Clause 22.3.4, the minimum end distance from the centre of the bolt to the end of the member is 1½ bolt diameters. The failure mode involves two parallel planes adjacent to each bolt hole.

Gross shear area:

$$A_{gv} = 3\,(2 \times 45)\,12 = 3240 \text{ mm}^2$$

$$T_r = \phi_u\,[0.60\,A_{gv}\,(F_y + F_u)/2] \qquad\qquad\qquad \text{Clause 13.11}$$

$$= 0.75\,[0.60 \times 3240\,(300 + 450)/2]$$

$$= 547 \text{ kN} > 480 \text{ kN}$$

Shear lag for the plate

Clause 12.3.3.3(b) in S16-09 provides for shear lag in plates that are connected by a pair of welds parallel to the load. The effective net area is reduced if the length of the welds is less than $2w$.

Distance between welds $w = 152$ mm

Try a weld length $L = w$

Plate area between the welds when $w = L$:

$$A_{n2} = 0.75 \times Lt = 0.75 \times 152 \times 12 = 1370 \text{ mm}^2 \qquad \text{Clause 12.3.3.3(b)(iii)}$$

Plate area on either side of the welds:

$$w = (240 - 152)/2 = 44 \text{ mm}$$

$$A_{n3} = \left(1 - \frac{\bar{x}}{L}\right)wt = 2\left(1 - \frac{44/2}{152}\right)44 \times 12 = 903 \text{ mm}^2 \qquad \text{Clause 12.3.3.3(c)(i)}$$

Total effective net area:

$$A_{ne} = A_{n2} + A_{n3} = 1370 + 903 = 2270 \text{ mm}^2$$

Tensile resistance of the plate

$$T_r = \phi_u\,A_{ne}\,F_u \qquad\qquad\qquad \text{Clause 13.2(a)(iii)}$$

$$= 0.75 \times 2270 \times 450$$

$$= 766 \text{ kN} > 480 \text{ kN}$$

Welds

Try a weld length $L = 150$ mm

Fillet weld size is $480 \text{ kN}/(4 \times 150 \times 0.156) = 5.12 \text{ mm}$ Use 6 mm

Shear lag for the HSS

Distance between the welds measured along the developed wall of the HSS:

$$w \approx 300 \text{ mm} > L$$

$$A_{n2} = 0.75\, L\, t \qquad\qquad \text{Clause 12.3.3.3(b)(iii)}$$

$$= 0.75 \times 150 \times 6.35 = 714 \text{ mm}^2$$

$$T_r = \phi_u A_{ne} F_u$$

$$= 0.75(2 \times 714)450$$

$$= 482 \text{ kN} > 480 \text{ kN}$$

Therefore a PL12×240 × 250 mm long, slotted 150 mm into the HSS, is adequate.

HOLE DIAMETERS FOR EFFECTIVE NET AREA

Table 3-48

Bolt Size		Specified Hole Diameter Clause 22.3.5		Diameter for Net Area** Clause 12.3.2	
Metric	Imperial	Nominal Size (mm)	Oversize (mm)	Nominal Size (mm)	Oversize (mm)
M16		18	20	20	22
	3/4	22*	—	24	—
M20		22*	24	24	26
M22		24*	26	26	28
	7/8	24*	—	26	—
M24		27*	30	29	32
	1	27*	—	29	—
M27		29	35	31	37
M30		32	38	34	40
M36		38	44	40	46

* For nominal diameter of hole, see CSA S16-09 Clause 22.3.5.1
** Diameter for net area is same as specified hole diameter if hole is drilled (Clause 12.3.2).

REDUCTION OF AREA FOR HOLES*

Table 3-49

Material Thickness (mm)	Diameter of Hole (mm)											
	20	22	24	26	28	29	31	32	34	37	40	44
5	100	110	120	130	140	145	155	160	170	185	200	220
6	120	132	144	156	168	174	186	192	204	222	240	264
7	140	154	168	182	196	203	217	224	238	259	280	308
8	160	176	192	208	224	232	248	256	272	296	320	352
9	180	198	216	234	252	261	279	288	306	333	360	396
10	200	220	240	260	280	290	310	320	340	370	400	440
11	220	242	264	286	308	319	341	352	374	407	440	484
12	240	264	288	312	336	348	372	384	408	444	480	528
13	260	286	312	338	364	377	403	416	442	481	520	572
14	280	308	336	364	392	406	434	448	476	518	560	616
16	320	352	384	416	448	464	496	512	544	592	640	704
18	360	396	432	468	504	522	558	576	612	666	720	792
20	400	440	480	520	560	580	620	640	680	740	800	880
22	440	484	528	572	616	638	682	704	748	814	880	968
25	500	550	600	650	700	725	775	800	850	925	1 000	1 100
28	560	616	672	728	784	812	868	896	952	1 040	1 120	1 230
30	600	660	720	780	840	870	930	960	1 020	1 110	1 200	1 320
32	640	704	768	832	896	928	992	1 020	1 090	1 180	1 280	1 410
35	700	770	840	910	980	1 020	1 090	1 120	1 190	1 300	1 400	1 540
38	760	836	912	988	1 060	1 100	1 180	1 220	1 290	1 410	1 520	1 670
40	800	880	960	1 040	1 120	1 160	1 240	1 280	1 360	1 480	1 600	1 760
45	900	990	1 080	1 170	1 260	1 310	1 400	1 440	1 530	1 670	1 800	1 980
50	1 000	1 100	1 200	1 300	1 400	1 450	1 550	1 600	1 700	1 850	2 000	2 200
55	1 100	1 210	1 320	1 430	1 540	1 600	1 710	1 760	1 870	2 040	2 200	2 420
60	1 200	1 320	1 440	1 560	1 680	1 740	1 860	1 920	2 040	2 220	2 400	2 640
70	1 400	1 540	1 680	1 820	1 960	2 030	2 170	2 240	2 380	2 590	2 800	3 080
80	1 600	1 760	1 920	2 080	2 240	2 320	2 480	2 560	2 720	2 960	3 200	3 520
90	1 800	1 980	2 160	2 340	2 520	2 610	2 790	2 880	3 060	3 330	3 600	3 960
100	2 000	2 200	2 400	2 600	2 800	2 900	3 100	3 200	3 400	3 700	4 000	4 400

* Area (mm²) = Diameter of hole (mm) times material thickness (mm).

Table 3-50 — STAGGERED HOLES IN TENSION MEMBERS
Values of $s^2/4g$

Pitch "s" (mm)	Gauge "g" (mm)															
	25	30	35	40	45	50	60	70	80	100	120	160	200	240	280	320
25					3.5	3.1	2.6	2.2	2.0	1.6	1.3	1.0	0.8	0.7	0.6	0.5
30				5.6	5.0	4.5	3.8	3.2	2.8	2.3	1.9	1.4	1.1	0.9	0.8	0.7
35			8.8	7.7	6.8	6.1	5.1	4.4	3.8	3.1	2.6	1.9	1.5	1.3	1.1	1.0
40		13.3	11.4	10.0	8.9	8.0	6.7	5.7	5.0	4.0	3.3	2.5	2.0	1.7	1.4	1.3
45	20.3	16.9	14.5	12.7	11.3	10.1	8.4	7.2	6.3	5.1	4.2	3.2	2.5	2.1	1.8	1.6
50	25.0	20.8	17.9	15.6	13.9	12.5	10.4	8.9	7.8	6.3	5.2	3.9	3.1	2.6	2.2	2.0
55	30.3	25.2	21.6	18.9	16.8	15.1	12.6	10.8	9.5	7.6	6.3	4.7	3.8	3.2	2.7	2.4
60	36.0	30.0	25.7	22.5	20.0	18.0	15.0	12.9	11.3	9.0	7.5	5.6	4.5	3.8	3.2	2.8
65	42.3	35.2	30.2	26.4	23.5	21.1	17.6	15.1	13.2	10.6	8.8	6.6	5.3	4.4	3.8	3.3
70	49.0	40.8	35.0	30.6	27.2	24.5	20.4	17.5	15.3	12.3	10.2	7.7	6.1	5.1	4.4	3.8
75		46.9	40.2	35.2	31.3	28.1	23.4	20.1	17.6	14.1	11.7	8.8	7.0	5.9	5.0	4.4
80			45.7	40.0	35.6	32.0	26.7	22.9	20.0	16.0	13.3	10.0	8.0	6.7	5.7	5.0
90				50.6	45.0	40.5	33.8	28.9	25.3	20.3	16.9	12.7	10.1	8.4	7.2	6.3
100						50.0	41.7	35.7	31.3	25.0	20.8	15.6	12.5	10.4	8.9	7.8
110							50.4	43.2	37.8	30.3	25.2	18.9	15.1	12.6	10.8	9.5
120									45.0	36.0	30.0	22.5	18.0	15.0	12.9	11.3
130										42.3	35.2	26.4	21.1	17.6	15.1	13.2
140										49.0	40.8	30.6	24.5	20.4	17.5	15.3
150											46.9	35.2	28.1	23.4	20.1	17.6
160												40.0	32.0	26.7	22.9	20.0
170												45.2	36.1	30.1	25.8	22.6
180												50.6	40.5	33.8	28.9	25.3
190													45.1	37.6	32.2	28.2
200													50.0	41.7	35.7	31.3
210														45.9	39.4	34.5
220														50.4	43.2	37.8
230															47.2	41.3
240																45.0

Table 3-51 — SHEAR LAG
Values of $1-\overline{x}/L$

L (mm)	$1-\overline{x}/L$ — Distance $\overline{x}$ (mm)															
	10	15	20	25	30	35	40	45	50	55	60	65	70	80	90	100
40	0.75	0.63	0.50	0.38	0.25	0.13										
80	0.88	0.81	0.75	0.69	0.63	0.56	0.50	0.44	0.38	0.31	0.25	0.19	0.13			
120	0.92	0.88	0.83	0.79	0.75	0.71	0.67	0.63	0.58	0.54	0.50	0.46	0.42	0.33	0.25	0.17
160	0.94	0.91	0.88	0.84	0.81	0.78	0.75	0.72	0.69	0.66	0.63	0.59	0.56	0.50	0.44	0.38
200	0.95	0.93	0.90	0.88	0.85	0.83	0.80	0.78	0.75	0.73	0.70	0.68	0.65	0.60	0.55	0.50
240	0.96	0.94	0.92	0.90	0.88	0.85	0.83	0.81	0.79	0.77	0.75	0.73	0.71	0.67	0.63	0.58
280	0.96	0.95	0.93	0.91	0.89	0.88	0.86	0.84	0.82	0.80	0.79	0.77	0.75	0.71	0.68	0.64
320	0.97	0.95	0.94	0.92	0.91	0.89	0.88	0.86	0.84	0.83	0.81	0.80	0.78	0.75	0.72	0.69
360		0.96	0.94	0.93	0.92	0.90	0.89	0.88	0.86	0.85	0.83	0.82	0.81	0.78	0.75	0.72
400		0.96	0.95	0.94	0.93	0.91	0.90	0.89	0.88	0.86	0.85	0.84	0.83	0.80	0.78	0.75
440			0.95	0.94	0.93	0.92	0.91	0.90	0.89	0.88	0.86	0.85	0.84	0.82	0.80	0.77
480			0.96	0.95	0.94	0.93	0.92	0.91	0.90	0.89	0.88	0.86	0.85	0.83	0.81	0.79

NOTES

PART FOUR
COMPRESSION MEMBERS

GENERAL INFORMATION

Limits on Width-to-Thickness Ratios

See page 4-5.

Unit Factored Compressive Resistances for Compression Members, C_r/A

Pages 4-13 to 4-17 provide tables of unit factored compressive resistance for slenderness ratios from 1 to 200 for various yield stresses of steel and values of n of 1.34 and 2.24. See page 4-12 for more information.

ω_1 — Equivalent Uniform Bending Coefficients

Table 4-6, page 4-18, lists values of ω_1 for various ratios M_{f1}/M_{f2} of factored end bending moments applied to beam-columns. The values of ω_1 are computed in accordance with the requirements of Clause 13.8.5, S16-09.

C_e/A — Euler Buckling Load per Unit Area

Table 4-7, page 4-19, lists values of C_e/A for KL/r ratios varying from 1 to 200. The values of C_e/A have been computed in accordance with the definition in Clause 2.2, S16-09.

Amplification Factor U

Table 4-8, page 4-20, has been prepared to facilitate the design of beam-columns in accordance with the requirements of Clause 13.8, S16-09 which incorporates the variable U in the factor U_1. Values of the amplification factor corresponding to various values of C_f/C_e are listed.

Factored Axial Compressive Resistances of Columns

These are the tables often referred to as "column load tables". See page 4-21 for a description of the contents and examples of use.

Design of Beam-Columns

For illustrative examples on the design of beam-columns, see page 4-114.

Factored Moment Resistances of Columns

For the factored moment resistances M_{rx} and M'_{rx} for various unbraced lengths for sections not listed in the Beam Selection Table, see page 4-117.

Double-Angle Struts

The tables of factored axial compressive resistances for double-angle struts, starting on page 4-122, are based on the requirements of Clause 13.3.1, CSA S16-09 with $n = 1.34$ for axis X-X and Clause 13.3.2 for axis Y-Y. For Class 4 angles, the resistances are computed based on the requirements of Clause 13.3.5.

Factored axial compressive resistances with respect to various effective lengths (in millimetres) relative to both the X-X and Y-Y axes, and the U-U and V-V axes for starred angles, are listed for angles made from CSA G40.21 300W. The yield stress F_y for G40.21 300W steel angles is 300 MPa for all thicknesses listed.

The resistances listed in the tables for axis Y-Y are based on closely spaced interconnectors; however, the resistances for axis Y-Y of double-angle struts in practical configurations are generally lower than the listed values because of the additional slenderness of the component angles between interconnectors. The actual number of interconnectors and method of interconnection should therefore be taken into account in accordance with Clause 19.1.4, S16-09. Consult the design example on page 4-142. For starred angles, these requirements may be waived provided interconnectors are spaced no further than at the one-third points, in accordance with Clause 19.1.5.

The factored axial compressive resistances pertaining to effective lengths based on the Y-Y axis have been computed for angles spaced 10 mm back-to-back. Consult the design example on page 4-142 to obtain factored compressive resistances for different spacings.

The value r_z appearing with the properties of double-angle struts is the minimum radius of gyration of a single angle about its minor principal axis. Values for r_x, r_y, r_u and r_v are those for a double-angle strut. See Part Six of this Handbook for a more comprehensive list of angle properties.

Column Base Plates

See page 4-148.

Anchor Rods

See page 4-153.

LIMITS ON WIDTH-TO-THICKNESS RATIOS

Table 4-1 below lists the particular width-to-thickness (b/t, h/w or D/t) ratio limits for various material yield strengths, for each general value given in Table 4-2.

Table 4-2, which is taken from Clause 11 of CSA S16-09, lists the width-to-thickness ratios for Class 1, 2, and 3 sections for various elements in compression. All sections not meeting these requirements are Class 4.

The class for webs in combined flexural and axial compression is a function of the ratio of the factored axial load to the axial compressive load at yield stress $C_f/(\phi C_y)$ as is shown in Table 4-2. Values of $C_f/(\phi C_y)$ at which the webs change class are tabulated in Table 4-3. Table 4-3 lists WWF and W members in G40.21 Grade 350W, when used as beam-columns. Some members with webs that are always Class 1 are controlled by flanges that are not Class 1. Therefore, these members and their flange classification are also included in the table.

Table 4-1
WIDTH-TO-THICKNESS LIMITS

General Value	F_y (MPa)											
	250	260	280	290	300	320	330	345	350	380	400	480
$145/\sqrt{F_y}$	9.17	8.99	8.67	8.51	8.37	8.11	7.98	7.81	7.75	7.44	7.25	6.62
$170/\sqrt{F_y}$	10.8	10.5	10.2	10.0	9.81	9.50	9.36	9.15	9.09	8.72	8.50	7.76
$200/\sqrt{F_y}$	12.6	12.4	12.0	11.7	11.5	11.2	11.0	10.8	10.7	10.3	10.0	9.13
$340/\sqrt{F_y}$	21.5	21.1	20.3	20.0	19.6	19.0	18.7	18.3	18.2	17.4	17.0	15.5
$420/\sqrt{F_y}$	26.6	26.0	25.1	24.7	24.2	23.5	23.1	22.6	22.4	21.5	21.0	19.2
$525/\sqrt{F_y}$	33.2	32.6	31.4	30.8	30.3	29.3	28.9	28.3	28.1	26.9	26.3	24.0
$670/\sqrt{F_y}$*	42.4	41.6	40.0	39.3	38.7	37.5	36.9	36.1	35.8	34.4	33.5	30.6
$840/\sqrt{F_y}$	53.1	52.1	50.2	49.3	48.5	47.0	46.2	45.2	44.9	43.1	42.0	38.3
$1100/\sqrt{F_y}$	69.6	68.2	65.7	64.6	63.5	61.5	60.6	59.2	58.8	56.4	55.0	50.2
$1700/\sqrt{F_y}$	108	105	102	99.8	98.1	95.0	93.6	91.5	90.9	87.2	85.0	77.6
$1900/\sqrt{F_y}$	120	118	114	112	110	106	105	102	102	97.5	95.0	86.7
$13\,000/F_y$	52.0	50.0	46.4	44.8	43.3	40.6	39.4	37.7	37.1	34.2	32.5	27.1
$18\,000/F_y$	72.0	69.2	64.3	62.1	60.0	56.3	54.5	52.2	51.4	47.4	45.0	37.5
$23\,000/F_y$	92.0	88.5	82.1	79.3	76.7	71.9	69.7	66.7	65.7	60.5	57.5	47.9
$66\,000/F_y$	264	254	236	228	220	206	200	191	189	174	165	138

* h/w limit for webs in pure compression, $C_f/(\phi C_y) = 1.0$

Description of Element	Maximum Width-to-Thickness Ratios: Elements in Axial Compression
Elements supported along one edge; flanges of I-sections, T-sections, and channels; legs of angles; plate-girder stiffeners	$\dfrac{b_{el}}{t} \leq \dfrac{200}{\sqrt{F_y}}$
Stems of T-sections	$\dfrac{b_{el}}{t} \leq \dfrac{340}{\sqrt{F_y}}$
Flanges of rectangular hollow sections; flanges of box sections; flange cover plates and diaphragm plates between lines of fasteners or welds	$\dfrac{b_{el}}{t} \leq \dfrac{670}{\sqrt{F_y}}$
Webs supported on both edges	$\dfrac{h}{t} \leq \dfrac{670}{\sqrt{F_y}}$
Perforated cover plates	$\dfrac{b_{el}}{t} \leq \dfrac{840}{\sqrt{F_y}}$
Circular hollow sections	$\dfrac{D}{t} \leq \dfrac{23\,000}{F_y}$

Description of Element	Maximum Width-to-Thickness Ratios: Elements in Flexural Compression		
	Class 1	Class 2	Class 3
Flanges of I-sections or T-sections; plates projecting from compression elements; outstanding legs of pairs of angles in continuous contact with an axis of symmetry in the plane of loading	$\dfrac{b_{el}}{t} \leq \dfrac{145}{\sqrt{F_y}}$	$\dfrac{b_{el}}{t} \leq \dfrac{170}{\sqrt{F_y}}$	$\dfrac{b_{el}}{t} \leq \dfrac{200}{\sqrt{F_y}}$
Stems of T-sections	$\dfrac{b_{el}}{t} \leq \dfrac{145}{\sqrt{F_y}}$	$\dfrac{b_{el}}{t} \leq \dfrac{170}{\sqrt{F_y}}$	$\dfrac{b_{el}}{t} \leq \dfrac{340}{\sqrt{F_y}}$
Flanges of rectangular hollow sections	$\dfrac{b_{el}}{t} \leq \dfrac{420}{\sqrt{F_y}}$	$\dfrac{b_{el}}{t} \leq \dfrac{525}{\sqrt{F_y}}$	$\dfrac{b_{el}}{t} \leq \dfrac{670}{\sqrt{F_y}}$
Flanges of box sections; flange cover plates and diaphragm plates between lines of fasteners or welds	$\dfrac{b_{el}}{t} \leq \dfrac{525}{\sqrt{F_y}}$	$\dfrac{b_{el}}{t} \leq \dfrac{525}{\sqrt{F_y}}$	$\dfrac{b_{el}}{t} \leq \dfrac{670}{\sqrt{F_y}}$
Webs	$\dfrac{h}{w} \leq \dfrac{1100}{\sqrt{F_y}}\left(1-0.39\dfrac{C_f}{\phi C_y}\right)$	$\dfrac{h}{w} \leq \dfrac{1700}{\sqrt{F_y}}\left(1-0.61\dfrac{C_f}{\phi C_y}\right)$	$\dfrac{h}{w} \leq \dfrac{1900}{\sqrt{F_y}}\left(1-0.65\dfrac{C_f}{\phi C_y}\right)$
Circular hollow sections	$\dfrac{D}{t} \leq \dfrac{13\,000}{F_y}$	$\dfrac{D}{t} \leq \dfrac{18\,000}{F_y}$	$\dfrac{D}{t} \leq \dfrac{66\,000}{F_y}$

See Clause 11 of CSA S16-09.

Table 4-3

CLASS OF SECTIONS FOR BEAM-COLUMNS
CSA G40.21 350W

Designation	Web 1 $C_f/\phi C_y \le$	Web 2 $C_f/\phi C_y \le$	Web 3 $C_f/\phi C_y \le$	Flange	Designation	Web 1 $C_f/\phi C_y \le$	Web 2 $C_f/\phi C_y \le$	Web 3 $C_f/\phi C_y \le$	Flange
WWF2000x732	—	—	0.099	1	WWF700x245	0.027	0.590	0.657	1
x648	—	—	0.084	1	x214	—	0.573	0.643	2
x607	—	—	0.077	2	x196	—	0.563	0.635	3
x542	—	—	0.069	2	x175	—	0.573	0.643	1
					x152	—	0.557	0.630	1
WWF1800x700	—	0.106	0.251	1					
x659	—	0.097	0.243	1	WWF650x864	1.0	—	—	1
x617	—	0.088	0.236	1	x739	1.0	—	—	1
x575	—	0.079	0.228	2	x598	1.0	—	—	1
x510	—	0.070	0.221	2	x499	1.0	—	—	2
					x400	1.0	—	—	4
WWF1600x622	—	—	0.118	1					
x580	—	—	0.109	1	WWF600x793	1.0	—	—	1
x538	—	—	0.099	1	x680	1.0	—	—	1
x496	—	—	0.090	2	x551	1.0	—	—	1
x431	—	—	0.080	2	x460	1.0	—	—	1
					x369	1.0	—	—	3
WWF1400x597	—	0.174	0.308	1					
x513	—	0.151	0.289	1	WWF550x721	1.0	—	—	1
x471	—	0.140	0.279	2	x620	1.0	—	—	1
x405	—	0.128	0.270	2	x503	1.0	—	—	1
x358	—	0.128	0.270	1	x420	1.0	—	—	1
					x280	1.0	—	—	4
WWF1200x487	—	0.376	0.478	1					
x418	—	0.365	0.469	1	WWF500x651	1.0	—	—	1
x380	—	0.354	0.459	2	x561	1.0	—	—	1
x333	—	0.354	0.459	1	x456	1.0	—	—	1
x302	—	0.343	0.450	2	x381	1.0	—	—	1
x263	—	0.343	0.450	1	x343	1.0	—	—	1
					x306	1.0	—	—	2
WWF1100x458	—	0.325	0.435	1	x276	1.0	—	—	2
x388	—	0.312	0.424	1	x254	1.0	—	—	3
x351	—	0.299	0.413	2	x223	1.0	—	—	4
x304	—	0.299	0.413	1	x197	0.740	0.885	0.905	4
x273	—	0.286	0.402	2					
x234	—	0.286	0.402	1	WWF450x503	1.0	—	—	1
					x409	1.0	—	—	1
WWF1000x447	—	0.454	0.543	1	x342	1.0	—	—	1
x377	—	0.441	0.532	1	x308	1.0	—	—	1
x340	—	0.428	0.521	2	x274	1.0	—	—	1
x293	—	0.428	0.521	1	x248	1.0	—	—	2
x262	—	0.415	0.511	2	x228	1.0	—	—	2
x223	—	0.415	0.511	1	x201	1.0	—	—	3
x200	—	0.402	0.500	1	x177	0.939	0.967	0.974	4
WWF900x417	—	0.294	0.409	1	WWF400x444	1.0	—	—	1
x347	—	0.278	0.395	1	x362	1.0	—	—	1
x309	—	0.262	0.382	2	x303	1.0	—	—	1
x262	—	0.262	0.382	1	x273	1.0	—	—	1
x231	—	0.245	0.368	2	x243	1.0	—	—	1
x192	—	0.245	0.368	1	x220	1.0	—	—	1
x169	—	0.229	0.354	1	x202	1.0	—	—	2
					x178	1.0	—	—	3
WWF800x339	—	0.442	0.533	1	x157	1.0	—	—	3
x300	—	0.426	0.519	2					
x253	—	0.426	0.519	1	WWF350x315	1.0	—	—	1
x223	—	0.409	0.506	2	x263	1.0	—	—	1
x184	—	0.409	0.506	1	x238	1.0	—	—	1
x161	—	0.393	0.492	1	x212	1.0	—	—	1
					x192	1.0	—	—	1
					x176	1.0	—	—	1
					x155	1.0	—	—	2
					x137	1.0	—	—	2

See Table 4-2 for width-thickness criteria.

— Indicates web is never that class.

$F_y = 350$ MPa

Designation	Web 1 $C_f/\phi C_y \leq$	Web 2 $C_f/\phi C_y \leq$	Web 3 $C_f/\phi C_y \leq$	Flange	Designation	Web 1 $C_f/\phi C_y \leq$	Web 2 $C_f/\phi C_y \leq$	Web 3 $C_f/\phi C_y \leq$	Flange
W1100x499	0.852	0.931	0.944	1	W840x251	0.534	0.800	0.833	1
x433	0.541	0.802	0.836	1	x226	0.420	0.752	0.794	1
x390	0.339	0.719	0.765	1	x210	0.323	0.712	0.760	1
x343	0.091	0.616	0.680	1	x193	0.218	0.669	0.723	1
					x176	0.098	0.619	0.682	1
W1000x883	1.0	—	—	1					
x748	1.0	—	—	1	W760x582	1.0	—	—	1
x642	1.0	—	—	1	x531	1.0	—	—	1
x591	1.0	—	—	1	x484	1.0	—	—	1
x554	1.0	—	—	1	x434	1.0	—	—	1
x539	1.0	—	—	1	x389	1.0	—	—	1
x483	0.982	0.985	0.989	1	x350	1.0	—	—	1
x443	0.861	0.935	0.947	1	x314	0.983	0.985	0.989	1
x412	0.660	0.852	0.877	1	x284	0.835	0.924	0.938	1
x371	0.450	0.765	0.804	1	x257	0.689	0.864	0.887	1
x321	0.129	0.632	0.693	1					
x296	0.130	0.632	0.693	1	W760x220	0.677	0.859	0.883	1
					x196	0.568	0.814	0.845	1
W1000x584	1.0	—	—	1	x185	0.475	0.775	0.813	1
x494	1.0	—	—	1	x173	0.403	0.745	0.788	1
x486	1.0	—	—	1	x161	0.307	0.706	0.754	1
x438	1.0	—	—	1	x147	0.206	0.664	0.719	1
x415	1.0	—	—	1	x134	—	0.557	0.630	2
x393	0.917	0.958	0.966	1					
x350	0.660	0.852	0.877	1	W690x548	1.0	—	—	1
x314	0.460	0.769	0.808	1	x500	1.0	—	—	1
x272	0.129	0.632	0.693	1	x457	1.0	—	—	1
x249	0.129	0.632	0.693	1	x419	1.0	—	—	1
x222	0.053	0.601	0.666	1	x384	1.0	—	—	1
					x350	1.0	—	—	1
W920x656	1.0	—	—	1	x323	1.0	—	—	1
x588	1.0	—	—	1	x289	1.0	—	—	1
x537	1.0	—	—	1	x265	1.0	—	—	1
x491	1.0	—	—	1	x240	0.899	0.950	0.960	1
x449	1.0	—	—	1	x217	0.750	0.889	0.908	1
x420	0.903	0.952	0.961	1					
x390	0.810	0.914	0.929	1	W690x192	0.759	0.893	0.911	1
x368	0.725	0.878	0.900	1	x170	0.636	0.842	0.869	1
x344	0.628	0.838	0.866	1	x152	0.430	0.756	0.797	1
					x140	0.308	0.706	0.755	1
W920x381	1.0	—	—	1	x125	0.176	0.651	0.709	1
x345	0.873	0.940	0.951	1					
x313	0.793	0.907	0.923	1	W610x551	1.0	—	—	1
x289	0.638	0.843	0.869	1	x498	1.0	—	—	1
x271	0.533	0.799	0.833	1	x455	1.0	—	—	1
x253	0.404	0.746	0.788	1	x415	1.0	—	—	1
x238	0.299	0.702	0.752	1	x372	1.0	—	—	1
x223	0.214	0.667	0.722	1	x341	1.0	—	—	1
x201	0.106	0.623	0.685	1	x307	1.0	—	—	1
					x285	1.0	—	—	1
W840x576	1.0	—	—	1	x262	1.0	—	—	1
x527	1.0	—	—	1	x241	1.0	—	—	1
x473	1.0	—	—	1	x217	1.0	—	—	1
x433	1.0	—	—	1	x195	0.953	0.973	0.979	1
x392	1.0	—	—	1	x174	0.793	0.907	0.923	1
x359	0.929	0.963	0.971	1	x155	0.611	0.831	0.860	2
x329	0.812	0.915	0.930	1					
x299	0.669	0.855	0.880	1					

— Indicates web is never that class.

$F_y = 345$ MPa

Table 4-3

CLASS OF SECTIONS FOR BEAM-COLUMNS
CSA G40.21 350W, ASTM A992, A572 gr. 50

Designation	Web 1 $C_f/\phi C_y \le$	Web 2 $C_f/\phi C_y \le$	Web 3 $C_f/\phi C_y \le$	Flange	Designation	Web 1 $C_f/\phi C_y \le$	Web 2 $C_f/\phi C_y \le$	Web 3 $C_f/\phi C_y \le$	Flange
W610x153	0.791	0.906	0.923	1	W410x149	1.0	—	—	1
x140	0.672	0.856	0.881	1	x132	1.0	—	—	1
x125	0.480	0.777	0.815	1	x114	1.0	—	—	1
x113	0.347	0.722	0.768	1	x100	0.914	0.957	0.965	1
x101	0.201	0.662	0.717	1					
x91	0.008	0.582	0.651	2	W410x85	1.0	—	—	1
x84	—	0.500	0.582	3	x74	0.863	0.936	0.948	1
					x67	0.689	0.863	0.887	1
W610x92	0.288	0.698	0.748	1	x60	0.420	0.752	0.794	1
x82	0.081	0.612	0.676	1	x54	0.363	0.729	0.774	2
W530x300	1.0	—	—	1	W410x46	0.210	0.665	0.721	1
x272	1.0	—	—	1	x39	—	0.572	0.642	2
x248	1.0	—	—	1					
x219	1.0	—	—	1	W360x1086	1.0	—	—	1
x196	1.0	—	—	1	x990	1.0	—	—	1
x182	1.0	—	—	1	x900	1.0	—	—	1
x165	1.0	—	—	1	x818	1.0	—	—	1
x150	0.851	0.931	0.944	1	x744	1.0	—	—	1
					x677	1.0	—	—	1
W530x138	1.0	—	—	1					
x123	0.906	0.954	0.963	1	W360x634	1.0	—	—	1
x109	0.693	0.865	0.888	1	x592	1.0	—	—	1
x101	0.569	0.814	0.846	1	x551	1.0	—	—	1
x92	0.434	0.758	0.799	1	x509	1.0	—	—	1
x82	0.279	0.694	0.745	2	x463	1.0	—	—	1
x72	0.121	0.629	0.690	3	x421	1.0	—	—	1
					x382	1.0	—	—	1
W530x85	0.454	0.766	0.805	1	x347	1.0	—	—	1
x74	0.324	0.713	0.760	1	x314	1.0	—	—	1
x66	0.121	0.629	0.690	1	x287	1.0	—	—	1
					x262	1.0	—	—	1
W460x464	1.0	—	—	1	x237	1.0	—	—	1
x421	1.0	—	—	1	x216	1.0	—	—	1
x384	1.0	—	—	1					
x349	1.0	—	—	1					
x315	1.0	—	—	1	W360x196	1.0	—	—	1
x286	1.0	—	—	1	x179	1.0	—	—	1
x260	1.0	—	—	1	x162	1.0	—	—	2
x235	1.0	—	—	1	x147	1.0	—	—	3
x213	1.0	—	—	1	x134	1.0	—	—	3
x193	1.0	—	—	1					
x177	1.0	—	—	1	W360x122	1.0	—	—	1
x158	1.0	—	—	1	x110	1.0	—	—	1
x144	1.0	—	—	1	x101	1.0	—	—	1
x128	1.0	—	—	1	x91	1.0	—	—	1
x113	0.847	0.929	0.942	2					
					W360x79	1.0	—	—	1
W460x106	1.0	—	—	1	x72	0.954	0.973	0.979	1
x97	0.939	0.967	0.974	1	x64	0.765	0.895	0.913	1
x89	0.801	0.910	0.926	1					
x82	0.692	0.865	0.888	1	W360x57	0.746	0.887	0.907	1
x74	0.505	0.788	0.823	1	x51	0.569	0.814	0.845	1
x67	0.381	0.736	0.780	1	x45	0.478	0.776	0.814	2
x61	0.274	0.692	0.743	2					
					W360x39	0.355	0.726	0.771	1
W460x68	0.527	0.797	0.831	1	x33	0.086	0.614	0.678	1
x60	0.246	0.680	0.733	1					
x52	0.124	0.630	0.691	1					

— Indicates web is never that class.

$F_y = 345$ MPa

CLASS OF SECTIONS FOR BEAM-COLUMNS
CSA G40.21 350W, ASTM A992, A572 gr. 50

Table 4-3

Designation	Web 1 $C_f/\phi C_y \le$	Web 2 $C_f/\phi C_y \le$	Web 3 $C_f/\phi C_y \le$	Flange	Designation	Web 1 $C_f/\phi C_y \le$	Web 2 $C_f/\phi C_y \le$	Web 3 $C_f/\phi C_y \le$	Flange
W310x500	1.0	—	—	1	W200x100	1.0	—	—	1
x454	1.0	—	—	1	x86	1.0	—	—	1
x415	1.0	—	—	1	x71	1.0	—	—	1
x375	1.0	—	—	1	x59	1.0	—	—	1
x342	1.0	—	—	1	x52	1.0	—	—	2
x313	1.0	—	—	1	x46	1.0	—	—	3
W310x283	1.0	—	—	1	W200x42	1.0	—	—	1
x253	1.0	—	—	1	x36	1.0	—	—	2
x226	1.0	—	—	1					
x202	1.0	—	—	1	W200x31	1.0	—	—	1
x179	1.0	—	—	1	x27	1.0	—	—	2
x158	1.0	—	—	1					
x143	1.0	—	—	1	W200x22	1.0	—	—	1
x129	1.0	—	—	1	x19	1.0	—	—	2
x118	1.0	—	—	2	x15	0.655	0.850	0.875	3
x107	1.0	—	—	2					
x97	1.0	—	—	3	W150x37	1.0	—	—	1
					x30	1.0	—	—	2
W310x86	1.0	—	—	1	x22	1.0	—	—	4
x79	1.0	—	—	2					
					W150x24	1.0	—	—	1
W310x74	1.0	—	—	1	x18	1.0	—	—	1
x67	1.0	—	—	1	x14	1.0	—	—	2
x60	0.966	0.978	0.983	1	x13	1.0	—	—	3
W310x52	0.903	0.952	0.961	1	W130x28	1.0	—	—	1
x45	0.658	0.851	0.876	1	x24	1.0	—	—	1
x39	0.395	0.742	0.785	2					
					W100x19	1.0	—	—	1
W310x33	0.652	0.849	0.874	1					
x28	0.463	0.770	0.809	1					
x24	0.310	0.707	0.755	1					
x21	0.089	0.615	0.679	2					
W250x167	1.0	—	—	1					
x149	1.0	—	—	1					
x131	1.0	—	—	1					
x115	1.0	—	—	1					
x101	1.0	—	—	1					
x89	1.0	—	—	1					
x80	1.0	—	—	2					
x73	1.0	—	—	2					
W250x67	1.0	—	—	1					
x58	1.0	—	—	1					
x49	1.0	—	—	3					
W250x45	1.0	—	—	1					
x39	1.0	—	—	1					
x33	0.862	0.935	0.947	2					
W250x28	0.940	0.968	0.974	1					
x25	0.859	0.934	0.946	1					
x22	0.771	0.898	0.916	1					
x18	0.396	0.742	0.785	3					

— Indicates web is never that class.

$F_y = 345$ MPa

NOTES

UNIT FACTORED COMPRESSIVE RESISTANCES
FOR COMPRESSION MEMBERS, C_r/A

General

Table 4-4 on pages 4-13 to 4-16 lists the unit factored compressive resistance C_r/A (in MPa) calculated in accordance with the requirements of Clause 13.3.1, CSA S16-09 for members with F_y varying from 250 to 700 MPa, for values of KL/r from 1 to 200 with $n = 1.34$. The values for $F_y = 350$ MPa are printed in boldface type. For hollow structural sections manufactured according to G40.20, Class C with $F_y = 350$ MPa, use values given in Table 4-4 for $F_y = 350$.

Table 4-5 on page 4-17 lists the unit factored compressive resistance C_r/A for compression members consisting of WWF shapes with oxy-flame-cut flange plates and $F_y = 300$ and 350 MPa, and HSS manufactured according to G40.20 Class H with $F_y = 350$ MPa. The resistances have been calculated for values of KL/r from 1 to 200, in accordance with the requirements of Clause 13.3.1, S16-09 with $n = 2.24$.

Use

To obtain the factored compressive resistance C_r for doubly symmetric Class 1, 2 or 3 sections, multiply the unit factored compressive resistance C_r/A for the appropriate F_y and KL/r ratio, by the cross-sectional area A of the column section. For Class 4 sections, see Clause 13.3.5.

Examples

1. Given:

    Find the factored compressive resistance of a W250x131 column of CSA G40.21 Grade 350W steel $(F_y = 350$ MPa) for a KL/r ratio of 89.

    Solution:

    From page 6-52, for W250x131, $A = 16\,700$ mm^2

    From Table 4-4, page 4-14, with $KL/r = 89$ and $F_y = 350$ MPa, $C_r/A = 155$ MPa

    Therefore, $C_r = 155$ MPa $\times 16\,700$ mm$^2 = 2\,590 \times 10^3$ N $= 2\,590$ kN

2. Given:

    Find the factored compressive resistance of an HSS 254x152x13 Class H column of CSA G40.21 Grade 350W $(F_y = 350$ MPa) and $KL/r = 89$.

    Solution:

    From page 6-100 for HSS 254x152x13, $A = 9\,260$ mm^2

    From Table 4-5, page 4-17, with $KL/r = 89$ and $F_y = 350$ MPa, $C_r/A = 189$ MPa

    Therefore, $C_r = 189$ MPa $\times 9\,260$ mm$^2 = 1\,750 \times 10^3$ N $= 1\,750$ kN

Notes:

1. Tables of C_r, factored axial compressive resistance, for columns in CSA G40.21 Grade 350W steels are given on pages 4-24 to 4-41.

2. Tables of C_r for HSS columns in G40.21 Grade 350W steel are given on pages 4-43 to 4-65 for Class C and pages 4-67 to 4-89 for Class H. Tables of C_r for HSS columns in ASTM A500 Grade C steel are given on pages 4-91 to 4-113.

3. For columns not manufactured in Canada, heavy sections, and built-up sections, see Clause 13.3 of the CISC Commentary in Part Two of this Handbook for more information on compressive resistance.

UNIT FACTORED COMPRESSIVE RESISTANCES, Cr/A (MPa)*

For compression members

$\phi = 0.90$ $n = 1.34$

$$\frac{KL}{r} = 1 \text{ to } 50$$

Table 4-4

$\frac{KL}{r}$	\multicolumn{12}{c}{F_y (MPa)}
	250	260	280	290	300	345	**350**	380	400	480	550	700
1	225	234	252	261	270	310	**315**	342	360	432	495	630
2	225	234	252	261	270	310	**315**	342	360	432	495	630
3	225	234	252	261	270	310	**315**	342	360	432	495	630
4	225	234	252	261	270	310	**315**	342	360	432	495	630
5	225	234	252	261	270	310	**315**	342	360	432	495	629
6	225	234	252	261	270	310	**315**	342	360	431	494	629
7	225	234	252	261	270	310	**315**	342	359	431	494	628
8	225	234	252	261	270	310	**314**	341	359	431	493	627
9	225	234	252	260	269	310	**314**	341	359	430	493	626
10	225	233	251	260	269	309	**314**	341	359	430	492	625
11	224	233	251	260	269	309	**314**	340	358	429	491	623
12	224	233	251	260	269	309	**313**	340	358	428	490	621
13	224	233	251	260	269	308	**313**	339	357	428	489	619
14	224	233	250	259	268	308	**312**	339	356	427	488	617
15	224	232	250	259	268	308	**312**	338	356	426	486	615
16	223	232	250	259	267	307	**311**	338	355	424	485	612
17	223	232	249	258	267	306	**311**	337	354	423	483	609
18	223	231	249	258	266	306	**310**	336	353	422	481	605
19	222	231	249	257	266	305	**309**	335	352	420	479	602
20	222	231	248	257	265	304	**308**	334	351	418	476	598
21	222	230	248	256	265	303	**307**	333	350	416	474	594
22	221	230	247	256	264	302	**307**	332	348	415	471	589
23	221	229	246	255	263	301	**305**	331	347	412	468	584
24	220	229	246	254	263	300	**304**	329	346	410	465	579
25	220	228	245	253	262	299	**303**	328	344	408	462	574
26	219	227	244	253	261	298	**302**	326	342	405	459	569
27	218	227	243	252	260	297	**301**	325	341	403	455	563
28	218	226	243	251	259	295	**299**	323	339	400	452	557
29	217	225	242	250	258	294	**298**	321	337	397	448	551
30	216	224	241	249	257	292	**296**	320	335	394	444	544
31	216	224	240	248	256	291	**295**	318	333	391	440	538
32	215	223	239	247	254	289	**293**	316	330	388	436	531
33	214	222	238	245	253	288	**291**	314	328	385	431	524
34	213	221	237	244	252	286	**290**	311	326	381	427	517
35	212	220	235	243	251	284	**288**	309	323	378	422	510
36	211	219	234	242	249	282	**286**	307	321	374	418	503
37	210	218	233	240	248	280	**284**	305	318	370	413	495
38	209	217	232	239	246	278	**282**	302	316	367	408	488
39	208	216	230	238	245	276	**280**	300	313	363	403	481
40	207	214	229	236	243	274	**278**	297	310	359	398	473
41	206	213	228	235	242	272	**275**	295	307	355	393	466
42	205	212	226	233	240	270	**273**	292	304	351	388	458
43	204	211	225	231	238	268	**271**	289	301	347	383	450
44	202	209	223	230	237	265	**269**	287	298	343	378	443
45	201	208	222	228	235	263	**266**	284	295	338	372	435
46	200	207	220	227	233	261	**264**	281	292	334	367	428
47	199	205	218	225	231	258	**261**	278	289	330	362	420
48	197	204	217	223	229	256	**259**	275	286	326	357	413
49	196	202	215	221	227	253	**256**	273	283	321	351	405
50	195	201	213	219	225	251	**254**	270	280	317	346	398

* Calculated in accordance with S16-09 Clause 13.3.1

For WWF sections and Class H Hollow Structural Sections, see Table 4-5 page 4-17.

$$\frac{KL}{r} = 51 \text{ to } 100$$

UNIT FACTORED COMPRESSIVE RESISTANCES, C_r/A (MPa)*
For compression members

Table 4-4

$\phi = 0.90 \quad n = 1.34$

KL/r	F_y (MPa)											
	250	260	280	290	300	345	350	380	400	480	550	700
51	193	200	212	218	223	249	251	267	277	313	341	391
52	192	198	210	216	222	246	249	264	273	308	335	383
53	190	196	208	214	220	243	246	261	270	304	330	376
54	189	195	206	212	218	241	243	258	267	300	325	369
55	188	193	205	210	215	238	241	255	264	296	320	362
56	186	192	203	208	213	236	238	252	260	291	315	355
57	185	190	201	206	211	233	235	249	257	287	310	349
58	183	189	199	204	209	230	233	246	254	283	305	342
59	181	187	197	202	207	228	230	243	250	279	300	336
60	180	185	195	200	205	225	227	240	247	274	295	329
61	178	184	193	198	203	223	225	236	244	270	290	323
62	177	182	192	196	201	220	222	233	241	266	285	317
63	175	180	190	194	199	217	219	230	237	262	280	310
64	174	178	188	192	197	215	217	227	234	258	275	305
65	172	177	186	190	194	212	214	224	231	254	271	299
66	170	175	184	188	192	210	211	221	228	250	266	293
67	169	173	182	186	190	207	209	219	225	246	262	287
68	167	172	180	184	188	204	206	216	222	242	257	282
69	166	170	178	182	186	202	203	213	218	238	253	276
70	164	168	176	180	184	199	201	210	215	235	249	271
71	162	167	174	178	182	197	198	207	212	231	244	266
72	161	165	172	176	180	194	196	204	209	227	240	261
73	159	163	171	174	178	192	193	201	206	224	236	256
74	158	161	169	172	175	189	191	198	203	220	232	251
75	156	160	167	170	173	187	188	196	200	217	228	246
76	154	158	165	168	171	184	186	193	198	213	224	242
77	153	156	163	166	169	182	183	190	195	210	220	237
78	151	155	161	164	167	179	181	188	192	206	217	233
79	149	153	159	162	165	177	178	185	189	203	213	228
80	148	151	157	160	163	175	176	182	186	200	209	224
81	146	150	156	158	161	172	173	180	184	197	206	220
82	145	148	154	157	159	170	171	177	181	194	202	216
83	143	146	152	155	157	168	169	175	178	190	199	212
84	142	145	150	153	155	165	166	172	176	187	195	208
85	140	143	148	151	153	163	164	170	173	184	192	204
86	138	141	147	149	151	161	162	167	171	182	189	200
87	137	140	145	147	150	159	160	165	168	179	186	197
88	135	138	143	145	148	157	158	163	166	176	183	193
89	134	137	141	144	146	155	155	160	163	173	180	190
90	132	135	140	142	144	152	153	158	161	170	177	186
91	131	133	138	140	142	150	151	156	159	168	174	183
92	129	132	136	138	140	148	149	154	156	165	171	180
93	128	130	135	137	139	146	147	151	154	162	168	177
94	127	129	133	135	137	144	145	149	152	160	165	174
95	125	127	131	133	135	142	143	147	150	157	163	171
96	124	126	130	132	133	140	141	145	147	155	160	168
97	122	124	128	130	132	139	139	143	145	153	158	165
98	121	123	127	128	130	137	137	141	143	150	155	162
99	119	121	125	127	128	135	135	139	141	148	153	159
100	118	120	124	125	127	133	134	137	139	146	150	157

* Calculated in accordance with S16-09 Clause 13.3.1

For WWF sections and Class H Hollow Structural Sections, see Table 4-5 page 4-17.

UNIT FACTORED COMPRESSIVE RESISTANCES, C_r / A (MPa)*

For compression members

$\phi = 0.90 \quad n = 1.34$

$\dfrac{KL}{r} = 101$ to 150

Table 4-4

$\dfrac{KL}{r}$	F_y (MPa)											
	250	260	280	290	300	345	**350**	380	400	480	550	700
101	117	119	122	124	125	131	**132**	135	137	144	148	154
102	115	117	121	122	124	129	**130**	133	135	141	145	151
103	114	116	119	121	122	128	**128**	131	133	139	143	149
104	113	114	118	119	121	126	**127**	130	131	137	141	147
105	111	113	116	118	119	124	**125**	128	129	135	139	144
106	110	112	115	116	118	123	**123**	126	128	133	137	142
107	109	110	113	115	116	121	**122**	124	126	131	134	140
108	108	109	112	113	115	119	**120**	123	124	129	132	137
109	106	108	111	112	113	118	**118**	121	122	127	130	135
110	105	107	109	111	112	116	**117**	119	121	125	128	133
111	104	105	108	109	110	115	**115**	118	119	124	127	131
112	103	104	107	108	109	113	**114**	116	117	122	125	129
113	102	103	105	107	108	112	**112**	114	116	120	123	127
114	100	102	104	105	106	110	**111**	113	114	118	121	125
115	99.2	100	103	104	105	109	**109**	111	113	117	119	123
116	98.1	99.3	102	103	104	107	**108**	110	111	115	117	121
117	96.9	98.2	100	101	102	106	**106**	108	110	113	116	119
118	95.8	97.0	99.2	100	101	105	**105**	107	108	112	114	117
119	94.7	95.9	98.0	98.9	99.8	103	**104**	106	107	110	112	116
120	93.6	94.8	96.8	97.7	98.6	102	**102**	104	105	109	111	114
121	92.6	93.7	95.6	96.5	97.4	101	**101**	103	104	107	109	112
122	91.5	92.6	94.5	95.4	96.2	99.4	**99.7**	101	102	106	108	111
123	90.5	91.5	93.4	94.2	95.0	98.1	**98.4**	100	101	104	106	109
124	89.4	90.4	92.3	93.1	93.9	96.9	**97.2**	98.8	99.7	103	105	107
125	88.4	89.4	91.2	92.0	92.7	95.7	**96.0**	97.5	98.4	101	103	106
126	87.4	88.4	90.1	90.9	91.6	94.5	**94.7**	96.2	97.1	99.9	102	104
127	86.4	87.4	89.0	89.8	90.5	93.3	**93.5**	95.0	95.9	98.6	100	103
128	85.4	86.4	88.0	88.7	89.4	92.1	**92.4**	93.8	94.6	97.3	98.9	101
129	84.5	85.4	87.0	87.7	88.4	91.0	**91.2**	92.6	93.4	96.0	97.6	99.9
130	83.5	84.4	85.9	86.6	87.3	89.8	**90.1**	91.4	92.2	94.7	96.2	98.5
131	82.6	83.4	84.9	85.6	86.3	88.7	**89.0**	90.3	91.0	93.4	94.9	97.1
132	81.7	82.5	84.0	84.6	85.2	87.6	**87.9**	89.1	89.9	92.2	93.7	95.8
133	80.8	81.5	83.0	83.6	84.2	86.6	**86.8**	88.0	88.7	91.0	92.4	94.5
134	79.9	80.6	82.0	82.6	83.2	85.5	**85.7**	86.9	87.6	89.8	91.2	93.2
135	79.0	79.7	81.1	81.7	82.3	84.5	**84.7**	85.8	86.5	88.6	90.0	91.9
136	78.1	78.8	80.1	80.7	81.3	83.4	**83.6**	84.8	85.4	87.5	88.8	90.7
137	77.2	77.9	79.2	79.8	80.4	82.4	**82.6**	83.7	84.4	86.4	87.6	89.4
138	76.4	77.1	78.3	78.9	79.4	81.4	**81.6**	82.7	83.3	85.3	86.5	88.2
139	75.5	76.2	77.4	78.0	78.5	80.5	**80.7**	81.7	82.3	84.2	85.4	87.1
140	74.7	75.4	76.6	77.1	77.6	79.5	**79.7**	80.7	81.3	83.1	84.3	85.9
141	73.9	74.5	75.7	76.2	76.7	78.6	**78.7**	79.7	80.3	82.1	83.2	84.8
142	73.1	73.7	74.8	75.3	75.8	77.6	**77.8**	78.7	79.3	81.0	82.1	83.7
143	72.3	72.9	74.0	74.5	74.9	76.7	**76.9**	77.8	78.3	80.0	81.1	82.6
144	71.5	72.1	73.2	73.6	74.1	75.8	**76.0**	76.9	77.4	79.0	80.0	81.5
145	70.7	71.3	72.3	72.8	73.3	74.9	**75.1**	76.0	76.5	78.0	79.0	80.5
146	70.0	70.5	71.5	72.0	72.4	74.1	**74.2**	75.0	75.5	77.1	78.1	79.4
147	69.2	69.8	70.7	71.2	71.6	73.2	**73.3**	74.2	74.6	76.1	77.1	78.4
148	68.5	69.0	70.0	70.4	70.8	72.3	**72.5**	73.3	73.8	75.2	76.1	77.4
149	67.7	68.3	69.2	69.6	70.0	71.5	**71.7**	72.4	72.9	74.3	75.2	76.5
150	67.0	67.5	68.4	68.8	69.2	70.7	**70.8**	71.6	72.0	73.4	74.3	75.5

* Calculated in accordance with S16-09 Clause 13.3.1

For WWF sections and Class H Hollow Structural Sections, see Table 4-5 page 4-17.

UNIT FACTORED COMPRESSIVE RESISTANCES, C_r/A (MPa)*
For compression members

Table 4-4

$\phi = 0.90$ $n = 1.34$

KL/r	\multicolumn{12}{c}{F_y (MPa)}										
	250	260	280	290	300	345	350	380	400	480	550	700
151	66.3	66.8	67.7	68.1	68.5	69.9	70.0	70.8	71.2	72.5	73.4	74.6
152	65.6	66.1	67.0	67.3	67.7	69.1	69.2	69.9	70.4	71.7	72.5	73.6
153	64.9	65.4	66.2	66.6	67.0	68.3	68.4	69.1	69.5	70.8	71.6	72.7
154	64.2	64.7	65.5	65.9	66.2	67.5	67.7	68.3	68.7	70.0	70.7	71.8
155	63.5	64.0	64.8	65.2	65.5	66.8	66.9	67.6	68.0	69.2	69.9	71.0
156	62.9	63.3	64.1	64.5	64.8	66.0	66.2	66.8	67.2	68.3	69.1	70.1
157	62.2	62.7	63.4	63.8	64.1	65.3	65.4	66.0	66.4	67.5	68.3	69.3
158	61.6	62.0	62.7	63.1	63.4	64.6	64.7	65.3	65.7	66.8	67.5	68.4
159	60.9	61.4	62.1	62.4	62.7	63.9	64.0	64.6	64.9	66.0	66.7	67.6
160	60.3	60.7	61.4	61.7	62.0	63.2	63.3	63.9	64.2	65.2	65.9	66.8
161	59.7	60.1	60.8	61.1	61.4	62.5	62.6	63.1	63.5	64.5	65.1	66.0
162	59.1	59.5	60.1	60.4	60.7	61.8	61.9	62.4	62.8	63.8	64.4	65.3
163	58.5	58.8	59.5	59.8	60.1	61.1	61.2	61.8	62.1	63.0	63.6	64.5
164	57.9	58.2	58.9	59.2	59.4	60.5	60.6	61.1	61.4	62.3	62.9	63.7
165	57.3	57.6	58.3	58.6	58.8	59.8	59.9	60.4	60.7	61.6	62.2	63.0
166	56.7	57.1	57.7	58.0	58.2	59.2	59.3	59.8	60.1	60.9	61.5	62.3
167	56.1	56.5	57.1	57.4	57.6	58.5	58.6	59.1	59.4	60.3	60.8	61.6
168	55.6	55.9	56.5	56.8	57.0	57.9	58.0	58.5	58.8	59.6	60.1	60.9
169	55.0	55.3	55.9	56.2	56.4	57.3	57.4	57.9	58.1	59.0	59.5	60.2
170	54.5	54.8	55.3	55.6	55.8	56.7	56.8	57.2	57.5	58.3	58.8	59.5
171	53.9	54.2	54.8	55.0	55.3	56.1	56.2	56.6	56.9	57.7	58.2	58.9
172	53.4	53.7	54.2	54.5	54.7	55.5	55.6	56.0	56.3	57.1	57.5	58.2
173	52.9	53.2	53.7	53.9	54.1	55.0	55.0	55.4	55.7	56.4	56.9	57.6
174	52.4	52.6	53.1	53.4	53.6	54.4	54.5	54.9	55.1	55.8	56.3	56.9
175	51.8	52.1	52.6	52.8	53.0	53.8	53.9	54.3	54.5	55.2	55.7	56.3
176	51.3	51.6	52.1	52.3	52.5	53.3	53.3	53.7	54.0	54.6	55.1	55.7
177	50.8	51.1	51.6	51.8	52.0	52.7	52.8	53.2	53.4	54.1	54.5	55.1
178	50.3	50.6	51.1	51.3	51.5	52.2	52.3	52.6	52.8	53.5	53.9	54.5
179	49.9	50.1	50.6	50.8	51.0	51.7	51.7	52.1	52.3	52.9	53.3	53.9
180	49.4	49.6	50.1	50.3	50.4	51.1	51.2	51.6	51.8	52.4	52.8	53.3
181	48.9	49.1	49.6	49.8	50.0	50.6	50.7	51.0	51.2	51.8	52.2	52.8
182	48.4	48.7	49.1	49.3	49.5	50.1	50.2	50.5	50.7	51.3	51.7	52.2
183	48.0	48.2	48.6	48.8	49.0	49.6	49.7	50.0	50.2	50.8	51.1	51.7
184	47.5	47.7	48.1	48.3	48.5	49.1	49.2	49.5	49.7	50.3	50.6	51.1
185	47.1	47.3	47.7	47.9	48.0	48.6	48.7	49.0	49.2	49.8	50.1	50.6
186	46.6	46.8	47.2	47.4	47.6	48.2	48.2	48.5	48.7	49.2	49.6	50.1
187	46.2	46.4	46.8	46.9	47.1	47.7	47.7	48.0	48.2	48.8	49.1	49.5
188	45.8	46.0	46.3	46.5	46.7	47.2	47.3	47.6	47.7	48.3	48.6	49.0
189	45.3	45.5	45.9	46.1	46.2	46.8	46.8	47.1	47.3	47.8	48.1	48.5
190	44.9	45.1	45.5	45.6	45.8	46.3	46.4	46.6	46.8	47.3	47.6	48.0
191	44.5	44.7	45.0	45.2	45.3	45.9	45.9	46.2	46.3	46.8	47.1	47.6
192	44.1	44.3	44.6	44.8	44.9	45.4	45.5	45.7	45.9	46.4	46.7	47.1
193	43.7	43.9	44.2	44.3	44.5	45.0	45.0	45.3	45.5	45.9	46.2	46.6
194	43.3	43.5	43.8	43.9	44.1	44.6	44.6	44.9	45.0	45.5	45.7	46.1
195	42.9	43.1	43.4	43.5	43.7	44.1	44.2	44.4	44.6	45.0	45.3	45.7
196	42.5	42.7	43.0	43.1	43.2	43.7	43.8	44.0	44.2	44.6	44.9	45.2
197	42.1	42.3	42.6	42.7	42.8	43.3	43.4	43.6	43.7	44.2	44.4	44.8
198	41.7	41.9	42.2	42.3	42.4	42.9	43.0	43.2	43.3	43.7	44.0	44.3
199	41.4	41.5	41.8	41.9	42.1	42.5	42.6	42.8	42.9	43.3	43.6	43.9
200	41.0	41.1	41.4	41.6	41.7	42.1	42.2	42.4	42.5	42.9	43.1	43.5

* Calculated in accordance with S16-09 Clause 13.3.1
For WWF sections and Class H Hollow Structural Sections, see Table 4-5 page 4-17.

UNIT FACTORED COMPRESSIVE RESISTANCES, C_r/A (MPa)*
For WWF and HSS Class H
$\phi = 0.90$ $n = 2.24$

Table 4-5

KL/r	WWF 300	WWF HSS 350	KL/r	WWF 300	WWF HSS 350	KL/r	WWF 300	WWF HSS 350	KL/r	WWF 300	WWF HSS 350
1	270	315	51	256	293	101	151	157	151	75.9	76.4
2	270	315	52	255	291	102	149	154	152	74.9	75.5
3	270	315	53	254	289	103	147	152	153	74.0	74.5
4	270	315	54	253	287	104	145	150	154	73.1	73.6
5	270	315	55	251	285	105	143	147	155	72.2	72.7
6	270	315	56	250	283	106	141	145	156	71.3	71.8
7	270	315	57	248	281	107	139	143	157	70.5	70.9
8	270	315	58	247	279	108	137	141	158	69.6	70.1
9	270	315	59	245	276	109	135	138	159	68.8	69.2
10	270	315	60	244	274	110	133	136	160	68.0	68.4
11	270	315	61	242	272	111	131	134	161	67.2	67.6
12	270	315	62	240	269	112	129	132	162	66.4	66.7
13	270	315	63	238	266	113	127	130	163	65.6	66.0
14	270	315	64	236	264	114	125	128	164	64.8	65.2
15	270	315	65	235	261	115	123	126	165	64.1	64.4
16	270	315	66	233	258	116	122	124	166	63.3	63.7
17	270	315	67	231	255	117	120	123	167	62.6	62.9
18	270	315	68	228	253	118	118	121	168	61.9	62.2
19	270	315	69	226	250	119	117	119	169	61.2	61.5
20	270	315	70	224	247	120	115	117	170	60.5	60.8
21	270	315	71	222	244	121	113	115	171	59.8	60.1
22	270	314	72	220	241	122	112	114	172	59.1	59.4
23	270	314	73	217	238	123	110	112	173	58.5	58.7
24	269	314	74	215	235	124	109	110	174	57.8	58.1
25	269	314	75	213	231	125	107	109	175	57.2	57.4
26	269	314	76	210	228	126	106	107	176	56.6	56.8
27	269	314	77	208	225	127	104	106	177	56.0	56.2
28	269	313	78	206	222	128	103	104	178	55.3	55.6
29	269	313	79	203	219	129	101	103	179	54.7	54.9
30	269	313	80	201	216	130	99.9	101	180	54.2	54.4
31	268	312	81	198	213	131	98.5	99.9	181	53.6	53.8
32	268	312	82	196	210	132	97.2	98.5	182	53.0	53.2
33	268	312	83	194	207	133	95.9	97.1	183	52.4	52.6
34	268	311	84	191	204	134	94.6	95.8	184	51.9	52.1
35	267	311	85	189	201	135	93.3	94.5	185	51.3	51.5
36	267	310	86	186	198	136	92.1	93.2	186	50.8	51.0
37	266	309	87	184	195	137	90.9	91.9	187	50.3	50.4
38	266	309	88	181	192	138	89.7	90.7	188	49.8	49.9
39	266	308	89	179	189	139	88.5	89.5	189	49.2	49.4
40	265	307	90	176	186	140	87.3	88.3	190	48.7	48.9
41	265	306	91	174	183	141	86.2	87.1	191	48.2	48.4
42	264	305	92	172	180	142	85.1	85.9	192	47.7	47.9
43	263	304	93	169	178	143	84.0	84.8	193	47.3	47.4
44	263	303	94	167	175	144	82.9	83.7	194	46.8	46.9
45	262	302	95	165	172	145	81.8	82.6	195	46.3	46.4
46	261	301	96	162	170	146	80.8	81.5	196	45.9	46.0
47	260	299	97	160	167	147	79.8	80.5	197	45.4	45.5
48	259	298	98	158	164	148	78.8	79.4	198	44.9	45.1
49	258	296	99	156	162	149	77.8	78.4	199	44.5	44.6
50	257	295	100	153	159	150	76.8	77.4	200	44.1	44.2

* Calculated in accordance with S16-09 Clause 13.3.1. WWF sections have oxy-flame-cut flange plates.
For Class C hollow structural sections, see Table 4-4 pages 4-13 to 4-16.

Single Curvature				Double Curvature			
$\dfrac{M_{f1}}{M_{f2}}$	ω_1	$\dfrac{M_{f1}}{M_{f2}}$	ω_1	$\dfrac{M_{f1}}{M_{f2}}$	ω_1	$\dfrac{M_{f1}}{M_{f2}}$	ω_1
1.00	1.00	0.50	0.80	0.00	0.60	0.55	0.40
0.95	0.98	0.45	0.78	0.05	0.58	0.60	0.40
0.90	0.96	0.40	0.76	0.10	0.56	0.65	0.40
0.85	0.94	0.35	0.74	0.15	0.54	0.70	0.40
0.80	0.92	0.30	0.72	0.20	0.52	0.75	0.40
0.75	0.90	0.25	0.70	0.25	0.50	0.80	0.40
0.70	0.88	0.20	0.68	0.30	0.48	0.85	0.40
0.65	0.86	0.15	0.66	0.35	0.46	0.90	0.40
0.60	0.84	0.10	0.64	0.40	0.44	0.95	0.40
0.55	0.82	0.05	0.62	0.45	0.42	1.00	0.40
		0.00	0.60	0.50	0.40		

* See Clause 13.8.5, CSA S16-09

The value of ω_1 is used to modify the bending term in the beam-column interaction expression to account for various end moment and transverse bending loading conditions of the columns.

For columns of a frame not subject to transverse loads between supports, use the values of ω_1 shown in Table 4-6.

For members subjected to distributed loads or a series of point loads between supports, $\omega_1 = 1.0$, and for members subjected to a concentrated load or moment between supports, $\omega_1 = 0.85$.

The values of ω_1 given in Table 4-6 are derived from:

$$\omega_1 = 0.6 - 0.4\,\kappa \geq 0.4$$

where:

κ = M_{f1}/M_{f2} for moments at opposite ends of the unbraced column length, positive for double curvature, and negative for single curvature in which,

M_{f1} = the smaller factored end moment, and

M_{f2} = the larger factored end moment.

C_e/A EULER BUCKLING LOAD
Per Unit of Area, MPa

Table 4-7

KL/r	C_e/A MPa	KL/r	C_e/A MPa	KL/r	C_e/A MPa	KL/r	C_e/A MPa	KL/r	C_e/A MPa
1	1 970 000	41	1 170	81	301	121	135	161	76.2
2	493 000	42	1 120	82	294	122	133	162	75.2
3	219 000	43	1 070	83	287	123	130	163	74.3
4	123 000	44	1 020	84	280	124	128	164	73.4
5	79 000	45	975	85	273	125	126	165	72.5
6	54 800	46	933	86	267	126	124	166	71.6
7	40 300	47	894	87	261	127	122	167	70.8
8	30 800	48	857	88	255	128	120	168	69.9
9	24 400	49	822	89	249	129	119	169	69.1
10	19 700	50	790	90	244	130	117	170	68.3
11	16 300	51	759	91	238	131	115	171	67.5
12	13 700	52	730	92	233	132	113	172	66.7
13	11 700	53	703	93	228	133	112	173	66.0
14	10 100	54	677	94	223	134	110	174	65.2
15	8 770	55	653	95	219	135	108	175	64.5
16	7 710	56	629	96	214	136	107	176	63.7
17	6 830	57	608	97	210	137	105	177	63.0
18	6 090	58	587	98	206	138	104	178	62.3
19	5 470	59	567	99	201	139	102	179	61.6
20	4 930	60	548	100	197	140	101	180	60.9
21	4 480	61	530	101	194	141	99.3	181	60.3
22	4 080	62	514	102	190	142	97.9	182	59.6
23	3 730	63	497	103	186	143	96.5	183	58.9
24	3 430	64	482	104	183	144	95.2	184	58.3
25	3 160	65	467	105	179	145	93.9	185	57.7
26	2 920	66	453	106	176	146	92.6	186	57.1
27	2 710	67	440	107	172	147	91.3	187	56.4
28	2 520	68	427	108	169	148	90.1	188	55.8
29	2 350	69	415	109	166	149	88.9	189	55.3
30	2 190	70	403	110	163	150	87.7	190	54.7
31	2 050	71	392	111	160	151	86.6	191	54.1
32	1 930	72	381	112	157	152	85.4	192	53.5
33	1 810	73	370	113	155	153	84.3	193	53.0
34	1 710	74	360	114	152	154	83.2	194	52.4
35	1 610	75	351	115	149	155	82.2	195	51.9
36	1 520	76	342	116	147	156	81.1	196	51.4
37	1 440	77	333	117	144	157	80.1	197	50.9
38	1 370	78	324	118	142	158	79.1	198	50.3
39	1 300	79	316	119	139	159	78.1	199	49.8
40	1 230	80	308	120	137	160	77.1	200	49.3

To obtain C_e, in kN, multiply the tabular value by the cross-sectional area, A, in mm^2, and divide by 1000.

AMPLIFICATION FACTOR *

Table 4-8

$$U = \frac{1}{1 - \dfrac{C_f}{C_e}}$$

$\dfrac{C_f}{C_e}$	U	$\dfrac{C_f}{C_e}$	U	$\dfrac{C_f}{C_e}$	U	$\dfrac{C_f}{C_e}$	U
0.01	1.01	0.26	1.35	0.51	2.04	0.76	4.17
0.02	1.02	0.27	1.37	0.52	2.08	0.77	4.35
0.03	1.03	0.28	1.39	0.53	2.13	0.78	4.55
0.04	1.04	0.29	1.41	0.54	2.17	0.79	4.76
0.05	1.05	0.30	1.43	0.55	2.22	0.80	5.00
0.06	1.06	0.31	1.45	0.56	2.27	0.81	5.26
0.07	1.08	0.32	1.47	0.57	2.33	0.82	5.56
0.08	1.09	0.33	1.49	0.58	2.38	0.83	5.88
0.09	1.10	0.34	1.52	0.59	2.44	0.84	6.25
0.10	1.11	0.35	1.54	0.60	2.50	0.85	6.67
0.11	1.12	0.36	1.56	0.61	2.56	0.86	7.14
0.12	1.14	0.37	1.59	0.62	2.63	0.87	7.69
0.13	1.15	0.38	1.61	0.63	2.70	0.88	8.33
0.14	1.16	0.39	1.64	0.64	2.78	0.89	9.09
0.15	1.18	0.40	1.67	0.65	2.86	0.90	10.0
0.16	1.19	0.41	1.69	0.66	2.94	0.91	11.1
0.17	1.20	0.42	1.72	0.67	3.03	0.92	12.5
0.18	1.22	0.43	1.75	0.68	3.13	0.93	14.3
0.19	1.23	0.44	1.79	0.69	3.23	0.94	16.7
0.20	1.25	0.45	1.82	0.70	3.33	0.95	20.0
0.21	1.27	0.46	1.85	0.71	3.45	0.96	25.0
0.22	1.28	0.47	1.89	0.72	3.57	0.97	33.3
0.23	1.30	0.48	1.92	0.73	3.70	0.98	50.0
0.24	1.32	0.49	1.96	0.74	3.85	0.99	100.0
0.25	1.33	0.50	2.00	0.75	4.00		

* See Clause 13.8.4 in CSA S16-09.

FACTORED AXIAL COMPRESSIVE RESISTANCES OF COLUMNS

Tables

The tables on the following pages list the factored axial compressive resistances C_r in kilonewtons for WWF shapes, W shapes, and HSS produced to the requirements of CSA Standard G40.20 (Class C and Class H) and ASTM A500. The resistances have been computed for effective lengths with respect to the least radius of gyration varying from 0 mm to 16 000 mm in accordance with the requirements of Clauses 13.3.1 and 13.3.5, CSA S16-09 with $n = 1.34$ for W shapes and for HSS produced to G40.20 Class C and to ASTM A500, and with $n = 2.24$ for WWF shapes and HSS produced to G40.20 Class H.

In all, five sets of tables are provided:

Set 1 — WWF shapes conforming to CSA G40.20 and with oxy-flame-cut flange plates

CSA G40.21 Grade 350W ($F_y = 350$ MPa, $n = 2.24$)

Set 2 — W shapes conforming to CSA G40.20

CSA G40.21 Grade 350W, ASTM A992, ASTM A572 grade 50

($F_y = 345$ MPa, $n = 1.34$)

Set 3 — HSS conforming to CSA G40.20, Class C

CSA G40.21 Grade 350W ($F_y = 350$ MPa, $n = 1.34$)

Set 4 — HSS conforming to CSA G40.20, Class H

CSA G40.21 Grade 350W ($F_y = 350$ MPa, $n = 2.24$)

Set 5 — HSS conforming to ASTM A500

ASTM A500 Grade C

($F_y = 345$ MPa for rectangular and square, $F_y = 317$ MPa for round, $n = 1.34$)

In each set of tables, sections which are either Class 3 or 4, in the grade of steel for which the loads have been computed, are identified. In Set 1, those welded sections in which the flange-to-web welds do not develop the entire web strength are identified. In Set 2, the minimum specified yield stress has been taken as $F_y = 345$ MPa, corresponding to the least value among the 3 grades represented (CSA G40.21 350W, ASTM A992 and A572 grade 50).

The factored axial compressive resistances for Class 4 sections have been computed in accordance with the requirements of Clause 13.3.5 of S16-09 and are so identified in the tables.

The applicable steel grade is listed at the top of each table, and the metric designation of each shape is given at the top of the columns, while the equivalent imperial size and weight are listed at the bottom of the tables. Properties and design data are included at the bottom of the tables as follows:

$Area$ = Total cross-sectional area, mm^2

Z_x = Plastic section modulus for bending about X-X axis, 10^3 mm^3

S_x = Elastic section modulus for bending about X-X axis, 10^3 mm^3

(S$_e$ is given for Class 4 sections; see Clause 13.5(c), CSA S16-09.)

r_x = Radius of gyration about the strong, X-X, axis, mm

Z_y = Plastic section modulus for bending about Y-Y axis, 10^3 mm^3

S_y = Elastic section modulus for bending about Y-Y axis, 10^3 mm^3 (S_e is given for Class 4 sections; see Clause 13.5(c), CSA S16-09.)

r_y = Radius of gyration about the weak, Y-Y, axis, mm

r_x / r_y = Ratio of radius of gyration of X-X axis to that of Y-Y axis

M_{rx} = Factored moment resistance for bending about the X-X axis, computed considering $L \leq L_u$, using the Class of the section considering bending about the X-X axis only and the value of F_y shown, for Class 1 and 2 sections, $\phi Z_x F_y \times 10^{-6}$; for Class 3 sections, $\phi S_x F_y \times 10^{-6}$; and for Class 4 sections, Clause 13.5(c) of S16-09, kN·m.

M_{ry} = Factored moment resistance for bending about the Y-Y axis, computed using the Class of the section considering bending about the Y-Y axis only and the value of F_y shown, for Class 1 and 2 section, $\phi Z_y F_y \times 10^{-6}$; for Class 3 sections, $\phi S_y F_y \times 10^{-6}$; and for class 4 sections, Clause 13.5(c) of S16-09, kN·m.

For hollow structural sections which have identical X-X and Y-Y axis properties, only one value of the relevant properties is shown.

The following additional constants are tabulated for the tables containing WWF and W shapes:

J = St. Venant torsional constant, 10^3 mm^4

C_w = Warping torsional constant, 10^9 mm^6

L_u = Maximum unsupported length of compression flange for which no reduction in M_r is required, mm

F_y = Specified minimum yield strength of the section, MPa

Design of Axially Loaded Columns

The design of axially loaded columns (columns theoretically not subjected to combined bending and compression) involves the determination of the governing effective length and the selection of a section with the required resistance at that effective length. Factored axial compressive resistance tables for columns enable a designer to select a suitable section directly, without following a trial-and-error procedure.

Since the factored axial compressive resistances C_r (listed in the tables supplied) have been computed on the basis of the least radius of gyration r_y for each section, the tables apply directly only to columns unbraced about the Y-Y axis. In certain cases, however, it is necessary to investigate the capacity of a column with reference to both the X-X axis and the Y-Y axis, or with reference only to the X-X axis. The ratio r_x / r_y included in the table of properties at the bottom of each resistance table provides a convenient means of investigating the strength of a column with respect to the X-X axis.

In general, a column having an effective length $K_x L_x$ with respect to the X-X axis will be able to carry a factored load equal to the tabulated factored axial compressive resistance based upon the effective length $K_y L_y$ with respect to the Y-Y axis if $K_x L_x < K_y L_y (r_x/r_y)$.

Resistances of HSS columns produced to ASTM A500

The tables of resistances for HSS used as columns (starting on page 4-91) were computed in accordance with CSA Standard S16-09, using a value of $\phi = 0.90$ as given in that standard, and with properties and dimensions based on the Design Wall Thickness and a value of $F_y = 345$ MPa for square and rectangular HSS and $F_y = 317$ for circular HSS MPa, as specified in ASTM A500 for grade C.

For HSS used as columns, the value of n = 1.34 (for the basic column curve, Clause 13.3, S16-09) was used in determining the factored axial compressive resistance as HSS produced under ASTM A500 grade C are generally cold-formed non-stress-relieved sections.

For more information on HSS produced to ASTM A500, see page 6-97.

Examples

1. Given:

   A W310 column is required to carry a factored axial load of 3 600 kN. The effective length $K_y L_y$ along the weak axis is 4 500 mm. The effective length $K_x L_x$ along the strong axis is 7 600 mm. Use CSA G40.21 Grade 350W steel.

Solution:

   With $K_y L_y = 4$ 500, the lightest W310 section with sufficient factored axial compressive resistance is W310x129. $C_r = 3$ 820 kN; $r_x/r_y = 1.76$.

   $K_x L_x = 7$ 600 mm (required)

   $K_y L_y (r_x/r_y) = 4 500 \times 1.76 = 7 920$ mm $> 7 600$ mm

   The W310x129 has a factored compressive resistance of 3 820 kN with an effective length of $K_x L_x = 7$ 920 mm, and hence the section is adequate. Use W310x129.

2. Given:

   Same as example 1, except $K_x L_x = 9$ 500 mm

Solution:

   $K_y L_y = 4$ 500 mm, $K_x L_x = 9$ 500 mm

   Equivalent $K_y L_y$, for $K_x L_x$ of 9 500 mm $= K_x L_x / (r_x/r_y)$

   Assuming that a heavy W310 section will be adequate, $r_x/r_y = 1.76$.

   Equivalent $K_y L_y = 9 500/1.76 = 5 400$ mm $> 4 500$ mm

   Therefore, $K_x L_x$ governs, and the effective $K_y L_y$ is 5 400 mm.

   With $K_y L_y = 5$ 400 mm, a W310x143 is the lightest W310 that has a factored axial compressive resistance greater than the factored axial load of 3 600 kN (C_r for 5 500 mm $= 3$ 630 kN; $r_x/r_y = 1.76$)

   Use W310x143.

4-23

Designation		WWF650			
Mass (kg/m)	864 ‡	739 ‡	598	499	400 **
Effective length (KL) in millimetres with respect to the least radius of gyration					
0	34 700	29 600	24 000	20 000	15 900
2 500	34 600	29 600	24 000	20 000	15 900
3 000	34 600	29 600	24 000	20 000	15 900
3 500	34 600	29 600	24 000	20 000	15 900
4 000	34 500	29 600	23 900	20 000	15 900
4 500	34 500	29 500	23 900	20 000	15 800
5 000	34 300	29 500	23 900	19 900	15 800
5 500	34 200	29 300	23 800	19 800	15 700
6 000	33 900	29 200	23 700	19 700	15 600
6 500	33 700	29 000	23 500	19 600	15 500
7 000	33 300	28 800	23 400	19 500	15 400
7 500	32 800	28 500	23 100	19 300	15 200
8 000	32 300	28 200	22 900	19 000	15 000
8 500	31 700	27 800	22 600	18 700	14 700
9 000	30 900	27 300	22 200	18 400	14 400
9 500	30 100	26 700	21 800	18 000	14 100
10 000	29 200	26 100	21 300	17 600	13 700
10 500	28 300	25 500	20 800	17 100	13 300
11 000	27 300	24 700	20 200	16 700	12 900
11 500	26 200	24 000	19 600	16 100	12 400
12 000	25 100	23 200	18 900	15 600	12 000
12 500	24 100	22 300	18 300	15 000	11 500
13 000	23 000	21 500	17 600	14 400	11 000
13 500	21 900	20 600	16 900	13 900	10 500
14 000	20 900	19 800	16 200	13 300	10 100
14 500	19 900	19 000	15 600	12 700	9 630
15 000	19 000	18 100	14 900	12 200	9 190
15 500	18 000	17 300	14 300	11 600	8 760
16 000	17 200	16 600	13 600	11 100	8 350
PROPERTIES AND DESIGN DATA					
Area (mm^2)	110 000	94 100	76 200	63 600	51 000
Z_x (10^3 mm^3)	27 300	25 200	21 100	17 500	13 900
S_x (10^3 mm^3)	23 300	22 100	18 900	15 900	12 500
r_x (mm)	262	277	284	285	284
Z_y (10^3 mm^3)	13 200	12 800	10 600	8 510	6 400
S_y (10^3 mm^3)	8 480	8 450	7 040	5 630	4 120
r_y (mm)	158	171	173	170	164
r_x / r_y	1.66	1.62	1.64	1.68	1.73
M_{rx} (kN·m) (L < L_u)	8 600	7 940	6 650	5 510	3 940
M_{ry} (kN·m)	4 160	4 030	3 340	2 680	1 300
J (10^3 mm^4)	132 000	98 400	55 600	29 300	13 300
C_w (10^9 mm^6)	240 000	239 000	206 000	170 000	132 000
L_u (mm)	13 000	12 600	11 500	10 500	10 300
F_y (MPa)	350	350	350	350	350
IMPERIAL SIZE AND WEIGHT					
Weight (lb./ft.)	580	497	402	336	269
Depth x Width (in.)			26 x 26		

‡ Welding does not fully develop web strength.

** Class 4: C_r calculated according to CSA S16-09 Clause 13.3.5; S_x, S_y, M_{rx}, M_{ry} according to 13.5(c).

CSA G40.21 350W
φ = 0.90
Oxy-Flame-Cut Flange Plates

WWF COLUMNS
Factored Axial Compressive Resistances, C_r (kN)

Designation	WWF600				
Mass (kg/m)	793 ‡	680 ‡	551	460	369 *
0	31 800	27 300	22 100	18 500	14 800
2 500	31 800	27 300	22 100	18 500	14 800
3 000	31 800	27 300	22 100	18 400	14 800
3 500	31 700	27 200	22 100	18 400	14 800
4 000	31 700	27 200	22 000	18 400	14 700
4 500	31 600	27 100	22 000	18 300	14 700
5 000	31 400	27 000	21 900	18 300	14 600
5 500	31 200	26 900	21 800	18 200	14 600
6 000	30 900	26 700	21 700	18 100	14 400
6 500	30 600	26 500	21 500	17 900	14 300
7 000	30 100	26 200	21 300	17 700	14 100
7 500	29 600	25 900	21 000	17 500	13 900
8 000	28 900	25 400	20 700	17 200	13 600
8 500	28 200	24 900	20 300	16 800	13 300
9 000	27 400	24 300	19 800	16 400	13 000
9 500	26 500	23 700	19 300	16 000	12 600
10 000	25 500	23 000	18 800	15 500	12 200
10 500	24 500	22 300	18 200	15 000	11 700
11 000	23 400	21 500	17 600	14 400	11 300
11 500	22 400	20 600	16 900	13 900	10 800
12 000	21 300	19 800	16 200	13 300	10 300
12 500	20 300	18 900	15 600	12 700	9 830
13 000	19 300	18 100	14 900	12 200	9 360
13 500	18 300	17 300	14 200	11 600	8 910
14 000	17 300	16 500	13 600	11 000	8 470
14 500	16 400	15 700	12 900	10 500	8 050
15 000	15 600	14 900	12 300	10 000	7 640
15 500	14 800	14 200	11 700	9 520	7 260
16 000	14 000	13 500	11 200	9 060	6 890

Effective length (KL) in millimetres with respect to the least radius of gyration

PROPERTIES AND DESIGN DATA

Area (mm²)	101 000	86 600	70 200	58 600	47 000
Z_x (10^3 mm³)	22 900	21 200	17 800	14 800	11 800
S_x (10^3 mm³)	19 400	18 500	15 900	13 400	10 700
r_x (mm)	240	253	261	262	261
Z_y (10^3 mm³)	11 200	10 900	9 050	7 250	5 460
S_y (10^3 mm³)	7 230	7 200	6 000	4 800	3 600
r_y (mm)	147	158	160	157	152
r_x / r_y	1.63	1.60	1.63	1.67	1.72
M_{rx} (kN·m) (L < L_u)	7 210	6 680	5 610	4 660	3 370
M_{ry} (kN·m)	3 530	3 430	2 850	2 280	1 130
J (10^3 mm⁴)	121 000	90 700	51 300	27 000	12 200
C_w (10^9 mm⁶)	158 000	158 000	136 000	113 000	87 800
L_u (mm)	12 800	12 300	11 100	9 970	9 630
F_y (MPa)	350	350	350	350	350

IMPERIAL SIZE AND WEIGHT

Weight (lb./ft.)	531	456	371	309	248
Depth x Width (in.)			24 x 24		

‡ Welding does not fully develop web strength.

* Class 3 flanges

WWF COLUMNS
Factored Axial Compressive Resistances, C_r (kN)

CSA G40.21 350W
$\phi = 0.90$

Oxy-Flame-Cut Flange Plates

Designation		WWF550					WWF500		
Mass (kg/m)		721 ‡	620 ‡	503	420	280 **	651 ‡	561 ‡	456
	0	29 000	24 900	20 200	16 900	11 000	26 100	22 600	18 300
	2 500	29 000	24 900	20 200	16 900	11 000	26 100	22 500	18 300
	3 000	28 900	24 900	20 200	16 900	11 000	26 100	22 500	18 300
	3 500	28 900	24 800	20 200	16 800	10 900	26 000	22 500	18 300
	4 000	28 800	24 800	20 100	16 800	10 900	25 900	22 400	18 200
	4 500	28 600	24 700	20 100	16 700	10 900	25 700	22 300	18 100
	5 000	28 500	24 600	20 000	16 700	10 800	25 400	22 100	18 000
	5 500	28 200	24 400	19 800	16 500	10 700	25 100	21 900	17 800
	6 000	27 800	24 200	19 700	16 400	10 600	24 600	21 600	17 600
	6 500	27 400	23 900	19 400	16 200	10 400	24 000	21 200	17 300
	7 000	26 800	23 500	19 100	15 900	10 300	23 300	20 700	16 900
	7 500	26 100	23 100	18 800	15 600	10 000	22 500	20 200	16 500
	8 000	25 400	22 500	18 400	15 200	9 780	21 700	19 500	16 000
	8 500	24 500	21 900	17 900	14 800	9 480	20 700	18 800	15 400
	9 000	23 600	21 300	17 400	14 400	9 160	19 700	18 000	14 800
	9 500	22 600	20 500	16 800	13 800	8 810	18 600	17 200	14 200
	10 000	21 600	19 800	16 200	13 300	8 440	17 600	16 400	13 500
	10 500	20 500	18 900	15 600	12 700	8 060	16 600	15 600	12 900
	11 000	19 500	18 100	14 900	12 200	7 680	15 600	14 700	12 200
	11 500	18 400	17 300	14 200	11 600	7 290	14 600	13 900	11 500
	12 000	17 400	16 400	13 500	11 000	6 920	13 700	13 100	10 900
	12 500	16 500	15 600	12 900	10 500	6 550	12 900	12 400	10 300
	13 000	15 500	14 800	12 200	9 930	6 200	12 100	11 700	9 710
	13 500	14 700	14 000	11 600	9 410	5 870	11 400	11 000	9 160
	14 000	13 800	13 300	11 000	8 920	5 550	10 700	10 400	8 640
	14 500	13 100	12 600	10 400	8 440	5 250	10 000	9 780	8 160
	15 000	12 300	11 900	9 900	8 000	4 960	9 450	9 230	7 700
	15 500	11 700	11 300	9 390	7 580	4 700	8 900	8 720	7 280
	16 000	11 000	10 700	8 910	7 180	4 450	8 400	8 240	6 880

Left axis label: Effective length (KL) in millimetres with respect to the least radius of gyration

PROPERTIES AND DESIGN DATA

	721	620	503	420	280	651	561	456
Area (mm²)	92 000	79 100	64 200	53 600	35 600	83 000	71 600	58 200
Z_x (10^3 mm³)	19 000	17 600	14 800	12 400	8 250	15 400	14 300	12 100
S_x (10^3 mm³)	16 000	15 200	13 100	11 100	7 330	12 800	12 300	10 600
r_x (mm)	218	230	237	239	241	196	207	214
Z_y (10^3 mm³)	9 470	9 180	7 610	6 100	3 810	7 850	7 590	6 290
S_y (10^3 mm³)	6 080	6 050	5 040	4 030	2 380	5 030	5 000	4 170
r_y (mm)	135	145	147	144	140	123	132	134
r_x / r_y	1.61	1.59	1.61	1.66	1.72	1.59	1.57	1.60
M_{rx} (kN·m) (L < L_u)	5 990	5 540	4 660	3 910	2 310	4 850	4 500	3 810
M_{ry} (kN·m)	2 980	2 890	2 400	1 920	750	2 470	2 390	1 980
J (10^3 mm⁴)	110 000	83 100	47 000	24 700	6 410	99 400	75 400	42 700
C_w (10^9 mm⁶)	100 000	99 900	86 700	72 100	47 800	60 800	60 500	52 700
L_u (mm)	12 500	12 100	10 700	9 410	8 790	12 500	11 900	10 300
F_y (MPa)	350	350	350	350	350	350	350	350

IMPERIAL SIZE AND WEIGHT

	721	620	503	420	280	651	561	456
Weight (lb./ft.)	484	416	338	282	188	437	377	306
Depth x Width (in.)			22 x 22				20 x 20	

‡ Welding does not fully develop web strength.

** Class 4: C_r calculated according to CSA S16-09 Clause 13.3.5; S_x, S_y, M_{rx}, M_{ry} according to 13.5(c).

CSA G40.21 350W
$\phi = 0.90$
Oxy-Flame-Cut Flange Plates

WWF COLUMNS
Factored Axial Compressive
Resistances, C_r (kN)

Designation		WWF500						
Mass (kg/m)		381	343	306	276	254 *	223 **	197 **
Effective length (KL) in millimetres with respect to the least radius of gyration	0	15 300	13 800	12 300	11 100	10 200	8 570	6 800
	2 500	15 300	13 800	12 300	11 100	10 200	8 560	6 790
	3 000	15 300	13 800	12 300	11 100	10 100	8 550	6 780
	3 500	15 200	13 700	12 200	11 000	10 100	8 520	6 770
	4 000	15 200	13 700	12 200	11 000	10 100	8 490	6 740
	4 500	15 100	13 600	12 100	10 900	10 000	8 440	6 700
	5 000	15 000	13 500	12 000	10 800	9 930	8 360	6 650
	5 500	14 800	13 300	11 800	10 700	9 810	8 260	6 570
	6 000	14 600	13 100	11 700	10 600	9 650	8 130	6 470
	6 500	14 300	12 900	11 400	10 300	9 450	7 960	6 340
	7 000	14 000	12 600	11 100	10 100	9 210	7 750	6 190
	7 500	13 600	12 200	10 800	9 800	8 930	7 520	6 010
	8 000	13 200	11 800	10 400	9 470	8 610	7 250	5 800
	8 500	12 700	11 300	9 970	9 100	8 260	6 950	5 580
	9 000	12 200	10 800	9 520	8 710	7 880	6 640	5 340
	9 500	11 600	10 300	9 050	8 290	7 500	6 310	5 080
	10 000	11 000	9 800	8 580	7 870	7 100	5 980	4 830
	10 500	10 500	9 270	8 110	7 450	6 710	5 650	4 570
	11 000	9 910	8 760	7 640	7 040	6 330	5 330	4 320
	11 500	9 360	8 260	7 200	6 640	5 960	5 020	4 070
	12 000	8 820	7 780	6 770	6 250	5 610	4 720	3 830
	12 500	8 320	7 320	6 370	5 890	5 270	4 440	3 610
	13 000	7 830	6 890	5 990	5 540	4 960	4 170	3 400
	13 500	7 380	6 490	5 630	5 210	4 660	3 930	3 200
	14 000	6 950	6 110	5 300	4 910	4 390	3 690	3 010
	14 500	6 560	5 750	4 990	4 620	4 130	3 480	2 840
	15 000	6 180	5 430	4 700	4 360	3 890	3 280	2 670
	15 500	5 840	5 120	4 430	4 110	3 670	3 090	2 520
	16 000	5 520	4 840	4 190	3 890	3 470	2 920	2 380

PROPERTIES AND DESIGN DATA

Area (mm²)		48 600	43 800	39 000	35 200	32 300	28 500	25 200
Z_x (10^3 mm³)		10 100	9 100	8 060	7 420	6 780	6 010	5 410
S_x (10^3 mm³)		9 010	8 140	7 240	6 740	6 160	5 180	4 330
r_x (mm)		215	216	215	219	218	220	223
Z_y (10^3 mm³)		5 040	4 420	3 800	3 530	3 160	2 770	2 510
S_y (10^3 mm³)		3 330	2 920	2 500	2 330	2 080	1 620	1 220
r_y (mm)		131	129	127	129	127	127	129
r_x / r_y		1.64	1.67	1.69	1.70	1.72	1.73	1.73
M_{rx} (kN·m) (L < L_u)		3 180	2 870	2 540	2 340	1 940	1 630	1 360
M_{ry} (kN·m)		1 590	1 390	1 200	1 110	655	511	384
J (10^3 mm⁴)		22 500	15 400	10 200	7 920	5 820	3 970	2 870
C_w (10^9 mm⁶)		44 100	39 400	34 500	32 500	29 400	26 200	24 000
L_u (mm)		8 970	8 390	7 930	7 830	8 040	8 090	8 360
F_y (MPa)		350	350	350	350	350	350	350

IMPERIAL SIZE AND WEIGHT

Weight (lb./ft.)		256	230	205	185	170	150	132
Depth x Width (in.)		20 x 20						

* Class 3 flanges

** Class 4: C_r calculated according to CSA S16-09 Clause 13.3.5; S_x, S_y, M_{rx}, M_{ry} according to 13.5(c).

Designation		WWF450								
Mass (kg/m)		503 ‡	409	342	308	274	248	228	201 *	177 **
Effective length (KL) in millimetres with respect to the least radius of gyration	0	20 200	16 400	13 700	12 400	11 000	9 950	9 140	8 060	6 780
	2 500	20 200	16 400	13 700	12 400	11 000	9 940	9 120	8 050	6 770
	3 000	20 100	16 400	13 700	12 300	11 000	9 920	9 100	8 030	6 760
	3 500	20 100	16 300	13 600	12 300	10 900	9 880	9 060	8 000	6 730
	4 000	20 000	16 300	13 600	12 200	10 900	9 820	9 000	7 950	6 690
	4 500	19 800	16 100	13 400	12 100	10 800	9 730	8 920	7 870	6 630
	5 000	19 600	16 000	13 300	11 900	10 600	9 610	8 790	7 760	6 540
	5 500	19 200	15 700	13 100	11 700	10 400	9 440	8 620	7 610	6 430
	6 000	18 800	15 400	12 800	11 500	10 200	9 220	8 410	7 420	6 280
	6 500	18 300	15 000	12 400	11 100	9 840	8 950	8 150	7 190	6 100
	7 000	17 700	14 600	12 000	10 700	9 470	8 630	7 850	6 930	5 880
	7 500	17 100	14 000	11 600	10 300	9 060	8 280	7 510	6 630	5 640
	8 000	16 300	13 500	11 000	9 810	8 610	7 890	7 140	6 300	5 380
	8 500	15 500	12 800	10 500	9 300	8 150	7 480	6 750	5 960	5 100
	9 000	14 700	12 200	9 920	8 780	7 670	7 060	6 360	5 610	4 810
	9 500	13 900	11 500	9 350	8 260	7 200	6 640	5 970	5 270	4 530
	10 000	13 100	10 900	8 790	7 750	6 750	6 230	5 590	4 930	4 250
	10 500	12 300	10 200	8 240	7 260	6 310	5 830	5 220	4 610	3 980
	11 000	11 500	9 580	7 720	6 790	5 890	5 460	4 880	4 310	3 720
	11 500	10 800	8 980	7 230	6 340	5 500	5 100	4 560	4 020	3 480
	12 000	10 100	8 420	6 760	5 930	5 130	4 770	4 250	3 760	3 250
	12 500	9 440	7 890	6 330	5 550	4 800	4 460	3 970	3 510	3 040
	13 000	8 840	7 400	5 930	5 190	4 490	4 170	3 720	3 280	2 840
	13 500	8 290	6 950	5 560	4 860	4 200	3 910	3 480	3 070	2 660
	14 000	7 780	6 520	5 210	4 560	3 930	3 660	3 260	2 880	2 500
	14 500	7 310	6 130	4 900	4 280	3 690	3 440	3 060	2 700	2 340
	15 000	6 870	5 770	4 600	4 020	3 470	3 230	2 870	2 540	2 200
	15 500	6 470	5 430	4 330	3 790	3 260	3 040	2 700	2 390	2 070
	16 000	6 100	5 130	4 090	3 570	3 070	2 870	2 550	2 250	1 950

PROPERTIES AND DESIGN DATA										
Area (mm^2)		64 100	52 200	43 600	39 300	35 000	31 600	29 000	25 600	22 600
Z_x (10^3 mm^3)		11 400	9 640	8 100	7 290	6 470	5 960	5 450	4 840	4 360
S_x (10^3 mm^3)		9 620	8 380	7 150	6 480	5 770	5 380	4 920	4 400	3 820
r_x (mm)		184	190	192	193	193	196	195	197	200
Z_y (10^3 mm^3)		6 150	5 100	4 090	3 580	3 080	2 860	2 560	2 250	2 040
S_y (10^3 mm^3)		4 050	3 380	2 700	2 360	2 030	1 890	1 690	1 490	1 220
r_y (mm)		119	121	118	116	114	116	114	114	116
r_x / r_y		1.55	1.57	1.63	1.66	1.69	1.69	1.71	1.73	1.72
M_{rx} (kN·m) (L < L_u)		3 590	3 040	2 550	2 300	2 040	1 880	1 720	1 390	1 200
M_{ry} (kN·m)		1 940	1 610	1 290	1 130	970	901	806	469	384
J (10^3 mm^4)		67 800	38 400	20 200	13 900	9 140	7 120	5 230	3 570	2 580
C_w (10^9 mm^6)		34 700	30 400	25 500	22 900	20 100	18 900	17 200	15 300	14 000
L_u (mm)		11 800	10 100	8 530	7 920	7 380	7 250	7 000	7 200	7 260
F_y (MPa)		350	350	350	350	350	350	350	350	350

IMPERIAL SIZE AND WEIGHT										
Weight (lb./ft.)		337	275	229	207	184	166	152	134	119
Depth x Width (in.)						18 x 18				

‡ Welding does not fully develop web strength.

* Class 3 flanges

** Class 4: C_r calculated according to CSA S16-09 Clause 13.3.5; S_x, S_y, M_{rx}, M_{ry} according to 13.5(c).

CSA G40.21 350W
$\phi = 0.90$
Oxy-Flame-Cut Flange Plates

WWF COLUMNS
Factored Axial Compressive
Resistances, C_r (kN)

Designation		\multicolumn{9}{c|}{WWF400}								
Mass (kg/m)	444 ‡	362	303	273	243	220	202	178 *	157 *
0	17 800	14 600	12 200	11 000	9 770	8 820	8 100	7 150	6 330
2 500	17 800	14 500	12 100	10 900	9 740	8 800	8 070	7 130	6 310
3 000	17 700	14 500	12 100	10 900	9 700	8 760	8 040	7 100	6 290
3 500	17 600	14 400	12 000	10 800	9 640	8 710	7 990	7 060	6 250
4 000	17 500	14 300	11 900	10 700	9 540	8 620	7 910	6 980	6 190
4 500	17 200	14 100	11 700	10 600	9 390	8 490	7 780	6 870	6 100
5 000	16 900	13 800	11 500	10 400	9 180	8 310	7 610	6 720	5 970
5 500	16 500	13 500	11 200	10 100	8 910	8 080	7 390	6 530	5 800
6 000	16 000	13 100	10 800	9 730	8 580	7 790	7 120	6 290	5 590
6 500	15 300	12 600	10 400	9 320	8 200	7 450	6 800	6 000	5 350
7 000	14 600	12 000	9 890	8 860	7 770	7 070	6 440	5 690	5 080
7 500	13 800	11 400	9 360	8 360	7 320	6 670	6 060	5 360	4 790
8 000	13 000	10 700	8 790	7 850	6 850	6 250	5 680	5 010	4 490
8 500	12 200	10 100	8 230	7 330	6 380	5 830	5 290	4 670	4 190
9 000	11 400	9 400	7 670	6 830	5 930	5 420	4 910	4 340	3 890
9 500	10 600	8 760	7 130	6 340	5 500	5 030	4 560	4 020	3 610
10 000	9 850	8 150	6 620	5 890	5 090	4 670	4 220	3 730	3 350
10 500	9 150	7 580	6 150	5 460	4 720	4 330	3 910	3 450	3 110
11 000	8 500	7 040	5 710	5 060	4 370	4 010	3 620	3 200	2 880
11 500	7 900	6 550	5 300	4 700	4 050	3 720	3 360	2 970	2 670
12 000	7 350	6 090	4 930	4 370	3 760	3 460	3 120	2 750	2 480
12 500	6 840	5 680	4 590	4 070	3 500	3 220	2 900	2 560	2 310
13 000	6 380	5 290	4 280	3 790	3 260	3 000	2 700	2 390	2 150
13 500	5 960	4 950	3 990	3 540	3 040	2 790	2 520	2 230	2 010
14 000	5 570	4 630	3 730	3 310	2 840	2 610	2 350	2 080	1 880
14 500	5 220	4 330	3 500	3 100	2 660	2 450	2 200	1 950	1 760
15 000	4 900	4 070	3 280	2 900	2 490	2 290	2 070	1 830	1 650
15 500	4 600	3 820	3 080	2 730	2 340	2 150	1 940	1 710	1 550
16 000	4 330	3 600	2 900	2 570	2 200	2 030	1 830	1 610	1 460

Effective length (KL) in millimetres with respect to the least radius of gyration

\multicolumn{10}{c	}{PROPERTIES AND DESIGN DATA}
Area (mm²)	56 600	46 200	38 600	34 800	31 000	28 000	25 700	22 700	20 100
Z_x (10^3 mm³)	8 770	7 480	6 300	5 680	5 050	4 660	4 260	3 790	3 420
S_x (10^3 mm³)	7 300	6 410	5 500	5 000	4 470	4 170	3 830	3 430	3 120
r_x (mm)	161	167	169	170	170	173	172	174	176
Z_y (10^3 mm³)	4 870	4 030	3 230	2 840	2 440	2 260	2 020	1 780	1 610
S_y (10^3 mm³)	3 200	2 670	2 130	1 870	1 600	1 490	1 330	1 170	1 070
r_y (mm)	106	107	105	104	102	103	102	102	103
r_x / r_y	1.52	1.56	1.61	1.63	1.67	1.68	1.69	1.71	1.71
M_{rx} (kN·m) (L < L_u)	2 760	2 360	1 980	1 790	1 590	1 470	1 340	1 080	983
M_{ry} (kN·m)	1 530	1 270	1 020	895	769	712	636	369	337
J (10^3 mm⁴)	60 100	34 100	17 900	12 300	8 110	6 320	4 640	3 170	2 290
C_w (10^9 mm⁶)	18 500	16 300	13 800	12 400	11 000	10 300	9 380	8 390	7 700
L_u (mm)	11 900	9 930	8 190	7 490	6 890	6 720	6 430	6 600	6 440
F_y (MPa)	350	350	350	350	350	350	350	350	350

\multicolumn{10}{c	}{IMPERIAL SIZE AND WEIGHT}
Weight (lb./ft.)	298	243	203	183	163	147	135	119	105
Depth x Width (in.)	\multicolumn{9}{c|}{16 x 16}								

‡ Welding does not fully develop web strength.

* Class 3 flanges

Designation					WWF350				
Mass (kg/m)		315	263	238	212	192	176	155	137
Effective length (KL) in millimetres with respect to the least radius of gyration	0	12 700	10 600	9 540	8 510	7 690	7 060	6 240	5 510
	2 500	12 600	10 500	9 500	8 460	7 650	7 020	6 200	5 480
	3 000	12 500	10 500	9 440	8 400	7 600	6 970	6 160	5 450
	3 500	12 400	10 400	9 340	8 310	7 520	6 890	6 090	5 390
	4 000	12 200	10 200	9 180	8 150	7 390	6 770	5 980	5 300
	4 500	12 000	9 970	8 950	7 930	7 200	6 580	5 820	5 160
	5 000	11 600	9 640	8 650	7 640	6 950	6 350	5 600	4 980
	5 500	11 200	9 240	8 270	7 290	6 640	6 050	5 340	4 760
	6 000	10 600	8 770	7 820	6 880	6 280	5 710	5 040	4 500
	6 500	10 000	8 240	7 340	6 430	5 880	5 340	4 710	4 210
	7 000	9 400	7 690	6 830	5 960	5 470	4 950	4 370	3 910
	7 500	8 740	7 130	6 310	5 500	5 060	4 570	4 030	3 620
	8 000	8 090	6 580	5 810	5 050	4 650	4 200	3 700	3 330
	8 500	7 470	6 050	5 340	4 630	4 270	3 850	3 390	3 060
	9 000	6 880	5 560	4 900	4 240	3 920	3 520	3 100	2 800
	9 500	6 330	5 110	4 500	3 890	3 600	3 230	2 840	2 570
	10 000	5 830	4 700	4 130	3 560	3 300	2 960	2 610	2 360
	10 500	5 370	4 320	3 800	3 270	3 030	2 720	2 400	2 170
	11 000	4 950	3 990	3 500	3 010	2 790	2 500	2 200	2 000
	11 500	4 580	3 680	3 230	2 780	2 580	2 310	2 030	1 840
	12 000	4 240	3 400	2 980	2 570	2 380	2 130	1 880	1 700
	12 500	3 930	3 160	2 770	2 380	2 210	1 980	1 740	1 580
	13 000	3 650	2 930	2 570	2 210	2 050	1 840	1 620	1 470
	13 500	3 400	2 730	2 390	2 050	1 910	1 710	1 500	1 360
	14 000	3 170	2 550	2 230	1 920	1 780	1 590	1 400	1 270
	14 500	2 970	2 380	2 080	1 790	1 660	1 490	1 310	1 190
	15 000	2 780	2 230	1 950	1 680	1 560	1 390	1 230	1 110
	15 500	2 610	2 090	1 830	1 570	1 460	1 310	1 150	1 040
	16 000	2 450	1 970	1 720	1 480	1 370	1 230	1 080	981

PROPERTIES AND DESIGN DATA								
Area (mm²)	40 200	33 600	30 300	27 000	24 400	22 400	19 800	17 500
Z_x (10³ mm³)	5 580	4 730	4 280	3 810	3 520	3 220	2 870	2 590
S_x (10³ mm³)	4 710	4 070	3 720	3 330	3 120	2 870	2 580	2 350
r_x (mm)	143	146	147	147	149	150	151	153
Z_y (10³ mm³)	3 090	2 480	2 170	1 870	1 740	1 550	1 360	1 240
S_y (10³ mm³)	2 040	1 630	1 430	1 230	1 140	1 020	899	817
r_y (mm)	94.3	92.3	90.9	89.2	90.5	89.3	89.1	90.3
r_x / r_y	1.52	1.58	1.62	1.65	1.65	1.68	1.69	1.69
M_{rx} (kN·m) (L < L_u)	1 760	1 490	1 350	1 200	1 110	1 010	904	816
M_{ry} (kN·m)	973	781	684	589	548	488	428	391
J (10³ mm⁴)	29 800	15 700	10 800	7 070	5 520	4 060	2 760	2 000
C_w (10⁹ mm⁶)	8 040	6 870	6 210	5 490	5 190	4 720	4 230	3 890
L_u (mm)	9 920	7 970	7 150	6 450	6 230	5 910	5 630	5 510
F_y (MPa)	350	350	350	350	350	350	350	350

IMPERIAL SIZE AND WEIGHT								
Weight (lb./ft.)	211	177	159	142	128	118	104	92
Depth x Width (in.)				14 x 14				

CSA G40.21 350W

ASTM A992, A572 grade 50

$\phi = 0.90$

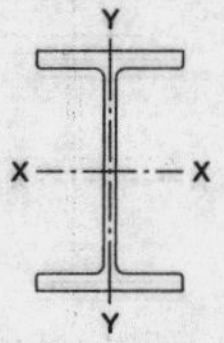

W COLUMNS

Factored Axial Compressive Resistances, C_r (kN)

Designation		W360					
Mass (kg/m)		1086	990	900	818	744	677
Effective length (KL) in millimetres with respect to the least radius of gyration	0	43 200	39 100	35 700	32 300	29 400	26 800
	2 500	42 100	38 200	34 800	31 400	28 600	26 000
	3 000	41 500	37 600	34 300	30 900	28 100	25 600
	3 500	40 800	36 900	33 600	30 300	27 500	25 000
	4 000	39 800	36 000	32 800	29 500	26 800	24 300
	4 500	38 700	34 900	31 800	28 600	26 000	23 600
	5 000	37 500	33 800	30 800	27 600	25 000	22 700
	5 500	36 200	32 600	29 600	26 600	24 000	21 800
	6 000	34 700	31 200	28 400	25 400	22 900	20 800
	6 500	33 300	29 800	27 100	24 200	21 800	19 800
	7 000	31 700	28 400	25 800	23 000	20 700	18 700
	7 500	30 200	27 000	24 500	21 800	19 600	17 700
	8 000	28 700	25 600	23 200	20 700	18 500	16 700
	8 500	27 200	24 300	22 000	19 500	17 500	15 800
	9 000	25 700	22 900	20 700	18 400	16 500	14 900
	9 500	24 300	21 700	19 600	17 400	15 500	14 000
	10 000	23 000	20 400	18 500	16 400	14 600	13 100
	10 500	21 700	19 300	17 400	15 400	13 700	12 400
	11 000	20 500	18 200	16 400	14 500	12 900	11 600
	11 500	19 400	17 200	15 500	13 700	12 200	10 900
	12 000	18 300	16 200	14 600	12 900	11 500	10 300
	12 500	17 300	15 300	13 800	12 200	10 800	9 690
	13 000	16 300	14 400	13 000	11 500	10 200	9 140
	13 500	15 400	13 600	12 300	10 800	9 600	8 620
	14 000	14 600	12 900	11 600	10 200	9 070	8 140
	14 500	13 800	12 200	11 000	9 680	8 570	7 690
	15 000	13 100	11 600	10 400	9 160	8 110	7 280
	15 500	12 400	11 000	9 880	8 680	7 680	6 890
	16 000	11 800	10 400	9 370	8 230	7 280	6 530
PROPERTIES AND DESIGN DATA							
Area (mm^2)		139 000	126 000	115 000	104 000	94 800	86 300
Z_x (10^3 mm^3)		27 200	24 300	21 600	19 300	17 200	15 300
S_x (10^3 mm^3)		20 900	18 900	17 000	15 300	13 700	12 400
r_x (mm)		207	203	198	194	190	186
Z_y (10^3 mm^3)		13 400	12 000	10 700	9 560	8 550	7 680
S_y (10^3 mm^3)		8 650	7 740	6 940	6 200	5 550	4 990
r_y (mm)		119	117	116	114	112	111
r_x / r_y		1.74	1.74	1.71	1.70	1.70	1.68
M_{rx} (kN·m) ($L < L_u$)		8 450	7 550	6 710	5 990	5 340	4 750
M_{ry} (kN·m)		4 160	3 730	3 320	2 970	2 650	2 380
J (10^3 mm^4)		605 000	469 000	364 000	279 000	214 000	165 000
C_w (10^9 mm^6)		96 700	82 000	69 200	58 900	50 200	43 100
L_u (mm)		21 200	19 600	18 300	17 000	15 700	14 700
F_y (MPa)		345	345	345	345	345	345
IMPERIAL SIZE AND WEIGHT							
Weight (lb/ft)		730	665	605	550	500	455
Depth x Width (in.)		22⅜ x 17⅞	21⅝ x 17⅝	20⅞ x 17⅜	20¼ x 17¼	19⅝ x 17	19 x 16⅞

W COLUMNS
Factored Axial Compressive Resistances, C_r (kN)

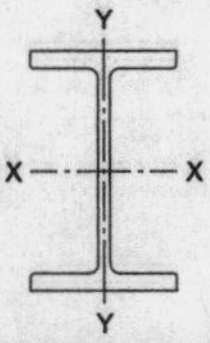

Designation		W360						
Mass (kg/m)		634	592	551	509	463	421	382
Effective length (KL) in millimetres with respect to the least radius of gyration	0	25 100	23 400	21 800	20 200	18 300	16 700	15 100
	2 500	24 400	22 800	21 100	19 500	17 800	16 100	14 600
	3 000	23 900	22 300	20 700	19 200	17 400	15 800	14 300
	3 500	23 400	21 800	20 200	18 700	17 000	15 400	14 000
	4 000	22 700	21 200	19 600	18 200	16 500	15 000	13 500
	4 500	22 000	20 500	19 000	17 600	15 900	14 400	13 100
	5 000	21 200	19 700	18 200	16 900	15 300	13 900	12 500
	5 500	20 300	18 900	17 400	16 100	14 600	13 200	11 900
	6 000	19 300	18 000	16 600	15 400	13 900	12 600	11 300
	6 500	18 400	17 100	15 800	14 600	13 200	11 900	10 700
	7 000	17 400	16 200	14 900	13 800	12 500	11 200	10 100
	7 500	16 500	15 300	14 100	13 000	11 700	10 600	9 530
	8 000	15 500	14 400	13 200	12 300	11 000	9 960	8 950
	8 500	14 600	13 500	12 500	11 500	10 400	9 350	8 400
	9 000	13 800	12 700	11 700	10 800	9 750	8 780	7 870
	9 500	12 900	12 000	11 000	10 200	9 150	8 230	7 380
	10 000	12 200	11 200	10 300	9 550	8 580	7 720	6 910
	10 500	11 400	10 600	9 690	8 970	8 050	7 240	6 480
	11 000	10 800	9 920	9 100	8 420	7 560	6 790	6 080
	11 500	10 100	9 320	8 540	7 910	7 100	6 370	5 700
	12 000	9 510	8 770	8 030	7 440	6 670	5 990	5 350
	12 500	8 960	8 250	7 560	7 000	6 270	5 630	5 030
	13 000	8 440	7 770	7 120	6 590	5 900	5 290	4 730
	13 500	7 960	7 330	6 710	6 210	5 560	4 990	4 450
	14 000	7 510	6 920	6 330	5 860	5 250	4 700	4 200
	14 500	7 100	6 530	5 970	5 530	4 950	4 440	3 960
	15 000	6 710	6 180	5 650	5 230	4 680	4 190	3 740
	15 500	6 350	5 850	5 340	4 950	4 430	3 970	3 540
	16 000	6 020	5 540	5 060	4 690	4 190	3 760	3 350

PROPERTIES AND DESIGN DATA

	634	592	551	509	463	421	382
Area (mm^2)	80 800	75 500	70 100	64 900	59 000	53 700	48 700
Z_x (10^3 mm^3)	14 200	13 100	12 100	11 000	9 880	8 880	7 970
S_x (10^3 mm^3)	11 600	10 800	9 940	9 170	8 280	7 510	6 790
r_x (mm)	184	182	180	178	175	172	170
Z_y (10^3 mm^3)	7 120	6 570	6 050	5 550	4 980	4 490	4 030
S_y (10^3 mm^3)	4 630	4 280	3 950	3 630	3 250	2 940	2 640
r_y (mm)	110	109	108	108	107	106	105
r_x / r_y	1.67	1.67	1.67	1.65	1.64	1.62	1.62
M_{rx} (kN·m) (L < L_u)	4 410	4 070	3 760	3 420	3 070	2 760	2 470
M_{ry} (kN·m)	2 210	2 040	1 880	1 720	1 550	1 390	1 250
J (10^3 mm^4)	138 000	114 000	92 500	74 000	56 500	43 400	32 900
C_w (10^9 mm^6)	38 700	34 800	31 000	27 700	23 900	20 800	18 200
L_u (mm)	13 900	13 200	12 400	11 700	10 800	10 100	9 440
F_y (MPa)	345	345	345	345	345	345	345

IMPERIAL SIZE AND WEIGHT

	634	592	551	509	463	421	382
Weight (lb/ft)	426	398	370	342	311	283	257
Depth x Width (in.)	18⅝ x 16¾	18¼ x 16⅝	17⅞ x 16½	17½ x 16⅜	17⅛ x 16¼	16¾ x 16⅛	16⅜ x 16

CSA G40.21 350W
ASTM A992, A572 grade 50
$\phi = 0.90$

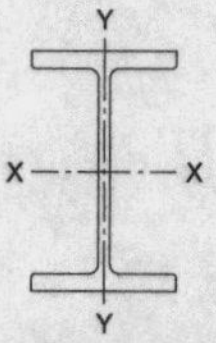

W COLUMNS
Factored Axial Compressive
Resistances, C_r (kN)

Designation	W360					
Mass (kg/m)	347	314	287	262	237	216
Effective length (KL) in millimetres with respect to the least radius of gyration — 0	13 700	12 400	11 400	10 400	9 350	8 570
2 500	13 300	12 000	11 000	10 000	9 020	8 260
3 000	13 000	11 700	10 700	9 820	8 830	8 080
3 500	12 700	11 400	10 500	9 560	8 590	7 860
4 000	12 300	11 000	10 100	9 240	8 300	7 590
4 500	11 800	10 600	9 740	8 880	7 980	7 290
5 000	11 300	10 200	9 320	8 490	7 630	6 960
5 500	10 800	9 670	8 870	8 080	7 260	6 620
6 000	10 200	9 170	8 410	7 650	6 870	6 260
6 500	9 670	8 660	7 950	7 220	6 490	5 900
7 000	9 110	8 160	7 480	6 790	6 100	5 550
7 500	8 570	7 660	7 030	6 380	5 730	5 200
8 000	8 040	7 190	6 590	5 980	5 370	4 870
8 500	7 540	6 740	6 180	5 590	5 030	4 560
9 000	7 070	6 310	5 780	5 230	4 700	4 260
9 500	6 620	5 900	5 410	4 890	4 400	3 980
10 000	6 200	5 520	5 070	4 580	4 110	3 720
10 500	5 800	5 170	4 740	4 280	3 850	3 480
11 000	5 440	4 840	4 440	4 010	3 600	3 260
11 500	5 100	4 540	4 160	3 760	3 380	3 050
12 000	4 790	4 260	3 910	3 520	3 170	2 860
12 500	4 500	4 000	3 670	3 310	2 970	2 680
13 000	4 230	3 760	3 450	3 110	2 790	2 520
13 500	3 980	3 540	3 240	2 920	2 630	2 370
14 000	3 750	3 330	3 060	2 750	2 470	2 230
14 500	3 540	3 140	2 880	2 600	2 330	2 100
15 000	3 340	2 970	2 720	2 450	2 200	1 980
15 500	3 160	2 810	2 570	2 320	2 080	1 880
16 000	2 990	2 650	2 440	2 190	1 970	1 770

PROPERTIES AND DESIGN DATA						
Area (mm^2)	44 200	39 900	36 600	33 500	30 100	27 600
Z_x (10^3 mm^3)	7 140	6 370	5 810	5 260	4 690	4 260
S_x (10^3 mm^3)	6 140	5 530	5 070	4 620	4 150	3 790
r_x (mm)	168	166	165	163	162	161
Z_y (10^3 mm^3)	3 630	3 240	2 960	2 680	2 390	2 180
S_y (10^3 mm^3)	2 380	2 120	1 940	1 760	1 570	1 430
r_y (mm)	104	103	103	102	102	101
r_x / r_y	1.62	1.61	1.60	1.60	1.59	1.59
M_{rx} (kN·m) (L < L_u)	2 220	1 980	1 800	1 630	1 460	1 320
M_{ry} (kN·m)	1 130	1 010	919	832	742	677
J (10^3 mm^4)	24 800	18 500	14 500	11 100	8 190	6 330
C_w (10^9 mm^6)	15 900	13 800	12 300	11 000	9 500	8 520
L_u (mm)	8 860	8 290	7 890	7 510	7 120	6 880
F_y (MPa)	345	345	345	345	345	345

IMPERIAL SIZE AND WEIGHT						
Weight (lb/ft)	233	211	193	176	159	145
Depth x Width (in.)	16 x 15⅞	15¾ x 15¾	15½ x 15¾	15¼ x 15⅝	15 x 15⅝	14¾ x 15½

W COLUMNS
Factored Axial Compressive
Resistances, C_r (kN)

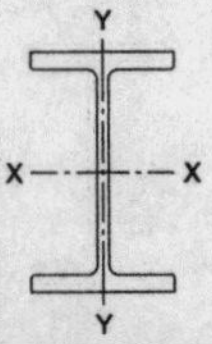

CSA G40.21 350W
ASTM A992, A572 grade 50
$\phi = 0.90$

Designation		**W360**					**W360**	
Mass (kg/m)		196	179	162	147*	134*	122	110
0		7 760	7 080	6 400	5 840	5 310	4 810	4 350
1 250		7 710	7 030	6 350	5 800	5 270	4 720	4 260
1 500		7 680	7 000	6 330	5 770	5 250	4 660	4 210
1 750		7 640	6 960	6 290	5 740	5 220	4 580	4 140
2 000		7 580	6 910	6 240	5 700	5 180	4 490	4 060
2 250		7 520	6 850	6 190	5 650	5 140	4 380	3 960
2 500		7 440	6 780	6 130	5 590	5 080	4 260	3 850
2 750		7 350	6 700	6 050	5 520	5 020	4 130	3 730
3 000		7 250	6 610	5 970	5 440	4 950	3 980	3 600
3 250		7 140	6 510	5 880	5 360	4 870	3 830	3 460
3 500		7 020	6 400	5 780	5 260	4 780	3 670	3 320
3 750		6 890	6 280	5 670	5 160	4 690	3 510	3 170
4 000		6 750	6 150	5 550	5 060	4 590	3 350	3 030
4 500		6 450	5 880	5 300	4 820	4 380	3 030	2 740
5 000		6 130	5 580	5 030	4 580	4 150	2 730	2 470
5 500		5 790	5 270	4 750	4 320	3 920	2 450	2 210
6 000		5 450	4 950	4 460	4 060	3 680	2 200	1 990
6 500		5 100	4 640	4 180	3 800	3 440	1 980	1 780
7 000		4 770	4 340	3 900	3 550	3 210	1 780	1 600
7 500		4 450	4 050	3 640	3 300	3 000	1 600	1 450
8 000		4 150	3 770	3 390	3 080	2 790	1 450	1 310
8 500		3 860	3 510	3 160	2 860	2 590	1 310	1 180
9 000		3 600	3 270	2 940	2 660	2 410	1 190	1 080
9 500		3 350	3 040	2 730	2 480	2 240	1 090	981
10 000		3 120	2 830	2 540	2 310	2 090	993	897
10 500		2 910	2 640	2 370	2 150	1 940	911	823
11 000		2 720	2 460	2 210	2 000	1 810	838	757
11 500		2 540	2 300	2 070	1 870	1 690	773	698
12 000		2 370	2 150	1 930	1 750	1 580	715	645

Effective length (KL) in millimetres with respect to the least radius of gyration

PROPERTIES AND DESIGN DATA								
Area (mm²)		25 000	22 800	20 600	18 800	17 100	15 500	14 000
Z_x (10^3 mm³)		3 840	3 480	3 140	2 840	2 560	2 270	2 060
S_x (10^3 mm³)		3 420	3 120	2 830	2 570	2 330	2 010	1 840
r_x (mm)		159	159	158	157	156	154	154
Z_y (10^3 mm³)		1 860	1 680	1 520	1 370	1 240	732	664
S_y (10^3 mm³)		1 220	1 110	1 000	904	817	478	435
r_y (mm)		95.5	95.2	94.8	94.3	94.0	63.0	63.0
r_x / r_y		1.66	1.67	1.67	1.66	1.66	2.44	2.44
M_{rx} (kN·m) (L < L_u)		1 190	1 080	975	798	723	705	640
M_{ry} (kN·m)		578	522	472	281	254	227	206
J (10^3 mm⁴)		5 140	3 910	2 940	2 230	1 680	2 110	1 600
C_w (10^9 mm⁶)		6 830	6 120	5 430	4 840	4 310	1 790	1 610
L_u (mm)		6 380	6 170	5 980	6 190	6 030	4 040	3 940
F_y (MPa)		345	345	345	345	345	345	345

IMPERIAL SIZE AND WEIGHT								
Weight (lb/ft)		132	120	109	99	90	82	74
Depth x Width (in.)		14⅝ x 14¾	14½ x 14⅝	14⅜ x 14⅝	14⅛ x 14⅝	14 x 14½	14¼ x 10⅛	14⅛ x 10⅛

* Class 3 in bending

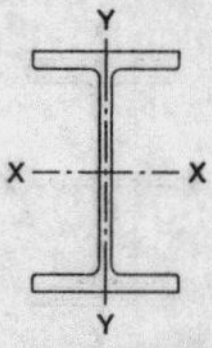

Designation	W360		W360			W310		
Mass (kg/m)	101	91	79	72**	64**	500	454	415
Effective length (KL) in millimetres with respect to the least radius of gyration								
0	4 010	3 600	3 140	2 800	2 430	19 800	17 900	16 400
1 250	3 920	3 530	3 010	2 690	2 330	19 600	17 800	16 300
1 500	3 870	3 480	2 940	2 620	2 270	19 500	17 700	16 200
1 750	3 810	3 420	2 850	2 540	2 200	19 400	17 600	16 100
2 000	3 730	3 350	2 750	2 450	2 120	19 200	17 400	15 900
2 250	3 640	3 270	2 630	2 340	2 020	19 000	17 200	15 700
2 500	3 540	3 180	2 510	2 230	1 920	18 800	17 000	15 500
2 750	3 430	3 070	2 370	2 110	1 820	18 500	16 700	15 300
3 000	3 310	2 960	2 240	1 990	1 710	18 200	16 500	15 000
3 250	3 180	2 850	2 100	1 870	1 610	17 900	16 100	14 700
3 500	3 050	2 730	1 970	1 750	1 500	17 500	15 800	14 400
3 750	2 910	2 610	1 840	1 630	1 400	17 100	15 400	14 100
4 000	2 780	2 480	1 720	1 520	1 310	16 700	15 100	13 700
4 500	2 510	2 250	1 500	1 320	1 140	15 800	14 200	13 000
5 000	2 260	2 020	1 300	1 150	986	14 900	13 400	12 200
5 500	2 030	1 810	1 140	1 000	858	14 000	12 500	11 400
6 000	1 820	1 620	995	877	750	13 000	11 600	10 600
6 500	1 630	1 460	875	771	659	12 100	10 800	9 800
7 000	1 470	1 310	773	681	582	11 200	10 000	9 070
7 500	1 320	1 180	687	605	517	10 400	9 260	8 380
8 000	1 190	1 060	613	541	463	9 610	8 560	7 740
8 500	1 080	963	550	486	417	8 890	7 910	7 150
9 000	983	875	496	438	377	8 230	7 320	6 610
9 500	896	797	449	397	343	7 630	6 770	6 110
10 000	819	729				7 070	6 280	5 660
10 500	751	668				6 570	5 820	5 250
11 000	691	614				6 100	5 410	4 880
11 500	637	567				5 680	5 030	4 540
12 000	589	524				5 300	4 690	4 230
PROPERTIES AND DESIGN DATA								
Area (mm^2)	12 900	11 600	10 100	9 100	8 140	63 800	57 800	52 900
Z_x (10^3 mm^3)	1 880	1 680	1 430	1 280	1 140	9 880	8 820	7 900
S_x (10^3 mm^3)	1 690	1 510	1 280	1 150	1 030	7 910	7 130	6 450
r_x (mm)	153	152	150	149	148	163	160	157
Z_y (10^3 mm^3)	605	538	362	322	284	4 490	4 000	3 610
S_y (10^3 mm^3)	397	353	236	210	186	2 910	2 600	2 340
r_y (mm)	62.7	62.3	48.9	48.5	48.1	88.0	86.8	86.0
r_x / r_y	2.44	2.44	3.07	3.07	3.08	1.85	1.84	1.83
M_{rx} (kN·m) ($L < L_u$)	584	522	444	397	354	3 070	2 740	2 450
M_{ry} (kN·m)	188	167	112	100	88.2	1 390	1 240	1 120
J (10^3 mm^4)	1 250	914	811	601	436	101 000	77 200	59 500
C_w (10^9 mm^6)	1 450	1 270	687	600	524	15 300	13 100	11 300
L_u (mm)	3 860	3 760	3 010	2 940	2 870	12 100	11 100	10 400
F_y (MPa)	345	345	345	345	345	345	345	345
IMPERIAL SIZE AND WEIGHT								
Weight (lb/ft)	68	61	53	48	43	336	305	279
Depth x Width (in.)	14 x 10	13⅞ x 10	13⅞ x 8	13¾ x 8	13⅝ x 8	16⅞ x 13⅜	16⅜ x 13¼	15⅞ x 13⅛

** Class 4

W COLUMNS
Factored Axial Compressive
Resistances, C$_r$ (kN)

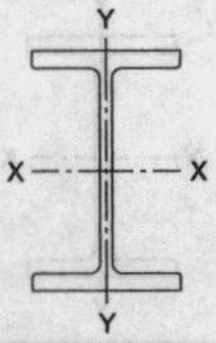

CSA G40.21 350W
ASTM A992, A572 grade 50
$\phi = 0.90$

Designation		W310					W310		
Mass (kg/m)		375	342	313	283	253	226	202	179
Effective length (KL) in millimetres with respect to the least radius of gyration	0	14 800	13 600	12 400	11 200	10 000	8 970	8 010	7 080
	1 250	14 700	13 400	12 300	11 100	9 900	8 880	7 930	7 000
	1 500	14 600	13 400	12 200	11 000	9 830	8 820	7 870	6 950
	1 750	14 500	13 300	12 100	10 900	9 750	8 750	7 800	6 890
	2 000	14 300	13 100	12 000	10 800	9 650	8 650	7 720	6 820
	2 250	14 200	13 000	11 800	10 700	9 530	8 540	7 620	6 720
	2 500	14 000	12 800	11 700	10 500	9 380	8 410	7 500	6 620
	2 750	13 800	12 600	11 500	10 300	9 220	8 260	7 360	6 490
	3 000	13 500	12 400	11 300	10 100	9 040	8 100	7 210	6 360
	3 250	13 200	12 100	11 000	9 920	8 840	7 920	7 050	6 210
	3 500	12 900	11 800	10 800	9 690	8 630	7 720	6 870	6 050
	3 750	12 600	11 500	10 500	9 440	8 400	7 520	6 680	5 880
	4 000	12 300	11 200	10 200	9 180	8 160	7 300	6 480	5 710
	4 500	11 600	10 600	9 610	8 630	7 660	6 850	6 070	5 340
	5 000	10 900	9 910	8 980	8 060	7 150	6 380	5 650	4 960
	5 500	10 100	9 230	8 360	7 490	6 630	5 910	5 230	4 590
	6 000	9 410	8 570	7 740	6 930	6 130	5 460	4 830	4 230
	6 500	8 710	7 920	7 150	6 400	5 650	5 030	4 440	3 890
	7 000	8 050	7 320	6 600	5 900	5 200	4 630	4 080	3 570
	7 500	7 430	6 750	6 080	5 430	4 780	4 250	3 750	3 280
	8 000	6 850	6 220	5 600	5 000	4 400	3 910	3 440	3 010
	8 500	6 330	5 740	5 160	4 600	4 050	3 600	3 170	2 760
	9 000	5 840	5 300	4 760	4 250	3 730	3 310	2 910	2 540
	9 500	5 400	4 900	4 400	3 920	3 440	3 050	2 680	2 340
	10 000	5 000	4 530	4 070	3 620	3 180	2 820	2 480	2 160
	10 500	4 630	4 200	3 770	3 350	2 940	2 610	2 290	2 000
	11 000	4 300	3 890	3 490	3 110	2 730	2 420	2 120	1 850
	11 500	4 000	3 620	3 250	2 890	2 530	2 240	1 970	1 720
	12 000	3 720	3 370	3 020	2 690	2 360	2 090	1 830	1 590

PROPERTIES AND DESIGN DATA

	375	342	313	283	253	226	202	179
Area (mm^2)	47 700	43 700	39 900	36 000	32 200	28 900	25 800	22 800
Z$_x$ (10^3 mm^3)	7 000	6 330	5 720	5 100	4 490	3 980	3 510	3 050
S$_x$ (10^3 mm^3)	5 770	5 260	4 790	4 310	3 830	3 420	3 050	2 680
r$_x$ (mm)	154	152	150	148	146	144	142	140
Z$_y$ (10^3 mm^3)	3 210	2 910	2 620	2 340	2 060	1 830	1 610	1 400
S$_y$ (10^3 mm^3)	2 080	1 890	1 700	1 530	1 350	1 190	1 050	919
r$_y$ (mm)	84.8	84.2	83.3	82.6	81.6	81.0	80.2	79.5
r$_x$ / r$_y$	1.82	1.81	1.80	1.79	1.79	1.78	1.77	1.76
M$_{rx}$ (kN·m) (L < L$_u$)	2 170	1 970	1 780	1 580	1 390	1 240	1 090	947
M$_{ry}$ (kN·m)	997	904	814	727	640	568	500	435
J (10^3 mm^4)	44 900	34 900	27 000	20 400	14 800	10 800	7 740	5 380
C$_w$ (10^9 mm^6)	9 570	8 420	7 350	6 330	5 370	4 620	3 960	3 340
L$_u$ (mm)	9 620	8 980	8 350	7 780	7 180	6 670	6 220	5 820
F$_y$ (MPa)	345	345	345	345	345	345	345	345

IMPERIAL SIZE AND WEIGHT

	375	342	313	283	253	226	202	179
Weight (lb/ft)	252	230	210	190	170	152	136	120
Depth x Width (in.)	15⅜ x 13	15 x 12⅞	14¾ x 12¾	14⅜ x 12⅝	14 x 12⅝	13¾ x 12½	13⅜ x 12⅜	13⅛ x 12⅜

CSA G40.21 350W
ASTM A992, A572 grade 50
$\phi = 0.90$

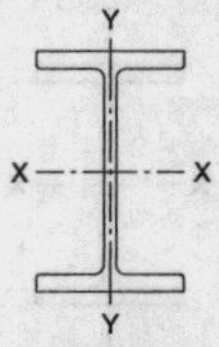

W COLUMNS
Factored Axial Compressive
Resistances, C_r (kN)

Designation		W310						W310	
Mass (kg/m)		158	143	129	118	107	97*	86	79
	0	6 240	5 650	5 120	4 660	4 220	3 820	3 420	3 140
	1 250	6 170	5 590	5 060	4 600	4 170	3 770	3 350	3 070
	1 500	6 130	5 550	5 030	4 570	4 140	3 750	3 310	3 030
	1 750	6 070	5 500	4 980	4 530	4 100	3 710	3 260	2 990
	2 000	6 000	5 430	4 920	4 470	4 050	3 660	3 190	2 930
	2 250	5 920	5 360	4 850	4 410	3 990	3 610	3 120	2 860
	2 500	5 820	5 270	4 770	4 330	3 930	3 550	3 030	2 780
	2 750	5 710	5 170	4 680	4 250	3 850	3 480	2 940	2 690
	3 000	5 590	5 060	4 580	4 150	3 760	3 400	2 840	2 590
	3 250	5 460	4 940	4 470	4 050	3 670	3 310	2 730	2 500
	3 500	5 320	4 810	4 350	3 940	3 570	3 220	2 620	2 390
	3 750	5 170	4 670	4 220	3 830	3 460	3 130	2 510	2 290
	4 000	5 010	4 530	4 090	3 710	3 350	3 030	2 390	2 180
	4 500	4 680	4 230	3 820	3 460	3 120	2 820	2 170	1 980
	5 000	4 350	3 930	3 540	3 200	2 890	2 610	1 960	1 780
	5 500	4 020	3 630	3 270	2 950	2 670	2 400	1 760	1 600
	6 000	3 700	3 340	3 000	2 720	2 450	2 210	1 580	1 430
	6 500	3 400	3 070	2 750	2 490	2 240	2 020	1 420	1 290
	7 000	3 120	2 810	2 520	2 280	2 050	1 850	1 280	1 160
	7 500	2 860	2 580	2 310	2 090	1 880	1 690	1 150	1 040
	8 000	2 620	2 360	2 120	1 910	1 720	1 550	1 040	942
	8 500	2 410	2 170	1 950	1 760	1 580	1 420	945	854
	9 000	2 220	1 990	1 790	1 610	1 450	1 300	859	776
	9 500	2 040	1 840	1 640	1 480	1 330	1 200	783	708
	10 000	1 880	1 690	1 520	1 370	1 230	1 100	716	647
	10 500	1 740	1 560	1 400	1 260	1 130	1 020	657	593
	11 000	1 610	1 450	1 300	1 170	1 050	943	605	546
	11 500	1 490	1 340	1 200	1 080	973	874	558	503
	12 000	1 390	1 250	1 120	1 010	904	812	516	466

(Left vertical label: Effective length (KL) in millimetres with respect to the least radius of gyration)

PROPERTIES AND DESIGN DATA

Area (mm²)	20 100	18 200	16 500	15 000	13 600	12 300	11 000	10 100
Z_x (10^3 mm³)	2 670	2 420	2 160	1 950	1 770	1 590	1 420	1 280
S_x (10^3 mm³)	2 360	2 150	1 940	1 750	1 590	1 440	1 280	1 160
r_x (mm)	139	138	137	136	135	134	134	133
Z_y (10^3 mm³)	1 220	1 110	991	893	806	725	533	478
S_y (10^3 mm³)	805	729	652	588	531	478	351	314
r_y (mm)	78.9	78.6	78.0	77.6	77.2	76.9	63.6	63.0
r_x / r_y	1.76	1.76	1.76	1.75	1.75	1.74	2.11	2.11
M_{rx} (kN·m) (L < L_u)	829	751	671	605	550	447	441	397
M_{ry} (kN·m)	379	345	308	277	250	148	165	148
J (10^3 mm⁴)	3 780	2 870	2 130	1 600	1 220	912	877	657
C_w (10^9 mm⁶)	2 840	2 540	2 220	1 970	1 760	1 560	961	847
L_u (mm)	5 490	5 280	5 080	4 920	4 790	4 970	3 900	3 810
F_y (MPa)	345	345	345	345	345	345	345	345

IMPERIAL SIZE AND WEIGHT

Weight (lb/ft)	106	96	87	79	72	65	58	53
Depth x Width (in.)	12⅞ x 12¼	12¾ x 12⅛	12½ x 12⅛	12⅜ x 12⅛	12¼ x 12	12⅛ x 12	12¼ x 10	12 x 10

* Class 3 in bending

W COLUMNS
Factored Axial Compressive Resistances, C_r (kN)

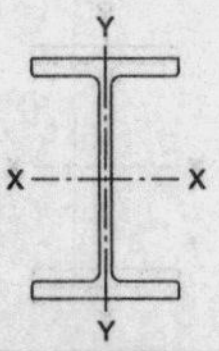

CSA G40.21 350W
ASTM A992, A572 grade 50
$\phi = 0.90$

Designation		W310			W250				
Mass (kg/m)		74	67	60**	167	149	131	115	101
Effective length (KL) in millimetres with respect to the least radius of gyration	0	2 930	2 620	2 320	6 610	5 900	5 190	4 530	4 010
	1 250	2 820	2 520	2 230	6 500	5 800	5 100	4 450	3 930
	1 500	2 760	2 470	2 180	6 440	5 740	5 040	4 400	3 890
	1 750	2 680	2 390	2 120	6 350	5 660	4 970	4 340	3 830
	2 000	2 580	2 310	2 040	6 250	5 560	4 880	4 260	3 760
	2 250	2 480	2 210	1 960	6 120	5 450	4 780	4 170	3 680
	2 500	2 360	2 110	1 870	5 980	5 320	4 670	4 070	3 590
	2 750	2 240	2 000	1 770	5 820	5 180	4 540	3 960	3 480
	3 000	2 120	1 890	1 670	5 650	5 020	4 400	3 830	3 370
	3 250	2 000	1 780	1 570	5 470	4 850	4 250	3 700	3 250
	3 500	1 880	1 670	1 470	5 270	4 680	4 090	3 560	3 130
	3 750	1 760	1 560	1 380	5 070	4 500	3 930	3 420	3 000
	4 000	1 640	1 460	1 290	4 870	4 310	3 770	3 270	2 870
	4 500	1 430	1 270	1 120	4 460	3 940	3 440	2 980	2 620
	5 000	1 250	1 110	977	4 060	3 590	3 120	2 710	2 370
	5 500	1 090	968	852	3 680	3 250	2 830	2 450	2 140
	6 000	959	849	747	3 330	2 940	2 550	2 210	1 930
	6 500	844	747	657	3 020	2 650	2 300	1 990	1 740
	7 000	747	661	581	2 730	2 400	2 080	1 800	1 570
	7 500	664	587	516	2 470	2 170	1 880	1 630	1 420
	8 000	594	524	461	2 240	1 970	1 710	1 470	1 280
	8 500	533	471	414	2 040	1 790	1 550	1 340	1 170
	9 000	480	424	374	1 860	1 630	1 420	1 220	1 060
	9 500	435	384	339	1 700	1 490	1 290	1 110	969
	10 000				1 560	1 370	1 180	1 020	887
	10 500				1 440	1 260	1 090	937	814
	11 000				1 320	1 160	1 000	862	750
	11 500				1 220	1 070	926	796	692
	12 000				1 130	991	857	737	641

PROPERTIES AND DESIGN DATA

Area (mm^2)	9 430	8 450	7 530	21 300	19 000	16 700	14 600	12 900
Z_x (10^3 mm^3)	1 180	1 050	933	2 430	2 130	1 850	1 600	1 400
S_x (10^3 mm^3)	1 060	942	842	2 080	1 840	1 610	1 410	1 240
r_x (mm)	132	131	130	119	117	115	114	113
Z_y (10^3 mm^3)	350	310	275	1 140	1 000	870	753	656
S_y (10^3 mm^3)	229	203	180	746	656	571	495	432
r_y (mm)	49.9	49.5	49.3	68.1	67.4	66.8	66.2	65.6
r_x / r_y	2.65	2.65	2.64	1.75	1.74	1.72	1.72	1.72
M_{rx} (kN·m) (L < L_u)	366	326	290	755	661	574	497	435
M_{ry} (kN·m)	109	96.3	85.4	354	311	270	234	204
J (10^3 mm^4)	718	522	378	6 310	4 510	3 120	2 130	1 490
C_w (10^9 mm^6)	505	439	384	1 630	1 390	1 160	976	829
L_u (mm)	3 100	3 020	2 960	5 900	5 480	5 080	4 740	4 470
F_y (MPa)	345	345	345	345	345	345	345	345

IMPERIAL SIZE AND WEIGHT

Weight (lb/ft)	50	45	40	112	100	88	77	68
Depth x Width (in.)	12¼ x 8⅛	12 x 8	12 x 8	11⅜ x 10⅜	11⅛ x 10⅜	10⅞ x 10¼	10⅝ x 10¼	10⅜ x 10⅛

** Class 4

4-38

CSA G40.21 350W
ASTM A992, A572 grade 50
$\phi = 0.90$

Designation		W250			W250		
Mass (kg/m)		89	80	73	67	58	49*
Effective length (KL) in millimetres with respect to the least radius of gyration	0	3 540	3 170	2 880	2 650	2 300	1 940
	1 250	3 470	3 110	2 830	2 560	2 220	1 870
	1 500	3 430	3 070	2 790	2 510	2 170	1 820
	1 750	3 380	3 030	2 750	2 440	2 110	1 770
	2 000	3 320	2 970	2 700	2 360	2 040	1 710
	2 250	3 250	2 900	2 640	2 270	1 960	1 630
	2 500	3 160	2 830	2 570	2 170	1 870	1 560
	2 750	3 070	2 750	2 490	2 060	1 780	1 470
	3 000	2 970	2 660	2 410	1 950	1 680	1 390
	3 250	2 860	2 560	2 320	1 840	1 580	1 310
	3 500	2 750	2 460	2 230	1 730	1 490	1 230
	3 750	2 640	2 360	2 140	1 630	1 400	1 150
	4 000	2 520	2 260	2 040	1 520	1 310	1 070
	4 500	2 300	2 050	1 860	1 340	1 140	934
	5 000	2 080	1 860	1 680	1 170	998	813
	5 500	1 870	1 670	1 510	1 020	873	710
	6 000	1 690	1 510	1 360	899	766	622
	6 500	1 520	1 360	1 220	793	675	547
	7 000	1 370	1 220	1 100	703	598	484
	7 500	1 240	1 100	996	625	532	430
	8 000	1 120	1 000	901	559	475	384
	8 500	1 020	908	818	502	427	344
	9 000	926	826	744	453	385	310
	9 500	845	754	679	411	349	281
	10 000	773	690	621	374	317	
	10 500	710	634	570			
	11 000	654	583	525			
	11 500	603	538	484			
	12 000	558	498	448			

PROPERTIES AND DESIGN DATA						
Area (mm^2)	11 400	10 200	9 280	8 550	7 420	6 250
Z_x (10^3 mm^3)	1 230	1 090	985	901	770	633
S_x (10^3 mm^3)	1 100	982	891	806	693	572
r_x (mm)	112	111	110	110	108	106
Z_y (10^3 mm^3)	574	513	463	332	283	228
S_y (10^3 mm^3)	378	338	306	218	186	150
r_y (mm)	65.1	65.0	64.6	51.0	50.4	49.2
r_x / r_y	1.72	1.71	1.70	2.16	2.14	2.15
M_{rx} (kN·m) (L < L_u)	382	338	306	280	239	178
M_{ry} (kN·m)	178	159	144	103	87.9	46.6
J (10^3 mm^4)	1 040	757	575	625	409	241
C_w (10^9 mm^6)	713	623	553	324	268	211
L_u (mm)	4 260	4 130	4 010	3 260	3 130	3 160
F_y (MPa)	345	345	345	345	345	345

IMPERIAL SIZE AND WEIGHT						
Weight (lb/ft)	60	54	49	45	39	33
Depth x Width (in.)	10¼ x 10⅛	10⅛ x 10	10 x 10	10⅛ x 8	9⅞ x 8	9¾ x 8

* Class 3 in bending

W COLUMNS
Factored Axial Compressive Resistances, C_r (kN)

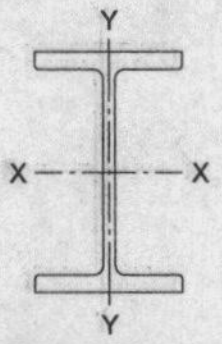

CSA G40.21 350W
ASTM A992, A572 grade 50
$\phi = 0.90$

Designation	W200					
Mass (kg/m)	100	86	71	59	52	46*
0	3 940	3 420	2 830	2 350	2 060	1 820
1 250	3 820	3 310	2 740	2 270	2 000	1 760
1 500	3 750	3 250	2 680	2 220	1 950	1 720
1 750	3 660	3 170	2 610	2 170	1 900	1 670
2 000	3 560	3 070	2 530	2 100	1 840	1 620
2 250	3 430	2 960	2 440	2 020	1 770	1 560
2 500	3 300	2 840	2 340	1 930	1 700	1 490
2 750	3 150	2 720	2 240	1 840	1 620	1 420
3 000	3 000	2 580	2 130	1 750	1 530	1 340
3 250	2 850	2 450	2 010	1 650	1 450	1 270
3 500	2 690	2 310	1 900	1 560	1 370	1 190
3 750	2 540	2 180	1 790	1 470	1 280	1 120
4 000	2 390	2 050	1 680	1 380	1 210	1 050
4 500	2 110	1 810	1 480	1 210	1 060	920
5 000	1 860	1 590	1 300	1 060	928	805
5 500	1 640	1 400	1 140	930	814	705
6 000	1 450	1 240	1 010	819	716	620
6 500	1 280	1 090	892	723	632	547
7 000	1 140	972	792	642	561	485
7 500	1 020	867	706	572	499	431
8 000	911	777	632	512	447	386
8 500	820	699	569	460	402	347
9 000	741	631	514	415	363	313
9 500	672	573	466	376	329	283
10 000	612	521	424	342	299	258
10 500	560	476	387			
11 000						
11 500						
12 000						

Effective length (KL) in millimetres with respect to the least radius of gyration

PROPERTIES AND DESIGN DATA

Area (mm^2)	12 700	11 000	9 100	7 560	6 650	5 860
Z_x (10^3 mm^3)	1 150	981	803	653	569	495
S_x (10^3 mm^3)	989	853	709	582	512	448
r_x (mm)	94.5	92.6	91.7	89.9	89.0	88.1
Z_y (10^3 mm^3)	533	458	375	303	266	229
S_y (10^3 mm^3)	349	300	246	199	175	151
r_y (mm)	53.8	53.3	52.8	52.0	51.8	51.2
r_x / r_y	1.76	1.74	1.74	1.73	1.72	1.72
M_{rx} (kN·m) (L < Lu)	357	305	249	203	177	139
M_{ry} (kN·m)	165	142	116	94.1	82.6	46.9
J (10^3 mm^4)	2 090	1 390	817	463	323	220
C_w (10^9 mm^6)	386	318	250	196	167	141
Lu (mm)	4 460	4 110	3 730	3 430	3 300	3 370
F_y (MPa)	345	345	345	345	345	345

IMPERIAL SIZE AND WEIGHT

Weight (lb/ft)	67	58	48	40	35	31
Depth x Width (in.)	9 x 8¼	8¾ x 8¼	8½ x 8⅛	8¼ x 8⅛	8⅛ x 8	8 x 8

* Class 3 in bending

CSA G40.21 350W
ASTM A992, A572 grade 50
$\phi = 0.90$

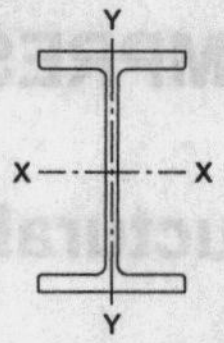

W COLUMNS
Factored Axial Compressive
Resistances, C_r (kN)

Designation		W200		W200		W150		
Mass (kg/m)		42	36	31	27	37	30	22**
Effective length (KL) in millimetres with respect to the least radius of gyration	0	1 650	1 420	1 240	1 050	1 470	1 180	844
	1 250	1 550	1 330	1 100	929	1 370	1 090	778
	1 500	1 490	1 280	1 030	867	1 310	1 050	742
	1 750	1 430	1 230	956	798	1 240	991	700
	2 000	1 350	1 160	875	727	1 170	930	654
	2 250	1 270	1 090	794	657	1 090	866	606
	2 500	1 190	1 020	716	591	1 010	801	558
	2 750	1 100	943	645	530	927	738	511
	3 000	1 020	872	579	475	852	677	467
	3 250	941	804	521	426	781	620	426
	3 500	867	740	469	383	715	567	388
	3 750	798	681	423	345	654	519	355
	4 000	735	626	383	311	599	475	325
	4 500	624	531	316	256	504	399	275
	5 000	532	453	263	214	427	338	233
	5 500	457	388	222	180	365	289	200
	6 000	395	336	190	154	314	248	172
	6 500	344	292			273	216	150
	7 000	301	256			239	188	131
	7 500	266	226			210	166	
	8 000	236	201					
	8 500							
	9 000							
	9 500							
	10 000							
	10 500							
	11 000							
	11 500							
	12 000							

PROPERTIES AND DESIGN DATA								
Area (mm^2)		5 310	4 570	4 000	3 390	4 730	3 790	2 850
Z_x (10^3 mm^3)		445	379	335	279	310	244	176
S_x (10^3 mm^3)		399	342	299	249	274	219	159
r_x (mm)		87.7	86.7	88.6	87.3	68.5	67.3	65.1
Z_y (10^3 mm^3)		165	141	93.8	76.1	140	111	77.6
S_y (10^3 mm^3)		108	92.6	61.1	49.6	91.8	72.6	50.9
r_y (mm)		41.2	40.9	32.0	31.2	38.6	38.3	36.9
r_x / r_y		2.13	2.12	2.77	2.80	1.77	1.76	1.76
M_{rx} (kN·m) (L < L$_u$)		138	118	104	86.6	96.3	75.8	46.6
M_{ry} (kN·m)		51.2	43.8	29.1	23.6	43.5	34.5	13.8
J (10^3 mm^4)		222	145	119	71.3	193	101	42.0
C_w (10^9 mm^6)		84.0	69.6	40.9	32.5	40.0	30.3	20.4
L_u (mm)		2 610	2 510	1 980	1 890	2 640	2 440	2 470
F_y (MPa)		345	345	345	345	345	345	345

IMPERIAL SIZE AND WEIGHT								
Weight (lb/ft)		28	24	21	18	25	20	15
Depth x Width (in.)		8 x 6½	7⅞ x 6½	8¼ x 5¼	8⅛ x 5¼	6⅜ x 6⅛	6¼ x 6	6 x 6

** Class 4

CSA G40.20/21 - Class C

For rectangular hollow sections, see page 4-43.

For square hollow sections, see page 4-50.

For round hollow sections, see page 4-58.

RECTANGULAR HOLLOW SECTIONS
Factored Axial Compressive Resistances, C_r (kN)

Designation (mm x mm x mm)		HSS 356 x 254		HSS 305 x 203			
		13	9.5 *	13	9.5	8.0 *	6.4 **
Mass (kg/m)		113	86.5	93.0	71.3	60.1	48.6
Effective length (KL) in millimetres with respect to the least radius of gyration	0	4 540	3 470	3 720	2 860	2 410	1 740
	400	4 530	3 460	3 720	2 860	2 410	1 740
	800	4 530	3 460	3 710	2 850	2 410	1 740
	1 200	4 510	3 450	3 680	2 840	2 390	1 730
	1 600	4 490	3 430	3 640	2 810	2 370	1 710
	2 000	4 450	3 400	3 580	2 760	2 330	1 680
	2 400	4 390	3 360	3 500	2 710	2 280	1 650
	2 800	4 320	3 310	3 410	2 630	2 220	1 610
	3 200	4 230	3 250	3 290	2 550	2 150	1 560
	3 600	4 130	3 170	3 160	2 450	2 070	1 500
	4 000	4 020	3 090	3 020	2 340	1 980	1 440
	4 400	3 900	3 000	2 870	2 230	1 890	1 370
	4 800	3 760	2 900	2 710	2 110	1 790	1 300
	5 200	3 620	2 790	2 560	2 000	1 690	1 230
	5 600	3 470	2 680	2 400	1 880	1 600	1 160
	6 000	3 320	2 570	2 250	1 770	1 500	1 090
	6 400	3 170	2 460	2 110	1 660	1 410	1 020
	6 800	3 020	2 340	1 970	1 550	1 320	961
	7 200	2 870	2 230	1 840	1 450	1 240	901
	7 600	2 730	2 120	1 720	1 360	1 160	844
	8 000	2 590	2 020	1 610	1 270	1 080	790
	8 400	2 450	1 910	1 500	1 190	1 010	740
	8 800	2 320	1 820	1 410	1 110	950	694
	9 200	2 200	1 720	1 320	1 040	891	651
	9 600	2 090	1 630	1 240	979	836	611
	10 000	1 980	1 550	1 160	919	785	574
	10 400	1 870	1 470	1 090	864	738	540
	10 800	1 780	1 400	1 020	813	694	508
	11 200	1 690	1 320	964	766	654	479
	11 600	1 600	1 260	909	722	617	452
	12 000	1 520	1 200	858	682	583	427

PROPERTIES AND DESIGN DATA							
Area (mm²)		14 400	11 000	11 800	9 090	7 660	6 190
Z_x (10³ mm³)		1 730	1 340	1 190	926	787	640
S_x (10³ mm³)		1 420	1 120	964	762	652	535
r_x (mm)		132	134	111	113	114	115
Z_y (10³ mm³)		1 370	1 060	897	701	596	486
S_y (10³ mm³)		1 180	931	769	611	525	368
r_y (mm)		102	104	81.2	82.7	83.4	84.1
r_x / r_y		1.29	1.29	1.37	1.37	1.37	1.37
M_{rx} (kN·m)		545	422	375	292	248	202
M_{ry} (kN·m)		432	293	283	221	165	116

IMPERIAL SIZE AND MASS							
Mass (lb./ft.)		76.1	58.1	62.5	47.9	40.4	32.6
Thickness (in.)		0.500	0.375	0.500	0.375	0.313	0.250
Size (in.)		14 x 10		12 x 8			

* Class 3 in bending about Y-Y axis
** Class 4: C_r calculated according to S16-09 Clause 13.3.5; S_y and M_{ry} according to Clause 13.5(c).

Designation (mm x mm x mm)		HSS 254 x 152				HSS 203 x 152				
		13	9.5	8.0	6.4 **	13	9.5	8.0	6.4	4.8 **
Mass (kg/m)		72.7	56.1	47.5	38.4	62.6	48.5	41.1	33.4	25.5
	0	2 920	2 250	1 910	1 540	2 510	1 950	1 650	1 340	985
	400	2 910	2 250	1 900	1 540	2 510	1 940	1 650	1 340	984
	800	2 900	2 240	1 890	1 530	2 490	1 930	1 640	1 330	978
	1 200	2 860	2 210	1 870	1 510	2 450	1 910	1 620	1 310	966
	1 600	2 790	2 160	1 830	1 480	2 390	1 860	1 580	1 280	945
	2 000	2 690	2 090	1 770	1 430	2 310	1 800	1 530	1 240	915
	2 400	2 570	2 000	1 700	1 380	2 200	1 720	1 460	1 190	877
	2 800	2 430	1 900	1 610	1 310	2 070	1 620	1 380	1 130	832
	3 200	2 280	1 780	1 520	1 230	1 930	1 510	1 290	1 060	782
	3 600	2 110	1 660	1 410	1 150	1 780	1 410	1 200	983	729
	4 000	1 950	1 530	1 310	1 070	1 640	1 290	1 110	909	675
	4 400	1 790	1 410	1 210	984	1 500	1 190	1 020	836	622
	4 800	1 640	1 300	1 110	906	1 370	1 090	934	767	571
	5 200	1 500	1 190	1 020	831	1 240	992	854	702	523
	5 600	1 360	1 080	931	762	1 130	905	780	642	479
	6 000	1 250	992	852	698	1 030	826	713	587	439
	6 400	1 140	908	781	640	940	755	652	537	402
	6 800	1 040	832	716	588	859	690	597	492	368
	7 200	955	764	658	540	786	632	547	452	338
	7 600	877	702	605	497	721	581	503	415	311
	8 000	807	647	557	458	662	534	463	382	287
	8 400	744	597	515	423	610	492	427	353	265
	8 800	688	552	476	392	563	455	395	326	245
	9 200	637	512	441	363	521	421	366	302	227
	9 600	591	475	410	338	484	391	339	281	211
	10 000	550	442	382	314	450	364	316	261	196
	10 400	512	412	356	293	419	339	294	244	183
	10 800	478	385	333	274	391	316	275	228	171
	11 200	448	361	311	257	366	296	257	213	160
	11 600	420	338	292	241	342	277	241	200	150
	12 000	394	317	274	226		261	226	188	141

Left axis label: Effective length (KL) in millimetres with respect to the least radius of gyration

PROPERTIES AND DESIGN DATA										
Area (mm^2)		9 260	7 150	6 050	4 900	7 970	6 180	5 240	4 250	3 250
Z_x (10^3 mm^3)		747	589	503	411	528	420	360	295	228
S_x (10^3 mm^3)		592	475	410	338	423	343	297	246	192
r_x (mm)		90.1	91.9	92.7	93.6	73.4	75.1	75.9	76.7	77.5
Z_y (10^3 mm^3)		522	413	354	290	432	344	295	243	188
S_y (10^3 mm^3)		442	357	309	255	359	292	254	211	157
r_y (mm)		60.3	61.7	62.4	63.1	58.6	60.0	60.8	61.5	62.2
r_x / r_y		1.49	1.49	1.49	1.48	1.25	1.25	1.25	1.25	1.25
M_{rx} (kN·m)		235	186	158	129	166	132	113	92.9	71.8
M_{ry} (kN·m)		164	130	112	80.3	136	108	92.9	76.5	49.3

IMPERIAL SIZE AND MASS										
Mass (lb./ft.)		48.9	37.7	31.9	25.8	42.1	32.6	27.6	22.4	17.1
Thickness (in.)		0.500	0.375	0.313	0.250	0.500	0.375	0.313	0.250	0.188
Size (in.)		10 x 6				8 x 6				

** Class 4: C_r calculated according to S16-09 Clause 13.3.5; S_y and M_{ry} according to Clause 13.5(c).

G40.21 350W
CLASS C
φ = 0.90

RECTANGULAR HOLLOW SECTIONS
Factored Axial Compressive
Resistances, C_r (kN)

Designation (mm x mm x mm)		HSS 203 x 102					HSS 178 x 127				
		13	9.5	8.0	6.4	4.8 **	13	9.5	8.0	6.4	4.8 *
Mass (kg/m)		52.4	40.9	34.8	28.3	21.7	52.4	40.9	34.8	28.3	21.7
Effective length (KL) in millimetres with respect to the least radius of gyration	0	2 100	1 640	1 400	1 140	831	2 100	1 640	1 400	1 140	869
	400	2 100	1 640	1 390	1 130	828	2 100	1 640	1 390	1 140	868
	800	2 060	1 610	1 370	1 120	816	2 080	1 620	1 380	1 120	860
	1 200	1 970	1 550	1 320	1 080	789	2 030	1 580	1 350	1 100	843
	1 600	1 840	1 450	1 240	1 020	746	1 940	1 520	1 300	1 060	814
	2 000	1 680	1 330	1 140	938	690	1 830	1 440	1 230	1 010	774
	2 400	1 490	1 190	1 030	848	626	1 700	1 340	1 150	943	726
	2 800	1 310	1 060	915	756	560	1 550	1 230	1 060	871	671
	3 200	1 150	928	806	668	496	1 400	1 120	964	795	614
	3 600	995	811	706	587	437	1 260	1 010	872	721	558
	4 000	865	708	618	515	384	1 120	908	784	650	504
	4 400	754	619	542	452	338	1 000	813	703	584	454
	4 800	660	544	476	398	298	895	728	630	524	408
	5 200	580	479	420	352	264	800	652	565	471	367
	5 600	512	424	372	312	234	716	585	508	424	330
	6 000	455	377	332	278	209	643	526	458	382	298
	6 400	406	337	297	249	187	579	475	413	345	270
	6 800	364	303	266	224	168	524	430	374	313	245
	7 200	328	273	240	202	152	475	390	340	285	223
	7 600	297	247	218	183	138	432	356	310	259	203
	8 000		225	198	167	125	395	325	283	237	186
	8 400				152	115	361	298	260	218	171
	8 800						332	274	239	200	157
	9 200						306	253	220	185	145
	9 600						283	233	204	171	134
	10 000								189	158	124
	10 400										
	10 800										
	11 200										
	11 600										
	12 000										

PROPERTIES AND DESIGN DATA

	HSS 203 x 102					HSS 178 x 127				
Area (mm^2)	6 680	5 210	4 430	3 610	2 760	6 680	5 210	4 430	3 610	2 760
Z_x (10^3 mm^3)	405	326	281	232	180	378	303	261	216	168
S_x (10^3 mm^3)	308	254	221	185	145	297	244	213	178	140
r_x (mm)	68.4	70.3	71.2	72.2	73.1	62.9	64.6	65.4	66.2	67.1
Z_y (10^3 mm^3)	246	199	172	143	111	298	240	207	171	133
S_y (10^3 mm^3)	201	169	148	125	93.3	244	202	177	148	117
r_y (mm)	39.1	40.5	41.3	42.0	42.7	48.1	49.6	50.3	51.1	51.8
r_x / r_y	1.75	1.74	1.72	1.72	1.71	1.31	1.30	1.30	1.30	1.30
M_{rx} (kN·m)	128	103	88.5	73.1	56.7	119	95.4	82.2	68.0	52.9
M_{ry} (kN·m)	77.5	62.7	54.2	45.0	29.4	93.9	75.6	65.2	53.9	36.9

IMPERIAL SIZE AND MASS

	HSS 203 x 102					HSS 178 x 127				
Mass (lb./ft.)	35.2	27.5	23.4	19.0	14.6	35.2	27.5	23.4	19.0	14.6
Thickness (in.)	0.500	0.375	0.313	0.250	0.188	0.500	0.375	0.313	0.250	0.188
Size (in.)			8 x 4					7 x 5		

* Class 3 in bending about Y-Y axis
** Class 4: C_r calculated according to S16-09 Clause 13.3.5; S_y and M_{ry} according to Clause 13.5(c).

Designation (mm x mm x mm)	HSS 152 x 102					HSS 152 x 76				
	13	9.5	8.0	6.4	4.8	13	9.5	8.0	6.4	4.8
Mass (kg/m)	42.3	33.3	28.4	23.2	17.9	37.3	29.5	25.3	20.7	16.0
0	1 700	1 340	1 140	932	718	1 500	1 180	1 010	832	643
400	1 690	1 330	1 140	929	716	1 480	1 180	1 010	826	639
800	1 660	1 310	1 120	914	704	1 420	1 130	970	797	618
1 200	1 580	1 250	1 070	879	679	1 290	1 040	895	739	574
1 600	1 470	1 170	1 000	825	639	1 120	911	791	657	513
2 000	1 330	1 060	917	757	588	936	774	677	565	445
2 400	1 170	950	822	680	530	772	647	568	477	378
2 800	1 020	836	725	602	471	635	536	474	400	318
3 200	887	729	635	529	415	524	446	395	335	267
3 600	766	634	553	462	363	436	373	331	281	225
4 000	663	551	482	404	318	366	314	280	238	191
4 400	576	480	421	353	279	310	267	238	203	163
4 800	502	420	369	310	245	266	230	205	175	141
5 200	440	370	325	273	216	230	199	178	152	122
5 600	388	327	287	242	192	200	174	155	133	107
6 000	344	290	255	215	171			137	117	94
6 400	307	259	228	192	153					
6 800	275	232	205	173	137					
7 200	248	209	185	156	124					
7 600		189	167	141	112					
8 000				128	102					
8 400										
8 800										
9 200										
9 600										
10 000										
10 400										
10 800										
11 200										
11 600										
12 000										

Effective length (KL) in millimetres with respect to the least radius of gyration

PROPERTIES AND DESIGN DATA

Area (mm^2)	5 390	4 240	3 620	2 960	2 280	4 750	3 760	3 220	2 640	2 040
Z_x (10^3 mm^3)	252	206	179	148	116	207	171	149	125	98.1
S_x (10^3 mm^3)	193	162	143	121	95.6	152	130	115	98.0	78.2
r_x (mm)	52.2	54.0	54.8	55.7	56.5	49.3	51.3	52.3	53.2	54.1
Z_y (10^3 mm^3)	189	155	135	112	87.8	124	104	91.2	76.6	60.5
S_y (10^3 mm^3)	151	128	113	96.2	76.6	97.3	85.0	76.3	65.5	52.9
r_y (mm)	37.7	39.2	39.9	40.6	41.3	28.0	29.4	30.1	30.8	31.5
r_x / r_y	1.38	1.38	1.37	1.37	1.37	1.76	1.74	1.74	1.73	1.72
M_{rx} (kN·m)	79.4	64.9	56.4	46.6	36.5	65.2	53.9	46.9	39.4	30.9
M_{ry} (kN·m)	59.5	48.8	42.5	35.3	27.7	39.1	32.8	28.7	24.1	19.1

IMPERIAL SIZE AND MASS

Mass (lb./ft.)	28.4	22.4	19.1	15.6	12.0	25.0	19.8	17.0	13.9	10.7
Thickness (in.)	0.500	0.375	0.313	0.250	0.188	0.500	0.375	0.313	0.250	0.188
Size (in.)	6 x 4					6 x 3				

G40.21 350W
CLASS C
φ = 0.90

RECTANGULAR HOLLOW SECTIONS
Factored Axial Compressive
Resistances, C_r (kN)

Designation (mm x mm x mm)	HSS 127 x 76				HSS 102 x 76				
	9.5	8.0	6.4	4.8	9.5	8.0	6.4	4.8	3.2
Mass (kg/m)	25.7	22.1	18.2	14.1	21.9	18.9	15.6	12.2	8.35
0	1 030	888	731	564	879	759	627	488	334
400	1 020	882	726	560	871	753	622	485	332
800	982	847	699	541	832	721	597	467	320
1 200	897	778	645	501	755	658	548	430	296
1 600	783	683	570	445	653	573	481	380	263
2 000	661	581	488	383	546	483	409	325	226
2 400	549	485	409	324	450	400	341	273	191
2 800	453	402	341	271	369	330	283	227	160
3 200	375	334	285	227	304	273	235	189	134
3 600	313	280	239	191	253	227	196	159	112
4 000	263	236	202	162	212	191	165	134	95
4 400	224	201	172	138	180	162	141	114	81
4 800	192	172	148	119	154	139	121	98	70
5 200	166	149	128	103	133	120	105	85	61
5 600	145	130	112	90		105	91	74	53
6 000			98	79				65	47
6 400									
6 800									
7 200									
7 600									
8 000									
8 400									
8 800									
9 200									
9 600									
10 000									
10 400									
10 800									
11 200									
11 600									
12 000									

Effective length (KL) in millimetres with respect to the least radius of gyration

PROPERTIES AND DESIGN DATA

Area (mm²)	3 280	2 820	2 320	1 790	2 790	2 410	1 990	1 550	1 060
Z_x (10³ mm³)	126	111	93.4	73.8	87.9	77.9	66.0	52.6	37.0
S_x (10³ mm³)	96.5	86.5	74.1	59.6	67.4	61.1	52.9	43.0	30.8
r_x (mm)	43.3	44.2	45.1	45.9	35.0	35.9	36.7	37.5	38.4
Z_y (10³ mm³)	87.8	77.4	65.3	51.8	71.6	63.6	54.0	43.1	30.4
S_y (10³ mm³)	70.8	63.9	55.2	44.8	56.6	51.5	44.8	36.6	26.4
r_y (mm)	28.7	29.4	30.1	30.8	27.8	28.5	29.3	30.0	30.7
r_x / r_y	1.51	1.50	1.50	1.49	1.26	1.26	1.25	1.25	1.25
M_{rx} (kN·m)	39.7	35.0	29.4	23.2	27.7	24.5	20.8	16.6	11.7
M_{ry} (kN·m)	27.7	24.4	20.6	16.3	22.6	20.0	17.0	13.6	9.58

IMPERIAL SIZE AND MASS

Mass (lb./ft.)	17.3	14.9	12.2	9.46	14.7	12.7	10.5	8.17	5.61
Thickness (in.)	0.375	0.313	0.250	0.188	0.375	0.313	0.250	0.188	0.125
Size (in.)	5 x 3				4 x 3				

RECTANGULAR HOLLOW SECTIONS
Factored Axial Compressive Resistances, C_r (kN)

G40.21 350W
CLASS C
$\phi = 0.90$

Designation (mm x mm x mm)	HSS 102 x 51					HSS 89 x 64			
	9.5	8.0	6.4	4.8	3.2	8.0	6.4	4.8	3.2
Mass (kg/m)	18.1	15.8	13.1	10.3	7.09	15.8	13.1	10.3	7.09
0	728	633	526	413	284	633	526	413	284
400	708	618	514	404	279	624	519	408	281
800	620	547	461	365	254	581	486	383	266
1 200	489	438	374	301	212	502	425	338	236
1 600	364	332	287	234	167	411	351	282	199
2 000	270	248	217	179	129	326	282	228	162
2 400	203	188	166	137	100	258	224	183	131
2 800	157	145	129	107	78	205	180	147	106
3 200	123	115	102	85	62	165	145	119	86
3 600	99	93	82	69	51	135	119	98	71
4 000				57	42	112	99	82	59
4 400						94	83	69	50
4 800							71	59	43
5 200									
5 600									
6 000									
6 400									
6 800									
7 200									
7 600									
8 000									
8 400									
8 800									
9 200									
9 600									
10 000									
10 400									
10 800									
11 200									
11 600									
12 000									

Effective length (KL) in millimetres with respect to the least radius of gyration

PROPERTIES AND DESIGN DATA

Area (mm²)	2 310	2 010	1 670	1 310	903	2 010	1 670	1 310	903
Z_x (10³ mm³)	65.6	59.0	50.7	40.8	29.0	55.1	47.2	38.0	27.0
S_x (10³ mm³)	47.1	43.6	38.5	31.8	23.1	42.2	37.1	30.6	22.3
r_x (mm)	32.2	33.2	34.2	35.1	36.1	30.6	31.4	32.3	33.1
Z_y (10³ mm³)	39.2	35.6	30.8	25.0	17.9	43.3	37.3	30.1	21.4
S_y (10³ mm³)	30.0	28.1	25.2	21.1	15.6	34.4	30.5	25.3	18.5
r_y (mm)	18.2	18.9	19.6	20.3	21.0	23.3	24.1	24.8	25.5
r_x / r_y	1.77	1.76	1.74	1.73	1.72	1.31	1.30	1.30	1.30
M_{rx} (kN·m)	20.7	18.6	16.0	12.9	9.14	17.4	14.9	12.0	8.51
M_{ry} (kN·m)	12.3	11.2	9.70	7.88	5.64	13.6	11.7	9.48	6.74

IMPERIAL SIZE AND MASS

Mass (lb./ft.)	12.2	10.6	8.81	6.89	4.76	10.6	8.81	6.89	4.76
Thickness (in.)	0.375	0.313	0.250	0.188	0.125	0.313	0.250	0.188	0.125
Size (in.)			4 x 2				3½ x 2½		

Designation (mm x mm x mm)	HSS 76 x 51			HSS 51 x 25	
	6.4	4.8	3.2	4.8	3.2
Mass (kg/m)	10.6	8.35	5.82	4.54	3.28

Effective length (KL) in millimetres with respect to the least radius of gyration

KL					
0	425	334	233	182	132
400	415	327	229	155	115
800	368	292	207	91	72
1 200	294	238	170	51	41
1 600	223	182	132	31	25
2 000	167	138	101		
2 400	126	105	78		
2 800	98	82	61		
3 200	77	65	48		
3 600	62	52	39		
4 000			32		
4 400					
4 800					
5 200					
5 600					
6 000					
6 400					
6 800					
7 200					
7 600					
8 000					
8 400					
8 800					
9 200					
9 600					
10 000					
10 400					
10 800					
11 200					
11 600					
12 000					

PROPERTIES AND DESIGN DATA

Area (mm^2)	1 350	1 060	741	578	418
Z_x (10^3 mm^3)	31.5	25.8	18.6	8.21	6.34
S_x (10^3 mm^3)	24.1	20.3	15.1	5.89	4.81
r_x (mm)	26.1	27.0	27.8	16.1	17.1
Z_y (10^3 mm^3)	23.6	19.4	14.0	4.91	3.85
S_y (10^3 mm^3)	18.9	16.1	12.0	3.75	3.15
r_y (mm)	18.9	19.6	20.3	9.08	9.78
r_x / r_y	1.38	1.38	1.37	1.77	1.75
M_{rx} (kN·m)	9.92	8.13	5.86	2.59	2.00
M_{ry} (kN·m)	7.43	6.11	4.41	1.55	1.21

IMPERIAL SIZE AND MASS

Mass (lb./ft.)	7.11	5.61	3.91	3.05	2.21
Thickness (in.)	0.250	0.188	0.125	0.188	0.125
Size (in.)	3 x 2			2 x 1	

SQUARE HOLLOW SECTIONS
Factored Axial Compressive
Resistances, C_r (kN)

G40.21 350W
CLASS C
$\phi = 0.90$

Designation (mm x mm x mm)		HSS 305 x 305					HSS 254 x 254			
		13	9.5	8.0 *	6.4 **		13	9.5	8.0	6.4 **
Mass (kg/m)		113	86.5	72.8	58.7		93.0	71.3	60.1	48.6
	0	4 540	3 470	2 920	1 940		3 720	2 860	2 410	1 940
	400	4 540	3 460	2 920	1 940		3 720	2 860	2 410	1 940
	800	4 530	3 460	2 920	1 940		3 710	2 860	2 410	1 940
	1 200	4 520	3 450	2 910	1 930		3 700	2 850	2 400	1 930
	1 600	4 500	3 440	2 900	1 930		3 670	2 830	2 380	1 920
	2 000	4 470	3 420	2 890	1 920		3 630	2 800	2 360	1 900
	2 400	4 440	3 390	2 860	1 900		3 580	2 760	2 330	1 880
	2 800	4 390	3 360	2 830	1 880		3 520	2 720	2 290	1 850
	3 200	4 330	3 310	2 800	1 860		3 440	2 660	2 240	1 810
	3 600	4 260	3 260	2 750	1 830		3 350	2 590	2 190	1 760
	4 000	4 170	3 200	2 700	1 790		3 250	2 520	2 130	1 710
	4 400	4 080	3 130	2 650	1 760		3 140	2 430	2 060	1 660
	4 800	3 980	3 050	2 580	1 710		3 020	2 340	1 980	1 600
	5 200	3 860	2 970	2 510	1 670		2 890	2 250	1 900	1 540
	5 600	3 750	2 880	2 440	1 620		2 770	2 150	1 820	1 480
	6 000	3 620	2 790	2 360	1 570		2 640	2 050	1 740	1 410
	6 400	3 500	2 700	2 290	1 520		2 510	1 960	1 660	1 340
	6 800	3 370	2 600	2 200	1 460		2 380	1 860	1 580	1 280
	7 200	3 230	2 500	2 120	1 410		2 260	1 760	1 500	1 220
	7 600	3 100	2 400	2 040	1 350		2 140	1 670	1 420	1 150
	8 000	2 970	2 300	1 960	1 300		2 020	1 580	1 350	1 090
	8 400	2 850	2 210	1 880	1 250		1 910	1 500	1 270	1 040
	8 800	2 720	2 110	1 800	1 190		1 810	1 420	1 210	982
	9 200	2 600	2 020	1 720	1 140		1 710	1 340	1 140	930
	9 600	2 490	1 930	1 650	1 090		1 610	1 270	1 080	881
	10 000	2 370	1 850	1 570	1 040		1 530	1 200	1 020	835
	10 400	2 270	1 770	1 500	998		1 440	1 140	968	791
	10 800	2 160	1 690	1 440	954		1 370	1 080	917	749
	11 200	2 060	1 610	1 370	912		1 290	1 020	869	711
	11 600	1 970	1 540	1 310	871		1 230	967	825	674
	12 000	1 880	1 470	1 250	833		1 160	917	783	640

Effective length (KL) in millimetres with respect to the least radius of gyration

PROPERTIES AND DESIGN DATA										
Area (mm²)		14 400	11 000	9 280	7 480		11 800	9 090	7 660	6 190
Z (10³ mm³)		1 560	1 210	1 030	833		1 060	825	702	571
S (10³ mm³)		1 330	1 040	886	625		889	703	602	492
r (mm)		118	120	121	121		97.6	99.1	99.9	101
M_r (kN·m)		491	381	279	197		334	260	221	155

IMPERIAL SIZE AND MASS										
Mass (lb./ft.)		76.1	58.1	48.9	39.4		62.5	47.9	40.4	32.6
Thickness (in.)		0.500	0.375	0.313	0.250		0.500	0.375	0.313	0.250
Size (in.)		12 x 12					10 x 10			

* Class 3 in bending
** Class 4: C_r calculated according to S16-09 Clause 13.3.5; S and M_r according to Clause 13.5(c).

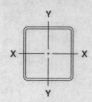

Designation (mm x mm x mm)		HSS 203 x 203					HSS 178 x 178	
		13	9.5	8.0	6.4		13	9.5
Mass (kg/m)		72.7	56.1	47.5	38.4		62.6	48.5
0		2 920	2 250	1 910	1 540		2 510	1 950
400		2 920	2 250	1 900	1 540		2 510	1 950
800		2 910	2 240	1 900	1 540		2 500	1 940
1 200		2 890	2 230	1 890	1 530		2 470	1 920
1 600		2 850	2 200	1 860	1 510		2 430	1 880
2 000		2 800	2 160	1 830	1 490		2 360	1 840
2 400		2 730	2 110	1 790	1 450		2 280	1 770
2 800		2 640	2 050	1 740	1 410		2 170	1 700
3 200		2 540	1 970	1 670	1 360		2 060	1 610
3 600		2 420	1 890	1 600	1 300		1 940	1 520
4 000		2 300	1 800	1 530	1 240		1 810	1 420
4 400		2 170	1 700	1 450	1 180		1 680	1 330
4 800		2 050	1 600	1 370	1 110		1 560	1 230
5 200		1 920	1 500	1 280	1 050		1 440	1 140
5 600		1 790	1 410	1 200	983		1 320	1 050
6 000		1 670	1 320	1 130	920		1 220	971
6 400		1 560	1 230	1 050	860		1 120	895
6 800		1 450	1 150	982	804		1 030	826
7 200		1 350	1 070	916	750		952	763
7 600		1 260	997	855	700		879	705
8 000		1 170	929	798	654		812	652
8 400		1 090	867	745	611		752	604
8 800		1 020	810	696	571		697	561
9 200		952	757	651	534		648	521
9 600		890	709	609	500		603	486
10 000		834	664	571	469		562	453
10 400		782	623	536	441		525	423
10 800		734	585	504	414		491	396
11 200		690	551	474	390		460	371
11 600		650	519	447	367		432	349
12 000		612	489	421	346		406	328

Effective length (KL) in millimetres with respect to the least radius of gyration

PROPERTIES AND DESIGN DATA								
Area (mm^2)		9 260	7 150	6 050	4 900		7 970	6 180
Z (10^3 mm^3)		651	513	439	359		484	385
S (10^3 mm^3)		538	432	373	308		396	322
r (mm)		76.9	78.4	79.2	79.9		66.5	68.0
M$_r$ (kN·m)		205	162	138	113		152	121

IMPERIAL SIZE AND MASS								
Mass (lb./ft.)		48.9	37.7	31.9	25.8		42.1	32.6
Thickness (in.)		0.500	0.375	0.313	0.250		0.500	0.375
Size (in.)			8 x 8				7 x 7	

SQUARE HOLLOW SECTIONS

Factored Axial Compressive Resistances, C_r (kN)

G40.21 350W
CLASS C
$\phi = 0.90$

Designation (mm x mm x mm)	HSS 178 x 178			HSS 152 x 152				
	8.0	6.4	4.8 *	13	9.5	8.0	6.4	4.8
Mass (kg/m)	41.1	33.4	25.5	52.4	40.9	34.8	28.3	21.7
0	1 650	1 340	1 020	2 100	1 640	1 400	1 140	869
400	1 650	1 340	1 020	2 100	1 640	1 390	1 140	868
800	1 640	1 330	1 020	2 090	1 630	1 380	1 130	863
1 200	1 630	1 320	1 010	2 050	1 600	1 360	1 110	851
1 600	1 600	1 300	994	1 990	1 560	1 330	1 090	831
2 000	1 560	1 270	971	1 910	1 500	1 280	1 050	802
2 400	1 510	1 230	940	1 810	1 430	1 220	998	766
2 800	1 450	1 180	903	1 700	1 340	1 150	941	723
3 200	1 380	1 120	861	1 570	1 250	1 070	878	676
3 600	1 300	1 060	815	1 440	1 150	988	813	627
4 000	1 220	995	766	1 320	1 050	907	748	578
4 400	1 140	930	716	1 200	962	829	685	530
4 800	1 060	865	667	1 090	875	756	625	484
5 200	978	802	620	987	796	688	570	442
5 600	904	743	574	895	723	626	520	403
6 000	835	686	531	812	658	570	474	368
6 400	771	634	491	739	599	520	432	336
6 800	712	586	454	673	547	475	395	307
7 200	657	542	420	614	500	434	362	282
7 600	608	502	389	562	458	398	332	259
8 000	563	465	361	516	421	366	305	238
8 400	522	431	335	475	387	337	281	219
8 800	485	400	311	438	357	311	260	203
9 200	451	373	290	405	331	288	240	188
9 600	420	347	270	375	307	267	223	174
10 000	392	324	252	348	285	248	207	162
10 400	366	303	236	324	265	231	193	151
10 800	343	284	221	302	248	216	180	141
11 200	322	266	207	283	231	202	169	132
11 600	302	250	195			189	158	124
12 000	284	235	183					

Effective length (KL) in millimetres with respect to the least radius of gyration

PROPERTIES AND DESIGN DATA

Area (mm^2)	5 240	4 250	3 250	6 680	5 210	4 430	3 610	2 760
Z (10^3 mm^3)	330	271	210	342	275	237	196	152
S (10^3 mm^3)	279	231	181	276	227	198	166	130
r (mm)	68.8	69.6	70.3	56.1	57.6	58.4	59.2	59.9
M_r (kN·m)	104	85.4	57.0	108	86.6	74.7	61.7	47.9

IMPERIAL SIZE AND MASS

Mass (lb./ft.)	27.6	22.4	17.1	35.2	27.5	23.4	19.0	14.6
Thickness (in.)	0.313	0.250	0.188	0.500	0.375	0.313	0.250	0.188
Size (in.)	7 x 7			6 x 6				

* Class 3 in bending

G40.21 350W
CLASS C
$\phi = 0.90$

SQUARE HOLLOW SECTIONS
Factored Axial Compressive
Resistances, C_r (kN)

Designation (mm x mm x mm)	HSS 127 x 127					HSS 114 x 114		
	13	9.5	8.0	6.4	4.8	13	9.5	8.0
Mass (kg/m)	42.3	33.3	28.4	23.2	17.9	37.3	29.5	25.3
0	1 700	1 340	1 140	932	718	1 500	1 180	1 010
400	1 690	1 330	1 140	931	717	1 490	1 180	1 010
800	1 670	1 320	1 130	921	710	1 470	1 160	996
1 200	1 630	1 280	1 100	899	693	1 410	1 120	963
1 600	1 550	1 230	1 050	863	667	1 320	1 060	911
2 000	1 450	1 160	991	815	631	1 210	978	843
2 400	1 330	1 070	919	757	588	1 090	885	766
2 800	1 210	973	839	694	540	964	789	685
3 200	1 080	877	759	629	491	846	698	607
3 600	963	786	681	566	443	739	613	535
4 000	855	700	608	507	397	646	538	471
4 400	758	624	542	453	356	565	473	414
4 800	673	555	484	405	318	496	416	365
5 200	598	495	432	362	285	437	368	323
5 600	534	443	387	324	256	386	326	287
6 000	478	397	347	292	230	344	291	256
6 400	429	358	313	263	208	307	260	229
6 800	387	323	283	238	188	276	234	206
7 200	350	293	256	216	171	249	211	186
7 600	318	266	233	196	156	225	192	169
8 000	290	243	213	179	142	205	174	154
8 400	266	223	195	164	130		159	141
8 800	244	204	179	151	120			
9 200		188	165	139	111			
9 600			153	129	102			
10 000								
10 400								
10 800								
11 200								
11 600								
12 000								

Effective length (KL) in millimetres with respect to the least radius of gyration

PROPERTIES AND DESIGN DATA

Area (mm²)	5 390	4 240	3 620	2 960	2 280	4 750	3 760	3 220
Z (10³ mm³)	225	183	159	132	103	175	144	126
S (10³ mm³)	177	149	132	111	88.1	136	116	103
r (mm)	45.7	47.3	48.0	48.8	49.6	40.5	42.1	42.8
M_r (kN·m)	70.9	57.6	50.1	41.6	32.4	55.1	45.4	39.7

IMPERIAL SIZE AND MASS

Mass (lb./ft.)	28.4	22.4	19.1	15.6	12.0	25.0	19.8	17.0
Thickness (in.)	0.500	0.375	0.313	0.250	0.188	0.500	0.375	0.313
Size (in.)	5 x 5					4½ x 4½		

SQUARE HOLLOW SECTIONS

Factored Axial Compressive Resistances, C_r (kN)

G40.21 350W
CLASS C
$\phi = 0.90$

Designation (mm x mm x mm)	HSS 114 x 114			HSS 102 x 102		
	6.4	4.8	3.2 *	13	9.5	8.0
Mass (kg/m)	20.7	16.0	10.9	32.2	25.7	22.1
Effective length (KL) in millimetres with respect to the least radius of gyration						
0	832	643	438	1 290	1 030	888
400	829	641	437	1 290	1 030	885
800	818	632	431	1 250	1 010	866
1 200	792	613	419	1 190	958	827
1 600	751	583	399	1 090	886	767
2 000	697	543	372	969	796	692
2 400	635	496	341	845	701	612
2 800	570	447	308	727	610	534
3 200	507	399	276	623	526	462
3 600	448	353	245	533	453	400
4 000	395	312	217	458	391	346
4 400	348	276	192	395	339	300
4 800	308	244	170	343	295	262
5 200	273	217	151	300	258	229
5 600	243	193	135	263	228	202
6 000	217	172	121	233	202	179
6 400	194	155	108	207	180	160
6 800	175	139	98	185	161	143
7 200	158	126	88		145	129
7 600	143	114	80			
8 000	131	104	73			
8 400	119	95	67			
8 800		87	61			
9 200						
9 600						
10 000						
10 400						
10 800						
11 200						
11 600						
12 000						
PROPERTIES AND DESIGN DATA						
Area (mm²)	2 640	2 040	1 390	4 100	3 280	2 820
Z (10³ mm³)	105	82.7	57.4	131	110	96.8
S (10³ mm³)	87.8	70.1	49.5	100	87.6	78.5
r (mm)	43.6	44.4	45.1	35.3	36.9	37.6
M_r (kN·m)	33.1	26.1	15.6	41.3	34.7	30.5
IMPERIAL SIZE AND MASS						
Mass (lb./ft.)	13.9	10.7	7.32	21.6	17.3	14.9
Thickness (in.)	0.250	0.188	0.125	0.500	0.375	0.313
Size (in.)		4½ x 4½			4 x 4	

* Class 3 in bending

Designation (mm x mm x mm)	HSS 102 x 102			HSS 89 x 89				
	6.4	4.8	3.2	9.5	8.0	6.4	4.8	3.2
Mass (kg/m)	18.2	14.1	9.62	21.9	18.9	15.6	12.2	8.35
0	731	564	387	879	759	627	488	334
400	728	562	386	873	755	623	486	332
800	714	551	379	845	732	606	473	324
1 200	683	529	364	787	684	568	445	306
1 600	635	494	341	705	615	514	405	280
2 000	576	450	312	611	537	451	357	248
2 400	512	401	280	520	459	388	309	216
2 800	448	353	247	438	388	330	264	185
3 200	390	308	216	368	328	279	225	158
3 600	338	268	189	311	277	237	191	135
4 000	293	233	164	264	236	202	164	116
4 400	255	203	144	226	202	174	141	100
4 800	223	177	126	194	174	150	122	87
5 200	195	156	111	169	152	131	106	76
5 600	172	138	98	148	133	115	93	66
6 000	153	122	87	130	117	101	82	59
6 400	137	109	78		104	90	73	52
6 800	122	98	70				65	47
7 200	110	88	63					
7 600	100	80	57					
8 000			52					
8 400								
8 800								
9 200								
9 600								
10 000								
10 400								
10 800								
11 200								
11 600								
12 000								

Effective length (KL) in millimetres with respect to the least radius of gyration

PROPERTIES AND DESIGN DATA

Area (mm^2)	2 320	1 790	1 230	2 790	2 410	1 990	1 550	1 060
Z (10^3 mm^3)	81.4	64.3	44.9	80.5	71.4	60.5	48.2	33.9
S (10^3 mm^3)	67.3	54.2	38.5	63.0	57.1	49.5	40.3	29.0
r (mm)	38.4	39.2	40.0	31.7	32.4	33.2	34.0	34.8
M$_r$ (kN·m)	25.6	20.3	14.1	25.4	22.5	19.1	15.2	10.7

IMPERIAL SIZE AND MASS

Mass (lb./ft.)	12.2	9.46	6.47	14.7	12.7	10.5	8.17	5.61
Thickness (in.)	0.250	0.188	0.125	0.375	0.313	0.250	0.188	0.125
Size (in.)	4 x 4			3½ x 3½				

SQUARE HOLLOW SECTIONS

Factored Axial Compressive Resistances, C_r (kN)

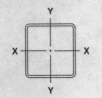

G40.21 350W
CLASS C
$\phi = 0.90$

Designation (mm x mm x mm)	HSS 76 x 76						HSS 64 x 64		
	9.5	8.0	6.4	4.8	3.2		6.4	4.8	3.2
Mass (kg/m)	18.1	15.8	13.1	10.3	7.09		10.6	8.35	5.82
0	728	633	526	413	284		425	334	233
400	720	627	522	409	282		419	329	231
800	684	597	498	392	271		388	307	216
1 200	613	539	453	359	250		333	267	190
1 600	523	463	392	313	220		270	219	157
2 000	432	385	329	265	187		214	175	127
2 400	351	316	272	220	156		168	138	101
2 800	286	258	223	182	130		133	110	81
3 200	234	212	184	151	108		107	89	66
3 600	194	176	153	126	90		87	73	54
4 000	162	147	129	106	76		72	61	45
4 400	137	125	109	90	65		61	51	38
4 800	117	107	93	77	56				32
5 200	101	92	81	67	48				
5 600			70	58	42				
6 000									
6 400									
6 800									
7 200									
7 600									
8 000									
8 400									
8 800									
9 200									
9 600									
10 000									
10 400									
10 800									
11 200									
11 600									
12 000									

Effective length (KL) in millimetres with respect to the least radius of gyration

PROPERTIES AND DESIGN DATA

Area (mm^2)	2 310	2 010	1 670	1 310	903		1 350	1 060	741
Z (10^3 mm^3)	55.5	49.8	42.8	34.4	24.5		28.1	23.0	16.6
S (10^3 mm^3)	42.4	39.1	34.5	28.5	20.7		22.2	18.7	13.9
r (mm)	26.5	27.2	28.0	28.8	29.6		22.8	23.6	24.4
M_r (kN·m)	17.5	15.7	13.5	10.8	7.72		8.85	7.25	5.23

IMPERIAL SIZE AND MASS

Mass (lb./ft.)	12.2	10.6	8.81	6.89	4.76		7.11	5.61	3.91
Thickness (in.)	0.375	0.313	0.250	0.188	0.125		0.250	0.188	0.125
Size (in.)			3 x 3					2½ x 2½	

G40.21 350W
CLASS C
$\phi = 0.90$

SQUARE HOLLOW SECTIONS
Factored Axial Compressive
Resistances, C_r (kN)

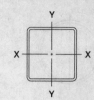

Designation (mm x mm x mm)	HSS 51 x 51			HSS 38 x 38	
	6.4	4.8	3.2	4.8	3.2
Mass (kg/m)	8.05	6.45	4.55	4.54	3.28
0	324	259	183	182	132
400	315	252	178	171	125
800	273	221	159	130	98
1 200	212	175	128	88	68
1 600	156	131	97	58	46
2 000	115	98	73	40	32
2 400	86	74	56	29	23
2 800	66	57	43		18
3 200	52	45	34		
3 600		36	28		
4 000					
4 400					
4 800					
5 200					
5 600					
6 000					
6 400					
6 800					
7 200					
7 600					
8 000					
8 400					
8 800					
9 200					
9 600					
10 000					
10 400					
10 800					
11 200					
11 600					
12 000					

Effective length (KL) in millimetres with respect to the least radius of gyration

PROPERTIES AND DESIGN DATA

Area (mm^2)	1 030	821	580	578	418
Z (10^3 mm^3)	16.4	13.8	10.2	6.95	5.35
S (10^3 mm^3)	12.6	11.0	8.42	5.30	4.31
r (mm)	17.6	18.4	19.2	13.2	14.0
M$_r$ (kN·m)	5.17	4.35	3.21	2.19	1.69

IMPERIAL SIZE AND MASS

Mass (lb./ft.)	5.41	4.33	3.06	3.05	2.21
Thickness (in.)	0.250	0.188	0.125	0.188	0.125
Size (in.)	2 x 2			1½ x 1½	

Factored Axial Compressive
Resistances, C_r (kN)

Designation (mm x mm)	HSS 406				HSS 356			HSS 324		
	13	9.5	6.4 *		13	9.5	6.4 *	13	9.5	6.4
Mass (kg/m)	123	93.3	62.6		107	81.3	54.7	97.5	73.9	49.7
0	4 950	3 750	2 510		4 320	3 280	2 200	3 910	2 960	1 990
400	4 940	3 750	2 510		4 310	3 280	2 200	3 910	2 960	1 990
800	4 940	3 750	2 510		4 310	3 270	2 190	3 900	2 960	1 990
1 200	4 930	3 740	2 510		4 300	3 270	2 190	3 890	2 950	1 990
1 600	4 920	3 730	2 500		4 290	3 250	2 180	3 870	2 940	1 980
2 000	4 900	3 720	2 490		4 260	3 240	2 170	3 840	2 920	1 960
2 400	4 870	3 700	2 480		4 230	3 210	2 150	3 800	2 890	1 940
2 800	4 840	3 670	2 460		4 180	3 180	2 130	3 750	2 850	1 920
3 200	4 800	3 640	2 440		4 130	3 140	2 100	3 690	2 800	1 890
3 600	4 740	3 600	2 410		4 060	3 090	2 070	3 620	2 750	1 850
4 000	4 680	3 550	2 380		3 990	3 030	2 040	3 530	2 690	1 810
4 400	4 610	3 500	2 350		3 910	2 970	1 990	3 440	2 620	1 770
4 800	4 530	3 440	2 310		3 810	2 900	1 950	3 340	2 540	1 720
5 200	4 440	3 370	2 270		3 710	2 830	1 900	3 230	2 460	1 660
5 600	4 350	3 300	2 220		3 600	2 750	1 850	3 120	2 380	1 610
6 000	4 250	3 230	2 170		3 490	2 660	1 790	3 000	2 290	1 550
6 400	4 140	3 150	2 120		3 370	2 570	1 730	2 880	2 200	1 490
6 800	4 030	3 060	2 060		3 250	2 480	1 670	2 760	2 110	1 430
7 200	3 910	2 980	2 000		3 130	2 390	1 610	2 640	2 020	1 370
7 600	3 790	2 890	1 940		3 010	2 300	1 550	2 520	1 930	1 310
8 000	3 670	2 800	1 880		2 890	2 210	1 490	2 400	1 840	1 250
8 400	3 550	2 710	1 820		2 770	2 120	1 430	2 290	1 750	1 190
8 800	3 430	2 610	1 760		2 650	2 030	1 370	2 180	1 670	1 130
9 200	3 310	2 520	1 700		2 540	1 940	1 310	2 070	1 590	1 080
9 600	3 190	2 430	1 640		2 430	1 860	1 260	1 970	1 510	1 030
10 000	3 070	2 350	1 580		2 320	1 780	1 200	1 880	1 440	980
10 400	2 960	2 260	1 530		2 220	1 700	1 150	1 790	1 370	933
10 800	2 850	2 170	1 470		2 120	1 630	1 100	1 700	1 310	888
11 200	2 740	2 090	1 410		2 030	1 560	1 050	1 620	1 240	846
11 600	2 630	2 010	1 360		1 940	1 490	1 010	1 540	1 180	806
12 000	2 530	1 940	1 310		1 850	1 420	963	1 470	1 130	768

Effective length (KL) in millimetres with respect to the least radius of gyration

PROPERTIES AND DESIGN DATA

	HSS 406				HSS 356			HSS 324		
Area (mm²)	15 700	11 900	7 980		13 700	10 400	6 970	12 400	9 410	6 330
Z (10³ mm³)	1 970	1 500	1 020		1 490	1 140	775	1 230	942	640
S (10³ mm³)	1 500	1 150	786		1 130	873	598	930	719	493
r (mm)	139	140	141		121	122	123	110	111	112
M_r (kN·m)	621	473	248		469	359	188	387	297	202

IMPERIAL SIZE AND MASS

	HSS 406				HSS 356			HSS 324		
Mass (lb./ft.)	82.9	62.7	42.1		72.2	54.7	36.8	65.5	49.7	33.4
Thickness (in.)	0.500	0.375	0.250		0.500	0.375	0.250	0.500	0.375	0.250
Size (in.)	16 OD				14 OD			12.75 OD		

* Class 3 in bending

G40.21 350W
CLASS C
$\phi = 0.90$

ROUND HOLLOW SECTIONS
Factored Axial Compressive
Resistances, C_r (kN)

Designation (mm x mm)		HSS 273				HSS 219			
		13	6.4	4.8 *		13	9.5	6.4	4.8
Mass (kg/m)		81.6	41.8	31.6		64.6	49.3	33.3	25.3
Effective length (KL) in millimetres with respect to the least radius of gyration	0	3 280	1 680	1 270		2 590	1 980	1 340	1 010
	400	3 270	1 680	1 270		2 590	1 970	1 330	1 010
	800	3 270	1 670	1 270		2 580	1 970	1 330	1 010
	1 200	3 250	1 670	1 260		2 560	1 950	1 320	1 000
	1 600	3 230	1 650	1 250		2 520	1 920	1 300	990
	2 000	3 190	1 630	1 240		2 470	1 890	1 280	971
	2 400	3 140	1 610	1 220		2 400	1 830	1 240	945
	2 800	3 080	1 580	1 200		2 310	1 770	1 200	914
	3 200	3 000	1 540	1 170		2 210	1 700	1 150	878
	3 600	2 910	1 500	1 140		2 100	1 610	1 100	837
	4 000	2 810	1 450	1 100		1 990	1 530	1 040	794
	4 400	2 700	1 390	1 060		1 870	1 440	982	749
	4 800	2 580	1 340	1 020		1 750	1 350	921	703
	5 200	2 460	1 280	972		1 630	1 260	862	658
	5 600	2 340	1 220	927		1 510	1 170	804	615
	6 000	2 220	1 160	881		1 410	1 090	749	573
	6 400	2 100	1 100	836		1 310	1 010	696	533
	6 800	1 990	1 040	792		1 210	940	647	496
	7 200	1 880	982	749		1 120	873	602	461
	7 600	1 770	928	708		1 040	811	560	429
	8 000	1 670	876	668		968	754	521	399
	8 400	1 570	826	631		900	701	485	372
	8 800	1 480	779	595		838	653	452	347
	9 200	1 390	735	562		781	609	422	324
	9 600	1 310	694	530		729	569	394	303
	10 000	1 240	655	501		682	532	369	283
	10 400	1 170	619	473		638	499	346	265
	10 800	1 100	585	447		598	468	324	249
	11 200	1 040	553	423		562	439	305	234
	11 600	988	524	401		528	413	287	220
	12 000	935	496	380		498	389	270	208

PROPERTIES AND DESIGN DATA

Area (mm^2)		10 400	5 320	4 030		8 230	6 270	4 240	3 220
Z (10^3 mm^3)		862	452	344		542	419	288	220
S (10^3 mm^3)		646	347	266		402	315	219	169
r (mm)		92.2	94.3	94.9		73.1	74.2	75.3	75.8
M$_r$ (kN·m)		272	142	83.8		171	132	90.7	69.3

IMPERIAL SIZE AND MASS

Mass (lb./ft.)		54.8	28.1	21.3		43.4	33.1	22.4	17.0
Thickness (in.)		0.500	0.250	0.188		0.500	0.375	0.250	0.188
Size (in.)			10.75 OD				8.625 OD		

* Class 3 in bending

ROUND HOLLOW SECTIONS

Factored Axial Compressive Resistances, C_r (kN)

G40.21 350W
CLASS C
$\phi = 0.90$

Designation (mm x mm)	HSS 178					HSS 168		
	13	9.5	8.0	6.4	4.8	13	9.5	8.0
Mass (kg/m)	51.7	39.5	33.3	26.8	20.4	48.7	37.3	31.4
0	2 080	1 590	1 340	1 080	819	1 960	1 500	1 260
400	2 070	1 590	1 330	1 080	818	1 950	1 490	1 260
800	2 060	1 580	1 330	1 070	813	1 940	1 480	1 250
1 200	2 030	1 550	1 310	1 060	803	1 910	1 460	1 230
1 600	1 980	1 520	1 280	1 030	785	1 850	1 420	1 200
2 000	1 910	1 460	1 230	997	759	1 770	1 360	1 150
2 400	1 810	1 400	1 180	953	726	1 670	1 290	1 090
2 800	1 710	1 320	1 110	901	687	1 560	1 210	1 020
3 200	1 590	1 230	1 040	844	644	1 450	1 120	949
3 600	1 470	1 140	965	784	599	1 330	1 030	873
4 000	1 350	1 050	890	724	554	1 210	939	799
4 400	1 240	963	816	665	509	1 100	855	728
4 800	1 130	880	747	609	467	993	776	661
5 200	1 030	803	682	557	427	899	703	600
5 600	934	732	622	508	390	814	638	545
6 000	851	667	568	464	357	738	579	495
6 400	776	609	519	425	327	670	527	451
6 800	708	557	475	389	299	610	480	411
7 200	648	510	435	356	274	556	438	375
7 600	594	468	399	327	252	509	401	344
8 000	546	431	367	301	232	467	368	316
8 400	503	397	339	278	214	429	339	290
8 800	465	367	313	257	198	395	312	268
9 200	430	340	290	238	183	365	289	248
9 600	399	315	269	221	170	338	267	230
10 000	371	293	250	205	158	314	248	213
10 400	345	273	233	192	148	292	231	199
10 800	322	255	218	179	138	273	216	185
11 200	301	238	204	167	129		202	173
11 600	282	223	191	157	121			
12 000			179	147	114			

Effective length (KL) in millimetres with respect to the least radius of gyration

PROPERTIES AND DESIGN DATA

Area (mm^2)	6 590	5 040	4 240	3 420	2 600	6 210	4 750	4 000
Z (10^3 mm^3)	347	270	230	187	143	308	241	205
S (10^3 mm^3)	254	201	172	142	109	225	179	153
r (mm)	58.5	59.6	60.1	60.7	61.2	55.2	56.2	56.8
M$_r$ (kN·m)	109	85.1	72.5	58.9	45.0	97.0	75.9	64.6

IMPERIAL SIZE AND MASS

Mass (lb./ft.)	34.7	26.6	22.4	18.0	13.7	32.7	25.1	21.1
Thickness (in.)	0.500	0.375	0.313	0.250	0.188	0.500	0.375	0.313
Size (in.)	7 OD					6.625 OD		

Designation (mm x mm)	HSS 168			HSS 152				
	6.4	4.8	3.2 *	9.5	8.0	6.4	4.8	3.2
Mass (kg/m)	25.4	19.3	12.9	33.6	28.3	22.9	17.4	11.7
0	1 020	775	520	1 350	1 140	917	699	469
400	1 020	774	519	1 350	1 140	915	698	469
800	1 010	769	516	1 330	1 120	907	692	465
1 200	993	757	508	1 300	1 100	888	678	456
1 600	967	737	495	1 260	1 060	858	655	441
2 000	930	710	477	1 190	1 010	816	624	420
2 400	883	675	454	1 110	943	764	586	395
2 800	829	634	427	1 030	871	707	542	366
3 200	770	590	398	936	795	647	497	336
3 600	710	544	368	847	721	587	452	306
4 000	650	499	338	762	650	530	408	277
4 400	593	456	309	684	584	477	368	250
4 800	539	415	282	614	524	429	331	226
5 200	490	377	256	551	471	386	298	203
5 600	445	343	233	495	424	347	269	183
6 000	405	312	212	446	382	314	243	166
6 400	369	284	194	403	345	284	220	150
6 800	336	260	177	365	313	257	199	136
7 200	307	237	162	332	285	234	181	124
7 600	282	218	148	302	259	213	166	113
8 000	259	200	136	277	237	195	151	104
8 400	238	184	126	254	218	179	139	95
8 800	220	170	116	233	200	165	128	88
9 200	203	157	107	215	185	152	118	81
9 600	188	146	100	199	171	141	109	75
10 000	175	135	92	184	158	131	101	69
10 400	163	126	86				94	65
10 800	152	118	80					
11 200	142	110	75					
11 600			70					
12 000								

Effective length (KL) in millimetres with respect to the least radius of gyration

PROPERTIES AND DESIGN DATA

Area (mm^2)	3 230	2 460	1 650	4 280	3 610	2 910	2 220	1 490
Z ($10^3 \ mm^3$)	167	128	86.7	195	166	136	104	70.8
S ($10^3 \ mm^3$)	126	97.6	66.8	144	124	102	79.3	54.5
r (mm)	57.3	57.8	58.4	50.6	51.1	51.7	52.2	52.8
M_r (kN·m)	52.6	40.3	21.0	61.4	52.3	42.8	32.8	22.3

IMPERIAL SIZE AND MASS

Mass (lb./ft.)	17.0	13.0	8.70	22.6	19.0	15.4	11.7	7.86
Thickness (in.)	0.250	0.188	0.125	0.375	0.313	0.250	0.188	0.125
Size (in.)	6.625 OD			6 OD				

* Class 3 in bending

ROUND HOLLOW SECTIONS

Factored Axial Compressive Resistances, C_r (kN)

G40.21 350W
CLASS C
$\phi = 0.90$

Designation (mm x mm)	HSS 141			HSS 127					
	9.5	6.4	4.8	13	9.5	8.0	6.4	4.8	3.2
Mass (kg/m)	31.0	21.1	16.1	35.8	27.6	23.3	18.9	14.4	9.71
0	1 240	847	646	1 440	1 110	936	759	580	391
400	1 240	846	644	1 430	1 110	933	757	578	390
800	1 230	836	637	1 410	1 090	918	746	570	384
1 200	1 190	815	622	1 350	1 050	887	721	551	372
1 600	1 140	781	597	1 270	989	837	682	522	353
2 000	1 070	736	563	1 170	911	773	631	484	328
2 400	988	681	522	1 050	823	700	572	440	299
2 800	898	622	477	930	733	625	512	395	269
3 200	808	562	432	817	647	552	454	350	239
3 600	722	504	388	714	568	486	400	309	212
4 000	643	450	347	624	497	426	351	272	187
4 400	571	401	310	546	436	375	309	240	165
4 800	508	357	276	479	384	330	272	212	146
5 200	453	319	247	422	339	292	241	187	129
5 600	405	286	221	374	301	259	214	167	115
6 000	363	256	199	333	268	231	191	149	102
6 400	326	231	179	297	240	206	171	133	92
6 800	294	209	162	267	215	186	154	120	83
7 200	267	189	147	241	194	168	139	108	75
7 600	243	172	134	218	176	152	126	98	68
8 000	221	157	122	199	160	138	115	89	62
8 400	203	144	112			126	105	82	57
8 800	186	132	103						
9 200	171	122	95						
9 600			87						
10 000									
10 400									
10 800									
11 200									
11 600									
12 000									

Effective length (KL) in millimetres with respect to the least radius of gyration

PROPERTIES AND DESIGN DATA

Area (mm^2)	3 950	2 690	2 050	4 560	3 520	2 970	2 410	1 840	1 240
Z (10^3 mm^3)	166	116	89.1	167	132	113	92.5	71.4	48.8
S (10^3 mm^3)	122	86.9	67.7	119	96.2	83.3	69.2	54.1	37.4
r (mm)	46.7	47.8	48.3	40.7	41.7	42.2	42.7	43.2	43.8
M_r (kN·m)	52.3	36.5	28.1	52.6	41.6	35.6	29.1	22.5	15.4

IMPERIAL SIZE AND MASS

Mass (lb./ft.)	20.8	14.2	10.8	24.1	18.6	15.7	12.7	9.68	6.53
Thickness (in.)	0.375	0.250	0.188	0.500	0.375	0.313	0.250	0.188	0.125
Size (in.)	5.563 OD			5 OD					

Designation (mm x mm)	HSS 114			HSS 102			
	9.5	4.8	3.2	8.0	6.4	4.8	3.2
Mass (kg/m)	24.6	12.9	8.71	18.4	14.9	11.4	7.72
0	989	517	350	737	599	457	310
400	985	515	348	733	595	454	308
800	964	505	342	712	579	442	300
1 200	919	484	328	668	545	417	284
1 600	850	451	306	604	495	380	259
2 000	766	410	279	530	436	336	230
2 400	676	365	249	456	377	291	200
2 800	588	320	219	388	321	249	172
3 200	508	279	191	329	273	212	147
3 600	439	242	166	279	232	181	125
4 000	379	210	145	238	199	155	107
4 400	329	183	126	204	171	133	93
4 800	286	160	110	177	148	116	80
5 200	251	141	97	154	129	101	70
5 600	221	124	86	135	113	89	62
6 000	196	110	76	119	100	78	54
6 400	175	98	68	106	89	70	48
6 800	156	88	61			62	43
7 200	141	79	55				
7 600		72	50				
8 000							
8 400							
8 800							
9 200							
9 600							
10 000							
10 400							
10 800							
11 200							
11 600							
12 000							

Effective length (KL) in millimetres with respect to the least radius of gyration

PROPERTIES AND DESIGN DATA

Area (mm^2)	3 140	1 640	1 110	2 340	1 900	1 450	983
Z (10^3 mm^3)	105	57.4	39.3	69.9	57.7	44.8	30.8
S (10^3 mm^3)	75.9	43.2	30.0	50.8	42.6	33.6	23.5
r (mm)	37.2	38.8	39.3	33.2	33.8	34.3	34.8
M$_r$ (kN·m)	33.1	18.1	12.4	22.0	18.2	14.1	9.70

IMPERIAL SIZE AND MASS

Mass (lb./ft.)	16.5	8.68	5.86	12.3	10.0	7.67	5.19
Thickness (in.)	0.375	0.188	0.125	0.313	0.250	0.188	0.125
Size (in.)	4.5 OD			4 OD			

Designation (mm x mm)		HSS 89			HSS 76		HSS 73		
		6.4	4.8	3.2	6.4	4.8	6.4	4.8	3.2
Mass (kg/m)		12.9	9.92	6.72	10.9	8.42	10.4	8.04	5.48
Effective length (KL) in millimetres with respect to the least radius of gyration	0	520	397	270	438	337	419	321	220
	400	516	394	268	433	333	413	317	217
	800	495	379	258	407	314	386	297	204
	1 200	455	349	238	358	278	335	260	180
	1 600	399	308	211	299	234	276	215	150
	2 000	339	263	181	242	191	220	173	121
	2 400	283	220	152	194	153	175	138	97
	2 800	234	183	127	156	124	139	110	78
	3 200	195	152	106	127	101	113	89	63
	3 600	163	128	89	104	83	92	73	52
	4 000	137	108	75	87	69	77	61	43
	4 400	117	92	64	73	58	64	51	36
	4 800	100	79	55	62	50		44	31
	5 200	87	68	48					
	5 600	76	60	42					
	6 000			37					
	6 400								
	6 800								
	7 200								
	7 600								
	8 000								
	8 400								
	8 800								
	9 200								
	9 600								
	10 000								
	10 400								
	10 800								
	11 200								
	11 600								
	12 000								

PROPERTIES AND DESIGN DATA

		HSS 89			HSS 76		HSS 73		
Area (mm^2)		1 650	1 260	856	1 390	1 070	1 330	1 020	698
Z (10^3 mm^3)		43.4	33.9	23.4	31.1	24.4	28.3	22.3	15.5
S (10^3 mm^3)		31.7	25.2	17.7	22.5	18.0	20.4	16.4	11.7
r (mm)		29.3	29.8	30.3	24.8	25.3	23.7	24.2	24.7
M$_r$ (kN·m)		13.7	10.7	7.37	9.80	7.69	8.91	7.02	4.88

IMPERIAL SIZE AND MASS

		HSS 89			HSS 76		HSS 73		
Mass (lb./ft.)		8.69	6.66	4.52	7.35	5.66	7.01	5.40	3.68
Thickness (in.)		0.250	0.188	0.125	0.250	0.188	0.250	0.188	0.125
Size (in.)		3.5 OD			3 OD		2.875 OD		

Designation (mm x mm)	HSS 64			HSS 60			HSS 48	
	6.4	4.8	3.2	6.4	4.8	3.2	4.8	3.2
Mass (kg/m)	8.95	6.92	4.73	8.45	6.54	4.48	5.13	3.54
0	359	278	190	340	263	180	206	142
400	352	273	187	332	257	176	198	137
800	318	248	171	296	230	159	163	114
1 200	262	206	143	238	188	131	119	85
1 600	204	162	114	181	144	101	84	60
2 000	155	124	88	136	109	77	60	43
2 400	119	96	68	104	83	59	44	32
2 800	93	75	54	80	65	46	33	24
3 200	74	60	43	64	51	37		19
3 600	60	48	35	51	42	30		
4 000	49	40	29			25		
4 400								
4 800								
5 200								
5 600								
6 000								
6 400								
6 800								
7 200								
7 600								
8 000								
8 400								
8 800								
9 200								
9 600								
10 000								
10 400								
10 800								
11 200								
11 600								
12 000								

Effective length (KL) in millimetres with respect to the least radius of gyration

PROPERTIES AND DESIGN DATA

Area (mm²)	1 140	882	603	1 080	834	571	654	451
Z (10^3 mm³)	20.8	16.5	11.6	18.6	14.8	10.4	9.09	6.48
S (10^3 mm³)	14.8	12.0	8.66	13.2	10.7	7.74	6.48	4.77
r (mm)	20.3	20.8	21.4	19.2	19.7	20.2	15.5	16.0
M_r (kN·m)	6.55	5.20	3.65	5.86	4.66	3.28	2.86	2.04

IMPERIAL SIZE AND MASS

Mass (lb./ft.)	6.01	4.65	3.18	5.68	4.40	3.01	3.45	2.38
Thickness (in.)	0.250	0.188	0.125	0.250	0.188	0.125	0.188	0.125
Size (in.)	2.5 OD			2.375 OD			1.9 OD	

CSA G40.20/21 - Class H

For rectangular hollow sections, see page 4-67.

For square hollow sections, see page 4-74.

For round hollow sections, see page 4-82.

RECTANGULAR HOLLOW SECTIONS
Factored Axial Compressive Resistances, C_r (kN)

Designation (mm x mm x mm)	HSS 356 x 254		HSS 305 x 203			
	13	9.5 *	13	9.5	8.0 *	6.4 **
Mass (kg/m)	113	86.5	93.0	71.3	60.1	48.6
0	4 540	3 470	3 720	2 860	2 410	1 740
400	4 540	3 460	3 720	2 860	2 410	1 740
800	4 540	3 460	3 720	2 860	2 410	1 740
1 200	4 540	3 460	3 720	2 860	2 410	1 740
1 600	4 530	3 460	3 710	2 860	2 410	1 740
2 000	4 530	3 460	3 710	2 860	2 410	1 740
2 400	4 520	3 460	3 690	2 850	2 400	1 730
2 800	4 510	3 450	3 670	2 830	2 380	1 720
3 200	4 500	3 440	3 630	2 800	2 360	1 710
3 600	4 470	3 420	3 570	2 760	2 330	1 680
4 000	4 430	3 390	3 490	2 700	2 280	1 650
4 400	4 380	3 350	3 390	2 630	2 220	1 610
4 800	4 310	3 300	3 260	2 530	2 140	1 550
5 200	4 220	3 240	3 110	2 420	2 050	1 490
5 600	4 110	3 160	2 950	2 300	1 950	1 420
6 000	3 990	3 070	2 770	2 170	1 840	1 340
6 400	3 850	2 970	2 590	2 040	1 730	1 260
6 800	3 690	2 860	2 410	1 900	1 620	1 180
7 200	3 530	2 740	2 240	1 770	1 510	1 100
7 600	3 350	2 610	2 080	1 640	1 400	1 020
8 000	3 180	2 480	1 920	1 520	1 300	951
8 400	3 010	2 350	1 780	1 410	1 210	882
8 800	2 840	2 220	1 650	1 310	1 120	819
9 200	2 670	2 100	1 530	1 220	1 040	761
9 600	2 510	1 980	1 420	1 130	966	707
10 000	2 360	1 860	1 320	1 050	899	659
10 400	2 220	1 750	1 230	979	838	614
10 800	2 090	1 650	1 150	913	782	573
11 200	1 970	1 550	1 070	854	731	536
11 600	1 850	1 460	1 000	799	684	502
12 000	1 750	1 380	940	750	642	471

(Leftmost column, rotated: Effective length (KL) in millimetres with respect to the least radius of gyration)

PROPERTIES AND DESIGN DATA						
Area (mm^2)	14 400	11 000	11 800	9 090	7 660	6 190
Z_x (10^3 mm^3)	1 730	1 340	1 190	926	787	640
S_x (10^3 mm^3)	1 420	1 120	964	762	652	535
r_x (mm)	132	134	111	113	114	115
Z_y (10^3 mm^3)	1 370	1 060	897	701	596	486
S_y (10^3 mm^3)	1 180	931	769	611	525	368
r_y (mm)	102	104	81.2	82.7	83.4	84.1
r_x / r_y	1.29	1.29	1.37	1.37	1.37	1.37
M_{rx} (kN·m)	545	422	375	292	248	202
M_{ry} (kN·m)	432	293	283	221	165	116

IMPERIAL SIZE AND MASS						
Mass (lb./ft.)	76.1	58.1	62.5	47.9	40.4	32.6
Thickness (in.)	0.500	0.375	0.500	0.375	0.313	0.250
Size (in.)	14 x 10		12 x 8			

* Class 3 in bending about Y-Y axis
** Class 4: C_r calculated according to S16-09 Clause 13.3.5; S_y and M_{ry} according to Clause 13.5(c).

Designation (mm x mm x mm)	HSS 254 x 152				HSS 203 x 152				
	13	9.5	8.0	6.4 **	13	9.5	8.0	6.4	4.8 **
Mass (kg/m)	72.7	56.1	47.5	38.4	62.6	48.5	41.1	33.4	25.5
0	2 920	2 250	1 910	1 540	2 510	1 950	1 650	1 340	985
400	2 920	2 250	1 910	1 540	2 510	1 950	1 650	1 340	985
800	2 920	2 250	1 910	1 540	2 510	1 950	1 650	1 340	985
1 200	2 910	2 250	1 900	1 540	2 510	1 940	1 650	1 340	984
1 600	2 900	2 240	1 900	1 530	2 500	1 940	1 640	1 330	981
2 000	2 880	2 230	1 890	1 520	2 480	1 920	1 630	1 320	975
2 400	2 840	2 200	1 860	1 510	2 440	1 900	1 610	1 310	963
2 800	2 780	2 150	1 830	1 480	2 380	1 850	1 570	1 280	944
3 200	2 680	2 080	1 770	1 430	2 280	1 780	1 520	1 240	913
3 600	2 540	1 990	1 690	1 370	2 160	1 690	1 450	1 180	873
4 000	2 380	1 870	1 590	1 300	2 010	1 580	1 360	1 110	822
4 400	2 200	1 740	1 480	1 210	1 840	1 460	1 260	1 030	764
4 800	2 010	1 590	1 360	1 110	1 680	1 340	1 150	944	703
5 200	1 830	1 450	1 250	1 020	1 510	1 210	1 040	859	641
5 600	1 650	1 320	1 130	927	1 360	1 090	944	778	582
6 000	1 490	1 190	1 020	840	1 220	984	852	703	526
6 400	1 340	1 070	926	761	1 100	887	769	635	476
6 800	1 210	972	838	689	991	801	694	574	431
7 200	1 090	880	760	625	895	724	629	520	390
7 600	993	799	690	569	811	657	570	472	355
8 000	904	728	629	518	737	598	519	430	323
8 400	825	665	575	474	673	545	474	393	295
8 800	755	609	527	434	616	499	434	360	271
9 200	694	560	484	399	565	459	399	331	249
9 600	639	516	446	368	521	423	368	305	229
10 000	591	477	412	340	481	390	340	282	212
10 400	547	442	382	315	445	362	315	261	196
10 800	508	410	355	293	414	336	292	242	182
11 200	473	382	331	273	385	313	272	226	170
11 600	442	357	309	255	359	292	254	211	159
12 000	413	334	289	238		273	238	197	148

Effective length (KL) in millimetres with respect to the least radius of gyration

PROPERTIES AND DESIGN DATA									
Area (mm²)	9 260	7 150	6 050	4 900	7 970	6 180	5 240	4 250	3 250
Z_x (10³ mm³)	747	589	503	411	528	420	360	295	228
S_x (10³ mm³)	592	475	410	338	423	343	297	246	192
r_x (mm)	90.1	91.9	92.7	93.6	73.4	75.1	75.9	76.7	77.5
Z_y (10³ mm³)	522	413	354	290	432	344	295	243	188
S_y (10³ mm³)	442	357	309	255	359	292	254	211	157
r_y (mm)	60.3	61.7	62.4	63.1	58.6	60.0	60.8	61.5	62.2
r_x / r_y	1.49	1.49	1.49	1.48	1.25	1.25	1.25	1.25	1.25
M_{rx} (kN·m)	235	186	158	129	166	132	113	92.9	71.8
M_{ry} (kN·m)	164	130	112	80.3	136	108	92.9	76.5	49.3

IMPERIAL SIZE AND MASS									
Mass (lb./ft.)	48.9	37.7	31.9	25.8	42.1	32.6	27.6	22.4	17.1
Thickness (in.)	0.500	0.375	0.313	0.250	0.500	0.375	0.313	0.250	0.188
Size (in.)	10 x 6				8 x 6				

** Class 4: C_r calculated according to S16-09 Clause 13.3.5; S_y and M_{ry} according to Clause 13.5(c).

G40.21 350W
CLASS H
$\phi = 0.90$

RECTANGULAR HOLLOW SECTIONS
Factored Axial Compressive
Resistances, C_r (kN)

Designation (mm x mm x mm)		HSS 203 x 102					HSS 178 x 127				
		13	9.5	8.0	6.4	4.8 **	13	9.5	8.0	6.4	4.8 *
Mass (kg/m)		52.4	40.9	34.8	28.3	21.7	52.4	40.9	34.8	28.3	21.7
Effective length (KL) in millimetres with respect to the least radius of gyration	0	2 100	1 640	1 400	1 140	831	2 100	1 640	1 400	1 140	869
	400	2 100	1 640	1 400	1 140	831	2 100	1 640	1 400	1 140	869
	800	2 100	1 640	1 390	1 140	830	2 100	1 640	1 390	1 140	869
	1 200	2 090	1 630	1 390	1 130	826	2 100	1 640	1 390	1 130	867
	1 600	2 050	1 600	1 360	1 110	815	2 080	1 620	1 380	1 130	862
	2 000	1 960	1 540	1 320	1 080	789	2 040	1 600	1 360	1 110	850
	2 400	1 810	1 440	1 230	1 010	746	1 970	1 550	1 320	1 080	828
	2 800	1 620	1 300	1 120	925	684	1 860	1 470	1 260	1 030	793
	3 200	1 410	1 140	991	822	611	1 720	1 370	1 170	965	744
	3 600	1 200	986	861	717	535	1 550	1 240	1 070	886	685
	4 000	1 030	846	741	619	464	1 380	1 120	964	799	620
	4 400	876	725	637	534	400	1 220	989	857	713	555
	4 800	751	624	549	461	346	1 070	873	758	632	493
	5 200	649	540	476	400	301	938	769	669	559	437
	5 600	565	471	415	349	263	826	679	592	495	387
	6 000	495	413	365	307	231	730	602	525	440	344
	6 400	437	365	322	271	204	648	535	467	392	307
	6 800	388	324	287	241	182	579	478	417	350	275
	7 200	347	290	256	216	163	519	429	375	315	247
	7 600	312	261	231	194	147	468	387	338	284	223
	8 000		236	208	176	132	424	351	306	257	202
	8 400				159	120	385	319	279	234	184
	8 800						352	291	255	214	168
	9 200						322	267	233	196	154
	9 600						296	246	215	180	142
	10 000								198	166	131
	10 400										
	10 800										
	11 200										
	11 600										
	12 000										

PROPERTIES AND DESIGN DATA

	13	9.5	8.0	6.4	4.8	13	9.5	8.0	6.4	4.8
Area (mm^2)	6 680	5 210	4 430	3 610	2 760	6 680	5 210	4 430	3 610	2 760
Z_x (10^3 mm^3)	405	326	281	232	180	378	303	261	216	168
S_x (10^3 mm^3)	308	254	221	185	145	297	244	213	178	140
r_x (mm)	68.4	70.3	71.2	72.2	73.1	62.9	64.6	65.4	66.2	67.1
Z_y (10^3 mm^3)	246	199	172	143	111	298	240	207	171	133
S_y (10^3 mm^3)	201	169	148	125	93.3	244	202	177	148	117
r_y (mm)	39.1	40.5	41.3	42.0	42.7	48.1	49.6	50.3	51.1	51.8
r_x / r_y	1.75	1.74	1.72	1.72	1.71	1.31	1.30	1.30	1.30	1.30
M_{rx} (kN·m)	128	103	88.5	73.1	56.7	119	95.4	82.2	68.0	52.9
M_{ry} (kN·m)	77.5	62.7	54.2	45.0	29.4	93.9	75.6	65.2	53.9	36.9

IMPERIAL SIZE AND MASS

	13	9.5	8.0	6.4	4.8	13	9.5	8.0	6.4	4.8
Mass (lb./ft.)	35.2	27.5	23.4	19.0	14.6	35.2	27.5	23.4	19.0	14.6
Thickness (in.)	0.500	0.375	0.313	0.250	0.188	0.500	0.375	0.313	0.250	0.188
Size (in.)			8 x 4					7 x 5		

* Class 3 in bending about Y-Y axis

** Class 4: C_r calculated according to S16-09 Clause 13.3.5; S_y and M_{ry} according to Clause 13.5(c).

RECTANGULAR HOLLOW SECTIONS

Factored Axial Compressive Resistances, C$_r$ (kN)

G40.21 350W
CLASS H
$\phi = 0.90$

Designation (mm x mm x mm)	HSS 152 x 102					HSS 152 x 76				
	13	9.5	8.0	6.4	4.8	13	9.5	8.0	6.4	4.8
Mass (kg/m)	42.3	33.3	28.4	23.2	17.9	37.3	29.5	25.3	20.7	16.0
0	1 700	1 340	1 140	932	718	1 500	1 180	1 010	832	643
400	1 700	1 340	1 140	932	718	1 500	1 180	1 010	831	643
800	1 700	1 330	1 140	931	717	1 490	1 180	1 010	828	640
1 200	1 680	1 330	1 130	926	714	1 450	1 150	989	813	629
1 600	1 640	1 300	1 110	910	702	1 330	1 080	931	769	598
2 000	1 560	1 240	1 070	876	677	1 150	949	827	690	541
2 400	1 430	1 150	991	818	635	944	793	698	587	465
2 800	1 260	1 030	891	739	577	757	645	572	485	386
3 200	1 080	895	780	650	510	606	522	465	396	317
3 600	921	767	671	562	443	491	425	380	324	260
4 000	780	654	574	482	381	404	350	313	268	216
4 400	663	558	491	414	328	336	292	262	224	181
4 800	567	479	422	356	283	284	247	222	190	153
5 200	489	414	365	308	245	243	212	190	163	131
5 600	425	360	318	269	214	210	183	164	141	114
6 000	372	316	279	236	188			143	123	99
6 400	328	279	246	208	166					
6 800	292	248	219	185	147					
7 200	261	221	196	166	132					
7 600		199	176	149	119					
8 000				135	107					
8 400										
8 800										
9 200										
9 600										
10 000										
10 400										
10 800										
11 200										
11 600										
12 000										

Effective length (KL) in millimetres with respect to the least radius of gyration

PROPERTIES AND DESIGN DATA

Area (mm^2)	5 390	4 240	3 620	2 960	2 280	4 750	3 760	3 220	2 640	2 040
Z$_x$ (10^3 mm^3)	252	206	179	148	116	207	171	149	125	98.1
S$_x$ (10^3 mm^3)	193	162	143	121	95.6	152	130	115	98.0	78.2
r$_x$ (mm)	52.2	54.0	54.8	55.7	56.5	49.3	51.3	52.3	53.2	54.1
Z$_y$ (10^3 mm^3)	189	155	135	112	87.8	124	104	91.2	76.6	60.5
S$_y$ (10^3 mm^3)	151	128	113	96.2	76.6	97.3	85.0	76.3	65.5	52.9
r$_y$ (mm)	37.7	39.2	39.9	40.6	41.3	28.0	29.4	30.1	30.8	31.5
r$_x$ / r$_y$	1.38	1.38	1.37	1.37	1.37	1.76	1.74	1.74	1.73	1.72
M$_{rx}$ (kN·m)	79.4	64.9	56.4	46.6	36.5	65.2	53.9	46.9	39.4	30.9
M$_{ry}$ (kN·m)	59.5	48.8	42.5	35.3	27.7	39.1	32.8	28.7	24.1	19.1

IMPERIAL SIZE AND MASS

Mass (lb./ft.)	28.4	22.4	19.1	15.6	12.0	25.0	19.8	17.0	13.9	10.7
Thickness (in.)	0.500	0.375	0.313	0.250	0.188	0.500	0.375	0.313	0.250	0.188
Size (in.)	6 x 4					6 x 3				

G40.21 350W
CLASS H
φ = 0.90

RECTANGULAR HOLLOW SECTIONS
Factored Axial Compressive
Resistances, C_r (kN)

Designation (mm x mm x mm)	HSS 127 x 76				HSS 102 x 76				
	9.5	8.0	6.4	4.8	9.5	8.0	6.4	4.8	3.2
Mass (kg/m)	25.7	22.1	18.2	14.1	21.9	18.9	15.6	12.2	8.35
0	1 030	888	731	564	879	759	627	488	334
400	1 030	888	731	564	879	759	627	488	334
800	1 030	884	728	562	874	755	624	486	333
1 200	1 000	864	712	551	848	735	609	476	326
1 600	931	808	671	521	781	682	569	447	308
2 000	812	712	596	468	672	593	501	397	276
2 400	672	595	503	398	549	490	418	335	235
2 800	543	484	412	329	439	395	340	274	194
3 200	437	391	335	268	352	317	275	222	158
3 600	355	319	273	220	285	257	224	182	129
4 000	292	263	226	182	234	212	184	150	107
4 400	244	219	189	152	195	177	154	125	89
4 800	206	185	160	129	165	149	130	106	76
5 200	176	159	137	110	141	128	111	91	65
5 600	152	137	118	95		110	96	78	56
6 000			103	83				68	49
6 400									
6 800									
7 200									
7 600									
8 000									
8 400									
8 800									
9 200									
9 600									
10 000									
10 400									
10 800									
11 200									
11 600									
12 000									

Effective length (KL) in millimetres with respect to the least radius of gyration

PROPERTIES AND DESIGN DATA

Area (mm²)	3 280	2 820	2 320	1 790	2 790	2 410	1 990	1 550	1 060
Z_x (10^3 mm³)	126	111	93.4	73.8	87.9	77.9	66.0	52.6	37.0
S_x (10^3 mm³)	96.5	86.5	74.1	59.6	67.4	61.1	52.9	43.0	30.8
r_x (mm)	43.3	44.2	45.1	45.9	35.0	35.9	36.7	37.5	38.4
Z_y (10^3 mm³)	87.8	77.4	65.3	51.8	71.6	63.6	54.0	43.1	30.4
S_y (10^3 mm³)	70.8	63.9	55.2	44.8	56.6	51.5	44.8	36.6	26.4
r_y (mm)	28.7	29.4	30.1	30.8	27.8	28.5	29.3	30.0	30.7
r_x / r_y	1.51	1.50	1.50	1.49	1.26	1.26	1.25	1.25	1.25
M_{rx} (kN·m)	39.7	35.0	29.4	23.2	27.7	24.5	20.8	16.6	11.7
M_{ry} (kN·m)	27.7	24.4	20.6	16.3	22.6	20.0	17.0	13.6	9.58

IMPERIAL SIZE AND MASS

Mass (lb./ft.)	17.3	14.9	12.2	9.46	14.7	12.7	10.5	8.17	5.61
Thickness (in.)	0.375	0.313	0.250	0.188	0.375	0.313	0.250	0.188	0.125
Size (in.)	5 x 3				4 x 3				

RECTANGULAR HOLLOW SECTIONS
Factored Axial Compressive Resistances, C_r (kN)

G40.21 350W
CLASS H
$\phi = 0.90$

Designation (mm x mm x mm)	HSS 102 x 51					HSS 89 x 64			
	9.5	8.0	6.4	4.8	3.2	8.0	6.4	4.8	3.2
Mass (kg/m)	18.1	15.8	13.1	10.3	7.09	15.8	13.1	10.3	7.09
0	728	633	526	413	284	633	526	413	284
400	726	632	525	412	284	633	526	412	284
800	700	613	511	403	279	625	520	409	282
1 200	597	533	453	362	254	587	493	389	270
1 600	444	406	352	288	206	504	429	344	241
2 000	315	292	258	214	155	399	345	280	199
2 400	228	213	189	158	115	305	268	219	158
2 800	170	159	142	119	87	235	207	171	123
3 200	131	123	110	92	68	184	163	135	98
3 600	104	98	87	73	54	147	130	108	78
4 000				60	44	120	106	88	64
4 400						99	88	73	53
4 800							74	62	45
5 200									
5 600									
6 000									
6 400									
6 800									
7 200									
7 600									
8 000									
8 400									
8 800									
9 200									
9 600									
10 000									
10 400									
10 800									
11 200									
11 600									
12 000									

Effective length (KL) in millimetres with respect to the least radius of gyration

PROPERTIES AND DESIGN DATA

Area (mm^2)	2 310	2 010	1 670	1 310	903	2 010	1 670	1 310	903
Z_x (10^3 mm^3)	65.6	59.0	50.7	40.8	29.0	55.1	47.2	38.0	27.0
S_x (10^3 mm^3)	47.1	43.6	38.5	31.8	23.1	42.2	37.1	30.6	22.3
r_x (mm)	32.2	33.2	34.2	35.1	36.1	30.6	31.4	32.3	33.1
Z_y (10^3 mm^3)	39.2	35.6	30.8	25.0	17.9	43.3	37.3	30.1	21.4
S_y (10^3 mm^3)	30.0	28.1	25.2	21.1	15.6	34.4	30.5	25.3	18.5
r_y (mm)	18.2	18.9	19.6	20.3	21.0	23.3	24.1	24.8	25.5
r_x / r_y	1.77	1.76	1.74	1.73	1.72	1.31	1.30	1.30	1.30
M_{rx} (kN·m)	20.7	18.6	16.0	12.9	9.14	17.4	14.9	12.0	8.51
M_{ry} (kN·m)	12.3	11.2	9.70	7.88	5.64	13.6	11.7	9.48	6.74

IMPERIAL SIZE AND MASS

Mass (lb./ft.)	12.2	10.6	8.81	6.89	4.76	10.6	8.81	6.89	4.76
Thickness (in.)	0.375	0.313	0.250	0.188	0.125	0.313	0.250	0.188	0.125
Size (in.)			4 x 2				3½ x 2½		

RECTANGULAR HOLLOW SECTIONS
Factored Axial Compressive
Resistances, C_r (kN)

Designation (mm x mm x mm)	HSS 76 x 51			HSS 51 x 25	
	6.4	4.8	3.2	4.8	3.2
Mass (kg/m)	10.6	8.35	5.82	4.54	3.28
Effective length (KL) in millimetres with respect to the least radius of gyration					
0	425	334	233	182	132
400	425	333	233	175	128
800	411	325	228	111	88
1 200	358	287	205	57	47
1 600	272	224	163	33	27
2 000	196	164	121		
2 400	143	120	89		
2 800	107	90	67		
3 200	83	70	52		
3 600	66	55	41		
4 000			34		
4 400					
4 800					
5 200					
5 600					
6 000					
6 400					
6 800					
7 200					
7 600					
8 000					
8 400					
8 800					
9 200					
9 600					
10 000					
10 400					
10 800					
11 200					
11 600					
12 000					
PROPERTIES AND DESIGN DATA					
Area (mm^2)	1 350	1 060	741	578	418
Z_x (10^3 mm^3)	31.5	25.8	18.6	8.21	6.34
S_x (10^3 mm^3)	24.1	20.3	15.1	5.89	4.81
r_x (mm)	26.1	27.0	27.8	16.1	17.1
Z_y (10^3 mm^3)	23.6	19.4	14.0	4.91	3.85
S_y (10^3 mm^3)	18.9	16.1	12.0	3.75	3.15
r_y (mm)	18.9	19.6	20.3	9.08	9.78
r_x / r_y	1.38	1.38	1.37	1.77	1.75
M_{rx} (kN·m)	9.92	8.13	5.86	2.59	2.00
M_{ry} (kN·m)	7.43	6.11	4.41	1.55	1.21
IMPERIAL SIZE AND MASS					
Mass (lb./ft.)	7.11	5.61	3.91	3.05	2.21
Thickness (in.)	0.250	0.188	0.125	0.188	0.125
Size (in.)	3 x 2			2 x 1	

SQUARE HOLLOW SECTIONS

Factored Axial Compressive Resistances, C_r (kN)

Designation (mm x mm x mm)		HSS 305 x 305					HSS 254 x 254			
		13	9.5	8.0 *	6.4 **		13	9.5	8.0	6.4 **
Mass (kg/m)		113	86.5	72.8	58.7		93.0	71.3	60.1	48.6
Effective length (KL) in millimetres with respect to the least radius of gyration	0	4 540	3 470	2 920	1 940		3 720	2 860	2 410	1 940
	400	4 540	3 460	2 920	1 940		3 720	2 860	2 410	1 940
	800	4 540	3 460	2 920	1 940		3 720	2 860	2 410	1 940
	1 200	4 540	3 460	2 920	1 940		3 720	2 860	2 410	1 940
	1 600	4 540	3 460	2 920	1 940		3 720	2 860	2 410	1 940
	2 000	4 530	3 460	2 920	1 940		3 710	2 860	2 410	1 940
	2 400	4 530	3 460	2 920	1 940		3 710	2 860	2 410	1 940
	2 800	4 520	3 460	2 920	1 940		3 690	2 850	2 400	1 930
	3 200	4 520	3 450	2 910	1 930		3 680	2 830	2 390	1 920
	3 600	4 500	3 440	2 900	1 930		3 650	2 820	2 370	1 910
	4 000	4 480	3 430	2 890	1 920		3 610	2 790	2 350	1 890
	4 400	4 450	3 400	2 870	1 910		3 560	2 750	2 320	1 870
	4 800	4 410	3 380	2 850	1 890		3 490	2 700	2 280	1 840
	5 200	4 360	3 340	2 820	1 870		3 410	2 640	2 230	1 800
	5 600	4 300	3 300	2 790	1 850		3 310	2 560	2 170	1 750
	6 000	4 220	3 240	2 740	1 820		3 190	2 480	2 100	1 700
	6 400	4 130	3 180	2 690	1 780		3 060	2 380	2 020	1 640
	6 800	4 030	3 100	2 620	1 740		2 920	2 280	1 930	1 570
	7 200	3 910	3 010	2 550	1 700		2 780	2 170	1 840	1 500
	7 600	3 780	2 920	2 480	1 640		2 630	2 060	1 750	1 420
	8 000	3 640	2 820	2 390	1 590		2 480	1 940	1 650	1 350
	8 400	3 500	2 710	2 300	1 530		2 330	1 830	1 560	1 270
	8 800	3 350	2 600	2 210	1 470		2 190	1 720	1 470	1 200
	9 200	3 200	2 490	2 120	1 410		2 060	1 620	1 380	1 130
	9 600	3 050	2 380	2 020	1 340		1 930	1 520	1 300	1 060
	10 000	2 900	2 260	1 930	1 280		1 810	1 430	1 220	996
	10 400	2 760	2 150	1 840	1 220		1 700	1 340	1 140	937
	10 800	2 620	2 050	1 750	1 160		1 590	1 260	1 080	880
	11 200	2 480	1 940	1 660	1 100		1 500	1 180	1 010	828
	11 600	2 360	1 850	1 580	1 050		1 410	1 110	951	780
	12 000	2 230	1 750	1 500	994		1 320	1 050	896	735

PROPERTIES AND DESIGN DATA

Area (mm²)		14 400	11 000	9 280	7 480		11 800	9 090	7 660	6 190
Z (10^3 mm³)		1 560	1 210	1 030	833		1 060	825	702	571
S (10^3 mm³)		1 330	1 040	886	625		889	703	602	492
r (mm)		118	120	121	121		97.6	99.1	99.9	101
M_r (kN·m)		491	381	279	197		334	260	221	155

IMPERIAL SIZE AND MASS

Mass (lb./ft.)		76.1	58.1	48.9	39.4		62.5	47.9	40.4	32.6
Thickness (in.)		0.500	0.375	0.313	0.250		0.500	0.375	0.313	0.250
Size (in.)		12 x 12					10 x 10			

* Class 3 in bending

** Class 4: C_r calculated according to S16-09 Clause 13.3.5; S and M_r according to Clause 13.5(c).

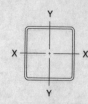
Designation (mm x mm x mm)	HSS 203 x 203					HSS 178 x 178	
	13	9.5	8.0	6.4		13	9.5
Mass (kg/m)	72.7	56.1	47.5	38.4		62.6	48.5
0	2 920	2 250	1 910	1 540		2 510	1 950
400	2 920	2 250	1 910	1 540		2 510	1 950
800	2 920	2 250	1 910	1 540		2 510	1 950
1 200	2 920	2 250	1 910	1 540		2 510	1 950
1 600	2 910	2 250	1 900	1 540		2 500	1 940
2 000	2 910	2 240	1 900	1 540		2 490	1 930
2 400	2 890	2 230	1 890	1 530		2 470	1 920
2 800	2 870	2 220	1 880	1 520		2 430	1 890
3 200	2 830	2 190	1 860	1 500		2 370	1 850
3 600	2 770	2 150	1 820	1 480		2 290	1 790
4 000	2 700	2 090	1 780	1 440		2 180	1 710
4 400	2 600	2 020	1 720	1 400		2 050	1 620
4 800	2 480	1 940	1 650	1 340		1 910	1 510
5 200	2 350	1 840	1 570	1 280		1 770	1 400
5 600	2 210	1 730	1 480	1 210		1 620	1 290
6 000	2 060	1 620	1 390	1 130		1 480	1 180
6 400	1 910	1 510	1 290	1 060		1 350	1 080
6 800	1 770	1 400	1 200	982		1 230	984
7 200	1 630	1 290	1 110	910		1 120	898
7 600	1 500	1 190	1 030	842		1 020	820
8 000	1 380	1 100	948	779		930	750
8 400	1 280	1 020	877	720		851	687
8 800	1 180	942	811	667		782	632
9 200	1 090	872	751	617		719	582
9 600	1 010	808	696	573		664	537
10 000	938	750	647	532		614	497
10 400	872	698	602	495		569	461
10 800	812	651	561	462		529	429
11 200	758	607	524	431		493	399
11 600	709	568	490	404		461	373
12 000	664	533	459	378		431	349
PROPERTIES AND DESIGN DATA							
Area (mm²)	9 260	7 150	6 050	4 900		7 970	6 180
Z (10^3 mm³)	651	513	439	359		484	385
S (10^3 mm³)	538	432	373	308		396	322
r (mm)	76.9	78.4	79.2	79.9		66.5	68.0
M_r (kN·m)	205	162	138	113		152	121
IMPERIAL SIZE AND MASS							
Mass (lb./ft.)	48.9	37.7	31.9	25.8		42.1	32.6
Thickness (in.)	0.500	0.375	0.313	0.250		0.500	0.375
Size (in.)	8 x 8					7 x 7	

The leftmost column label reads: Effective length (KL) in millimetres with respect to the least radius of gyration

SQUARE HOLLOW SECTIONS
Factored Axial Compressive Resistances, C_r (kN)

G40.21 350W
CLASS H
$\phi = 0.90$

Designation (mm x mm x mm)	HSS 178 x 178			HSS 152 x 152				
	8.0	6.4	4.8 *	13	9.5	8.0	6.4	4.8
Mass (kg/m)	41.1	33.4	25.5	52.4	40.9	34.8	28.3	21.7
0	1 650	1 340	1 020	2 100	1 640	1 400	1 140	869
400	1 650	1 340	1 020	2 100	1 640	1 400	1 140	869
800	1 650	1 340	1 020	2 100	1 640	1 400	1 140	869
1 200	1 650	1 340	1 020	2 100	1 640	1 390	1 140	868
1 600	1 650	1 340	1 020	2 090	1 630	1 390	1 130	866
2 000	1 640	1 330	1 020	2 070	1 620	1 380	1 120	859
2 400	1 630	1 320	1 010	2 030	1 590	1 360	1 110	847
2 800	1 610	1 300	998	1 970	1 550	1 320	1 080	827
3 200	1 570	1 280	979	1 880	1 480	1 270	1 040	796
3 600	1 520	1 240	951	1 760	1 390	1 200	982	756
4 000	1 460	1 190	914	1 620	1 290	1 110	916	707
4 400	1 380	1 130	869	1 480	1 180	1 020	843	652
4 800	1 300	1 060	818	1 330	1 070	927	768	595
5 200	1 200	987	763	1 190	966	837	695	539
5 600	1 110	912	706	1 070	867	752	626	487
6 000	1 020	838	649	955	777	676	563	438
6 400	931	767	595	855	698	608	507	395
6 800	850	702	545	769	628	547	457	356
7 200	776	641	498	693	567	494	413	322
7 600	709	587	456	627	514	448	374	292
8 000	649	537	418	569	467	407	340	266
8 400	595	493	384	519	426	372	311	243
8 800	547	453	353	475	389	340	284	222
9 200	504	418	325	435	357	312	261	204
9 600	465	386	301	401	329	287	240	188
10 000	431	357	278	370	304	265	222	174
10 400	400	331	258	343	281	246	206	161
10 800	372	308	240	318	261	228	191	150
11 200	346	287	224	296	243	213	178	139
11 600	324	268	209			198	166	130
12 000	303	251	196					

Effective length (KL) in millimetres with respect to the least radius of gyration

PROPERTIES AND DESIGN DATA

Area (mm²)	5 240	4 250	3 250	6 680	5 210	4 430	3 610	2 760
Z (10^3 mm³)	330	271	210	342	275	237	196	152
S (10^3 mm³)	279	231	181	276	227	198	166	130
r (mm)	68.8	69.6	70.3	56.1	57.6	58.4	59.2	59.9
M_r (kN·m)	104	85.4	57.0	108	86.6	74.7	61.7	47.9

IMPERIAL SIZE AND MASS

Mass (lb./ft.)	27.6	22.4	17.1	35.2	27.5	23.4	19.0	14.6
Thickness (in.)	0.313	0.250	0.188	0.500	0.375	0.313	0.250	0.188
Size (in.)	7 x 7					6 x 6		

* Class 3 in bending

Designation (mm x mm x mm)	HSS 127 x 127					HSS 114 x 114		
	13	9.5	8.0	6.4	4.8	13	9.5	8.0
Mass (kg/m)	42.3	33.3	28.4	23.2	17.9	37.3	29.5	25.3
0	1 700	1 340	1 140	932	718	1 500	1 180	1 010
400	1 700	1 340	1 140	932	718	1 500	1 180	1 010
800	1 700	1 330	1 140	932	718	1 490	1 180	1 010
1 200	1 690	1 330	1 140	930	716	1 490	1 180	1 010
1 600	1 670	1 320	1 130	922	711	1 460	1 160	995
2 000	1 630	1 290	1 110	906	699	1 400	1 120	964
2 400	1 560	1 240	1 070	876	678	1 310	1 060	912
2 800	1 460	1 170	1 010	830	644	1 180	966	837
3 200	1 330	1 070	928	768	598	1 040	859	748
3 600	1 180	967	838	696	545	899	749	655
4 000	1 040	857	745	622	488	771	647	568
4 400	910	753	657	550	433	661	558	491
4 800	794	660	577	484	382	569	482	425
5 200	693	579	506	426	337	492	418	369
5 600	608	509	446	375	297	429	365	322
6 000	536	449	394	332	263	377	321	283
6 400	475	399	350	295	234	333	284	251
6 800	424	356	312	264	209	296	252	223
7 200	380	319	280	237	188	265	226	200
7 600	342	288	253	213	169	238	203	180
8 000	309	260	229	193	153	215	184	163
8 400	281	237	208	176	140		167	148
8 800	257	216	190	160	127			
9 200		198	174	147	117			
9 600			160	135	107			
10 000								
10 400								
10 800								
11 200								
11 600								
12 000								

Effective length (KL) in millimetres with respect to the least radius of gyration

PROPERTIES AND DESIGN DATA

Area (mm^2)	5 390	4 240	3 620	2 960	2 280	4 750	3 760	3 220
Z (10^3 mm^3)	225	183	159	132	103	175	144	126
S (10^3 mm^3)	177	149	132	111	88.1	136	116	103
r (mm)	45.7	47.3	48.0	48.8	49.6	40.5	42.1	42.8
M_r (kN·m)	70.9	57.6	50.1	41.6	32.4	55.1	45.4	39.7

IMPERIAL SIZE AND MASS

Mass (lb./ft.)	28.4	22.4	19.1	15.6	12.0	25.0	19.8	17.0
Thickness (in.)	0.500	0.375	0.313	0.250	0.188	0.500	0.375	0.313
Size (in.)	5 x 5					4½ x 4½		

Designation (mm x mm x mm)	HSS 114 x 114			HSS 102 x 102		
	6.4	4.8	3.2 *	13	9.5	8.0
Mass (kg/m)	20.7	16.0	10.9	32.2	25.7	22.1
0	832	643	438	1 290	1 030	888
400	832	643	438	1 290	1 030	888
800	831	642	438	1 290	1 030	887
1 200	827	640	436	1 280	1 020	880
1 600	817	632	431	1 240	996	859
2 000	794	616	421	1 160	941	815
2 400	753	586	402	1 040	856	745
2 800	695	543	374	894	750	657
3 200	624	490	339	755	642	565
3 600	550	434	301	633	543	480
4 000	478	379	264	531	458	407
4 400	414	330	230	449	389	345
4 800	359	286	200	382	332	295
5 200	313	250	175	329	286	255
5 600	274	219	153	285	248	221
6 000	241	192	135	249	217	194
6 400	213	170	120	220	192	171
6 800	190	152	107	195	170	152
7 200	170	136	95		152	136
7 600	153	122	86			
8 000	138	111	78			
8 400	126	101	71			
8 800		92	64			
9 200						
9 600						
10 000						
10 400						
10 800						
11 200						
11 600						
12 000						

Effective length (KL) in millimetres with respect to the least radius of gyration

PROPERTIES AND DESIGN DATA

Area (mm^2)	2 640	2 040	1 390	4 100	3 280	2 820
Z (10^3 mm^3)	105	82.7	57.4	131	110	96.8
S (10^3 mm^3)	87.8	70.1	49.5	100	87.6	78.5
r (mm)	43.6	44.4	45.1	35.3	36.9	37.6
M$_r$ (kN·m)	33.1	26.1	15.6	41.3	34.7	30.5

IMPERIAL SIZE AND MASS

Mass (lb./ft.)	13.9	10.7	7.32	21.6	17.3	14.9
Thickness (in.)	0.250	0.188	0.125	0.500	0.375	0.313
Size (in.)	4½ x 4½			4 x 4		

* Class 3 in bending

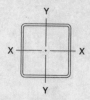

Designation (mm x mm x mm)	HSS 102 x 102			HSS 89 x 89				
	6.4	4.8	3.2	9.5	8.0	6.4	4.8	3.2
Mass (kg/m)	18.2	14.1	9.62	21.9	18.9	15.6	12.2	8.35
0	731	564	387	879	759	627	488	334
400	731	564	387	879	759	627	488	334
800	730	563	387	876	757	625	487	333
1 200	724	559	385	861	745	617	481	329
1 600	709	548	378	820	712	592	464	319
2 000	675	524	362	743	650	544	429	297
2 400	621	485	337	640	565	477	380	265
2 800	552	434	303	533	474	404	324	227
3 200	478	378	266	438	391	335	271	191
3 600	407	324	229	360	323	278	225	160
4 000	346	276	196	299	268	232	188	134
4 400	295	236	168	250	225	195	158	113
4 800	253	202	144	212	191	165	135	96
5 200	218	175	125	182	164	142	116	83
5 600	190	152	109	157	142	123	100	72
6 000	166	133	95	137	124	107	88	63
6 400	147	118	84		109	95	77	55
6 800	130	105	75				68	49
7 200	116	94	67					
7 600	105	84	60					
8 000			54					
8 400								
8 800								
9 200								
9 600								
10 000								
10 400								
10 800								
11 200								
11 600								
12 000								

Effective length (KL) in millimetres with respect to the least radius of gyration

PROPERTIES AND DESIGN DATA

Area (mm²)	2 320	1 790	1 230	2 790	2 410	1 990	1 550	1 060
Z (10³ mm³)	81.4	64.3	44.9	80.5	71.4	60.5	48.2	33.9
S (10³ mm³)	67.3	54.2	38.5	63.0	57.1	49.5	40.3	29.0
r (mm)	38.4	39.2	40.0	31.7	32.4	33.2	34.0	34.8
M_r (kN·m)	25.6	20.3	14.1	25.4	22.5	19.1	15.2	10.7

IMPERIAL SIZE AND MASS

Mass (lb./ft.)	12.2	9.46	6.47	14.7	12.7	10.5	8.17	5.61
Thickness (in.)	0.250	0.188	0.125	0.375	0.313	0.250	0.188	0.125
Size (in.)	4 x 4			3½ x 3½				

SQUARE HOLLOW SECTIONS
Factored Axial Compressive Resistances, C_r (kN)

Designation (mm x mm x mm)	HSS 76 x 76						HSS 64 x 64		
	9.5	8.0	6.4	4.8	3.2		6.4	4.8	3.2
Mass (kg/m)	18.1	15.8	13.1	10.3	7.09		10.6	8.35	5.82
0	728	633	526	413	284		425	334	233
400	727	633	526	413	284		425	334	233
800	722	629	523	411	283		419	330	231
1 200	696	609	508	400	277		392	311	219
1 600	631	557	469	372	259		332	268	192
2 000	531	474	405	325	229		260	214	156
2 400	426	384	332	270	192		198	164	121
2 800	337	306	266	218	157		152	127	94
3 200	268	244	213	176	127		119	99	74
3 600	216	197	173	143	103		95	79	59
4 000	177	162	142	117	85		77	65	48
4 400	147	135	118	98	71		64	54	40
4 800	124	114	100	83	60				34
5 200	106	97	85	71	51				
5 600			74	61	45				
6 000									
6 400									
6 800									
7 200									
7 600									
8 000									
8 400									
8 800									
9 200									
9 600									
10 000									
10 400									
10 800									
11 200									
11 600									
12 000									

Effective length (KL) in millimetres with respect to the least radius of gyration

PROPERTIES AND DESIGN DATA

Area (mm^2)	2 310	2 010	1 670	1 310	903		1 350	1 060	741
Z (10^3 mm^3)	55.5	49.8	42.8	34.4	24.5		28.1	23.0	16.6
S (10^3 mm^3)	42.4	39.1	34.5	28.5	20.7		22.2	18.7	13.9
r (mm)	26.5	27.2	28.0	28.8	29.6		22.8	23.6	24.4
M$_r$ (kN·m)	17.5	15.7	13.5	10.8	7.72		8.85	7.25	5.23

IMPERIAL SIZE AND MASS

Mass (lb./ft.)	12.2	10.6	8.81	6.89	4.76		7.11	5.61	3.91
Thickness (in.)	0.375	0.313	0.250	0.188	0.125		0.250	0.188	0.125
Size (in.)	3 x 3						2½ x 2½		

G40.21 350W CLASS H
$\phi = 0.90$

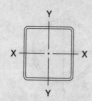

SQUARE HOLLOW SECTIONS
Factored Axial Compressive Resistances, C_r (kN)

Designation (mm x mm x mm)		HSS 51 x 51			HSS 38 x 38	
		6.4	4.8	3.2	4.8	3.2
Mass (kg/m)		8.05	6.45	4.55	4.54	3.28
Effective length (KL) in millimetres with respect to the least radius of gyration	0	324	259	183	182	132
	400	324	258	182	181	131
	800	310	249	177	158	117
	1 200	260	214	155	106	83
	1 600	189	160	119	67	53
	2 000	133	114	87	44	36
	2 400	96	83	63	31	25
	2 800	71	62	47		18
	3 200	55	48	37		
	3 600		38	29		
	4 000					
	4 400					
	4 800					
	5 200					
	5 600					
	6 000					
	6 400					
	6 800					
	7 200					
	7 600					
	8 000					
	8 400					
	8 800					
	9 200					
	9 600					
	10 000					
	10 400					
	10 800					
	11 200					
	11 600					
	12 000					

PROPERTIES AND DESIGN DATA

	HSS 51 x 51			HSS 38 x 38	
Area (mm^2)	1 030	821	580	578	418
Z (10^3 mm^3)	16.4	13.8	10.2	6.95	5.35
S (10^3 mm^3)	12.6	11.0	8.42	5.30	4.31
r (mm)	17.6	18.4	19.2	13.2	14.0
M$_r$ (kN·m)	5.17	4.35	3.21	2.19	1.69

IMPERIAL SIZE AND MASS

	HSS 51 x 51			HSS 38 x 38	
Mass (lb./ft.)	5.41	4.33	3.06	3.05	2.21
Thickness (in.)	0.250	0.188	0.125	0.188	0.125
Size (in.)	2 x 2			1½ x 1½	

ROUND HOLLOW SECTIONS
Factored Axial Compressive
Resistances, C$_r$ (kN)

G40.21 350W
CLASS H
$\phi = 0.90$

Designation (mm x mm)	HSS 406				HSS 356			HSS 324		
	13	9.5	6.4 *		13	9.5	6.4 *	13	9.5	6.4
Mass (kg/m)	123	93.3	62.6		107	81.3	54.7	97.5	73.9	49.7
0	4 950	3 750	2 510		4 320	3 280	2 200	3 910	2 960	1 990
400	4 950	3 750	2 510		4 320	3 280	2 200	3 910	2 960	1 990
800	4 950	3 750	2 510		4 320	3 280	2 200	3 910	2 960	1 990
1 200	4 950	3 750	2 510		4 320	3 280	2 200	3 910	2 960	1 990
1 600	4 950	3 750	2 510		4 310	3 280	2 200	3 900	2 960	1 990
2 000	4 940	3 750	2 510		4 310	3 270	2 190	3 900	2 960	1 990
2 400	4 940	3 750	2 510		4 310	3 270	2 190	3 900	2 960	1 990
2 800	4 940	3 740	2 510		4 310	3 270	2 190	3 890	2 950	1 990
3 200	4 930	3 740	2 510		4 300	3 260	2 190	3 880	2 950	1 980
3 600	4 930	3 730	2 500		4 290	3 250	2 180	3 860	2 930	1 970
4 000	4 920	3 730	2 500		4 270	3 240	2 170	3 840	2 920	1 960
4 400	4 900	3 720	2 490		4 240	3 220	2 160	3 810	2 890	1 950
4 800	4 880	3 700	2 480		4 210	3 200	2 150	3 760	2 860	1 930
5 200	4 850	3 680	2 470		4 170	3 170	2 120	3 700	2 820	1 900
5 600	4 820	3 650	2 450		4 110	3 130	2 100	3 630	2 770	1 860
6 000	4 770	3 620	2 430		4 050	3 080	2 070	3 550	2 700	1 820
6 400	4 720	3 580	2 400		3 970	3 020	2 030	3 450	2 630	1 780
6 800	4 650	3 530	2 370		3 870	2 950	1 980	3 340	2 550	1 720
7 200	4 580	3 480	2 340		3 770	2 880	1 930	3 220	2 460	1 660
7 600	4 490	3 410	2 290		3 660	2 790	1 880	3 090	2 360	1 600
8 000	4 390	3 340	2 250		3 530	2 700	1 820	2 960	2 260	1 530
8 400	4 290	3 260	2 200		3 400	2 600	1 750	2 820	2 160	1 470
8 800	4 170	3 170	2 140		3 270	2 500	1 690	2 680	2 050	1 400
9 200	4 050	3 080	2 080		3 130	2 390	1 620	2 540	1 950	1 330
9 600	3 920	2 990	2 010		2 990	2 290	1 550	2 410	1 850	1 260
10 000	3 780	2 880	1 950		2 850	2 180	1 480	2 280	1 750	1 190
10 400	3 640	2 780	1 880		2 710	2 080	1 410	2 150	1 650	1 130
10 800	3 500	2 680	1 810		2 580	1 980	1 340	2 030	1 560	1 070
11 200	3 360	2 570	1 740		2 450	1 880	1 280	1 920	1 480	1 010
11 600	3 230	2 470	1 670		2 330	1 790	1 210	1 810	1 400	953
12 000	3 090	2 360	1 600		2 210	1 700	1 150	1 710	1 320	902

Effective length (KL) in millimetres with respect to the least radius of gyration

PROPERTIES AND DESIGN DATA

	HSS 406				HSS 356			HSS 324		
Area (mm^2)	15 700	11 900	7 980		13 700	10 400	6 970	12 400	9 410	6 330
Z (10^3 mm^3)	1 970	1 500	1 020		1 490	1 140	775	1 230	942	640
S (10^3 mm^3)	1 500	1 150	786		1 130	873	598	930	719	493
r (mm)	139	140	141		121	122	123	110	111	112
M$_r$ (kN·m)	621	473	248		469	359	188	387	297	202

IMPERIAL SIZE AND MASS

	HSS 406				HSS 356			HSS 324		
Mass (lb./ft.)	82.9	62.7	42.1		72.2	54.7	36.8	65.5	49.7	33.4
Thickness (in.)	0.500	0.375	0.250		0.500	0.375	0.250	0.500	0.375	0.250
Size (in.)	16 OD				14 OD			12.75 OD		

* Class 3 in bending

Designation (mm x mm)	HSS 273				HSS 219			
	13	6.4	4.8 *		13	9.5	6.4	4.8
Mass (kg/m)	81.6	41.8	31.6		64.6	49.3	33.3	25.3
0	3 280	1 680	1 270		2 590	1 980	1 340	1 010
400	3 280	1 680	1 270		2 590	1 980	1 340	1 010
800	3 280	1 680	1 270		2 590	1 970	1 340	1 010
1 200	3 280	1 680	1 270		2 590	1 970	1 340	1 010
1 600	3 270	1 670	1 270		2 590	1 970	1 340	1 010
2 000	3 270	1 670	1 270		2 580	1 970	1 330	1 010
2 400	3 260	1 670	1 270		2 560	1 960	1 320	1 000
2 800	3 250	1 660	1 260		2 540	1 940	1 310	996
3 200	3 230	1 650	1 250		2 500	1 910	1 290	982
3 600	3 200	1 640	1 240		2 430	1 860	1 260	961
4 000	3 160	1 620	1 230		2 350	1 800	1 230	933
4 400	3 100	1 590	1 210		2 250	1 730	1 180	897
4 800	3 030	1 560	1 180		2 130	1 640	1 120	855
5 200	2 940	1 520	1 150		2 000	1 540	1 060	807
5 600	2 830	1 470	1 110		1 860	1 440	990	756
6 000	2 710	1 410	1 070		1 730	1 340	920	704
6 400	2 580	1 350	1 020		1 590	1 240	851	652
6 800	2 450	1 280	974		1 460	1 140	785	602
7 200	2 310	1 210	922		1 340	1 050	723	555
7 600	2 170	1 140	870		1 230	961	666	511
8 000	2 030	1 070	818		1 130	884	613	470
8 400	1 900	1 000	767		1 040	814	564	433
8 800	1 780	941	719		959	750	521	400
9 200	1 660	880	673		885	693	481	370
9 600	1 550	824	630		819	641	445	342
10 000	1 450	771	590		759	594	413	318
10 400	1 360	722	553		705	552	384	295
10 800	1 270	677	518		656	514	358	275
11 200	1 190	635	486		612	480	334	257
11 600	1 120	596	457		572	448	312	240
12 000	1 050	561	430		535	420	292	225

Effective length (KL) in millimetres with respect to the least radius of gyration

PROPERTIES AND DESIGN DATA								
Area (mm^2)	10 400	5 320	4 030		8 230	6 270	4 240	3 220
Z (10^3 mm^3)	862	452	344		542	419	288	220
S (10^3 mm^3)	646	347	266		402	315	219	169
r (mm)	92.2	94.3	94.9		73.1	74.2	75.3	75.8
M$_r$ (kN·m)	272	142	83.8		171	132	90.7	69.3

IMPERIAL SIZE AND MASS								
Mass (lb./ft.)	54.8	28.1	21.3		43.4	33.1	22.4	17.0
Thickness (in.)	0.500	0.250	0.188		0.500	0.375	0.250	0.188
Size (in.)	10.75 OD				8.625 OD			

* Class 3 in bending

ROUND HOLLOW SECTIONS
Factored Axial Compressive
Resistances, C$_r$ (kN)

G40.21 350W
CLASS H
$\phi = 0.90$

Designation (mm x mm)		HSS 178					HSS 168		
		13	9.5	8.0	6.4	4.8	13	9.5	8.0
Mass (kg/m)		51.7	39.5	33.3	26.8	20.4	48.7	37.3	31.4
Effective length (KL) in millimetres with respect to the least radius of gyration	0	2 080	1 590	1 340	1 080	819	1 960	1 500	1 260
	400	2 080	1 590	1 340	1 080	819	1 960	1 500	1 260
	800	2 080	1 590	1 340	1 080	819	1 960	1 500	1 260
	1 200	2 070	1 590	1 330	1 080	818	1 950	1 490	1 260
	1 600	2 070	1 580	1 330	1 070	816	1 940	1 490	1 250
	2 000	2 050	1 570	1 320	1 070	810	1 920	1 470	1 240
	2 400	2 020	1 550	1 300	1 050	800	1 890	1 450	1 220
	2 800	1 960	1 510	1 270	1 030	782	1 820	1 400	1 180
	3 200	1 880	1 450	1 220	991	756	1 730	1 340	1 130
	3 600	1 780	1 380	1 160	943	720	1 620	1 250	1 060
	4 000	1 660	1 290	1 090	884	676	1 490	1 150	982
	4 400	1 520	1 180	1 000	818	626	1 350	1 050	895
	4 800	1 380	1 080	918	749	574	1 210	948	809
	5 200	1 250	978	832	680	522	1 080	850	727
	5 600	1 120	882	751	615	473	967	761	651
	6 000	1 010	794	677	555	427	864	681	583
	6 400	907	715	610	500	386	773	610	523
	6 800	817	645	551	452	348	694	548	471
	7 200	738	584	498	409	316	625	494	425
	7 600	669	529	452	371	286	566	447	384
	8 000	608	481	411	338	261	513	406	349
	8 400	554	439	375	309	238	468	370	318
	8 800	507	402	344	283	218	428	339	291
	9 200	466	369	316	260	200	392	311	267
	9 600	429	340	291	239	185	361	286	246
	10 000	396	314	269	221	171	333	264	227
	10 400	367	291	249	205	158	309	245	210
	10 800	341	270	231	190	147	286	227	195
	11 200	317	252	215	177	137		211	182
	11 600	296	235	201	165	128			
	12 000			188	155	119			

PROPERTIES AND DESIGN DATA									
Area (mm^2)		6 590	5 040	4 240	3 420	2 600	6 210	4 750	4 000
Z (10^3 mm^3)		347	270	230	187	143	308	241	205
S (10^3 mm^3)		254	201	172	142	109	225	179	153
r (mm)		58.5	59.6	60.1	60.7	61.2	55.2	56.2	56.8
M$_r$ (kN·m)		109	85.1	72.5	58.9	45.0	97.0	75.9	64.6

IMPERIAL SIZE AND MASS									
Mass (lb./ft.)		34.7	26.6	22.4	18.0	13.7	32.7	25.1	21.1
Thickness (in.)		0.500	0.375	0.313	0.250	0.188	0.500	0.375	0.313
Size (in.)				7 OD				6.625 OD	

G40.21 350W CLASS H
$\phi = 0.90$

ROUND HOLLOW SECTIONS
Factored Axial Compressive Resistances, C_r (kN)

Designation (mm x mm)	HSS 168			HSS 152				
	6.4	4.8	3.2 *	9.5	8.0	6.4	4.8	3.2
Mass (kg/m)	25.4	19.3	12.9	33.6	28.3	22.9	17.4	11.7
0	1 020	775	520	1 350	1 140	917	699	469
400	1 020	775	520	1 350	1 140	917	699	469
800	1 020	775	520	1 350	1 140	916	699	469
1 200	1 020	774	519	1 340	1 130	915	698	468
1 600	1 010	771	517	1 340	1 130	909	694	466
2 000	1 000	764	513	1 320	1 110	896	685	460
2 400	986	752	505	1 280	1 080	873	667	449
2 800	957	731	491	1 220	1 030	835	640	431
3 200	916	700	472	1 140	965	784	601	406
3 600	862	660	445	1 040	886	721	554	375
4 000	798	613	414	937	799	652	503	341
4 400	730	561	380	834	713	583	451	307
4 800	661	509	345	739	632	518	401	273
5 200	594	458	312	653	559	459	356	243
5 600	533	411	280	577	495	407	316	216
6 000	478	369	252	512	440	362	281	192
6 400	429	332	226	456	392	322	250	171
6 800	386	299	204	408	350	289	224	154
7 200	348	270	184	366	315	259	202	138
7 600	315	244	167	331	284	234	182	125
8 000	287	222	152	299	257	212	165	113
8 400	261	202	138	272	234	193	150	103
8 800	239	185	127	249	214	176	137	94
9 200	219	170	116	228	196	162	126	86
9 600	202	156	107	210	180	149	116	79
10 000	187	144	99	194	166	137	107	73
10 400	173	134	92				99	68
10 800	160	124	85					
11 200	149	116	79					
11 600			74					
12 000								

Effective length (KL) in millimetres with respect to the least radius of gyration

PROPERTIES AND DESIGN DATA

Area (mm²)	3 230	2 460	1 650	4 280	3 610	2 910	2 220	1 490
Z (10^3 mm³)	167	128	86.7	195	166	136	104	70.8
S (10^3 mm³)	126	97.6	66.8	144	124	102	79.3	54.5
r (mm)	57.3	57.8	58.4	50.6	51.1	51.7	52.2	52.8
M_r (kN·m)	52.6	40.3	21.0	61.4	52.3	42.8	32.8	22.3

IMPERIAL SIZE AND MASS

Mass (lb./ft.)	17.0	13.0	8.70	22.6	19.0	15.4	11.7	7.86
Thickness (in.)	0.250	0.188	0.125	0.375	0.313	0.250	0.188	0.125
Size (in.)	6.625 OD			6 OD				

* Class 3 in bending

ROUND HOLLOW SECTIONS
Factored Axial Compressive Resistances, C_r (kN)

Designation (mm x mm)		HSS 141			HSS 127					
		9.5	6.4	4.8	13	9.5	8.0	6.4	4.8	3.2
Mass (kg/m)		31.0	21.1	16.1	35.8	27.6	23.3	18.9	14.4	9.71
Effective length (KL) in millimetres with respect to the least radius of gyration	0	1 240	847	646	1 440	1 110	936	759	580	391
	400	1 240	847	646	1 440	1 110	936	759	580	391
	800	1 240	847	645	1 430	1 110	935	758	579	390
	1 200	1 240	845	644	1 430	1 100	930	755	577	389
	1 600	1 230	837	639	1 400	1 090	917	745	569	384
	2 000	1 200	821	627	1 350	1 050	887	722	552	373
	2 400	1 150	792	605	1 260	985	836	682	523	354
	2 800	1 080	746	572	1 140	898	764	625	481	327
	3 200	991	687	528	1 000	796	680	558	431	294
	3 600	889	620	477	869	693	594	489	379	260
	4 000	785	551	425	746	598	513	424	329	226
	4 400	689	485	375	640	514	443	366	285	196
	4 800	602	426	330	551	444	382	317	247	170
	5 200	527	374	290	477	385	332	275	214	148
	5 600	463	329	255	416	336	290	240	187	130
	6 000	409	291	226	365	295	255	211	165	114
	6 400	363	258	201	322	261	225	187	146	101
	6 800	324	230	179	287	232	200	166	130	90
	7 200	290	207	161	256	208	179	149	116	80
	7 600	261	186	145	231	187	161	134	105	72
	8 000	237	169	131	208	169	146	121	95	65
	8 400	215	153	119			132	110	86	59
	8 800	196	140	109						
	9 200	180	128	100						
	9 600			92						
	10 000									
	10 400									
	10 800									
	11 200									
	11 600									
	12 000									

PROPERTIES AND DESIGN DATA

Area (mm²)		3 950	2 690	2 050	4 560	3 520	2 970	2 410	1 840	1 240
Z (10^3 mm³)		166	116	89.1	167	132	113	92.5	71.4	48.8
S (10^3 mm³)		122	86.9	67.7	119	96.2	83.3	69.2	54.1	37.4
r (mm)		46.7	47.8	48.3	40.7	41.7	42.2	42.7	43.2	43.8
M_r (kN·m)		52.3	36.5	28.1	52.6	41.6	35.6	29.1	22.5	15.4

IMPERIAL SIZE AND MASS

Mass (lb./ft.)		20.8	14.2	10.8	24.1	18.6	15.7	12.7	9.68	6.53
Thickness (in.)		0.375	0.250	0.188	0.500	0.375	0.313	0.250	0.188	0.125
Size (in.)			5.563 OD				5 OD			

G40.21 350W
CLASS H
$\phi = 0.90$

Designation (mm x mm)	HSS 114			HSS 102			
	9.5	4.8	3.2	8.0	6.4	4.8	3.2
Mass (kg/m)	24.6	12.9	8.71	18.4	14.9	11.4	7.72
Effective length (KL) in millimetres with respect to the least radius of gyration							
0	989	517	350	737	599	457	310
400	989	517	350	737	598	457	310
800	987	516	349	735	597	456	309
1 200	979	512	347	725	589	456	309
1 600	955	502	340	696	568	450	306
2 000	904	479	325	640	525	403	275
2 400	824	442	301	561	463	358	245
2 800	724	394	270	475	394	306	211
3 200	621	342	235	394	329	256	178
3 600	526	292	202	327	273	214	148
4 000	445	249	172	272	228	179	124
4 400	377	212	147	229	192	151	105
4 800	323	182	126	194	163	128	89
5 200	278	157	109	167	140	110	77
5 600	241	137	95	144	121	95	66
6 000	211	120	83	126	106	83	58
6 400	186	106	73	111	93	73	51
6 800	166	94	65			65	45
7 200	148	84	58				
7 600		75	52				
8 000							
8 400							
8 800							
9 200							
9 600							
10 000							
10 400							
10 800							
11 200							
11 600							
12 000							

PROPERTIES AND DESIGN DATA

Area (mm²)	3 140	1 640	1 110	2 340	1 900	1 450	983
Z (10³ mm³)	105	57.4	39.3	69.9	57.7	44.8	30.8
S (10³ mm³)	75.9	43.2	30.0	50.8	42.6	33.6	23.5
r (mm)	37.2	38.8	39.3	33.2	33.8	34.3	34.8
M_r (kN·m)	33.1	18.1	12.4	22.0	18.2	14.1	9.70

IMPERIAL SIZE AND MASS

Mass (lb./ft.)	16.5	8.68	5.86	12.3	10.0	7.67	5.19
Thickness (in.)	0.375	0.188	0.125	0.313	0.250	0.188	0.125
Size (in.)	4.5 OD			4 OD			

ROUND HOLLOW SECTIONS
Factored Axial Compressive Resistances, C_r (kN)

G40.21 350W
CLASS H
$\phi = 0.90$

Designation (mm x mm)		HSS 89			HSS 76		HSS 73		
		6.4	4.8	3.2	6.4	4.8	6.4	4.8	3.2
Mass (kg/m)		12.9	9.92	6.72	10.9	8.42	10.4	8.04	5.48
	0	520	397	270	438	337	419	321	220
	400	520	397	270	438	337	419	321	220
	800	517	395	269	433	334	414	318	218
	1 200	505	386	263	413	319	390	301	207
	1 600	472	363	248	365	284	338	263	183
	2 000	415	321	221	298	234	270	212	149
	2 400	347	270	187	233	185	208	165	116
	2 800	282	221	153	181	144	160	127	90
	3 200	228	179	125	143	114	126	100	71
	3 600	185	146	102	115	92	101	80	57
	4 000	153	120	84	94	75	82	65	47
	4 400	127	101	70	78	62	68	54	39
	4 800	108	85	60	65	52		46	33
	5 200	92	73	51					
	5 600	80	63	44					
	6 000			39					
	6 400								
	6 800								
	7 200								
	7 600								
	8 000								
	8 400								
	8 800								
	9 200								
	9 600								
	10 000								
	10 400								
	10 800								
	11 200								
	11 600								
	12 000								

Effective length (KL) in millimetres with respect to the least radius of gyration

PROPERTIES AND DESIGN DATA

Area (mm²)		1 650	1 260	856	1 390	1 070	1 330	1 020	698
Z (10^3 mm³)		43.4	33.9	23.4	31.1	24.4	28.3	22.3	15.5
S (10^3 mm³)		31.7	25.2	17.7	22.5	18.0	20.4	16.4	11.7
r (mm)		29.3	29.8	30.3	24.8	25.3	23.7	24.2	24.7
M_r (kN·m)		13.7	10.7	7.37	9.80	7.69	8.91	7.02	4.88

IMPERIAL SIZE AND MASS

Mass (lb./ft.)		8.69	6.66	4.52	7.35	5.66	7.01	5.40	3.68
Thickness (in.)		0.250	0.188	0.125	0.250	0.188	0.250	0.188	0.125
Size (in.)		3.5 OD			3 OD		2.875 OD		

G40.21 350W
CLASS H
φ = 0.90

Designation (mm x mm)	HSS 64			HSS 60			HSS 48	
	6.4	4.8	3.2	6.4	4.8	3.2	4.8	3.2
Mass (kg/m)	8.95	6.92	4.73	8.45	6.54	4.48	5.13	3.54
0	359	278	190	340	263	180	206	142
400	359	278	190	340	262	180	205	142
800	351	272	186	330	256	175	191	133
1 200	315	247	171	289	227	157	146	104
1 600	250	199	140	222	177	125	99	72
2 000	186	149	106	161	130	92	67	49
2 400	137	111	80	118	95	68	48	35
2 800	103	84	60	88	72	51	35	26
3 200	80	65	47	68	55	40		20
3 600	64	52	37	54	44	32		
4 000	52	42	30			26		
4 400								
4 800								
5 200								
5 600								
6 000								
6 400								
6 800								
7 200								
7 600								
8 000								
8 400								
8 800								
9 200								
9 600								
10 000								
10 400								
10 800								
11 200								
11 600								
12 000								

Effective length (KL) in millimetres with respect to the least radius of gyration

PROPERTIES AND DESIGN DATA

	HSS 64			HSS 60			HSS 48	
Area (mm²)	1 140	882	603	1 080	834	571	654	451
Z (10³ mm³)	20.8	16.5	11.6	18.6	14.8	10.4	9.09	6.48
S (10³ mm³)	14.8	12.0	8.66	13.2	10.7	7.74	6.48	4.77
r (mm)	20.3	20.8	21.4	19.2	19.7	20.2	15.5	16.0
M_r (kN·m)	6.55	5.20	3.65	5.86	4.66	3.28	2.86	2.04

IMPERIAL SIZE AND MASS

	HSS 64			HSS 60			HSS 48	
Mass (lb./ft.)	6.01	4.65	3.18	5.68	4.40	3.01	3.45	2.38
Thickness (in.)	0.250	0.188	0.125	0.250	0.188	0.125	0.188	0.125
Size (in.)	2.5 OD			2.375 OD			1.9 OD	

Hollow Structural Sections

ASTM A500 Grade C

For rectangular hollow sections, see page 4-91.

For square hollow sections, see page 4-98.

For round hollow sections, see page 4-106.

ASTM A500 Grade C
F_y = 345 MPa

RECTANGULAR HOLLOW SECTIONS
Factored Axial Compressive Resistances, C_r (kN) ϕ = 0.90

Designation (mm x mm x mm)		HSS 356 x 254			HSS 305 x 203				
		16	13	9.5 **	16	13	9.5 *	8.0 **	6.4 **
Mass (kg/m)		139	113	86.5	114	93.0	71.3	60.1	48.6
	0	5 000	4 070	3 030	4 100	3 350	2 560	2 070	1 470
	400	5 000	4 070	3 030	4 100	3 350	2 550	2 070	1 470
	800	4 990	4 060	3 030	4 090	3 340	2 550	2 070	1 460
	1 200	4 970	4 050	3 020	4 060	3 320	2 530	2 050	1 450
	1 600	4 940	4 020	3 000	4 020	3 290	2 510	2 030	1 440
	2 000	4 900	3 990	2 980	3 950	3 240	2 470	2 000	1 420
	2 400	4 840	3 940	2 940	3 860	3 170	2 420	1 960	1 390
	2 800	4 760	3 880	2 900	3 750	3 080	2 360	1 910	1 360
	3 200	4 670	3 810	2 840	3 630	2 980	2 280	1 850	1 320
	3 600	4 550	3 720	2 780	3 480	2 870	2 200	1 790	1 270
	4 000	4 430	3 620	2 710	3 320	2 740	2 100	1 710	1 220
	4 400	4 290	3 510	2 630	3 160	2 610	2 000	1 630	1 160
	4 800	4 140	3 400	2 540	2 990	2 470	1 900	1 550	1 100
	5 200	3 980	3 270	2 450	2 810	2 330	1 800	1 470	1 040
	5 600	3 820	3 140	2 360	2 640	2 190	1 690	1 380	986
	6 000	3 650	3 010	2 260	2 480	2 060	1 590	1 300	928
	6 400	3 480	2 880	2 160	2 320	1 930	1 500	1 220	872
	6 800	3 320	2 740	2 060	2 170	1 810	1 400	1 150	819
	7 200	3 150	2 610	1 970	2 030	1 690	1 310	1 080	768
	7 600	3 000	2 480	1 870	1 900	1 580	1 230	1 010	720
	8 000	2 840	2 360	1 780	1 770	1 480	1 150	944	675
	8 400	2 690	2 240	1 690	1 660	1 390	1 080	885	633
	8 800	2 550	2 130	1 600	1 550	1 300	1 010	830	593
	9 200	2 420	2 020	1 520	1 450	1 220	948	778	557
	9 600	2 290	1 910	1 440	1 360	1 140	890	731	523
	10 000	2 170	1 810	1 370	1 280	1 070	836	687	492
	10 400	2 060	1 720	1 300	1 200	1 010	786	646	462
	10 800	1 950	1 630	1 230	1 130	946	740	608	435
	11 200	1 850	1 550	1 170	1 060	891	697	573	411
	11 600	1 760	1 470	1 110	1 000	840	658	541	387
	12 000	1 670	1 400	1 060	943	793	621	511	366

(Left axis label: Effective length (KL) in millimetres with respect to the least radius of gyration)

PROPERTIES AND DESIGN DATA

	HSS 356 x 254			HSS 305 x 203				
Area (mm^2)	16 100	13 100	9 970	13 200	10 800	8 230	6 930	5 590
Z_x (10^3 mm^3)	1 910	1 570	1 210	1 310	1 090	843	715	581
S_x (10^3 mm^3)	1 570	1 300	1 020	1 060	886	697	595	486
r_x (mm)	132	133	135	111	112	114	114	115
Z_y (10^3 mm^3)	1 520	1 250	965	989	821	638	542	441
S_y (10^3 mm^3)	1 300	1 090	826	841	709	560	454	309
r_y (mm)	101	103	104	80.5	81.8	83.1	83.8	84.4
r_x / r_y	1.31	1.29	1.30	1.38	1.37	1.37	1.36	1.36
M_{rx} (kN·m)	593	487	376	407	338	262	222	151
M_{ry} (kN·m)	472	388	257	307	255	174	141	95.9

IMPERIAL SIZE AND MASS

	HSS 356 x 254			HSS 305 x 203				
Mass (lb./ft.)	93.4	76.1	58.1	76.4	62.5	47.9	40.4	32.6
Thickness† (in.)	0.563	0.450	0.338	0.563	0.450	0.338	0.282	0.225
Size (in.)	14 x 10			12 x 8				

* Class 3 in bending about Y-Y axis

** Class 4: C_r calculated according to S16-09 Clause 13.3.5; S_y and M_{ry} according to Clause 13.5(c).

† Design wall thickness

RECTANGULAR HOLLOW SECTIONS
Factored Axial Compressive Resistances, C_r (kN) $\phi = 0.90$

ASTM A500
Grade C
$F_y = 345$ MPa

Designation (mm x mm x mm)		HSS 254 x 152					HSS 203 x 152				
		16	13	9.5	8.0 *	6.4 **	13	9.5	8.0	6.4 *	4.8 **
Mass (kg/m)		88.3	72.7	56.1	47.5	38.4	62.6	48.5	41.1	33.4	25.5
Effective length (KL) in millimetres with respect to the least radius of gyration	0	3 200	2 620	2 020	1 700	1 290	2 260	1 750	1 470	1 200	830
	400	3 190	2 610	2 010	1 700	1 290	2 250	1 740	1 470	1 190	830
	800	3 180	2 600	2 000	1 690	1 280	2 240	1 730	1 460	1 190	825
	1 200	3 130	2 570	1 980	1 670	1 260	2 210	1 710	1 450	1 170	815
	1 600	3 060	2 510	1 940	1 640	1 240	2 160	1 670	1 410	1 150	798
	2 000	2 950	2 430	1 870	1 590	1 200	2 080	1 620	1 370	1 110	773
	2 400	2 820	2 320	1 800	1 520	1 160	1 980	1 540	1 310	1 060	742
	2 800	2 660	2 200	1 710	1 450	1 100	1 870	1 460	1 240	1 010	704
	3 200	2 490	2 060	1 600	1 360	1 040	1 750	1 370	1 160	949	663
	3 600	2 310	1 920	1 500	1 270	969	1 620	1 270	1 080	885	619
	4 000	2 130	1 770	1 390	1 180	900	1 490	1 180	1 000	819	574
	4 400	1 950	1 630	1 280	1 090	832	1 370	1 080	922	755	529
	4 800	1 790	1 490	1 180	1 000	767	1 250	990	846	694	487
	5 200	1 630	1 370	1 080	922	705	1 140	906	774	636	447
	5 600	1 490	1 250	987	845	647	1 040	827	708	582	409
	6 000	1 360	1 140	904	775	593	947	756	648	533	375
	6 400	1 240	1 040	828	710	545	865	691	593	488	344
	6 800	1 130	957	760	652	500	791	633	543	448	315
	7 200	1 040	878	698	599	460	724	581	498	411	290
	7 600	955	807	642	552	424	665	533	458	378	267
	8 000	878	743	592	509	391	611	491	422	348	246
	8 400	810	685	546	470	361	563	453	389	322	227
	8 800	748	634	506	435	334	521	419	360	297	210
	9 200	693	587	469	403	310	482	388	334	276	195
	9 600	643	545	435	375	288	447	360	310	256	181
	10 000	598	507	405	349	269	416	335	288	238	168
	10 400	557	473	378	326	251	387	312	269	222	157
	10 800	520	442	353	304	234	362	292	251	208	147
	11 200	487	413	331	285	219	338	273	235	194	137
	11 600	456	387	310	267	206	317	256	220	182	129
	12 000		364	291	251	193		240	207	171	121

PROPERTIES AND DESIGN DATA

Area (mm^2)		10 300	8 430	6 490	5 480	4 430	7 270	5 620	4 750	3 850	2 940
Z_x (10^3 mm^3)		820	686	538	458	374	486	384	328	269	207
S_x (10^3 mm^3)		644	548	436	375	308	393	316	272	225	175
r_x (mm)		89.2	90.8	92.4	93.2	94.0	74.1	75.6	76.3	77.1	77.8
Z_y (10^3 mm^3)		572	480	378	322	263	398	315	270	221	170
S_y (10^3 mm^3)		478	410	329	283	214	334	269	233	193	132
r_y (mm)		59.6	60.8	62.1	62.8	63.4	59.1	60.5	61.1	61.8	62.4
r_x / r_y		1.50	1.49	1.49	1.48	1.48	1.25	1.25	1.25	1.25	1.25
M_{rx} (kN·m)		255	213	167	142	116	151	119	102	83.5	54.3
M_{ry} (kN·m)		178	149	117	87.9	66.3	124	97.8	83.8	59.9	40.9

IMPERIAL SIZE AND MASS

Mass (lb./ft.)		59.3	48.9	37.7	31.9	25.8	42.1	32.6	27.6	22.4	17.1
Thickness† (in.)		0.563	0.450	0.338	0.282	0.225	0.450	0.338	0.282	0.225	0.169
Size (in.)		10 x 6					8 x 6				

* Class 3 in bending about Y-Y axis

** Class 4: C_r calculated according to S16-09 Clause 13.3.5; S_y and M_{ry} according to Clause 13.5(c).

† Design wall thickness

Designation (mm x mm x mm)	HSS 203 x 102					HSS 178 x 127				
	13	9.5	8.0	6.4 *	4.8 **	13	9.5	8.0	6.4	4.8 **
Mass (kg/m)	52.4	40.9	34.8	28.3	21.7	52.4	40.9	34.8	28.3	21.7
0	1 900	1 470	1 250	1 020	694	1 900	1 470	1 250	1 020	762
400	1 890	1 470	1 250	1 010	692	1 890	1 470	1 250	1 010	760
800	1 860	1 440	1 230	997	682	1 870	1 450	1 240	1 000	754
1 200	1 780	1 390	1 190	964	660	1 830	1 420	1 210	984	739
1 600	1 670	1 310	1 120	911	625	1 760	1 370	1 170	950	714
2 000	1 530	1 200	1 030	842	579	1 660	1 300	1 110	904	680
2 400	1 370	1 090	932	763	527	1 540	1 210	1 040	847	639
2 800	1 210	965	831	682	472	1 420	1 120	958	784	592
3 200	1 060	850	733	604	419	1 280	1 020	875	717	543
3 600	923	745	644	532	370	1 160	920	793	651	493
4 000	805	652	565	467	326	1 040	828	714	588	446
4 400	703	571	496	411	287	927	743	642	529	402
4 800	616	502	437	362	253	829	666	576	476	362
5 200	542	443	386	320	224	742	597	518	428	326
5 600	480	393	342	284	199	665	537	466	386	294
6 000	426	350	305	253	178	598	483	420	348	266
6 400	381	313	273	227	159	539	437	380	315	240
6 800	342	281	245	204	143	488	395	344	286	218
7 200	308	254	221	184	130	443	359	313	260	199
7 600	279	230	201	167	118	403	328	285	237	199
8 000		209	183	152	107	368	299	261	217	181
8 400				139	98	338	275	239	199	166
8 800						310	252	220	183	152
9 200						286	233	203	169	140
9 600						264	215	188	156	129
10 000							200	174	145	120
10 400										111
10 800										103
11 200										
11 600										
12 000										

Effective length (KL) in millimetres with respect to the least radius of gyration

PROPERTIES AND DESIGN DATA

Area (mm^2)	6 110	4 740	4 030	3 270	2 500	6 110	4 740	4 030	3 270	2 500
Z_x (10^3 mm^3)	375	299	257	211	164	350	278	239	197	152
S_x (10^3 mm^3)	288	235	204	169	132	278	226	196	163	127
r_x (mm)	69.2	70.9	71.7	72.5	73.3	63.6	65.1	65.8	66.6	67.3
Z_y (10^3 mm^3)	228	183	158	130	101	276	221	190	156	121
S_y (10^3 mm^3)	190	157	137	115	78.2	228	187	163	136	104
r_y (mm)	39.7	41.0	41.6	42.2	42.9	48.7	50.0	50.7	51.4	52.0
r_x / r_y	1.74	1.73	1.72	1.72	1.71	1.31	1.30	1.30	1.30	1.29
M_{rx} (kN·m)	116	92.8	79.8	65.5	50.9	109	86.3	74.2	61.2	47.2
M_{ry} (kN·m)	70.8	56.8	49.1	35.7	24.3	85.7	68.6	59.0	48.4	32.2

IMPERIAL SIZE AND MASS

Mass (lb./ft.)	35.2	27.5	23.4	19.0	14.6	35.2	27.5	23.4	19.0	14.6
Thickness† (in.)	0.450	0.338	0.282	0.225	0.169	0.450	0.338	0.282	0.225	0.169
Size (in.)	8 x 4					7 x 5				

* Class 3 in bending about Y-Y axis

** Class 4: C_r calculated according to S16-09 Clause 13.3.5; S_y and M_{ry} according to Clause 13.5(c).

† Design wall thickness

RECTANGULAR HOLLOW SECTIONS

Factored Axial Compressive Resistances, C_r (kN) $\phi = 0.90$

ASTM A500 Grade C
$F_y = 345$ MPa

Designation (mm x mm x mm)	HSS 152 x 102					HSS 152 x 76				
	13	9.5	8.0	6.4	4.8 *	13	9.5	8.0	6.4	4.8 *
Mass (kg/m)	42.3	33.3	28.4	23.2	17.9	37.3	29.5	25.3	20.7	16.0
0	1 540	1 200	1 020	835	640	1 360	1 070	910	745	574
400	1 530	1 200	1 020	833	638	1 350	1 060	904	740	571
800	1 500	1 180	1 000	819	628	1 290	1 020	872	715	553
1 200	1 440	1 130	966	789	606	1 180	941	807	664	515
1 600	1 340	1 060	907	743	571	1 030	831	716	593	462
2 000	1 210	967	831	683	527	869	711	616	512	402
2 400	1 080	866	747	615	476	721	596	519	434	342
2 800	947	764	662	547	425	595	497	434	364	289
3 200	824	669	581	481	375	493	414	363	306	243
3 600	715	583	508	421	329	411	347	305	257	205
4 000	620	508	444	369	289	346	293	258	218	174
4 400	540	443	388	323	254	294	250	220	186	149
4 800	472	389	341	284	223	252	215	189	161	129
5 200	414	342	300	250	197	218	186	164	139	112
5 600	366	303	266	222	175	190	163	144	122	98
6 000	324	269	236	198	156			126	107	86
6 400	289	240	211	177	139					
6 800	260	216	190	159	125					
7 200	234	194	171	143	113					
7 600	212	176	155	130	103					
8 000			141	118	93					
8 400										
8 800										
9 200										
9 600										
10 000										
10 400										
10 800										
11 200										
11 600										
12 000										

Effective length (KL) in millimetres with respect to the least radius of gyration

PROPERTIES AND DESIGN DATA

Area (mm^2)	4 950	3 870	3 300	2 690	2 060	4 370	3 440	2 930	2 400	1 850
Z_x (10^3 mm^3)	235	190	164	136	106	194	158	138	114	89.4
S_x (10^3 mm^3)	182	151	132	111	87.3	144	121	107	90.3	71.6
r_x (mm)	52.9	54.5	55.3	56.0	56.8	50.1	51.9	52.7	53.6	54.4
Z_y (10^3 mm^3)	176	143	124	103	80.0	117	96.4	84.1	70.3	55.2
S_y (10^3 mm^3)	143	120	105	88.6	70.1	93.2	80.0	71.2	60.7	48.6
r_y (mm)	38.3	39.6	40.3	40.9	41.6	28.5	29.8	30.4	31.0	31.7
r_x / r_y	1.38	1.38	1.37	1.37	1.37	1.76	1.74	1.73	1.73	1.72
M_{rx} (kN·m)	73.0	59.0	50.9	42.2	32.9	60.2	49.1	42.8	35.4	27.8
M_{ry} (kN·m)	54.6	44.4	38.5	32.0	21.8	36.3	29.9	26.1	21.8	15.1

IMPERIAL SIZE AND MASS

Mass (lb./ft.)	28.4	22.4	19.1	15.6	12.0	25.0	19.8	17.0	13.9	10.7
Thickness[†] (in.)	0.450	0.338	0.282	0.225	0.169	0.450	0.338	0.282	0.225	0.169
Size (in.)	6 x 4					6 x 3				

* Class 3 in bending about Y-Y axis

[†] Design wall thickness

ASTM A500 Grade C
$F_y = 345$ MPa

RECTANGULAR HOLLOW SECTIONS
Factored Axial Compressive Resistances, C_r (kN) $\phi = 0.90$

Designation (mm x mm x mm)	HSS 127 x 76				HSS 102 x 76				
	9.5	8.0	6.4	4.8	9.5	8.0	6.4	4.8	3.2 *
Mass (kg/m)	25.7	22.1	18.2	14.1	21.9	18.9	15.6	12.2	8.35
0	932	798	655	506	798	686	565	438	299
400	924	792	651	503	791	681	561	435	297
800	888	763	628	486	758	654	540	419	287
1 200	815	703	581	452	690	599	497	387	267
1 600	715	621	516	403	601	525	438	343	238
2 000	607	531	443	349	506	445	374	295	205
2 400	507	446	374	296	419	370	313	248	174
2 800	420	371	313	248	345	307	261	207	146
3 200	349	310	261	209	285	255	217	173	122
3 600	292	259	220	176	238	213	182	145	103
4 000	246	219	186	149	200	179	153	123	87
4 400	209	187	159	127	170	152	131	105	74
4 800	180	160	136	110	145	131	112	90	64
5 200	155	139	118	95	126	113	97	78	56
5 600	136	121	103	83	110	99	85	68	49
6 000			91	73				60	43
6 400									
6 800									
7 200									
7 600									
8 000									
8 400									
8 800									
9 200									
9 600									
10 000									
10 400									
10 800									
11 200									
11 600									
12 000									

Effective length (KL) in millimetres with respect to the least radius of gyration

PROPERTIES AND DESIGN DATA

Area (mm²)	3 000	2 570	2 110	1 630	2 570	2 210	1 820	1 410	964
Z_x (10^3 mm³)	117	103	85.7	67.4	82.1	72.2	60.8	48.1	33.6
S_x (10^3 mm³)	90.7	80.6	68.5	54.7	63.8	57.2	49.1	39.6	28.2
r_x (mm)	43.8	44.6	45.4	46.2	35.5	36.3	37.0	37.8	38.5
Z_y (10^3 mm³)	81.7	71.6	60.0	47.3	67.0	59.0	49.8	39.5	27.6
S_y (10^3 mm³)	66.9	59.8	51.2	41.2	53.7	48.4	41.7	33.8	24.1
r_y (mm)	29.1	29.8	30.4	31.1	28.2	28.9	29.6	30.2	30.9
r_x / r_y	1.51	1.50	1.49	1.49	1.26	1.26	1.25	1.25	1.25
M_{rx} (kN·m)	36.3	32.0	26.6	20.9	25.5	22.4	18.9	14.9	10.4
M_{ry} (kN·m)	25.4	22.2	18.6	14.7	20.8	18.3	15.5	12.3	7.48

IMPERIAL SIZE AND MASS

Mass (lb./ft.)	17.3	14.9	12.2	9.46	14.7	12.7	10.5	8.17	5.61
Thickness† (in.)	0.338	0.282	0.225	0.169	0.338	0.282	0.225	0.169	0.113
Size (in.)	5 x 3				4 x 3				

* Class 3 in bending about Y-Y axis

† Design wall thickness

RECTANGULAR HOLLOW SECTIONS
Factored Axial Compressive
Resistances, C$_r$ (kN) $\phi = 0.90$

ASTM A500
Grade C
F$_y$ = 345 MPa

Designation (mm x mm x mm)		HSS 102 x 51					HSS 89 x 64			
		9.5	8.0	6.4	4.8	3.2 *	8.0	6.4	4.8	3.2
Mass (kg/m)		18.1	15.8	13.1	10.3	7.09	15.8	13.1	10.3	7.09
Effective length (KL) in millimetres with respect to the least radius of gyration	0	661	571	475	369	254	571	475	369	254
	400	645	558	465	362	249	564	469	365	251
	800	570	498	419	329	228	527	441	344	238
	1 200	455	402	343	273	191	459	387	305	212
	1 600	343	307	266	213	151	378	322	256	179
	2 000	256	231	202	164	117	303	260	208	147
	2 400	194	176	155	126	91	241	208	167	119
	2 800	150	137	121	99	71	192	167	135	96
	3 200	118	108	96	79	57	155	136	110	79
	3 600	95	87	78	64	46	127	111	90	65
	4 000				52	38	106	93	75	54
	4 400						89	78	63	46
	4 800							66	54	39
	5 200									
	5 600									
	6 000									
	6 400									
	6 800									
	7 200									
	7 600									
	8 000									
	8 400									
	8 800									
	9 200									
	9 600									
	10 000									
	10 400									
	10 800									
	11 200									
	11 600									
	12 000									

PROPERTIES AND DESIGN DATA

Area (mm^2)		2 130	1 840	1 530	1 190	818	1 840	1 530	1 190	818
Z$_x$ (10^3 mm^3)		61.8	55.1	46.9	37.5	26.4	51.4	43.7	34.9	24.6
S$_x$ (10^3 mm^3)		45.2	41.2	36.0	29.4	21.2	39.9	34.7	28.3	20.4
r$_x$ (mm)		32.8	33.7	34.6	35.4	36.3	31.0	31.8	32.5	33.3
Z$_y$ (10^3 mm^3)		37.1	33.3	28.6	23.0	16.3	40.5	34.5	27.6	19.5
S$_y$ (10^3 mm^3)		29.0	26.8	23.7	19.6	14.4	32.6	28.6	23.4	17.0
r$_y$ (mm)		18.6	19.2	19.9	20.5	21.1	23.7	24.4	25.0	25.7
r$_x$ / r$_y$		1.76	1.76	1.74	1.73	1.72	1.31	1.30	1.30	1.30
M$_{rx}$ (kN·m)		19.2	17.1	14.6	11.6	8.20	16.0	13.6	10.8	7.64
M$_{ry}$ (kN·m)		11.5	10.3	8.88	7.14	4.47	12.6	10.7	8.57	6.05

IMPERIAL SIZE AND MASS

Mass (lb./ft.)		12.2	10.6	8.81	6.89	4.76	10.6	8.81	6.89	4.76
Thickness[†] (in.)		0.338	0.282	0.225	0.169	0.113	0.282	0.225	0.169	0.113
Size (in.)			4 x 2					3½ x 2½		

* Class 3 in bending about Y-Y axis

[†] Design wall thickness

RECTANGULAR HOLLOW SECTIONS
Factored Axial Compressive Resistances, C_r (kN) $\phi = 0.90$

Designation (mm x mm x mm)		HSS 76 x 51				HSS 51 x 25	
		8.0	6.4	4.8	3.2	4.8	3.2
Mass (kg/m)		12.6	10.6	8.35	5.82	4.54	3.28
	0	460	385	301	209	166	119
	400	448	376	295	205	143	104
	800	395	335	265	186	86	66
	1 200	314	270	217	154	48	38
	1 600	237	206	168	121	30	24
	2 000	177	155	127	93		
	2 400	133	118	98	71		
	2 800	103	91	76	56		
	3 200	81	72	60	44		
	3 600	66	58	49	36		
	4 000				30		
	4 400						
	4 800						
	5 200						
	5 600						
	6 000						
	6 400						
	6 800						
	7 200						
	7 600						
	8 000						
	8 400						
	8 800						
	9 200						
	9 600						
	10 000						
	10 400						
	10 800						
	11 200						
	11 600						
	12 000						

Effective length (KL) in millimetres with respect to the least radius of gyration

PROPERTIES AND DESIGN DATA

	8.0	6.4	4.8	3.2	4.8	3.2
Area (mm^2)	1 480	1 240	971	673	534	382
Z_x (10^3 mm^3)	34.0	29.3	23.8	17.0	7.74	5.87
S_x (10^3 mm^3)	25.6	22.7	18.9	13.9	5.65	4.50
r_x (mm)	25.7	26.5	27.2	28.0	16.4	17.3
Z_y (10^3 mm^3)	25.4	22.0	17.9	12.8	4.65	3.57
S_y (10^3 mm^3)	19.9	17.9	15.0	11.1	3.63	2.96
r_y (mm)	18.5	19.1	19.8	20.5	9.29	9.92
r_x / r_y	1.39	1.39	1.37	1.37	1.77	1.74
M_{rx} (kN·m)	10.6	9.10	7.39	5.28	2.40	1.82
M_{ry} (kN·m)	7.89	6.83	5.56	3.97	1.44	1.11

IMPERIAL SIZE AND MASS

	8.0	6.4	4.8	3.2	4.8	3.2
Mass (lb./ft.)	8.46	7.11	5.61	3.91	3.05	2.21
Thickness[†] (in.)	0.282	0.225	0.169	0.113	0.169	0.113
Size (in.)	3 x 2				2 x 1	

[†] Design wall thickness

SQUARE HOLLOW SECTIONS

Factored Axial Compressive Resistances, C_r (kN) $\phi = 0.90$

ASTM A500 Grade C
$F_y = 345$ MPa

Designation (mm x mm x mm)		HSS 305 x 305					HSS 254 x 254				
		16	13	9.5 *	8.0 **	6.4 **	16	13	9.5	8.0 *	6.4 **
Mass (kg/m)		139	113	86.5	72.8	58.7	114	93.0	71.3	60.1	48.6
	0	5 000	4 070	3 100	2 450	1 560	4 100	3 350	2 560	2 150	1 560
	400	5 000	4 070	3 100	2 450	1 560	4 100	3 350	2 550	2 150	1 560
	800	4 990	4 060	3 090	2 440	1 560	4 090	3 350	2 550	2 150	1 560
	1 200	4 980	4 050	3 090	2 440	1 550	4 070	3 330	2 540	2 140	1 550
	1 600	4 960	4 040	3 070	2 430	1 550	4 050	3 310	2 530	2 130	1 540
	2 000	4 930	4 010	3 060	2 420	1 540	4 010	3 280	2 500	2 110	1 530
	2 400	4 890	3 980	3 030	2 400	1 530	3 950	3 240	2 470	2 080	1 510
	2 800	4 840	3 940	3 000	2 370	1 510	3 880	3 180	2 430	2 050	1 480
	3 200	4 770	3 890	2 960	2 340	1 490	3 790	3 110	2 380	2 000	1 460
	3 600	4 690	3 830	2 920	2 310	1 470	3 690	3 030	2 320	1 960	1 420
	4 000	4 600	3 750	2 860	2 260	1 450	3 580	2 940	2 250	1 900	1 380
	4 400	4 500	3 670	2 800	2 220	1 420	3 460	2 850	2 180	1 840	1 340
	4 800	4 390	3 580	2 730	2 170	1 380	3 330	2 740	2 100	1 770	1 290
	5 200	4 270	3 490	2 660	2 110	1 350	3 190	2 630	2 020	1 700	1 240
	5 600	4 140	3 380	2 580	2 050	1 310	3 050	2 520	1 940	1 630	1 190
	6 000	4 010	3 270	2 500	1 990	1 270	2 900	2 400	1 850	1 560	1 140
	6 400	3 870	3 160	2 420	1 920	1 230	2 760	2 290	1 760	1 490	1 090
	6 800	3 730	3 050	2 330	1 850	1 190	2 620	2 170	1 680	1 420	1 040
	7 200	3 580	2 930	2 250	1 780	1 140	2 480	2 060	1 590	1 350	984
	7 600	3 440	2 820	2 160	1 720	1 100	2 350	1 950	1 510	1 280	935
	8 000	3 300	2 700	2 070	1 650	1 060	2 220	1 850	1 430	1 210	887
	8 400	3 160	2 590	1 990	1 580	1 010	2 100	1 750	1 360	1 150	841
	8 800	3 020	2 480	1 900	1 520	973	1 990	1 660	1 280	1 090	796
	9 200	2 890	2 370	1 820	1 450	932	1 880	1 570	1 210	1 030	755
	9 600	2 760	2 270	1 740	1 390	892	1 780	1 480	1 150	974	715
	10 000	2 640	2 170	1 660	1 330	854	1 680	1 400	1 090	922	677
	10 400	2 520	2 070	1 590	1 270	817	1 590	1 330	1 030	873	642
	10 800	2 400	1 980	1 520	1 210	781	1 500	1 260	977	828	609
	11 200	2 300	1 890	1 450	1 160	747	1 420	1 190	927	785	577
	11 600	2 190	1 800	1 390	1 110	714	1 350	1 130	879	745	548
	12 000	2 090	1 720	1 330	1 060	683	1 280	1 070	834	707	520

Effective length (KL) in millimetres with respect to the least radius of gyration

PROPERTIES AND DESIGN DATA

Area (mm²)		16 100	13 100	9 970	8 390	6 750	13 200	10 800	8 230	6 930	5 590
Z (10^3 mm³)		1 730	1 430	1 100	931	754	1 170	968	751	638	518
S (10^3 mm³)		1 460	1 210	948	770	529	973	817	643	549	414
r (mm)		118	119	120	121	122	96.8	98.2	99.6	100	101
M_r (kN·m)		537	444	294	239	164	363	301	233	170	129

IMPERIAL SIZE AND MASS

Mass (lb./ft.)		93.4	76.1	58.1	48.9	39.4	76.4	62.5	47.9	40.4	32.6
Thickness† (in.)		0.563	0.450	0.338	0.282	0.225	0.563	0.450	0.338	0.282	0.225
Size (in.)		12 x 12					10 x 10				

* Class 3 in bending
** Class 4: C_r calculated according to S16-09 Clause 13.3.5; S and M_r according to Clause 13.5(c).

† Design wall thickness

Designation (mm x mm x mm)	HSS 203 x 203					HSS 178 x 178		
	16	13	9.5	8.0	6.4 *	16	13	9.5
Mass (kg/m)	88.3	72.7	56.1	47.5	38.4	75.6	62.6	48.5
0	3 200	2 620	2 020	1 700	1 380	2 740	2 260	1 750
400	3 200	2 620	2 010	1 700	1 370	2 740	2 260	1 740
800	3 190	2 610	2 010	1 700	1 370	2 720	2 250	1 740
1 200	3 160	2 590	1 990	1 680	1 360	2 690	2 220	1 720
1 600	3 120	2 560	1 970	1 670	1 350	2 640	2 180	1 690
2 000	3 060	2 510	1 940	1 640	1 330	2 570	2 130	1 650
2 400	2 990	2 450	1 890	1 600	1 300	2 480	2 050	1 600
2 800	2 890	2 380	1 840	1 550	1 260	2 370	1 970	1 530
3 200	2 780	2 290	1 770	1 500	1 220	2 240	1 870	1 460
3 600	2 650	2 190	1 700	1 440	1 170	2 110	1 760	1 370
4 000	2 520	2 080	1 620	1 370	1 110	1 970	1 640	1 290
4 400	2 380	1 970	1 530	1 300	1 060	1 830	1 530	1 200
4 800	2 240	1 860	1 450	1 230	1 000	1 690	1 420	1 120
5 200	2 100	1 740	1 360	1 160	942	1 560	1 310	1 040
5 600	1 960	1 630	1 280	1 090	885	1 440	1 210	959
6 000	1 830	1 520	1 190	1 020	829	1 320	1 120	886
6 400	1 700	1 420	1 120	951	776	1 220	1 030	818
6 800	1 580	1 330	1 040	888	725	1 120	950	755
7 200	1 470	1 240	973	829	678	1 030	876	698
7 600	1 370	1 150	908	774	633	952	810	645
8 000	1 280	1 070	847	723	591	879	749	598
8 400	1 190	1 000	791	675	553	814	694	554
8 800	1 110	935	740	631	517	755	644	515
9 200	1 040	874	692	591	484	701	598	479
9 600	971	818	648	554	454	652	557	446
10 000	909	767	607	519	426	608	520	416
10 400	853	719	570	487	400	568	486	389
10 800	800	675	536	458	376	531	454	364
11 200	752	635	504	431	354	498	426	342
11 600	708	598	475	406	333	467	400	321
12 000	668	564	448	383	315	439	376	302

Effective length (KL) in millimetres with respect to the least radius of gyration

PROPERTIES AND DESIGN DATA

Area (mm^2)	10 300	8 430	6 490	5 480	4 430	8 820	7 270	5 620
Z (10^3 mm^3)	714	598	469	399	326	529	446	352
S (10^3 mm^3)	585	498	397	341	281	428	368	296
r (mm)	76.1	77.5	78.9	79.5	80.2	65.7	67.1	68.5
M_r (kN·m)	222	186	146	124	87.3	164	138	109

IMPERIAL SIZE AND MASS

Mass (lb./ft.)	59.3	48.9	37.7	31.9	25.8	50.8	42.1	32.6
Thickness[†] (in.)	0.563	0.450	0.338	0.282	0.225	0.563	0.450	0.338
Size (in.)	8 x 8					7 x 7		

* Class 3 in bending

[†] Design wall thickness

SQUARE HOLLOW SECTIONS

Factored Axial Compressive Resistances, C_r (kN) $\phi = 0.90$

ASTM A500 Grade C
$F_y = 345$ MPa

Designation (mm x mm x mm)	HSS 178 x 178			HSS 152 x 152				
	8.0	6.4	4.8 **	13	9.5	8.0	6.4	4.8 *
Mass (kg/m)	41.1	33.4	25.5	52.4	40.9	34.8	28.3	21.7
0	1 470	1 200	884	1 900	1 470	1 250	1 020	776
400	1 470	1 190	883	1 890	1 470	1 250	1 010	775
800	1 470	1 190	879	1 880	1 460	1 240	1 010	771
1 200	1 450	1 180	872	1 850	1 440	1 220	994	760
1 600	1 430	1 160	858	1 800	1 400	1 190	970	743
2 000	1 400	1 130	839	1 730	1 350	1 150	937	718
2 400	1 350	1 100	813	1 640	1 290	1 100	894	686
2 800	1 300	1 060	782	1 540	1 210	1 040	844	649
3 200	1 240	1 010	746	1 430	1 130	966	789	608
3 600	1 170	952	707	1 320	1 040	895	732	564
4 000	1 100	895	665	1 210	958	823	675	521
4 400	1 030	837	623	1 100	876	754	619	479
4 800	954	780	581	1 000	799	689	566	438
5 200	885	724	540	910	728	628	517	400
5 600	819	671	501	827	662	572	471	366
6 000	758	621	464	751	603	522	430	334
6 400	700	575	429	684	550	476	393	305
6 800	647	532	397	624	502	435	359	280
7 200	598	492	368	570	460	398	329	256
7 600	554	455	341	522	422	365	302	235
8 000	513	422	316	479	387	336	278	217
8 400	476	392	293	441	357	310	256	200
8 800	442	364	273	407	330	286	237	185
9 200	411	339	254	377	305	265	219	171
9 600	383	316	237	349	283	246	204	159
10 000	358	295	221	324	263	228	189	148
10 400	335	276	207	302	245	213	176	138
10 800	313	259	194	282	229	199	165	129
11 200	294	243	182	263	214	186	154	120
11 600	276	228	171		200	174	144	113
12 000	260	215	161					106

Effective length (KL) in millimetres with respect to the least radius of gyration

PROPERTIES AND DESIGN DATA

Area (mm^2)	4 750	3 850	2 940	6 110	4 740	4 030	3 270	2 500
Z (10^3 mm^3)	301	247	190	317	252	217	178	138
S (10^3 mm^3)	256	211	160	258	210	183	152	119
r (mm)	69.2	69.9	70.5	56.7	58.1	58.8	59.5	60.2
M_r (kN·m)	93.5	76.7	49.8	98.4	78.2	67.4	55.3	36.9

IMPERIAL SIZE AND MASS

Mass (lb./ft.)	27.6	22.4	17.1	35.2	27.5	23.4	19.0	14.6
Thickness[†] (in.)	0.282	0.225	0.169	0.450	0.338	0.282	0.225	0.169
Size (in.)	7 x 7			6 x 6				

* Class 3 in bending

** Class 4: C_r calculated according to S16-09 Clause 13.3.5; S and M_r according to Clause 13.5(c).

[†] Design wall thickness

ASTM A500
Grade C
F_y = 345 MPa

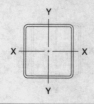

SQUARE HOLLOW SECTIONS
Factored Axial Compressive
Resistances, C_r (kN) ϕ = 0.90

Designation (mm x mm x mm)	HSS 127 x 127					HSS 114 x 114		
	13	9.5	8.0	6.4	4.8	13	9.5	8.0
Mass (kg/m)	42.3	33.3	28.4	23.2	17.9	37.3	29.5	25.3
0	1 540	1 200	1 020	835	640	1 360	1 070	910
400	1 530	1 200	1 020	834	638	1 350	1 070	907
800	1 520	1 190	1 010	825	632	1 330	1 050	894
1 200	1 480	1 160	988	806	618	1 280	1 010	866
1 600	1 410	1 110	949	775	595	1 210	960	821
2 000	1 320	1 050	896	733	564	1 110	888	762
2 400	1 220	968	832	683	526	1 000	807	694
2 800	1 110	885	762	627	484	892	722	623
3 200	997	800	690	569	441	785	640	554
3 600	891	718	621	513	398	689	564	489
4 000	793	642	556	461	358	603	496	431
4 400	705	572	497	412	321	529	436	380
4 800	627	511	444	369	288	465	385	336
5 200	558	456	397	330	258	410	340	297
5 600	499	408	356	297	232	364	302	264
6 000	447	367	320	267	209	324	270	236
6 400	402	330	288	241	189	290	242	212
6 800	363	298	261	218	171	260	217	190
7 200	329	271	237	198	155	235	196	172
7 600	299	246	215	180	141	213	178	156
8 000	273	225	197	165	129	194	162	142
8 400	250	206	180	151	118		148	130
8 800	229	189	166	139	109			
9 200	211	174	153	128	100			
9 600			141	118	93			
10 000								
10 400								
10 800								
11 200								
11 600								
12 000								

Effective length (KL) in millimetres with respect to the least radius of gyration

PROPERTIES AND DESIGN DATA

Area (mm^2)	4 950	3 870	3 300	2 690	2 060	4 370	3 440	2 930
Z (10^3 mm^3)	209	169	146	121	94.2	164	134	116
S (10^3 mm^3)	167	139	122	102	80.6	129	109	95.9
r (mm)	46.3	47.7	48.4	49.1	49.8	41.1	42.5	43.2
M_r (kN·m)	64.9	52.5	45.3	37.6	29.2	50.9	41.6	36.0

IMPERIAL SIZE AND MASS

Mass (lb./ft.)	28.4	22.4	19.1	15.6	12.0	25.0	19.8	17.0
Thickness[†] (in.)	0.450	0.338	0.282	0.225	0.169	0.450	0.338	0.282
Size (in.)	5 x 5					4½ x 4½		

[†] Design wall thickness

SQUARE HOLLOW SECTIONS

Factored Axial Compressive Resistances, C$_r$ (kN) ϕ = 0.90

ASTM A500
Grade C
F$_y$ = 345 MPa

Designation (mm x mm x mm)	HSS 114 x 114			HSS 102 x 102		
	6.4	4.8	3.2 *	13	9.5	8.0
Mass (kg/m)	20.7	16.0	10.9	32.2	25.7	22.1
Effective length (KL) in millimetres with respect to the least radius of gyration						
0	745	574	388	1 180	932	798
400	743	573	387	1 170	928	795
800	733	566	382	1 140	908	779
1 200	711	549	372	1 090	867	745
1 600	675	522	354	1 000	804	693
2 000	628	487	331	896	726	628
2 400	574	447	304	786	642	558
2 800	517	403	276	680	560	488
3 200	461	360	247	585	484	424
3 600	408	320	220	502	419	367
4 000	360	283	195	433	362	318
4 400	318	251	173	374	314	277
4 800	282	222	153	325	274	242
5 200	250	197	136	284	240	212
5 600	222	176	122	250	212	187
6 000	199	157	109	222	188	166
6 400	178	141	98	197	167	148
6 800	160	127	88	177	150	133
7 200	145	115	80		135	120
7 600	132	104	73			108
8 000	120	95	66			
8 400	110	87	61			
8 800		80	56			
9 200						
9 600						
10 000						
10 400						
10 800						
11 200						
11 600						
12 000						

PROPERTIES AND DESIGN DATA						
Area (mm^2)	2 400	1 850	1 250	3 790	3 000	2 570
Z (10^3 mm^3)	96.5	75.4	52.1	124	102	89.4
S (10^3 mm^3)	81.0	64.2	45.0	96.1	82.4	73.2
r (mm)	43.9	44.6	45.3	35.9	37.3	38.0
M$_r$ (kN·m)	30.0	23.4	14.0	38.5	31.7	27.8

IMPERIAL SIZE AND MASS						
Mass (lb./ft.)	13.9	10.7	7.32	21.6	17.3	14.9
Thickness[†] (in.)	0.225	0.169	0.113	0.450	0.338	0.282
Size (in.)		4½ x 4½			4 x 4	

* Class 3 in bending

[†] Design wall thickness

ASTM A500
Grade C
F_y = 345 MPa

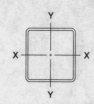

SQUARE HOLLOW SECTIONS
Factored Axial Compressive
Resistances, C_r (kN) ϕ = 0.90

Designation (mm x mm x mm)	HSS 102 x 102			HSS 89 x 89				
	6.4	4.8	3.2 *	9.5	8.0	6.4	4.8	3.2
Mass (kg/m)	18.2	14.1	9.62	21.9	18.9	15.6	12.2	8.35
0	655	506	345	798	686	565	438	299
400	653	504	344	793	682	562	436	298
800	640	495	338	769	663	547	424	291
1 200	614	475	325	718	621	514	400	275
1 600	572	445	305	646	561	467	365	252
2 000	521	406	279	563	492	411	323	224
2 400	464	363	250	481	423	355	280	195
2 800	408	320	222	407	359	303	240	168
3 200	355	280	194	343	304	257	205	144
3 600	309	244	170	290	258	219	175	123
4 000	268	212	148	247	220	187	150	105
4 400	234	185	130	212	189	161	129	91
4 800	204	162	114	183	163	139	112	79
5 200	180	143	100	159	142	121	97	69
5 600	159	126	89	139	124	106	85	61
6 000	141	112	79	123	110	94	76	54
6 400	126	100	70	109	97	83	67	48
6 800	113	90	63				60	43
7 200	102	81	57					
7 600	92	73	52					
8 000			47					
8 400								
8 800								
9 200								
9 600								
10 000								
10 400								
10 800								
11 200								
11 600								
12 000								

Effective length (KL) in millimetres with respect to the least radius of gyration

PROPERTIES AND DESIGN DATA

Area (mm²)	2 110	1 630	1 110	2 570	2 210	1 820	1 410	964
Z (10^3 mm³)	74.7	58.7	40.8	75.2	66.2	55.8	44.1	30.9
S (10^3 mm³)	62.3	49.8	35.1	59.6	53.6	46.0	37.1	26.5
r (mm)	38.7	39.4	40.1	32.1	32.8	33.5	34.2	34.9
M_r (kN·m)	23.2	18.2	10.9	23.3	20.6	17.3	13.7	9.59

IMPERIAL SIZE AND MASS

Mass (lb./ft.)	12.2	9.46	6.47	14.7	12.7	10.5	8.17	5.61
Thickness[†] (in.)	0.225	0.169	0.113	0.338	0.282	0.225	0.169	0.113
Size (in.)	4 x 4			3½ x 3½				

* Class 3 in bending

[†] Design wall thickness

SQUARE HOLLOW SECTIONS
Factored Axial Compressive Resistances, C_r (kN) $\phi = 0.90$

ASTM A500 Grade C
$F_y = 345$ MPa

Designation (mm x mm x mm)	HSS 76 x 76					HSS 64 x 64			
	9.5	8.0	6.4	4.8	3.2	8.0	6.4	4.8	3.2
Mass (kg/m)	18.1	15.8	13.1	10.3	7.09	12.6	10.6	8.35	5.82
0	661	571	475	369	254	460	385	301	209
400	655	566	471	367	252	453	380	298	206
800	624	541	451	352	243	418	353	278	194
1 200	562	491	412	323	224	358	306	243	171
1 600	483	424	359	283	197	289	250	201	143
2 000	401	355	303	240	169	228	199	161	115
2 400	328	292	251	200	141	179	157	128	93
2 800	268	240	207	166	118	142	125	103	74
3 200	220	198	172	138	98	114	101	83	60
3 600	183	164	143	115	82	93	83	68	50
4 000	153	138	120	97	69	77	69	57	41
4 400	129	117	102	82	59	64	58	48	35
4 800	111	100	88	71	51				30
5 200	96	87	76	61	44				
5 600			66	53	38				
6 000									
6 400									
6 800									
7 200									
7 600									
8 000									
8 400									
8 800									
9 200									
9 600									
10 000									
10 400									
10 800									
11 200									
11 600									
12 000									

Effective length (KL) in millimetres with respect to the least radius of gyration

PROPERTIES AND DESIGN DATA

Area (mm²)	2 130	1 840	1 530	1 190	818	1 480	1 240	971	673
Z (10^3 mm³)	52.2	46.5	39.6	31.6	22.3	30.2	26.1	21.2	15.1
S (10^3 mm³)	40.6	37.0	32.2	26.3	19.0	23.5	20.9	17.4	12.8
r (mm)	26.9	27.6	28.4	29.0	29.7	22.4	23.2	23.9	24.6
M_r (kN·m)	16.2	14.4	12.3	9.81	6.92	9.38	8.10	6.58	4.69

IMPERIAL SIZE AND MASS

Mass (lb./ft.)	12.2	10.6	8.81	6.89	4.76	8.46	7.11	5.61	3.91
Thickness[†] (in.)	0.338	0.282	0.225	0.169	0.113	0.282	0.225	0.169	0.113
Size (in.)	3 x 3					2½ x 2½			

[†] Design wall thickness

ASTM A500 Grade C
$F_y = 345$ MPa

SQUARE HOLLOW SECTIONS
Factored Axial Compressive Resistances, C_r (kN) $\phi = 0.90$

Designation (mm x mm x mm)	HSS 51 x 51			HSS 38 x 38	
	6.4	4.8	3.2	4.8	3.2
Mass (kg/m)	8.05	6.45	4.55	4.54	3.28
Effective length (KL) in millimetres with respect to the least radius of gyration					
0	294	233	164	166	119
400	286	228	160	156	113
800	250	202	143	121	90
1 200	197	161	116	83	63
1 600	147	122	89	56	43
2 000	109	91	67	39	30
2 400	82	69	51	28	22
2 800	63	53	40		17
3 200	50	42	32		
3 600	40	34	26		
4 000					
4 400					
4 800					
5 200					
5 600					
6 000					
6 400					
6 800					
7 200					
7 600					
8 000					
8 400					
8 800					
9 200					
9 600					
10 000					
10 400					
10 800					
11 200					
11 600					
12 000					
PROPERTIES AND DESIGN DATA					
Area (mm^2)	947	752	528	534	382
Z (10^3 mm^3)	15.5	12.8	9.35	6.54	4.95
S (10^3 mm^3)	12.0	10.3	7.79	5.08	4.03
r (mm)	18.0	18.7	19.4	13.5	14.2
M$_r$ (kN·m)	4.81	3.97	2.90	2.03	1.54
IMPERIAL SIZE AND MASS					
Mass (lb./ft.)	5.41	4.33	3.06	3.05	2.21
Thickness[†] (in.)	0.225	0.169	0.113	0.169	0.113
Size (in.)	2 x 2			1½ x 1½	

[†] Design wall thickness

ROUND HOLLOW SECTIONS
Factored Axial Compressive Resistances, C_r (kN) $\phi = 0.90$

ASTM A500 Grade C
$F_y = 317$ MPa

Designation (mm x mm)	HSS 406			HSS 356				HSS 324		
	13	9.5	6.4 *	16	13	9.5	6.4 *	13	9.5	6.4
Mass (kg/m)	123	93.3	62.6	133	107	81.3	54.7	97.5	73.9	49.7
0	4 050	3 050	2 050	4 370	3 540	2 670	1 790	3 200	2 430	1 630
400	4 050	3 050	2 050	4 360	3 540	2 670	1 790	3 190	2 420	1 630
800	4 050	3 050	2 050	4 360	3 530	2 670	1 790	3 190	2 420	1 630
1 200	4 040	3 050	2 050	4 350	3 530	2 660	1 790	3 180	2 420	1 620
1 600	4 030	3 040	2 040	4 340	3 520	2 650	1 780	3 170	2 410	1 620
2 000	4 020	3 030	2 040	4 320	3 500	2 640	1 770	3 150	2 390	1 610
2 400	4 000	3 020	2 030	4 290	3 480	2 620	1 760	3 120	2 370	1 590
2 800	3 980	3 000	2 010	4 250	3 440	2 600	1 750	3 090	2 350	1 580
3 200	3 950	2 970	2 000	4 200	3 410	2 570	1 730	3 040	2 310	1 560
3 600	3 910	2 950	1 980	4 140	3 360	2 540	1 710	2 990	2 270	1 530
4 000	3 860	2 910	1 960	4 070	3 310	2 500	1 680	2 930	2 230	1 500
4 400	3 810	2 880	1 930	4 000	3 250	2 450	1 650	2 860	2 180	1 470
4 800	3 760	2 830	1 910	3 910	3 180	2 400	1 620	2 790	2 120	1 430
5 200	3 690	2 790	1 880	3 820	3 100	2 350	1 580	2 710	2 060	1 390
5 600	3 620	2 730	1 840	3 720	3 020	2 290	1 540	2 620	2 000	1 350
6 000	3 550	2 680	1 800	3 610	2 940	2 220	1 500	2 540	1 930	1 310
6 400	3 470	2 620	1 770	3 500	2 850	2 160	1 460	2 450	1 870	1 260
6 800	3 380	2 560	1 720	3 390	2 760	2 090	1 410	2 350	1 800	1 210
7 200	3 300	2 490	1 680	3 280	2 670	2 020	1 370	2 260	1 730	1 170
7 600	3 210	2 430	1 640	3 160	2 570	1 950	1 320	2 170	1 660	1 120
8 000	3 120	2 360	1 590	3 040	2 480	1 880	1 270	2 070	1 590	1 070
8 400	3 020	2 290	1 550	2 930	2 390	1 810	1 230	1 980	1 520	1 030
8 800	2 930	2 220	1 500	2 810	2 290	1 740	1 180	1 900	1 450	984
9 200	2 840	2 150	1 450	2 700	2 200	1 670	1 130	1 810	1 390	941
9 600	2 740	2 080	1 400	2 590	2 110	1 610	1 090	1 730	1 320	899
10 000	2 650	2 010	1 360	2 480	2 030	1 540	1 040	1 650	1 260	858
10 400	2 560	1 940	1 310	2 380	1 940	1 480	1 000	1 570	1 210	820
10 800	2 470	1 870	1 270	2 280	1 860	1 420	961	1 500	1 150	783
11 200	2 380	1 810	1 220	2 180	1 790	1 360	922	1 430	1 100	747
11 600	2 300	1 740	1 180	2 090	1 710	1 300	884	1 370	1 050	713
12 000	2 210	1 680	1 140	2 000	1 640	1 250	847	1 300	1 000	681

Effective length (KL) in millimetres with respect to the least radius of gyration

PROPERTIES AND DESIGN DATA

Area (mm²)	14 200	10 700	7 190	15 300	12 400	9 350	6 280	11 200	8 500	5 710
Z (10^3 mm³)	1 780	1 360	918	1 670	1 350	1 030	700	1 120	853	579
S (10^3 mm³)	1 360	1 040	711	1 260	1 030	792	541	847	653	447
r (mm)	140	141	142	121	122	123	124	111	112	113
M_r (kN·m)	508	388	203	476	385	294	154	320	243	165

IMPERIAL SIZE AND MASS

Mass (lb./ft.)	82.9	62.7	42.1	89.4	72.2	54.7	36.8	65.5	49.7	33.4
Thickness[†] (in.)	0.450	0.338	0.225	0.563	0.450	0.338	0.225	0.450	0.338	0.225
Size (in.)	16 OD			14 OD				12.75 OD		

* Class 3 in bending

† Design wall thickness

ASTM A500
Grade C
F_y = 317 MPa

ROUND HOLLOW SECTIONS
Factored Axial Compressive
Resistances, C_r (kN) ϕ = 0.90

Designation (mm x mm)	HSS 273			HSS 219				
	13	6.4	4.8 *	16	13	9.5	6.4	4.8
Mass (kg/m)	81.6	41.8	31.6	79.6	64.6	49.3	33.3	25.3
0	2 680	1 370	1 040	2 620	2 130	1 620	1 090	827
400	2 680	1 370	1 040	2 620	2 130	1 620	1 090	827
800	2 680	1 370	1 030	2 610	2 120	1 610	1 090	825
1 200	2 670	1 360	1 030	2 600	2 110	1 600	1 080	819
1 600	2 650	1 350	1 020	2 560	2 080	1 580	1 070	810
2 000	2 620	1 340	1 010	2 510	2 040	1 550	1 050	796
2 400	2 580	1 320	1 000	2 450	1 990	1 520	1 030	778
2 800	2 540	1 300	984	2 370	1 930	1 470	996	755
3 200	2 480	1 270	963	2 280	1 850	1 420	960	729
3 600	2 420	1 240	939	2 170	1 770	1 350	920	699
4 000	2 340	1 200	912	2 060	1 680	1 290	876	666
4 400	2 260	1 160	882	1 950	1 590	1 220	831	632
4 800	2 170	1 120	850	1 830	1 500	1 150	784	596
5 200	2 080	1 080	816	1 710	1 400	1 080	737	561
5 600	1 990	1 030	782	1 600	1 310	1 010	691	527
6 000	1 900	984	747	1 490	1 230	945	647	493
6 400	1 800	937	711	1 390	1 140	882	604	461
6 800	1 710	891	676	1 290	1 060	822	564	430
7 200	1 620	846	642	1 200	991	766	526	402
7 600	1 540	802	609	1 120	923	714	491	375
8 000	1 450	759	577	1 040	860	666	458	350
8 400	1 370	719	546	971	802	622	428	327
8 800	1 300	680	517	906	748	581	400	306
9 200	1 230	644	489	846	699	543	374	286
9 600	1 160	609	463	791	654	508	350	268
10 000	1 100	576	438	741	613	476	328	251
10 400	1 040	546	415	694	574	446	308	236
10 800	981	517	393	652	539	419	290	222
11 200	929	490	373	612	507	394	273	209
11 600	880	464	354	576	478	371	257	197
12 000	835	441	336	543	450	350	242	185

Effective length (KL) in millimetres with respect to the least radius of gyration

PROPERTIES AND DESIGN DATA

Area (mm^2)	9 400	4 800	3 630	9 200	7 460	5 670	3 830	2 900
Z (10^3 mm^3)	783	409	311	600	493	380	260	199
S (10^3 mm^3)	590	314	240	442	368	287	199	153
r (mm)	92.6	94.6	95.0	72.6	73.5	74.5	75.5	76.0
M$_r$ (kN·m)	223	117	68.5	171	141	108	74.2	56.8

IMPERIAL SIZE AND MASS

Mass (lb./ft.)	54.8	28.1	21.3	53.5	43.4	33.1	22.4	17.0
Thickness[†] (in.)	0.450	0.225	0.169	0.563	0.450	0.338	0.225	0.169
Size (in.)	10.75 OD			8.625 OD				

* Class 3 in bending

[†] Design wall thickness

Designation (mm x mm)		HSS 178					HSS 168		
		13	9.5	8.0	6.4	4.8	13	9.5	8.0
Mass (kg/m)		51.7	39.5	33.3	26.8	20.4	48.7	37.3	31.4
Effective length (KL) in millimetres with respect to the least radius of gyration	0	1 700	1 300	1 100	882	668	1 610	1 230	1 030
	400	1 700	1 300	1 090	881	667	1 600	1 230	1 030
	800	1 690	1 290	1 090	876	664	1 590	1 220	1 030
	1 200	1 670	1 280	1 080	866	656	1 570	1 200	1 010
	1 600	1 630	1 250	1 050	849	643	1 530	1 170	987
	2 000	1 580	1 210	1 020	824	625	1 470	1 130	953
	2 400	1 520	1 160	981	791	601	1 400	1 080	909
	2 800	1 440	1 100	933	753	572	1 320	1 020	859
	3 200	1 350	1 040	879	710	540	1 230	950	803
	3 600	1 260	970	821	664	506	1 140	880	744
	4 000	1 160	900	762	617	470	1 040	810	686
	4 400	1 070	830	704	571	436	955	742	629
	4 800	984	764	648	526	402	871	678	575
	5 200	902	701	596	484	370	793	619	525
	5 600	825	642	546	444	340	721	564	479
	6 000	755	589	501	407	312	657	514	437
	6 400	692	539	460	374	286	599	469	399
	6 800	634	495	422	344	263	547	429	365
	7 200	582	455	388	316	242	500	393	335
	7 600	535	419	357	291	223	459	361	307
	8 000	493	386	329	268	206	422	332	283
	8 400	455	356	304	248	190	388	306	260
	8 800	421	330	282	230	176	359	282	241
	9 200	390	306	261	213	164	332	261	223
	9 600	362	284	243	198	152	308	243	207
	10 000	337	265	226	185	142	286	226	192
	10 400	314	247	211	172	132	266	210	179
	10 800	294	231	197	161	124	249	196	167
	11 200	275	216	185	151	116		184	157
	11 600	258	203	173	141	109			
	12 000			163	133	102			

PROPERTIES AND DESIGN DATA

Area (mm^2)		5 970	4 560	3 840	3 090	2 340	5 630	4 300	3 620
Z (10^3 mm^3)		317	246	208	169	130	282	219	186
S (10^3 mm^3)		234	184	157	129	99.3	207	164	140
r (mm)		59.0	59.9	60.4	60.9	61.4	55.6	56.6	57.0
M$_r$ (kN·m)		90.4	70.2	59.3	48.2	37.1	80.5	62.5	53.1

IMPERIAL SIZE AND MASS

Mass (lb./ft.)		34.7	26.6	22.4	18.0	13.7	32.7	25.1	21.1
Thickness† (in.)		0.450	0.338	0.282	0.225	0.169	0.450	0.338	0.282
Size (in.)				7 OD				6.625 OD	

† Design wall thickness

ASTM A500
Grade C
F_y = 317 MPa

ROUND HOLLOW SECTIONS
Factored Axial Compressive
Resistances, C_r (kN) ϕ = 0.90

Designation (mm x mm)	HSS 168			HSS 152				
	6.4	4.8	3.2 *	9.5	8.0	6.4	4.8	3.2
Mass (kg/m)	25.4	19.3	12.9	33.6	28.3	22.9	17.4	11.7
0	833	633	425	1 110	930	750	571	382
400	832	633	425	1 110	929	749	570	382
800	827	629	422	1 100	921	743	565	379
1 200	816	621	417	1 080	904	730	556	373
1 600	797	606	407	1 040	877	708	539	362
2 000	770	586	394	995	838	678	517	347
2 400	736	561	377	936	790	640	488	328
2 800	695	531	357	870	735	596	456	307
3 200	651	497	335	801	677	550	421	284
3 600	604	462	312	730	619	503	386	260
4 000	557	427	288	663	562	458	351	238
4 400	512	392	265	599	509	415	319	216
4 800	468	359	243	541	460	375	289	196
5 200	428	329	223	488	415	339	261	177
5 600	391	300	204	441	375	307	237	161
6 000	357	274	186	398	340	278	214	146
6 400	326	251	171	361	308	252	195	132
6 800	298	230	156	328	280	229	177	121
7 200	274	211	143	299	255	209	162	110
7 600	251	194	132	273	233	191	148	101
8 000	231	178	121	250	214	175	136	92
8 400	213	164	112	230	196	161	125	85
8 800	197	152	104	212	181	148	115	78
9 200	183	141	96	195	167	137	106	72
9 600	169	131	89	181	155	127	98	67
10 000	158	122	83	168	144	118	91	62
10 400	147	113	77				85	58
10 800	137	106	72					
11 200	128	99	68					
11 600		93	63					
12 000								

Effective length (KL) in millimetres with respect to the least radius of gyration

PROPERTIES AND DESIGN DATA

Area (mm²)	2 920	2 220	1 490	3 880	3 260	2 630	2 000	1 340
Z (10^3 mm³)	151	116	78.3	178	151	123	94.4	64.0
S (10^3 mm³)	115	88.6	60.5	132	113	93.1	72.1	49.3
r (mm)	57.5	58.0	58.5	50.9	51.4	51.9	52.4	52.9
M_r (kN·m)	43.1	33.1	17.3	50.8	43.1	35.1	26.9	18.3

IMPERIAL SIZE AND MASS

Mass (lb./ft.)	17.0	13.0	8.70	22.6	19.0	15.4	11.7	7.86
Thickness† (in.)	0.225	0.169	0.113	0.338	0.282	0.225	0.169	0.113
Size (in.)	6.625 OD			6 OD				

* Class 3 in bending

† Design wall thickness

ROUND HOLLOW SECTIONS
Factored Axial Compressive
Resistances, C_r (kN) $\phi = 0.90$

ASTM A500
Grade C
$F_y = 317$ MPa

Designation (mm x mm)	HSS 141			HSS 127					
	9.5	6.4	4.8	13	9.5	8.0	6.4	4.8	3.2
Mass (kg/m)	31.0	21.1	16.1	35.8	27.6	23.3	18.9	14.4	9.71
0	1 020	693	528	1 180	910	767	622	474	320
400	1 020	692	527	1 180	908	766	620	472	319
800	1 010	685	522	1 160	895	755	612	467	315
1 200	986	670	511	1 130	868	733	595	453	306
1 600	948	646	493	1 070	824	697	566	432	292
2 000	896	612	468	988	767	649	528	404	274
2 400	834	572	437	899	700	594	484	371	252
2 800	766	527	404	806	630	535	438	336	229
3 200	696	480	368	715	561	478	391	301	205
3 600	627	434	334	631	497	424	348	268	183
4 000	562	391	301	556	439	375	308	238	163
4 400	503	351	270	490	388	331	273	211	144
4 800	450	314	243	432	343	293	242	187	128
5 200	403	282	218	383	304	260	215	166	114
5 600	362	253	196	340	271	232	191	148	102
6 000	325	228	177	303	242	207	171	133	91
6 400	294	206	160	272	217	186	154	119	82
6 800	266	187	145	245	195	167	138	108	74
7 200	241	170	131	221	177	151	125	97	67
7 600	220	155	120	201	160	138	114	88	61
8 000	201	141	110	183	146	125	104	81	56
8 400	184	130	101		134	115	95	74	51
8 800	169	119	93						
9 200	156	110	85						
9 600		102	79						
10 000									
10 400									
10 800									
11 200									
11 600									
12 000									

Effective length (KL) in millimetres with respect to the least radius of gyration

PROPERTIES AND DESIGN DATA

	HSS 141			HSS 127					
Area (mm^2)	3 580	2 430	1 850	4 150	3 190	2 690	2 180	1 660	1 120
Z (10^3 mm^3)	151	105	80.8	153	120	103	84.1	64.8	44.1
S (10^3 mm^3)	112	79.3	61.5	110	88.6	76.4	63.2	49.2	33.9
r (mm)	47.0	48.0	48.5	41.1	42.0	42.4	42.9	43.4	43.9
M$_r$ (kN·m)	43.1	30.0	23.1	43.7	34.2	29.4	24.0	18.5	12.6

IMPERIAL SIZE AND MASS

	HSS 141			HSS 127					
Mass (lb./ft.)	20.8	14.2	10.8	24.1	18.6	15.7	12.7	9.68	6.53
Thickness[†] (in.)	0.338	0.225	0.169	0.450	0.338	0.282	0.225	0.169	0.113
Size (in.)	5.563 OD			5 OD					

[†] Design wall thickness

ASTM A500
Grade C
F_y = 317 MPa

ROUND HOLLOW SECTIONS
Factored Axial Compressive
Resistances, C_r (kN) ϕ = 0.90

Designation (mm x mm)	HSS 114			HSS 102			
	9.5	4.8	3.2	8.0	6.4	4.8	3.2
Mass (kg/m)	24.6	12.9	8.71	18.4	14.9	11.4	7.72
Effective length (KL) in millimetres with respect to the least radius of gyration							
0	813	425	285	605	491	374	253
400	810	424	284	602	488	372	252
800	795	417	280	587	477	364	247
1 200	763	401	270	556	452	345	235
1 600	713	377	254	509	415	318	217
2 000	650	346	234	453	371	285	195
2 400	581	311	211	395	324	249	171
2 800	511	276	187	340	280	216	149
3 200	446	243	165	291	240	186	128
3 600	388	212	145	249	206	159	110
4 000	338	186	127	214	177	137	95
4 400	295	163	111	184	153	119	82
4 800	258	143	98	160	133	103	72
5 200	227	126	86	140	116	90	63
5 600	201	112	76	123	102	79	55
6 000	178	99	68	109	90	70	49
6 400	159	89	61	97	80	63	44
6 800	143	80	55		72	56	39
7 200	129	72	49				
7 600		65	45				
8 000							
8 400							
8 800							
9 200							
9 600							
10 000							
10 400							
10 800							
11 200							
11 600							
12 000							

PROPERTIES AND DESIGN DATA

Area (mm^2)	2 850	1 490	1 000	2 120	1 720	1 310	888
Z (10^3 mm^3)	96.1	52.1	35.5	63.9	52.6	40.8	27.9
S (10^3 mm^3)	70.1	39.4	27.2	46.9	39.1	30.7	21.3
r (mm)	37.5	38.9	39.4	33.5	34.0	34.4	34.9
M_r (kN·m)	27.4	14.9	10.1	18.2	15.0	11.6	7.96

IMPERIAL SIZE AND MASS

Mass (lb./ft.)	16.5	8.68	5.86	12.3	10.0	7.67	5.19
Thickness[†] (in.)	0.338	0.169	0.113	0.282	0.225	0.169	0.113
Size (in.)	4.5 OD			4 OD			

[†] Design wall thickness

ROUND HOLLOW SECTIONS

Factored Axial Compressive
Resistances, C_r (kN) $\phi = 0.90$

ASTM A500
Grade C
$F_y = 317$ MPa

Designation (mm x mm)	HSS 89				HSS 76		HSS 73		
	8.0	6.4	4.8	3.2	6.4	4.8	6.4	4.8	3.2
Mass (kg/m)	15.9	12.9	9.92	6.72	10.9	8.42	10.4	8.04	5.48
0	525	425	325	221	362	277	345	265	180
400	521	422	323	219	359	275	341	262	178
800	503	408	312	213	340	261	321	247	169
1 200	465	378	291	198	304	235	284	220	151
1 600	412	337	260	178	259	201	238	185	128
2 000	354	290	225	154	213	166	194	151	105
2 400	298	246	191	132	173	136	156	122	85
2 800	249	206	160	111	141	111	125	99	69
3 200	208	173	135	93	115	91	102	80	56
3 600	175	145	113	79	95	75	84	66	47
4 000	148	123	96	67	79	63	70	55	39
4 400	126	105	82	57	67	53	59	47	33
4 800	108	90	71	50	57	45		40	28
5 200	94	78	62	43					
5 600	82	69	54	38					
6 000				33					
6 400									
6 800									
7 200									
7 600									
8 000									
8 400									
8 800									
9 200									
9 600									
10 000									
10 400									
10 800									
11 200									
11 600									
12 000									

Effective length (KL) in millimetres with respect to the least radius of gyration

PROPERTIES AND DESIGN DATA

Area (mm²)	1 840	1 490	1 140	774	1 270	972	1 210	928	631
Z (10^3 mm³)	47.9	39.6	30.8	21.2	28.5	22.3	25.9	20.3	14.1
S (10^3 mm³)	34.8	29.2	23.1	16.1	20.8	16.5	18.9	15.1	10.6
r (mm)	29.0	29.5	29.9	30.4	25.0	25.5	23.9	24.3	24.8
M_r (kN·m)	13.7	11.3	8.79	6.05	8.13	6.36	7.39	5.79	4.02

IMPERIAL SIZE AND MASS

Mass (lb./ft.)	10.7	8.69	6.66	4.52	7.35	5.66	7.01	5.40	3.68
Thickness[†] (in.)	0.282	0.225	0.169	0.113	0.225	0.169	0.225	0.169	0.113
Size (in.)	3.5 OD				3 OD		2.875 OD		

† Design wall thickness

Designation (mm x mm)		HSS 64			HSS 60			HSS 48	
		6.4	4.8	3.2	6.4	4.8	3.2	4.8	3.2
Mass (kg/m)		8.95	6.92	4.73	8.45	6.54	4.48	5.13	3.54
Effective length (KL) in millimetres with respect to the least radius of gyration	0	297	228	155	280	216	147	170	117
	400	292	225	153	274	212	145	164	113
	800	267	207	142	248	193	132	138	97
	1 200	225	176	121	204	161	111	104	73
	1 600	179	141	98	159	126	88	74	53
	2 000	139	110	77	122	97	68	54	39
	2 400	108	86	61	94	75	53	40	29
	2 800	85	68	48	73	59	41	30	22
	3 200	68	54	39	58	47	33		17
	3 600	55	44	31	47	38	27		
	4 000	46	37	26			22		
	4 400								
	4 800								
	5 200								
	5 600								
	6 000								
	6 400								
	6 800								
	7 200								
	7 600								
	8 000								
	8 400								
	8 800								
	9 200								
	9 600								
	10 000								
	10 400								
	10 800								
	11 200								
	11 600								
	12 000								

PROPERTIES AND DESIGN DATA

	HSS 64 6.4	4.8	3.2	HSS 60 6.4	4.8	3.2	HSS 48 4.8	3.2
Area (mm²)	1 040	800	545	980	757	516	595	409
Z (10^3 mm³)	19.1	15.1	10.5	17.1	13.5	9.45	8.35	5.92
S (10^3 mm³)	13.8	11.1	7.91	12.2	9.90	7.08	6.02	4.38
r (mm)	20.5	21.0	21.5	19.4	19.9	20.3	15.6	16.1
M_r (kN·m)	5.45	4.31	3.00	4.88	3.85	2.70	2.38	1.69

IMPERIAL SIZE AND MASS

	HSS 64 6.4	4.8	3.2	HSS 60 6.4	4.8	3.2	HSS 48 4.8	3.2
Mass (lb./ft.)	6.01	4.65	3.18	5.68	4.40	3.01	3.45	2.38
Thickness[†] (in.)	0.225	0.169	0.113	0.225	0.169	0.113	0.169	0.113
Size (in.)		2.5 OD			2.375 OD			1.9 OD

[†] Design wall thickness

DESIGN OF BEAM-COLUMNS

Examples

1. Given:

Design a steel column in a braced frame for the factored loads shown. The moments cause bending about the X-X axis of the column. The P-Δ effects have been included in the analysis. The steel grade is ASTM A992 ($F_y = 345$ MPa).

Solution:

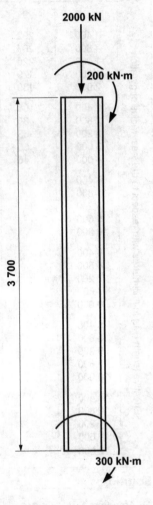

2000 kN

200 kN·m

3 700

300 kN·m

$L = 3\,700$ mm $M_{f1} = 200$ kN·m

$C_f = 2\,000$ kN $M_{f2} = 300$ kN·m

Try a W310x118 column.

Although Table 5-1, Class of Sections in Bending, page 5-8, lists the W310x118 as Class 2, the addition of axial load might change that class (as per Table 2 in Clause 11.2 of S16-09). However, an examination of Table 4-3, Class of Sections for Beam-Columns, page 4-10, shows that the W310x118 is always a Class 2 section, and Clause 13.8.2 applies:

$$\frac{C_f}{C_r} + \frac{0.85 U_{1x} M_{fx}}{M_{rx}} + \frac{\beta U_{1y} M_{fy}}{M_{ry}} \le 1.0$$

i) *Cross-sectional strength*

$C_f = 2\,000$ kN

$M_{fx} = 300$ kN·m

From Table of Factored Axial Compressive Resistances, page 4-37, $C_r = C_{ro} = 4\,660$ kN, and $M_{rx} = 606$ kN·m

$M_{f1} / M_{f2} = 200/300 = 0.67$ (double curvature)

From Table 4-6, page 4-18, $\omega_{1x} = 0.40$

$KL_x/r_x = 1.0\,(3\,700/136) = 27.2$

From Table 4-7, page 4-19, $C_e/A = 2\,664$ MPa (by interpolation)

$C_e = 2\,664 \times 15\,000$ mm$^2 = 40\,000$ kN, $C_f/C_e = 2\,000/40\,000 = 0.05$

From Table 4-8, page 4-20, $U = 1.05$

$U_{1x} = \omega_{1x} U = 0.40 \times 1.05 = 0.42\ < 1.0$

Therefore, $U_{1x} = 1.0$

$$\frac{2\,000}{4\,660} + \frac{0.85 \times 1.0 \times 300}{606} = 0.429 + 0.421 = 0.85 < 1.0$$

ii) Overall member strength

$KL_x/r_x = 27.2$, From Table 4-4 (page 4-13), $C_r/A = 297$ MPa, for $F_y = 345$ MPa

$C_r = C_{rx} = 297 \times 15\,000/10^3 = 4\,460$ kN (uniaxial bending about axis X-X)

$U_{1x} = 0.4 \times 1.05 = 0.42$ (for braced frames)

$$\frac{2\,000}{4\,460} + \frac{0.85 \times 0.42 \times 300}{606} = 0.448 + 0.177 = 0.625 < 1.0$$

iii) Lateral-torsional buckling strength

$C_r = C_{ry} = C_{rL} = 3\,850$ kN   (by interpolation, table on page 4-37)

$L = 3\,700$ mm $< L_u = 4\,920$ mm, $M_{rx} = 606$ kN·m

$U_{1x} = 1.0$

$$\frac{2\,000}{3\,850} + \frac{0.85 \times 1.0 \times 300}{606} = 0.519 + 0.421 = 0.940 < 1.0$$

The W310x118 column section is adequate.

Comments:

1. C_r could be more accurately determined by computing the KL/r values and entering the tables of Unit Factored Compressive Resistances for the larger KL/r and multiplying that value by the area of the column.

2. When $L > L_u$ the tables on pages 4-118 to 4-120, Factored Moment Resistances of Columns, will be more useful. (Caution: if a column section changes from Class 2 to Class 3 on account of high axial loads, M_{rx} or M'_{rx} values need to be adjusted as noted on page 4-117.)

2. Given:

Same as example 1, except that the column is part of an unbraced (sway) frame. Additional moments of 50 kN·m at each end of the column cause bending about the Y-Y axis, such that double curvature is induced in the column.

Solution:

$L = 3\,700$ mm $M_{fx1} = 200$ kN·m $M_{fy1} = 50$ kN·m

$C_f = 2\,000$ kN $M_{fx2} = 300$ kN·m $M_{fy2} = 50$ kN·m

Try a W310x129 column.

This section is a heavier one of the same series as the W310x118 used in Example 1, but is a Class 1 section. S16-09 Clause 13.8.2 applies.

i) Cross-sectional strength

For members in unbraced frames, the cross-sectional strength check does not govern.

ii) Overall member strength

$C_f = 2\,000$ kN, $M_{fx} = 300$ kN·m, $M_{fy} = 50$ kN·m

$KL_x/r_x = 1.0\,(3\,700/137) = 27.0$, $KL_y/r_y = 1.0\,(3\,700/78.0) = 47.4$

From Table 4-4 (page 4-13), $C_r/A = 257$ MPa (for $KL/r = 47.4$)

$C_r = 257 \times 16\,500/10^3 = 4\,240$ kN

From Table of Factored Axial Compressive Resistances, page 4-37,

$M_{rx} = 671$ kN·m and $M_{ry} = 308$ kN·m

$U_{1x} = 1.0$ and $U_{1y} = 1.0$ (unbraced frame)

$$\lambda_y = \frac{KL_y}{r_y}\sqrt{\frac{F_y}{\pi^2 E}} = 47.4\sqrt{\frac{345}{\pi^2\,200\,000}} = 0.627$$

$\beta = 0.6 + 4.0\,\lambda_y = 0.6 + 0.4 \times 0.627 = 0.851 > 0.85$, Therefore, $\beta = 0.85$

$$\frac{2\,000}{4\,240} + \frac{0.85 \times 1.0 \times 300}{671} + \frac{0.85 \times 1.0 \times 50}{308} = 0.472 + 0.380 + 0.138 = 0.990 < 1.0$$

iii) Lateral-torsional buckling

$C_r = C_{ry} = C_{rL} = 4\,240$ kN (previously calculated)

$L = 3\,700$ mm $< L_u = 5\,080$ mm, $M_{rx} = 671$ kN·m

$U_{1x} = 1.0$ and $U_{1y} = 1.0$

$\beta = 0.85$ (previously calculated)

$$\frac{2\,000}{4\,240} + \frac{0.85 \times 1.0 \times 300}{671} + \frac{0.85 \times 1.0 \times 50}{308} = 0.472 + 0.380 + 0.138 = 0.990 < 1.0$$

The W310x129 column section is adequate.

iv) Biaxial bending interaction

$$\frac{M_{fx}}{M_{rx}} + \frac{M_{fy}}{M_{ry}} = \frac{300}{671} + \frac{50}{308} = 0.447 + 0.162 = 0.609 < 1.0$$

Shear

Where beams with large end moments are connected to columns with thin webs, a check for shear capacity in the column web will be necessary.

Note

For further design examples of beam-columns, see "Limit States Design in Structural Steel", G.L. Kulak and G.Y. Grondin, Canadian Institute of Steel Construction.

FACTORED MOMENT RESISTANCES OF COLUMNS

The tables on pages 4-118 to 4-120 list: 1) the factored moment resistance for strong-axis bending M_{rx} for cases where the unsupported length of compression flange L is less than L_u, and 2) the factored moment resistance M'_{rx} where L is greater than L_u. The tables are based on CSA G40.21-350W for WWF shapes, and on CSA G40.21-350W, ASTM A992 and A572 Grade 50 for W shapes normally used as columns. Sections are ordered as in Part Six of this Handbook, with all of the sections of the same nominal dimensions listed together.

The M_{rx} and M'_{rx} values are based on the class of the section in bending about the X-X axis, without axial load. However, the class of a section used as a beam-column is a function of the ratio of the factored axial load to the factored axial compressive load at yield stress $C_f/\phi\, C_y$ in accordance with CAN/CSA S16-09 Clause 11.2. For example, a W410x39 of ASTM A992 steel becomes a Class 3 section when $C_f/\phi\, C_y$ exceeds 0.572, based on the Class 2 limit for h/w of:

$$\frac{1700}{\sqrt{F_y}}\left(1 - 0.61\frac{C_f}{\phi C_y}\right)$$

Table 4-3 on page 4-7 lists the classes for sections when they are used as beam-columns, and the values of $C_f/\phi\, C_y$ at which the class changes.

Thus, sections whose loading causes a change from Class 2 to Class 3 need to have their tabulated values of M_{rx} and M'_{rx} adjusted. A conservative method is to multiply the listed values by the factor S_x/Z_x.

FACTORED MOMENT RESISTANCES OF COLUMNS, M_{rx} and M'_{rx} (kN·m)

CSA G40.21 350W

$\phi = 0.90$

Designation	M_{rx}	M'_{rx} for the following unsupported lengths in millimetres									
		8 000	9 000	10 000	11 000	12 000	13 000	14 000	16 000	18 000	20 000
WWF650x864	8 600	—	—	—	—	—	8 600	8 470	8 230	8 000	7 760
WWF650x739	7 940	—	—	—	—	—	7 890	7 770	7 530	7 300	7 060
WWF650x598	6 650	—	—	—	—	6 590	6 460	6 340	6 090	5 850	5 600
WWF650x499	5 510	—	—	—	5 450	5 330	5 200	5 070	4 810	4 540	4 280
** WWF650x400	3 940	—	—	—	3 870	3 770	3 660	3 550	3 330	3 110	2 880
WWF600x793	7 210	—	—	—	—	—	7 190	7 090	6 890	6 700	6 510
WWF600x680	6 680	—	—	—	—	—	6 610	6 510	6 310	6 120	5 930
WWF600x551	5 610	—	—	—	—	5 510	5 410	5 300	5 100	4 890	4 690
WWF600x460	4 660	—	—	4 660	4 550	4 440	4 330	4 220	4 000	3 780	3 560
* WWF600x369	3 370	—	—	3 340	3 250	3 150	3 060	2 960	2 770	2 570	2 370
WWF550x721	5 990	—	—	—	—	—	5 950	5 870	5 710	5 550	5 390
WWF550x620	5 540	—	—	—	—	—	5 470	5 390	5 230	5 070	4 910
WWF550x503	4 660	—	—	—	4 630	4 550	4 460	4 380	4 210	4 050	3 890
WWF550x420	3 910	—	—	3 850	3 760	3 670	3 580	3 480	3 300	3 120	2 940
** WWF550x280	2 310	—	2 300	2 230	2 150	2 080	2 000	1 920	1 770	1 610	1 420
WWF500x651	4 850	—	—	—	—	—	4 820	4 760	4 630	4 510	4 380
WWF500x561	4 500	—	—	—	—	4 500	4 440	4 370	4 250	4 120	4 000
WWF500x456	3 810	—	—	—	3 760	3 700	3 630	3 560	3 430	3 300	3 170
WWF500x381	3 180	—	3 180	3 110	3 030	2 960	2 880	2 810	2 670	2 520	2 380
WWF500x343	2 870	—	2 820	2 740	2 670	2 590	2 510	2 430	2 280	2 130	1 980
WWF500x306	2 540	2 530	2 460	2 380	2 300	2 220	2 140	2 060	1 900	1 740	1 550
WWF500x276	2 340	2 320	2 250	2 170	2 090	2 010	1 930	1 850	1 690	1 520	1 340
* WWF500x254	1 940	—	1 880	1 820	1 750	1 690	1 620	1 550	1 410	1 270	1 110
** WWF500x223	1 630	—	1 580	1 530	1 470	1 410	1 350	1 290	1 170	1 030	892
** WWF500x197	1 360	—	1 340	1 290	1 240	1 190	1 140	1 090	986	869	752
WWF450x503	3 590	—	—	—	—	3 580	3 530	3 480	3 390	3 290	3 190
WWF450x409	3 040	—	—	—	2 990	2 940	2 880	2 830	2 730	2 630	2 530
WWF450x342	2 550	—	2 520	2 470	2 410	2 350	2 290	2 240	2 120	2 010	1 900
WWF450x308	2 300	2 290	2 230	2 170	2 110	2 050	1 990	1 930	1 810	1 690	1 570
WWF450x274	2 040	2 000	1 940	1 870	1 810	1 740	1 680	1 620	1 490	1 360	1 210
WWF450x248	1 880	1 830	1 770	1 710	1 640	1 580	1 510	1 450	1 320	1 180	1 040
WWF450x228	1 720	1 660	1 590	1 530	1 460	1 400	1 330	1 260	1 130	976	861
* WWF450x201	1 390	1 350	1 290	1 240	1 190	1 130	1 080	1 020	905	779	684
** WWF450x177	1 200	1 170	1 120	1 080	1 030	978	927	876	763	653	570
WWF400x444	2 760	—	—	—	—	2 760	2 720	2 690	2 610	2 540	2 470
WWF400x362	2 360	—	—	2 350	2 310	2 270	2 240	2 200	2 120	2 040	1 970
WWF400x303	1 980	—	1 950	1 900	1 860	1 820	1 770	1 730	1 640	1 560	1 480
WWF400x273	1 790	1 770	1 720	1 670	1 630	1 580	1 530	1 490	1 400	1 310	1 220
WWF400x243	1 590	1 540	1 490	1 440	1 390	1 340	1 290	1 240	1 140	1 040	932
WWF400x220	1 470	1 410	1 360	1 310	1 260	1 210	1 160	1 110	1 010	900	801
WWF400x202	1 340	1 260	1 210	1 160	1 110	1 060	1 010	959	846	739	656
* WWF400x178	1 080	1 020	982	940	897	854	811	769	673	585	518
* WWF400x157	983	921	879	836	793	749	706	662	560	484	427

F_y taken as 350 MPa for WWF shapes and 345 MPa for W shapes.   * Class 3 section   ** Class 4 section

Note: Moment resistances are based on class of section for X-X axis of bending only, $\omega_2 = 1.0$.

FACTORED MOMENT RESISTANCES OF COLUMNS, M_{rx} and M'_{rx} (kN·m)

$\phi = 0.90$

Designation	M_{rx}	M'_{rx} for the following unsupported lengths in millimetres									
		6 000	7 000	8 000	9 000	10 000	11 000	12 000	14 000	16 000	18 000
WWF350x315	1 760	—	—	—	—	1 760	1 730	1 700	1 640	1 590	1 530
WWF350x263	1 490	—	—	1 490	1 460	1 430	1 390	1 360	1 300	1 240	1 180
WWF350x238	1 350	—	—	1 320	1 280	1 250	1 220	1 180	1 120	1 050	985
WWF350x212	1 200	—	1 180	1 140	1 110	1 070	1 030	999	928	858	783
WWF350x192	1 110	—	1 080	1 040	1 010	970	934	898	827	756	671
WWF350x176	1 010	1 010	973	935	897	859	821	784	710	625	549
WWF350x155	904	890	852	813	774	734	695	656	572	490	430
WWF350x137	816	798	760	722	682	643	604	565	475	405	354

Designation	M_{rx}	M'_{rx} for the following unsupported lengths in millimetres									
		8 000	9 000	10 000	12 000	14 000	16 000	18 000	20 000	24 000	28 000
W360x1086	8 450	—	—	—	—	—	—	—	—	8 270	8 030
W360x990	7 550	—	—	—	—	—	—	—	7 520	7 290	7 060
W360x900	6 710	—	—	—	—	—	—	—	6 610	6 390	6 170
W360x818	5 990	—	—	—	—	—	—	5 940	5 830	5 610	5 400
W360x744	5 340	—	—	—	—	—	5 320	5 220	5 120	4 910	4 700
W360x677	4 750	—	—	—	—	—	4 680	4 590	4 490	4 290	4 090
W360x634	4 410	—	—	—	—	4 400	4 310	4 210	4 110	3 920	3 720
W360x592	4 070	—	—	—	—	4 030	3 930	3 840	3 740	3 550	3 360
W360x551	3 760	—	—	—	—	3 680	3 580	3 490	3 390	3 200	3 010
W360x509	3 420	—	—	—	3 400	3 310	3 220	3 120	3 030	2 850	2 670
W360x463	3 070	—	—	—	3 010	2 920	2 830	2 740	2 650	2 470	2 290
W360x421	2 760	—	—	—	2 670	2 580	2 500	2 410	2 320	2 140	1 970
W360x382	2 470	—	—	2 450	2 360	2 270	2 190	2 100	2 010	1 840	1 670
W360x347	2 220	—	2 210	2 170	2 080	1 990	1 910	1 820	1 740	1 570	1 380
W360x314	1 980	—	1 950	1 900	1 820	1 730	1 650	1 570	1 480	1 320	1 130
W360x287	1 800	1 800	1 760	1 710	1 630	1 550	1 460	1 380	1 300	1 120	953
W360x262	1 630	1 610	1 570	1 530	1 440	1 360	1 280	1 200	1 120	931	794
W360x237	1 460	1 420	1 380	1 340	1 250	1 170	1 090	1 010	916	755	643
W360x216	1 320	1 280	1 240	1 190	1 110	1 030	951	868	774	637	542
W360x196	1 190	1 130	1 080	1 040	961	880	800	703	627	516	439
W360x179	1 080	1 010	965	924	843	762	671	588	524	430	366
W360x162	975	895	855	814	733	653	558	488	434	356	302
* W360x147	798	740	708	675	609	544	467	407	361	295	250
* W360x134	723	663	630	598	532	461	392	341	302	246	208
W310x500	3 070	—	—	—	—	2 990	2 910	2 840	2 760	2 600	2 450
W310x454	2 740	—	—	—	2 710	2 630	2 550	2 480	2 400	2 250	2 100
W310x415	2 450	—	—	—	2 390	2 320	2 250	2 170	2 100	1 960	1 810
W310x375	2 170	—	—	2 160	2 090	2 020	1 950	1 880	1 810	1 670	1 530
W310x342	1 970	—	1 960	1 930	1 860	1 790	1 720	1 650	1 580	1 450	1 310
W310x313	1 780	—	1 750	1 720	1 650	1 580	1 510	1 450	1 380	1 240	1 090

F_y taken as 350 MPa for WWF shapes and 345 MPa for W shapes.   * Class 3 section

Note: Moment resistances are based on class of section for X-X axis of bending only, $\omega_2 = 1.0$.

See page 6-20

FACTORED MOMENT RESISTANCES OF COLUMNS, M_{rx} and M'_{rx} (kN·m)

$\phi = 0.90$

Designation	M_{rx}	M'_{rx} for the following unsupported lengths in millimetres									
		4 000	5 000	6 000	7 000	8 000	9 000	10 000	12 000	14 000	16 000
W310x283	1 580	—	—	—	—	1 580	1 540	1 510	1 440	1 380	1 310
W310x253	1 390	—	—	—	—	1 370	1 330	1 300	1 240	1 170	1 110
W310x226	1 240	—	—	—	1 220	1 190	1 160	1 130	1 060	999	935
W310x202	1 090	—	—	—	1 060	1 030	999	967	904	841	779
W310x179	947	—	—	941	909	877	846	814	752	691	629
W310x158	829	—	—	813	781	750	719	688	626	566	494
W310x143	751	—	—	729	698	666	635	604	543	477	412
W310x129	671	—	—	643	612	581	551	520	460	390	336
W310x118	605	—	603	574	543	513	482	452	388	324	279
W310x107	550	—	544	515	485	455	424	394	326	272	234
* W310x97	447	—	446	424	400	376	351	327	272	226	194
W250x167	755	—	—	752	730	708	687	665	622	580	537
W250x149	661	—	—	650	628	607	586	565	523	481	439
W250x131	574	—	—	555	533	512	492	471	430	389	341
W250x115	497	—	491	470	449	429	408	388	348	301	262
W250x101	435	—	424	403	382	362	342	322	279	236	205
W250x89	382	—	367	346	326	306	285	265	220	186	161
W250x80	338	—	321	302	282	262	242	221	179	151	130
W250x73	306	—	287	268	248	228	209	185	149	126	108
W200x100	357	—	349	335	321	307	294	280	253	222	194
W200x86	305	—	292	279	265	252	238	225	197	168	147
W200x71	249	246	232	219	205	192	179	166	137	116	101
W200x59	203	195	182	169	155	142	128	114	93.2	79.1	68.8
W200x52	177	168	155	142	129	116	101	89.5	73.3	62.1	53.9
* W200x46	139	133	122	112	101	90.2	78.4	69.5	56.6	47.9	41.5
W150x37	96.3	85.5	77.6	69.9	61.6	53.3	47.0	42.1	34.8	29.7	25.9
W150x30	75.8	64.0	56.4	48.3	40.4	34.8	30.6	27.3	22.5	19.1	16.7
** W150x22	46.6	38.8	33.4	27.4	22.6	19.3	16.9	15.0	12.3	10.4	9.05

F_y taken as 350 MPa for WWF shapes and 345 MPa for W shapes.   * Class 3 section   ** Class 4 section

Note: Moment resistances are based on class of section for X-X axis of bending only, $\omega_2 = 1.0$.

FACTORED AXIAL COMPRESSIVE RESISTANCES

Double-Angle Struts

Back-to-Back Double Angles, CSA G40.21-300W

For equal-leg angles, see page 4-122.

For unequal-leg angles, long legs back-to-back, see page 4-126.

For unequal-leg angles, short legs back-to-back, see page 4-132.

Star-Shaped Double Angles, CSA G40.21-300W

For star-shaped angles, see page 4-138.

DOUBLE ANGLE STRUTS

Equal-Leg Angles

Factored Axial Compressive Resistances (kN)

Legs 10 mm Back-to-Back *

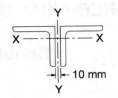

G40.21
300W
$\phi = 0.90$

Designation (mm x mm x mm)			L203x203	L 152 x 152				L 127 x 127				
			13 **	19	16	13 **	9.5 **	19	16	13	9.5 **	7.9 **
Mass (kg/m)			78.4	85.4	71.9	58.1	44.1	70.4	59.4	48.1	36.6	30.7
Effective length (KL) in millimetres with respect to indicated axis	X-X Axis	0	1 920	2 940	2 470	1 920	1 080	2 420	2 040	1 660	1 080	753
		1 000	1 910	2 880	2 420	1 890	1 060	2 340	1 980	1 600	1 050	729
		2 000	1 820	2 590	2 190	1 700	962	1 980	1 680	1 370	900	627
		3 000	1 650	2 120	1 800	1 410	797	1 490	1 270	1 040	688	481
		4 000	1 420	1 640	1 390	1 090	623	1 080	920	755	501	351
		5 000	1 180	1 250	1 060	836	477	778	667	549	365	257
		6 000	972	956	814	642	367	577	496	408	272	191
		7 000	796	745	635	501	287	440	379	312	208	147
		8 000	655	591	505	399	228					
		9 000	543	479	409	323	185					
		10 000	456									
		11 000	386									
		12 000	330									
	Y-Y Axis	0	1 920	2 940	2 470	1 920	1 080	2 420	2 040	1 660	1 080	753
		1 000	1 180	2 640	2 090	1 450	647	2 250	1 820	1 360	749	442
		2 000	1 140	2 590	2 040	1 420	630	2 170	1 770	1 330	730	431
		3 000	1 120	2 450	1 960	1 370	615	1 950	1 610	1 230	698	416
		4 000	1 100	2 180	1 780	1 280	591	1 640	1 360	1 060	630	388
		5 000	1 060	1 870	1 530	1 130	550	1 340	1 110	871	534	343
		6 000	1 020	1 570	1 290	967	491	1 080	892	704	439	290
		7 000	948	1 310	1 080	813	424	871	720	570	358	240
		8 000	864	1 090	900	681	362	709	586	464	293	198
		9 000	774	915	755	573	308	584	483	383	243	165
		10 000	687	773	639	486	263	487	403	319	203	138
		11 000	608	659	544	415	225	411	340	270	172	117
		12 000	537	567	468	357	195					

PROPERTIES OF 2 ANGLES - 10 mm BACK-TO-BACK										
Area (mm²)	9 990	10 900	9 160	7 400	5 610	8 970	7 570	6 130	4 660	3 910
r_x (mm)	63.6	46.3	46.7	47.1	47.6	38.3	38.7	39.1	39.5	39.8
r_y (mm)	87.7	68.1	67.6	67.1	66.6	58.1	57.5	57.0	56.4	56.2
* r_z (mm)	40.3	29.7	29.8	30.0	30.2	24.8	24.8	25.0	25.1	25.2

IMPERIAL SIZE AND MASS										
Mass (lb/ft)	52.7	57.4	48.3	39.0	29.6	47.3	39.9	32.3	24.6	20.6
Thickness (in)	½	¾	⅝	½	⅜	¾	⅝	½	⅜	⁵⁄₁₆
Size (in)	8 x 8	6 x 6				5 x 5				

* See page 4-4 for more information. Interconnectors are assumed to be closely spaced.
** Factored axial compressive resistances calculated according to S16-09 Clause 13.3.5.

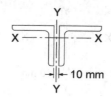

G40.21 300W

$\phi = 0.90$

10 mm

DOUBLE ANGLE STRUTS
Equal-Leg Angles
Factored Axial Compressive Resistances (kN)
Legs 10 mm Back-to-Back *

Designation (mm x mm x mm)			L 102 x 102					L 89 x 89		
		19	13	9.5	7.9 **	6.4 **	13	9.5	7.9	6.4 **
Mass (kg/m)		55.4	38.1	29.1	24.4	19.7	32.9	25.2	21.2	17.1
X-X Axis	0	1 910	1 310	1 000	751	481	1 130	867	729	482
	500	1 890	1 300	992	744	477	1 120	855	719	475
	1 000	1 790	1 240	945	710	455	1 040	797	671	444
	1 500	1 600	1 110	853	641	412	896	692	584	388
	2 000	1 360	952	733	552	355	732	568	481	320
	2 500	1 120	789	610	460	297	581	453	384	256
	3 000	907	645	500	378	244	459	359	305	204
	3 500	736	526	409	309	200	365	286	244	163
	4 000	602	431	336	254	164	294	231	197	132
	4 500	497	357	279	211	137	241	189	161	108
	5 000	415	299	233	177	115	200	157	134	89.6
	5 500	351	253	198	150	97.0			113	75.4
	6 000	300	216	169	128	83.0				
Y-Y Axis	0	1 910	1 310	1 000	751	481	1 130	867	729	482
	1 000	1 820	1 160	788	527	277	1 030	723	556	313
	2 000	1 670	1 100	756	509	268	932	673	525	300
	3 000	1 400	924	665	463	252	738	544	440	265
	4 000	1 100	725	532	381	221	551	409	334	210
	5 000	845	556	411	299	180	409	304	250	159
	6 000	653	429	318	232	143	308	229	189	121
	7 000	512	336	249	183	113	238	176	146	93.9
	8 000	408	267	199	146	91.0	187	139	115	74.4
	9 000	331	217	161	119	74.3				
	10 000									
	11 000									
	12 000									
PROPERTIES OF 2 ANGLES - 10 mm BACK-TO-BACK										
Area (mm²)		7 060	4 860	3 710	3 110	2 510	4 190	3 210	2 700	2 180
r_x (mm)		30.3	31.1	31.5	31.7	31.9	26.9	27.3	27.5	27.7
r_y (mm)		48.1	46.9	46.4	46.1	45.8	41.7	41.1	40.8	40.5
* r_z (mm)		19.8	19.9	20.1	20.2	20.3	17.3	17.4	17.5	17.6
IMPERIAL SIZE AND MASS										
Mass (lb/ft)		37.3	25.6	19.6	16.4	13.2	22.1	16.9	14.2	11.5
Thickness (in)		¾	½	⅜	⁵⁄₁₆	¼	½	⅜	⁵⁄₁₆	¼
Size (in)				4 x 4				3 ½ x 3 ½		

Effective length (KL) in millimetres with respect to indicated axis

* See page 4-4 for more information. Interconnectors are assumed to be closely spaced.
** Factored axial compressive resistances calculated according to S16-09 Clause 13.3.5.

DOUBLE ANGLE STRUTS

Equal-Leg Angles

Factored Axial Compressive Resistances (kN)

Legs 10 mm Back-to-Back *

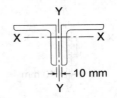

G40.21
300W
$\phi = 0.90$

Designation		L 76 x 76					L 64 x 64				
(mm x mm x mm)		13	9.5	7.9	6.4 **	4.8 **	13	9.5	7.9	6.4	4.8 **
Mass (kg/m)		27.9	21.4	18.0	14.6	11.0	22.8	17.6	14.8	12.0	9.14
X-X Axis	0	959	734	618	480	272	783	605	510	413	269
	500	938	719	606	470	266	755	584	493	400	261
	1 000	841	648	547	425	242	635	495	419	341	224
	1 500	684	531	450	351	200	474	372	317	259	171
	2 000	526	411	349	273	157	339	268	229	188	125
	2 500	398	313	266	209	120	244	193	166	136	91.1
	3 000	304	239	204	161	92.7	181	143	123	102	67.9
	3 500	236	187	159	125	72.5	138	109	94.1	77.6	52.0
	4 000	187	148	127	99.7	57.7					
	4 500	152	120	103	80.8	46.8					
	5 000										
	5 500										
	6 000										
Y-Y Axis	0	959	734	618	480	272	783	605	510	413	269
	500	904	652	515	354	156	752	558	450	334	181
	1 000	889	641	506	347	152	728	544	440	327	177
	1 500	839	616	490	338	150	660	498	409	311	171
	2 000	755	560	453	321	145	569	429	355	275	159
	2 500	656	488	399	291	138	475	357	295	231	139
	3 000	559	415	341	253	126	390	292	242	190	117
	3 500	471	350	288	216	112	319	239	197	155	97.1
	4 000	397	295	243	183	96.8	263	196	162	128	80.4
	4 500	335	249	205	155	83.2	218	163	134	106	67.0
	5 000	285	211	174	132	71.5	183	136	113	88.7	56.3
	5 500	244	181	149	113	61.7	155	115	95.4	75.1	47.8
	6 000	210	156	129	97.6	53.5	133	98.7	81.6	64.2	41.0

Effective length (KL) in millimetres with respect to indicated axis

PROPERTIES OF 2 ANGLES - 10 mm BACK-TO-BACK										
Area (mm^2)	3 550	2 720	2 290	1 850	1 410	2 900	2 240	1 890	1 530	1 160
r_x (mm)	22.8	23.2	23.4	23.6	23.9	18.8	19.1	19.3	19.5	19.8
r_y (mm)	36.6	36.0	35.7	35.4	35.2	31.6	31.0	30.7	30.3	30.1
* r_z (mm)	14.8	14.9	15.0	15.0	15.1	12.4	12.4	12.4	12.5	12.6

IMPERIAL SIZE AND MASS										
Mass (lb/ft)	18.7	14.4	12.1	9.78	7.41	15.3	11.8	9.97	8.08	6.14
Thickness (in)	$\frac{1}{2}$	$\frac{3}{8}$	$\frac{5}{16}$	$\frac{1}{4}$	$\frac{3}{16}$	$\frac{1}{2}$	$\frac{3}{8}$	$\frac{5}{16}$	$\frac{1}{4}$	$\frac{3}{16}$
Size (in)	3 x 3					2 $\frac{1}{2}$ x 2 $\frac{1}{2}$				

* See page 4-4 for more information. Interconnectors are assumed to be closely spaced.

** Factored axial compressive resistances calculated according to S16-09 Clause 13.3.5.

G40.21
300W
$\phi = 0.90$

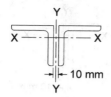

10 mm

DOUBLE ANGLE STRUTS
Equal-Leg Angles
Factored Axial Compressive Resistances (kN)
Legs 10 mm Back-to-Back *

Designation (mm x mm x mm)			L 51 x 51					L 44 x 44			L 38 x 38		
		9.5	7.9	6.4	4.8	3.2 **	6.4	4.8	3.2 **	6.4	4.8	3.2 **
Mass (kg/m)		13.8	11.7	9.50	7.24	4.91	8.24	6.30	4.28	6.96	5.34	3.65
X-X Axis	0	473	402	327	249	121	284	217	121	239	184	121
	500	443	378	308	235	114	260	199	111	210	162	107
	1 000	336	289	237	182	88.9	183	142	80.4	131	103	68.7
	1 500	224	194	160	124	60.9	114	90.2	51.3	76.0	59.9	40.4
	2 000	148	129	107	83.1	41.1	73.3	58.1	33.2	46.8	37.0	25.1
	2 500	102	89.1	74.0	57.7	28.6	49.7	39.5	22.6			
	3 000	73.8	64.4	53.5	41.8	20.7						
	3 500											
	4 000											
	4 500											
	5 000											
	5 500											
	6 000											
Y-Y Axis	0	473	402	327	249	121	284	217	121	239	184	121
	500	448	371	285	191	66.6	255	177	74.8	221	158	83.8
	1 000	423	353	275	186	65.0	239	169	72.6	197	145	80.0
	1 500	363	304	240	170	62.3	198	145	67.4	154	114	68.4
	2 000	294	245	194	141	56.9	153	113	56.9	113	84.5	52.0
	2 500	231	192	153	112	48.4	116	86.1	44.9	83.5	62.2	38.6
	3 000	182	151	120	88.1	39.5	89.1	66.0	34.9	62.6	46.6	29.1
	3 500	144	119	94.5	69.8	31.9	69.4	51.5	27.4	48.1	35.8	22.4
	4 000	116	95.7	75.9	56.1	25.9	55.1	40.9	21.9	37.9	28.2	
	4 500	94.3	78.0	61.9	45.8	21.2	44.6	33.1				
	5 000	78.1	64.6	51.2	38.0							
	5 500											
	6 000											

Effective length (KL) in millimetres with respect to indicated axis

PROPERTIES OF 2 ANGLES - 10 mm BACK-TO-BACK

Area (mm²)	1 750	1 490	1 210	922	626	1 050	802	546	887	680	464
r_x (mm)	15.1	15.3	15.5	15.7	15.9	13.4	13.7	13.9	11.4	11.6	11.8
r_y (mm)	26.0	25.6	25.3	25.0	24.7	22.8	22.5	22.2	20.3	20.0	19.6
* r_z (mm)	9.89	9.90	9.93	10.0	10.1	8.68	8.73	8.82	7.42	7.45	7.52

IMPERIAL SIZE AND MASS

Mass (lb/ft)	9.26	7.85	6.38	4.86	3.30	5.54	4.23	2.88	4.68	3.59	2.45
Thickness (in)	$\frac{3}{8}$	$\frac{5}{16}$	$\frac{1}{4}$	$\frac{3}{16}$	$\frac{1}{8}$	$\frac{1}{4}$	$\frac{3}{16}$	$\frac{1}{8}$	$\frac{1}{4}$	$\frac{3}{16}$	$\frac{1}{8}$
Size (in)			2 x 2				$1\frac{3}{4}$ x $1\frac{3}{4}$			$1\frac{1}{2}$ x $1\frac{1}{2}$	

* See page 4-4 for more information. Interconnectors are assumed to be closely spaced.

** Factored axial compressive resistances calculated according to S16-09 Clause 13.3.5.

DOUBLE ANGLE STRUTS
Unequal-Leg Angles
Factored Axial Compressive Resistances (kN)
Long Legs 10 mm Back-to-Back *

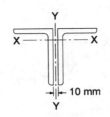

G40.21
300W
$\phi = 0.90$

Designation (mm x mm x mm)		L 178 x 102		L 152 x 102					L 152 x 89			
		13 **	9.5 **	19	16	13 **	9.5 **	7.9 **	16	13 **	9.5 **	7.9 **
Mass (kg/m)		53.3	40.5	70.4	59.4	48.1	36.6	30.7	56.2	45.5	34.6	29.0
X-X Axis	0	1 620	1 040	2 420	2 040	1 620	1 040	753	1 930	1 530	975	740
	1 000	1 600	1 030	2 370	2 000	1 590	1 020	739	1 900	1 500	957	727
	2 000	1 500	971	2 150	1 820	1 450	933	675	1 720	1 370	874	664
	3 000	1 320	857	1 780	1 510	1 210	781	566	1 430	1 140	732	557
	4 000	1 100	717	1 390	1 190	949	616	448	1 130	898	579	441
	5 000	894	582	1 070	911	731	476	346	866	693	447	342
	6 000	716	467	821	702	565	368	268	668	535	347	265
	7 000	575	376	642	549	442	289	211	523	420	272	208
	8 000	467	305	511	438	353	230	168	417	335	217	166
	9 000	384	251	414	355	286	187	137	338	272	176	135
	10 000	319	209									
	11 000	269	176									
	12 000											
Y-Y Axis	0	1 620	1 040	2 420	2 040	1 620	1 040	753	1 930	1 530	975	740
	1 000	1 200	616	2 210	1 780	1 300	694	422	1 680	1 220	653	420
	2 000	1 090	564	1 990	1 620	1 190	644	395	1 430	1 060	580	379
	3 000	892	487	1 600	1 310	978	556	352	1 080	808	462	315
	4 000	685	392	1 220	996	752	444	292	775	585	344	243
	5 000	518	305	915	749	569	343	232	561	425	254	183
	6 000	395	237	696	570	434	265	182	417	317	191	139
	7 000	307	186	539	442	337	207	144	319	242	147	108
	8 000	243		427	350	268	165	115				
	9 000											
	10 000											
	11 000											
	12 000											

Effective length (KL) in millimetres with respect to indicated axis

PROPERTIES OF 2 ANGLES - 10 mm BACK-TO-BACK												
Area (mm²)	6 790	5 160	8 970	7 570	6 130	4 660	3 910	7 160	5 800	4 410	3 700
r_x (mm)	57.3	57.8	47.6	48.0	48.5	48.9	49.2	48.2	48.6	49.1	49.3
r_y (mm)	40.2	39.7	43.3	42.7	42.1	41.6	41.3	36.6	36.0	35.4	35.2
* r_z (mm)	22.2	22.4	21.9	22.0	22.2	22.4	22.5	19.1	19.3	19.5	19.6

IMPERIAL SIZE AND MASS												
Mass (lb/ft)	35.8	27.2	47.3	39.9	32.3	24.6	20.6	37.7	30.6	23.3	19.5
Thickness (in)	½	⅜	¾	⅝	½	⅜	⁵⁄₁₆	⅝	½	⅜	⁵⁄₁₆
Size (in)	7 x 4		6 x 4					6 x 3 ½			

* See page 4-4 for more information. Interconnectors are assumed to be closely spaced.

** Factored axial compressive resistances calculated according to S16-09 Clause 13.3.5.

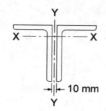

DOUBLE ANGLE STRUTS
Unequal-Leg Angles
Factored Axial Compressive Resistances (kN)
Long Legs 10 mm Back-to-Back *

Designation (mm x mm x mm)			L 127 x 89				L 127 x 76			
			13	9.5 **	7.9 **	6.4 **	13	9.5 **	7.9 **	6.4 **
Mass (kg/m)			40.5	30.9	25.9	20.9	38.0	29.0	24.3	19.6
	X-X Axis	0	1 390	974	740	481	1 310	909	686	481
		1 000	1 350	945	718	467	1 270	883	666	467
		2 000	1 160	818	623	406	1 090	765	578	407
		3 000	897	634	483	315	845	594	450	317
		4 000	657	466	356	233	620	438	332	235
		5 000	480	342	262	171	454	322	244	173
		6 000	359	256	196	128	339	241	183	130
		7 000	275	196	150	98.7	260	185	141	99.6
		8 000	216	154	118	77.6	204	145	111	78.4
		9 000								
		10 000								
		11 000								
		12 000								
	Y-Y Axis	0	1 390	974	740	481	1 310	909	686	481
		500	1 220	752	504	266	1 150	710	475	271
		1 000	1 190	725	482	252	1 100	676	450	256
		1 500	1 130	697	465	244	1 020	632	424	243
		2 000	1 040	654	441	234	894	565	386	226
		2 500	926	592	407	221	758	486	338	204
		3 000	803	521	365	204	631	409	289	180
		3 500	687	451	321	184	522	341	243	155
		4 000	585	387	278	164	433	284	204	132
		4 500	499	332	240	144	362	238	172	113
		5 000	427	285	208	126	305	201	146	96.8
		5 500	368	246	180	110	259	172	125	83.3
		6 000	319	214	157	96.9	223	148	108	72.2

Effective length (KL) in millimetres with respect to indicated axis

PROPERTIES OF 2 ANGLES - 10 mm BACK-TO-BACK										
Area (mm^2)			5 160	3 930	3 300	2 660	4 840	3 690	3 100	2 500
r_x (mm)			40.1	40.6	40.8	41.0	40.3	40.8	41.0	41.2
r_y (mm)			37.9	37.4	37.1	36.8	32.0	31.4	31.1	30.8
* r_z (mm)			19.2	19.3	19.4	19.6	16.5	16.6	16.7	16.8
IMPERIAL SIZE AND MASS										
Mass (lb/ft)			27.2	20.7	17.4	14.0	25.5	19.5	16.4	13.2
Thickness (in)			½	⅜	5/16	¼	½	⅜	5/16	¼
Size (in)			5 x 3 ½				5 x 3			

* See page 4-4 for more information. Interconnectors are assumed to be closely spaced.
** Factored axial compressive resistances calculated according to S16-09 Clause 13.3.5.

DOUBLE ANGLE STRUTS

Unequal-Leg Angles

Factored Axial Compressive Resistances (kN)

Long Legs 10 mm Back-to-Back *

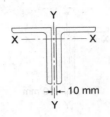

G40.21
300W
$\phi = 0.90$

Designation		L 102 x 89				L 102 x 76			
(mm x mm x mm)		13	9.5	7.9 **	6.4 **	13	9.5	7.9 **	6.4 **
Mass (kg/m)		35.5	27.1	22.8	18.4	33.0	25.2	21.2	17.1
X-X Axis	0	1 220	934	741	480	1 130	867	685	480
	500	1 210	926	735	476	1 120	859	679	476
	1 000	1 150	883	702	455	1 070	820	649	456
	1 500	1 040	800	636	413	969	744	589	415
	2 000	895	690	550	357	836	644	511	361
	2 500	745	576	460	299	697	539	428	303
	3 000	610	473	379	247	573	444	353	251
	3 500	499	388	311	203	469	365	291	206
	4 000	410	319	256	167	386	301	240	171
	4 500	340	265	213	139	320	250	199	142
	5 000	285	222	178	117	268	210	167	119
	5 500	241	188	151	99.0	227	178	142	101
	6 000	206	161	129	84.8	195	152	122	86.7
Y-Y Axis	0	1 220	934	741	480	1 130	867	685	480
	500	1 110	772	556	303	1 040	730	528	316
	1 000	1 090	755	541	293	1 010	708	510	304
	1 500	1 050	735	527	287	943	669	486	292
	2 000	978	695	505	278	836	602	445	273
	2 500	875	632	468	263	716	519	389	246
	3 000	765	558	420	243	601	438	331	214
	3 500	659	483	368	219	501	366	278	183
	4 000	565	416	318	193	418	306	234	155
	4 500	484	357	275	168	350	257	197	132
	5 000	416	307	237	147	296	217	167	112
	5 500	360	266	206	128	253	185	143	96.4
	6 000	312	231	179	112	217	159	123	83.3

Left column label: Effective length (KL) in millimetres with respect to indicated axis

PROPERTIES OF 2 ANGLES - 10 mm BACK-TO-BACK

Area (mm²)		4 530	3 460	2 910	2 340	4 200	3 210	2 700	2 180
r_x (mm)		31.5	31.9	32.1	32.3	31.8	32.2	32.4	32.7
r_y (mm)		40.2	39.7	39.4	39.1	34.0	33.4	33.1	32.8
* r_z (mm)		18.4	18.5	18.6	18.7	16.2	16.4	16.5	16.6

IMPERIAL SIZE AND MASS

Mass (lb/ft)		23.9	18.2	15.3	12.4	22.2	17.0	14.3	11.5
Thickness (in)		½	⅜	⁵⁄₁₆	¼	½	⅜	⁵⁄₁₆	¼
Size (in)		4 x 3 ½				4 x 3			

* See page 4-4 for more information. Interconnectors are assumed to be closely spaced.
** Factored axial compressive resistances calculated according to S16-09 Clause 13.3.5.

G40.21
300W
$\phi = 0.90$

DOUBLE ANGLE STRUTS
Unequal-Leg Angles
Factored Axial Compressive Resistances (kN)
Long Legs 10 mm Back-to-Back *

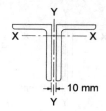

10 mm

Designation (mm x mm x mm)			L 89 x 76				L 89 x 64			
		13	9.5	7.9	6.4 **	13	9.5	7.9	6.4 **
Mass (kg/m)		30.4	23.3	19.6	15.8	27.9	21.4	18.0	14.6
X-X Axis	0	1 040	802	675	482	959	734	618	446
	500	1 030	791	666	476	946	725	611	441
	1 000	961	740	624	446	884	679	572	414
	1 500	834	645	545	391	770	594	502	363
	2 000	685	532	451	324	634	492	417	302
	2 500	546	426	362	261	508	395	335	244
	3 000	433	339	288	208	403	315	268	195
	3 500	345	271	231	167	322	252	215	157
	4 000	279	219	187	135	260	204	174	127
	4 500	228	179	153	111	213	167	143	104
	5 000	189	149	127	92.0	177	139	119	86.7
	5 500		125	107	77.4	149	117	99.9	73.0
	6 000								
Y-Y Axis	0	1 040	802	675	482	959	734	618	446
	500	974	696	543	338	898	647	509	325
	1 000	952	680	530	328	858	619	488	311
	1 500	893	647	508	318	765	557	445	289
	2 000	797	585	467	299	645	471	381	253
	2 500	687	507	410	270	526	385	313	212
	3 000	580	429	349	235	425	310	253	174
	3 500	486	359	294	201	344	251	205	142
	4 000	407	301	247	170	280	204	167	116
	4 500	343	253	208	144	231	168	138	96.2
	5 000	290	215	177	123	193	141	115	80.5
	5 500	248	183	151	105	163	119	97.4	68.2
	6 000	213	158	130	90.8				

Effective length (KL) in millimetres with respect to indicated axis

PROPERTIES OF 2 ANGLES - 10 mm BACK-TO-BACK									
Area (mm²)		3 870	2 970	2 500	2 020	3 550	2 720	2 290	1 850
r_x (mm)		27.3	27.7	27.9	28.1	27.6	28.0	28.2	28.4
r_y (mm)		35.2	34.6	34.3	34.1	29.1	28.4	28.1	27.8
* r_z (mm)		15.8	15.9	15.9	16.0	13.6	13.6	13.7	13.8

IMPERIAL SIZE AND MASS									
Mass (lb/ft)		20.4	15.6	13.2	10.6	18.7	14.4	12.1	9.78
Thickness (in)		½	³⁄₈	⁵⁄₁₆	¼	½	³⁄₈	⁵⁄₁₆	¼
Size (in)		3 ½ x 3				3 ½ x 2 ½			

* See page 4-4 for more information. Interconnectors are assumed to be closely spaced.
** Factored axial compressive resistances calculated according to S16-09 Clause 13.3.5.

DOUBLE ANGLE STRUTS
Unequal-Leg Angles
Factored Axial Compressive Resistances (kN)

Long Legs 10 mm Back-to-Back *

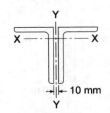

G40.21
300W
$\phi = 0.90$

Designation (mm x mm x mm)		L 76 x 64			L 76 x 51				
		9.5	7.9	6.4 **	13	9.5	7.9	6.4 **	4.8 **
Mass (kg/m)		19.5	16.4	13.3	22.8	17.6	14.8	12.0	9.14
X-X Axis	0	670	564	446	783	605	510	403	259
	500	656	553	438	767	593	501	396	254
	1 000	593	501	398	693	538	455	360	232
	1 500	490	415	330	571	446	379	301	194
	2 000	382	324	259	444	349	297	237	153
	2 500	292	249	199	339	268	229	183	118
	3 000	224	191	153	260	206	176	141	91.6
	3 500	175	150	120	203	161	138	111	71.9
	4 000	139	119	95.6	162	129	110	88.2	57.4
	4 500	113	96.5	77.5	131	104	89.3	71.6	46.6
	5 000								
	5 500								
	6 000								
Y-Y Axis	0	670	564	446	783	605	510	403	259
	500	606	484	345	744	550	443	320	169
	1 000	585	468	334	682	507	410	298	159
	1 500	531	431	313	571	423	344	256	142
	2 000	453	370	276	450	332	271	203	118
	2 500	372	306	231	348	255	208	158	93.5
	3 000	302	248	189	269	197	161	122	73.6
	3 500	245	202	154	212	155	126	95.9	58.3
	4 000	201	165	127	169	123	100	76.7	46.9
	4 500	166	137	105	137	100	81.5	62.3	38.3
	5 000	139	114	87.9					
	5 500	117	96.5	74.4					
	6 000								

Effective length (KL) in millimetres with respect to indicated axis

PROPERTIES OF 2 ANGLES - 10 mm BACK-TO-BACK									
Area (mm^2)		2 480	2 090	1 690	2 900	2 240	1 890	1 530	1 160
r_x (mm)		23.6	23.8	24.0	23.5	23.9	24.1	24.3	24.5
r_y (mm)		29.6	29.3	29.0	24.2	23.5	23.1	22.8	22.5
* r_z (mm)		13.3	13.3	13.4	10.9	10.9	11.0	11.0	11.1

IMPERIAL SIZE AND MASS									
Mass (lb/ft)		13.1	11.0	8.93	15.3	11.8	9.97	8.08	6.14
Thickness (in)		$\frac{3}{8}$	$\frac{5}{16}$	$\frac{1}{4}$	$\frac{1}{2}$	$\frac{3}{8}$	$\frac{5}{16}$	$\frac{1}{4}$	$\frac{3}{16}$
Size (in)			3 x 2 $\frac{1}{2}$				3 x 2		

* See page 4-4 for more information. Interconnectors are assumed to be closely spaced.
** Factored axial compressive resistances calculated according to S16-09 Clause 13.3.5.

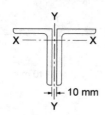

Y
X ——— X
Y
10 mm

DOUBLE ANGLE STRUTS
Unequal-Leg Angles
Factored Axial Compressive Resistances (kN)
Long Legs 10 mm Back-to-Back *

Designation (mm x mm x mm)			L 64 x 51				L 51 x 38		
			9.5	7.9	6.4	4.8 **	6.4	4.8	3.2 **
Mass (kg/m)			15.7	13.3	10.8	8.19	8.23	6.29	4.28
Effective length (KL) in millimetres with respect to indicated axis	X-X Axis	0	540	456	370	259	284	216	121
		500	522	442	358	251	268	205	114
		1 000	446	378	308	217	208	160	90.3
		1 500	339	289	236	167	142	110	62.7
		2 000	246	210	173	122	95.5	74.3	42.6
		2 500	178	153	126	89.6	66.4	51.8	29.8
		3 000	133	114	94.1	66.9	48.1	37.5	21.7
		3 500	101	87.3	72.0	51.3			
		4 000				40.3			
		4 500							
		5 000							
		5 500							
		6 000							
	Y-Y Axis	0	540	456	370	259	284	216	121
		500	504	411	310	186	253	175	74.2
		1 000	469	385	294	178	221	157	69.0
		1 500	396	327	254	160	168	121	58.2
		2 000	315	260	203	132	122	88.2	44.6
		2 500	245	202	158	104	88.4	64.3	33.3
		3 000	190	157	123	82.0	65.8	47.9	25.1
		3 500	150	123	96.5	64.9	50.3	36.7	19.4
		4 000	120	98.7	77.2	52.1			
		4 500	97.4	80.3	62.8	42.5			
		5 000							
		5 500							
		6 000							

PROPERTIES OF 2 ANGLES - 10 mm BACK-TO-BACK									
Area (mm²)			2 000	1 690	1 370	1 040	1 050	801	545
r_x (mm)			19.5	19.7	19.9	20.1	15.8	16.0	16.3
r_y (mm)			24.6	24.3	23.9	23.6	19.0	18.6	18.3
* r_z (mm)			10.7	10.7	10.8	10.9	8.12	8.18	8.27

IMPERIAL SIZE AND MASS									
Mass (lb/ft)			10.5	8.91	7.23	5.50	5.53	4.23	2.88
Thickness (in)			$^3/_8$	$^5/_{16}$	$^1/_4$	$^3/_{16}$	$^1/_4$	$^3/_{16}$	$^1/_8$
Size (in)					$2^1/_2$ x 2			2 x $1^1/_2$	

* See page 4-4 for more information. Interconnectors are assumed to be closely spaced.
** Factored axial compressive resistances calculated according to S16-09 Clause 13.3.5.

DOUBLE ANGLE STRUTS
Unequal-Leg Angles
Factored Axial Compressive Resistances (kN)
Short Legs 10 mm Back-to-Back *

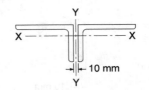

G40.21
300W
φ = 0.90

Designation (mm x mm x mm)		L 178 x 102		L 152 x 102					L 152 x 89			
		13 **	9.5 **	19	16	13 **	9.5 **	7.9 **	16	13 **	9.5 **	7.9 **
Mass (kg/m)		53.3	40.5	70.4	59.4	48.1	36.6	30.7	56.2	45.5	34.6	29.0
X-X Axis	0	1 620	1 040	2 420	2 040	1 620	1 040	753	1 930	1 530	975	740
	500	1 600	1 030	2 390	2 020	1 600	1 030	745	1 900	1 500	958	728
	1 000	1 500	971	2 250	1 900	1 510	975	705	1 730	1 370	879	669
	1 500	1 320	857	1 980	1 680	1 340	868	629	1 440	1 150	742	566
	2 000	1 100	717	1 650	1 400	1 120	733	532	1 140	913	591	453
	2 500	888	582	1 330	1 140	916	600	437	875	707	460	353
	3 000	711	467	1 070	915	737	485	354	677	549	358	275
	3 500	571	376	859	736	595	393	287	530	431	282	217
	4 000	463	305	697	598	484	320	234	423	344	226	174
	4 500	380	251	573	492	399	264	193	343	280	183	141
	5 000	317	209	477	410	332	221	161			152	117
	5 500	267	176	402	345	280	186	136				
	6 000							116				
Y-Y Axis	0	1 620	1 040	2 420	2 040	1 620	1 040	753	1 930	1 530	975	740
	1 000	1 190	600	2 220	1 790	1 290	682	412	1 690	1 220	643	409
	2 000	1 170	588	2 200	1 770	1 270	672	405	1 680	1 210	635	403
	3 000	1 170	585	2 140	1 740	1 260	666	402	1 660	1 200	631	400
	4 000	1 160	582	1 940	1 610	1 210	656	397	1 550	1 170	625	397
	5 000	1 140	578	1 690	1 410	1 090	629	389	1 370	1 060	607	392
	6 000	1 070	569	1 450	1 210	938	570	371	1 180	917	557	379
	7 000	955	549	1 230	1 020	794	493	336	1 000	780	483	348
	8 000	835	507	1 030	862	671	420	293	847	660	411	304
	9 000	725	451	876	729	568	356	251	719	560	350	261
	10 000	630	395	745	620	483	304	215	613	478	299	223
	11 000	548	345	639	531	414	261	185	526	410	256	192
	12 000	479	303	551	458	357	225	160	454	354	222	166

Effective length (KL) in millimetres with respect to indicated axis

PROPERTIES OF 2 ANGLES - 10 mm BACK-TO-BACK												
Area (mm²)		6 790	5 160	8 970	7 570	6 130	4 660	3 910	7 160	5 800	4 410	3 700
r_x (mm)		28.5	28.9	28.6	28.9	29.3	29.8	30.0	24.3	24.7	25.1	25.3
r_y (mm)		87.7	87.1	74.7	74.1	73.5	72.9	72.6	76.1	75.5	74.9	74.6
* r_z (mm)		22.2	22.4	21.9	22.0	22.2	22.4	22.5	19.1	19.3	19.5	19.6

IMPERIAL SIZE AND MASS												
Mass (lb/ft)		35.8	27.2	47.3	39.9	32.3	24.6	20.6	37.7	30.6	23.3	19.5
Thickness (in)		½	³⁄₈	¾	⁵⁄₈	½	³⁄₈	⁵⁄₁₆	⁵⁄₈	½	³⁄₈	⁵⁄₁₆
Size (in)		7 x 4		6 x 4					6 x 3 ½			

* See page 4-4 for more information. Interconnectors are assumed to be closely spaced.
** Factored axial compressive resistances calculated according to S16-09 Clause 13.3.5.

G40.21 300W

φ = 0.90

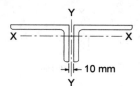

Y

X ——— X

← 10 mm

Y

DOUBLE ANGLE STRUTS
Unequal-Leg Angles
Factored Axial Compressive Resistances (kN)
Short Legs 10 mm Back-to-Back *

Designation (mm x mm x mm)			L 127 x 89				L 127 x 76			
			13	9.5 **	7.9 **	6.4 **	13	9.5 **	7.9 **	6.4 **
Mass (kg/m)			40.5	30.9	25.9	20.9	38.0	29.0	24.3	19.6
Effective length (KL) in millimetres with respect to indicated axis	X-X Axis	0	1 390	974	740	481	1 310	909	686	481
		500	1 370	959	728	474	1 270	886	669	469
		1 000	1 260	886	674	439	1 120	781	591	416
		1 500	1 070	757	577	377	879	621	472	333
		2 000	862	611	467	306	656	467	356	252
		2 500	674	480	368	242	486	348	266	189
		3 000	527	377	289	190	366	263	201	143
		3 500	416	298	229	151	282	203	155	111
		4 000	333	239	184	121	222	160	123	87.6
		4 500	272	195	150	98.9				
		5 000	225	161	124	82.0				
		5 500								
		6 000								
	Y-Y Axis	0	1 390	974	740	481	1 310	909	686	481
		1 000	1 190	720	475	246	1 120	677	445	249
		2 000	1 180	711	469	242	1 110	671	440	246
		3 000	1 130	697	462	239	1 080	663	436	244
		4 000	986	649	445	235	952	628	426	241
		5 000	822	555	401	224	798	541	391	234
		6 000	673	458	338	203	658	448	331	216
		7 000	550	375	279	173	540	368	273	185
		8 000	451	309	230	145	445	304	226	155
		9 000	374	256	191	121	370	252	188	129
		10 000	313	214	161	102	310	212	158	109
		11 000	265	182	136	86.9	263	179	134	92.6
		12 000	227	155	116	74.5	225	154	115	79.4

PROPERTIES OF 2 ANGLES - 10 mm BACK-TO-BACK

	13	9.5	7.9	6.4	13	9.5	7.9	6.4
Area (mm²)	5 160	3 930	3 300	2 660	4 840	3 690	3 100	2 500
r_x (mm)	25.6	26.0	26.2	26.4	21.1	21.5	21.7	21.9
r_y (mm)	61.9	61.3	61.0	60.7	63.8	63.2	62.9	62.6
* r_z (mm)	19.2	19.3	19.4	19.6	16.5	16.6	16.7	16.8

IMPERIAL SIZE AND MASS

	13	9.5	7.9	6.4	13	9.5	7.9	6.4
Mass (lb/ft)	27.2	20.7	17.4	14.0	25.5	19.5	16.4	13.2
Thickness (in)	½	³⁄₈	⁵⁄₁₆	¼	½	³⁄₈	⁵⁄₁₆	¼
Size (in)	5 x 3 ½				5 x 3			

* See page 4-4 for more information. Interconnectors are assumed to be closely spaced.
** Factored axial compressive resistances calculated according to S16-09 Clause 13.3.5.

DOUBLE ANGLE STRUTS
Unequal-Leg Angles
Factored Axial Compressive Resistances (kN)
Short Legs 10 mm Back-to-Back *

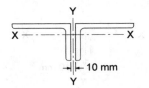

Designation (mm x mm x mm)		L 102 x 89				L 102 x 76			
		13	9.5	7.9 **	6.4 **	13	9.5	7.9 **	6.4 **
Mass (kg/m)		35.5	27.1	22.8	18.4	33.0	25.2	21.2	17.1
X-X Axis	0	1 220	934	741	480	1 130	867	685	480
	500	1 200	921	731	474	1 110	847	669	470
	1 000	1 120	856	681	441	981	754	598	421
	1 500	959	739	590	383	786	609	484	342
	2 000	778	603	483	315	595	464	370	262
	2 500	615	478	384	251	445	349	279	198
	3 000	483	377	304	199	338	266	213	151
	3 500	384	300	242	159	261	206	165	118
	4 000	308	242	195	128	206	163	131	93.2
	4 500	252	197	160	105			106	75.4
	5 000	209	164	133	86.9				
	5 500								
	6 000								
Y-Y Axis	0	1 220	934	741	480	1 130	867	685	480
	1 000	1 100	755	539	290	1 030	712	510	301
	2 000	1 050	733	525	284	992	698	501	296
	3 000	891	650	484	270	851	629	470	286
	4 000	705	522	400	239	681	508	391	256
	5 000	546	405	314	194	531	397	308	208
	6 000	423	314	244	153	414	309	240	164
	7 000	332	247	192	122	326	244	190	130
	8 000	265	197	154	97.7	261	195	152	105
	9 000	215	160	125	79.7	213	159	124	85.3
	10 000					176			
	11 000								
	12 000								
PROPERTIES OF 2 ANGLES - 10 mm BACK-TO-BACK									
Area (mm²)		4 530	3 460	2 910	2 340	4 200	3 210	2 700	2 180
r_x (mm)		26.4	26.8	27.1	27.3	21.9	22.3	22.5	22.7
r_y (mm)		48.5	47.9	47.6	47.4	50.2	49.6	49.3	49.0
* r_z (mm)		18.4	18.5	18.6	18.7	16.2	16.4	16.5	16.6
IMPERIAL SIZE AND MASS									
Mass (lb/ft)		23.9	18.2	15.3	12.4	22.2	17.0	14.3	11.5
Thickness (in)		½	⅜	⁵⁄₁₆	¼	½	⅜	⁵⁄₁₆	¼
Size (in)		4 x 3 ½				4 x 3			

Effective length (KL) in millimetres with respect to indicated axis

* See page 4-4 for more information. Interconnectors are assumed to be closely spaced.
** Factored axial compressive resistances calculated according to S16-09 Clause 13.3.5.

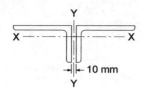

DOUBLE ANGLE STRUTS
Unequal-Leg Angles
Factored Axial Compressive Resistances (kN)
Short Legs 10 mm Back-to-Back *

Designation (mm x mm x mm)			L 89 x 76				L 89 x 64			
		13	9.5	7.9	6.4 **	13	9.5	7.9	6.4 **
Mass (kg/m)		30.4	23.3	19.6	15.8	27.9	21.4	18.0	14.6
X-X Axis	0	1 040	802	675	482	959	734	618	446
	500	1 020	784	661	472	919	706	595	430
	1 000	911	703	594	425	759	588	498	361
	1 500	736	573	485	349	553	433	369	269
	2 000	562	440	374	270	388	307	262	192
	2 500	424	333	284	205	277	220	188	138
	3 000	322	254	217	157	203	162	139	102
	3 500	250	198	169	122	154	123	106	77.7
	4 000	198	157	134	97.2				
	4 500		127	108	78.7				
	5 000								
	5 500								
	6 000								
Y-Y Axis	0	1 040	802	675	482	959	734	618	446
	1 000	963	684	531	327	891	635	496	312
	2 000	882	647	509	317	828	611	483	306
	3 000	707	528	431	286	673	505	416	282
	4 000	534	399	329	227	516	387	321	225
	5 000	400	298	247	172	390	292	242	171
	6 000	303	226	187	131	297	222	184	131
	7 000	234	175	145	102	231	172	143	102
	8 000	185	138	114	80.5	183	136	113	80.5
	9 000					148			
	10 000								
	11 000								
	12 000								

Effective length (KL) in millimetres with respect to indicated axis

PROPERTIES OF 2 ANGLES - 10 mm BACK-TO-BACK									
Area (mm^2)		3 870	2 970	2 500	2 020	3 550	2 720	2 290	1 850
r_x (mm)		22.4	22.8	23.0	23.2	17.9	18.3	18.5	18.7
r_y (mm)		43.2	42.6	42.3	42.1	45.0	44.4	44.1	43.8
* r_z (mm)		15.8	15.9	15.9	16.0	13.6	13.6	13.7	13.8

IMPERIAL SIZE AND MASS									
Mass (lb/ft)		20.4	15.6	13.2	10.6	18.7	14.4	12.1	9.78
Thickness (in)		$\frac{1}{2}$	$\frac{3}{8}$	$\frac{5}{16}$	$\frac{1}{4}$	$\frac{1}{2}$	$\frac{3}{8}$	$\frac{5}{16}$	$\frac{1}{4}$
Size (in)		$3\frac{1}{2}$ x 3				$3\frac{1}{2}$ x $2\frac{1}{2}$			

* See page 4-4 for more information. Interconnectors are assumed to be closely spaced.
** Factored axial compressive resistances calculated according to S16-09 Clause 13.3.5.

DOUBLE ANGLE STRUTS

Unequal-Leg Angles

Factored Axial Compressive Resistances (kN)

Short Legs 10 mm Back-to-Back *

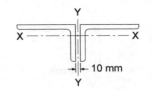

G40.21
300W
$\phi = 0.90$

Designation		L 76 x 64			L 76 x 51				
(mm x mm x mm)		9.5	7.9	6.4 **	13	9.5	7.9	6.4 **	4.8 **
Mass (kg/m)		19.5	16.4	13.3	22.8	17.6	14.8	12.0	9.14
X-X Axis	0	670	564	446	783	605	510	403	259
	500	645	544	431	723	561	474	376	242
	1 000	542	459	365	521	410	350	279	181
	1 500	404	344	275	333	264	227	183	119
	2 000	288	246	198	215	172	149	120	78.7
	2 500	207	178	143	147	118	102	82.3	54.1
	3 000	153	131	106					
	3 500	117	100	80.8					
	4 000								
	4 500								
	5 000								
	5 500								
	6 000								
Y-Y Axis	0	670	564	446	783	605	510	403	259
	500	603	480	341	746	549	439	313	163
	1 000	597	475	336	742	545	436	310	161
	1 500	579	464	331	712	535	431	308	159
	2 000	530	434	318	652	495	409	301	158
	2 500	466	385	291	578	439	366	279	154
	3 000	400	331	254	502	380	317	245	145
	3 500	339	281	217	431	325	271	211	129
	4 000	287	238	184	368	277	231	179	111
	4 500	243	202	156	314	236	197	153	95.5
	5 000	207	172	133	270	202	168	131	82.0
	5 500	178	148	114	232	174	145	113	70.7
	6 000	154	127	98.9	201	151	125	97.5	61.3
PROPERTIES OF 2 ANGLES - 10 mm BACK-TO-BACK									
Area (mm²)		2 480	2 090	1 690	2 900	2 240	1 890	1 530	1 160
r_x (mm)		18.7	18.9	19.1	13.9	14.2	14.4	14.6	14.8
r_y (mm)		37.6	37.3	37.0	40.1	39.4	39.1	38.8	38.5
* r_z (mm)		13.3	13.3	13.4	10.9	10.9	11.0	11.0	11.1
IMPERIAL SIZE AND MASS									
Mass (lb/ft)		13.1	11.0	8.93	15.3	11.8	9.97	8.08	6.14
Thickness (in)		³/₈	⁵/₁₆	¼	½	³/₈	⁵/₁₆	¼	³/₁₆
Size (in)			3 x 2 ½				3 x 2		

Effective length (KL) in millimetres with respect to indicated axis

* See page 4-4 for more information. Interconnectors are assumed to be closely spaced.
** Factored axial compressive resistances calculated according to S16-09 Clause 13.3.5.

DOUBLE ANGLE STRUTS
Unequal-Leg Angles
Factored Axial Compressive Resistances (kN)
Short Legs 10 mm Back-to-Back *

Designation		L 64 x 51				L 51 x 38		
(mm x mm x mm)		9.5	7.9	6.4	4.8 **	6.4	4.8	3.2 **
Mass (kg/m)		15.7	13.3	10.8	8.19	8.23	6.29	4.28

Effective length (KL) in millimetres with respect to indicated axis

X-X Axis

		L 64 x 51				L 51 x 38		
	0	540	456	370	259	284	216	121
	500	503	426	346	243	246	189	106
	1 000	374	319	262	185	149	116	66.2
	1 500	245	211	174	124	85.0	66.7	38.3
	2 000	161	139	115	82.1	52.0	41.0	23.6
	2 500	110	95.4	79.2	56.7			
	3 000			57.1	40.9			
	3 500							
	4 000							
	4 500							
	5 000							
	5 500							
	6 000							

Y-Y Axis

		L 64 x 51				L 51 x 38		
	0	540	456	370	259	284	216	121
	500	504	409	308	183	253	173	71.7
	1 000	496	404	304	180	248	171	70.8
	1 500	460	381	293	177	221	160	69.3
	2 000	400	334	263	167	182	135	65.1
	2 500	337	281	223	148	145	108	55.9
	3 000	279	232	185	124	115	85.2	45.3
	3 500	230	191	152	103	91.6	67.9	36.5
	4 000	190	158	126	85.1	73.9	54.8	29.5
	4 500	158	131	105	71.0	60.5	44.8	24.2
	5 000	133	110	87.8	59.7	50.2	37.2	20.1
	5 500	113	93.7	74.5	50.7			
	6 000	96.7	80.3	63.9	43.5			

PROPERTIES OF 2 ANGLES - 10 mm BACK-TO-BACK

	9.5	7.9	6.4	4.8	6.4	4.8	3.2
Area (mm²)	2 000	1 690	1 370	1 040	1 050	801	545
r_x (mm)	14.6	14.8	15.0	15.2	11.0	11.2	11.4
r_y (mm)	32.6	32.3	32.0	31.6	27.0	26.6	26.3
* r_z (mm)	10.7	10.7	10.8	10.9	8.12	8.18	8.27

IMPERIAL SIZE AND MASS

	9.5	7.9	6.4	4.8	6.4	4.8	3.2
Mass (lb/ft)	10.5	8.91	7.23	5.50	5.53	4.23	2.88
Thickness (in)	$\frac{3}{8}$	$\frac{5}{16}$	$\frac{1}{4}$	$\frac{3}{16}$	$\frac{1}{4}$	$\frac{3}{16}$	$\frac{1}{8}$
Size (in)	2 ½ x 2				2 x 1 ½		

* See page 4-4 for more information. Interconnectors are assumed to be closely spaced.
** Factored axial compressive resistances calculated according to S16-09 Clause 13.3.5.

DOUBLE ANGLE STRUTS

Star-Shaped *

Factored Axial Compressive Resistances (kN)

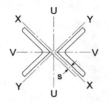

CSA G40.21
300W
$\phi = 0.90$

Designation (mm x mm x mm)		L152x152	L127x127		L102x102	
		16	16	13	13	9.5
Mass (kg/m)		72.0	59.4	48.2	38.2	29.0
Spacing, s		12 mm	12 mm		10 mm	
U-U Axis	0	2 470	2 050	1 650	1 310	999
	1 000	2 030	1 780	1 310	1 140	762
	2 000	2 010	1 780	1 310	1 140	758
	3 000	2 010	1 770	1 300	1 040	757
	4 000	2 010	1 550	1 230	846	628
	5 000	1 780	1 310	1 040	672	494
	6 000	1 530	1 090	856	530	388
	7 000	1 300	898	703	421	307
	8 000	1 100	744	581	339	246
	9 000	932	620	483	277	201
	10 000	795	522	406	230	166
	11 000	682	443	344		
	12 000	589	380	295		
V-V Axis	0	2 470	2 050	1 650	1 310	999
	1 000	2 030	1 780	1 310	1 140	762
	2 000	2 010	1 780	1 310	1 080	758
	3 000	2 010	1 530	1 240	825	637
	4 000	1 720	1 200	985	599	465
	5 000	1 410	929	762	435	339
	6 000	1 130	719	591	324	253
	7 000	916	563	464	248	194
	8 000	746	449	371		
	9 000	615	365	301		
	10 000	513				

Effective length (KL) in millimetres with respect to indicated axis

PROPERTIES OF 2 STARRED ANGLES						
Area (mm^2)		9 160	7 580	6 120	4 860	3 700
r_u (mm)		76.6	66.5	65.0	53.6	52.1
r_v (mm)		58.9	48.7	49.3	39.1	39.7
r_z (mm)		29.8	24.8	25.0	19.9	20.1

IMPERIAL SIZE AND WEIGHT						
Weight (lb/ft)		48.4	40.0	32.4	25.6	19.6
Thickness (in)		$\frac{5}{8}$	$\frac{5}{8}$	$\frac{1}{2}$	$\frac{1}{2}$	$\frac{3}{8}$
Size (in)		6 x 6	5 x 5		4 x 4	

* See page 4-4 for more information. Interconnectors are assumed to be closely spaced.
See CSA S16-09 Clauses 19.1.4 and 19.1.5 for interconnecting requirements.

CSA G40.21 300W
$\phi = 0.90$

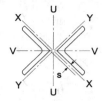

DOUBLE ANGLE STRUTS
Star-Shaped *
Factored Axial Compressive Resistances (kN)

Designation (mm x mm x mm)			L89x89			L76x76			L64x64
			13	9.5	7.9	13	9.5	7.9	6.4
Mass (kg/m)			33.0	25.2	21.2	27.8	21.4	18.0	12.0
Spacing, s			8 mm			8 mm			8 mm
Effective length (KL) in millimetres with respect to indicated axis	U-U Axis	0	1 130	864	729	956	734	621	414
		1 000	1 020	709	541	888	636	498	322
		2 000	1 000	707	539	813	615	497	317
		3 000	827	616	514	639	475	396	224
		4 000	643	473	393	475	349	289	154
		5 000	491	358	296	352	255	211	109
		6 000	377	273	225	264	191	157	79.2
		7 000	294	212	175	204	146	120	
		8 000	234	168	138	160	115		
		9 000	189	136					
	V-V Axis	0	1 130	864	729	956	734	621	414
		500	1 030	716	549	891	639	502	324
		1 000	1 020	709	541	887	636	498	322
		1 500	991	707	539	781	606	498	312
		2 000	869	669	539	651	509	434	247
		2 500	737	570	485	527	414	354	191
		3 000	614	477	407	422	333	285	148
		3 500	509	397	339	339	269	231	117
		4 000	423	330	282	275	219	188	93.1
		4 500	353	277	237	226	180	155	75.6
		5 000	298	233	200	188	150	129	
		5 500	253	199	170	158	126	109	
		6 000	217	171	146				
		6 500	188	148	127				
PROPERTIES OF 2 STARRED ANGLES									
Area (mm^2)			4 200	3 200	2 700	3 540	2 720	2 300	1 530
r_u (mm)			47.0	45.5	44.9	41.9	40.3	39.7	33.8
r_v (mm)			33.8	34.4	34.7	28.6	29.2	29.5	24.7
r_z (mm)			17.3	17.4	17.5	14.8	14.9	15.0	12.5
IMPERIAL SIZE AND WEIGHT									
Weight (lb/ft)			22.2	16.9	14.2	18.7	14.4	12.1	8.08
Thickness (in)			½	⅜	⁵⁄₁₆	½	⅜	⁵⁄₁₆	¼
Size (in)			3 ½ x 3 ½			3 x 3			2 ½ x 2 ½

* See page 4-4 for more information. Interconnectors are assumed to be closely spaced.
See CSA S16-09 Clauses 19.1.4 and 19.1.5 for interconnecting requirements.

DOUBLE ANGLE STRUTS
Star-Shaped *
Factored Axial Compressive Resistances (kN)

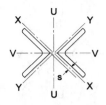

CSA G40.21
300W
$\phi = 0.90$

Designation (mm x mm x mm)		L51x51				L44x44		L38x38
		9.5	7.9	6.4	4.8	6.4	4.8	4.8
Mass (kg/m)		13.8	11.7	9.50	7.24	8.24	6.30	5.34
Spacing, s		6 mm				6 mm		6 mm
U-U Axis	0	474	402	327	249	284	217	184
	500	447	368	282	188	253	174	156
	1 000	440	367	281	187	253	174	156
	1 500	389	326	261	187	214	161	126
	2 000	325	270	214	160	170	126	94.5
	2 500	264	217	171	127	132	97.1	70.5
	3 000	212	173	136	100.0	102	75.0	53.3
	3 500	171	139	108	79.4	80.2	58.7	41.1
	4 000	139	112	87.2	63.9	64.1	46.8	32.5
	4 500	114	92.2	71.4	52.2	52.1	37.9	
	5 000	94.9	76.7	59.3	43.3			
	5 500	80.0	64.5					
V-V Axis	0	474	402	327	249	284	217	184
	500	447	368	282	188	253	174	156
	1 000	385	329	270	187	217	168	127
	1 500	288	248	205	158	154	120	83.3
	2 000	207	179	149	115	106	82.8	54.6
	2 500	149	130	108	84.2	74.4	58.5	37.5
	3 000	110	96.1	80.3	62.8	54.3	42.8	
	3 500	84.1	73.4	61.4	48.0			

Effective length (KL) in millimetres with respect to indicated axis

PROPERTIES OF 2 STARRED ANGLES

	L51x51 9.5	7.9	6.4	4.8	L44x44 6.4	4.8	L38x38 4.8
Area (mm^2)	1 750	1 490	1 210	922	1 050	802	680
r_u (mm)	28.9	28.1	27.3	26.7	24.8	24.1	21.6
r_v (mm)	18.9	19.2	19.5	19.8	16.9	17.2	14.6
r_z (mm)	9.89	9.90	9.93	10.0	8.68	8.73	7.45

IMPERIAL SIZE AND WEIGHT

Weight (lb/ft)	9.26	7.84	6.38	4.86	5.54	4.24	3.58
Thickness (in)	$\frac{3}{8}$	$\frac{5}{16}$	$\frac{1}{4}$	$\frac{3}{16}$	$\frac{1}{4}$	$\frac{3}{16}$	$\frac{3}{16}$
Size (in)	2 x 2				$1\frac{3}{4}$ x $1\frac{3}{4}$		$1\frac{1}{2}$ x $1\frac{1}{2}$

* See page 4-4 for more information. Interconnectors are assumed to be closely spaced.
See CSA S16-09 Clauses 19.1.4 and 19.1.5 for interconnecting requirements.

Double Angle Strut – Design Example

General

The following example illustrates the design of a double angle strut in accordance with S16-09 Clauses 13.3 and 19.1. Also see page 4-4 and the tables of factored axial compressive resistances starting on page 4-122.

Given:

Find the factored axial compressive resistance of a 2L102x76x6.4 double angle strut, with long legs 10 mm back-to-back. The steel grade is G40.21 300W ($F_y = 300$ MPa), $L = 2\,000$ mm, and there are two welded intermediate connectors at the one-third points.

Solution:

A. Class of Section

Width-to-thickness ratios, S16-09 Clause 11.2

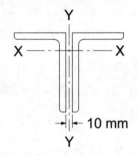

$$\frac{d}{t} = \frac{102}{6.35} = 16.1 > \frac{200}{\sqrt{F_y}} = 11.5$$

$$\frac{b}{t} = \frac{76.2}{6.35} = 12.0 > \frac{200}{\sqrt{F_y}} = 11.5$$

The angle is therefore a Class 4 section in axial compression.

B. Effective Area

Effective area according to Clause 13.3.5

$$A_e = A - 2\left(\frac{d}{t} + \frac{b}{t} - 2 \times \frac{200}{\sqrt{F_y}}\right)t^2$$

$$= 2180 - 2\,(16.1 + 12.0 - 2 \times 11.5)\,6.35^2 \approx 1\,770 \text{ mm}^2$$

C. Compressive Resistance about Axis X-X, Flexural Mode

Slenderness parameter, Clause 13.3.1

$$\lambda = \left(\frac{KL}{r}\right)_x \sqrt{\frac{F_y}{\pi^2 E}} = \frac{2\,000}{32.7} \sqrt{\frac{300}{\pi^2 \times 200 \times 10^3}} = 0.754$$

$$C_{rx} = \phi A_e F_y \left(1 + \lambda^{2n}\right)^{-1/n}$$

$$= 0.90 \times 1\,770 \times 300 \left(1 + 0.754^{2 \times 1.34}\right)^{-1/1.34} = 359 \text{ kN}$$

The table on page 4-128 indicates a compressive resistance of 361 kN.

D. *Compressive Resistance about Axis Y-Y, Torsional-Flexural Mode (Detailed Calculation)*

Shear centre location, Clause 13.3.2

$$x_o = 0 \qquad y_o = y - \frac{t}{2} = 31.6 - \frac{6.35}{2} = 28.4 \text{ mm}$$

Torsional-flexural section properties

$$\bar{r}_o^2 = x_o^2 + y_o^2 + r_x^2 + r_y^2 = 0^2 + 28.4^2 + 32.7^2 + 32.8^2 = 2\,950 \text{ mm}^2$$

$$\Omega = 1 - \left(\frac{x_o^2 + y_o^2}{\bar{r}_o^2}\right) = 1 - \left(\frac{0^2 + 28.4^2}{2\,950}\right) = 0.727$$

Slenderness ratio of the built-up member, Clause 19.1.4 (b)

$$\rho_o = \left(\frac{K L}{r}\right)_y = \frac{2\,000}{32.8} = 61.0$$

Slenderness ratio of a component angle, with two welded intermediate connectors spaced at $L / 3 = 2\,000 / 3 = 667$ mm and $K = 0.65$

$$\rho_i = \left(\frac{K L}{r}\right)_z = \frac{0.65 \times 667}{16.6} = 26.1$$

Equivalent slenderness ratio

$$\rho_e = \sqrt{\rho_o^2 + \rho_i^2} = \sqrt{61.0^2 + 26.1^2} = 66.3$$

$$F_{ey} = \frac{\pi^2 E}{\rho_e^2} = \frac{\pi^2 \times 200 \times 10^3}{66.3^2} = 449 \text{ MPa}$$

$$F_{ez} = \left(\frac{\pi^2 E C_w}{(K_z L_z)^2} + G J \right) \frac{1}{A \bar{r}_o^2}$$

$$= \left(\frac{\pi^2 \times 200 \times 10^3 \times 19.3 \times 10^6}{2\,000^2} + 77 \times 10^3 \times 29.3 \times 10^3 \right) \frac{1}{2\,180 \times 2\,950} = 352 \text{ MPa}$$

$$F_e = F_{eyz} = \frac{F_{ey} + F_{ez}}{2\Omega} \left(1 - \sqrt{1 - \frac{4 F_{ey} F_{ez} \Omega}{(F_{ey} + F_{ez})^2}} \right)$$

$$= \frac{449 + 352}{2 \times 0.727} \left(1 - \sqrt{1 - \frac{4 \times 449 \times 352 \times 0.727}{(449 + 352)^2}} \right) = 257 \text{ MPa}$$

Slenderness parameter

$$\lambda = \sqrt{\frac{F_y}{F_e}} = \sqrt{\frac{300}{257}} = 1.08$$

Compressive resistance

$$C_{ry} = \phi A_e F_y \left(1 + \lambda^{2n} \right)^{-1/n}$$

$$= 0.90 \times 1\,770 \times 300 \left(1 + 1.08^{2 \times 1.34} \right)^{-1/1.34} = 263 \text{ kN}$$

E. Compressive Resistance about Axis Y-Y using the Table on Page 4-128

The actual length $L = 2\,000$ mm is replaced by an equivalent length L_e that accounts for the slenderness of the component angles between the connectors.

$$L_e = r_y \sqrt{\left(\frac{K L}{r} \right)_y^2 + \left(\frac{K L}{r} \right)_z^2} = 32.8 \sqrt{\left(\frac{2\,000}{32.8} \right)^2 + \left(\frac{0.65 \times 667}{16.6} \right)^2} = 2\,180 \text{ mm}$$

The table indicates $C_r = 273$ kN for $L = 2\,000$ mm and $C_r = 246$ kN for $L = 2\,500$ mm, for closely spaced interconnectors. The compressive resistance for interconnectors spaced at the one-third points is obtained by linear interpolation:

$$C_r = 263 \text{ kN}$$

This resistance is equal to the value previously obtained by detailed calculation.

F. Approximate Compressive Resistance of Struts with Back-to-Back Spacings Other Than 10 mm

The actual length is replaced by an equivalent length based on the radius of gyration of the built-up section r'_y and the slenderness ratio of the component angles. Consider a double angle strut with long legs spaced 16 mm back-to-back ($r'_y = 35.0$ mm).

$$L_e = r_y \sqrt{\left(\frac{KL}{r'}\right)_y^2 + \left(\frac{KL}{r}\right)_z^2} = 32.8 \sqrt{\left(\frac{2\,000}{35.0}\right)^2 + \left(\frac{0.65 \times 667}{16.6}\right)^2} = 2\,060 \text{ mm}$$

By interpolation:

$C_r = 270$ kN

BRACING ASSEMBLIES

General

The following example illustrates the design of a bracing assembly in accordance with CSA S16-09 Clause 9.2.6.2.

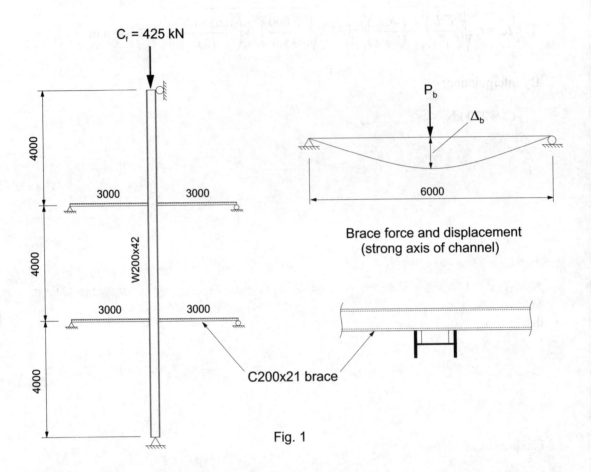

Fig. 1

Example

A W200x42 column is braced about its weak axis by channels located at the one-third points, as shown on Fig. 1. Given a factored axial load of 425 kN acting on the 12-m column, design the channel braces.

Solution

The design objective consists in sizing the channel braces with sufficient strength and stiffness to force the column into a buckling mode between bracing points.

A. Initial Imperfections

For the assumed imperfect shape shown on Fig. 2, the initial imperfection is:

$$\Delta_o = 8.0 \text{ mm}$$

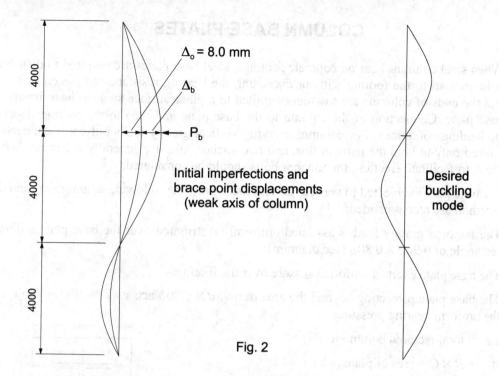

Fig. 2

B. Strength Requirement

The required flexural strength of the channel braces is calculated using the "Direct Method" in Clause 9.2.6.2. For two equally spaced braces, $\beta = 3$. The brace point displacement is assumed to be equal to the initial imperfection:

$\Delta_b = \Delta_o = 8.0$ mm

The factored bracing force is given by:

$$P_b = \frac{\beta(\Delta_o + \Delta_b) C_f}{L} = \frac{3(8.0 + 8.0) 425}{4000} = 5.1 \text{ kN}$$

Factored moment acting on a channel:

$$M_f = P_b L / 4 = 5.1 \times 6.0 / 4 = 7.65 \text{ kN} \cdot \text{m}$$

Try C200x21 channels. The factored moment resistance of a C200x21 channel with unbraced length $L/2 = 3000$ mm and $F_y = 300$ MPa may be determined using the Beam Selection Table, p. 5-100.

$M_r' = 27.5$ kN·m > 7.65 kN

C. Stiffness Requirement

For channels of length $L = 6000$ mm and strong-axis moment of inertia $I_x = 14.9 \times 10^6$ mm^4, the brace point displacement is given by:

$$\Delta_b = \frac{P_b L^3}{48 E I_x} = \frac{5.1 \times 10^3 \times 6000^3}{48 \times 200 \times 10^3 \times 14.9 \times 10^6} = 7.7 \text{ mm} < \Delta_o = 8.0 \text{ mm}$$

The selected channel section is adequate.

COLUMN BASE PLATES

When steel columns bear on concrete footings, steel base plates are required to distribute the column load to the footing without exceeding the bearing resistance of the concrete. In general the ends of columns are saw-cut or milled to a plane surface so as to bear evenly on the base plate. Connection of the column to the base plate and then to the footing depends on the loading conditions. For columns carrying vertical gravity loads only, this connection is required only to hold the parts in line, and two anchor bolts are generally sufficient. When practical, to facilitate erection, four anchor bolts should be considered.

For base plates subjected to vertical gravity loads only, the following assumptions and design method are recommended:

1. The factored gravity load is assumed uniformly distributed over the base plate within a rectangle of $0.95d \times 0.80b$ (see diagram).

2. The base plate exerts a uniform pressure over the footing.

3. The base plate projecting beyond the area of $0.95d \times 0.80b$ acts as a cantilever subject to the uniform bearing pressure.

C_f = total factored column load (kN)

A = $B \times C$ = area of plate (mm²)

t_p = plate thickness (mm)

F_y = specified minimum yield strength of base plate steel (MPa)

f'_c = specified 28-day strength of concrete (MPa)

ϕ = 0.90 for steel

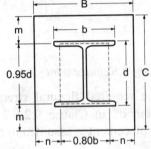

1. Determine the required area $A = C_f/B_r$ where B_r is the factored bearing resistance per unit of bearing area. For concrete, B_r is assumed to be $0.85\phi_c f'_c$ where $\phi_c = 0.65$ in bearing. (Clause 10.8 of CSA A23.3-04 states when B_r may be increased.)

2. Determine B and C so that the dimensions m and n (the projections of the plate beyond the area $0.95d \times 0.80b$) are approximately equal.

3. Determine m and n and solve for t_p, where

$$t_p = \sqrt{\frac{2C_f m^2}{BC\phi F_y}} \quad \text{or} \quad \sqrt{\frac{2C_f n^2}{BC\phi F_y}} \quad \text{whichever is greater.}$$

These formulae were derived by equating the factored moment acting on the portion of the plate taken as a cantilever to the factored moment resistance of the plate ($M_r = \phi Z F_y$) and solving for the plate thickness t_p.

To minimize deflection of the base plate, the thickness should be generally not less than about 1/5 of the overhang, m or n.

Examples

1. Given:

A W310x118 column subjected to a factored axial load of 2 500 kN is supported by a concrete foundation whose 28-day specified strength is 20 MPa. Design the base plate assuming 300 MPa steel.

Solution:

For W310x118, $b = 307$ mm, $d = 314$ mm.

$$\text{Area of plate required} = \frac{2\,500}{0.85 \times 0.65 \times 20/10^3} = 226\,000 \text{ mm}^2$$

Try $B = C = 480$ mm; $A = 230\,000$ mm^2

Determine m and n

$0.95d = 0.95 \times 314 = 298$ mm   Therefore, $m = (480 - 298)/2 = 91$ mm

$0.80b = 0.80 \times 307 = 246$ mm   Therefore, $n = (480 - 246)/2 = 117$ mm

Use n for design

$$\text{Plate thickness required} = \sqrt{\frac{2 \times 2\,500 \times 117^2}{480 \times 480 \times 0.9 \times 300/10^3}} = 33.2 \text{ mm}$$

$$\frac{n}{5} = \frac{117}{5} = 23.4 \text{ mm} \ < 33.2 \text{ mm} \quad \text{OK} \quad \text{Use 35 mm.}$$

Since the plate thickness of 35 mm is less than 65 mm, $F_y = 300$ MPa for G40.21 Grade 300W steel. For plates greater than 65 mm in thickness, $F_y = 280$ MPa for 300W steel (see Table 6-3). Therefore, use PL 35x480x480 for the base plate.

2. Given:

An HSS 203x203x9.5 column supports a factored axial load of 1 550 kN.

Select a base plate assuming $f'_c = 20$ MPa and $F_y = 300$ MPa.

Solution:

$$\text{Area required is } \frac{1550}{0.85 \times 0.65 \times 20/10^3} = 140\,000 \text{ mm}^2$$

$$B = C = \sqrt{A} = \sqrt{140 \times 10^3} = 374 \text{ mm} \quad \text{Use 380 mm}$$

$$n = \frac{380 - (203 - 9.5)}{2} = 93.3 \text{ mm}$$

$$\text{Therefore, } t_p = \sqrt{\frac{2 \times 1550 \times 93.3^2}{380 \times 380 \times 0.9 \times 300/10^3}} = 26.3 \text{ mm}$$

Use 30 mm.

Therefore, use PL 30x380x380 for the base plate.

Design Chart

As an alternative to computing the plate thickness, Figure 4-1 provides a means of selecting t_p knowing the length of cantilever m or n and the unit factored bearing resistance.

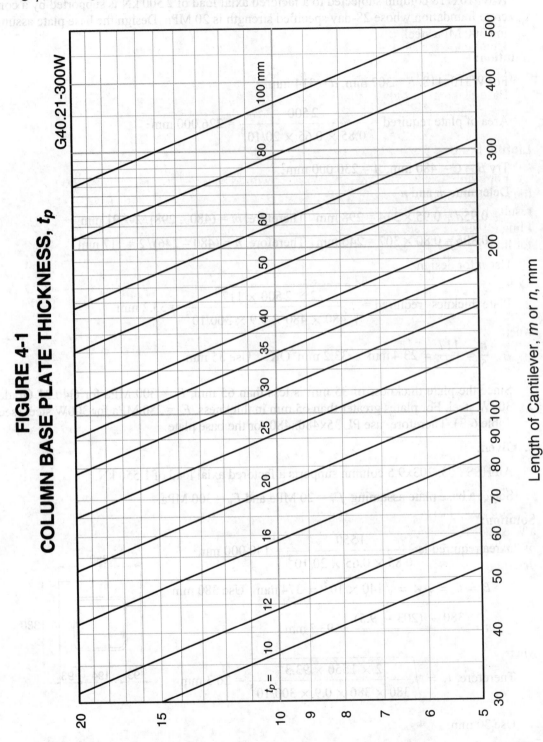

FIGURE 4-1

COLUMN BASE PLATE THICKNESS, t_p

G40.21-300W

Unit Factored Bearing Resistance, B_r, MPa

Length of Cantilever, m or n, mm

Example

Given:

Same as example 1

Solution:

Unit factored bearing resistance is $0.85 \times 0.65 \times 20 = 11.1$ MPa

From Figure 4-1 for 11.1 MPa and $n = 117$, select $t_p = 35$ mm.

Base plate assemblies (including anchor rods) that are subjected to applied bending moments, uplift tension, and shear forces must be designed to resist all such forces.

Lightly Loaded Base Plates

For lightly loaded base plates where the required bearing area is less than or about equal to the area bounded by the column dimensions b and d, the above method does not give realistic results for the base plate thickness, and other methods have been proposed in the literature. Fling (1970) uses a yield line theory to derive an equation for plate thickness. When modified for limit states design the equation becomes:

$$t_p = 0.43 b \beta \sqrt{\frac{B_r}{\phi F_y (1 - \beta^2)}}$$

where

$$B_r = 0.85 \phi_c f'_c$$

$$\beta = \sqrt{0.75 + \frac{1}{4\lambda^2}} - \frac{1}{2\lambda}$$

$$\lambda = 2d/b$$

b = column width (mm)

d = column depth (mm)

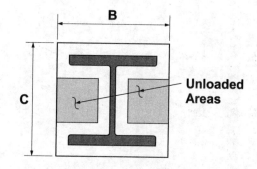

Stockwell (1975) assumes an effective bearing area where only an H-shaped pattern under a W column is loaded, and that the remainder of the base plate is unloaded. The assumed width of flange strips can be derived from the required bearing area, and the thickness of plate can be determined by the expression:

$$t_p = \sqrt{\frac{2C_f m^2}{A \phi F_y}}$$

where

A = effective bearing area

m = half the width of the bearing strips

References

FLING, R.S. 1970. Design of steel bearing plates. Engineering Journal, American Institute of Steel Construction, **7**(2), April.

STOCKWELL, F.J.JR. 1975. Preliminary base plate selection. Engineering Journal, American Institute of Steel Construction, **12**(3), Third Quarter.

ANCHOR RODS

Theoretically, anchor rods are not required at base plates for concentrically loaded columns carrying gravity loads only since neither end moments nor horizontal forces are present. According to CSA S16-09 Clause 25.2, however, at least four anchor rods are required in order to locate the column base, to provide a means for levelling the base plate, and to resist nominal end moments and horizontal forces which may occur. *Note: the expression "anchor rod" has replaced "anchor bolt" in order to avoid confusion with bolts produced to ASTM A325 and A490 (See ASTM F1554).*

Fabricators normally supply anchor rods manufactured from round bar stock. The bars are threaded at one end to receive a washer and nut and may be bent at the other end to form a hook, or both ends may be threaded. The material used for most common applications is usually produced to CSA G40.21 Grade 300W (F_y = 300 MPa) or to ASTM A36 (F_y = 248 MPa). However, ASTM A36 round bar stock is generally more readily available, and should be assumed for anchor rod design in most situations. For specialized applications, fastener suppliers or fabricators should be consulted.

The diameter of anchor rod holes in base plates should provide for possible horizontal adjustments for alignment purposes. The following table can be used as a guide, although actual sizes used by fabricators may vary depending on shop and field practices. If hole diameters other than those suggested are required, the reference below provides information on larger hole sizes and washers used in common practice.

References

AISC. 2005. Steel construction manual. 13th Edition. American Institute of Steel Construction, Chicago, IL.

SUGGESTED ANCHOR ROD HOLE SIZES

Rod Diameter in.	Hole Diameter mm	Rod Diameter in.	Hole Diameter mm
¾	27	1½	50
⅞	30	1¾	56
1	34	2	64
1¼	40	2½	78

CSA S16-09 Clause 25 covers design requirements for column bases in situations where anchor rods transfer end moments and horizontal forces due to lateral loads. If such requirements are necessary, they should be clearly identified in the contract documents.

PART FIVE
FLEXURAL MEMBERS

GENERAL INFORMATION

Class of Sections in Bending

See page 5-4.

Factored Shear Resistance of Girder Webs

The tables on pages 5-9 to 5-11 list the factored shear resistance ϕF_s in a girder web, computed in accordance with the requirements of Clause 13.4.1.1 of CSA S16-09, and the required gross area of pairs of intermediate stiffeners, computed in accordance with the requirements of Clause 14.5.3. Values are provided for minimum specified yield strength levels F_y of 250, 300 and 350 MPa, for aspect ratios (a/h) from 0.50 to 3.00, and for web slenderness ratios (h/w) varying between 60 and 320 for $F_y = 250$, between 50 and 260 for $F_y = 300$, and between 50 and 220 for $F_y = 350$. The required gross area of stiffeners is provided as a percentage of the web area $(h\,w)$ and is shown in italics.

Plate Girders

For design information and an illustrative example, see page 5-12.

Composite Beams

Tables for the Factored Shear Resistance of Shear Studs in solid slabs and in deck-slabs are given on pages 5-17 to 5-19. Formulas for calculating the area of the concrete pull-out pyramid and an illustrative example are given on pages 5-20 to 5-22. The calculation of the factored resistance of a shear stud is illustrated on page 5-23. Trial Selection Tables for composite beams with various combinations of cover slab and cellular steel deck (hollow composite construction) are given on pages 5-26 to 5-75. See page 5-14 for explanatory text.

Deflection of Flexural Members

See page 5-76 for design chart, table, and illustrative examples.

Factored Resistance of Beams

Beam Selection Tables, which list the factored moment resistance of beams under various conditions of lateral support, are provided on pages 5-86 to 5-103 to facilitate the design of flexural members. See page 5-80 for explanatory text.

Beam Load Tables which list total uniformly distributed factored loads for laterally supported beams of various spans are provided on pages 5-104 to 5-145. For explanatory text, see page 5-82.

Beam Diagrams and Formulae

Pages 5-146 to 5-164 contain diagrams and formulae to facilitate the design of flexural members in accordance with elastic theory.

Beam Bearing Plates

See page 5-165 for design information, design chart and illustrative example.

Beams with Web Holes

See page 5-168 for design information, design tables and illustrative example.

Guide for Floor Vibration

See Annex E of CSA S16-09.

CLASS OF SECTIONS IN BENDING

Table 5-1 lists the class of section in bending of WWF sizes and W shapes for common grades of steel including CSA G40.21-350W, ASTM A992 and A572 grade 50. Listed are the WWF sizes and W shapes provided in Part Six of this Handbook. The class of section in bending is based on F_y = 350 MPa for WWF shapes and on F_y = 345 MPa for W shapes. For these steel grades all S shapes are Class 1, and all C and MC shapes are Class 3.

Table 5-1 also lists for each section size the ratios b/t and h/w, where b = one-half the flange width, t = flange thickness, h = clear distance between flanges and w = web thickness. See also "Limits on Width-Thickness Ratios", page 4-5.

Table 5-1

Designation	Class	b / t	h / w	Designation	Class	b / t	h / w
WWF2000x732	3	5.50	95.0	WWF700x245	1	6.67	58.2
x648	3	6.88	96.0	x214	2	8.00	59.1
x607	3	7.86	96.5	x196	3	9.09	59.6
x542	3	8.33	97.0	x175	2	6.00	59.1
				x152	2	7.50	60.0
WWF1800x700	2	5.50	85.0				
x659	2	6.11	85.5	WWF650x864	1	5.42	8.83
x617	2	6.88	86.0	x739	1	5.42	17.7
x575	2	7.86	86.5	x598	1	6.50	27.5
x510	2	8.33	87.0	x499	2	8.13	28.5
				x400	4	10.8	29.5
WWF1600x622	3	5.50	93.8				
x580	3	6.11	94.4	WWF600x793	1	5.00	8.00
x538	3	6.88	95.0	x680	1	5.00	16.0
x496	3	7.86	95.6	x551	1	6.00	25.0
x431	3	8.33	96.3	x460	1	7.50	26.0
				x369	3	10.0	27.0
WWF1400x597	2	5.50	81.3				
x513	2	6.88	82.5	WWF550x721	1	4.58	7.17
x471	2	7.86	83.1	x620	1	4.58	14.3
x405	2	8.33	83.8	x503	1	5.50	22.5
x358	2	6.67	83.8	x420	1	6.88	23.5
				x280	4	11.0	31.3
WWF1200x487	2	6.88	70.0				
x418	2	7.14	70.6	WWF500x651	1	4.17	6.33
x380	2	8.33	71.3	x561	1	4.17	12.7
x333	2	6.67	71.3	x456	1	5.00	20.0
x302	2	8.00	71.9	x381	1	6.25	21.0
x263	2	6.00	71.9	x343	1	7.14	21.5
				x306	2	8.33	22.0
WWF1100x458	2	6.88	72.9	x276	2	8.93	27.8
x388	2	7.14	73.6	x254	3	10.0	28.1
x351	2	8.33	74.3	x223	4	11.4	32.6
x304	2	6.67	74.3	x197	4	12.5	41.8
x273	2	8.00	75.0				
x234	2	6.00	75.0	WWF450x503	1	3.75	11.0
				x409	1	4.50	17.5
WWF1000x447	2	6.88	65.7	x342	1	5.63	18.5
x377	2	7.14	66.4	x308	1	6.43	19.0
x340	2	8.33	67.1	x274	1	7.50	19.5
x293	2	6.67	67.1	x248	2	8.04	24.6
x262	2	8.00	67.9	x228	2	9.00	25.0
x223	2	6.00	67.9	x201	3	10.2	29.0
x200	2	7.50	68.6	x177	4	11.3	37.3
WWF900x417	2	6.88	74.5	WWF400x444	1	3.33	9.33
x347	2	7.14	75.5	x362	1	4.00	15.0
x309	2	8.33	76.4	x303	1	5.00	16.0
x262	2	6.67	76.4	x273	1	5.71	16.5
x231	2	8.00	77.3	x243	1	6.67	17.0
x192	2	6.00	77.3	x220	1	7.14	21.5
x169	2	7.50	78.2	x202	2	8.00	21.9
				x178	3	9.09	25.4
WWF800x339	2	7.14	66.4	x157	3	10.0	32.7
x300	2	8.33	67.3				
x253	2	6.67	67.3	WWF350x315	1	3.50	12.5
x223	2	8.00	68.2	x263	1	4.38	13.5
x184	2	6.00	68.2	x238	1	5.00	14.0
x161	2	7.50	69.1	x212	1	5.83	14.5
				x192	1	6.25	18.4
				x176	1	7.00	18.8
				x155	2	7.95	21.9
				x137	2	8.75	28.2

F_y = 350 MPa

CLASS OF SECTIONS IN BENDING

CSA G40.21 350W, ASTM A992, A572 gr. 50

Table 5-1

Designation	Class	b/t	h/w	Designation	Class	b/t	h/w
W1100x499	1	4.50	39.5	W840x251	1	4.71	46.9
x433	1	5.03	46.7	x226	1	5.49	49.5
x390	1	5.56	51.4	x210	1	6.00	51.8
x343	1	6.45	57.1	x193	1	6.73	54.2
				x176	1	7.77	57.0
W1000x883	1	2.59	20.4				
x748	1	2.98	23.8	W760x582	1	3.19	20.8
x642	1	3.43	27.3	x531	1	3.45	22.8
x591	1	3.66	29.9	x484	1	3.74	24.8
x554	1	3.92	31.5	x434	1	4.12	27.8
x539	1	3.98	32.7	x389	1	4.59	30.5
x483	1	4.39	36.5	x350	1	5.01	34.1
x443	1	4.80	39.3	x314	1	5.75	36.5
x412	1	5.03	44.0	x284	1	6.35	39.9
x371	1	5.54	48.8	x257	1	7.03	43.3
x321	1	6.45	56.2				
x296	1	7.38	56.2	W760x220	1	4.43	43.6
				x196	1	5.28	46.1
W1000x584	1	2.45	25.8	x185	1	5.66	48.2
x494	1	2.86	29.9	x173	1	6.18	49.9
x486	1	2.85	30.9	x161	1	6.89	52.1
x438	1	3.11	34.5	x147	1	7.79	54.5
x415	1	3.30	35.7	x134	2	8.52	60.4
x393	1	3.45	38.0				
x350	1	3.78	44.0	W690x548	1	2.95	18.4
x314	1	4.18	48.6	x500	1	3.19	20.2
x272	1	4.84	56.2	x457	1	3.46	21.9
x249	1	5.77	56.2	x419	1	3.71	24.0
x222	1	7.11	58.0	x384	1	4.02	25.9
				x350	1	4.40	28.0
W920x656	1	3.48	25.0	x323	1	4.71	30.6
x588	1	3.82	27.8	x289	1	5.24	34.0
x537	1	4.16	30.4	x265	1	5.93	35.1
x491	1	4.49	33.3	x240	1	6.50	38.5
x449	1	4.95	35.9	x217	1	7.16	41.9
x420	1	5.29	38.4				
x390	1	5.74	40.5	W690x192	1	4.55	41.7
x368	1	6.11	42.5	x170	1	5.42	44.5
x344	1	6.53	44.7	x152	1	6.02	49.3
				x140	1	6.72	52.1
W920x381	1	3.53	35.4	x125	1	7.76	55.2
x345	1	3.86	39.1				
x313	1	4.48	40.9	W610x551	1	2.51	14.8
x289	1	4.81	44.5	x498	1	2.72	16.3
x271	1	5.12	46.9	x455	1	2.94	17.9
x253	1	5.48	49.9	x415	1	3.18	19.4
x238	1	5.89	52.3	x372	1	3.49	21.7
x223	1	6.36	54.3	x341	1	3.79	23.5
x201	1	7.56	56.8	x307	1	4.14	25.9
				x285	1	4.43	27.8
W840x576	1	3.55	24.9	x262	1	4.81	30.2
x527	1	3.85	27.0	x241	1	5.31	32.0
x473	1	4.23	30.2	x217	1	5.92	34.7
x433	1	4.60	32.7	x195	1	6.70	37.2
x392	1	5.03	36.1	x174	1	7.52	40.9
x359	1	5.66	37.8	x155	2	8.53	45.1
x329	1	6.19	40.5				
x299	1	6.85	43.8				

$F_y = 345$ MPa

Table 5-1

CLASS OF SECTIONS IN BENDING
CSA G40.21 350W, ASTM A992, A572 gr. 50

Designation	Class	b/t	h/w	Designation	Class	b/t	h/w
W610x153	1	4.60	40.9	W410x149	1	5.30	25.6
x140	1	5.18	43.7	x132	1	5.92	28.6
x125	1	5.84	48.1	x114	1	6.76	32.9
x113	1	6.59	51.2	x100	1	7.69	38.1
x101	1	7.65	54.6				
x91	2	8.94	59.0	W410x85	1	4.97	34.9
x84	3	9.66	63.6	x74	1	5.63	39.3
				x67	1	6.22	43.3
W610x92	1	5.97	52.6	x60	1	6.95	49.5
x82	1	6.95	57.3	x54	2	8.12	50.8
W530x300	1	3.85	21.7	W410x46	1	6.25	54.4
x272	1	4.23	23.8	x39	2	7.95	59.6
x248	1	4.57	26.4				
x219	1	5.45	27.4	W360x1086	1	1.82	4.09
x196	1	6.01	30.4	x990	1	1.95	4.45
x182	1	6.45	33.0	x900	1	2.08	4.84
x165	1	7.05	35.8	x818	1	2.25	5.29
x150	1	7.68	39.6	x744	1	2.43	5.76
				x677	1	2.63	6.25
W530x138	1	4.53	34.1				
x123	1	5.00	38.3	W360x634	1	2.75	6.72
x109	1	5.61	43.2	x592	1	2.91	7.12
x101	1	6.03	46.1	x551	1	3.09	7.61
x92	1	6.70	49.2	x509	1	3.32	8.20
x82	2	7.86	52.8	x463	1	3.59	8.94
x72	3	9.50	56.4	x421	1	3.89	9.75
				x382	1	4.23	10.7
W530x85	1	5.03	48.7	x347	1	4.62	11.8
x74	1	6.10	51.7	x314	1	5.06	12.8
x66	1	7.24	56.4	x287	1	5.45	14.2
				x262	1	5.98	15.2
W460x464	1	2.19	11.1	x237	1	6.54	16.9
x421	1	2.38	12.0	x216	1	7.11	18.5
x384	1	2.56	13.2				
x349	1	2.76	14.5	W360x196	1	7.14	19.5
x315	1	3.02	15.9	x179	1	7.80	21.3
x286	1	3.28	17.5	x162	2	8.51	24.1
x260	1	3.58	18.9	x147	3	9.34	26.0
x235	1	3.92	20.8	x134	3	10.3	28.6
x213	1	4.25	23.1				
x193	1	4.64	25.2	W360x122	1	5.92	24.6
x177	1	5.32	25.8	x110	1	6.43	28.1
x158	1	5.94	28.5	x101	1	6.97	30.5
x144	1	6.40	31.5	x91	1	7.74	33.7
x128	1	7.19	35.1				
x113	2	8.09	39.7	W360x79	1	6.10	34.1
				x72	1	6.75	37.2
W460x106	1	4.71	34.0	x64	1	7.52	41.6
x97	1	5.08	37.5				
x89	1	5.42	40.7	W360x57	1	6.56	42.0
x82	1	5.97	43.2	x51	1	7.37	46.1
x74	1	6.55	47.6	x45	2	8.72	48.2
x67	1	7.48	50.4				
x61	2	8.75	52.9	W360x39	1	5.98	51.0
				x33	1	7.47	57.2
W460x68	1	5.00	47.1				
x60	1	5.75	53.6				
x52	1	7.04	56.4				

F_y = 345 MPa

Designation	Class	b / t	h / w	Designation	Class	b / t	h / w
W310x500	1	2.26	6.14	W200x100	1	4.43	12.5
x454	1	2.45	6.72	x86	1	5.07	13.9
x415	1	2.66	7.14	x71	1	5.92	17.8
x375	1	2.88	7.81	x59	1	7.22	20.0
x342	1	3.12	8.49	x52	2	8.10	22.9
x313	1	3.36	9.25	x46	3	9.23	25.1
W310x283	1	3.65	10.3	W200x42	1	7.03	25.2
x253	1	4.03	11.3	x36	2	8.09	29.1
x226	1	4.45	12.5				
x202	1	4.95	13.8	W200x31	1	6.57	29.6
x179	1	5.57	15.4	x27	2	7.92	32.8
x158	1	6.18	17.9				
x143	1	6.75	19.8	W200x22	1	6.38	30.6
x129	1	7.48	21.1	x19	2	7.85	32.8
x118	2	8.21	23.2	x15	3	9.62	44.1
x107	2	9.00	25.4				
x97	3	9.90	28.0	W150x37	1	6.64	17.1
				x30	2	8.23	21.0
W310x86	1	7.79	30.5	x22	4	11.5	23.9
x79	2	8.70	31.5				
				W150x24	1	4.95	21.1
W310x74	1	6.29	29.5	x18	1	7.18	23.9
x67	1	6.99	32.6	x14	2	9.09	32.3
x60	1	7.75	36.9	x13	3	10.2	32.1
W310x52	1	6.33	38.4	W130x28	1	5.87	15.8
x45	1	7.41	44.0	x24	1	6.98	17.8
x39	2	8.51	50.1				
				W100x19	1	5.85	12.5
W310x33	1	4.72	44.2				
x28	1	5.73	48.5				
x24	1	7.54	52.1				
x21	2	8.86	57.2				
W250x167	1	4.17	11.7				
x149	1	4.63	13.0				
x131	1	5.20	14.6				
x115	1	5.86	16.7				
x101	1	6.56	18.9				
x89	1	7.40	21.1				
x80	2	8.17	23.9				
x73	2	8.94	26.1				
W250x67	1	6.50	25.3				
x58	1	7.52	28.1				
x49	3	9.18	30.4				
W250x45	1	5.69	31.6				
x39	1	6.56	36.3				
x33	2	8.02	39.3				
W250x28	1	5.10	37.5				
x25	1	6.07	39.4				
x22	1	7.39	41.4				
x18	3	9.53	50.1				

F_y = 345 MPa

Factored Shear Resistance of Girder Webs

$F_y = 250$ MPa

Top number = Factored shear stress, ϕF_s (MPa)

$\phi = 0.90$

Bottom number = Required Gross Area of Pairs of Intermediate Stiffeners,
Percent of Web Area, h x w

Web h/w Ratio	Panel Aspect Ratio: a/h = Stiffener Spacing / Web Depth										No Intermediate Stiffeners
	0.50	0.67	0.75	1.00	1.25	1.50	1.75	2.00	2.50	3.00	
50											149
60									149 / 0.77		149
70							149 / 1.15	148 / 1.06	144 / 0.89	142 / 0.77	136
80				149 / 1.46	145 / 1.37	138 / 1.26	133 / 1.15	130 / 1.06	127 / 0.89	126 / 0.77	119
90			149 / 1.50	140 / 1.46	129 / 1.37	126 / 1.26	123 / 1.15	121 / 1.06	118 / 0.89	116 / 0.88	106
100			149 / 1.50	128 / 1.46	124 / 1.37	120 / 1.48	116 / 2.03	113 / 2.26	107 / 2.31	104 / 2.18	86.5
120	149 / 1.38	137 / 1.49	129 / 1.50	120 / 2.87	111 / 4.38	104 / 4.88	98.5 / 4.93	94.0 / 4.79	87.4 / 4.34	82.8 / 3.86	60.1
140	148 / 1.38	126 / 1.49	123 / 2.20	109 / 5.99	100 / 6.85	93.0 / 6.92	87.1 / 6.68	82.4 / 6.32	75.3 / 5.56	70.3 / 4.88	44.1
160	130 / 1.38	122 / 3.42	116 / 5.20	102 / 8.02	93.2 / 8.45	85.8 / 8.25	79.8 / 7.82	74.9 / 7.32	67.5 / 6.35		33.8
180	127 / 1.38	116 / 5.82	111 / 7.25	97.7 / 9.41	88.4 / 9.55	80.9 / 9.16	74.8 / 8.60	69.7 / 8.00			26.7
200	124 / 2.96	112 / 7.53	107 / 8.73	94.2 / 10.4	85.0 / 10.3	77.4 / 9.82					21.6
220	120 / 4.84	108 / 8.80	104 / 9.81	91.7 / 11.1	82.4 / 10.9						17.9
240	117 / 6.27	106 / 9.77	102 / 10.6	89.7 / 11.7							15.0
260	114 / 7.39	104 / 10.5	99.9 / 11.3								12.8
280	112 / 8.28	103 / 11.1	98.6 / 11.8		**Not Permitted**						11.0
300	111 / 8.99	101 / 11.6	97.5 / 12.2								9.61
320	110 / 9.58										8.45

Notes:
- For shear resistance and stiffener area, see S16-09 Clauses 13.4.1.1 and 14.5.3, respectively.
- For maximum web slenderness and stiffener spacing, see S16-09 Clauses 14.3.1 and 14.5.2, respectively.
- For single stiffeners on one side of web only, multiply percentages shown by 1.8 for angle stiffeners and by 2.4 for plate stiffeners.
- When the stiffener F_y is not the same as the web F_y, multiply gross area by the ratio ($F_{y\,web} / F_{y\,stiffener}$).

Factored Shear Resistance of Girder Webs

$F_y = 300$ MPa

Top number = Factored shear stress, ϕF_s (MPa)

$\phi = 0.90$

Bottom number = Required Gross Area of Pairs of Intermediate Stiffeners, Percent of Web Area, h x w

Web h / w Ratio	Panel Aspect Ratio: a / h = Stiffener Spacing / Web Depth										No Inter-mediate Stiffeners
	0.50	0.67	0.75	1.00	1.25	1.50	1.75	2.00	2.50	3.00	
50											178
60										178 / 0.77	174
70					178 / 1.37	172 / 1.26	166 / 1.15	163 / 1.06	158 / 0.89	155 / 0.77	149
80			178 / 1.50	173 / 1.46	159 / 1.37	153 / 1.26	150 / 1.15	148 / 1.06	144 / 0.89	141 / 0.77	131
90			178 / 1.50	155 / 1.46	149 / 1.37	145 / 1.26	141 / 1.75	138 / 2.02	131 / 2.12	127 / 2.02	107
100		178 / 1.49	166 / 1.50	149 / 1.46	143 / 2.52	135 / 3.33	128 / 3.61	123 / 3.64	116 / 3.42	111 / 3.10	86.5
110	178 / 1.38	164 / 1.49	154 / 1.50	144 / 2.96	133 / 4.46	124 / 4.94	118 / 4.99	112 / 4.84	104 / 4.37	98.9 / 3.90	71.5
120	178 / 1.38	154 / 1.49	151 / 1.50	136 / 4.83	125 / 5.93	116 / 6.16	110 / 6.03	104 / 5.75	95.8 / 5.10	89.9 / 4.50	60.1
130	175 / 1.38	151 / 1.49	147 / 2.62	130 / 6.28	119 / 7.08	110 / 7.11	103 / 6.84	97.6 / 6.46	89.0 / 5.67	83.0 / 4.98	51.2
140	163 / 1.38	148 / 2.41	142 / 4.33	125 / 7.43	114 / 7.99	105 / 7.87	98.3 / 7.49	92.5 / 7.03	83.7 / 6.12	77.4 / 5.35	44.1
150	155 / 1.38	144 / 4.01	138 / 5.70	122 / 8.36	110 / 8.73	102 / 8.48	94.3 / 8.01	88.3 / 7.48	79.3 / 6.49	72.9 / 5.65	38.4
160	153 / 1.38	140 / 5.32	134 / 6.83	118 / 9.12	107 / 9.33	98.3 / 8.98	91.0 / 8.44	85.0 / 7.86	75.8 / 6.78		33.8
180	149 / 2.64	134 / 7.32	129 / 8.54	114 / 10.3	102 / 10.2	93.4 / 9.74	85.9 / 9.09	79.8 / 8.42			26.7
200	144 / 4.77	130 / 8.75	125 / 9.77	110 / 11.1	99.0 / 10.9	89.9 / 10.3					21.6
220	140 / 6.34	127 / 9.81	122 / 10.7	108 / 11.7	96.5 / 11.4						17.9
240	137 / 7.53	125 / 10.6	120 / 11.4	106 / 12.2			**Not Permitted**				15.0
260	134 / 8.46	123 / 11.2	118 / 11.9								12.8

Notes:

- For shear resistance and stiffener area, see S16-09 Clauses 13.4.1.1 and 14.5.3, respectively.
- For maximum web slenderness and stiffener spacing, see S16-09 Clauses 14.3.1 and 14.5.2, respectively.
- For single stiffeners on one side of web only, multiply percentages shown by 1.8 for angle stiffeners and by 2.4 for plate stiffeners.
- When the stiffener F_y is not the same as the web F_y, multiply gross area by the ratio ($F_{y\,web}$ / $F_{y\,stiffener}$).

Factored Shear Resistance of Girder Webs F_y = 350 MPa

Top number = Factored shear stress, ϕF_s (MPa) $\phi = 0.90$

Bottom number = Required Gross Area of Pairs of Intermediate Stiffeners,
Percent of Web Area, h x w

Web h/w Ratio	Panel Aspect Ratio: **a/h** = Stiffener Spacing / Web Depth										No Intermediate Stiffeners
	0.50	**0.67**	**0.75**	**1.00**	**1.25**	**1.50**	**1.75**	**2.00**	**2.50**	**3.00**	
50										208 / 0.77	208
60							208 / 1.15	205 / 1.06	199 / 0.89	196 / 0.77	188
70				208 / 1.46	196 / 1.37	186 / 1.26	181 / 1.15	178 / 1.06	174 / 0.89	172 / 0.77	161
80			208 / 1.50	187 / 1.46	177 / 1.37	172 / 1.26	168 / 1.15	165 / 1.29	160 / 1.54	156 / 1.54	135
90		208 / 1.49	199 / 1.50	176 / 1.46	168 / 1.86	161 / 2.79	154 / 3.15	148 / 3.24	140 / 3.09	134 / 2.83	107
100	208 / 1.38	195 / 1.49	181 / 1.50	169 / 2.53	157 / 4.11	147 / 4.66	140 / 4.74	133 / 4.63	124 / 4.21	118 / 3.75	86.5
110	208 / 1.38	180 / 1.49	176 / 1.50	160 / 4.63	147 / 5.78	137 / 6.03	129 / 5.92	122 / 5.66	113 / 5.03	106 / 4.44	71.5
120	205 / 1.38	176 / 1.49	172 / 2.55	152 / 6.23	139 / 7.04	129 / 7.08	121 / 6.82	114 / 6.44	104 / 5.65	97.1 / 4.96	60.1
130	189 / 1.38	173 / 2.48	166 / 4.39	146 / 7.48	133 / 8.03	123 / 7.90	114 / 7.51	108 / 7.05	97.4 / 6.14	90.1 / 5.36	51.2
140	180 / 1.38	168 / 4.18	160 / 5.85	141 / 8.46	128 / 8.81	118 / 8.54	109 / 8.07	103 / 7.53	92.0 / 6.52	84.5 / 5.69	44.1
150	178 / 1.38	163 / 5.56	156 / 7.03	137 / 9.26	124 / 9.44	114 / 9.07	105 / 8.51	98.4 / 7.92	87.7 / 6.84	80.0 / 5.94	38.4
160	176 / 1.69	159 / 6.68	152 / 8.00	134 / 9.91	121 / 9.95	111 / 9.49	102 / 8.88	95.0 / 8.24	84.2 / 7.09		33.8
170	173 / 3.08	156 / 7.62	149 / 8.80	132 / 10.5	119 / 10.4	108 / 9.85	99.4 / 9.18	92.2 / 8.51			29.9
180	169 / 4.24	153 / 8.40	147 / 9.47	129 / 10.9	117 / 10.7	106 / 10.1	97.1 / 9.43	89.9 / 8.73			26.7
190	167 / 5.22	151 / 9.06	145 / 10.0	128 / 11.3	115 / 11.0	104 / 10.4	95.2 / 9.65				24.0
200	164 / 6.06	149 / 9.63	143 / 10.5	126 / 11.6	113 / 11.3	102 / 10.6	**Not Permitted**				21.6
220	160 / 7.41	146 / 10.5	140 / 11.3	123 / 12.1	111 / 11.7						17.9

Notes:

- For shear resistance and stiffener area, see S16-09 Clauses 13.4.1.1 and 14.5.3, respectively.
- For maximum web slenderness and stiffener spacing, see S16-09 Clauses 14.3.1 and 14.5.2, respectively.
- For single stiffeners on one side of web only, multiply percentages shown by 1.8 for angle stiffeners and by 2.4 for plate stiffeners.
- When the stiffener F_y is not the same as the web F_y, multiply gross area by the ratio ($F_{y\,web}$ / $F_{y\,stiffener}$).

PLATE GIRDERS – WEB SHEAR RESISTANCE

Design Example

Given:

Find the shear resistance of a simply supported welded plate girder spanning 22 m and loaded as shown. The grade of steel is G40.21-350W.

Girder cross-sectional dimensions:

$d = 1800$ mm, $b = 500$ mm, $t = 30$ mm, $w = 10$ mm, $h = d - 2t = 1740$ mm

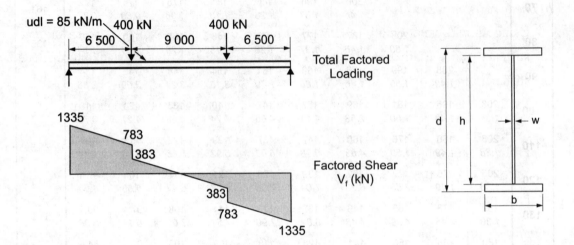

Solution:

a) Shear resistance of end panels

Factored ultimate shear force in girder web: $V_f = 1335$ kN

Maximum h/w permitted $= 83\,000/F_y = 83\,000/350 = 237$ (S16-09 Clause 14.3.1)

Web slenderness ratio: $h/w = 1740/10 = 174 < 237$

Maximum a/h permitted $= 67\,500/(h/w)^2$

$\qquad = 67\,500/174^2 = 2.23$ for $h/w > 150$ (Clause 14.5.2)

Size the end panel without the tension-field action, in accordance with Clause 14.5.1.

Find the maximum stiffener spacing:

Assuming that Clause 13.4.1.1(d) applies, for $h/w = 174$ and $F_s = F_{cre}$

$$V_r = \phi A_w \frac{180000\,k_v}{(h/w)^2} = 0.9 \times 17\,400 \times \frac{180000\,k_v}{174^2} = 93\,100\,k_v$$

Equating V_r to $V_f = 1335$ kN gives $k_v = 14.34$

$$k_v = 4 + \frac{5.34}{(a/h)^2} = 14.34, \quad a/h = \sqrt{\frac{5.34}{14.34 - 4}} = 0.719$$

Therefore, the maximum end panel length is $0.719 \times 1740 = 1250$ mm.

Try $a = 1000$ mm. The panel aspect ratio is $a/h = 1000 / 1740 = 0.575$

$$k_v = 4 + \frac{5.34}{(a/h)^2} = 4 + \frac{5.34}{0.575^2} = 20.2$$

$$\frac{h}{w} = 174 > 621\sqrt{\frac{k_v}{F_y}} = 621\sqrt{\frac{20.2}{350}} = 149$$

This confirms that Clause 13.4.1.1(d) applies, as assumed above.

b) Shear resistance between end panel and concentrated load

Using an end panel length of $a = 1000$ mm and two equal panels between the end stiffener and the stiffener at the interior concentrated load gives an intermediate stiffener spacing of: $(6500 - 1000) / 2 = 2750$ mm

Factored shear force at the first intermediate stiffener, by linear interpolation:

$V_f = 1335 - (1335 - 783)(1000 / 6500) = 1250$ kN

From the table on page 5-11 for $h/w = 174$ and $a/h = 2750/1740 = 1.58$

$\phi F_s = 104$ MPa (by interpolation)

Factored shear resistance: $V_r = A_w(\phi F_s) = 17\,400 \times 104 = 1810$ kN $> V_f = 1250$ kN

c) Intermediate Stiffener Size

From the table on page 5-11 for $h/w = 174$ and $a/h = 1.58$, by interpolation:

The required total area of a pair of intermediate stiffeners is 9.74% of the web area.

$A_s = 0.0974 \times 17\,400 = 1690$ mm^2

Required $I_s = (h/50)^4 = (1740/50)^4 = 1.47 \times 10^6$ mm^4 (Clause 14.5.3)

Maximum $b/t = 200/\sqrt{F_y} = 10.7$ Use two 10×100 stiffeners

$A_s = 2 \times 10 \times 100 = 2000 > 1690$ mm^2 $I_s = 10 \times 210^3/12 = 7.72 \times 10^6 > 1.47 \times 10^6$ mm^4

$b/t = 100/10 = 10.0 < 10.7$

d) Shear resistance between concentrated loads

Factored ultimate shear force in girder web: $V_f = 383$ kN   Try an unstiffened web.

Using the table on page 5-11, for $h/w = 174$: $\phi F_s = 28.6$ MPa (by interpolation)

Factored shear resistance: $V_r = A_w(\phi F_s) = 17\,400 \times 28.6 = 498$ kN > 383 kN

Therefore, stiffeners are not required between the two concentrated loads (but are required at the concentrated load locations). Design checks for bearing at concentrated loads, moment, and combined shear and moment are not shown. See "Limit States Design in Structural Steel", Kulak and Grondin, CISC, 2009.

COMPOSITE BEAMS

General

A composite beam, in general, consists of a steel beam and a concrete slab so interconnected that both the steel beam and the slab act jointly to resist bending. Several combinations which effectively act as composite beams occur in practice. These include a steel beam or girder with a concrete slab interconnected with mechanical shear connectors, a steel beam or girder with a ribbed concrete slab formed by steel deck interconnected by mechanical shear connectors, and a steel beam or girder fully encased by the concrete in such a way that the encased beam and the concrete slab behave monolithically. Clause 17 of CSA S16-09 contains requirements for composite beams.

Some advantages of composite construction are:

- Reduced weight of steel members
- Reduced depth of steel members
- Reduced deflections under superimposed load
- Simplified changes to electrical services when steel deck is used

Composite construction is most advantageous when heavy loads and long spans are involved. For this reason composite construction is widely used for bridges. For building construction, composite beams consisting of steel beams with steel deck and concrete cover slab utilizing steel stud shear connectors welded to the beam top flange are most frequently used. Other types of composite construction used in buildings include composite trusses and joists, and stub-girders.

A comprehensive examination of the design and behaviour of steel-concrete composite floor systems and their components is contained in the CISC publication *Design and Construction of Composite Floor Systems* (Chien and Ritchie 1984). This book contains design aids and examples for composite beams, girders, trusses, and stub-girders.

Tables

The Composite Beam Trial Selection Tables from pages 5-26 to 5-75 are based on CSA G40.21-350W steel for WWF shapes, and on CSA G40.21-350W, ASTM A992 and A572 grade 50 for W-shapes (using the lowest value of $F_y = 345$ MPa among the three grades). The tables list composite members for the practical range of rolled W-shapes from 200 mm to 760 mm nominal depth, and for eight WWF sizes. Tables are provided for the following combinations of deck-slab concrete strength and concrete density:

- 75 mm steel deck with 65 mm cover slab with f'_c of 25 MPa, 2300 kg/m³ concrete
- 75 mm steel deck with 75 mm cover slab with f'_c of 25 MPa, 2300 kg/m³ concrete
- 75 mm steel deck with 90 mm cover slab with f'_c of 25 MPa, 2300 kg/m³ concrete
- 75 mm steel deck with 85 mm cover slab with f'_c of 25 MPa, 1850 kg/m³ concrete
- 75 mm steel deck with 85 mm cover slab with f'_c of 25 MPa, 2000 kg/m³ concrete

The tables show steel shapes listed in descending order of nominal depth and mass, and include the following properties, design data and resistances:

b = flange width of steel shape (mm)

t = flange thickness of steel shape (mm)

d = overall depth of steel shape (mm)

b_l = effective width of slab used in computing values of M_{rc}, Q_r, I_t, S_t and I_{ts} (mm). (Refer to Clause 17.4 of S16-09 for appropriate design effective width.)

M_{rc} = factored moment resistance of composite beam for percentage of full shear connection equal to 100%, 70% and 40% (kN·m)

Q_r = required sum of factored shear resistances between adjacent points of maximum and zero moment for 100% shear connection, (kN). Q_r = lesser of $\phi A_s F_y$ or $\phi_c \alpha_1 b_l t_c f'_c$, where t_c = effective slab thickness or effective cover slab thickness

I_t = moment of inertia of the composite section, transformed into steel properties, computed using mass density as shown on each table (10^6 mm^4)

S_t = section modulus of the composite section related to the extreme fibre of the bottom flange of the steel beam based on the value of I_t (10^3 mm^3)

I_{ts} = transformed moment of inertia for calculating shrinkage deflections, based on the modular ratio n_s. (See S16-09 Annex H for further information).

M_r = factored moment resistance of laterally supported bare steel section (kN·m)

V_r = factored shear resistance of the bare steel beam (kN)

L_u = maximum unsupported length of compression flange of the steel beam alone for which no reduction in M_r is required (mm)

I_x = moment of inertia about the x-x axis of the bare steel beam (10^6 mm^4)

S_x = section modulus of the bare steel beam (10^3 mm^3)

M'_r = factored moment resistance of the bare steel beam for an unsupported length L' (kN·m).

Since the concrete slab and/or the steel deck prevent movement of the top flange, lateral buckling is not a consideration at composite action. During construction, however, the unsupported length of the compression flange may be greater than L_u, and the moment resistance for the non-composite shape for the appropriate unsupported length of compression flange must be used.

The tabulated factored shear resistance V_r is computed according to Clause 13.4.1.1 of S16-09 for the appropriate h/w ratio.

Shear Connectors

Clauses 17.9.5 and 17.9.6 of S16-09 stipulate the amount of total factored horizontal shear force that must be resisted by shear connectors.

For full (i.e. 100%) shear connection, the total factored horizontal shear force V_h to be transferred between the point of maximum positive moment and adjacent points of zero moment is either:

- $\phi A_s F_y$ when the plastic neutral axis is in the slab, or

- $\phi_c \alpha_1 b_1 t_c f'_c$ when the plastic neutral axis is in the steel section.

For partial shear connection the total factored horizontal shear force V_h is the sum of the factored resistances of all the shear connectors between the point of maximum positive moment and each adjacent point of zero moment. S16-09 Clause 17.9.4 limits the minimum amount of partial shear connection to 40% of either $\phi A_s F_y$ or $\phi_c \alpha_1 b_1 t_c f'_c$, whichever is the lesser, when computing flexural strength.

Generally, shear connectors may be uniformly spaced in regions of positive or negative bending. However, when a concentrated load occurs within a region of positive bending, the number of shear connectors and the shear connector spacing is determined by Clause 17.9.8.

Tables 5-2, 5-3 and 5-4 provide values of the factored shear resistance q_r for the most common sizes of end-welded shear studs according to the requirements of Clause 17.7 when the stud height is at least four stud diameters, and when the stud projection in a ribbed slab is at least two stud diameters above the top surface of the steel deck.

Table 5-2 on page 5-17 gives values of q_r for stud diameters of 3/4 inch (19 mm), 5/8 inch (15.9 mm), and 1/2 inch (12.7 mm) in solid slabs, or in deck-slabs with ribs parallel to the beam, based on three concrete strength levels f'_c of 20 MPa, 25 MPa, and 30 MPa for both normal density (2300 kg/m³) and semi-low density (1850 kg/m³) concrete. Values are calculated according to Clause 17.7.2.2 and Clause 17.7.2.3.

Table 5-3 on page 5-18 and Table 5-4 on page 5-19 give values of q_{rr} for 3/4 inch (19 mm) and 5/8 inch (15.9 mm) diameter studs respectively in ribbed slabs for 75 mm or 38 mm deck, with ribs perpendicular to the beam, calculated according to Clause 17.7.2.4. Values are given for three concrete strength levels f'_c of 20 MPa, 25 MPa, and 30 MPa for both normal density (2300 kg/m³) and semi-low density (1850 kg/m³) concrete.

Deflections

Composite beams are stiffer than similar non-composite beams, and deflections are reduced when composite construction is used. Due to creep of the concrete slab over time, maximum deflections may increase, especially if the full load is sustained. Annex H of CSA S16-09 provides guidance for estimating deflections caused by shrinkage of the concrete slab. Beam deflection during construction, due to loads supported prior to hardening of the concrete while the steel beam alone supports the loads, should be checked. Cambering or the use of temporary shores will reduce the total final deflection.

For steel beams unshored during construction, S16-09 Clause 17.11 limits the stress (caused by the total of the specified loads applied before the concrete strength reaches $0.75 f'_c$ and, at the same location, the remaining specified loads acting on the composite section) in the tension flange to F_y.

Other Composite Members

Other composite members suitable for floor construction include composite trusses, composite open-web steel joists, and stub-girders. Optimum spans for performance and economy depend on overall building considerations such as storey height restrictions and integration of building services.

For composite trusses and joists, Clause 17.9.2 of S16-09 stipulates that the area of the top chord shall be neglected in determining the properties of the composite section, and that the factored moment resistance of the composite truss or joist shall be computed on the basis of full shear connection with the plastic neutral axis in the slab.

Composite stub-girders use wide-flange column shapes with short W-shape stubs shop-welded to the top of the girders and interconnected with the deck-slab by shear connectors to provide Vierendeel girder action. Deck-slabs usually consist of a 75 mm composite steel deck with 75 mm or 85 mm cover slabs.

Examples

An example to illustrate the use of the tables in this book follows on page 5-24. Further examples and design information for composite trusses, composite joists and stub girders, including design tables for stub girders, are contained in the CISC publication *Design and Construction of Composite Floor Systems* (see below).

References

PART TWO of this Handbook. See CISC Commentary on Clause 17.

CHIEN, E.Y.L., RITCHIE, J.K., 1984. Design and Construction of Composite Floor Systems. Canadian Institute of Steel Construction, Willowdale, Ontario.

KULAK, G.L., GRONDIN, G.Y. 2009. Limit States Design in Structural Steel, 8th Edition. Canadian Institute of Steel Construction, Markham, Ontario.

PICARD, A., BEAULIEU, D. 1991. Calcul des charpentes d'acier. Canadian Institute of Steel Construction, Willowdale, Ontario.

Factored Shear Resistance of Shear Studs   Table 5-2

in Solid Slabs and in Deck-Slabs with Ribs Parallel to Beam $(3.0 > w_d / h_d \geq 1.5)$

Stud in a Solid Slab, q_{rs} (kN)						
Stud Diameter	f'_c (γ_c = 2300 kg/m³)			f'_c (γ_c = 1850 kg/m³)		
	20 MPa	25 MPa	30 MPa	20 MPa	25 MPa	30 MPa
3/4" (19 mm)	74.6	86.7	98.2	63.4	73.7	83.4
5/8" (15.9 mm)	52.3	60.7	68.7	44.4	51.6	58.4
1/2" (12.7 mm)	33.3	38.8	43.9	28.3	32.9	37.3

Stud in a Deck-Slab with Ribs Parallel to Beam, q_{rr} (kN)							
Stud Diameter	**w_d / h_d**	f'_c (γ_c = 2300 kg/m³)			f'_c (γ_c = 1850 kg/m³)		
		20 MPa	25 MPa	30 MPa	20 MPa	25 MPa	30 MPa
3/4" (19 mm)	2.5	68.4	79.5	90.0	58.1	67.6	76.5
	2.4	67.2	78.1	88.4	57.1	66.3	75.1
	2.0	62.2	72.3	81.8	52.8	61.4	69.5
5/8" (15.9 mm)	2.5	47.9	55.7	63.0	40.7	47.3	53.5
	2.4	47.1	54.7	61.9	40.0	46.5	52.6
	2.0	43.6	50.6	57.3	37.0	43.0	48.7
1/2" (12.7 mm)	2.5	30.6	35.5	40.2	26.0	30.2	34.2
	2.4	30.0	34.9	39.5	25.5	29.6	33.5
	2.0	27.8	32.3	36.6	23.6	27.4	31.0

Factored Resistance of Shear Studs

Table 5-3

Ribs Perpendicular to Beam
3/4" (19 mm) Diameter Studs, F_u = 450 MPa
75 mm or 38 mm-Deep Steel Deck

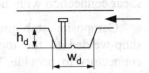

Deck		Stud connector(s)				Pull-out area A_p	Factored shear resistance of stud(s), q_{rr} (kN)					
							f'_c (γ_c = 2300 kg/m³)			f'_c (γ_c = 1850 kg/m³)		
h_d	w_d / h_d	Dia.	Length	n	Edge distance		20 MPa	25 MPa	30 MPa	20 MPa	25 MPa	30 MPa
mm	mm	mm	mm		mm	10³ mm²						
75	2.4	3/4" (19)	115	1	Int.	52.0	65.2	72.9	79.8	55.4	61.9	67.8
				1	65	40.7	51.0	57.0	62.5	43.4	48.5	53.1
				1	35	33.9	42.5	47.5	52.1	36.1	40.4	44.2
				2	Int.	69.2	86.7	96.9	106	73.7	82.4	90.3
			150	1	Int.	82.7	74.6	86.7	98.2	63.4	73.7	83.4
				1	65	60.7	74.6	84.9	93.0	63.4	72.2	79.1
				1	35	51.8	64.8	72.5	79.4	55.1	61.6	67.5
				2	Int.	105	132	147	161	112	125	137
75	2.0	3/4" (19)	115	1	Int.	49.1	61.4	68.7	75.3	52.2	58.4	64.0
				1	65	38.5	48.2	53.9	59.0	40.9	45.8	50.1
				1	35	32.1	40.2	44.9	49.2	34.2	38.2	41.8
				2	Int.	65.5	82.0	91.6	100	69.7	77.9	85.3
			150	1	Int.	71.6	74.6	86.7	98.2	63.4	73.7	83.4
				1	65	53.0	66.4	74.2	81.3	56.4	63.1	69.1
				1	35	45.1	56.4	63.1	69.1	48.0	53.6	58.8
				2	Int.	91.7	115	128	141	97.7	109	120
38	2.5	3/4" (19)	75	1	Int.	20.2	44.0	49.2	53.9	37.4	41.8	45.8
				1	65	18.8	41.0	45.9	50.3	34.9	39.0	42.7
				1	35	14.8	32.3	36.1	39.5	27.4	30.7	33.6
				2	Int.	30.4	66.3	74.1	81.2	56.3	63.0	69.0
			100	1	Int.	32.0	69.7	78.0	85.4	59.3	66.3	72.6
				1	65	27.3	59.5	66.5	72.8	50.6	56.5	61.9
				1	35	22.1	48.3	54.0	59.1	41.0	45.9	50.2
				2	Int.	45.3	98.8	110	121	84.0	93.9	103
38	1.4	3/4" (19)	75	1	Int.	13.5	29.4	32.8	36.0	25.0	27.9	30.6
				1	65	12.7	27.7	31.0	34.0	23.6	26.4	28.9
				1	35	10.4	22.7	25.4	27.8	19.3	21.6	23.6
				2	Int.	21.4	46.7	52.3	57.2	39.7	44.4	48.7
			100	1	Int.	27.5	59.9	67.0	73.4	50.9	57.0	62.4
				1	65	24.8	54.2	60.6	66.4	46.1	51.5	56.4
				1	35	19.9	43.4	48.5	53.1	36.9	41.2	45.1
				2	Int.	40.8	89.0	99.5	109	75.7	84.6	92.7

Factored shear resistances are calculated in accordance with CSA S16-09 Clause 17.7.2.4.

Notes:
1. n = number of studs per rib, γ_c = density of concrete
2. Stud length listed is the length after welding.
   Minimum length prior to welding ≈ stud length listed + 10 mm fusion allowance.
3. Double studs transversely spaced at minimum 4 stud diameters.
4. Int. = interior condition
5. Studs placed off-centre in ribs of 75 mm deck and on-centre in ribs of 38 mm deck.

Table 5-4

Factored Resistance of Shear Studs
Ribs Perpendicular to Beam
5/8" (15.9 mm) Diameter Studs, F_u = 450 MPa
75 mm or 38 mm-Deep Steel Deck

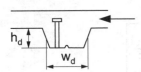

Deck		Stud connector(s)				Pull-out area A_p	Factored shear resistance of stud(s), q_{rr} (kN)					
h_d	$\dfrac{w_d}{h_d}$	Dia.	Length	n	Edge distance		f'_c (γ_c = 2300 kg/m^3)			f'_c (γ_c = 1850 kg/m^3)		
mm		mm	mm		mm	10^3 mm^2	20 MPa	25 MPa	30 MPa	20 MPa	25 MPa	30 MPa
75	2.4	5/8" (15.9)	115	1	Int.	52.0	52.3	60.7	68.7	44.4	51.6	58.4
				1	65	40.7	51.0	57.0	62.5	43.4	48.5	53.1
				1	35	33.9	42.5	47.5	52.1	36.1	40.4	44.2
				2	Int.	66.4	83.2	93.0	102	70.7	79.1	86.6
			150	1	Int.	82.7	52.3	60.7	68.7	44.4	51.6	58.4
				1	65	60.7	52.3	60.7	68.7	44.4	51.6	58.4
				1	35	51.8	52.3	60.7	68.7	44.4	51.6	58.4
				2	Int.	102	105	121	137	88.8	103	117
75	2.0	5/8" (15.9)	115	1	Int.	49.1	52.3	60.7	68.7	44.4	51.6	58.4
				1	65	38.5	48.2	53.9	59.0	40.9	45.8	50.1
				1	35	32.1	40.2	44.9	49.2	34.2	38.2	41.8
				2	Int.	62.8	78.6	87.9	96.3	66.8	74.7	81.9
			150	1	Int.	71.6	52.3	60.7	68.7	44.4	51.6	58.4
				1	65	53.0	52.3	60.7	68.7	44.4	51.6	58.4
				1	35	45.1	52.3	60.7	68.7	44.4	51.6	58.4
				2	Int.	88.5	105	121	136	88.8	103	115
38	2.5	5/8" (15.9)	75	1	Int.	20.2	44.0	49.2	53.9	37.4	41.8	45.8
				1	65	18.8	41.0	45.9	50.3	34.9	39.0	42.7
				1	35	14.8	32.3	36.1	39.5	27.4	30.7	33.6
				2	Int.	28.7	62.6	70.0	76.7	53.2	59.5	65.2
			100	1	Int.	32.0	52.3	60.7	68.7	44.4	51.6	58.4
				1	65	27.3	52.3	60.7	68.7	44.4	51.6	58.4
				1	35	22.1	48.3	54.0	59.1	41.0	45.9	50.2
				2	Int.	43.1	94.1	105	115	80.0	89.4	97.9
38	1.4	5/8" (15.9)	75	1	Int.	13.5	29.4	32.8	36.0	25.0	27.9	30.6
				1	65	12.7	27.7	31.0	34.0	23.6	26.4	28.9
				1	35	10.4	22.7	25.4	27.8	19.3	21.6	23.6
				2	Int.	20.1	43.9	49.1	53.8	37.3	41.7	45.7
			100	1	Int.	27.5	52.3	60.7	68.7	44.4	51.6	58.4
				1	65	24.8	52.3	60.6	66.4	44.4	51.5	56.4
				1	35	19.9	43.4	48.5	53.1	36.9	41.2	45.1
				2	Int.	38.6	84.3	94.2	103	71.6	80.1	87.7

Factored shear resistances are calculated in accordance with CSA S16-09 Clause 17.7.2.4.

Notes:
1. n = number of studs per rib, γ_c = density of concrete
2. Stud length listed is the length after welding.
   Minimum length prior to welding ≈ stud length listed + 10 mm fusion allowance.
3. Double studs transversely spaced at minimum 4 stud diameters.
4. Int. = interior condition
5. Studs placed off-centre in ribs of 75 mm deck and on-centre in ribs of 38 mm deck.

Pull-out Area, A$_p$

Studs placed on-centre in ribs

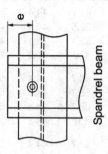

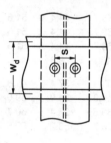

n = 2, s ≥ 4 dia.

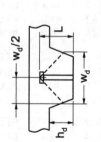

Spandrel beam

Stud length, L	A$_p$	If double studs (n=2), add:	If spandrel beam and e < L, subtract:	
a) $L \leq w_d/2$	$4\sqrt{2}\,L^2$	$2\sqrt{2}\,sL$	$2\sqrt{2}\,L(L-e)$	
b) $w_d/2 < L \leq w_d/2 + h_d$	$2\sqrt{2}\,L\,w_d$	$\sqrt{2}\,s\,w_d$	$\sqrt{2}\,w_d(L-e)$	
c) $L > w_d/2 + h_d$	$2\sqrt{2}\,[2(L-h_d)^2 + h_d\,w_d]$	$2\sqrt{2}\,s(L-h_d)$	i) $e \geq L - h_d$	$\sqrt{2}\,w_d(L-e)$
			ii) $e < L - h_d$	$\sqrt{2}\,[2(L-h_d)^2 + w_d\,h_d - 2e(L-h_d)]$

See CSA S16-09 Clause 17.7.2.4.

Pull-out Area, A_p

Studs placed off-centre in ribs

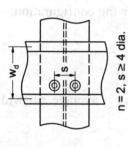

Spandrel beam

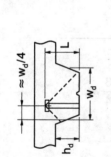

$n=2$, $s \geq 4$ dia.

Stud length, L	A_p	If double studs (n=2), add:		If spandrel beam and e < L, subtract:
a) $L \leq w_d/4$	$4\sqrt{2}\,L^2$	$2\sqrt{2}\,s L$		$2\sqrt{2}\,L(L-e)$
b) $w_d/4 < L \leq 3w_d/4$ and $L \leq w_d/4 + h_d$	$\sqrt{2}\,L(2L + w_d/2)$	$\sqrt{2}\,s(L + w_d/4)$		$\sqrt{2}\,(w_d/4 + L)(L-e)$
c) $3w_d/4 < L \leq w_d/4 + h_d$	$2\sqrt{2}\,L w_d$	$\sqrt{2}\,s w_d$		$\sqrt{2}\,w_d(L-e)$
d) $w_d/4 + h_d < L \leq 3w_d/4$	$\sqrt{2}\,(4L^2 - 4L h_d + 2h_d^2 + h_d w_d/2)$	$\sqrt{2}\,s(2L - h_d)$	i) $e \geq L - h_d$	$\sqrt{2}\,(w_d/4 + L)(L-e)$
			iii) $e < L - h_d$	$\sqrt{2}\,[(w_d/4 - e)(L-e) + (L - h_d - e)(L - h_d - w_d/4)]$
e) $L > w_d/4 + h_d$ and $3w_d/4 < L \leq 3w_d/4 + h_d$	$\sqrt{2}\,[2(L-h_d)^2 + h_d w_d/2 + 3L w_d/2]$	$\sqrt{2}\,s(L - h_d + 3w_d/4)$	i) $e \geq L - h_d$	$\sqrt{2}\,w_d(L-e)$
			iii) $e < L - h_d$	$\sqrt{2}\,[w_d(L-e) + (L - h_d - e)(L - h_d - w_d/4)]$
f) $L > 3w_d/4 + h_d$	$\sqrt{2}\,[4(L - h_d)^2 + 2h_d w_d]$	$2\sqrt{2}\,s(L - h_d)$	i) $e \geq L - h_d$	$\sqrt{2}\,w_d(L-e)$
			iii) $e < L - h_d$	$\sqrt{2}\,[2(L - h_d)^2 + w_d h_d - 2e(L - h_d)]$

See CSA S16-09 Clause 17.7.2.4.

Design Example: Area of Concrete Pull-Out Pyramid, A_p

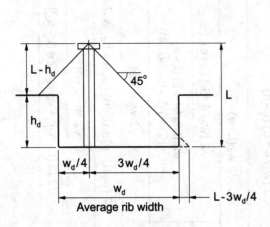

Idealized geometry: vertical rib walls

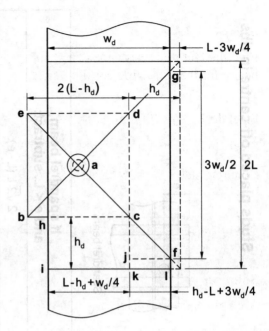

Find the area of the concrete pull-out pyramid for a single stud placed off-centre in a rib, in accordance with CSA S16-09 Clause 17.7.2.4, for the following configuration:

$$L > \frac{w_d}{4} + h_d \quad \text{and} \quad \frac{3}{4}w_d < L \le \frac{3}{4}w_d + h_d$$

For simplicity, rib walls are assumed to be vertical, with w_d = average rib width. For other deck and stud configurations, see pages 5-20 and 5-21.

Surface	Area
abc + acd + ade + aeb	$4\sqrt{2}\left(L - h_d\right)^2$
cfgd	$\dfrac{\sqrt{2}}{2}\left[\dfrac{3}{2}w_d + 2\left(L - h_d\right)\right]\left(h_d - L + \dfrac{3}{4}w_d\right)$
2 × hikc	$2\sqrt{2}\,h_d\left(L - h_d + \dfrac{w_d}{4}\right)$
2 × cjf	$\sqrt{2}\left(h_d - L + \dfrac{3}{4}w_d\right)^2$
2 × jklf	$2\sqrt{2}\left(h_d - L + \dfrac{3}{4}w_d\right)\left(L - \dfrac{3}{4}w_d\right)$
Total area:	$A_p = \sqrt{2}\left[2\left(L - h_d\right)^2 + \dfrac{1}{2}h_d w_d + \dfrac{3}{2}L w_d\right]$

Design Example: Factored Resistance of a Shear Stud

Given

Find the factored resistance of a shear stud placed off-centre in ribs perpendicular to the beam, for the following configuration:

Steel deck: $h_d = 75$ mm, $w_d = 180$ mm (average rib width)

Steel stud: diameter $= 19$ mm, $L = 150$ mm, $F_u = 450$ MPa, $\phi_{sc} = 0.80$

Concrete slab: $f'_c = 25$ MPa, $\gamma_c = 2\,300$ kg/m^3, $\rho = 1.0$ (normal-density concrete)

Assume a spandrel beam condition with edge distance, $e = 65$ mm.

Solution

Area of concrete pull-out pyramid, S16-09 Clause 17.7.2.4:

$L = 150 > w_d/4 + h_d = 120$ mm, $3\,w_d/4 = 135 < L = 150 < 3\,w_d/4 + h_d = 210$ mm.

See page 5-21, case (e).

$A_p = \sqrt{2}\,[2\,(L - h_d)^2 + h_d w_d/2 + 3\,L\,w_d/2] = 82\,700$ mm^2 (for an interior condition)

Edge distance, $e = 65 < L - h_d = 75$ mm, page 5-21, case (e) (ii)

Subtract: $\sqrt{2}\,[w_d\,(L - e) + (L - h_d - e)(L - h_d - w_d/4)] = 22\,100$ mm^2

$A_p = 82\,700 - 22\,100 = 60\,600$ mm^2 ($\approx 60\,700$ mm^2, Table 5-3, page 5-18)

$A_{sc} = \pi\,(19/2)^2 = 284$ mm^2

$E_c = (3\,300\,\sqrt{f'_c} + 6\,900)\,(\gamma_c/2\,300)^{1.5} = 23\,400$ MPa, S16-09 Clause 2.1

Clause 17.7.2.2, $q_{rs} = 0.50\,\phi_{sc}\,A_{sc}\,\sqrt{f'_c\,E_c} = 86.9$ kN $< \phi_{sc}\,A_{sc}\,F_u = 102$ kN

Clause 17.7.2.4(a), $q_{rr} = 0.35\,\phi_{sc}\,\rho\,A_p\,\sqrt{f'_c} = 84.8$ kN $< q_{rs} = 86.9$ kN

Factored shear resistance: $q_{rr} = 84.8$ kN (≈ 84.9 kN, Table 5-3, page 5-18)

Design Example

Given:

Select a simply-supported composite beam to span 12 m and carry a uniformly distributed specified live load of 18 kN/m and a dead load of 12 kN/m. Beams are spaced at 3 m on centre and support a 75 mm steel deck (ribs perpendicular to the beam) with a 65 mm cover slab of 25 MPa normal density concrete. Calculations are based on F_y = 345 MPa, representing the lowest value among CSA G40.21-350W, ASTM A992 and A572 Grade 50 steels. Live load deflections are limited to $L/300$.

Solution:

Total factored load $= (1.25 \times 12) + (1.50 \times 18) = 42.0$ kN/m

Therefore $M_f = 42.0 \times 12^2 / 8 = 756$ kN·m and $V_f = 42.0 \times 12 / 2 = 252$ kN

Compute minimum I_{reqd} for deflection limit $L/300$ using Figure 5-1 and Table 5-5 on pages 5-78 and 5-79.

Total specified live load, $W = 18 \times 12 = 216$ kN

B_d = 1.0   simple span UDL   (Table 5-5)

C_d = 2.8   for 12 m span and $L / \Delta = 300$ (Figure 5-1)

I_{reqd} = $W \times C_d \times B_d$

        = $(216 \times 2.8 \times 1.0)\, 1.15 = 696 \times 10^6$ mm^4 (with 15% allowance for creep)

Effective Width   (S16-09 Clause 17.4.1)

a) $0.25\,L = 0.25 \times 12\,000$ mm $= 3\,000$ mm

b) beam spacing $= 3$ m $= 3\,000$ mm

Therefore, effective width $= 3\,000$ mm

Beam Selection

From composite beam selection tables for 75 mm steel deck with 65 mm cover slab and $b_1 = 3\,000$ mm, page 5-31, a suitable shape is a W460x74 with M_{rc} for 40% shear connection $= 783$ kN·m > 756 kN·m

$V_r = 843$ kN > 252 kN

I_t = $1\,100 \times 10^6$ mm^4

For 40% shear connection, $I_e = I_s + 0.85\,p^{0.25}\,(I_t - I_s)$ (Clause 17.3.1(a))

      = $333 + 0.85\,(0.4)^{0.25}\,(1\,100 - 333) = 851 \times 10^6$ mm$^4 > 696 \times 10^6$ mm^4

$Q_r = 2\,570$ kN ; $S_t = 2\,350 \times 10^3$ mm^3 ; $M_r = 512$ kN·m ; $L_u = 2\,530$ mm

Clause 17.12 requires that the steel section alone must be capable of supporting all factored loads applied before concrete hardens. In this case the steel deck will provide lateral support to the compression flange of the beam.

Thus $M_r = 512$ kN·m applies.

Assuming dead load due to deck-slab and steel beam as 8 kN/m and construction live load as 2.5 kN/m, the total factored load applied before the concrete hardens is

$$(1.25 \times 8) + (1.5 \times 2.5) = 13.8 \text{ kN/m}$$

$$M_f = 13.8 \times 12^2 / 8 = 248 \text{ kN·m} < 512 \text{ kN·m}$$

Check Unshored Beam Tension Flange (Clause 17.11)

Assume that the load applied before concrete strength reaches $0.75 f'_c$ is the specified dead load (8 kN/m), and that the remaining dead load ($12 - 8 = 4$ kN/m) and the specified live load acts on the composite section.

Stress in tension flange due to specified load acting on steel beam alone:

S_x of steel beam $= 1\,460 \times 10^3$ mm^3

$$f_1 = \frac{M_1}{S_x} = \frac{8 \times 12\,000^2}{8 \times 1\,460 \times 10^3} = 98.6 \text{ MPa}$$

Stress in tension flange due to specified live and superimposed dead loads acting on composite section:

$$f_2 = \frac{M_2}{S_t} = \frac{(18+4) \times 12\,000^2}{8 \times 2\,350 \times 10^3} = 169 \text{ MPa}$$

$$f_1 + f_2 = 98.6 + 169 = 268 \text{ MPa} < 345 \text{ MPa}$$

Shear Connectors

Q_r (100% connection) $= 2\,570$ kN

Assume 3/4 inch (19 mm) diameter studs, length $L = 115$ mm.

Minimum flange thickness $= 19 / 2.5 = 7.6$ mm < 14.5 mm (Clause 17.6.5)

From Table 5-3 (page 5-18), for 3/4 inch diameter studs, $h_d = 75$ mm, $w_d / h_d = 2.0$, 25 MPa, 2 300 kg/m^3 concrete, factored shear resistance per stud q_{rr} is 68.7 kN

Number of studs required:

$$= \frac{2 \times Q_r \times (\% \text{ shear connection} / 100)}{q_{rr}} = \frac{2 \times 2\,570 \times (40/100)}{68.7} = 29.9 \quad \text{Use 30 studs.}$$

Since there are no concentrated loads, the studs can be spaced uniformly along the full length of the beam as permitted by the deck flutes.

COMPOSITE BEAMS
Trial Selection Table
75 mm Deck with 65 mm Slab

$\phi = 0.90$, $\phi_c = 0.65$

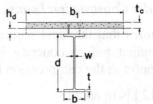

G40.21 350W
$f'_c = 25$ MPa

Steel section	b_1	M_{rc} (kN·m) for % shear connection			Q_r	I_t	S_t	I_{ts}	Steel section data	Non-composite Unbraced condition			
		100%	70%	40%	100%					L'	M_r'	L'	M_r'
	mm				(kN)	10^6 mm⁴	10^3 mm³	10^6 mm⁴		mm	kN·m	mm	kN·m
WWF1000x223	6 000	4 990	4 800	4 360	5 150	11 100	12 700	8 270	M_r 3 310	4 000	3 250	14 000	729
WWF39x150	5 000	4 880	4 650	4 210	4 290	10 600	12 500	7 850	V_r 2 210	6 000	2 620	16 000	602
b = 300	4 000	4 730	4 460	4 060	3 430	10 000	12 300	7 370	L_u 3 790	8 000	1 790	18 000	512
t = 25	3 000	4 500	4 230	3 890	2 570	9 270	12 000	6 820	I_x 4 590	10 000	1 230	20 000	446
d = 1000	2 000	4 180	3 960	3 700	1 720	8 250	11 600	6 190	S_x 9 190	12 000	920	22 000	394
WWF1000x200	6 000	4 560	4 380	3 930	5 150	10 000	11 300	7 490	M_r 2 890	4 000	2 790	14 000	549
WWF39x134	5 000	4 460	4 230	3 790	4 290	9 600	11 100	7 090	V_r 2 210	6 000	2 180	16 000	449
b = 300	4 000	4 310	4 040	3 630	3 430	9 080	10 900	6 640	L_u 3 610	8 000	1 390	18 000	379
t = 20	3 000	4 070	3 810	3 460	2 570	8 400	10 700	6 120	I_x 3 940	10 000	945	20 000	328
d = 1000	2 000	3 750	3 530	3 280	1 720	7 470	10 300	5 520	S_x 7 880	12 000	699	22 000	289
WWF900x192	6 000	4 010	3 850	3 590	5 150	8 430	10 400	6 400	M_r 2 710	4 000	2 700	14 000	670
WWF35x128	5 000	3 900	3 770	3 480	4 290	8 100	10 300	6 080	V_r 1 350	6 000	2 240	16 000	555
b = 300	4 000	3 790	3 660	3 360	3 430	7 690	10 100	5 710	L_u 3 980	8 000	1 630	18 000	473
t = 25	3 000	3 670	3 490	3 220	2 570	7 140	9 930	5 280	I_x 3 460	10 000	1 120	20 000	412
d = 900	2 000	3 450	3 280	3 060	1 720	6 380	9 620	4 780	S_x 7 680	12 000	842	22 000	365
WWF900x169	5 000	3 510	3 380	3 090	4 290	7 220	8 970	5 430	M_r 2 320	4 500	2 190	12 000	625
WWF35x113	4 000	3 400	3 270	2 970	3 430	6 870	8 850	5 090	V_r 1 340	5 000	2 080	14 000	491
b = 300	3 000	3 280	3 100	2 830	2 570	6 390	8 670	4 690	L_u 3 820	6 000	1 850	16 000	402
t = 20	2 000	3 060	2 890	2 670	1 720	5 710	8 390	4 220	I_x 2 930	8 000	1 250	18 000	339
d = 900	1 000	2 730	2 620	2 500	858	4 680	7 860	3 640	S_x 6 510	10 000	845	20 000	293
WWF800x184	5 000	3 380	3 250	3 020	4 290	6 400	8 970	4 800	M_r 2 330	4 500	2 260	12 000	791
WWF31x123	4 000	3 280	3 160	2 920	3 430	6 080	8 850	4 500	V_r 1 370	5 000	2 170	14 000	634
b = 300	3 000	3 160	3 030	2 790	2 570	5 640	8 670	4 150	L_u 4 060	6 000	1 970	16 000	529
t = 25	2 000	2 990	2 840	2 650	1 720	5 040	8 400	3 740	I_x 2 660	8 000	1 490	18 000	454
d = 800	1 000	2 710	2 610	2 490	858	4 140	7 900	3 260	S_x 6 640	10 000	1 040	20 000	398
WWF800x161	5 000	3 030	2 900	2 680	4 290	5 690	7 800	4 280	M_r 1 990	4 500	1 940	12 000	581
WWF31x108	4 000	2 930	2 820	2 570	3 430	5 410	7 700	4 010	V_r 1 370	5 000	1 810	14 000	460
b = 300	3 000	2 820	2 680	2 450	2 570	5 040	7 550	3 690	L_u 3 900	6 000	1 620	16 000	379
t = 20	2 000	2 640	2 500	2 310	1 720	4 500	7 310	3 310	I_x 2 250	8 000	1 130	18 000	322
d = 800	1 000	2 360	2 260	2 150	858	3 680	6 850	2 840	S_x 5 610	10 000	778	20 000	280
WWF700x175	5 000	2 900	2 770	2 580	4 290	4 930	7 720	3 680	M_r 1 970	4 500	1 930	12 000	741
WWF28x117	4 000	2 790	2 680	2 490	3 430	4 670	7 610	3 440	V_r 1 370	5 000	1 850	14 000	601
b = 300	3 000	2 680	2 580	2 380	2 570	4 340	7 460	3 170	L_u 4 160	6 000	1 700	16 000	505
t = 25	2 000	2 540	2 430	2 260	1 720	3 870	7 220	2 840	I_x 1 970	8 000	1 350	18 000	436
d = 700	1 000	2 310	2 220	2 120	858	3 160	6 780	2 450	S_x 5 640	10 000	965	20 000	384
WWF700x152	5 000	2 590	2 470	2 280	4 290	4 360	6 680	3 280	M_r 1 680	4 500	1 610	12 000	537
WWF28x102	4 000	2 490	2 380	2 190	3 430	4 150	6 590	3 070	V_r 1 370	5 000	1 540	14 000	429
b = 300	3 000	2 380	2 280	2 080	2 570	3 860	6 470	2 810	L_u 3 990	6 000	1 390	16 000	356
t = 20	2 000	2 250	2 130	1 960	1 720	3 450	6 260	2 510	I_x 1 660	8 000	1 020	18 000	305
d = 700	1 000	2 010	1 920	1 820	858	2 810	5 860	2 130	S_x 4 760	10 000	711	20 000	266

Note: Resistances are based on a concrete density of 2300 kg/m³.

Units: M_r - kN·m, V_r - kN, L_u - mm, I_x - 10^6 mm⁴, S_x - 10^3 mm³, b - mm, t - mm, d - mm

$F_y = 350$ MPa

G40.21 350W
ASTM A992
A572 Grade 50
f′c = 25 MPa

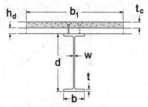

COMPOSITE BEAMS
Trial Selection Table
75 mm Deck with 65 mm Slab
φ = 0.90, φc = 0.65

Steel section	b₁	Mrc (kN·m) for % shear connection			Qr	It	St	Its	Steel section data	Unbraced condition			
		100%	70%	40%	100%	10⁶	10³	10⁶		L′	Mr′	L′	Mr′
	mm				(kN)	mm⁴	mm³	mm⁴		mm	kN·m	mm	kN·m
W760x185	5 000	3 230	3 080	2 780	4 290	5 740	8 360	4 230	Mr 2 080	4 000	1 980	12 000	576
W30x124	4 000	3 120	2 960	2 660	3 430	5 430	8 230	3 950	Vr 2 340	5 000	1 780	14 000	470
b = 267	3 000	2 970	2 790	2 520	2 570	5 020	8 040	3 630	Lu 3 450	6 000	1 550	16 000	397
t = 23.6	2 000	2 740	2 580	2 380	1 720	4 460	7 740	3 240	Ix 2 230	8 000	1 040	18 000	344
d = 766	1 000	2 440	2 330	2 220	858	3 620	7 190	2 790	Sx 5 820	10 000	743	20 000	304
W760x173	5 000	3 060	2 920	2 620	4 290	5 410	7 840	4 000	Mr 1 930	4 000	1 830	12 000	506
W30x116	4 000	2 950	2 800	2 510	3 430	5 130	7 720	3 730	Vr 2 250	5 000	1 630	14 000	411
b = 267	3 000	2 810	2 630	2 370	2 570	4 750	7 550	3 420	Lu 3 410	6 000	1 410	16 000	346
t = 21.6	2 000	2 590	2 430	2 230	1 720	4 220	7 270	3 050	Ix 2 060	8 000	924	18 000	299
d = 762	1 000	2 290	2 190	2 070	858	3 410	6 740	2 610	Sx 5 400	10 000	657	20 000	264
W760x161	5 000	2 850	2 720	2 440	4 290	5 020	7 210	3 730	Mr 1 760	4 000	1 650	12 000	429
W30x108	4 000	2 740	2 610	2 330	3 430	4 760	7 100	3 480	Vr 2 140	5 000	1 460	14 000	347
b = 266	3 000	2 620	2 450	2 200	2 570	4 420	6 950	3 180	Lu 3 330	6 000	1 250	16 000	291
t = 19.3	2 000	2 410	2 250	2 060	1 720	3 930	6 690	2 830	Ix 1 860	8 000	793	18 000	251
d = 758	1 000	2 110	2 010	1 900	858	3 170	6 210	2 400	Sx 4 900	10 000	560	20 000	220
W760x147	5 000	2 640	2 510	2 260	4 290	4 610	6 580	3 440	Mr 1 580	4 000	1 470	12 000	358
W30x99	4 000	2 540	2 410	2 150	3 430	4 380	6 480	3 210	Vr 2 040	5 000	1 290	14 000	288
b = 265	3 000	2 420	2 260	2 020	2 570	4 080	6 340	2 940	Lu 3 260	6 000	1 090	16 000	241
t = 17	2 000	2 220	2 070	1 880	1 720	3 630	6 120	2 600	Ix 1 660	8 000	671	18 000	207
d = 753	1 000	1 940	1 840	1 730	858	2 930	5 670	2 190	Sx 4 410	10 000	470	20 000	181
W760x134	5 000	2 440	2 320	2 090	4 290	4 250	6 000	3 200	Mr 1 440	4 000	1 330	12 000	308
W30x90	4 000	2 340	2 230	1 990	3 430	4 050	5 920	2 990	Vr 1 650	5 000	1 160	14 000	246
b = 264	3 000	2 230	2 100	1 870	2 570	3 780	5 800	2 730	Lu 3 230	6 000	967	16 000	205
t = 15.5	2 000	2 060	1 920	1 730	1 720	3 370	5 600	2 420	Ix 1 500	8 000	587	18 000	175
d = 750	1 000	1 780	1 690	1 580	858	2 730	5 200	2 020	Sx 4 010	10 000	408	20 000	153
W690x192	5 000	3 090	2 940	2 660	4 290	5 120	8 120	3 750	Mr 2 010	4 000	1 910	12 000	635
W27x129	4 000	2 970	2 830	2 550	3 430	4 840	7 990	3 500	Vr 2 230	5 000	1 730	14 000	526
b = 254	3 000	2 840	2 670	2 430	2 570	4 470	7 800	3 210	Lu 3 440	6 000	1 540	16 000	449
t = 27.9	2 000	2 630	2 480	2 290	1 720	3 960	7 500	2 870	Ix 1 980	8 000	1 090	18 000	393
d = 702	1 000	2 350	2 250	2 150	858	3 200	6 960	2 470	Sx 5 640	10 000	802	20 000	349
W690x170	5 000	2 770	2 630	2 380	4 290	4 550	7 160	3 360	Mr 1 750	4 000	1 650	12 000	497
W27x114	4 000	2 660	2 530	2 280	3 430	4 310	7 050	3 140	Vr 2 060	5 000	1 480	14 000	409
b = 256	3 000	2 540	2 390	2 160	2 570	3 990	6 890	2 870	Lu 3 380	6 000	1 290	16 000	347
t = 23.6	2 000	2 350	2 210	2 030	1 720	3 540	6 640	2 550	Ix 1 700	8 000	875	18 000	302
d = 693	1 000	2 080	1 990	1 880	858	2 860	6 160	2 170	Sx 4 910	10 000	635	20 000	268
W690x152	5 000	2 520	2 400	2 180	4 290	4 140	6 440	3 090	Mr 1 550	4 000	1 460	12 000	406
W27x102	4 000	2 420	2 310	2 080	3 430	3 940	6 350	2 880	Vr 1 850	5 000	1 290	14 000	332
b = 254	3 000	2 310	2 180	1 960	2 570	3 660	6 220	2 630	Lu 3 320	6 000	1 110	16 000	281
t = 21.1	2 000	2 140	2 010	1 830	1 720	3 250	6 000	2 340	Ix 1 510	8 000	728	18 000	244
d = 688	1 000	1 880	1 790	1 690	858	2 630	5 570	1 970	Sx 4 380	10 000	523	20 000	216

Note: Resistances are based on a concrete density of 2300 kg/m³.

Units: Mr - kN·m, Vr - kN, Lu - mm, Ix - 10⁶ mm⁴, Sx - 10³ mm³, b - mm, t - mm, d - mm

Fy = 345 MPa

COMPOSITE BEAMS
Trial Selection Table
75 mm Deck with 65 mm Slab
$\phi = 0.90$, $\phi_c = 0.65$

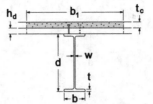

G40.21 350W
ASTM A992
A572 Grade 50
$f'_c = 25$ MPa

Steel section	b_1	M_{rc} (kN·m) for % shear connection			Q_r (kN)	I_t 10^6	S_t 10^3	I_{ts} 10^6	Steel section data	Unbraced condition			
										L'	M_r'	L'	M_r'
	mm	100%	70%	40%	100%	mm⁴	mm³	mm⁴		mm	kN·m	mm	kN·m
W690x140	5 000	2 350	2 220	2 020	4 290	3 820	5 900	2 870	M_r 1 410	4 000	1 320	10 000	447
W27x94	4 000	2 250	2 140	1 920	3 430	3 640	5 820	2 680	V_r 1 740	5 000	1 160	12 000	345
b = 254	3 000	2 140	2 020	1 810	2 570	3 390	5 700	2 450	L_u 3 270	6 000	987	14 000	280
t = 18.9	2 000	1 990	1 860	1 690	1 720	3 020	5 500	2 170	I_x 1 360	7 000	778	16 000	236
d = 684	1 000	1 740	1 650	1 550	858	2 440	5 120	1 810	S_x 3 980	8 000	628	18 000	204
W690x125	5 000	2 140	2 020	1 840	4 290	3 450	5 280	2 610	M_r 1 250	4 000	1 140	10 000	362
W27x84	4 000	2 050	1 940	1 750	3 430	3 290	5 210	2 440	V_r 1 610	5 000	999	12 000	277
b = 253	3 000	1 940	1 840	1 640	2 570	3 070	5 110	2 230	L_u 3 190	6 000	834	14 000	224
t = 16.3	2 000	1 800	1 680	1 520	1 720	2 750	4 940	1 970	I_x 1 190	7 000	641	16 000	188
d = 678	1 000	1 570	1 480	1 380	858	2 220	4 600	1 630	S_x 3 500	8 000	514	18 000	162
W610x174	5 000	2 570	2 440	2 240	4 290	3 900	6 840	2 880	M_r 1 660	4 500	1 660	10 000	924
W24x117	4 000	2 460	2 350	2 150	3 430	3 700	6 740	2 680	V_r 1 770	5 000	1 610	12 000	709
b = 325	3 000	2 350	2 240	2 040	2 570	3 420	6 600	2 460	L_u 4 480	6 000	1 490	14 000	574
t = 21.6	2 000	2 200	2 090	1 930	1 720	3 030	6 360	2 190	I_x 1 470	7 000	1 370	16 000	482
d = 616	1 000	1 970	1 890	1 800	858	2 450	5 920	1 870	S_x 4 780	8 000	1 230	18 000	415
W610x155	5 000	2 320	2 200	2 020	4 290	3 520	6 090	2 620	M_r 1 470	4 500	1 460	10 000	762
W24x104	4 000	2 220	2 120	1 940	3 430	3 340	6 010	2 440	V_r 1 590	5 000	1 410	12 000	579
b = 324	3 000	2 110	2 020	1 840	2 570	3 100	5 880	2 240	L_u 4 400	6 000	1 300	14 000	465
t = 19	2 000	1 980	1 880	1 730	1 720	2 760	5 680	1 980	I_x 1 290	7 000	1 180	16 000	388
d = 611	1 000	1 770	1 690	1 600	858	2 230	5 300	1 680	S_x 4 220	8 000	1 050	18 000	333
W610x140	5 000	2 170	2 040	1 850	4 290	3 240	5 480	2 420	M_r 1 290	4 000	1 170	10 000	422
W24x94	4 000	2 070	1 960	1 770	3 430	3 080	5 400	2 250	V_r 1 660	5 000	1 030	12 000	334
b = 230	3 000	1 960	1 860	1 670	2 570	2 860	5 290	2 050	L_u 3 070	6 000	874	14 000	277
t = 22.2	2 000	1 820	1 710	1 550	1 720	2 550	5 100	1 810	I_x 1 120	7 000	695	16 000	237
d = 617	1 000	1 590	1 510	1 420	858	2 050	4 730	1 510	S_x 3 630	8 000	573	18 000	207
W610x125	5 000	1 970	1 850	1 680	4 290	2 920	4 880	2 200	M_r 1 140	4 000	1 020	10 000	342
W24x84	4 000	1 870	1 770	1 600	3 430	2 780	4 820	2 050	V_r 1 490	5 000	889	12 000	269
b = 229	3 000	1 770	1 680	1 510	2 570	2 600	4 720	1 870	L_u 3 020	6 000	733	14 000	222
t = 19.6	2 000	1 650	1 540	1 400	1 720	2 320	4 560	1 650	I_x 985	7 000	575	16 000	189
d = 612	1 000	1 440	1 360	1 270	858	1 870	4 250	1 360	S_x 3 220	8 000	470	18 000	165
W610x113	5 000	1 820	1 700	1 540	4 290	2 660	4 410	2 030	M_r 1 020	4 000	906	10 000	282
W24x76	4 000	1 720	1 630	1 470	3 430	2 540	4 360	1 890	V_r 1 400	5 000	775	12 000	220
b = 228	3 000	1 620	1 540	1 380	2 570	2 380	4 270	1 730	L_u 2 950	6 000	617	14 000	180
t = 17.3	2 000	1 510	1 420	1 270	1 720	2 130	4 140	1 520	I_x 875	7 000	481	16 000	153
d = 608	1 000	1 310	1 240	1 150	858	1 720	3 860	1 240	S_x 2 880	8 000	391	18 000	133
W610x101	5 000	1 660	1 550	1 400	4 040	2 400	3 960	1 850	M_r 900	4 000	787	10 000	228
W24x68	4 000	1 580	1 490	1 340	3 430	2 300	3 910	1 730	V_r 1 300	5 000	664	12 000	176
b = 228	3 000	1 490	1 410	1 260	2 570	2 160	3 840	1 570	L_u 2 890	6 000	512	14 000	144
t = 14.9	2 000	1 380	1 290	1 150	1 720	1 940	3 720	1 380	I_x 764	7 000	396	16 000	121
d = 603	1 000	1 190	1 120	1 030	858	1 570	3 470	1 120	S_x 2 530	8 000	320	18 000	105

Note: Resistances are based on a concrete density of 2300 kg/m³.

Units: M_r - kN·m, V_r - kN, L_u - mm, I_x - 10^6 mm⁴, S_x - 10^3 mm³, b - mm, t - mm, d - mm

$F_y = 345$ MPa

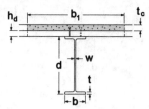

G40.21 350W
ASTM A992
A572 Grade 50
f′_c = 25 MPa

COMPOSITE BEAMS
Trial Selection Table
75 mm Deck with 65 mm Slab
$\phi = 0.90, \phi_c = 0.65$

Steel section	b_1	M_{rc} (kN·m) for % shear connection			Q_r (kN)	I_t 10^6	S_t 10^3	I_{ts} 10^6	Steel section data	Unbraced condition			
		100%	70%	40%	100%					L'	M_r'	L'	M_r'
	mm					mm⁴	mm³	mm⁴		mm	kN·m	mm	kN·m
W610x91	4 000	1 440	1 340	1 210	3 430	2 050	3 450	1 560	M_r 782	3 000	768	8 000	257
W24x61	3 000	1 340	1 270	1 130	2 570	1 930	3 390	1 420	V_r 1 100	4 000	672	10 000	181
b = 227	2 000	1 240	1 160	1 030	1 720	1 740	3 290	1 240	L_u 2 820	5 000	557	12 000	139
t = 12.7	1 000	1 070	996	910	858	1 420	3 070	1 000	I_x 657	6 000	416	14 000	112
d = 598	500	934	891	843	429	1 130	2 830	848	S_x 2 200	7 000	320	16 000	94.2
W610x82	4 000	1 330	1 240	1 100	3 260	1 870	3 100	1 430	M_r 686	3 000	589	8 000	147
W24x55	3 000	1 250	1 180	1 030	2 570	1 760	3 050	1 300	V_r 1 170	4 000	450	10 000	108
b = 178	2 000	1 150	1 070	932	1 720	1 600	2 960	1 140	L_u 2 110	5 000	306	12 000	84.8
t = 12.8	1 000	969	897	810	858	1 300	2 760	907	I_x 565	6 000	227	14 000	70.1
d = 599	500	834	791	742	429	1 030	2 520	754	S_x 1 880	7 000	179	16 000	59.8
W530x138	4 000	1 850	1 750	1 560	3 430	2 500	4 840	1 810	M_r 1 120	3 000	1 110	8 000	515
W21x93	3 000	1 750	1 650	1 470	2 570	2 320	4 730	1 640	V_r 1 650	4 000	1 000	10 000	390
b = 214	2 000	1 610	1 510	1 360	1 720	2 060	4 550	1 440	L_u 2 930	5 000	884	12 000	314
t = 23.6	1 000	1 400	1 330	1 240	858	1 640	4 200	1 190	I_x 861	6 000	759	14 000	263
d = 549	500	1 270	1 230	1 180	429	1 320	3 850	1 040	S_x 3 140	7 000	616	16 000	227
W530x123	4 000	1 690	1 580	1 420	3 430	2 260	4 330	1 660	M_r 997	3 000	984	8 000	421
W21x83	3 000	1 580	1 500	1 340	2 570	2 110	4 240	1 510	V_r 1 460	4 000	879	10 000	316
b = 212	2 000	1 460	1 370	1 230	1 720	1 880	4 100	1 320	L_u 2 860	5 000	762	12 000	253
t = 21.2	1 000	1 270	1 200	1 120	858	1 500	3 790	1 080	I_x 761	6 000	631	14 000	211
d = 544	500	1 140	1 100	1 050	429	1 200	3 480	932	S_x 2 800	7 000	505	16 000	182
W530x109	4 000	1 530	1 430	1 290	3 430	2 030	3 850	1 510	M_r 879	3 000	862	8 000	342
W21x73	3 000	1 430	1 350	1 210	2 570	1 900	3 780	1 370	V_r 1 280	4 000	764	10 000	254
b = 211	2 000	1 320	1 240	1 110	1 720	1 700	3 650	1 200	L_u 2 810	5 000	652	12 000	202
t = 18.8	1 000	1 140	1 080	997	858	1 370	3 400	975	I_x 667	6 000	520	14 000	168
d = 539	500	1 020	979	934	429	1 090	3 120	834	S_x 2 480	7 000	413	16 000	144
W530x101	4 000	1 440	1 350	1 210	3 430	1 910	3 580	1 430	M_r 814	3 000	794	8 000	301
W21x68	3 000	1 340	1 270	1 140	2 570	1 790	3 520	1 300	V_r 1 200	4 000	699	10 000	222
b = 210	2 000	1 240	1 170	1 040	1 720	1 610	3 410	1 140	L_u 2 770	5 000	591	12 000	176
t = 17.4	1 000	1 080	1 010	932	858	1 300	3 180	920	I_x 617	6 000	462	14 000	146
d = 537	500	953	914	869	429	1 030	2 920	782	S_x 2 300	7 000	365	16 000	125
W530x92	4 000	1 350	1 250	1 130	3 430	1 750	3 270	1 320	M_r 733	3 000	711	8 000	253
W21x62	3 000	1 250	1 170	1 050	2 570	1 650	3 210	1 210	V_r 1 110	4 000	621	9 000	214
b = 209	2 000	1 150	1 080	961	1 720	1 490	3 120	1 050	L_u 2 720	5 000	516	10 000	185
t = 15.6	1 000	993	930	851	858	1 200	2 910	847	I_x 552	6 000	393	12 000	146
d = 533	500	872	833	790	429	956	2 670	714	S_x 2 070	7 000	309	14 000	120
W530x82	4 000	1 220	1 130	1 010	3 260	1 560	2 900	1 200	M_r 640	3 000	616	8 000	203
W21x55	3 000	1 140	1 060	952	2 570	1 480	2 850	1 090	V_r 1 030	4 000	531	9 000	170
b = 209	2 000	1 040	976	864	1 720	1 340	2 770	954	L_u 2 660	5 000	433	10 000	147
t = 13.3	1 000	894	833	757	858	1 090	2 590	762	I_x 477	6 000	320	12 000	115
d = 528	500	777	739	696	429	864	2 380	635	S_x 1 810	7 000	249	14 000	94.0

Note: Resistances are based on a concrete density of 2300 kg/m³. $F_y = 345$ MPa

Units: M_r - kN·m, V_r - kN, L_u - mm, I_x - 10^6 mm⁴, S_x - 10^3 mm³, b - mm, t - mm, d - mm

COMPOSITE BEAMS
Trial Selection Table
75 mm Deck with 65 mm Slab
$\phi = 0.90$, $\phi_c = 0.65$

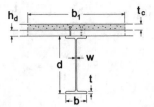

G40.21 350W
ASTM A992
A572 Grade 50
$f'_c = 25$ MPa

Steel section	b_1	M_{rc} (kN·m) for % shear connection			Q_r (kN)	I_t 10^6	S_t 10^3	I_{ts} 10^6	Steel section data		Unbraced condition			
											L'	M_r'	L'	M_r'
	mm	100%	70%	40%	100%	mm⁴	mm³	mm⁴			mm	kN·m	mm	kN·m
W530x74	4 000	1 110	1 030	908	2 960	1 430	2 600	1 100	M_r	562	3 000	474	8 000	123
W21x50	3 000	1 060	987	873	2 570	1 350	2 560	1 000	V_r	1 050	4 000	357	9 000	105
b = 166	2 000	959	898	785	1 720	1 230	2 490	874	L_u	2 040	5 000	247	10 000	91.7
t = 13.6	1 000	815	754	678	858	999	2 320	691	I_x	411	6 000	186	12 000	73.2
d = 529	500	698	660	617	429	788	2 130	568	S_x	1 550	7 000	148	14 000	61.0
W530x66	4 000	982	903	793	2 600	1 260	2 280	985	M_r	484	3 000	398	8 000	94.9
W21x44	3 000	959	890	787	2 570	1 200	2 250	902	V_r	927	4 000	284	9 000	80.6
b = 165	2 000	863	809	704	1 720	1 100	2 190	788	L_u	1 980	5 000	195	10 000	70.0
t = 11.4	1 000	732	674	600	858	899	2 050	620	I_x	351	6 000	145	12 000	55.5
d = 525	500	619	582	540	429	710	1 880	503	S_x	1 340	7 000	115	14 000	46.0
W460x158	4 000	1 830	1 730	1 570	3 430	2 250	5 050	1 610	M_r	1 170	4 500	1 150	9 000	795
W18x106	3 000	1 720	1 640	1 490	2 570	2 080	4 930	1 460	V_r	1 460	5 000	1 110	10 000	697
b = 284	2 000	1 610	1 520	1 390	1 720	1 830	4 740	1 280	L_u	4 190	6 000	1 040	11 000	618
t = 23.9	1 000	1 430	1 360	1 290	858	1 460	4 380	1 070	I_x	796	7 000	957	12 000	556
d = 476	500	1 310	1 270	1 230	429	1 180	4 020	940	S_x	3 350	8 000	876	14 000	463
W460x144	4 000	1 700	1 600	1 460	3 430	2 090	4 640	1 510	M_r	1 070	4 500	1 050	9 000	693
W18x97	3 000	1 600	1 520	1 380	2 570	1 940	4 540	1 370	V_r	1 320	5 000	1 010	10 000	602
b = 283	2 000	1 490	1 410	1 290	1 720	1 710	4 380	1 200	L_u	4 130	6 000	936	11 000	533
t = 22.1	1 000	1 320	1 260	1 190	858	1 360	4 050	992	I_x	726	7 000	858	12 000	478
d = 472	500	1 200	1 170	1 130	429	1 100	3 730	868	S_x	3 080	8 000	779	14 000	396
W460x128	4 000	1 550	1 450	1 320	3 430	1 890	4 150	1 370	M_r	947	4 500	918	9 000	567
W18x86	3 000	1 450	1 370	1 250	2 570	1 750	4 060	1 250	V_r	1 170	5 000	884	10 000	490
b = 282	2 000	1 340	1 270	1 160	1 720	1 560	3 920	1 090	L_u	4 040	6 000	812	11 000	432
t = 19.6	1 000	1 190	1 130	1 060	858	1 240	3 640	895	I_x	637	7 000	736	12 000	386
d = 467	500	1 080	1 040	1 000	429	997	3 350	776	S_x	2 730	8 000	658	14 000	318
W460x113	4 000	1 400	1 300	1 180	3 430	1 690	3 660	1 250	M_r	829	4 500	796	9 000	458
W18x76	3 000	1 300	1 230	1 120	2 570	1 580	3 590	1 130	V_r	1 020	5 000	765	10 000	394
b = 280	2 000	1 200	1 140	1 040	1 720	1 410	3 480	992	L_u	3 950	6 000	696	11 000	345
t = 17.3	1 000	1 060	1 010	940	858	1 130	3 240	807	I_x	556	7 000	623	12 000	307
d = 463	500	958	923	884	429	903	2 990	692	S_x	2 400	8 000	545	14 000	252
W460x106	3 000	1 250	1 170	1 040	2 570	1 490	3 310	1 060	M_r	742	3 000	719	8 000	308
W18x71	2 000	1 140	1 070	957	1 720	1 330	3 200	924	V_r	1 210	4 000	637	9 000	266
b = 194	1 500	1 080	1 000	907	1 290	1 220	3 110	839	L_u	2 690	5 000	549	10 000	235
t = 20.6	1 000	986	926	853	858	1 060	2 960	741	I_x	488	6 000	450	11 000	210
d = 469	500	872	837	796	429	836	2 700	625	S_x	2 080	7 000	366	12 000	190
W460x97	3 000	1 160	1 080	971	2 570	1 380	3 040	996	M_r	677	3 000	652	8 000	264
W18x65	2 000	1 060	994	887	1 720	1 240	2 940	866	V_r	1 090	4 000	574	9 000	227
b = 193	1 500	997	933	840	1 290	1 140	2 860	786	L_u	2 650	5 000	488	10 000	200
t = 19	1 000	914	858	788	858	993	2 730	692	I_x	445	6 000	389	11 000	178
d = 466	500	806	771	731	429	783	2 500	580	S_x	1 910	7 000	314	12 000	161

Note: Resistances are based on a concrete density of 2300 kg/m³.

Units: M_r - kN·m, V_r - kN, L_u - mm, I_x - 10^6 mm⁴, S_x - 10^3 mm³, b - mm, t - mm, d - mm

$F_y = 345$ MPa

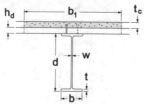

Steel section	b_1	Composite							Non-composite				
		M_{rc} (kN·m) for % shear connection			Q_r	I_t	S_t	I_{ts}	Steel section data	Unbraced condition			
		100%	70%	40%	100%	10^6	10^3	10^6		L'	M_r'	L'	M_r'
	mm	100%	70%	40%	(kN)	mm⁴	mm³	mm⁴		mm	kN·m	mm	kN·m
W460x89	3 000	1 090	1 020	912	2 570	1 290	2 820	940	M_r 624	3 000	598	8 000	231
W18x60	2 000	990	934	833	1 720	1 160	2 740	818	V_r 996	4 000	523	9 000	198
b = 192	1 500	935	876	786	1 290	1 070	2 670	741	L_u 2 620	5 000	439	10 000	174
t = 17.7	1 000	858	804	735	858	937	2 550	651	I_x 410	6 000	343	11 000	155
d = 463	500	752	718	679	429	739	2 340	543	S_x 1 770	7 000	276	12 000	140
W460x82	3 000	1 020	945	846	2 570	1 190	2 580	876	M_r 568	3 000	540	8 000	195
W18x55	2 000	918	865	771	1 720	1 080	2 510	763	V_r 933	4 000	467	9 000	167
b = 191	1 500	865	811	726	1 290	994	2 440	691	L_u 2 560	5 000	385	10 000	146
t = 16	1 000	794	743	676	858	873	2 340	605	I_x 370	6 000	292	11 000	129
d = 460	500	693	660	621	429	689	2 150	500	S_x 1 610	7 000	234	12 000	117
W460x74	3 000	947	876	783	2 570	1 100	2 350	814	M_r 512	3 000	484	8 000	164
W18x50	2 000	849	799	712	1 720	996	2 290	710	V_r 843	4 000	414	9 000	140
b = 190	1 500	797	750	668	1 290	921	2 230	643	L_u 2 530	5 000	332	10 000	122
t = 14.5	1 000	733	685	620	858	811	2 140	561	I_x 333	6 000	249	11 000	108
d = 457	500	636	604	566	429	640	1 970	461	S_x 1 460	7 000	198	12 000	96.9
W460x67	3 000	880	812	721	2 570	1 000	2 130	751	M_r 456	3 000	427	8 000	135
W18x45	2 000	784	735	654	1 720	913	2 070	655	V_r 791	4 000	361	9 000	115
b = 190	1 500	734	690	612	1 290	846	2 020	593	L_u 2 480	5 000	280	10 000	99.4
t = 12.7	1 000	674	628	564	858	748	1 950	516	I_x 295	6 000	208	11 000	87.8
d = 454	500	580	548	511	429	591	1 790	420	S_x 1 300	7 000	164	12 000	78.6
W460x61	3 000	795	729	644	2 370	895	1 890	680	M_r 401	3 000	370	8 000	107
W18x41	2 000	716	669	592	1 720	822	1 840	595	V_r 747	4 000	306	9 000	90.5
b = 189	1 500	667	626	551	1 290	764	1 800	538	L_u 2 410	5 000	227	10 000	78.1
t = 10.8	1 000	610	567	505	858	678	1 730	467	I_x 254	6 000	168	11 000	68.7
d = 450	500	520	489	452	429	536	1 600	376	S_x 1 130	7 000	131	12 000	61.3
W460x52	3 000	698	637	557	2 060	788	1 630	608	M_r 338	3 000	269	8 000	63.7
W18x35	2 000	647	600	528	1 720	728	1 590	533	V_r 680	4 000	185	9 000	54.4
b = 152	1 500	598	560	488	1 290	680	1 560	482	L_u 1 890	5 000	128	10 000	47.4
t = 10.8	1 000	545	503	442	858	606	1 510	417	I_x 212	6 000	96.3	11 000	42.1
d = 450	500	458	427	390	429	481	1 390	331	S_x 943	7 000	76.8	12 000	37.9
W410x149	3 000	1 530	1 440	1 310	2 570	1 720	4 400	1 200	M_r 1 020	4 500	993	8 000	773
W16x100	2 000	1 410	1 340	1 220	1 720	1 520	4 230	1 050	V_r 1 320	5 000	963	9 000	710
b = 265	1 500	1 340	1 270	1 170	1 290	1 380	4 100	960	L_u 4 080	5 500	931	10 000	637
t = 25	1 000	1 250	1 190	1 120	858	1 200	3 890	862	I_x 625	6 000	900	11 000	569
d = 431	500	1 140	1 100	1 060	429	957	3 560	751	S_x 2 900	7 000	836	12 000	515
W410x132	3 000	1 380	1 300	1 170	2 570	1 550	3 920	1 090	M_r 897	4 500	865	8 000	647
W16x89	2 000	1 270	1 200	1 090	1 720	1 370	3 770	950	V_r 1 160	5 000	835	9 000	579
b = 263	1 500	1 200	1 140	1 040	1 290	1 250	3 660	867	L_u 3 940	5 500	804	10 000	508
t = 22.2	1 000	1 120	1 060	992	858	1 090	3 490	774	I_x 545	6 000	773	11 000	453
d = 425	500	1 010	976	938	429	865	3 190	667	S_x 2 560	7 000	710	12 000	409

Note: Resistances are based on a concrete density of 2300 kg/m³.

Units: M_r - kN·m, V_r - kN, L_u - mm, I_x - 10^6 mm⁴, S_x - 10^3 mm³, b - mm, t - mm, d - mm

F_y = 345 MPa

COMPOSITE BEAMS
Trial Selection Table
75 mm Deck with 65 mm Slab
$\phi = 0.90$, $\phi_c = 0.65$

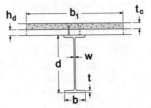

G40.21 350W
ASTM A992
A572 Grade 50
$f'_c = 25$ MPa

Steel section	b_1	\multicolumn{3}{c}{Composite M_{rc} (kN·m) for % shear connection}	Q_r	I_t	S_t	I_{ts}	\multicolumn{2}{c}{Non-composite Steel section data}	\multicolumn{4}{c}{Unbraced condition}
		100%	70%	40%	100%	10^6	10^3	10^6			L'	M_r'	L'	M_r'
	mm					mm^4	mm^3	mm^4			mm	kN·m	mm	kN·m
W410x114	3 000	1 230	1 150	1 040	2 570	1 380	3 430	980	M_r 773		4 500	736	8 000	525
W16x77	2 000	1 120	1 070	965	1 720	1 230	3 310	853	V_r 998		5 000	707	9 000	451
b = 261	1 500	1 070	1 010	919	1 290	1 120	3 220	777	L_u 3 810		5 500	678	10 000	394
t = 19.3	1 000	990	936	869	858	977	3 070	689	I_x 468		6 000	648	11 000	350
d = 420	500	886	853	815	429	774	2 820	587	S_x 2 230		7 000	587	12 000	315
W410x100	3 000	1 100	1 030	930	2 570	1 230	3 010	884	M_r 671		4 500	632	8 000	423
W16x67	2 000	999	947	857	1 720	1 100	2 920	769	V_r 850		5 000	605	9 000	359
b = 260	1 500	947	896	814	1 290	1 010	2 840	699	L_u 3 730		5 500	577	10 000	312
t = 16.9	1 000	879	830	766	858	881	2 720	617	I_x 404		6 000	548	11 000	276
d = 415	500	782	750	713	429	697	2 500	520	S_x 1 950		7 000	489	12 000	247
W410x85	3 000	973	900	801	2 570	1 050	2 490	766	M_r 537		3 000	509	8 000	205
W16x57	2 000	872	819	728	1 720	951	2 420	664	V_r 931		4 000	444	9 000	178
b = 181	1 500	819	767	685	1 290	873	2 350	599	L_u 2 520		5 000	376	10 000	157
t = 18.2	1 000	750	701	638	858	763	2 250	523	I_x 315		6 000	297	11 000	141
d = 417	500	654	622	586	429	597	2 050	430	S_x 1 510		7 000	243	12 000	127
W410x74	3 000	888	818	725	2 570	947	2 210	697	M_r 469		3 000	440	8 000	163
W16x50	2 000	790	739	657	1 720	859	2 150	605	V_r 821		4 000	379	9 000	140
b = 180	1 500	738	693	616	1 290	792	2 100	546	L_u 2 470		5 000	312	10 000	124
t = 16	1 000	677	632	571	858	695	2 010	475	I_x 275		6 000	239	11 000	110
d = 413	500	586	555	520	429	544	1 840	387	S_x 1 330		7 000	194	12 000	99.8
W410x67	3 000	824	755	666	2 570	864	2 000	645	M_r 422		3 000	392	8 000	135
W16x45	2 000	728	679	604	1 720	788	1 950	561	V_r 739		4 000	333	9 000	116
b = 179	1 500	677	637	565	1 290	729	1 900	507	L_u 2 420		5 000	264	10 000	102
t = 14.4	1 000	621	579	521	858	643	1 830	440	I_x 246		6 000	201	11 000	90.5
d = 410	500	535	506	471	429	505	1 680	355	S_x 1 200		7 000	161	12 000	81.7
W410x60	3 000	739	673	591	2 350	774	1 770	588	M_r 369		3 000	341	8 000	109
W16x40	2 000	662	614	547	1 720	711	1 730	513	V_r 642		4 000	286	9 000	93.2
b = 178	1 500	612	575	511	1 290	660	1 690	464	L_u 2 390		5 000	218	10 000	81.4
t = 12.8	1 000	560	524	469	858	586	1 630	402	I_x 216		6 000	165	11 000	72.2
d = 407	500	482	454	420	429	462	1 500	322	S_x 1 060		7 000	131	12 000	65.0
W410x54	3 000	666	604	528	2 110	695	1 580	533	M_r 326		3 000	295	8 000	86.1
W16x36	2 000	610	563	499	1 720	640	1 540	467	V_r 619		4 000	242	9 000	73.2
b = 177	1 500	561	525	463	1 290	597	1 510	422	L_u 2 310		5 000	176	10 000	63.6
t = 10.9	1 000	511	476	422	858	532	1 460	365	I_x 186		6 000	132	11 000	56.3
d = 403	500	435	407	374	429	420	1 350	289	S_x 924		7 000	104	12 000	50.5
W410x46	3 000	582	525	456	1 830	611	1 370	477	M_r 275		2 000	265	7 000	61.7
W16x31	2 000	553	507	445	1 720	567	1 340	419	V_r 578		3 000	210	8 000	51.8
b = 140	1 500	505	469	411	1 290	531	1 310	379	L_u 1 790		4 000	142	9 000	44.6
t = 11.2	1 000	455	423	371	858	476	1 270	327	I_x 156		5 000	99.9	10 000	39.2
d = 403	500	384	357	323	429	378	1 170	257	S_x 773		6 000	76.4	11 000	35.0

Note: Resistances are based on a concrete density of 2300 kg/m³.

Units: M_r - kN·m, V_r - kN, L_u - mm, I_x - 10^6 mm⁴, S_x - 10^3 mm³, b - mm, t - mm, d - mm

$F_y = 345$ MPa

G40.21 350W
ASTM A992
A572 Grade 50
f'_c = 25 MPa

COMPOSITE BEAMS
Trial Selection Table
75 mm Deck with 65 mm Slab
$\phi = 0.90$, $\phi_c = 0.65$

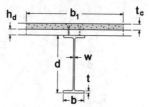

Steel section	b_1	Composite M_{rc} (kN·m) for % shear connection			Q_r (kN)	I_t 10^6 mm⁴	S_t 10^3 mm³	I_{ts} 10^6 mm⁴	Non-composite Steel section data		Unbraced condition			
	mm	100%	70%	40%	100%						L' mm	M_r' kN·m	L' mm	M_r' kN·m
W410x39	3 000	496	445	383	1 550	521	1 150	415	M_r	227	2 000	216	7 000	44.1
W16x26	2 000	481	437	380	1 550	486	1 130	367	V_r	480	3 000	166	8 000	36.6
b = 140	1 500	447	412	360	1 290	458	1 110	333	L_u	1 730	4 000	105	9 000	31.3
t = 8.8	1 000	399	370	321	858	414	1 070	287	I_x	127	5 000	73.1	10 000	27.4
d = 399	500	333	307	275	429	332	998	223	S_x	634	6 000	55.2	11 000	24.3
W360x79	3 000	831	759	668	2 570	801	2 140	582	M_r	444	3 500	425	7 000	267
W14x53	2 000	732	681	611	1 720	723	2 080	503	V_r	682	4 000	404	8 000	225
b = 205	1 500	680	640	574	1 290	664	2 020	453	L_u	3 010	4 500	383	9 000	194
t = 16.8	1 000	625	587	533	858	580	1 940	392	I_x	226	5 000	361	10 000	171
d = 354	500	546	519	487	429	451	1 770	318	S_x	1 280	6 000	317	11 000	153
W360x72	3 000	771	702	613	2 570	728	1 930	536	M_r	397	3 500	377	7 000	222
W14x48	2 000	674	625	559	1 720	661	1 880	464	V_r	617	4 000	357	8 000	186
b = 204	1 500	624	585	525	1 290	609	1 830	418	L_u	2 940	4 500	336	9 000	160
t = 15.1	1 000	571	537	485	858	534	1 760	361	I_x	201	5 000	315	10 000	141
d = 350	500	497	471	439	429	416	1 610	291	S_x	1 150	6 000	272	11 000	126
W360x64	3 000	712	644	558	2 530	660	1 730	493	M_r	354	3 500	332	7 000	183
W14x43	2 000	620	572	510	1 720	602	1 690	428	V_r	548	4 000	313	8 000	153
b = 203	1 500	571	534	478	1 290	557	1 650	385	L_u	2 870	4 500	293	9 000	131
t = 13.5	1 000	520	489	440	858	491	1 590	333	I_x	178	5 000	273	10 000	115
d = 347	500	451	426	395	429	384	1 460	266	S_x	1 030	6 000	228	11 000	102
W360x57	3 000	652	588	508	2 240	619	1 560	469	M_r	314	3 000	289	7 000	119
W14x38	2 000	585	537	475	1 720	568	1 520	409	V_r	580	3 500	267	8 000	99.8
b = 172	1 500	535	499	442	1 290	528	1 490	368	L_u	2 360	4 000	244	9 000	86.0
t = 13.1	1 000	485	453	404	858	468	1 430	317	I_x	161	5 000	192	10 000	75.7
d = 358	500	415	390	359	429	367	1 320	251	S_x	897	6 000	147	11 000	67.6
W360x51	3 000	585	525	453	2 000	557	1 390	428	M_r	278	3 000	253	7 000	97.0
W14x34	2 000	540	493	434	1 720	514	1 360	375	V_r	524	3 500	232	8 000	81.0
b = 171	1 500	491	455	403	1 290	480	1 330	338	L_u	2 320	4 000	210	9 000	69.5
t = 11.6	1 000	442	414	367	858	427	1 290	291	I_x	141	5 000	159	10 000	60.9
d = 355	500	377	353	323	429	337	1 190	228	S_x	796	6 000	121	11 000	54.2
W360x45	3 000	522	467	401	1 780	498	1 240	388	M_r	242	3 000	217	7 000	76.5
W14x30	2 000	498	452	394	1 720	462	1 210	341	V_r	498	3 500	197	8 000	63.4
b = 171	1 500	450	415	365	1 290	433	1 190	308	L_u	2 260	4 000	176	9 000	54.1
t = 9.8	1 000	401	375	330	858	387	1 150	265	I_x	122	5 000	128	10 000	47.2
d = 352	500	340	317	287	429	307	1 060	207	S_x	691	6 000	96.1	11 000	41.9
W360x39	2 500	453	405	348	1 550	427	1 060	330	M_r	206	2 000	193	6 000	54.2
W14x26	2 000	444	401	346	1 550	410	1 050	307	V_r	470	2 500	172	7 000	44.3
b = 128	1 500	411	376	328	1 290	386	1 030	278	L_u	1 660	3 000	148	8 000	37.5
t = 10.7	1 000	362	337	293	858	347	998	239	I_x	102	4 000	97.2	9 000	32.5
d = 353	500	303	280	251	429	277	926	185	S_x	580	5 000	69.8	10 000	28.8

Note: Resistances are based on a concrete density of 2300 kg/m³. F_y = 345 MPa

Units: M_r - kN·m, V_r - kN, L_u - mm, I_x - 10^6 mm⁴, S_x - 10^3 mm³, b - mm, t - mm, d - mm

COMPOSITE BEAMS
Trial Selection Table
75 mm Deck with 65 mm Slab
$\phi = 0.90$, $\phi_c = 0.65$

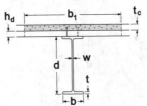

G40.21 350W
ASTM A992
A572 Grade 50
$f'_c = 25$ MPa

Steel section	b₁	Mrc (kN·m) for % shear connection 100%	70%	40%	Qr (kN) 100%	It 10⁶ mm⁴	St 10³ mm³	Its 10⁶ mm⁴	Steel section data		L' mm	Mr' kN·m	L' mm	Mr' kN·m
W360x33	2 500	382	339	289	1 290	361	891	286	Mr	168	2 000	155	6 000	38.1
W14x22	2 000	375	336	288	1 290	348	880	267	Vr	396	2 500	136	7 000	30.8
b = 127	1 500	364	331	286	1 290	330	865	243	Lu	1 600	3 000	113	8 000	25.9
t = 8.5	1 000	317	293	253	858	300	840	210	Ix	82.7	4 000	70.3	9 000	22.3
d = 349	500	262	241	213	429	242	784	161	Sx	474	5 000	49.7	10 000	19.6
W310x74	2 500	682	622	546	2 150	605	1 830	429	Mr	366	3 500	354	6 000	274
W12x50	2 000	633	583	519	1 720	570	1 800	394	Vr	597	4 000	339	7 000	240
b = 205	1 500	582	543	487	1 290	524	1 750	353	Lu	3 100	4 500	323	8 000	204
t = 16.3	1 000	529	498	450	858	457	1 680	304	Ix	164	5 000	307	9 000	177
d = 310	500	461	437	408	429	352	1 530	242	Sx	1 060	5 500	291	10 000	156
W310x67	2 500	631	573	498	2 150	548	1 640	393	Mr	326	3 500	312	6 000	234
W12x45	2 000	583	534	473	1 720	518	1 620	362	Vr	533	4 000	297	7 000	198
b = 204	1 500	533	495	443	1 290	477	1 580	325	Lu	3 020	4 500	282	8 000	167
t = 14.6	1 000	481	453	408	858	418	1 510	278	Ix	144	5 000	266	9 000	144
d = 306	500	418	395	367	429	323	1 380	220	Sx	942	5 500	250	10 000	127
W310x60	2 500	585	528	455	2 150	497	1 470	362	Mr	290	3 500	275	6 000	199
W12x40	2 000	537	490	431	1 720	471	1 450	334	Vr	466	4 000	261	7 000	163
b = 203	1 500	488	452	403	1 290	436	1 420	300	Lu	2 960	4 500	246	8 000	137
t = 13.1	1 000	438	412	370	858	384	1 370	257	Ix	128	5 000	231	9 000	118
d = 303	500	379	358	330	429	299	1 250	202	Sx	842	5 500	215	10 000	104
W310x52	2 500	554	499	427	2 070	476	1 340	353	Mr	261	3 000	241	6 000	130
W12x35	2 000	513	467	407	1 720	454	1 320	327	Vr	495	3 500	224	7 000	106
b = 167	1 500	465	428	379	1 290	422	1 290	293	Lu	2 370	4 000	206	8 000	89.4
t = 13.2	1 000	414	388	345	858	374	1 240	251	Ix	119	4 500	188	9 000	77.5
d = 318	500	355	333	305	429	292	1 140	196	Sx	750	5 000	167	10 000	68.4
W310x45	2 500	477	425	362	1 770	411	1 140	311	Mr	220	3 000	200	6 000	98.2
W12x30	2 000	461	416	358	1 720	393	1 130	289	Vr	423	3 500	184	7 000	79.3
b = 166	1 500	414	379	333	1 290	368	1 110	260	Lu	2 310	4 000	167	8 000	66.5
t = 11.2	1 000	365	340	302	858	329	1 070	223	Ix	99.2	4 500	150	9 000	57.3
d = 313	500	310	290	263	429	259	989	172	Sx	634	5 000	128	10 000	50.4
W310x39	2 500	417	370	314	1 530	362	996	279	Mr	189	3 000	170	6 000	77.7
W12x26	2 000	408	365	312	1 530	347	984	260	Vr	368	3 500	155	7 000	62.2
b = 165	1 500	376	341	298	1 290	327	966	235	Lu	2 260	4 000	139	8 000	51.8
t = 9.7	1 000	328	304	269	858	294	936	202	Ix	85.1	4 500	121	9 000	44.3
d = 310	500	276	258	232	429	234	871	156	Sx	549	5 000	103	10 000	38.8
W250x67	2 500	571	512	437	2 150	439	1 510	310	Mr	280	3 500	275	6 000	223
W10x45	2 000	522	474	413	1 720	414	1 480	284	Vr	469	4 000	265	6 500	212
b = 204	1 500	472	435	386	1 290	380	1 440	253	Lu	3 260	4 500	254	7 000	202
t = 15.7	1 000	421	395	355	858	331	1 380	215	Ix	104	5 000	244	7 500	192
d = 257	500	363	343	317	429	252	1 250	166	Sx	806	5 500	233	8 000	180

Note: Resistances are based on a concrete density of 2300 kg/m³.

Units: Mr - kN·m, Vr - kN, Lu - mm, Ix - 10⁶ mm⁴, Sx - 10³ mm³, b - mm, t - mm, d - mm

$F_y = 345$ MPa

G40.21 350W
ASTM A992
A572 Grade 50
f′$_c$ = 25 MPa

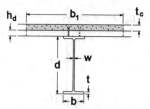

COMPOSITE BEAMS
Trial Selection Table
75 mm Deck with 65 mm Slab
φ = 0.90, φ$_c$ = 0.65

Steel section	b$_1$	M$_{rc}$ (kN·m) for % shear connection			Q$_r$	I$_t$	S$_t$	I$_{ts}$	Steel section data		Unbraced condition			
		100%	70%	40%	(kN) 100%	10^6	10^3	10^6			L′	M$_r$′	L′	M$_r$′
	mm					mm^4	mm^3	mm^4			mm	kN·m	mm	kN·m
W250x58	2 500	521	464	391	2 150	385	1 310	277	M$_r$	239	3 500	232	6 000	181
W10x39	2 000	473	426	367	1 720	365	1 290	254	V$_r$	413	4 000	222	6 500	171
b = 203	1 500	425	388	342	1 290	336	1 260	227	L$_u$	3 130	4 500	212	7 000	161
t = 13.5	1 000	374	349	312	858	295	1 210	192	I$_x$	87.3	5 000	202	7 500	148
d = 252	500	320	301	276	429	226	1 100	147	S$_x$	693	5 500	192	8 000	137
W250x45	2 500	437	385	322	1 780	332	1 040	248	M$_r$	187	3 000	167	5 500	101
W10x30	2 000	421	375	317	1 720	317	1 030	229	V$_r$	414	3 500	155	6 000	90.6
b = 148	1 500	373	338	293	1 290	295	1 010	205	L$_u$	2 170	4 000	142	6 500	82.2
t = 13	1 000	324	299	263	858	263	972	174	I$_x$	71.1	4 500	129	7 000	75.2
d = 266	500	270	252	227	429	205	893	132	S$_x$	534	5 000	114	7 500	69.3
W250x39	2 500	379	331	275	1 530	289	902	221	M$_r$	159	3 000	140	5 500	77.5
W10x26	2 000	370	327	274	1 530	277	890	205	V$_r$	354	3 500	128	6 000	69.2
b = 147	1 500	338	304	260	1 290	260	872	184	L$_u$	2 110	4 000	115	6 500	62.5
t = 11.2	1 000	290	266	233	858	233	844	157	I$_x$	60.1	4 500	102	7 000	57.0
d = 262	500	239	222	199	429	183	781	118	S$_x$	459	5 000	88.0	7 500	52.4
W250x33	2 500	323	281	232	1 290	247	764	192	M$_r$	132	3 000	112	5 500	55.6
W10x22	2 000	317	278	231	1 290	237	754	179	V$_r$	323	3 500	100	6 000	49.4
b = 146	1 500	305	272	229	1 290	224	740	162	L$_u$	2 020	4 000	88.4	6 500	44.4
t = 9.1	1 000	258	235	204	858	202	718	139	I$_x$	48.9	4 500	74.1	7 000	40.3
d = 258	500	209	193	171	429	161	668	104	S$_x$	379	5 000	63.6	7 500	36.9
W200x42	2 500	359	309	250	1 650	231	865	171	M$_r$	138	3 000	133	5 500	99.6
W8x28	2 000	348	304	248	1 650	220	852	158	V$_r$	302	3 500	126	6 000	92.9
b = 166	1 500	307	272	228	1 290	205	833	141	L$_u$	2 610	4 000	120	6 500	84.6
t = 11.8	1 000	258	234	203	858	181	802	118	I$_x$	40.9	4 500	113	7 000	77.5
d = 205	500	208	194	173	429	140	736	86.8	S$_x$	399	5 000	106	7 500	71.6
W200x36	2 500	311	266	214	1 420	200	748	152	M$_r$	118	3 000	112	5 500	79.3
W8x24	2 000	303	262	212	1 420	192	736	141	V$_r$	255	3 500	105	6 000	71.3
b = 165	1 500	281	247	204	1 290	180	721	126	L$_u$	2 510	4 000	99.0	6 500	64.6
t = 10.2	1 000	233	210	180	858	161	697	106	I$_x$	34.4	4 500	92.5	7 000	59.0
d = 201	500	184	171	152	429	126	644	78.1	S$_x$	342	5 000	85.9	7 500	54.4
W200x31	2 500	281	240	193	1 240	187	668	145	M$_r$	104	2 000	104	4 500	65.2
W8x21	2 000	275	237	192	1 240	180	658	135	V$_r$	275	2 500	96.7	5 000	57.0
b = 134	1 500	265	232	190	1 240	169	645	121	L$_u$	1 980	3 000	89.3	5 500	50.6
t = 10.2	1 000	222	198	169	858	152	624	103	I$_x$	31.4	3 500	81.7	6 000	45.6
d = 210	500	173	159	139	429	121	579	75.6	S$_x$	299	4 000	74.0	6 500	41.5
W200x27	2 500	240	203	163	1 050	161	568	127	M$_r$	86.6	2 000	85.3	4 500	47.5
W8x18	2 000	235	201	162	1 050	155	560	118	V$_r$	246	2 500	78.7	5 000	41.2
b = 133	1 500	228	198	161	1 050	146	549	107	L$_u$	1 890	3 000	71.5	5 500	36.4
t = 8.4	1 000	201	178	149	858	133	533	91.6	I$_x$	25.8	3 500	64.1	6 000	32.6
d = 207	500	153	140	121	429	107	497	67.6	S$_x$	249	4 000	56.0	6 500	29.6

Note: Resistances are based on a concrete density of 2300 kg/m^3.

Units: M$_r$ - kN·m, V$_r$ - kN, L$_u$ - mm, I$_x$ - 10^6 mm^4, S$_x$ - 10^3 mm^3, b - mm, t - mm, d - mm

F$_y$ = 345 MPa

COMPOSITE BEAMS
Trial Selection Table
75 mm Deck with 75 mm Slab
$\phi = 0.90$, $\phi_c = 0.65$

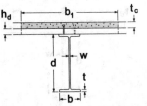

G40.21 350W
$f'_c = 25$ MPa

Steel section	b_1	M_{rc} (kN·m) for % shear connection			Q_r	I_t	S_t	I_{ts}	Steel section data	Unbraced condition			
		100%	70%	40%	100%	10^6	10^3	10^6		L'	M_r'	L'	M_r'
	mm				(kN)	mm⁴	mm³	mm⁴		mm	kN·m	mm	kN·m
WWF1000x223	6 000	5 120	4 930	4 500	5 940	11 500	12 800	8 690	M_r 3 310	4 000	3 250	14 000	729
WWF39x150	5 000	4 990	4 790	4 340	4 950	11 100	12 700	8 240	V_r 2 210	6 000	2 620	16 000	602
b = 300	4 000	4 850	4 600	4 170	3 960	10 500	12 500	7 730	L_u 3 790	8 000	1 790	18 000	512
t = 25	3 000	4 630	4 360	3 980	2 970	9 730	12 200	7 130	I_x 4 590	10 000	1 230	20 000	446
d = 1000	2 000	4 300	4 060	3 770	1 980	8 670	11 800	6 430	S_x 9 190	12 000	920	22 000	394
WWF1000x200	6 000	4 690	4 510	4 070	5 940	10 400	11 400	7 880	M_r 2 890	4 000	2 790	14 000	549
WWF39x134	5 000	4 560	4 370	3 910	4 950	10 000	11 300	7 460	V_r 2 210	6 000	2 180	16 000	449
b = 300	4 000	4 430	4 180	3 740	3 960	9 510	11 100	6 980	L_u 3 610	8 000	1 390	18 000	379
t = 20	3 000	4 200	3 930	3 550	2 970	8 820	10 900	6 410	I_x 3 940	10 000	945	20 000	328
d = 1000	2 000	3 870	3 630	3 340	1 980	7 850	10 500	5 740	S_x 7 880	12 000	699	22 000	289
WWF900x192	6 000	4 130	3 950	3 690	5 940	8 770	10 500	6 720	M_r 2 710	4 000	2 700	14 000	670
WWF35x128	5 000	4 010	3 850	3 580	4 950	8 450	10 400	6 380	V_r 1 350	6 000	2 240	16 000	555
b = 300	4 000	3 880	3 750	3 450	3 960	8 040	10 300	5 990	L_u 3 980	8 000	1 630	18 000	473
t = 25	3 000	3 750	3 590	3 290	2 970	7 490	10 100	5 520	I_x 3 460	10 000	1 120	20 000	412
d = 900	2 000	3 540	3 360	3 120	1 980	6 700	9 790	4 970	S_x 7 680	12 000	842	22 000	365
WWF900x169	5 000	3 610	3 460	3 190	4 950	7 530	9 110	5 710	M_r 2 320	4 500	2 190	12 000	625
WWF35x113	4 000	3 490	3 360	3 060	3 960	7 180	8 990	5 350	V_r 1 340	5 000	2 080	14 000	491
b = 300	3 000	3 360	3 200	2 900	2 970	6 700	8 820	4 920	L_u 3 820	6 000	1 850	16 000	402
t = 20	2 000	3 150	2 970	2 730	1 980	6 000	8 550	4 400	I_x 2 930	8 000	1 250	18 000	339
d = 900	1 000	2 800	2 670	2 530	990	4 910	8 010	3 750	S_x 6 510	10 000	845	20 000	293
WWF800x184	5 000	3 490	3 340	3 110	4 950	6 690	9 110	5 040	M_r 2 330	4 500	2 260	12 000	791
WWF31x123	4 000	3 360	3 240	3 000	3 960	6 360	9 000	4 730	V_r 1 370	5 000	2 170	14 000	634
b = 300	3 000	3 230	3 110	2 860	2 970	5 930	8 830	4 350	L_u 4 060	6 000	1 970	16 000	529
t = 25	2 000	3 060	2 910	2 700	1 980	5 300	8 560	3 900	I_x 2 660	8 000	1 490	18 000	454
d = 800	1 000	2 760	2 650	2 520	990	4 340	8 040	3 350	S_x 6 640	10 000	1 040	20 000	398
WWF800x161	5 000	3 130	2 990	2 760	4 950	5 940	7 930	4 510	M_r 1 990	4 500	1 900	12 000	581
WWF31x108	4 000	3 010	2 890	2 650	3 960	5 670	7 830	4 220	V_r 1 370	5 000	1 810	14 000	460
b = 300	3 000	2 890	2 760	2 520	2 970	5 290	7 690	3 880	L_u 3 900	6 000	1 620	16 000	379
t = 20	2 000	2 720	2 570	2 360	1 980	4 740	7 450	3 460	I_x 2 250	8 000	1 130	18 000	322
d = 800	1 000	2 420	2 310	2 180	990	3 870	6 990	2 930	S_x 5 610	10 000	778	20 000	280
WWF700x175	5 000	3 000	2 850	2 650	4 950	5 150	7 850	3 880	M_r 1 970	4 500	1 930	12 000	741
WWF28x117	4 000	2 880	2 750	2 560	3 960	4 900	7 750	3 630	V_r 1 370	5 000	1 850	14 000	601
b = 300	3 000	2 750	2 650	2 440	2 970	4 560	7 600	3 330	L_u 4 160	6 000	1 700	16 000	505
t = 25	2 000	2 610	2 490	2 300	1 980	4 080	7 370	2 970	I_x 1 970	8 000	1 350	18 000	436
d = 700	1 000	2 350	2 260	2 140	990	3 320	6 910	2 530	S_x 5 640	10 000	965	20 000	384
WWF700x152	5 000	2 690	2 550	2 350	4 950	4 560	6 800	3 460	M_r 1 680	4 500	1 610	12 000	537
WWF28x102	4 000	2 570	2 450	2 260	3 960	4 350	6 710	3 240	V_r 1 370	5 000	1 540	14 000	429
b = 300	3 000	2 450	2 350	2 140	2 970	4 060	6 590	2 970	L_u 3 990	6 000	1 390	16 000	356
t = 20	2 000	2 310	2 190	2 010	1 980	3 640	6 390	2 630	I_x 1 660	8 000	1 020	18 000	305
d = 700	1 000	2 060	1 960	1 850	990	2 960	5 980	2 210	S_x 4 760	10 000	711	20 000	266

Note: Resistances are based on a concrete density of 2300 kg/m³.
Units: M_r - kN·m, V_r - kN, L_u - mm, I_x - 10^6 mm⁴, S_x - 10^3 mm³, b - mm, t - mm, d - mm

F_y = 350 MPa

G40.21 350W
ASTM A992
A572 Grade 50
f'_c = 25 MPa

COMPOSITE BEAMS
Trial Selection Table
75 mm Deck with 75 mm Slab
ϕ = 0.90, ϕ_c = 0.65

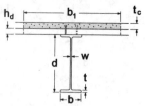

Steel section	b_1	M_{rc} (kN·m) for % shear connection			Q_r	I_t	S_t	I_{ts}	Steel section data	Unbraced condition			
		100%	70%	40%	100%	10^6	10^3	10^6		L'	M_r'	L'	M_r'
	mm				(kN)	mm^4	mm^3	mm^4		mm	kN·m	mm	kN·m
W760x185	5 000	3 340	3 180	2 880	4 950	6 010	8 510	4 460	M_r 2 080	4 000	1 980	12 000	576
W30x124	4 000	3 210	3 060	2 740	3 960	5 700	8 390	4 170	V_r 2 340	5 000	1 780	14 000	470
b = 267	3 000	3 060	2 880	2 600	2 970	5 290	8 210	3 810	L_u 3 450	6 000	1 550	16 000	397
t = 23.6	2 000	2 830	2 660	2 430	1 980	4 700	7 910	3 390	I_x 2 230	8 000	1 040	18 000	344
d = 766	1 000	2 490	2 380	2 250	990	3 800	7 350	2 880	S_x 5 820	10 000	743	20 000	304
W760x173	5 000	3 160	3 010	2 720	4 950	5 660	7 980	4 220	M_r 1 930	4 000	1 830	12 000	506
W30x116	4 000	3 030	2 890	2 590	3 960	5 380	7 870	3 940	V_r 2 250	5 000	1 630	14 000	411
b = 267	3 000	2 900	2 730	2 450	2 970	5 000	7 700	3 600	L_u 3 410	6 000	1 410	16 000	346
t = 21.6	2 000	2 680	2 510	2 280	1 980	4 450	7 420	3 200	I_x 2 060	8 000	924	18 000	299
d = 762	1 000	2 340	2 230	2 100	990	3 590	6 890	2 700	S_x 5 400	10 000	657	20 000	264
W760x161	5 000	2 950	2 800	2 540	4 950	5 240	7 340	3 940	M_r 1 760	4 000	1 650	12 000	429
W30x108	4 000	2 830	2 700	2 410	3 960	4 990	7 240	3 670	V_r 2 140	5 000	1 460	14 000	347
b = 266	3 000	2 700	2 540	2 270	2 970	4 650	7 090	3 360	L_u 3 330	6 000	1 250	16 000	291
t = 19.3	2 000	2 490	2 330	2 110	1 980	4 150	6 840	2 970	I_x 1 860	8 000	793	18 000	251
d = 758	1 000	2 170	2 060	1 930	990	3 350	6 350	2 480	S_x 4 900	10 000	560	20 000	220
W760x147	5 000	2 740	2 600	2 350	4 950	4 820	6 690	3 640	M_r 1 580	4 000	1 470	12 000	358
W30x99	4 000	2 620	2 500	2 230	3 960	4 590	6 600	3 400	V_r 2 040	5 000	1 290	14 000	288
b = 265	3 000	2 500	2 350	2 090	2 970	4 290	6 470	3 100	L_u 3 260	6 000	1 090	16 000	241
t = 17	2 000	2 300	2 150	1 930	1 980	3 830	6 250	2 740	I_x 1 660	8 000	671	18 000	207
d = 753	1 000	1 990	1 880	1 760	990	3 090	5 810	2 270	S_x 4 410	10 000	470	20 000	181
W760x134	5 000	2 540	2 400	2 180	4 950	4 430	6 100	3 390	M_r 1 440	4 000	1 330	12 000	308
W30x90	4 000	2 420	2 300	2 070	3 960	4 240	6 030	3 160	V_r 1 650	5 000	1 160	14 000	246
b = 264	3 000	2 300	2 180	1 930	2 970	3 970	5 910	2 890	L_u 3 230	6 000	967	16 000	205
t = 15.5	2 000	2 130	1 990	1 780	1 980	3 560	5 720	2 540	I_x 1 500	8 000	587	18 000	175
d = 750	1 000	1 840	1 730	1 610	990	2 880	5 320	2 100	S_x 4 010	10 000	408	20 000	153
W690x192	5 000	3 190	3 030	2 760	4 950	5 370	8 270	3 960	M_r 2 010	4 000	1 910	12 000	635
W27x129	4 000	3 060	2 920	2 640	3 960	5 090	8 150	3 700	V_r 2 230	5 000	1 730	14 000	526
b = 254	3 000	2 920	2 760	2 500	2 970	4 710	7 970	3 380	L_u 3 440	6 000	1 540	16 000	449
t = 27.9	2 000	2 710	2 550	2 340	1 980	4 180	7 670	3 000	I_x 1 980	8 000	1 090	18 000	393
d = 702	1 000	2 400	2 290	2 170	990	3 370	7 120	2 550	S_x 5 640	10 000	802	20 000	349
W690x170	5 000	2 870	2 720	2 470	4 950	4 770	7 290	3 550	M_r 1 750	4 000	1 650	12 000	497
W27x114	4 000	2 750	2 620	2 360	3 960	4 530	7 190	3 310	V_r 2 060	5 000	1 480	14 000	409
b = 256	3 000	2 610	2 470	2 230	2 970	4 210	7 040	3 030	L_u 3 380	6 000	1 290	16 000	347
t = 23.6	2 000	2 430	2 280	2 080	1 980	3 750	6 790	2 680	I_x 1 700	8 000	875	18 000	302
d = 693	1 000	2 130	2 030	1 910	990	3 020	6 300	2 250	S_x 4 910	10 000	635	20 000	268
W690x152	5 000	2 630	2 480	2 260	4 950	4 330	6 560	3 260	M_r 1 550	4 000	1 460	12 000	406
W27x102	4 000	2 500	2 380	2 150	3 960	4 130	6 470	3 050	V_r 1 850	5 000	1 290	14 000	332
b = 254	3 000	2 380	2 260	2 030	2 970	3 850	6 340	2 780	L_u 3 320	6 000	1 110	16 000	281
t = 21.1	2 000	2 210	2 080	1 880	1 980	3 440	6 130	2 460	I_x 1 510	8 000	728	18 000	244
d = 688	1 000	1 930	1 830	1 720	990	2 770	5 700	2 050	S_x 4 380	10 000	523	20 000	216

Note: Resistances are based on a concrete density of 2300 kg/m^3.

Units: M_r - kN·m, V_r - kN, L_u - mm, I_x - 10^6 mm^4, S_x - 10^3 mm^3, b - mm, t - mm, d - mm

F_y = 345 MPa

COMPOSITE BEAMS
Trial Selection Table
75 mm Deck with 75 mm Slab
$\phi = 0.90$, $\phi_c = 0.65$

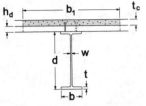

G40.21 350W
ASTM A992
A572 Grade 50
$f'_c = 25$ MPa

Steel section	b₁	Composite Mrc (kN·m) for % shear connection			Qr (kN)	It 10⁶	St 10³	Its 10⁶	Non-composite Steel section data	Unbraced condition			
		100%	70%	40%	100%	mm⁴	mm³	mm⁴		L' mm	Mr' kN·m	L' mm	Mr' kN·m
W690x140	5 000	2 450	2 310	2 100	4 950	4 000	6 010	3 030	M_r 1 410	4 000	1 320	10 000	447
W27x94	4 000	2 330	2 210	2 000	3 960	3 820	5 930	2 830	V_r 1 740	5 000	1 160	12 000	345
b = 254	3 000	2 200	2 100	1 880	2 970	3 570	5 820	2 590	L_u 3 270	6 000	987	14 000	280
t = 18.9	2 000	2 050	1 920	1 740	1 980	3 190	5 630	2 280	I_x 1 360	7 000	778	16 000	236
d = 684	1 000	1 790	1 690	1 570	990	2 580	5 240	1 880	S_x 3 980	8 000	628	18 000	204
W690x125	5 000	2 240	2 110	1 910	4 950	3 600	5 380	2 760	M_r 1 250	4 000	1 140	10 000	362
W27x84	4 000	2 130	2 010	1 820	3 960	3 450	5 310	2 580	V_r 1 610	5 000	999	12 000	277
b = 253	3 000	2 010	1 910	1 700	2 970	3 230	5 210	2 360	L_u 3 190	6 000	834	14 000	224
t = 16.3	2 000	1 870	1 750	1 560	1 980	2 900	5 050	2 070	I_x 1 190	7 000	641	16 000	188
d = 678	1 000	1 610	1 520	1 410	990	2 350	4 710	1 700	S_x 3 500	8 000	514	18 000	162
W610x174	5 000	2 670	2 520	2 310	4 950	4 100	6 980	3 050	M_r 1 660	4 500	1 660	10 000	924
W24x117	4 000	2 550	2 420	2 220	3 960	3 890	6 880	2 840	V_r 1 770	5 000	1 610	12 000	709
b = 325	3 000	2 420	2 310	2 100	2 970	3 610	6 740	2 590	L_u 4 480	6 000	1 490	14 000	574
t = 21.6	2 000	2 270	2 150	1 970	1 980	3 210	6 510	2 300	I_x 1 470	7 000	1 370	16 000	482
d = 616	1 000	2 020	1 930	1 820	990	2 590	6 050	1 930	S_x 4 780	8 000	1 230	18 000	415
W610x155	5 000	2 420	2 280	2 090	4 950	3 690	6 210	2 770	M_r 1 470	4 500	1 460	10 000	762
W24x104	4 000	2 300	2 180	2 000	3 960	3 510	6 130	2 590	V_r 1 590	5 000	1 410	12 000	579
b = 324	3 000	2 180	2 080	1 890	2 970	3 270	6 010	2 360	L_u 4 400	6 000	1 300	14 000	465
t = 19	2 000	2 040	1 930	1 770	1 980	2 920	5 810	2 090	I_x 1 290	7 000	1 180	16 000	388
d = 611	1 000	1 810	1 730	1 620	990	2 350	5 420	1 740	S_x 4 220	8 000	1 050	18 000	333
W610x140	5 000	2 270	2 130	1 930	4 950	3 390	5 590	2 560	M_r 1 290	4 000	1 170	10 000	422
W24x94	4 000	2 150	2 030	1 840	3 960	3 240	5 510	2 390	V_r 1 660	5 000	1 030	12 000	334
b = 230	3 000	2 030	1 920	1 720	2 970	3 020	5 400	2 170	L_u 3 070	6 000	874	14 000	277
t = 22.2	2 000	1 880	1 770	1 590	1 980	2 700	5 220	1 910	I_x 1 120	7 000	695	16 000	237
d = 617	1 000	1 640	1 550	1 450	990	2 170	4 850	1 570	S_x 3 630	8 000	573	18 000	207
W610x125	5 000	2 070	1 930	1 740	4 940	3 050	4 970	2 330	M_r 1 140	4 000	1 020	10 000	342
W24x84	4 000	1 950	1 840	1 660	3 960	2 920	4 910	2 180	V_r 1 490	5 000	889	12 000	269
b = 229	3 000	1 830	1 740	1 560	2 970	2 730	4 820	1 990	L_u 3 020	6 000	733	14 000	222
t = 19.6	2 000	1 700	1 600	1 440	1 980	2 450	4 670	1 740	I_x 985	7 000	575	16 000	189
d = 612	1 000	1 480	1 400	1 290	990	1 980	4 350	1 420	S_x 3 220	8 000	470	18 000	165
W610x113	5 000	1 880	1 750	1 570	4 470	2 780	4 500	2 150	M_r 1 020	4 000	906	10 000	282
W24x76	4 000	1 800	1 690	1 530	3 960	2 660	4 440	2 010	V_r 1 400	5 000	775	12 000	220
b = 228	3 000	1 690	1 600	1 430	2 970	2 500	4 360	1 830	L_u 2 950	6 000	617	14 000	180
t = 17.3	2 000	1 560	1 470	1 320	1 980	2 260	4 230	1 600	I_x 875	7 000	481	16 000	153
d = 608	1 000	1 360	1 270	1 170	990	1 820	3 950	1 300	S_x 2 880	8 000	391	18 000	133
W610x101	5 000	1 700	1 580	1 410	4 040	2 500	4 030	1 960	M_r 900	4 000	787	10 000	228
W24x68	4 000	1 660	1 550	1 400	3 960	2 410	3 990	1 830	V_r 1 300	5 000	664	12 000	176
b = 228	3 000	1 550	1 460	1 310	2 970	2 270	3 920	1 670	L_u 2 890	6 000	512	14 000	144
t = 14.9	2 000	1 420	1 340	1 190	1 980	2 050	3 810	1 460	I_x 764	7 000	396	16 000	121
d = 603	1 000	1 230	1 150	1 050	990	1 670	3 560	1 180	S_x 2 530	8 000	320	18 000	105

Note: Resistances are based on a concrete density of 2300 kg/m³.

$F_y = 345$ MPa

Units: M_r - kN·m, V_r - kN, L_u - mm, I_x - 10^6 mm⁴, S_x - 10^3 mm³, b - mm, t - mm, d - mm

G40.21 350W
ASTM A992
A572 Grade 50
f'$_c$ = 25 MPa

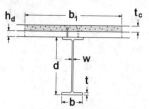

Steel section	b$_1$	Composite M$_{rc}$ (kN·m) for % shear connection			Q$_r$ (kN)	I$_t$ 10^6	S$_t$ 10^3	I$_{ts}$ 10^6	Steel section data		Non-composite Unbraced condition			
	mm	100%	70%	40%	100%	mm^4	mm^3	mm^4			L' mm	M$_r$' kN·m	L' mm	M$_r$' kN·m
W610x91	4 000	1 480	1 380	1 240	3 570	2 140	3 510	1 650	M$_r$	782	3 000	768	8 000	257
W24x61	3 000	1 400	1 320	1 180	2 970	2 020	3 460	1 510	V$_r$	1 100	4 000	672	10 000	181
b = 227	2 000	1 280	1 210	1 070	1 980	1 840	3 360	1 320	L$_u$	2 820	5 000	557	12 000	139
t = 12.7	1 000	1 110	1 030	933	990	1 500	3 150	1 060	I$_x$	657	6 000	416	14 000	112
d = 598	500	959	910	855	495	1 200	2 900	879	S$_x$	2 200	7 000	320	16 000	94.2
W610x82	4 000	1 360	1 270	1 120	3 260	1 950	3 170	1 510	M$_r$	686	3 000	589	8 000	147
W24x55	3 000	1 310	1 230	1 080	2 970	1 850	3 120	1 380	V$_r$	1 170	4 000	450	10 000	108
b = 178	2 000	1 190	1 120	972	1 980	1 690	3 030	1 210	L$_u$	2 110	5 000	306	12 000	84.8
t = 12.8	1 000	1 010	932	833	990	1 380	2 830	958	I$_x$	565	6 000	227	14 000	70.1
d = 599	500	859	810	755	495	1 090	2 600	785	S$_x$	1 880	7 000	179	16 000	59.8
W530x138	4 000	1 940	1 820	1 630	3 960	2 630	4 950	1 930	M$_r$	1 120	3 000	1 110	8 000	515
W21x93	3 000	1 810	1 710	1 530	2 970	2 450	4 840	1 750	V$_r$	1 650	4 000	1 000	10 000	390
b = 214	2 000	1 670	1 560	1 400	1 980	2 190	4 670	1 530	L$_u$	2 930	5 000	884	12 000	314
t = 23.6	1 000	1 440	1 360	1 270	990	1 740	4 320	1 240	I$_x$	861	6 000	759	14 000	263
d = 549	500	1 290	1 240	1 190	495	1 390	3 950	1 070	S$_x$	3 140	7 000	616	16 000	227
W530x123	4 000	1 770	1 650	1 480	3 960	2 380	4 430	1 760	M$_r$	997	3 000	984	8 000	421
W21x83	3 000	1 650	1 550	1 390	2 970	2 230	4 340	1 600	V$_r$	1 460	4 000	879	10 000	316
b = 212	2 000	1 520	1 420	1 270	1 980	1 990	4 200	1 400	L$_u$	2 860	5 000	762	12 000	253
t = 21.2	1 000	1 310	1 230	1 140	990	1 600	3 900	1 130	I$_x$	761	6 000	631	14 000	211
d = 544	500	1 160	1 120	1 060	495	1 270	3 570	961	S$_x$	2 800	7 000	505	16 000	182
W530x109	4 000	1 610	1 500	1 340	3 960	2 140	3 930	1 600	M$_r$	879	3 000	862	8 000	342
W21x73	3 000	1 490	1 400	1 260	2 970	2 010	3 860	1 460	V$_r$	1 280	4 000	764	10 000	254
b = 211	2 000	1 370	1 290	1 150	1 980	1 810	3 740	1 270	L$_u$	2 810	5 000	652	12 000	202
t = 18.8	1 000	1 180	1 110	1 020	990	1 460	3 490	1 020	I$_x$	667	6 000	520	14 000	168
d = 539	500	1 040	997	946	495	1 160	3 200	862	S$_x$	2 480	7 000	413	16 000	144
W530x101	4 000	1 520	1 410	1 270	3 960	2 000	3 660	1 520	M$_r$	814	3 000	794	8 000	301
W21x68	3 000	1 410	1 320	1 180	2 970	1 890	3 600	1 380	V$_r$	1 200	4 000	699	10 000	222
b = 210	2 000	1 280	1 210	1 080	1 980	1 700	3 490	1 210	L$_u$	2 770	5 000	591	12 000	176
t = 17.4	1 000	1 110	1 040	953	990	1 380	3 260	967	I$_x$	617	6 000	462	14 000	146
d = 537	500	976	932	881	495	1 090	3 000	810	S$_x$	2 300	7 000	365	16 000	125
W530x92	4 000	1 400	1 290	1 160	3 660	1 840	3 340	1 410	M$_r$	733	3 000	711	8 000	253
W21x62	3 000	1 310	1 220	1 100	2 970	1 730	3 280	1 280	V$_r$	1 110	4 000	621	9 000	214
b = 209	2 000	1 190	1 120	998	1 980	1 570	3 190	1 120	L$_u$	2 720	5 000	516	10 000	185
t = 15.6	1 000	1 030	961	873	990	1 280	2 990	893	I$_x$	552	6 000	393	12 000	146
d = 533	500	895	851	801	495	1 010	2 740	741	S$_x$	2 070	7 000	309	14 000	120
W530x82	4 000	1 250	1 150	1 020	3 260	1 640	2 960	1 270	M$_r$	640	3 000	616	8 000	203
W21x55	3 000	1 190	1 110	995	2 970	1 550	2 910	1 160	V$_r$	1 030	4 000	531	9 000	170
b = 209	2 000	1 080	1 020	900	1 980	1 420	2 840	1 020	L$_u$	2 660	5 000	433	10 000	147
t = 13.3	1 000	928	864	778	990	1 160	2 660	805	I$_x$	477	6 000	320	12 000	115
d = 528	500	800	757	707	495	918	2 450	661	S$_x$	1 810	7 000	249	14 000	94.0

Note: Resistances are based on a concrete density of 2300 kg/m^3.

Units: M$_r$ - kN·m, V$_r$ - kN, L$_u$ - mm, I$_x$ - 10^6 mm^4, S$_x$ - 10^3 mm^3, b - mm, t - mm, d - mm

F$_y$ = 345 MPa

COMPOSITE BEAMS
Trial Selection Table
75 mm Deck with 75 mm Slab
$\phi = 0.90$, $\phi_c = 0.65$

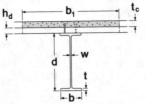

G40.21 350W
ASTM A992
A572 Grade 50
$f'_c = 25$ MPa

Steel section	b₁	Composite Mrc (kN·m) for % shear connection			Qr (kN)	It 10⁶	St 10³	Its 10⁶	Non-composite Steel section data	Unbraced condition			
		100%	70%	40%	100%	mm⁴	mm³	mm⁴		L' mm	Mr' kN·m	L' mm	Mr' kN·m
W530x74	4 000	1 140	1 050	920	2 960	1 490	2 660	1 170	Mr 562	3 000	474	8 000	123
W21x50	3 000	1 110	1 030	916	2 960	1 420	2 620	1 070	Vr 1 050	4 000	357	9 000	105
b = 166	2 000	1 000	939	821	1 980	1 300	2 550	932	Lu 2 040	5 000	247	10 000	91.7
t = 13.6	1 000	850	785	699	990	1 060	2 390	733	Ix 411	6 000	186	12 000	73.2
d = 529	500	721	678	628	495	840	2 190	593	Sx 1 550	7 000	148	14 000	61.0
W530x66	4 000	1 010	921	803	2 600	1 320	2 330	1 050	Mr 484	3 000	398	8 000	94.9
W21x44	3 000	987	910	800	2 600	1 260	2 300	960	Vr 927	4 000	284	9 000	80.6
b = 165	2 000	903	846	738	1 980	1 160	2 240	841	Lu 1 980	5 000	195	10 000	70.0
t = 11.4	1 000	764	704	620	990	958	2 110	659	Ix 351	6 000	145	12 000	55.5
d = 525	500	641	600	551	495	758	1 940	528	Sx 1 340	7 000	115	14 000	46.0
W460x158	4 000	1 920	1 790	1 630	3 960	2 380	5 170	1 720	Mr 1 170	4 500	1 150	9 000	795
W18x106	3 000	1 790	1 690	1 540	2 970	2 210	5 060	1 560	Vr 1 460	5 000	1 110	10 000	697
b = 284	2 000	1 660	1 570	1 430	1 980	1 960	4 870	1 360	Lu 4 190	6 000	1 040	11 000	618
t = 23.9	1 000	1 460	1 390	1 310	990	1 550	4 500	1 110	Ix 796	7 000	957	12 000	556
d = 476	500	1 330	1 290	1 240	495	1 240	4 120	966	Sx 3 350	8 000	876	14 000	463
W460x144	4 000	1 790	1 670	1 510	3 960	2 210	4 750	1 610	Mr 1 070	4 500	1 050	9 000	693
W18x97	3 000	1 660	1 570	1 430	2 970	2 050	4 660	1 460	Vr 1 320	5 000	1 010	10 000	602
b = 283	2 000	1 530	1 460	1 330	1 980	1 830	4 490	1 270	Lu 4 130	6 000	936	11 000	533
t = 22.1	1 000	1 360	1 290	1 210	990	1 450	4 170	1 040	Ix 726	7 000	858	12 000	478
d = 472	500	1 230	1 190	1 140	495	1 160	3 820	893	Sx 3 080	8 000	779	14 000	396
W460x128	4 000	1 630	1 520	1 370	3 960	1 990	4 240	1 460	Mr 947	4 500	918	9 000	567
W18x86	3 000	1 510	1 420	1 290	2 970	1 860	4 160	1 330	Vr 1 170	5 000	884	10 000	490
b = 282	2 000	1 380	1 320	1 200	1 980	1 660	4 030	1 160	Lu 4 040	6 000	812	11 000	432
t = 19.6	1 000	1 220	1 160	1 080	990	1 330	3 740	938	Ix 637	7 000	736	12 000	386
d = 467	500	1 100	1 060	1 010	495	1 050	3 440	800	Sx 2 730	8 000	658	14 000	318
W460x113	4 000	1 480	1 370	1 230	3 960	1 780	3 750	1 330	Mr 829	4 500	796	9 000	458
W18x76	3 000	1 360	1 280	1 160	2 970	1 670	3 680	1 210	Vr 1 020	5 000	765	10 000	394
b = 280	2 000	1 240	1 180	1 070	1 980	1 500	3 570	1 050	Lu 3 950	6 000	696	11 000	345
t = 17.3	1 000	1 100	1 040	959	990	1 210	3 330	847	Ix 556	7 000	623	12 000	307
d = 463	500	978	940	895	495	956	3 070	715	Sx 2 400	8 000	545	14 000	252
W460x106	3 000	1 310	1 220	1 090	2 970	1 570	3 390	1 140	Mr 742	3 000	719	8 000	308
W18x71	2 000	1 190	1 120	992	1 980	1 410	3 290	986	Vr 1 210	4 000	637	9 000	266
b = 194	1 500	1 120	1 040	935	1 490	1 300	3 200	892	Lu 2 690	5 000	549	10 000	235
t = 20.6	1 000	1 020	956	873	990	1 130	3 050	781	Ix 488	6 000	450	11 000	210
d = 469	500	894	853	807	495	889	2 780	649	Sx 2 080	7 000	366	12 000	190
W460x97	3 000	1 220	1 130	1 010	2 970	1 460	3 110	1 060	Mr 677	3 000	652	8 000	264
W18x65	2 000	1 100	1 040	921	1 980	1 320	3 020	924	Vr 1 090	4 000	574	9 000	227
b = 193	1 500	1 030	970	867	1 490	1 210	2 940	836	Lu 2 650	5 000	488	10 000	200
t = 19	1 000	948	887	807	990	1 060	2 810	731	Ix 445	6 000	389	11 000	178
d = 466	500	827	787	742	495	833	2 570	603	Sx 1 910	7 000	314	12 000	161

Note: Resistances are based on a concrete density of 2300 kg/m³.

Units: Mr - kN·m, Vr - kN, Lu - mm, Ix - 10⁶ mm⁴, Sx - 10³ mm³, b - mm, t - mm, d - mm

$F_y = 345$ MPa

G40.21 350W
ASTM A992
A572 Grade 50
f′c = 25 MPa

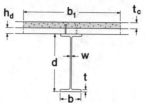

COMPOSITE BEAMS
Trial Selection Table
75 mm Deck with 75 mm Slab
φ = 0.90, φc = 0.65

Steel section	b₁	Composite Mrc (kN·m) for % shear connection 100%	70%	40%	Qr (kN) 100%	It 10⁶ mm⁴	St 10³ mm³	Its 10⁶ mm⁴	Non-composite Steel section data	Unbraced condition L′ mm	Mr′ kN·m	L′ mm	Mr′ kN·m
W460x89	3 000	1 150	1 070	952	2 970	1 360	2 890	1 000	Mr 624	3 000	598	8 000	231
W18x60	2 000	1 030	971	865	1 980	1 240	2 810	873	Vr 996	4 000	523	9 000	198
b = 192	1 500	969	911	813	1 490	1 140	2 740	790	Lu 2 620	5 000	439	10 000	174
t = 17.7	1 000	890	832	754	990	1 000	2 630	689	Ix 410	6 000	343	11 000	155
d = 463	500	773	735	689	495	787	2 410	565	Sx 1 770	7 000	276	12 000	140
W460x82	3 000	1 080	994	884	2 970	1 260	2 640	935	Mr 568	3 000	540	8 000	195
W18x55	2 000	959	900	802	1 980	1 140	2 570	815	Vr 933	4 000	467	9 000	167
b = 191	1 500	897	845	752	1 490	1 060	2 510	737	Lu 2 560	5 000	385	10 000	146
t = 16	1 000	824	770	695	990	932	2 410	641	Ix 370	6 000	292	11 000	129
d = 460	500	713	676	632	495	734	2 210	522	Sx 1 610	7 000	234	12 000	117
W460x74	3 000	1 000	922	816	2 930	1 150	2 410	869	Mr 512	3 000	484	8 000	164
W18x50	2 000	889	832	742	1 980	1 060	2 340	758	Vr 843	4 000	414	9 000	140
b = 190	1 500	829	781	694	1 490	979	2 290	686	Lu 2 530	5 000	332	10 000	122
t = 14.5	1 000	761	711	638	990	866	2 210	596	Ix 333	6 000	249	11 000	108
d = 457	500	656	619	576	495	683	2 030	482	Sx 1 460	7 000	198	12 000	96.9
W460x67	3 000	913	836	737	2 660	1 050	2 180	801	Mr 456	3 000	427	8 000	135
W18x45	2 000	824	768	683	1 980	966	2 120	701	Vr 791	4 000	361	9 000	115
b = 190	1 500	765	720	637	1 490	899	2 080	634	Lu 2 480	5 000	280	10 000	99.4
t = 12.7	1 000	700	653	582	990	799	2 000	549	Ix 295	6 000	208	11 000	87.8
d = 454	500	599	564	521	495	631	1 850	441	Sx 1 300	7 000	164	12 000	78.6
W460x61	3 000	819	746	654	2 370	941	1 930	725	Mr 401	3 000	370	8 000	107
W18x41	2 000	756	701	621	1 980	869	1 890	636	Vr 747	4 000	306	9 000	90.5
b = 189	1 500	698	654	576	1 490	811	1 850	575	Lu 2 410	5 000	227	10 000	78.1
t = 10.8	1 000	636	591	523	990	723	1 780	498	Ix 254	6 000	168	11 000	68.7
d = 450	500	539	504	462	495	574	1 650	396	Sx 1 130	7 000	131	12 000	61.3
W460x52	3 000	718	651	565	2 060	828	1 670	648	Mr 338	3 000	269	8 000	63.7
W18x35	2 000	686	632	555	1 980	768	1 630	571	Vr 680	4 000	185	9 000	54.4
b = 152	1 500	629	586	512	1 490	720	1 600	517	Lu 1 890	5 000	128	10 000	47.4
t = 10.8	1 000	568	527	460	990	646	1 550	446	Ix 212	6 000	96.3	11 000	42.1
d = 450	500	476	442	400	495	515	1 430	350	Sx 943	7 000	76.8	12 000	37.9
W410x149	3 000	1 590	1 500	1 350	2 970	1 830	4 520	1 280	Mr 1 020	4 500	993	8 000	773
W16x100	2 000	1 460	1 380	1 250	1 980	1 620	4 350	1 110	Vr 1 320	5 000	963	9 000	710
b = 265	1 500	1 380	1 310	1 200	1 490	1 470	4 220	1 010	Lu 4 080	5 500	931	10 000	637
t = 25	1 000	1 280	1 220	1 140	990	1 280	4 010	902	Ix 625	6 000	900	11 000	569
d = 431	500	1 160	1 120	1 070	495	1 010	3 660	773	Sx 2 900	7 000	836	12 000	515
W410x132	3 000	1 440	1 350	1 220	2 970	1 650	4 020	1 160	Mr 897	4 500	865	8 000	647
W16x89	2 000	1 310	1 240	1 120	1 980	1 470	3 880	1 010	Vr 1 160	5 000	835	9 000	579
b = 263	1 500	1 240	1 170	1 070	1 490	1 330	3 770	918	Lu 3 940	5 500	804	10 000	508
t = 22.2	1 000	1 150	1 090	1 010	990	1 160	3 590	812	Ix 545	6 000	773	11 000	453
d = 425	500	1 030	992	948	495	915	3 280	689	Sx 2 560	7 000	710	12 000	409

Note: Resistances are based on a concrete density of 2300 kg/m³.

Fy = 345 MPa

Units: Mr - kN·m, Vr - kN, Lu - mm, Ix - 10⁶ mm⁴, Sx - 10³ mm³, b - mm, t - mm, d - mm

COMPOSITE BEAMS
Trial Selection Table
75 mm Deck with 75 mm Slab
$\phi = 0.90$, $\phi_c = 0.65$

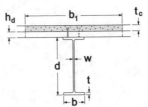

G40.21 350W
ASTM A992
A572 Grade 50
$f'_c = 25$ MPa

Steel section	b_1	M_{rc} (kN·m) for % shear connection 100%	70%	40%	Q_r (kN) 100%	I_t 10^6 mm⁴	S_t 10^3 mm³	I_{ts} 10^6 mm⁴	Steel section data	L' mm	M_r' kN·m	L' mm	M_r' kN·m
W410x114	3 000	1 290	1 200	1 080	2 970	1 470	3 520	1 050	M_r 773	4 500	736	8 000	525
W16x77	2 000	1 170	1 100	997	1 980	1 310	3 410	910	V_r 998	5 000	707	9 000	451
b = 261	1 500	1 100	1 040	945	1 490	1 200	3 310	825	L_u 3 810	5 500	678	10 000	394
t = 19.3	1 000	1 020	964	888	990	1 050	3 170	725	I_x 468	6 000	648	11 000	350
d = 420	500	906	869	825	495	822	2 900	608	S_x 2 230	7 000	587	12 000	315
W410x100	3 000	1 160	1 080	966	2 970	1 300	3 090	946	M_r 671	4 500	632	8 000	423
W16x67	2 000	1 040	981	888	1 980	1 170	2 990	822	V_r 850	5 000	605	9 000	359
b = 260	1 500	979	928	839	1 490	1 080	2 920	744	L_u 3 730	5 500	577	10 000	312
t = 16.9	1 000	908	857	784	990	943	2 800	651	I_x 404	6 000	548	11 000	276
d = 415	500	801	766	723	495	741	2 570	540	S_x 1 950	7 000	489	12 000	247
W410x85	3 000	1 030	949	838	2 970	1 120	2 560	821	M_r 537	3 000	509	8 000	205
W16x57	2 000	914	854	759	1 980	1 010	2 490	711	V_r 931	4 000	444	9 000	178
b = 181	1 500	851	799	710	1 490	932	2 420	641	L_u 2 520	5 000	376	10 000	157
t = 18.2	1 000	779	727	656	990	818	2 320	555	I_x 315	6 000	297	11 000	141
d = 417	500	673	638	596	495	639	2 120	450	S_x 1 510	7 000	243	12 000	127
W410x74	3 000	946	866	758	2 970	1 000	2 270	747	M_r 469	3 000	440	8 000	163
W16x50	2 000	831	773	687	1 980	913	2 210	649	V_r 821	4 000	379	9 000	140
b = 180	1 500	770	723	641	1 490	844	2 160	585	L_u 2 470	5 000	312	10 000	124
t = 16	1 000	704	657	588	990	744	2 070	506	I_x 275	6 000	239	11 000	110
d = 413	500	604	570	530	495	583	1 900	406	S_x 1 330	7 000	194	12 000	99.8
W410x67	3 000	858	781	682	2 670	912	2 050	690	M_r 422	3 000	392	8 000	135
W16x45	2 000	768	712	632	1 980	836	2 000	602	V_r 739	4 000	333	9 000	116
b = 179	1 500	708	664	589	1 490	777	1 960	543	L_u 2 420	5 000	264	10 000	102
t = 14.4	1 000	646	603	538	990	688	1 880	469	I_x 246	6 000	201	11 000	90.5
d = 410	500	553	521	481	495	541	1 730	374	S_x 1 200	7 000	161	12 000	81.7
W410x60	3 000	762	690	600	2 350	816	1 820	628	M_r 369	3 000	341	8 000	109
W16x40	2 000	701	646	573	1 980	753	1 770	550	V_r 642	4 000	286	9 000	93.2
b = 178	1 500	643	600	533	1 490	702	1 740	497	L_u 2 390	5 000	218	10 000	81.4
t = 12.8	1 000	582	546	486	990	626	1 680	430	I_x 216	6 000	165	11 000	72.2
d = 407	500	499	469	430	495	496	1 550	340	S_x 1 060	7 000	131	12 000	65.0
W410x54	3 000	687	619	536	2 110	732	1 620	570	M_r 326	3 000	295	8 000	86.1
W16x36	2 000	649	595	523	1 980	678	1 590	501	V_r 619	4 000	242	9 000	73.2
b = 177	1 500	591	549	485	1 490	635	1 550	453	L_u 2 310	5 000	176	10 000	63.6
t = 10.9	1 000	532	498	438	990	568	1 500	390	I_x 186	6 000	132	11 000	56.3
d = 403	500	452	421	383	495	451	1 390	306	S_x 924	7 000	104	12 000	50.5
W410x46	3 000	601	538	463	1 830	643	1 400	509	M_r 275	2 000	265	7 000	61.7
W16x31	2 000	580	528	460	1 830	599	1 370	450	V_r 578	3 000	210	8 000	51.8
b = 140	1 500	535	494	433	1 490	563	1 350	407	L_u 1 790	4 000	142	9 000	44.6
t = 11.2	1 000	476	444	387	990	508	1 300	351	I_x 156	5 000	99.9	10 000	39.2
d = 403	500	400	371	333	495	406	1 210	273	S_x 773	6 000	76.4	11 000	35.0

Note: Resistances are based on a concrete density of 2300 kg/m³.

Units: M_r - kN·m, V_r - kN, L_u - mm, I_x - 10^6 mm⁴, S_x - 10^3 mm³, b - mm, t - mm, d - mm

$F_y = 345$ MPa

G40.21 350W
ASTM A992
A572 Grade 50
f'_c = 25 MPa

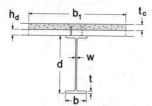

COMPOSITE BEAMS
Trial Selection Table
75 mm Deck with 75 mm Slab
ϕ = 0.90, ϕ_c = 0.65

Steel section	b_1	M_{rc} (kN·m) for % shear connection			Q_r	I_t	S_t	I_{ts}	Steel section data		Unbraced condition			
											L'	M_r'	L'	M_r'
	mm	100%	70%	40%	(kN)	10^6 mm⁴	10^3 mm³	10^6 mm⁴			mm	kN·m	mm	kN·m
W410x39	3 000	511	456	389	1 550	548	1 190	442	M_r	227	2 000	216	7 000	44.1
W16x26	2 000	496	448	387	1 550	513	1 160	393	V_r	480	3 000	166	8 000	36.6
b = 140	1 500	476	436	380	1 490	485	1 140	358	L_u 1 730		4 000	105	9 000	31.3
t = 8.8	1 000	419	390	337	990	441	1 110	309	I_x	127	5 000	73.1	10 000	27.4
d = 399	500	348	321	284	495	356	1 030	239	S_x	634	6 000	55.2	11 000	24.3
W360x79	3 000	889	808	701	2 970	850	2 200	626	M_r	444	3 500	425	7 000	267
W14x53	2 000	773	715	637	1 980	772	2 140	541	V_r	682	4 000	404	8 000	225
b = 205	1 500	711	666	597	1 490	711	2 090	486	L_u 3 010		4 500	383	9 000	194
t = 16.8	1 000	648	610	550	990	624	2 000	419	I_x	226	5 000	361	10 000	171
d = 354	500	563	533	496	495	484	1 830	335	S_x 1 280		6 000	317	11 000	153
W360x72	3 000	818	739	637	2 830	772	1 990	576	M_r	397	3 500	377	7 000	222
W14x48	2 000	714	658	584	1 980	705	1 930	500	V_r	617	4 000	357	8 000	186
b = 204	1 500	654	611	546	1 490	652	1 890	449	L_u 2 940		4 500	336	9 000	160
t = 15.1	1 000	593	558	501	990	574	1 820	387	I_x	201	5 000	315	10 000	141
d = 350	500	513	484	448	495	448	1 670	307	S_x 1 150		6 000	272	11 000	126
W360x64	3 000	737	662	568	2 530	699	1 780	529	M_r	354	3 500	332	7 000	183
W14x43	2 000	660	605	533	1 980	641	1 740	461	V_r	548	4 000	313	8 000	153
b = 203	1 500	601	558	499	1 490	596	1 700	415	L_u 2 870		4 500	293	9 000	131
t = 13.5	1 000	541	509	455	990	528	1 640	357	I_x	178	5 000	273	10 000	115
d = 347	500	467	439	404	495	413	1 510	281	S_x 1 030		6 000	228	11 000	102
W360x57	3 000	674	603	517	2 240	655	1 610	503	M_r	314	3 000	289	7 000	119
W14x38	2 000	624	569	498	1 980	604	1 570	440	V_r	580	3 500	267	8 000	99.8
b = 172	1 500	566	523	463	1 490	563	1 530	396	L_u 2 360		4 000	244	9 000	86.0
t = 13.1	1 000	505	474	419	990	502	1 480	340	I_x	161	5 000	192	10 000	75.7
d = 358	500	431	403	368	495	395	1 370	266	S_x	897	6 000	147	11 000	67.6
W360x51	3 000	605	539	461	2 000	589	1 440	459	M_r	278	3 000	253	7 000	97.0
W14x34	2 000	578	525	456	1 980	546	1 400	403	V_r	524	3 500	232	8 000	81.0
b = 171	1 500	521	480	423	1 490	511	1 370	364	L_u 2 320		4 000	210	9 000	69.5
t = 11.6	1 000	462	433	382	990	458	1 330	313	I_x	141	5 000	159	10 000	60.9
d = 355	500	392	366	332	495	363	1 230	243	S_x	796	6 000	121	11 000	54.2
W360x45	3 000	540	479	408	1 780	526	1 270	416	M_r	242	3 000	217	7 000	76.5
W14x30	2 000	520	469	405	1 780	490	1 240	367	V_r	498	3 500	197	8 000	63.4
b = 171	1 500	480	439	384	1 490	460	1 220	332	L_u 2 260		4 000	176	9 000	54.1
t = 9.8	1 000	422	393	344	990	415	1 180	286	I_x	122	5 000	128	10 000	47.2
d = 352	500	354	329	295	495	331	1 100	220	S_x	691	6 000	96.1	11 000	41.9
W360x39	2 500	469	416	354	1 550	451	1 100	354	M_r	206	2 000	193	6 000	54.2
W14x26	2 000	460	412	352	1 550	434	1 080	330	V_r	470	2 500	172	7 000	44.3
b = 128	1 500	440	400	346	1 490	410	1 060	300	L_u 1 660		3 000	148	8 000	37.5
t = 10.7	1 000	382	354	308	990	371	1 030	258	I_x	102	4 000	97.2	9 000	32.5
d = 353	500	317	292	259	495	299	958	198	S_x	580	5 000	69.8	10 000	28.8

Note: Resistances are based on a concrete density of 2300 kg/m³.

Units: M_r - kN·m, V_r - kN, L_u - mm, I_x - 10^6 mm⁴, S_x - 10^3 mm³, b - mm, t - mm, d - mm

F_y = 345 MPa

COMPOSITE BEAMS
Trial Selection Table
75 mm Deck with 75 mm Slab
$\phi = 0.90$, $\phi_c = 0.65$

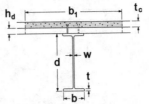

G40.21 350W
ASTM A992
A572 Grade 50
$f'_c = 25$ MPa

Steel section	b_1	M_{rc} (kN·m) for % shear connection			Q_r (kN)	I_t 10^6	S_t 10^3	I_{ts} 10^6	Steel section data		Unbraced condition			
		100%	70%	40%	100%						L'	M_r'	L'	M_r'
	mm					mm⁴	mm³	mm⁴			mm	kN·m	mm	kN·m
W360x33	2 500	395	348	294	1 290	382	918	306	M_r	168	2 000	155	6 000	38.1
W14x22	2 000	388	345	293	1 290	368	907	287	V_r	396	2 500	136	7 000	30.8
b = 127	1 500	378	340	292	1 290	350	891	262	L_u	1 600	3 000	113	8 000	25.9
t = 8.5	1 000	337	309	267	990	320	866	226	I_x	82.7	4 000	70.3	9 000	22.3
d = 349	500	275	253	221	495	261	811	173	S_x	474	5 000	49.7	10 000	19.6
W310x74	2 500	732	663	573	2 480	646	1 890	464	M_r	366	3 500	354	6 000	274
W12x50	2 000	673	616	543	1 980	611	1 860	427	V_r	597	4 000	339	7 000	240
b = 205	1 500	613	569	507	1 490	563	1 810	382	L_u	3 100	4 500	323	8 000	204
t = 16.3	1 000	550	518	465	990	493	1 740	326	I_x	164	5 000	307	9 000	177
d = 310	500	476	450	416	495	380	1 590	256	S_x	1 060	5 500	291	10 000	156
W310x67	2 500	680	613	525	2 480	584	1 700	425	M_r	326	3 500	312	6 000	234
W12x45	2 000	623	567	495	1 980	554	1 670	392	V_r	533	4 000	297	7 000	198
b = 204	1 500	563	520	462	1 490	513	1 630	351	L_u	3 020	4 500	282	8 000	167
t = 14.6	1 000	502	472	422	990	452	1 570	300	I_x	144	5 000	266	9 000	144
d = 306	500	432	407	375	495	350	1 430	233	S_x	942	5 500	250	10 000	127
W310x60	2 500	622	557	473	2 340	529	1 520	391	M_r	290	3 500	275	6 000	199
W12x40	2 000	577	522	452	1 980	503	1 500	361	V_r	466	4 000	261	7 000	163
b = 203	1 500	518	476	421	1 490	468	1 470	324	L_u	2 960	4 500	246	8 000	137
t = 13.1	1 000	458	429	384	990	415	1 410	277	I_x	128	5 000	231	9 000	118
d = 303	500	393	369	338	495	323	1 300	215	S_x	842	5 500	215	10 000	104
W310x52	2 500	575	513	436	2 070	506	1 380	381	M_r	261	3 000	241	6 000	130
W12x35	2 000	552	499	428	1 980	483	1 360	353	V_r	495	3 500	224	7 000	106
b = 167	1 500	495	453	398	1 490	451	1 330	317	L_u	2 370	4 000	206	8 000	89.4
t = 13.2	1 000	435	406	360	990	402	1 280	271	I_x	119	4 500	188	9 000	77.5
d = 318	500	369	345	313	495	316	1 190	209	S_x	750	5 000	167	10 000	68.4
W310x45	2 500	494	437	369	1 770	436	1 180	335	M_r	220	3 000	200	6 000	98.2
W12x30	2 000	482	432	368	1 770	418	1 160	312	V_r	423	3 500	184	7 000	79.3
b = 166	1 500	443	403	350	1 490	393	1 140	282	L_u	2 310	4 000	167	8 000	66.5
t = 11.2	1 000	385	357	315	990	353	1 100	241	I_x	99.2	4 500	150	9 000	57.3
d = 313	500	323	301	271	495	281	1 030	185	S_x	634	5 000	128	10 000	50.4
W310x39	2 500	432	380	320	1 530	384	1 030	300	M_r	189	3 000	170	6 000	77.7
W12x26	2 000	423	376	319	1 530	369	1 010	280	V_r	368	3 500	155	7 000	62.2
b = 165	1 500	405	365	314	1 490	348	997	254	L_u	2 260	4 000	139	8 000	51.8
t = 9.7	1 000	348	320	282	990	315	967	219	I_x	85.1	4 500	121	9 000	44.3
d = 310	500	288	269	240	495	253	902	167	S_x	549	5 000	103	10 000	38.8
W250x67	2 500	620	552	464	2 480	472	1 560	338	M_r	280	3 500	275	6 000	223
W10x45	2 000	562	506	434	1 980	446	1 540	310	V_r	469	4 000	265	6 500	212
b = 204	1 500	503	460	404	1 490	411	1 500	276	L_u	3 260	4 500	254	7 000	202
t = 15.7	1 000	442	412	368	990	360	1 440	233	I_x	104	5 000	244	7 500	192
d = 257	500	376	354	325	495	274	1 310	178	S_x	806	5 500	233	8 000	180

Note: Resistances are based on a concrete density of 2300 kg/m³.

Units: M_r - kN·m, V_r - kN, L_u - mm, I_x - 10^6 mm⁴, S_x - 10^3 mm³, b - mm, t - mm, d - mm

$F_y = 345$ MPa

COMPOSITE BEAMS
Trial Selection Table
75 mm Deck with 75 mm Slab
$\phi = 0.90$, $\phi_c = 0.65$

G40.21 350W
ASTM A992
A572 Grade 50
$f'_c = 25$ MPa

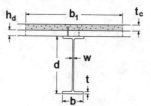

Steel section	b_1	M_{rc} (kN·m) for % shear connection			Q_r	I_t	S_t	I_{ts}	Steel section data		Unbraced condition			
		100%	70%	40%	100%	10^6	10^3	10^6			L'	M_r'	L'	M_r'
	mm				(kN)	mm^4	mm^3	mm^4			mm	kN·m	mm	kN·m
W250x58	2 500	555	491	408	2 300	413	1 360	301	M_r	239	3 500	232	6 000	181
W10x39	2 000	513	459	388	1 980	392	1 340	277	V_r	413	4 000	222	6 500	171
b = 203	1 500	455	413	359	1 490	363	1 300	247	L_u 3 130		4 500	212	7 000	161
t = 13.5	1 000	395	366	325	990	320	1 250	209	I_x	87.3	5 000	202	7 500	148
d = 252	500	332	312	284	495	246	1 150	158	S_x	693	5 500	192	8 000	137
W250x45	2 500	455	398	329	1 780	355	1 080	269	M_r	187	3 000	167	5 500	101
W10x30	2 000	443	392	327	1 780	339	1 070	249	V_r	414	3 500	155	6 000	90.6
b = 148	1 500	403	362	309	1 490	318	1 040	224	L_u 2 170		4 000	142	6 500	82.2
t = 13	1 000	344	316	276	990	284	1 010	190	I_x	71.1	4 500	129	7 000	75.2
d = 266	500	282	262	235	495	223	930	143	S_x	534	5 000	114	7 500	69.3
W250x39	2 500	394	342	282	1 530	309	936	239	M_r	159	3 000	140	5 500	77.5
W10x26	2 000	385	338	280	1 530	296	922	222	V_r	354	3 500	128	6 000	69.2
b = 147	1 500	367	327	276	1 490	279	904	200	L_u 2 110		4 000	115	6 500	62.5
t = 11.2	1 000	310	282	245	990	251	875	171	I_x	60.1	4 500	102	7 000	57.0
d = 262	500	250	232	206	495	200	812	128	S_x	459	5 000	88.0	7 500	52.4
W250x33	2 500	336	290	237	1 290	264	794	208	M_r	132	3 000	112	5 500	55.6
W10x22	2 000	330	287	236	1 290	254	783	194	V_r	323	3 500	100	6 000	49.4
b = 146	1 500	319	281	235	1 290	240	767	176	L_u 2 020		4 000	88.4	6 500	44.4
t = 9.1	1 000	278	251	215	990	218	744	151	I_x	48.9	4 500	74.1	7 000	40.3
d = 258	500	219	203	178	495	176	695	113	S_x	379	5 000	63.6	7 500	36.9
W200x42	2 500	375	321	257	1 650	249	903	187	M_r	138	3 000	133	5 500	99.6
W8x28	2 000	365	316	255	1 650	238	888	173	V_r	302	3 500	126	6 000	92.9
b = 166	1 500	336	296	244	1 490	222	868	155	L_u 2 610		4 000	120	6 500	84.6
t = 11.8	1 000	278	250	215	990	198	837	130	I_x	40.9	4 500	113	7 000	77.5
d = 205	500	218	203	180	495	154	771	95.0	S_x	399	5 000	106	7 500	71.6
W200x36	2 500	325	276	219	1 420	216	781	166	M_r	118	3 000	112	5 500	79.3
W8x24	2 000	317	272	218	1 420	207	769	154	V_r	255	3 500	105	6 000	71.3
b = 165	1 500	305	266	216	1 420	194	752	139	L_u 2 510		4 000	99.0	6 500	64.6
t = 10.2	1 000	253	226	191	990	175	727	117	I_x	34.4	4 500	92.5	7 000	59.0
d = 201	500	194	180	158	495	138	674	85.7	S_x	342	5 000	85.9	7 500	54.4
W200x31	2 500	293	249	198	1 240	202	698	158	M_r	104	2 000	104	4 500	65.2
W8x21	2 000	288	246	197	1 240	194	687	147	V_r	275	2 500	96.7	5 000	57.0
b = 134	1 500	278	241	195	1 240	183	672	133	L_u 1 980		3 000	89.3	5 500	50.6
t = 10.2	1 000	241	214	180	990	165	651	113	I_x	31.4	3 500	81.7	6 000	45.6
d = 210	500	183	168	146	495	132	605	83.1	S_x	299	4 000	74.0	6 500	41.5
W200x27	2 500	250	211	167	1 050	173	594	138	M_r	86.6	2 000	85.3	4 500	47.5
W8x18	2 000	246	209	166	1 050	167	585	129	V_r	246	2 500	78.7	5 000	41.2
b = 133	1 500	239	205	165	1 050	158	573	117	L_u 1 890		3 000	71.5	5 500	36.4
t = 8.4	1 000	220	194	160	990	144	555	101	I_x	25.8	3 500	64.1	6 000	32.6
d = 207	500	163	149	128	495	117	520	74.5	S_x	249	4 000	56.0	6 500	29.6

Note: Resistances are based on a concrete density of 2300 kg/m^3.

$F_y = 345$ MPa

Units: M_r - kN·m, V_r - kN, L_u - mm, I_x - 10^6 mm^4, S_x - 10^3 mm^3, b - mm, t - mm, d - mm

COMPOSITE BEAMS
Trial Selection Table
75 mm Deck with 90 mm Slab
$\phi = 0.90$, $\phi_c = 0.65$

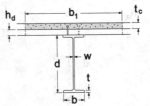

G40.21 350W
$f'_c = 25$ MPa

Steel section	b_1	M_{rc} (kN·m) for % shear connection			Q_r (kN)	I_t 10^6	S_t 10^3	I_{ts} 10^6	Steel section data	Unbraced condition			
		100%	70%	40%	100%					L'	M_r'	L'	M_r'
	mm					mm^4	mm^3	mm^4		mm	kN·m	mm	kN·m
WWF1000x223	6 000	5 320	5 100	4 690	7 130	12 200	13 100	9 280	M_r 3 310	4 000	3 250	14 000	729
WWF39x150	5 000	5 160	4 970	4 520	5 940	11 700	13 000	8 800	V_r 2 210	6 000	2 620	16 000	602
b = 300	4 000	5 000	4 790	4 330	4 750	11 100	12 800	8 230	L_u 3 790	8 000	1 790	18 000	512
t = 25	3 000	4 800	4 540	4 110	3 560	10 400	12 500	7 570	I_x 4 590	10 000	1 230	20 000	446
d = 1000	2 000	4 460	4 200	3 870	2 380	9 250	12 100	6 780	S_x 9 190	12 000	920	22 000	394
WWF1000x200	6 000	4 890	4 670	4 270	7 130	11 000	11 700	8 420	M_r 2 890	4 000	2 790	14 000	549
WWF39x134	5 000	4 730	4 550	4 100	5 940	10 600	11 600	7 980	V_r 2 210	6 000	2 180	16 000	449
b = 300	4 000	4 570	4 370	3 900	4 750	10 100	11 400	7 460	L_u 3 610	8 000	1 390	18 000	379
t = 20	3 000	4 380	4 110	3 680	3 560	9 400	11 200	6 830	I_x 3 940	10 000	945	20 000	328
d = 1000	2 000	4 030	3 770	3 440	2 380	8 400	10 800	6 080	S_x 7 880	12 000	699	22 000	289
WWF900x192	6 000	4 330	4 120	3 830	7 130	9 240	10 700	7 170	M_r 2 710	4 000	2 700	14 000	670
WWF35x128	5 000	4 180	3 990	3 720	5 940	8 930	10 600	6 810	V_r 1 350	6 000	2 240	16 000	555
b = 300	4 000	4 020	3 870	3 580	4 750	8 520	10 500	6 390	L_u 3 980	8 000	1 630	18 000	473
t = 25	3 000	3 860	3 720	3 410	3 560	7 960	10 300	5 880	I_x 3 460	10 000	1 120	20 000	412
d = 900	2 000	3 660	3 480	3 200	2 380	7 150	10 000	5 250	S_x 7 680	12 000	842	22 000	365
WWF900x169	5 000	3 770	3 600	3 330	5 940	7 940	9 300	6 100	M_r 2 320	4 500	2 190	12 000	625
WWF35x113	4 000	3 620	3 470	3 190	4 750	7 600	9 190	5 720	V_r 1 340	5 000	2 080	14 000	491
b = 300	3 000	3 460	3 330	3 020	3 560	7 120	9 030	5 250	L_u 3 820	6 000	1 850	16 000	402
t = 20	2 000	3 270	3 090	2 810	2 380	6 410	8 760	4 670	I_x 2 930	8 000	1 250	18 000	339
d = 900	1 000	2 890	2 740	2 570	1 190	5 240	8 220	3 920	S_x 6 510	10 000	845	20 000	293
WWF800x184	5 000	3 660	3 480	3 230	5 940	7 080	9 310	5 400	M_r 2 330	4 500	2 260	12 000	791
WWF31x123	4 000	3 500	3 350	3 110	4 750	6 760	9 200	5 060	V_r 1 370	5 000	2 170	14 000	634
b = 300	3 000	3 340	3 220	2 960	3 560	6 320	9 040	4 640	L_u 4 060	6 000	1 970	16 000	529
t = 25	2 000	3 160	3 020	2 780	2 380	5 670	8 770	4 140	I_x 2 660	8 000	1 490	18 000	454
d = 800	1 000	2 840	2 720	2 560	1 190	4 630	8 250	3 490	S_x 6 640	10 000	1 040	20 000	398
WWF800x161	5 000	3 300	3 120	2 880	5 940	6 280	8 100	4 830	M_r 1 990	4 500	1 900	12 000	581
WWF31x108	4 000	3 150	3 000	2 770	4 750	6 010	8 010	4 530	V_r 1 370	5 000	1 810	14 000	460
b = 300	3 000	2 990	2 870	2 620	3 560	5 630	7 870	4 150	L_u 3 900	6 000	1 620	16 000	379
t = 20	2 000	2 820	2 670	2 440	2 380	5 070	7 650	3 680	I_x 2 250	8 000	1 130	18 000	322
d = 800	1 000	2 500	2 370	2 220	1 190	4 140	7 180	3 070	S_x 5 610	10 000	778	20 000	280
WWF700x175	5 000	3 170	2 990	2 750	5 940	5 470	8 040	4 160	M_r 1 970	4 500	1 930	12 000	741
WWF28x117	4 000	3 020	2 870	2 660	4 750	5 220	7 940	3 890	V_r 1 370	5 000	1 850	14 000	601
b = 300	3 000	2 850	2 740	2 530	3 560	4 880	7 800	3 570	L_u 4 160	6 000	1 700	16 000	505
t = 25	2 000	2 690	2 580	2 370	2 380	4 380	7 570	3 160	I_x 1 970	8 000	1 350	18 000	436
d = 700	1 000	2 430	2 320	2 180	1 190	3 560	7 100	2 650	S_x 5 640	10 000	965	20 000	384
WWF700x152	5 000	2 850	2 680	2 450	5 940	4 830	6 960	3 720	M_r 1 680	4 500	1 610	12 000	537
WWF28x102	4 000	2 700	2 560	2 360	4 750	4 620	6 880	3 480	V_r 1 370	5 000	1 540	14 000	429
b = 300	3 000	2 550	2 440	2 230	3 560	4 340	6 760	3 180	L_u 3 990	6 000	1 390	16 000	356
t = 20	2 000	2 390	2 280	2 080	2 380	3 900	6 570	2 810	I_x 1 660	8 000	1 020	18 000	305
d = 700	1 000	2 130	2 020	1 890	1 190	3 170	6 160	2 320	S_x 4 760	10 000	711	20 000	266

Note: Resistances are based on a concrete density of 2300 kg/m^3.

Units: M_r - kN·m, V_r - kN, L_u - mm, I_x - 10^6 mm^4, S_x - 10^3 mm^3, b - mm, t - mm, d - mm

$F_y = 350$ MPa

G40.21 350W
ASTM A992
A572 Grade 50
f'$_c$ = 25 MPa

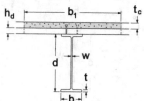

COMPOSITE BEAMS
Trial Selection Table
75 mm Deck with 90 mm Slab
$\phi = 0.90$, $\phi_c = 0.65$

Steel section	b_1	M_{rc} (kN·m) for % shear connection			Q_r (kN)	I_t 10^6	S_t 10^3	I_{ts} 10^6	Steel section data	L'	M_r'	L'	M_r'
	mm	100%	70%	40%	100%	mm^4	mm^3	mm^4		mm	kN·m	mm	kN·m
W760x185	5 000	3 500	3 320	3 020	5 940	6 380	8 730	4 800	M_r 2 080	4 000	1 980	12 000	576
W30x124	4 000	3 350	3 190	2 870	4 750	6 070	8 610	4 480	V_r 2 340	5 000	1 780	14 000	470
b = 267	3 000	3 180	3 020	2 700	3 560	5 660	8 430	4 090	L_u 3 450	6 000	1 550	16 000	397
t = 23.6	2 000	2 960	2 770	2 510	2 380	5 050	8 140	3 610	I_x 2 230	8 000	1 040	18 000	344
d = 766	1 000	2 580	2 450	2 290	1 190	4 080	7 570	3 010	S_x 5 820	10 000	743	20 000	304
W760x173	5 000	3 320	3 150	2 860	5 940	6 000	8 180	4 540	M_r 1 930	4 000	1 830	12 000	506
W30x116	4 000	3 170	3 020	2 720	4 750	5 730	8 070	4 240	V_r 2 250	5 000	1 630	14 000	411
b = 267	3 000	3 010	2 860	2 550	3 560	5 350	7 910	3 870	L_u 3 410	6 000	1 410	16 000	346
t = 21.6	2 000	2 800	2 620	2 360	2 380	4 780	7 640	3 410	I_x 2 060	8 000	924	18 000	299
d = 762	1 000	2 430	2 300	2 150	1 190	3 860	7 110	2 830	S_x 5 400	10 000	657	20 000	264
W760x161	5 000	3 110	2 940	2 670	5 940	5 560	7 520	4 230	M_r 1 760	4 000	1 650	12 000	429
W30x108	4 000	2 960	2 820	2 530	4 750	5 310	7 430	3 950	V_r 2 140	5 000	1 460	14 000	347
b = 266	3 000	2 810	2 670	2 370	3 560	4 970	7 280	3 610	L_u 3 330	6 000	1 250	16 000	291
t = 19.3	2 000	2 610	2 440	2 190	2 380	4 450	7 040	3 170	I_x 1 860	8 000	793	18 000	251
d = 758	1 000	2 250	2 120	1 970	1 190	3 600	6 550	2 610	S_x 4 900	10 000	560	20 000	220
W760x147	5 000	2 890	2 720	2 460	5 810	5 100	6 860	3 910	M_r 1 580	4 000	1 470	12 000	358
W30x99	4 000	2 750	2 610	2 350	4 750	4 880	6 780	3 660	V_r 2 040	5 000	1 290	14 000	288
b = 265	3 000	2 600	2 470	2 190	3 560	4 580	6 650	3 340	L_u 3 260	6 000	1 090	16 000	241
t = 17	2 000	2 410	2 250	2 010	2 380	4 120	6 440	2 930	I_x 1 660	8 000	671	18 000	207
d = 753	1 000	2 070	1 950	1 800	1 190	3 330	5 990	2 400	S_x 4 410	10 000	470	20 000	181
W760x134	5 000	2 640	2 480	2 240	5 280	4 680	6 250	3 640	M_r 1 440	4 000	1 330	12 000	308
W30x90	4 000	2 550	2 410	2 180	4 750	4 500	6 180	3 400	V_r 1 650	5 000	1 160	14 000	246
b = 264	3 000	2 400	2 290	2 030	3 560	4 230	6 070	3 110	L_u 3 230	6 000	967	16 000	205
t = 15.5	2 000	2 230	2 090	1 860	2 380	3 820	5 890	2 730	I_x 1 500	8 000	587	18 000	175
d = 750	1 000	1 920	1 800	1 650	1 190	3 100	5 490	2 220	S_x 4 010	10 000	408	20 000	153
W690x192	5 000	3 360	3 180	2 890	5 940	5 710	8 490	4 270	M_r 2 010	4 000	1 910	12 000	635
W27x129	4 000	3 200	3 050	2 760	4 750	5 440	8 370	3 980	V_r 2 230	5 000	1 730	14 000	526
b = 254	3 000	3 040	2 890	2 600	3 560	5 060	8 200	3 630	L_u 3 440	6 000	1 540	16 000	449
t = 27.9	2 000	2 830	2 660	2 420	2 380	4 500	7 910	3 200	I_x 1 980	8 000	1 090	18 000	393
d = 702	1 000	2 480	2 360	2 210	1 190	3 620	7 340	2 670	S_x 5 640	10 000	802	20 000	349
W690x170	5 000	3 040	2 860	2 600	5 940	5 070	7 480	3 830	M_r 1 750	4 000	1 650	12 000	497
W27x114	4 000	2 880	2 730	2 470	4 750	4 840	7 380	3 570	V_r 2 060	5 000	1 480	14 000	409
b = 256	3 000	2 720	2 590	2 320	3 560	4 510	7 240	3 260	L_u 3 380	6 000	1 290	16 000	347
t = 23.6	2 000	2 530	2 380	2 150	2 380	4 030	7 000	2 870	I_x 1 700	8 000	875	18 000	302
d = 693	1 000	2 210	2 090	1 950	1 190	3 250	6 500	2 360	S_x 4 910	10 000	635	20 000	268
W690x152	5 000	2 790	2 620	2 370	5 940	4 600	6 730	3 520	M_r 1 550	4 000	1 460	12 000	406
W27x102	4 000	2 640	2 490	2 260	4 750	4 400	6 650	3 280	V_r 1 850	5 000	1 290	14 000	332
b = 254	3 000	2 480	2 360	2 120	3 560	4 120	6 520	3 000	L_u 3 320	6 000	1 110	16 000	281
t = 21.1	2 000	2 310	2 170	1 950	2 380	3 700	6 320	2 630	I_x 1 510	8 000	728	18 000	244
d = 688	1 000	2 010	1 900	1 760	1 190	2 990	5 890	2 160	S_x 4 380	10 000	523	20 000	216

Note: Resistances are based on a concrete density of 2300 kg/m^3.

F_y = 345 MPa

Units: M_r - kN·m, V_r - kN, L_u - mm, I_x - 10^6 mm^4, S_x - 10^3 mm^3, b - mm, t - mm, d - mm

COMPOSITE BEAMS
Trial Selection Table
75 mm Deck with 90 mm Slab
$\phi = 0.90$, $\phi_c = 0.65$

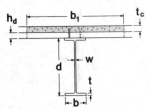

Steel section	b₁	Composite M_rc (kN·m) for % shear connection			Q_r	I_t	S_t	I_ts	Non-composite Steel section data	Unbraced condition			
		100%	70%	40%	100%	10⁶	10³	10⁶		L'	M_r'	L'	M_r'
	mm				(kN)	mm⁴	mm³	mm⁴		mm	kN·m	mm	kN·m
W690x140	5 000	2 570	2 410	2 180	5 530	4 230	6 160	3 270	M_r 1 410	4 000	1 320	10 000	447
W27x94	4 000	2 460	2 320	2 100	4 750	4 060	6 090	3 050	V_r 1 740	5 000	1 160	12 000	345
b = 254	3 000	2 310	2 190	1 970	3 560	3 810	5 980	2 790	L_u 3 270	6 000	987	14 000	280
t = 18.9	2 000	2 140	2 020	1 810	2 380	3 430	5 800	2 450	I_x 1 360	7 000	778	16 000	236
d = 684	1 000	1 860	1 750	1 610	1 190	2 780	5 410	1 990	S_x 3 980	8 000	628	18 000	204
W690x125	5 000	2 320	2 160	1 940	4 970	3 810	5 510	2 970	M_r 1 250	4 000	1 140	10 000	362
W27x84	4 000	2 250	2 120	1 920	4 750	3 660	5 450	2 780	V_r 1 610	5 000	999	12 000	277
b = 253	3 000	2 110	2 000	1 790	3 560	3 450	5 360	2 540	L_u 3 190	6 000	834	14 000	224
t = 16.3	2 000	1 950	1 840	1 630	2 380	3 120	5 200	2 230	I_x 1 190	7 000	641	16 000	188
d = 678	1 000	1 680	1 580	1 440	1 190	2 540	4 860	1 800	S_x 3 500	8 000	514	18 000	162
W610x174	5 000	2 830	2 660	2 420	5 940	4 370	7 170	3 290	M_r 1 660	4 500	1 660	10 000	924
W24x117	4 000	2 680	2 540	2 320	4 750	4 160	7 070	3 060	V_r 1 770	5 000	1 610	12 000	709
b = 325	3 000	2 520	2 410	2 190	3 560	3 880	6 940	2 790	L_u 4 480	6 000	1 490	14 000	574
t = 21.6	2 000	2 360	2 240	2 040	2 380	3 460	6 710	2 460	I_x 1 470	7 000	1 370	16 000	482
d = 616	1 000	2 090	1 980	1 860	1 190	2 790	6 250	2 030	S_x 4 780	8 000	1 230	18 000	415
W610x155	5 000	2 580	2 410	2 180	5 940	3 920	6 370	2 990	M_r 1 470	4 500	1 460	10 000	762
W24x104	4 000	2 430	2 290	2 090	4 750	3 750	6 300	2 790	V_r 1 590	5 000	1 410	12 000	579
b = 324	3 000	2 280	2 170	1 980	3 560	3 510	6 180	2 550	L_u 4 400	6 000	1 300	14 000	465
t = 19	2 000	2 120	2 020	1 830	2 380	3 150	5 990	2 240	I_x 1 290	7 000	1 180	16 000	388
d = 611	1 000	1 880	1 780	1 660	1 190	2 540	5 600	1 840	S_x 4 220	8 000	1 050	18 000	333
W610x140	5 000	2 400	2 230	2 000	5 560	3 610	5 740	2 770	M_r 1 290	4 000	1 170	10 000	422
W24x94	4 000	2 280	2 140	1 930	4 750	3 450	5 670	2 580	V_r 1 660	5 000	1 030	12 000	334
b = 230	3 000	2 130	2 010	1 810	3 560	3 240	5 570	2 350	L_u 3 070	6 000	874	14 000	277
t = 22.2	2 000	1 960	1 850	1 660	2 380	2 910	5 390	2 060	I_x 1 120	7 000	695	16 000	237
d = 617	1 000	1 710	1 610	1 480	1 190	2 340	5 020	1 670	S_x 3 630	8 000	573	18 000	207
W610x125	5 000	2 140	1 980	1 770	4 940	3 240	5 110	2 520	M_r 1 140	4 000	1 020	10 000	342
W24x84	4 000	2 080	1 950	1 750	4 750	3 110	5 050	2 350	V_r 1 490	5 000	889	12 000	269
b = 229	3 000	1 930	1 820	1 640	3 560	2 930	4 960	2 150	L_u 3 020	6 000	733	14 000	222
t = 19.6	2 000	1 770	1 680	1 500	2 380	2 640	4 820	1 880	I_x 985	7 000	575	16 000	189
d = 612	1 000	1 540	1 450	1 330	1 190	2 140	4 500	1 510	S_x 3 220	8 000	470	18 000	165
W610x113	5 000	1 950	1 800	1 600	4 470	2 940	4 620	2 320	M_r 1 020	4 000	906	10 000	282
W24x76	4 000	1 910	1 780	1 590	4 470	2 830	4 570	2 170	V_r 1 400	5 000	775	12 000	220
b = 228	3 000	1 780	1 680	1 510	3 560	2 670	4 490	1 980	L_u 2 950	6 000	617	14 000	180
t = 17.3	2 000	1 630	1 540	1 380	2 380	2 430	4 370	1 730	I_x 875	7 000	481	16 000	153
d = 608	1 000	1 420	1 330	1 210	1 190	1 980	4 090	1 390	S_x 2 880	8 000	391	18 000	133
W610x101	5 000	1 760	1 620	1 440	4 040	2 650	4 150	2 110	M_r 900	4 000	787	10 000	228
W24x68	4 000	1 730	1 600	1 430	4 040	2 560	4 100	1 980	V_r 1 300	5 000	664	12 000	176
b = 228	3 000	1 640	1 540	1 380	3 560	2 420	4 040	1 810	L_u 2 890	6 000	512	14 000	144
t = 14.9	2 000	1 490	1 410	1 250	2 380	2 210	3 920	1 580	I_x 764	7 000	396	16 000	121
d = 603	1 000	1 290	1 200	1 090	1 190	1 800	3 680	1 260	S_x 2 530	8 000	320	18 000	105

Note: Resistances are based on a concrete density of 2300 kg/m³.

F_y = 345 MPa

Units: M_r - kN·m, V_r - kN, L_u - mm, I_x - 10⁶ mm⁴, S_x - 10³ mm³, b - mm, t - mm, d - mm

G40.21 350W
ASTM A992
A572 Grade 50
f'c = 25 MPa

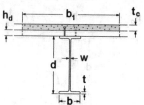

COMPOSITE BEAMS
Trial Selection Table
75 mm Deck with 90 mm Slab
φ = 0.90, φc = 0.65

Steel section	b₁	Composite			Qr	Iₜ	Sₜ	Iₜₛ	Non-composite				
		Mrc (kN·m) for % shear connection							Steel section data	Unbraced condition			
		100%	70%	40%	100%	10⁶	10³	10⁶		L'	Mr'	L'	Mr'
	mm				(kN)	mm⁴	mm³	mm⁴		mm	kN·m	mm	kN·m
W610x91	4 000	1 540	1 420	1 260	3 570	2 270	3 620	1 780	Mr 782	3 000	768	8 000	257
W24x61	3 000	1 500	1 400	1 250	3 560	2 160	3 560	1 630	Vr 1 100	4 000	672	10 000	181
b = 227	2 000	1 350	1 280	1 130	2 380	1 980	3 470	1 430	Lu 2 820	5 000	557	12 000	139
t = 12.7	1 000	1 160	1 080	968	1 190	1 630	3 260	1 140	Ix 657	6 000	416	14 000	112
d = 598	500	996	940	874	594	1 290	3 010	928	Sx 2 200	7 000	320	16 000	94.2
W610x82	4 000	1 410	1 300	1 140	3 260	2 070	3 260	1 640	Mr 686	3 000	589	8 000	147
W24x55	3 000	1 380	1 280	1 130	3 260	1 970	3 210	1 500	Vr 1 170	4 000	450	10 000	108
b = 178	2 000	1 260	1 180	1 030	2 380	1 810	3 130	1 310	Lu 2 110	5 000	306	12 000	84.8
t = 12.8	1 000	1 070	983	869	1 190	1 500	2 940	1 030	Ix 565	6 000	227	14 000	70.1
d = 599	500	897	840	774	594	1 190	2 700	833	Sx 1 880	7 000	179	16 000	59.8
W530x138	4 000	2 070	1 930	1 720	4 750	2 820	5 100	2 090	Mr 1 120	3 000	1 110	8 000	515
W21x93	3 000	1 910	1 800	1 610	3 560	2 640	5 000	1 900	Vr 1 650	4 000	1 000	10 000	390
b = 214	2 000	1 750	1 650	1 470	2 380	2 370	4 840	1 650	Lu 2 930	5 000	884	12 000	314
t = 23.6	1 000	1 510	1 420	1 300	1 190	1 890	4 480	1 320	Ix 861	6 000	759	14 000	263
d = 549	500	1 330	1 270	1 210	594	1 500	4 090	1 110	Sx 3 140	7 000	616	16 000	227
W530x123	4 000	1 900	1 760	1 570	4 750	2 550	4 570	1 920	Mr 997	3 000	984	8 000	421
W21x83	3 000	1 750	1 640	1 470	3 560	2 390	4 480	1 740	Vr 1 460	4 000	879	10 000	316
b = 212	2 000	1 590	1 500	1 330	2 380	2 160	4 340	1 520	Lu 2 860	5 000	762	12 000	253
t = 21.2	1 000	1 370	1 280	1 170	1 190	1 740	4 040	1 210	Ix 761	6 000	631	14 000	211
d = 544	500	1 200	1 150	1 080	594	1 370	3 700	1 010	Sx 2 800	7 000	505	16 000	182
W530x109	4 000	1 700	1 570	1 390	4 320	2 280	4 060	1 740	Mr 879	3 000	862	8 000	342
W21x73	3 000	1 590	1 480	1 330	3 560	2 150	3 990	1 590	Vr 1 280	4 000	764	10 000	254
b = 211	2 000	1 430	1 360	1 210	2 380	1 950	3 870	1 380	Lu 2 810	5 000	652	12 000	202
t = 18.8	1 000	1 240	1 160	1 050	1 190	1 580	3 620	1 100	Ix 667	6 000	520	14 000	168
d = 539	500	1 080	1 030	964	594	1 250	3 320	907	Sx 2 480	7 000	413	16 000	144
W530x101	4 000	1 580	1 460	1 290	4 010	2 140	3 770	1 650	Mr 814	3 000	794	8 000	301
W21x68	3 000	1 500	1 400	1 250	3 560	2 020	3 710	1 500	Vr 1 200	4 000	699	10 000	222
b = 210	2 000	1 350	1 280	1 140	2 380	1 840	3 610	1 310	Lu 2 770	5 000	591	12 000	176
t = 17.4	1 000	1 170	1 090	986	1 190	1 500	3 380	1 040	Ix 617	6 000	462	14 000	146
d = 537	500	1 010	959	899	594	1 180	3 110	853	Sx 2 300	7 000	365	16 000	125
W530x92	4 000	1 450	1 330	1 180	3 660	1 960	3 440	1 520	Mr 733	3 000	711	8 000	253
W21x62	3 000	1 400	1 300	1 160	3 560	1 860	3 390	1 390	Vr 1 110	4 000	621	9 000	214
b = 209	2 000	1 260	1 180	1 050	2 380	1 700	3 300	1 220	Lu 2 720	5 000	516	10 000	185
t = 15.6	1 000	1 080	1 010	905	1 190	1 390	3 100	962	Ix 552	6 000	393	12 000	146
d = 533	500	929	879	819	594	1 100	2 850	783	Sx 2 070	7 000	309	14 000	120
W530x82	4 000	1 300	1 180	1 040	3 260	1 740	3 050	1 380	Mr 640	3 000	616	8 000	203
W21x55	3 000	1 260	1 170	1 040	3 260	1 660	3 010	1 260	Vr 1 030	4 000	531	9 000	170
b = 209	2 000	1 140	1 070	952	2 380	1 520	2 930	1 110	Lu 2 660	5 000	433	10 000	147
t = 13.3	1 000	977	909	810	1 190	1 260	2 760	870	Ix 477	6 000	320	12 000	115
d = 528	500	833	784	724	594	998	2 540	702	Sx 1 810	7 000	249	14 000	94.0

Note: Resistances are based on a concrete density of 2300 kg/m³.

Units: Mr - kN·m, Vr - kN, Lu - mm, Ix - 10⁶ mm⁴, Sx - 10³ mm³, b - mm, t - mm, d - mm

Fy = 345 MPa

COMPOSITE BEAMS
Trial Selection Table
75 mm Deck with 90 mm Slab
$\phi = 0.90$, $\phi_c = 0.65$

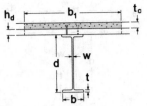

Steel section	b₁	M_rc (kN·m) for % shear connection			Q_r	I_t	S_t	I_ts	Steel section data	Non-composite Unbraced condition			
		100%	70%	40%	100%	10⁶	10³	10⁶		L'	M_r'	L'	M_r'
	mm	mm	mm	mm	kN	mm⁴	mm³	mm⁴		mm	kN·m	mm	kN·m
W530x74	4 000	1 190	1 080	938	2 960	1 590	2 750	1 260	M_r 562	3 000	474	8 000	123
W21x50	3 000	1 160	1 070	933	2 960	1 510	2 700	1 160	V_r 1 050	4 000	357	9 000	105
b = 166	2 000	1 070	996	874	2 380	1 390	2 630	1 020	L_u 2 040	5 000	247	10 000	91.7
t = 13.6	1 000	899	830	731	1 190	1 160	2 480	795	I_x 411	6 000	186	12 000	73.2
d = 529	500	754	705	646	594	916	2 280	633	S_x 1 550	7 000	148	14 000	61.0
W530x66	4 000	1 050	948	819	2 600	1 400	2 410	1 130	M_r 484	3 000	398	8 000	94.9
W21x44	3 000	1 030	938	815	2 600	1 340	2 370	1 040	V_r 927	4 000	284	9 000	80.6
b = 165	2 000	967	900	789	2 380	1 240	2 320	917	L_u 1 980	5 000	195	10 000	70.0
t = 11.4	1 000	810	747	652	1 190	1 040	2 190	718	I_x 351	6 000	145	12 000	55.5
d = 525	500	674	626	568	594	827	2 020	566	S_x 1 340	7 000	115	14 000	46.0
W460x158	4 000	2 050	1 910	1 710	4 750	2 570	5 350	1 870	M_r 1 170	4 500	1 150	9 000	795
W18x106	3 000	1 890	1 780	1 610	3 560	2 390	5 240	1 690	V_r 1 460	5 000	1 110	10 000	697
b = 284	2 000	1 730	1 640	1 490	2 380	2 130	5 050	1 470	L_u 4 190	6 000	1 040	11 000	618
t = 23.9	1 000	1 520	1 440	1 340	1 190	1 690	4 680	1 180	I_x 796	7 000	957	12 000	556
d = 476	500	1 360	1 310	1 260	594	1 330	4 270	1 010	S_x 3 350	8 000	876	14 000	463
W460x144	4 000	1 920	1 780	1 590	4 750	2 380	4 910	1 750	M_r 1 070	4 500	1 050	9 000	693
W18x97	3 000	1 760	1 650	1 500	3 560	2 220	4 820	1 590	V_r 1 320	5 000	1 010	10 000	602
b = 283	2 000	1 600	1 520	1 380	2 380	1 980	4 660	1 380	L_u 4 130	6 000	936	11 000	533
t = 22.1	1 000	1 410	1 340	1 240	1 190	1 580	4 330	1 110	I_x 726	7 000	858	12 000	478
d = 472	500	1 260	1 210	1 160	594	1 250	3 960	932	S_x 3 080	8 000	779	14 000	396
W460x128	4 000	1 760	1 620	1 440	4 750	2 140	4 390	1 600	M_r 947	4 500	918	9 000	567
W18x86	3 000	1 610	1 500	1 360	3 560	2 010	4 310	1 450	V_r 1 170	5 000	884	10 000	490
b = 282	2 000	1 450	1 380	1 250	2 380	1 800	4 170	1 260	L_u 4 040	6 000	812	11 000	432
t = 19.6	1 000	1 270	1 200	1 110	1 190	1 450	3 890	1 000	I_x 637	7 000	736	12 000	386
d = 467	500	1 130	1 080	1 030	594	1 140	3 560	838	S_x 2 730	8 000	658	14 000	318
W460x113	4 000	1 580	1 450	1 280	4 470	1 910	3 870	1 450	M_r 829	4 500	796	9 000	458
W18x76	3 000	1 460	1 360	1 220	3 560	1 800	3 800	1 320	V_r 1 020	5 000	765	10 000	394
b = 280	2 000	1 310	1 230	1 120	2 380	1 630	3 700	1 150	L_u 3 950	6 000	696	11 000	345
t = 17.3	1 000	1 140	1 080	989	1 190	1 310	3 460	910	I_x 556	7 000	623	12 000	307
d = 463	500	1 010	965	911	594	1 040	3 180	752	S_x 2 400	8 000	545	14 000	252
W460x106	3 000	1 410	1 300	1 160	3 560	1 700	3 520	1 240	M_r 742	3 000	719	8 000	308
W18x71	2 000	1 250	1 180	1 040	2 380	1 540	3 410	1 080	V_r 1 210	4 000	637	9 000	266
b = 194	1 500	1 170	1 100	978	1 780	1 410	3 320	971	L_u 2 690	5 000	549	10 000	235
t = 20.6	1 000	1 070	1 000	904	1 190	1 240	3 180	843	I_x 488	6 000	450	11 000	210
d = 469	500	926	879	823	594	968	2 900	686	S_x 2 080	7 000	366	12 000	190
W460x97	3 000	1 320	1 220	1 070	3 560	1 570	3 220	1 160	M_r 677	3 000	652	8 000	264
W18x65	2 000	1 170	1 090	972	2 380	1 430	3 130	1 010	V_r 1 090	4 000	574	9 000	227
b = 193	1 500	1 090	1 020	909	1 780	1 320	3 050	911	L_u 2 650	5 000	488	10 000	200
t = 19	1 000	995	930	837	1 190	1 160	2 930	790	I_x 445	6 000	389	11 000	178
d = 466	500	858	813	758	594	908	2 680	639	S_x 1 910	7 000	314	12 000	161

Note: Resistances are based on a concrete density of 2300 kg/m³.

Units: M_r - kN·m, V_r - kN, L_u - mm, I_x - 10^6 mm⁴, S_x - 10^3 mm³, b - mm, t - mm, d - mm

$F_y = 345$ MPa

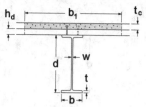

COMPOSITE BEAMS
Trial Selection Table
75 mm Deck with 90 mm Slab
$\phi = 0.90$, $\phi_c = 0.65$

G40.21 350W
ASTM A992
A572 Grade 50
$f'_c = 25$ MPa

Steel section	b_1	M_{rc} (kN·m) for % shear connection			Q_r (kN)	I_t 10^6	S_t 10^3	I_{ts} 10^6	Steel section data		Unbraced condition			
		100%	70%	40%	100%						L'	M_r'	L'	M_r'
	mm					mm⁴	mm³	mm⁴			mm	kN·m	mm	kN·m
W460x89	3 000	1 250	1 150	1 010	3 540	1 470	2 990	1 100	M_r	624	3 000	598	8 000	231
W18x60	2 000	1 100	1 030	914	2 380	1 340	2 910	955	V_r	996	4 000	523	9 000	198
b = 192	1 500	1 020	962	854	1 780	1 240	2 840	862	L_u 2 620		5 000	439	10 000	174
t = 17.7	1 000	935	874	784	1 190	1 090	2 730	746	I_x	410	6 000	343	11 000	155
d = 463	500	804	760	706	594	859	2 510	601	S_x 1 770		7 000	276	12 000	140
W460x82	3 000	1 140	1 050	919	3 230	1 350	2 740	1 020	M_r	568	3 000	540	8 000	195
W18x55	2 000	1 020	954	849	2 380	1 240	2 660	891	V_r	933	4 000	467	9 000	167
b = 191	1 500	948	892	791	1 780	1 150	2 600	805	L_u 2 560		5 000	385	10 000	146
t = 16	1 000	866	810	724	1 190	1 020	2 510	696	I_x	370	6 000	292	11 000	129
d = 460	500	743	700	648	594	802	2 310	557	S_x 1 610		7 000	234	12 000	117
W460x74	3 000	1 050	953	833	2 930	1 240	2 490	948	M_r	512	3 000	484	8 000	164
W18x50	2 000	954	886	787	2 380	1 140	2 430	830	V_r	843	4 000	414	9 000	140
b = 190	1 500	879	825	732	1 780	1 060	2 380	750	L_u 2 530		5 000	332	10 000	122
t = 14.5	1 000	800	750	667	1 190	945	2 290	648	I_x	333	6 000	249	11 000	108
d = 457	500	685	644	592	594	747	2 120	515	S_x 1 460		7 000	198	12 000	96.9
W460x67	3 000	953	864	753	2 660	1 130	2 250	873	M_r	456	3 000	427	8 000	135
W18x45	2 000	888	821	727	2 380	1 040	2 200	767	V_r	791	4 000	361	9 000	115
b = 190	1 500	814	761	674	1 780	974	2 150	693	L_u 2 480		5 000	280	10 000	99.4
t = 12.7	1 000	737	691	611	1 190	871	2 080	599	I_x	295	6 000	208	11 000	87.8
d = 454	500	628	588	537	594	691	1 920	473	S_x 1 300		7 000	164	12 000	78.6
W460x61	3 000	854	771	668	2 370	1 010	2 000	790	M_r	401	3 000	370	8 000	107
W18x41	2 000	819	753	662	2 370	935	1 960	696	V_r	747	4 000	306	9 000	90.5
b = 189	1 500	746	695	612	1 780	878	1 920	631	L_u 2 410		5 000	227	10 000	78.1
t = 10.8	1 000	670	628	551	1 190	788	1 850	545	I_x	254	6 000	168	11 000	68.7
d = 450	500	567	528	478	594	629	1 720	426	S_x 1 130		7 000	131	12 000	61.3
W460x52	3 000	749	673	578	2 060	886	1 740	705	M_r	338	3 000	269	8 000	63.7
W18x35	2 000	723	660	573	2 060	826	1 700	625	V_r	680	4 000	185	9 000	54.4
b = 152	1 500	677	626	548	1 780	778	1 660	567	L_u 1 890		5 000	128	10 000	47.4
t = 10.8	1 000	602	562	488	1 190	703	1 610	489	I_x	212	6 000	96.3	11 000	42.1
d = 450	500	503	465	416	594	565	1 500	380	S_x	943	7 000	76.8	12 000	37.9
W410x149	3 000	1 700	1 580	1 420	3 560	1 990	4 690	1 400	M_r 1 020		4 500	993	8 000	773
W16x100	2 000	1 530	1 450	1 310	2 380	1 770	4 530	1 210	V_r 1 320		5 000	963	9 000	710
b = 265	1 500	1 450	1 370	1 240	1 780	1 610	4 390	1 100	L_u 4 080		5 500	931	10 000	637
t = 25	1 000	1 340	1 260	1 170	1 190	1 400	4 180	964	I_x	625	6 000	900	11 000	569
d = 431	500	1 190	1 140	1 090	594	1 090	3 800	809	S_x 2 900		7 000	836	12 000	515
W410x132	3 000	1 540	1 430	1 280	3 560	1 790	4 170	1 280	M_r	897	4 500	865	8 000	647
W16x89	2 000	1 380	1 300	1 180	2 380	1 600	4 030	1 100	V_r 1 160		5 000	835	9 000	579
b = 263	1 500	1 300	1 230	1 110	1 780	1 460	3 920	996	L_u 3 940		5 500	804	10 000	508
t = 22.2	1 000	1 200	1 130	1 040	1 190	1 270	3 740	872	I_x	545	6 000	773	11 000	453
d = 425	500	1 060	1 020	964	594	993	3 410	724	S_x 2 560		7 000	710	12 000	409

Note: Resistances are based on a concrete density of 2300 kg/m³.

Units: M_r - kN·m, V_r - kN, L_u - mm, I_x - 10^6 mm⁴, S_x - 10^3 mm³, b - mm, t - mm, d - mm

$F_y = 345$ MPa

COMPOSITE BEAMS
Trial Selection Table
75 mm Deck with 90 mm Slab
$\phi = 0.90$, $\phi_c = 0.65$

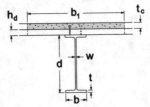

G40.21 350W
ASTM A992
A572 Grade 50
$f'_c = 25$ MPa

Steel section	b_1	Composite M_{rc} (kN·m) for % shear connection			Q_r	I_t	S_t	I_{ts}	Steel section data		Non-composite Unbraced condition			
		100%	70%	40%	100%	10^6	10^3	10^6			L'	M_r'	L'	M_r'
	mm				kN	mm⁴	mm³	mm⁴			mm	kN·m	mm	kN·m
W410x114	3 000	1 390	1 280	1 140	3 560	1 590	3 650	1 150	M_r	773	4 500	736	8 000	525
W16x77	2 000	1 240	1 160	1 050	2 380	1 430	3 540	995	V_r	998	5 000	707	9 000	451
b = 261	1 500	1 150	1 090	986	1 780	1 310	3 450	898	L_u	3 810	5 500	678	10 000	394
t = 19.3	1 000	1 070	1 010	917	1 190	1 150	3 300	782	I_x	468	6 000	648	11 000	350
d = 420	500	936	893	841	594	894	3 020	642	S_x	2 230	7 000	587	12 000	315
W410x100	3 000	1 260	1 160	1 020	3 560	1 410	3 200	1 040	M_r	671	4 500	632	8 000	423
W16x67	2 000	1 110	1 040	934	2 380	1 280	3 110	899	V_r	850	5 000	605	9 000	359
b = 260	1 500	1 030	974		1 780	1 180	3 030	811	L_u	3 730	5 500	577	10 000	312
t = 16.9	1 000	949	896	813	1 190	1 030	2 910	705	I_x	404	6 000	548	11 000	276
d = 415	500	830	789	739	594	809	2 670	572	S_x	1 950	7 000	489	12 000	247
W410x85	3 000	1 110	1 010	880	3 350	1 200	2 660	900	M_r	537	3 000	509	8 000	205
W16x57	2 000	980	909	804	2 380	1 100	2 580	782	V_r	931	4 000	444	9 000	178
b = 181	1 500	902	846	748	1 780	1 020	2 520	703	L_u	2 520	5 000	376	10 000	157
t = 18.2	1 000	820	766	684	1 190	897	2 420	605	I_x	315	6 000	297	11 000	141
d = 417	500	701	661	611	594	701	2 220	480	S_x	1 510	7 000	243	12 000	127
W410x74	3 000	991	897	776	2 970	1 080	2 360	819	M_r	469	3 000	440	8 000	163
W16x50	2 000	896	827	730	2 380	990	2 300	714	V_r	821	4 000	379	9 000	140
b = 180	1 500	820	766	678	1 780	920	2 240	643	L_u	2 470	5 000	312	10 000	124
t = 16	1 000	741	694	616	1 190	816	2 160	553	I_x	275	6 000	239	11 000	110
d = 413	500	632	593	545	594	640	1 990	436	S_x	1 330	7 000	194	12 000	99.8
W410x67	3 000	898	809	698	2 670	981	2 130	755	M_r	422	3 000	392	8 000	135
W16x45	2 000	832	765	673	2 380	905	2 080	661	V_r	739	4 000	333	9 000	116
b = 179	1 500	758	705	624	1 780	845	2 030	597	L_u	2 420	5 000	264	10 000	102
t = 14.4	1 000	680	638	565	1 190	753	1 960	513	I_x	246	6 000	201	11 000	90.5
d = 410	500	580	543	496	594	594	1 810	402	S_x	1 200	7 000	161	12 000	81.7
W410x60	3 000	797	714	614	2 350	877	1 890	686	M_r	369	3 000	341	8 000	109
W16x40	2 000	762	697	608	2 350	814	1 840	604	V_r	642	4 000	286	9 000	93.2
b = 178	1 500	691	640	566	1 780	763	1 810	547	L_u	2 390	5 000	218	10 000	81.4
t = 12.8	1 000	615	578	511	1 190	684	1 750	471	I_x	216	6 000	165	11 000	72.2
d = 407	500	524	490	444	594	545	1 620	368	S_x	1 060	7 000	131	12 000	65.0
W410x54	3 000	719	641	549	2 110	786	1 690	622	M_r	326	3 000	295	8 000	86.1
W16x36	2 000	690	627	544	2 110	732	1 650	550	V_r	619	4 000	242	9 000	73.2
b = 177	1 500	639	589	518	1 780	689	1 620	498	L_u	2 310	5 000	176	10 000	63.6
t = 10.9	1 000	565	529	464	1 190	621	1 560	429	I_x	186	6 000	132	11 000	56.3
d = 403	500	476	443	398	594	496	1 450	333	S_x	924	7 000	104	12 000	50.5
W410x46	3 000	628	557	474	1 830	690	1 460	555	M_r	275	2 000	265	7 000	61.7
W16x31	2 000	607	547	470	1 830	646	1 430	493	V_r	578	3 000	210	8 000	51.8
b = 140	1 500	582	533	464	1 780	610	1 400	448	L_u	1 790	4 000	142	9 000	44.6
t = 11.2	1 000	509	474	412	1 190	554	1 360	387	I_x	156	5 000	99.9	10 000	39.2
d = 403	500	424	391	347	594	447	1 270	298	S_x	773	6 000	76.4	11 000	35.0

Note: Resistances are based on a concrete density of 2300 kg/m³.

Units: M_r - kN·m, V_r - kN, L_u - mm, I_x - 10^6 mm⁴, S_x - 10^3 mm³, b - mm, t - mm, d - mm

$F_y = 345$ MPa

G40.21 350W
ASTM A992
A572 Grade 50
$f'_c = 25$ MPa

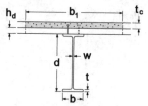

COMPOSITE BEAMS
Trial Selection Table
75 mm Deck with 90 mm Slab
$\phi = 0.90$, $\phi_c = 0.65$

Steel section	b_1	M_{rc} (kN·m) for % shear connection			Q_r	I_t	S_t	I_{ts}	Steel section data		Non-composite Unbraced condition			
		100%	70%	40%	(kN) 100%	10^6	10^3	10^6			L'	M_r'	L'	M_r'
	mm					mm^4	mm^3	mm^4			mm	kN·m	mm	kN·m
W410x39	3 000	534	472	398	1 550	588	1 240	481	M_r 227		2 000	216	7 000	44.1
W16x26	2 000	519	465	396	1 550	553	1 210	431	V_r 480		3 000	166	8 000	36.6
b = 140	1 500	504	457	393	1 550	525	1 190	393	L_u 1 730		4 000	105	9 000	31.3
t = 8.8	1 000	451	417	361	1 190	480	1 150	341	I_x 127		5 000	73.1	10 000	27.4
d = 399	500	371	341	298	594	392	1 080	262	S_x 634		6 000	55.2	11 000	24.3
W360x79	3 000	948	853	728	3 140	922	2 290	690	M_r 444		3 500	425	7 000	267
W14x53	2 000	838	769	676	2 380	842	2 230	598	V_r 682		4 000	404	8 000	225
b = 205	1 500	762	708	630	1 780	780	2 180	537	L_u 3 010		4 500	383	9 000	194
t = 16.8	1 000	683	643	575	1 190	688	2 090	460	I_x 226		5 000	361	10 000	171
d = 354	500	588	554	510	594	535	1 920	360	S_x 1 280		6 000	317	11 000	153
W360x72	3 000	860	769	653	2 830	837	2 070	635	M_r 397		3 500	377	7 000	222
W14x48	2 000	779	711	620	2 380	768	2 020	553	V_r 617		4 000	357	8 000	186
b = 204	1 500	704	651	578	1 780	714	1 970	497	L_u 2 940		4 500	336	9 000	160
t = 15.1	1 000	626	589	525	1 190	633	1 900	425	I_x 201		5 000	315	10 000	141
d = 350	500	537	505	462	594	495	1 750	331	S_x 1 150		6 000	272	11 000	126
W360x64	3 000	775	689	583	2 530	757	1 860	582	M_r 354		3 500	332	7 000	183
W14x43	2 000	724	658	568	2 380	698	1 810	509	V_r 548		4 000	313	8 000	153
b = 203	1 500	650	599	529	1 780	651	1 770	459	L_u 2 870		4 500	293	9 000	131
t = 13.5	1 000	574	538	479	1 190	581	1 710	393	I_x 178		5 000	273	10 000	115
d = 347	500	490	459	418	594	457	1 580	305	S_x 1 030		6 000	228	11 000	102
W360x57	3 000	708	627	531	2 240	708	1 680	553	M_r 314		3 000	289	7 000	119
W14x38	2 000	676	611	526	2 240	656	1 630	486	V_r 580		3 500	267	8 000	99.8
b = 172	1 500	614	563	494	1 780	615	1 600	438	L_u 2 360		4 000	244	9 000	86.0
t = 13.1	1 000	539	503	443	1 190	551	1 550	376	I_x 161		5 000	192	10 000	75.7
d = 358	500	454	423	382	594	437	1 430	289	S_x 897		6 000	147	11 000	67.6
W360x51	3 000	635	560	473	2 000	636	1 500	503	M_r 278		3 000	253	7 000	97.0
W14x34	2 000	610	548	469	2 000	592	1 460	445	V_r 524		3 500	232	8 000	81.0
b = 171	1 500	569	519	452	1 780	557	1 430	403	L_u 2 320		4 000	210	9 000	69.5
t = 11.6	1 000	495	460	405	1 190	502	1 390	346	I_x 141		5 000	159	10 000	60.9
d = 355	500	414	386	345	594	401	1 290	265	S_x 796		6 000	121	11 000	54.2
W360x45	3 000	567	498	419	1 780	568	1 330	455	M_r 242		3 000	217	7 000	76.5
W14x30	2 000	547	488	416	1 780	531	1 300	404	V_r 498		3 500	197	8 000	63.4
b = 171	1 500	527	478	412	1 780	501	1 270	367	L_u 2 260		4 000	176	9 000	54.1
t = 9.8	1 000	454	420	367	1 190	454	1 240	316	I_x 122		5 000	128	10 000	47.2
d = 352	500	375	348	309	594	366	1 150	242	S_x 691		6 000	96.1	11 000	41.9
W360x39	2 500	492	432	363	1 550	488	1 150	388	M_r 206		2 000	193	6 000	54.2
W14x26	2 000	483	428	362	1 550	470	1 130	364	V_r 470		2 500	172	7 000	44.3
b = 128	1 500	468	421	359	1 550	446	1 110	332	L_u 1 660		3 000	148	8 000	37.5
t = 10.7	1 000	415	381	330	1 190	406	1 080	286	I_x 102		4 000	97.2	9 000	32.5
d = 353	500	337	311	272	594	331	1 010	218	S_x 580		5 000	69.8	10 000	28.8

Note: Resistances are based on a concrete density of 2300 kg/m³.

Units: M_r - kN·m, V_r - kN, L_u - mm, I_x - 10^6 mm⁴, S_x - 10^3 mm³, b - mm, t - mm, d - mm

$F_y = 345$ MPa

COMPOSITE BEAMS
Trial Selection Table
75 mm Deck with 90 mm Slab
$\phi = 0.90$, $\phi_c = 0.65$

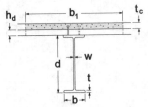

G40.21 350W
ASTM A992
A572 Grade 50
$f'_c = 25$ MPa

Steel section	b_1	M_{rc} (kN·m) for % shear connection			Q_r	I_t	S_t	I_{ts}	Steel section data		Non-composite Unbraced condition			
		100%	70%	40%	100%	10^6	10^3	10^6			L'	M_r'	L'	M_r'
	mm				(kN)	mm⁴	mm³	mm⁴			mm	kN·m	mm	kN·m
W360x33	2 500	414	362	302	1 290	413	962	335	M_r	168	2 000	155	6 000	38.1
W14x22	2 000	408	359	301	1 290	399	949	315	V_r	396	2 500	136	7 000	30.8
b = 127	1 500	397	354	299	1 290	379	931	289	L_u	1 600	3 000	113	8 000	25.9
t = 8.5	1 000	368	336	289	1 190	349	905	251	I_x	82.7	4 000	70.3	9 000	22.3
d = 349	500	294	271	234	594	288	850	192	S_x	474	5 000	49.7	10 000	19.6
W310x74	2 500	807	725	614	2 930	707	1 980	515	M_r	366	3 500	354	6 000	274
W12x50	2 000	738	670	578	2 380	671	1 940	475	V_r	597	4 000	339	7 000	240
b = 205	1 500	663	609	538	1 780	621	1 900	425	L_u	3 100	4 500	323	8 000	204
t = 16.3	1 000	585	548	488	1 190	547	1 820	361	I_x	164	5 000	307	9 000	177
d = 310	500	498	469	429	594	423	1 670	278	S_x	1 060	5 500	291	10 000	156
W310x67	2 500	730	651	548	2 620	639	1 780	472	M_r	326	3 500	312	6 000	234
W12x45	2 000	686	620	530	2 380	608	1 750	436	V_r	533	4 000	297	7 000	198
b = 204	1 500	613	561	491	1 780	565	1 710	391	L_u	3 020	4 500	282	8 000	167
t = 14.6	1 000	536	500	445	1 190	501	1 640	332	I_x	144	5 000	266	9 000	144
d = 306	500	454	426	388	594	389	1 510	254	S_x	942	5 500	250	10 000	127
W310x60	2 500	657	582	487	2 340	577	1 590	434	M_r	290	3 500	275	6 000	199
W12x40	2 000	636	572	484	2 340	551	1 570	402	V_r	466	4 000	261	7 000	163
b = 203	1 500	567	516	449	1 780	515	1 530	361	L_u	2 960	4 500	246	8 000	137
t = 13.1	1 000	492	456	406	1 190	459	1 480	308	I_x	128	5 000	231	9 000	118
d = 303	500	413	388	351	594	360	1 370	235	S_x	842	5 500	215	10 000	104
W310x52	2 500	606	535	448	2 070	551	1 440	421	M_r	261	3 000	241	6 000	130
W12x35	2 000	590	527	446	2 070	528	1 420	391	V_r	495	3 500	224	7 000	106
b = 167	1 500	543	493	425	1 780	495	1 390	353	L_u	2 370	4 000	206	8 000	89.4
t = 13.2	1 000	468	433	382	1 190	444	1 350	302	I_x	119	4 500	188	9 000	77.5
d = 318	500	389	363	326	594	352	1 250	229	S_x	750	5 000	167	10 000	68.4
W310x45	2 500	521	456	380	1 770	475	1 240	370	M_r	220	3 000	200	6 000	98.2
W12x30	2 000	509	450	378	1 770	456	1 220	345	V_r	423	3 500	184	7 000	79.3
b = 166	1 500	489	441	375	1 770	430	1 190	313	L_u	2 310	4 000	167	8 000	66.5
t = 11.2	1 000	417	383	336	1 190	389	1 160	269	I_x	99.2	4 500	150	9 000	57.3
d = 313	500	341	319	284	594	312	1 080	204	S_x	634	5 000	128	10 000	50.4
W310x39	2 500	455	396	329	1 530	417	1 080	331	M_r	189	3 000	170	6 000	77.7
W12x26	2 000	446	392	328	1 530	402	1 060	310	V_r	368	3 500	155	7 000	62.2
b = 165	1 500	431	385	325	1 530	380	1 040	282	L_u	2 260	4 000	139	8 000	51.8
t = 9.7	1 000	380	346	302	1 190	346	1 010	244	I_x	85.1	4 500	121	9 000	44.3
d = 310	500	305	285	252	594	281	948	185	S_x	549	5 000	103	10 000	38.8
W250x67	2 500	672	593	489	2 650	520	1 650	379	M_r	280	3 500	275	6 000	223
W10x45	2 000	626	559	469	2 380	494	1 620	348	V_r	469	4 000	265	6 500	212
b = 204	1 500	552	500	431	1 780	457	1 580	310	L_u	3 260	4 500	254	7 000	202
t = 15.7	1 000	475	439	389	1 190	402	1 520	261	I_x	104	5 000	244	7 500	192
d = 257	500	395	371	337	594	309	1 380	196	S_x	806	5 500	233	8 000	180

$F_y = 345$ MPa

Note: Resistances are based on a concrete density of 2300 kg/m³.

Units: M_r - kN·m, V_r - kN, L_u - mm, I_x - 10^6 mm⁴, S_x - 10^3 mm³, b - mm, t - mm, d - mm

G40.21 350W
ASTM A992
A572 Grade 50
f'_c = 25 MPa

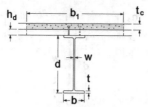

COMPOSITE BEAMS
Trial Selection Table
75 mm Deck with 90 mm Slab
$\phi = 0.90$, $\phi_c = 0.65$

Steel section	b_1	Composite M_{rc} (kN·m) for % shear connection			Q_r	I_t	S_t	I_{ts}	Non-composite Steel section data		Unbraced condition			
	mm	100%	70%	40%	100% (kN)	10^6 mm^4	10^3 mm^3	10^6 mm^4			L' mm	M_r' kN·m	L' mm	M_r' kN·m
W250x58	2 500	590	515	422	2 300	455	1 430	338	M_r	239	3 500	232	6 000	181
W10x39	2 000	570	505	419	2 300	434	1 410	311	V_r	413	4 000	222	6 500	171
b = 203	1 500	503	452	385	1 780	403	1 380	278	L_u	3 130	4 500	212	7 000	161
t = 13.5	1 000	428	393	345	1 190	358	1 320	235	I_x	87.3	5 000	202	7 500	148
d = 252	500	350	328	295	594	277	1 220	175	S_x	693	5 500	192	8 000	137
W250x45	2 500	481	416	340	1 780	390	1 140	300	M_r	187	3 000	167	5 500	101
W10x30	2 000	470	411	338	1 780	373	1 120	279	V_r	414	3 500	155	6 000	90.6
b = 148	1 500	450	401	335	1 780	351	1 100	251	L_u	2 170	4 000	142	6 500	82.2
t = 13	1 000	377	342	296	1 190	315	1 060	214	I_x	71.1	4 500	129	7 000	75.2
d = 266	500	300	279	246	594	250	984	159	S_x	534	5 000	114	7 500	69.3
W250x39	2 500	417	358	291	1 530	339	989	265	M_r	159	3 000	140	5 500	77.5
W10x26	2 000	408	354	289	1 530	326	973	248	V_r	354	3 500	128	6 000	69.2
b = 147	1 500	393	347	287	1 530	307	953	225	L_u	2 110	4 000	115	6 500	62.5
t = 11.2	1 000	342	309	264	1 190	278	922	192	I_x	60.1	4 500	102	7 000	57.0
d = 262	500	267	248	218	594	224	859	143	S_x	459	5 000	88.0	7 500	52.4
W250x33	2 500	355	303	245	1 290	290	841	231	M_r	132	3 000	112	5 500	55.6
W10x22	2 000	349	300	244	1 290	279	828	216	V_r	323	3 500	100	6 000	49.4
b = 146	1 500	338	295	242	1 290	264	810	197	L_u	2 020	4 000	88.4	6 500	44.4
t = 9.1	1 000	310	277	233	1 190	241	785	170	I_x	48.9	4 500	74.1	7 000	40.3
d = 258	500	236	218	189	594	197	734	127	S_x	379	5 000	63.6	7 500	36.9
W200x42	2 500	400	338	266	1 650	277	963	211	M_r	138	3 000	133	5 500	99.6
W8x28	2 000	390	333	265	1 650	265	946	196	V_r	302	3 500	126	6 000	92.9
b = 166	1 500	372	325	262	1 650	248	923	176	L_u	2 610	4 000	120	6 500	84.6
t = 11.8	1 000	311	277	232	1 190	223	890	149	I_x	40.9	4 500	113	7 000	77.5
d = 205	500	235	217	190	594	175	822	108	S_x	399	5 000	106	7 500	71.6
W200x36	2 500	346	291	228	1 420	241	834	187	M_r	118	3 000	112	5 500	79.3
W8x24	2 000	339	287	227	1 420	231	820	174	V_r	255	3 500	105	6 000	71.3
b = 165	1 500	326	281	225	1 420	217	801	157	L_u	2 510	4 000	99.0	6 500	64.6
t = 10.2	1 000	285	252	208	1 190	196	773	134	I_x	34.4	4 500	92.5	7 000	59.0
d = 201	500	211	193	168	594	157	718	97.7	S_x	342	5 000	85.9	7 500	54.4
W200x31	2 500	312	262	205	1 240	225	744	177	M_r	104	2 000	104	4 500	65.2
W8x21	2 000	306	259	204	1 240	216	733	166	V_r	275	2 500	96.7	5 000	57.0
b = 134	1 500	296	254	203	1 240	204	716	151	L_u	1 980	3 000	89.3	5 500	50.6
t = 10.2	1 000	273	240	197	1 190	185	691	129	I_x	31.4	3 500	81.7	6 000	45.6
d = 210	500	199	182	156	594	150	644	94.8	S_x	299	4 000	74.0	6 500	41.5
W200x27	2 500	266	222	173	1 050	193	634	154	M_r	86.6	2 000	85.3	4 500	47.5
W8x18	2 000	262	220	173	1 050	186	625	145	V_r	246	2 500	78.7	5 000	41.2
b = 133	1 500	255	216	172	1 050	176	611	133	L_u	1 890	3 000	71.5	5 500	36.4
t = 8.4	1 000	241	209	169	1 050	161	591	115	I_x	25.8	3 500	64.1	6 000	32.6
d = 207	500	179	162	138	594	132	553	85.1	S_x	249	4 000	56.0	6 500	29.6

Note: Resistances are based on a concrete density of 2300 kg/m^3.

Units: M_r - kN·m, V_r - kN, L_u - mm, I_x - 10^6 mm^4, S_x - 10^3 mm^3, b - mm, t - mm, d - mm

$F_y = 345$ MPa

COMPOSITE BEAMS
Trial Selection Table
75 mm Deck with 85 mm Slab
$\phi = 0.90$, $\phi_c = 0.65$

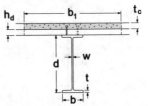

G40.21 350W
$f'_c = 25$ MPa

Steel section	b_1	M_{rc} (kN·m) for % shear connection			Q_r	I_t	S_t	I_{ts}	Steel section data	Unbraced condition			
		100%	70%	40%	(kN)	10^6	10^3	10^6		L'	M_r'	L'	M_r'
	mm					mm⁴	mm³	mm⁴		mm	kN·m	mm	kN·m
WWF1000x223	6 000	5 250	5 040	4 630	6 730	11 100	12 800	8 260	M_r 3 310	4 000	3 250	14 000	729
WWF39x150	5 000	5 100	4 910	4 460	5 610	10 700	12 600	7 830	V_r 2 210	6 000	2 620	16 000	602
b = 300	4 000	4 950	4 730	4 280	4 490	10 000	12 400	7 340	L_u 3 790	8 000	1 790	18 000	512
t = 25	3 000	4 750	4 480	4 070	3 370	9 270	12 100	6 800	I_x 4 590	10 000	1 230	20 000	446
d = 1000	2 000	4 410	4 150	3 830	2 240	8 230	11 600	6 170	S_x 9 190	12 000	920	22 000	394
WWF1000x200	6 000	4 820	4 620	4 200	6 730	10 100	11 400	7 480	M_r 2 890	4 000	2 790	14 000	549
WWF39x134	5 000	4 680	4 490	4 040	5 610	9 660	11 200	7 080	V_r 2 210	6 000	2 180	16 000	449
b = 300	4 000	4 530	4 310	3 850	4 490	9 120	11 000	6 620	L_u 3 610	8 000	1 390	18 000	379
t = 20	3 000	4 320	4 050	3 640	3 370	8 410	10 800	6 100	I_x 3 940	10 000	945	20 000	328
d = 1000	2 000	3 980	3 730	3 400	2 240	7 450	10 300	5 490	S_x 7 880	12 000	699	22 000	289
WWF900x192	6 000	4 260	4 060	3 790	6 730	8 510	10 500	6 400	M_r 2 710	4 000	2 700	14 000	670
WWF35x128	5 000	4 120	3 950	3 680	5 610	8 170	10 400	6 070	V_r 1 350	6 000	2 240	16 000	555
b = 300	4 000	3 970	3 830	3 540	4 490	7 730	10 200	5 700	L_u 3 980	8 000	1 630	18 000	473
t = 25	3 000	3 820	3 680	3 370	3 370	7 160	10 000	5 260	I_x 3 460	10 000	1 120	20 000	412
d = 900	2 000	3 620	3 440	3 170	2 240	6 380	9 680	4 760	S_x 7 680	12 000	842	22 000	365
WWF900x169	5 000	3 720	3 550	3 290	5 610	7 290	9 070	5 430	M_r 2 320	4 500	2 190	12 000	625
WWF35x113	4 000	3 580	3 440	3 150	4 490	6 920	8 940	5 090	V_r 1 340	5 000	2 080	14 000	491
b = 300	3 000	3 430	3 290	2 980	3 370	6 410	8 750	4 680	L_u 3 820	6 000	1 850	16 000	402
t = 20	2 000	3 230	3 050	2 780	2 240	5 720	8 450	4 200	I_x 2 930	8 000	1 250	18 000	339
d = 900	1 000	2 860	2 720	2 560	1 120	4 670	7 890	3 630	S_x 6 510	10 000	845	20 000	293
WWF800x184	5 000	3 600	3 430	3 190	5 610	6 470	9 080	4 800	M_r 2 330	4 500	2 260	12 000	791
WWF31x123	4 000	3 450	3 310	3 070	4 490	6 130	8 950	4 500	V_r 1 370	5 000	2 170	14 000	634
b = 300	3 000	3 300	3 180	2 930	3 370	5 680	8 760	4 150	L_u 4 060	6 000	1 970	16 000	529
t = 25	2 000	3 130	2 980	2 750	2 240	5 050	8 460	3 730	I_x 2 660	8 000	1 490	18 000	454
d = 800	1 000	2 820	2 700	2 550	1 120	4 130	7 930	3 250	S_x 6 640	10 000	1 040	20 000	398
WWF800x161	5 000	3 240	3 080	2 840	5 610	5 770	7 900	4 290	M_r 1 990	4 500	1 900	12 000	581
WWF31x108	4 000	3 100	2 960	2 730	4 490	5 470	7 790	4 010	V_r 1 370	5 000	1 810	14 000	460
b = 300	3 000	2 950	2 840	2 580	3 370	5 070	7 630	3 690	L_u 3 900	6 000	1 620	16 000	379
t = 20	2 000	2 790	2 640	2 410	2 240	4 520	7 370	3 300	I_x 2 250	8 000	1 130	18 000	322
d = 800	1 000	2 470	2 350	2 210	1 120	3 680	6 880	2 830	S_x 5 610	10 000	778	20 000	280
WWF700x175	5 000	3 110	2 940	2 720	5 610	5 000	7 830	3 690	M_r 1 970	4 500	1 930	12 000	741
WWF28x117	4 000	2 970	2 830	2 630	4 490	4 730	7 720	3 450	V_r 1 370	5 000	1 850	14 000	601
b = 300	3 000	2 820	2 710	2 500	3 370	4 380	7 550	3 170	L_u 4 160	6 000	1 700	16 000	505
t = 25	2 000	2 660	2 550	2 350	2 240	3 890	7 290	2 840	I_x 1 970	8 000	1 350	18 000	436
d = 700	1 000	2 400	2 300	2 170	1 120	3 160	6 810	2 450	S_x 5 640	10 000	965	20 000	384
WWF700x152	5 000	2 800	2 640	2 420	5 610	4 430	6 780	3 290	M_r 1 680	4 500	1 610	12 000	537
WWF28x102	4 000	2 660	2 520	2 330	4 490	4 210	6 690	3 080	V_r 1 370	5 000	1 540	14 000	429
b = 300	3 000	2 510	2 410	2 200	3 370	3 900	6 550	2 820	L_u 3 990	6 000	1 390	16 000	356
t = 20	2 000	2 360	2 250	2 050	2 240	3 470	6 330	2 510	I_x 1 660	8 000	1 020	18 000	305
d = 700	1 000	2 100	2 000	1 870	1 120	2 810	5 900	2 130	S_x 4 760	10 000	711	20 000	266

The table is divided into **Composite** (columns M_{rc}, Q_r, I_t, S_t, I_{ts}) and **Non-composite** (Steel section data, Unbraced condition) sections.

Note: Resistances are based on a concrete density of 1850 kg/m³.

Units: M_r - kN·m, V_r - kN, L_u - mm, I_x - 10^6 mm⁴, S_x - 10^3 mm³, b - mm, t - mm, d - mm

$F_y = 350$ MPa

G40.21 350W
ASTM A992
A572 Grade 50
f′_c = 25 MPa

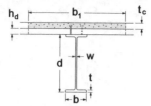

COMPOSITE BEAMS
Trial Selection Table
75 mm Deck with 85 mm Slab
$\phi = 0.90$, $\phi_c = 0.65$

Steel section	b_1	M_{rc} (kN·m) for % shear connection			Q_r	I_t	S_t	I_{ts}	Steel section data	Unbraced condition			
		100%	70%	40%	100%	10^6	10^3	10^6		L′	M_r′	L′	M_r′
	mm				(kN)	mm⁴	mm³	mm⁴		mm	kN·m	mm	kN·m
W760×185	5 000	3 450	3 270	2 970	5 610	5 810	8 470	4 240	M_r 2 080	4 000	1 980	12 000	576
W30×124	4 000	3 300	3 150	2 830	4 490	5 480	8 330	3 950	V_r 2 340	5 000	1 780	14 000	470
b = 267	3 000	3 140	2 970	2 670	3 370	5 060	8 130	3 620	L_u 3 450	6 000	1 550	16 000	397
t = 23.6	2 000	2 920	2 730	2 480	2 240	4 470	7 810	3 240	I_x 2 230	8 000	1 040	18 000	344
d = 766	1 000	2 550	2 420	2 280	1 120	3 610	7 220	2 780	S_x 5 820	10 000	743	20 000	304
W760×173	5 000	3 270	3 100	2 810	5 610	5 480	7 950	4 010	M_r 1 930	4 000	1 830	12 000	506
W30×116	4 000	3 120	2 980	2 680	4 490	5 180	7 820	3 740	V_r 2 250	5 000	1 630	14 000	411
b = 267	3 000	2 970	2 820	2 520	3 370	4 780	7 630	3 420	L_u 3 410	6 000	1 410	16 000	346
t = 21.6	2 000	2 760	2 580	2 340	2 240	4 230	7 330	3 050	I_x 2 060	8 000	924	18 000	299
d = 762	1 000	2 400	2 280	2 130	1 120	3 410	6 780	2 600	S_x 5 400	10 000	657	20 000	264
W760×161	5 000	3 060	2 890	2 630	5 610	5 090	7 310	3 740	M_r 1 760	4 000	1 650	12 000	429
W30×108	4 000	2 920	2 780	2 490	4 490	4 820	7 200	3 480	V_r 2 140	5 000	1 460	14 000	347
b = 266	3 000	2 770	2 630	2 340	3 370	4 450	7 030	3 180	L_u 3 330	6 000	1 250	16 000	291
t = 19.3	2 000	2 570	2 400	2 160	2 240	3 950	6 760	2 830	I_x 1 860	8 000	793	18 000	251
d = 758	1 000	2 220	2 100	1 960	1 120	3 170	6 240	2 390	S_x 4 900	10 000	560	20 000	220
W760×147	5 000	2 850	2 690	2 430	5 610	4 680	6 680	3 460	M_r 1 580	4 000	1 470	12 000	358
W30×99	4 000	2 710	2 570	2 310	4 490	4 440	6 570	3 220	V_r 2 040	5 000	1 290	14 000	288
b = 265	3 000	2 560	2 430	2 160	3 370	4 110	6 420	2 940	L_u 3 260	6 000	1 090	16 000	241
t = 17	2 000	2 380	2 220	1 980	2 240	3 650	6 180	2 600	I_x 1 660	8 000	671	18 000	207
d = 753	1 000	2 050	1 930	1 780	1 120	2 930	5 710	2 180	S_x 4 410	10 000	470	20 000	181
W760×134	5 000	2 610	2 460	2 230	5 280	4 320	6 090	3 220	M_r 1 440	4 000	1 330	12 000	308
W30×90	4 000	2 510	2 370	2 140	4 490	4 110	6 000	3 000	V_r 1 650	5 000	1 160	14 000	246
b = 264	3 000	2 360	2 250	2 000	3 370	3 820	5 870	2 740	L_u 3 230	6 000	967	16 000	205
t = 15.5	2 000	2 200	2 050	1 830	2 240	3 400	5 660	2 420	I_x 1 500	8 000	587	18 000	175
d = 750	1 000	1 890	1 770	1 630	1 120	2 730	5 230	2 010	S_x 4 010	10 000	408	20 000	153
W690×192	5 000	3 310	3 130	2 850	5 610	5 190	8 240	3 760	M_r 2 010	4 000	1 910	12 000	635
W27×129	4 000	3 160	3 010	2 720	4 490	4 890	8 100	3 500	V_r 2 230	5 000	1 730	14 000	526
b = 254	3 000	3 000	2 850	2 570	3 370	4 500	7 890	3 210	L_u 3 440	6 000	1 540	16 000	449
t = 27.9	2 000	2 790	2 620	2 390	2 240	3 970	7 570	2 870	I_x 1 980	8 000	1 090	18 000	393
d = 702	1 000	2 450	2 340	2 200	1 120	3 200	7 000	2 460	S_x 5 640	10 000	802	20 000	349
W690×170	5 000	2 980	2 810	2 560	5 610	4 620	7 270	3 370	M_r 1 750	4 000	1 650	12 000	497
W27×114	4 000	2 840	2 690	2 430	4 490	4 370	7 150	3 140	V_r 2 060	5 000	1 480	14 000	409
b = 256	3 000	2 680	2 550	2 290	3 370	4 030	6 980	2 870	L_u 3 380	6 000	1 290	16 000	347
t = 23.6	2 000	2 500	2 350	2 120	2 240	3 560	6 700	2 550	I_x 1 700	8 000	875	18 000	302
d = 693	1 000	2 180	2 070	1 940	1 120	2 860	6 200	2 170	S_x 4 910	10 000	635	20 000	268
W690×152	5 000	2 730	2 570	2 340	5 610	4 210	6 550	3 100	M_r 1 550	4 000	1 460	12 000	406
W27×102	4 000	2 590	2 460	2 230	4 490	3 990	6 450	2 890	V_r 1 850	5 000	1 290	14 000	332
b = 254	3 000	2 450	2 330	2 090	3 370	3 700	6 300	2 640	L_u 3 320	6 000	1 110	16 000	281
t = 21.1	2 000	2 280	2 140	1 930	2 240	3 280	6 060	2 340	I_x 1 510	8 000	728	18 000	244
d = 688	1 000	1 980	1 870	1 740	1 120	2 630	5 610	1 970	S_x 4 380	10 000	523	20 000	216

Note: Resistances are based on a concrete density of 1850 kg/m³.

Units: M_r - kN·m, V_r - kN, L_u - mm, I_x - 10^6 mm⁴, S_x - 10^3 mm³, b - mm, t - mm, d - mm

$F_y = 345$ MPa

COMPOSITE BEAMS
Trial Selection Table
75 mm Deck with 85 mm Slab
$\phi = 0.90$, $\phi_c = 0.65$

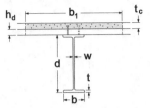

G40.21 350W
ASTM A992
A572 Grade 50
$f'_c = 25$ MPa

Steel section	b_1	M_{rc} (kN·m) for % shear connection 100%	70%	40%	Q_r (kN) 100%	I_t 10^6 mm⁴	S_t 10^3 mm³	I_{ts} 10^6 mm⁴	Steel section data	L' mm	M_r' kN·m	L' mm	M_r' kN·m
W690x140	5 000	2 540	2 390	2 170	5 530	3 890	6 000	2 890	M_r 1 410	4 000	1 320	10 000	447
W27x94	4 000	2 410	2 280	2 070	4 490	3 700	5 910	2 690	V_r 1 740	5 000	1 160	12 000	345
b = 254	3 000	2 270	2 160	1 940	3 370	3 430	5 780	2 450	L_u 3 270	6 000	987	14 000	280
t = 18.9	2 000	2 110	1 990	1 780	2 240	3 050	5 570	2 160	I_x 1 360	7 000	778	16 000	236
d = 684	1 000	1 840	1 730	1 600	1 120	2 440	5 160	1 810	S_x 3 980	8 000	628	18 000	204
W690x125	5 000	2 290	2 140	1 930	4 970	3 520	5 370	2 630	M_r 1 250	4 000	1 140	10 000	362
W27x84	4 000	2 210	2 080	1 880	4 490	3 350	5 300	2 450	V_r 1 610	5 000	999	12 000	277
b = 253	3 000	2 070	1 970	1 760	3 370	3 120	5 190	2 230	L_u 3 190	6 000	834	14 000	224
t = 16.3	2 000	1 920	1 810	1 610	2 240	2 780	5 000	1 970	I_x 1 190	7 000	641	16 000	188
d = 678	1 000	1 660	1 560	1 430	1 120	2 230	4 640	1 630	S_x 3 500	8 000	514	18 000	162
W610x174	5 000	2 780	2 610	2 390	5 610	3 970	6 960	2 890	M_r 1 660	4 500	1 660	10 000	924
W24x117	4 000	2 640	2 500	2 290	4 490	3 750	6 850	2 690	V_r 1 770	5 000	1 610	12 000	709
b = 325	3 000	2 490	2 380	2 160	3 370	3 460	6 690	2 460	L_u 4 480	6 000	1 490	14 000	574
t = 21.6	2 000	2 330	2 210	2 020	2 240	3 060	6 430	2 190	I_x 1 470	7 000	1 370	16 000	482
d = 616	1 000	2 060	1 960	1 850	1 120	2 460	5 960	1 870	S_x 4 780	8 000	1 230	18 000	415
W610x155	5 000	2 530	2 370	2 150	5 610	3 590	6 200	2 640	M_r 1 470	4 500	1 460	10 000	762
W24x104	4 000	2 390	2 260	2 060	4 490	3 400	6 110	2 460	V_r 1 590	5 000	1 410	12 000	579
b = 324	3 000	2 250	2 140	1 950	3 370	3 140	5 970	2 240	L_u 4 400	6 000	1 300	14 000	465
t = 19	2 000	2 100	1 990	1 810	2 240	2 780	5 760	1 990	I_x 1 290	7 000	1 180	16 000	388
d = 611	1 000	1 850	1 760	1 650	1 120	2 240	5 340	1 680	S_x 4 220	8 000	1 050	18 000	333
W610x140	5 000	2 370	2 210	1 990	5 560	3 310	5 580	2 440	M_r 1 290	4 000	1 170	10 000	422
W24x94	4 000	2 240	2 100	1 900	4 490	3 140	5 500	2 260	V_r 1 660	5 000	1 030	12 000	334
b = 230	3 000	2 090	1 990	1 780	3 370	2 910	5 370	2 060	L_u 3 070	6 000	874	14 000	277
t = 22.2	2 000	1 940	1 830	1 640	2 240	2 570	5 170	1 810	I_x 1 120	7 000	695	16 000	237
d = 617	1 000	1 680	1 590	1 470	1 120	2 050	4 770	1 510	S_x 3 630	8 000	573	18 000	207
W610x125	5 000	2 120	1 970	1 760	4 940	2 980	4 980	2 220	M_r 1 140	4 000	1 020	10 000	342
W24x84	4 000	2 040	1 910	1 720	4 490	2 840	4 900	2 070	V_r 1 490	5 000	889	12 000	269
b = 229	3 000	1 900	1 790	1 620	3 370	2 640	4 800	1 880	L_u 3 020	6 000	733	14 000	222
t = 19.6	2 000	1 750	1 650	1 480	2 240	2 350	4 630	1 650	I_x 985	7 000	575	16 000	189
d = 612	1 000	1 520	1 430	1 320	1 120	1 880	4 290	1 360	S_x 3 220	8 000	470	18 000	165
W610x113	5 000	1 920	1 780	1 590	4 470	2 720	4 500	2 050	M_r 1 020	4 000	906	10 000	282
W24x76	4 000	1 890	1 760	1 590	4 470	2 600	4 440	1 910	V_r 1 400	5 000	775	12 000	220
b = 228	3 000	1 750	1 650	1 490	3 370	2 420	4 350	1 740	L_u 2 950	6 000	617	14 000	180
t = 17.3	2 000	1 610	1 520	1 360	2 240	2 160	4 200	1 520	I_x 875	7 000	481	16 000	153
d = 608	1 000	1 400	1 310	1 200	1 120	1 730	3 900	1 240	S_x 2 880	8 000	391	18 000	133
W610x101	5 000	1 740	1 600	1 430	4 040	2 460	4 040	1 870	M_r 900	4 000	787	10 000	228
W24x68	4 000	1 710	1 590	1 420	4 040	2 350	3 990	1 740	V_r 1 300	5 000	664	12 000	176
b = 228	3 000	1 610	1 510	1 360	3 370	2 200	3 910	1 590	L_u 2 890	6 000	512	14 000	144
t = 14.9	2 000	1 470	1 390	1 230	2 240	1 970	3 780	1 390	I_x 764	7 000	396	16 000	121
d = 603	1 000	1 270	1 190	1 080	1 120	1 580	3 510	1 120	S_x 2 530	8 000	320	18 000	105

Note: Resistances are based on a concrete density of 1850 kg/m³.

Units: M_r - kN·m, V_r - kN, L_u - mm, I_x - 10^6 mm⁴, S_x - 10^3 mm³, b - mm, t - mm, d - mm

$F_y = 345$ MPa

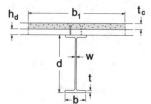

COMPOSITE BEAMS
Trial Selection Table
75 mm Deck with 85 mm Slab
ϕ = 0.90, ϕ_c = 0.65

Steel section	b$_1$	M_{rc} (kN·m) for % shear connection			Q_r	I_t	S_t	I_{ts}	Steel section data	L'	M_r'	L'	M_r'
		Composite								**Non-composite** Unbraced condition			
	mm	100%	70%	40%	(kN) 100%	10^6 mm^4	10^3 mm^3	10^6 mm^4		mm	kN·m	mm	kN·m
W610x91	4 000	1 520	1 400	1 250	3 570	2 100	3 520	1 570	M$_r$ 782	3 000	768	8 000	257
W24x61	3 000	1 460	1 370	1 230	3 370	1 970	3 450	1 430	V$_r$ 1 100	4 000	672	10 000	181
b = 227	2 000	1 330	1 250	1 110	2 240	1 770	3 340	1 250	L$_u$ 2 820	5 000	557	12 000	139
t = 12.7	1 000	1 140	1 060	956	1 120	1 430	3 110	1 000	I$_x$ 657	6 000	416	14 000	112
d = 598	500	983	930	868	561	1 130	2 850	847	S$_x$ 2 200	7 000	320	16 000	94.2
W610x82	4 000	1 400	1 290	1 130	3 260	1 920	3 170	1 450	M$_r$ 686	3 000	589	8 000	147
W24x55	3 000	1 360	1 270	1 120	3 260	1 810	3 110	1 310	V$_r$ 1 170	4 000	450	10 000	108
b = 178	2 000	1 240	1 160	1 010	2 240	1 630	3 010	1 140	L$_u$ 2 110	5 000	306	12 000	84.8
t = 12.8	1 000	1 050	966	857	1 120	1 310	2 800	908	I$_x$ 565	6 000	227	14 000	70.1
d = 599	500	884	830	767	561	1 030	2 540	754	S$_x$ 1 880	7 000	179	16 000	59.8
W530x138	4 000	2 020	1 890	1 690	4 490	2 550	4 940	1 830	M$_r$ 1 120	3 000	1 110	8 000	515
W21x93	3 000	1 880	1 770	1 580	3 370	2 360	4 820	1 650	V$_r$ 1 650	4 000	1 000	10 000	390
b = 214	2 000	1 720	1 620	1 450	2 240	2 080	4 630	1 450	L$_u$ 2 930	5 000	884	12 000	314
t = 23.6	1 000	1 490	1 400	1 290	1 120	1 650	4 250	1 190	I$_x$ 861	6 000	759	14 000	263
d = 549	500	1 320	1 260	1 200	561	1 320	3 880	1 040	S$_x$ 3 140	7 000	616	16 000	227
W530x123	4 000	1 850	1 720	1 540	4 490	2 320	4 430	1 670	M$_r$ 997	3 000	984	8 000	421
W21x83	3 000	1 710	1 610	1 440	3 370	2 150	4 330	1 520	V$_r$ 1 460	4 000	879	10 000	316
b = 212	2 000	1 560	1 470	1 310	2 240	1 910	4 160	1 320	L$_u$ 2 860	5 000	762	12 000	253
t = 21.2	1 000	1 350	1 270	1 160	1 120	1 510	3 840	1 080	I$_x$ 761	6 000	631	14 000	211
d = 544	500	1 190	1 140	1 080	561	1 210	3 500	932	S$_x$ 2 800	7 000	505	16 000	182
W530x109	4 000	1 680	1 550	1 380	4 320	2 090	3 940	1 530	M$_r$ 879	3 000	862	8 000	342
W21x73	3 000	1 560	1 460	1 310	3 370	1 940	3 850	1 380	V$_r$ 1 280	4 000	764	10 000	254
b = 211	2 000	1 410	1 330	1 190	2 240	1 730	3 720	1 210	L$_u$ 2 810	5 000	652	12 000	202
t = 18.8	1 000	1 220	1 140	1 040	1 120	1 380	3 440	977	I$_x$ 667	6 000	520	14 000	168
d = 539	500	1 070	1 020	957	561	1 100	3 140	834	S$_x$ 2 480	7 000	413	16 000	144
W530x101	4 000	1 560	1 440	1 280	4 010	1 960	3 670	1 450	M$_r$ 814	3 000	794	8 000	301
W21x68	3 000	1 470	1 370	1 230	3 370	1 830	3 590	1 310	V$_r$ 1 200	4 000	699	10 000	222
b = 210	2 000	1 330	1 260	1 120	2 240	1 640	3 470	1 140	L$_u$ 2 770	5 000	591	12 000	176
t = 17.4	1 000	1 150	1 070	975	1 120	1 310	3 220	922	I$_x$ 617	6 000	462	14 000	146
d = 537	500	999	950	893	561	1 040	2 940	782	S$_x$ 2 300	7 000	365	16 000	125
W530x92	4 000	1 440	1 320	1 170	3 660	1 800	3 350	1 340	M$_r$ 733	3 000	711	8 000	253
W21x62	3 000	1 370	1 280	1 140	3 370	1 690	3 280	1 220	V$_r$ 1 110	4 000	621	9 000	214
b = 209	2 000	1 230	1 160	1 030	2 240	1 520	3 180	1 060	L$_u$ 2 720	5 000	516	10 000	185
t = 15.6	1 000	1 060	992	894	1 120	1 210	2 950	849	I$_x$ 552	6 000	393	12 000	146
d = 533	500	918	870	813	561	960	2 700	714	S$_x$ 2 070	7 000	309	14 000	120
W530x82	4 000	1 280	1 170	1 030	3 260	1 610	2 970	1 220	M$_r$ 640	3 000	616	8 000	203
W21x55	3 000	1 250	1 160	1 030	3 260	1 520	2 920	1 110	V$_r$ 1 030	4 000	531	9 000	170
b = 209	2 000	1 120	1 050	935	2 240	1 370	2 820	961	L$_u$ 2 660	5 000	433	10 000	147
t = 13.3	1 000	961	894	799	1 120	1 100	2 630	764	I$_x$ 477	6 000	320	12 000	115
d = 528	500	822	775	719	561	868	2 400	635	S$_x$ 1 810	7 000	249	14 000	94.0

Note: Resistances are based on a concrete density of 1850 kg/m^3.

Units: M_r - kN·m, V_r - kN, L_u - mm, I_x - 10^6 mm^4, S_x - 10^3 mm^3, b - mm, t - mm, d - mm

F$_y$ = 345 MPa

COMPOSITE BEAMS
Trial Selection Table
75 mm Deck with 85 mm Slab
$\phi = 0.90$, $\phi_c = 0.65$

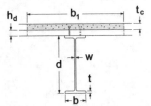

G40.21 350W
ASTM A992
A572 Grade 50
$f'_c = 25$ MPa

Steel section	b_1	Composite M_{rc} (kN·m) for % shear connection			Q_r (kN)	I_t 10^6 mm⁴	S_t 10^3 mm³	I_{ts} 10^6 mm⁴	Steel section data		Non-composite Unbraced condition			
	mm	100%	70%	40%	100%	mm⁴	mm³	mm⁴			L' mm	M_r' kN·m	L' mm	M_r' kN·m
W530x74	4 000	1 170	1 070	932	2 960	1 470	2 670	1 120	M_r	562	3 000	474	8 000	123
W21x50	3 000	1 140	1 060	927	2 960	1 390	2 620	1 020	V_r 1 050		4 000	357	9 000	105
b = 166	2 000	1 040	977	856	2 240	1 250	2 540	881	L_u 2 040		5 000	247	10 000	91.7
t = 13.6	1 000	883	815	720	1 120	1 010	2 360	694	I_x 411		6 000	186	12 000	73.2
d = 529	500	743	696	640	561	793	2 150	568	S_x 1 550		7 000	148	14 000	61.0
W530x66	4 000	1 030	939	813	2 600	1 300	2 340	1 000	M_r 484		3 000	398	8 000	94.9
W21x44	3 000	1 010	929	810	2 600	1 230	2 300	916	V_r 927		4 000	284	9 000	80.6
b = 165	2 000	945	882	772	2 240	1 120	2 230	796	L_u 1 980		5 000	195	10 000	70.0
t = 11.4	1 000	795	733	641	1 120	913	2 090	623	I_x 351		6 000	145	12 000	55.5
d = 525	500	663	617	562	561	716	1 900	504	S_x 1 340		7 000	115	14 000	46.0
W460x158	4 000	2 000	1 870	1 680	4 490	2 310	5 160	1 630	M_r 1 170		4 500	1 150	9 000	795
W18x106	3 000	1 860	1 750	1 590	3 370	2 120	5 030	1 470	V_r 1 460		5 000	1 110	10 000	697
b = 284	2 000	1 700	1 620	1 470	2 240	1 860	4 820	1 290	L_u 4 190		6 000	1 040	11 000	618
t = 23.9	1 000	1 500	1 430	1 330	1 120	1 470	4 430	1 070	I_x 796		7 000	957	12 000	556
d = 476	500	1 350	1 300	1 250	561	1 180	4 050	941	S_x 3 350		8 000	876	14 000	463
W460x144	4 000	1 870	1 740	1 560	4 490	2 140	4 750	1 520	M_r 1 070		4 500	1 050	9 000	693
W18x97	3 000	1 730	1 620	1 470	3 370	1 980	4 640	1 380	V_r 1 320		5 000	1 010	10 000	602
b = 283	2 000	1 580	1 500	1 360	2 240	1 740	4 460	1 210	L_u 4 130		6 000	936	11 000	533
t = 22.1	1 000	1 390	1 320	1 230	1 120	1 380	4 100	994	I_x 726		7 000	858	12 000	478
d = 472	500	1 250	1 200	1 150	561	1 100	3 760	868	S_x 3 080		8 000	779	14 000	396
W460x128	4 000	1 720	1 590	1 410	4 490	1 940	4 250	1 390	M_r 947		4 500	918	9 000	567
W18x86	3 000	1 580	1 470	1 340	3 370	1 800	4 150	1 260	V_r 1 170		5 000	884	10 000	490
b = 282	2 000	1 430	1 360	1 230	2 240	1 590	4 000	1 100	L_u 4 040		6 000	812	11 000	432
t = 19.6	1 000	1 260	1 190	1 100	1 120	1 260	3 690	898	I_x 637		7 000	736	12 000	386
d = 467	500	1 120	1 080	1 020	561	1 000	3 380	776	S_x 2 730		8 000	658	14 000	318
W460x113	4 000	1 560	1 440	1 270	4 470	1 740	3 750	1 270	M_r 829		4 500	796	9 000	458
W18x76	3 000	1 430	1 330	1 200	3 370	1 620	3 680	1 150	V_r 1 020		5 000	765	10 000	394
b = 280	2 000	1 280	1 220	1 100	2 240	1 440	3 550	999	L_u 3 950		6 000	696	11 000	345
t = 17.3	1 000	1 130	1 070	979	1 120	1 140	3 290	809	I_x 556		7 000	623	12 000	307
d = 463	500	999	956	905	561	908	3 020	692	S_x 2 400		8 000	545	14 000	252
W460x106	3 000	1 380	1 280	1 130	3 370	1 530	3 390	1 080	M_r 742		3 000	719	8 000	308
W18x71	2 000	1 230	1 160	1 030	2 240	1 360	3 270	932	V_r 1 210		4 000	637	9 000	266
b = 194	1 500	1 150	1 080	964	1 680	1 240	3 170	844	L_u 2 690		5 000	549	10 000	235
t = 20.6	1 000	1 060	986	894	1 120	1 070	3 010	743	I_x 488		6 000	450	11 000	210
d = 469	500	915	871	818	561	841	2 730	626	S_x 2 080		7 000	366	12 000	190
W460x97	3 000	1 280	1 190	1 050	3 370	1 420	3 110	1 010	M_r 677		3 000	652	8 000	264
W18x65	2 000	1 140	1 070	955	2 240	1 270	3 000	874	V_r 1 090		4 000	574	9 000	227
b = 193	1 500	1 070	1 010	895	1 680	1 160	2 920	791	L_u 2 650		5 000	488	10 000	200
t = 19	1 000	980	916	827	1 120	1 010	2 780	694	I_x 445		6 000	389	11 000	178
d = 466	500	848	804	753	561	788	2 530	581	S_x 1 910		7 000	314	12 000	161

Note: Resistances are based on a concrete density of 1850 kg/m³.

$F_y = 345$ MPa

Units: M_r - kN·m, V_r - kN, L_u - mm, I_x - 10^6 mm⁴, S_x - 10^3 mm³, b - mm, t - mm, d - mm

G40.21 350W
ASTM A992
A572 Grade 50
f'$_c$ = 25 MPa

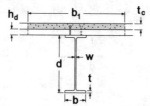

COMPOSITE BEAMS
Trial Selection Table
75 mm Deck with 85 mm Slab
ϕ = 0.90, ϕ_c = 0.65

Steel section	b$_1$	M$_{rc}$ (kN·m) for % shear connection			Q$_r$	I$_t$	S$_t$	I$_{ts}$	Steel section data		Unbraced condition			
											L'	M$_r$'	L'	M$_r$'
	mm	100%	70%	40%	100%	mm^4	10^3 mm^3	10^6 mm^4			mm	kN·m	mm	kN·m
W460x89	3 000	1 210	1 120	991	3 370	1 330	2 890	954	M$_r$	624	3 000	598	8 000	231
W18x60	2 000	1 080	1 010	898	2 240	1 190	2 800	826	V$_r$	996	4 000	523	9 000	198
b = 192	1 500	1 000	945	840	1 680	1 090	2 720	747	L$_u$	2 620	5 000	439	10 000	174
t = 17.7	1 000	920	860	774	1 120	951	2 600	654	I$_x$	410	6 000	343	11 000	155
d = 463	500	794	751	700	561	744	2 360	544	S$_x$	1 770	7 000	276	12 000	140
W460x82	3 000	1 130	1 040	912	3 230	1 230	2 650	890	M$_r$	568	3 000	540	8 000	195
W18x55	2 000	1 000	936	834	2 240	1 110	2 570	771	V$_r$	933	4 000	467	9 000	167
b = 191	1 500	930	877	778	1 680	1 020	2 500	697	L$_u$	2 560	5 000	385	10 000	146
t = 16	1 000	852	797	714	1 120	887	2 390	608	I$_x$	370	6 000	292	11 000	129
d = 460	500	733	692	642	561	694	2 180	501	S$_x$	1 610	7 000	234	12 000	117
W460x74	3 000	1 030	943	828	2 930	1 130	2 410	828	M$_r$	512	3 000	484	8 000	164
W18x50	2 000	932	867	772	2 240	1 020	2 340	719	V$_r$	843	4 000	414	9 000	140
b = 190	1 500	862	811	719	1 680	942	2 280	649	L$_u$	2 530	5 000	332	10 000	122
t = 14.5	1 000	788	737	657	1 120	826	2 190	565	I$_x$	333	6 000	249	11 000	108
d = 457	500	675	635	586	561	646	2 000	462	S$_x$	1 460	7 000	198	12 000	96.9
W460x67	3 000	939	855	748	2 660	1 030	2 190	765	M$_r$	456	3 000	427	8 000	135
W18x45	2 000	866	803	712	2 240	940	2 120	664	V$_r$	791	4 000	361	9 000	115
b = 190	1 500	797	748	662	1 680	867	2 070	599	L$_u$	2 480	5 000	280	10 000	99.4
t = 12.7	1 000	725	678	601	1 120	763	1 990	520	I$_x$	295	6 000	208	11 000	87.8
d = 454	500	618	580	531	561	597	1 820	421	S$_x$	1 300	7 000	164	12 000	78.6
W460x61	3 000	842	762	663	2 370	928	1 940	695	M$_r$	401	3 000	370	8 000	107
W18x41	2 000	797	736	649	2 240	847	1 890	604	V$_r$	747	4 000	306	9 000	90.5
b = 189	1 500	730	681	600	1 680	785	1 840	544	L$_u$	2 410	5 000	227	10 000	78.1
t = 10.8	1 000	659	616	541	1 120	692	1 770	471	I$_x$	254	6 000	168	11 000	68.7
d = 450	500	558	520	472	561	543	1 620	377	S$_x$	1 130	7 000	131	12 000	61.3
W460x52	3 000	739	666	574	2 060	820	1 680	622	M$_r$	338	3 000	269	8 000	63.7
W18x35	2 000	712	652	569	2 060	753	1 640	543	V$_r$	680	4 000	185	9 000	54.4
b = 152	1 500	660	613	536	1 680	700	1 600	489	L$_u$	1 890	5 000	128	10 000	47.4
t = 10.8	1 000	590	550	479	1 120	621	1 540	421	I$_x$	212	6 000	96.3	11 000	42.1
d = 450	500	494	458	411	561	487	1 410	333	S$_x$	943	7 000	76.8	12 000	37.9
W410x149	3 000	1 660	1 550	1 400	3 370	1 760	4 500	1 210	M$_r$	1 020	4 500	993	8 000	773
W16x100	2 000	1 510	1 430	1 290	2 240	1 540	4 310	1 060	V$_r$	1 320	5 000	963	9 000	710
b = 265	1 500	1 430	1 350	1 230	1 680	1 400	4 170	965	L$_u$	4 080	5 500	931	10 000	637
t = 25	1 000	1 320	1 250	1 160	1 120	1 210	3 950	864	I$_x$	625	6 000	900	11 000	569
d = 431	500	1 180	1 130	1 080	561	962	3 590	752	S$_x$	2 900	7 000	836	12 000	515
W410x132	3 000	1 510	1 400	1 260	3 370	1 590	4 010	1 100	M$_r$	897	4 500	865	8 000	647
W16x89	2 000	1 360	1 280	1 160	2 240	1 400	3 850	957	V$_r$	1 160	5 000	835	9 000	579
b = 263	1 500	1 280	1 210	1 100	1 680	1 270	3 730	872	L$_u$	3 940	5 500	804	10 000	508
t = 22.2	1 000	1 180	1 120	1 030	1 120	1 100	3 540	777	I$_x$	545	6 000	773	11 000	453
d = 425	500	1 050	1 010	958	561	870	3 220	668	S$_x$	2 560	7 000	710	12 000	409

Note: Resistances are based on a concrete density of 1850 kg/m^3.

F$_y$ = 345 MPa

Units: M$_r$ - kN·m, V$_r$ - kN, L$_u$ - mm, I$_x$ - 10^6 mm^4, S$_x$ - 10^3 mm^3, b - mm, t - mm, d - mm

COMPOSITE BEAMS
Trial Selection Table
75 mm Deck with 85 mm Slab
$\phi = 0.90$, $\phi_c = 0.65$

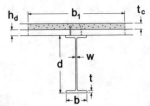

G40.21 350W
ASTM A992
A572 Grade 50
$f'_c = 25$ MPa

Steel section	b₁	Mrc (kN·m) for % shear connection 100%	70%	40%	Qr (kN) 100%	It 10⁶ mm⁴	St 10³ mm³	Its 10⁶ mm⁴	Steel section data	L' mm	Mr' kN·m	L' mm	Mr' kN·m
W410x114	3 000	1 360	1 260	1 120	3 370	1 420	3 520	994	Mr 773	4 500	736	8 000	525
W16x77	2 000	1 210	1 140	1 030	2 240	1 260	3 390	861	Vr 998	5 000	707	9 000	451
b = 261	1 500	1 140	1 080	972	1 680	1 140	3 280	782	Lu 3 810	5 500	678	10 000	394
t = 19.3	1 000	1 050	992	907	1 120	991	3 130	692	Ix 468	6 000	648	11 000	350
d = 420	500	926	885	836	561	780	2 850	588	Sx 2 230	7 000	587	12 000	315
W410x100	3 000	1 230	1 130	1 000	3 370	1 270	3 090	898	Mr 671	4 500	632	8 000	423
W16x67	2 000	1 090	1 020	918	2 240	1 130	2 980	778	Vr 850	5 000	605	9 000	359
b = 260	1 500	1 010	959	865	1 680	1 030	2 900	705	Lu 3 730	5 500	577	10 000	312
t = 16.9	1 000	935	883	803	1 120	895	2 770	620	Ix 404	6 000	548	11 000	276
d = 415	500	821	781	733	561	703	2 530	521	Sx 1 950	7 000	489	12 000	247
W410x85	3 000	1 090	1 000	873	3 350	1 090	2 570	780	Mr 537	3 000	509	8 000	205
W16x57	2 000	957	890	789	2 240	979	2 480	673	Vr 931	4 000	444	9 000	178
b = 181	1 500	885	830	736	1 680	894	2 410	605	Lu 2 520	5 000	376	10 000	157
t = 18.2	1 000	807	753	675	1 120	777	2 300	526	Ix 315	6 000	297	11 000	141
d = 417	500	692	653	606	561	603	2 080	431	Sx 1 510	7 000	243	12 000	127
W410x74	3 000	976	887	770	2 970	982	2 280	712	Mr 469	3 000	440	8 000	163
W16x50	2 000	874	808	715	2 240	886	2 210	615	Vr 821	4 000	379	9 000	140
b = 180	1 500	803	752	665	1 680	813	2 150	553	Lu 2 470	5 000	312	10 000	124
t = 16	1 000	729	681	607	1 120	709	2 050	479	Ix 275	6 000	239	11 000	110
d = 413	500	623	586	540	561	551	1 870	388	Sx 1 330	7 000	194	12 000	99.8
W410x67	3 000	885	799	692	2 670	898	2 060	659	Mr 422	3 000	392	8 000	135
W16x45	2 000	810	747	659	2 240	814	2 000	571	Vr 739	4 000	333	9 000	116
b = 179	1 500	741	691	612	1 680	750	1 950	513	Lu 2 420	5 000	264	10 000	102
t = 14.4	1 000	668	627	556	1 120	657	1 870	444	Ix 246	6 000	201	11 000	90.5
d = 410	500	571	535	490	561	511	1 710	357	Sx 1 200	7 000	161	12 000	81.7
W410x60	3 000	786	706	609	2 350	807	1 830	602	Mr 369	3 000	341	8 000	109
W16x40	2 000	743	681	598	2 240	736	1 780	523	Vr 642	4 000	286	9 000	93.2
b = 178	1 500	675	626	555	1 680	681	1 740	471	Lu 2 390	5 000	218	10 000	81.4
t = 12.8	1 000	604	568	503	1 120	600	1 670	406	Ix 216	6 000	165	11 000	72.2
d = 407	500	516	483	440	561	469	1 530	324	Sx 1 060	7 000	131	12 000	65.0
W410x54	3 000	708	633	545	2 110	725	1 630	548	Mr 326	3 000	295	8 000	86.1
W16x36	2 000	680	620	540	2 110	665	1 590	476	Vr 619	4 000	242	9 000	73.2
b = 177	1 500	623	576	507	1 680	617	1 550	429	Lu 2 310	5 000	176	10 000	63.6
t = 10.9	1 000	553	519	455	1 120	546	1 490	369	Ix 186	6 000	132	11 000	56.3
d = 403	500	468	436	393	561	427	1 370	291	Sx 924	7 000	104	12 000	50.5
W410x46	3 000	619	551	470	1 830	640	1 420	491	Mr 275	2 000	265	7 000	61.7
W16x31	2 000	598	541	467	1 830	590	1 380	429	Vr 578	3 000	210	8 000	51.8
b = 140	1 500	566	520	454	1 680	550	1 350	386	Lu 1 790	4 000	142	9 000	44.6
t = 11.2	1 000	498	464	404	1 120	489	1 300	332	Ix 156	5 000	99.9	10 000	39.2
d = 403	500	416	384	342	561	385	1 190	259	Sx 773	6 000	76.4	11 000	35.0

Note: Resistances are based on a concrete density of 1850 kg/m³.

Units: M_r - kN·m, V_r - kN, L_u - mm, I_x - 10^6 mm⁴, S_x - 10^3 mm³, b - mm, t - mm, d - mm

$F_y = 345$ MPa

COMPOSITE BEAMS
Trial Selection Table
75 mm Deck with 85 mm Slab
$\phi = 0.90$, $\phi_c = 0.65$

G40.21 350W
ASTM A992
A572 Grade 50
$f'_c = 25$ MPa

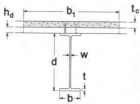

Steel section	b_1	Composite							Non-composite				
		M_{rc} (kN·m) for % shear connection			Q_r	I_t	S_t	I_{ts}	Steel section data	Unbraced condition			
					(kN)	10^6	10^3	10^6		L'	M_r'	L'	M_r'
	mm	100%	70%	40%	100%	mm⁴	mm³	mm⁴		mm	kN·m	mm	kN·m
W410x39	3 000	527	467	395	1 550	547	1 200	428	M_r 227	2 000	216	7 000	44.1
W16x26	2 000	512	459	393	1 550	508	1 170	377	V_r 480	3 000	166	8 000	36.6
b = 140	1 500	496	452	390	1 550	476	1 140	340	L_u 1 730	4 000	105	9 000	31.3
t = 8.8	1 000	440	408	353	1 120	427	1 110	292	I_x 127	5 000	73.1	10 000	27.4
d = 399	500	363	334	293	561	339	1 020	225	S_x 634	6 000	55.2	11 000	24.3
W360x79	3 000	933	842	722	3 140	835	2 210	596	M_r 444	3 500	425	7 000	267
W14x53	2 000	816	750	663	2 240	749	2 140	512	V_r 682	4 000	404	8 000	225
b = 205	1 500	745	694	619	1 680	684	2 080	459	L_u 3 010	4 500	383	9 000	194
t = 16.8	1 000	671	632	566	1 120	594	1 980	396	I_x 226	5 000	361	10 000	171
d = 354	500	579	547	505	561	458	1 800	320	S_x 1 280	6 000	317	11 000	153
W360x72	3 000	846	759	648	2 830	761	2 000	550	M_r 397	3 500	377	7 000	222
W14x48	2 000	757	693	608	2 240	686	1 940	474	V_r 617	4 000	357	8 000	186
b = 204	1 500	687	637	567	1 680	629	1 890	425	L_u 2 940	4 500	336	9 000	160
t = 15.1	1 000	615	579	517	1 120	549	1 800	366	I_x 201	5 000	315	10 000	141
d = 350	500	529	498	457	561	423	1 640	293	S_x 1 150	6 000	272	11 000	126
W360x64	3 000	762	680	578	2 530	691	1 800	507	M_r 354	3 500	332	7 000	183
W14x43	2 000	702	640	556	2 240	626	1 740	438	V_r 548	4 000	313	8 000	153
b = 203	1 500	633	585	519	1 680	577	1 700	392	L_u 2 870	4 500	293	9 000	131
t = 13.5	1 000	563	529	471	1 120	505	1 630	337	I_x 178	5 000	273	10 000	115
d = 347	500	482	453	413	561	391	1 490	268	S_x 1 030	6 000	228	11 000	102
W360x57	3 000	697	619	526	2 240	649	1 620	483	M_r 314	3 000	289	7 000	119
W14x38	2 000	665	604	521	2 240	592	1 570	418	V_r 580	3 500	267	8 000	99.8
b = 172	1 500	598	549	483	1 680	547	1 540	375	L_u 2 360	4 000	244	9 000	86.0
t = 13.1	1 000	527	493	435	1 120	482	1 470	322	I_x 161	5 000	192	10 000	75.7
d = 358	500	446	417	377	561	374	1 350	253	S_x 897	6 000	147	11 000	67.6
W360x51	3 000	625	553	469	2 000	586	1 450	442	M_r 278	3 000	253	7 000	97.0
W14x34	2 000	600	541	465	2 000	537	1 410	384	V_r 524	3 500	232	8 000	81.0
b = 171	1 500	553	506	442	1 680	498	1 380	345	L_u 2 320	4 000	210	9 000	69.5
t = 11.6	1 000	484	451	397	1 120	441	1 320	295	I_x 141	5 000	159	10 000	60.9
d = 355	500	407	379	341	561	344	1 220	230	S_x 796	6 000	121	11 000	54.2
W360x45	3 000	558	491	415	1 780	525	1 290	402	M_r 242	3 000	217	7 000	76.5
W14x30	2 000	538	482	412	1 780	483	1 250	351	V_r 498	3 500	197	8 000	63.4
b = 171	1 500	511	465	403	1 680	451	1 230	315	L_u 2 260	4 000	176	9 000	54.1
t = 9.8	1 000	443	411	360	1 120	401	1 180	270	I_x 122	5 000	128	10 000	47.2
d = 352	500	369	342	304	561	314	1 090	209	S_x 691	6 000	96.1	11 000	41.9
W360x39	2 500	484	427	360	1 550	450	1 110	342	M_r 206	2 000	193	6 000	54.2
W14x26	2 000	475	423	359	1 550	430	1 090	317	V_r 470	2 500	172	7 000	44.3
b = 128	1 500	460	415	356	1 550	403	1 070	285	L_u 1 660	3 000	148	8 000	37.5
t = 10.7	1 000	404	372	322	1 120	360	1 030	244	I_x 102	4 000	97.2	9 000	32.5
d = 353	500	331	305	268	561	284	949	187	S_x 580	5 000	69.8	10 000	28.8

Note: Resistances are based on a concrete density of 1850 kg/m³.

Units: M_r - kN·m, V_r - kN, L_u - mm, I_x - 10^6 mm⁴, S_x - 10^3 mm³, b - mm, t - mm, d - mm

$F_y = 345$ MPa

COMPOSITE BEAMS
Trial Selection Table
75 mm Deck with 85 mm Slab
$\phi = 0.90$, $\phi_c = 0.65$

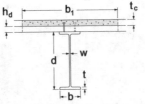

G40.21 350W
ASTM A992
A572 Grade 50
$f'_c = 25$ MPa

Steel section	b_1	Composite							Non-composite				
		M_{rc} (kN·m) for % shear connection			Q_r	I_t	S_t	I_{ts}	Steel section data	Unbraced condition			
					(kN)	10^6	10^3	10^6		L'	M_r'	L'	M_r'
	mm	100%	70%	40%	100%	mm⁴	mm³	mm⁴		mm	kN·m	mm	kN·m
W360x33	2 500	408	358	299	1 290	382	928	297	M_r 168	2 000	155	6 000	38.1
W14x22	2 000	401	354	298	1 290	367	915	276	V_r 396	2 500	136	7 000	30.8
b = 127	1 500	391	349	297	1 290	345	897	250	L_u 1 600	3 000	113	8 000	25.9
t = 8.5	1 000	358	327	282	1 120	312	868	215	I_x 82.7	4 000	70.3	9 000	22.3
d = 349	500	288	265	230	561	249	805	163	S_x 474	5 000	49.7	10 000	19.6
W310x74	2 500	783	706	602	2 810	634	1 900	441	M_r 366	3 500	354	6 000	274
W12x50	2 000	716	651	566	2 240	595	1 860	404	V_r 597	4 000	339	7 000	240
b = 205	1 500	646	595	528	1 680	544	1 810	361	L_u 3 100	4 500	323	8 000	204
t = 16.3	1 000	573	538	481	1 120	471	1 730	308	I_x 164	5 000	307	9 000	177
d = 310	500	491	462	425	561	359	1 560	244	S_x 1 060	5 500	291	10 000	156
W310x67	2 500	717	642	543	2 620	575	1 710	405	M_r 326	3 500	312	6 000	234
W12x45	2 000	665	602	518	2 240	542	1 680	372	V_r 533	4 000	297	7 000	198
b = 204	1 500	596	547	482	1 680	497	1 630	332	L_u 3 020	4 500	282	8 000	167
t = 14.6	1 000	524	490	437	1 120	432	1 560	283	I_x 144	5 000	266	9 000	144
d = 306	500	446	420	383	561	330	1 410	222	S_x 942	5 500	250	10 000	127
W310x60	2 500	646	574	483	2 340	523	1 530	374	M_r 290	3 500	275	6 000	199
W12x40	2 000	618	557	474	2 240	494	1 510	344	V_r 466	4 000	261	7 000	163
b = 203	1 500	550	502	439	1 680	455	1 470	307	L_u 2 960	4 500	246	8 000	137
t = 13.1	1 000	480	447	398	1 120	398	1 410	262	I_x 128	5 000	231	9 000	118
d = 303	500	406	381	347	561	306	1 280	204	S_x 842	5 500	215	10 000	104
W310x52	2 500	596	528	444	2 070	502	1 390	365	M_r 261	3 000	241	6 000	130
W12x35	2 000	579	520	441	2 070	476	1 370	336	V_r 495	3 500	224	7 000	106
b = 167	1 500	526	479	416	1 680	440	1 340	301	L_u 2 370	4 000	206	8 000	89.4
t = 13.2	1 000	457	424	374	1 120	388	1 280	256	I_x 119	4 500	188	9 000	77.5
d = 318	500	382	357	322	561	299	1 170	198	S_x 750	5 000	167	10 000	68.4
W310x45	2 500	512	450	377	1 770	434	1 190	323	M_r 220	3 000	200	6 000	98.2
W12x30	2 000	500	444	375	1 770	414	1 170	298	V_r 423	3 500	184	7 000	79.3
b = 166	1 500	474	428	367	1 680	385	1 150	268	L_u 2 310	4 000	167	8 000	66.5
t = 11.2	1 000	406	374	329	1 120	342	1 100	228	I_x 99.2	4 500	150	9 000	57.3
d = 313	500	335	313	279	561	267	1 020	175	S_x 634	5 000	128	10 000	50.4
W310x39	2 500	448	391	326	1 530	384	1 040	290	M_r 189	3 000	170	6 000	77.7
W12x26	2 000	439	387	325	1 530	367	1 020	269	V_r 368	3 500	155	7 000	62.2
b = 165	1 500	424	379	322	1 530	343	1 000	242	L_u 2 260	4 000	139	8 000	51.8
t = 9.7	1 000	369	337	295	1 120	307	969	207	I_x 85.1	4 500	121	9 000	44.3
d = 310	500	299	280	248	561	242	896	158	S_x 549	5 000	103	10 000	38.8
W250x67	2 500	659	584	484	2 650	465	1 580	322	M_r 280	3 500	275	6 000	223
W10x45	2 000	604	541	457	2 240	437	1 550	294	V_r 469	4 000	265	6 500	212
b = 204	1 500	535	486	422	1 680	399	1 500	260	L_u 3 260	4 500	254	7 000	202
t = 15.7	1 000	464	430	382	1 120	344	1 430	219	I_x 104	5 000	244	7 500	192
d = 257	500	389	366	333	561	259	1 290	169	S_x 806	5 500	233	8 000	180

Note: Resistances are based on a concrete density of 1850 kg/m³.

Units: M_r - kN·m, V_r - kN, L_u - mm, I_x - 10^6 mm⁴, S_x - 10^3 mm³, b - mm, t - mm, d - mm

$F_y = 345$ MPa

COMPOSITE BEAMS
Trial Selection Table
75 mm Deck with 85 mm Slab
$\phi = 0.90$, $\phi_c = 0.65$

G40.21 350W
ASTM A992
A572 Grade 50
$f'_c = 25$ MPa

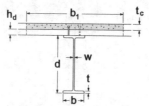

Steel section	b_1	M_{rc} (kN·m) for % shear connection			Q_r	I_t	S_t	I_{ts}	Steel section data		Unbraced condition			
		100%	70%	40%	100%	10^6	10^3	10^6			L'	M_r'	L'	M_r'
	mm				(kN)	mm⁴	mm³	mm⁴			mm	kN·m	mm	kN·m
W250x58	2 500	579	507	417	2 300	409	1 370	288	M_r	239	3 500	232	6 000	181
W10x39	2 000	554	493	411	2 240	386	1 350	264	V_r	413	4 000	222	6 500	171
b = 203	1 500	487	439	376	1 680	354	1 310	234	L_u 3 130		4 500	212	7 000	161
t = 13.5	1 000	417	383	339	1 120	308	1 250	197	I_x	87.3	5 000	202	7 500	148
d = 252	500	344	323	291	561	233	1 130	150	S_x	693	5 500	192	8 000	137
W250x45	2 500	473	410	336	1 780	354	1 100	259	M_r	187	3 000	167	5 500	101
W10x30	2 000	461	404	334	1 780	336	1 080	238	V_r	414	3 500	155	6 000	90.6
b = 148	1 500	434	388	326	1 680	312	1 050	212	L_u 2 170		4 000	142	6 500	82.2
t = 13	1 000	366	333	289	1 120	275	1 010	179	I_x	71.1	4 500	129	7 000	75.2
d = 266	500	294	273	242	561	212	922	134	S_x	534	5 000	114	7 500	69.3
W250x39	2 500	409	353	288	1 530	309	949	231	M_r	159	3 000	140	5 500	77.5
W10x26	2 000	400	348	286	1 530	295	933	214	V_r	354	3 500	128	6 000	69.2
b = 147	1 500	386	341	284	1 530	275	912	191	L_u 2 110		4 000	115	6 500	62.5
t = 11.2	1 000	331	299	258	1 120	245	879	162	I_x	60.1	4 500	102	7 000	57.0
d = 262	500	261	243	214	561	190	807	121	S_x	459	5 000	88.0	7 500	52.4
W250x33	2 500	349	299	243	1 290	265	806	202	M_r	132	3 000	112	5 500	55.6
W10x22	2 000	342	296	241	1 290	254	793	188	V_r	323	3 500	100	6 000	49.4
b = 146	1 500	332	290	240	1 290	238	776	169	L_u 2 020		4 000	88.4	6 500	44.4
t = 9.1	1 000	299	268	227	1 120	213	749	143	I_x	48.9	4 500	74.1	7 000	40.3
d = 258	500	230	213	185	561	168	692	107	S_x	379	5 000	63.6	7 500	36.9
W200x42	2 500	392	332	263	1 650	250	918	181	M_r	138	3 000	133	5 500	99.6
W8x28	2 000	381	327	262	1 650	237	901	166	V_r	302	3 500	126	6 000	92.9
b = 166	1 500	364	319	259	1 650	219	879	147	L_u 2 610		4 000	120	6 500	84.6
t = 11.8	1 000	300	268	226	1 120	193	843	123	I_x	40.9	4 500	113	7 000	77.5
d = 205	500	229	212	187	561	147	767	89.2	S_x	399	5 000	106	7 500	71.6
W200x36	2 500	339	286	225	1 420	218	796	162	M_r	118	3 000	112	5 500	79.3
W8x24	2 000	332	282	224	1 420	208	782	149	V_r	255	3 500	105	6 000	71.3
b = 165	1 500	319	276	222	1 420	193	763	133	L_u 2 510		4 000	99.0	6 500	64.6
t = 10.2	1 000	274	243	202	1 120	171	733	111	I_x	34.4	4 500	92.5	7 000	59.0
d = 201	500	205	189	165	561	132	673	80.5	S_x	342	5 000	85.9	7 500	54.4
W200x31	2 500	306	257	203	1 240	204	711	154	M_r	104	2 000	104	4 500	65.2
W8x21	2 000	300	254	202	1 240	195	699	143	V_r	275	2 500	96.7	5 000	57.0
b = 134	1 500	290	250	200	1 240	182	682	128	L_u 1 980		3 000	89.3	5 500	50.6
t = 10.2	1 000	262	231	191	1 120	163	657	107	I_x	31.4	3 500	81.7	6 000	45.6
d = 210	500	194	177	153	561	127	605	78.0	S_x	299	4 000	74.0	6 500	41.5
W200x27	2 500	261	218	171	1 050	176	607	135	M_r	86.6	2 000	85.3	4 500	47.5
W8x18	2 000	256	216	171	1 050	168	596	126	V_r	246	2 500	78.7	5 000	41.2
b = 133	1 500	249	213	169	1 050	158	583	114	L_u 1 890		3 000	71.5	5 500	36.4
t = 8.4	1 000	235	206	167	1 050	143	562	96.1	I_x	25.8	3 500	64.1	6 000	32.6
d = 207	500	173	157	134	561	113	521	70.0	S_x	249	4 000	56.0	6 500	29.6

Note: Resistances are based on a concrete density of 1850 kg/m³.

$F_y = 345$ MPa

Units: M_r - kN·m, V_r - kN, L_u - mm, I_x - 10^6 mm⁴, S_x - 10^3 mm³, b - mm, t - mm, d - mm

COMPOSITE BEAMS
Trial Selection Table
75 mm Deck with 85 mm Slab
$\phi = 0.90$, $\phi_c = 0.65$

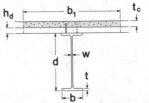

G40.21 350W
$f'_c = 25$ MPa

Steel section	b_1	Composite M_{rc} (kN·m) for % shear connection			Q_r	I_t	S_t	I_{ts}	Steel section data	Non-composite Unbraced condition			
		100%	70%	40%	100%	10^6	10^3	10^6		L'	M_r'	L'	M_r'
	mm				(kN)	mm⁴	mm³	mm⁴		mm	kN·m	mm	kN·m
WWF1000x223	6 000	5 250	5 040	4 630	6 730	11 400	12 900	8 550	M_r 3 310	4 000	3 250	14 000	729
WWF39x150	5 000	5 100	4 910	4 460	5 610	11 000	12 700	8 100	V_r 2 210	6 000	2 620	16 000	602
b = 300	4 000	4 950	4 730	4 280	4 490	10 400	12 500	7 590	L_u 3 790	8 000	1 790	18 000	512
t = 25	3 000	4 750	4 480	4 070	3 370	9 590	12 200	7 010	I_x 4 590	10 000	1 230	20 000	446
d = 1000	2 000	4 410	4 150	3 830	2 240	8 520	11 800	6 330	S_x 9 190	12 000	920	22 000	394
WWF1000x200	6 000	4 820	4 620	4 200	6 730	10 400	11 500	7 750	M_r 2 890	4 000	2 790	14 000	549
WWF39x134	5 000	4 680	4 490	4 040	5 610	9 930	11 300	7 330	V_r 2 210	6 000	2 180	16 000	449
b = 300	4 000	4 530	4 310	3 850	4 490	9 400	11 100	6 850	L_u 3 610	8 000	1 390	18 000	379
t = 20	3 000	4 320	4 050	3 640	3 370	8 700	10 900	6 300	I_x 3 940	10 000	945	20 000	328
d = 1000	2 000	3 980	3 730	3 400	2 240	7 720	10 500	5 650	S_x 7 880	12 000	699	22 000	289
WWF900x192	6 000	4 260	4 060	3 790	6 730	8 730	10 600	6 620	M_r 2 710	4 000	2 700	14 000	670
WWF35x128	5 000	4 120	3 950	3 680	5 610	8 390	10 500	6 280	V_r 1 350	6 000	2 240	16 000	555
b = 300	4 000	3 970	3 830	3 540	4 490	7 960	10 300	5 890	L_u 3 980	8 000	1 630	18 000	473
t = 25	3 000	3 820	3 680	3 370	3 370	7 390	10 100	5 430	I_x 3 460	10 000	1 120	20 000	412
d = 900	2 000	3 620	3 440	3 170	2 240	6 600	9 780	4 890	S_x 7 680	12 000	842	22 000	365
WWF900x169	5 000	3 720	3 550	3 290	5 610	7 480	9 130	5 620	M_r 2 320	4 500	2 190	12 000	625
WWF35x113	4 000	3 580	3 440	3 150	4 490	7 120	9 010	5 260	V_r 1 340	5 000	2 080	14 000	491
b = 300	3 000	3 430	3 290	2 980	3 370	6 620	8 830	4 840	L_u 3 820	6 000	1 850	16 000	402
t = 20	2 000	3 230	3 050	2 780	2 240	5 910	8 540	4 330	I_x 2 930	8 000	1 250	18 000	339
d = 900	1 000	2 860	2 720	2 560	1 120	4 830	7 990	3 710	S_x 6 510	10 000	845	20 000	293
WWF800x184	5 000	3 600	3 430	3 190	5 610	6 650	9 140	4 970	M_r 2 330	4 500	2 260	12 000	791
WWF31x123	4 000	3 450	3 310	3 070	4 490	6 310	9 020	4 650	V_r 1 370	5 000	2 170	14 000	634
b = 300	3 000	3 300	3 180	2 930	3 370	5 860	8 840	4 280	L_u 4 060	6 000	1 970	16 000	529
t = 25	2 000	3 130	2 980	2 750	2 240	5 230	8 550	3 840	I_x 2 660	8 000	1 490	18 000	454
d = 800	1 000	2 820	2 700	2 550	1 120	4 270	8 020	3 310	S_x 6 640	10 000		20 000	398
WWF800x161	5 000	3 240	3 080	2 840	5 610	5 910	7 960	4 440	M_r 1 990	4 500	1 900	12 000	581
WWF31x108	4 000	3 100	2 960	2 730	4 490	5 630	7 850	4 160	V_r 1 370	5 000	1 810	14 000	460
b = 300	3 000	2 950	2 840	2 580	3 370	5 240	7 700	3 820	L_u 3 900	6 000	1 620	16 000	379
t = 20	2 000	2 790	2 640	2 410	2 240	4 680	7 450	3 400	I_x 2 250	8 000	1 130	18 000	322
d = 800	1 000	2 470	2 350	2 210	1 120	3 800	6 970	2 890	S_x 5 610	10 000	778	20 000	280
WWF700x175	5 000	3 110	2 940	2 720	5 610	5 130	7 880	3 820	M_r 1 970	4 500	1 930	12 000	741
WWF28x117	4 000	2 970	2 830	2 630	4 490	4 870	7 780	3 570	V_r 1 370	5 000	1 850	14 000	601
b = 300	3 000	2 820	2 710	2 500	3 370	4 520	7 620	3 280	L_u 4 160	6 000	1 700	16 000	505
t = 25	2 000	2 660	2 550	2 350	2 240	4 030	7 370	2 930	I_x 1 970	8 000	1 350	18 000	436
d = 700	1 000	2 400	2 300	2 170	1 120	3 270	6 890	2 500	S_x 5 640	10 000	965	20 000	384
WWF700x152	5 000	2 800	2 640	2 420	5 610	4 550	6 830	3 410	M_r 1 680	4 500	1 610	12 000	537
WWF28x102	4 000	2 660	2 520	2 330	4 490	4 330	6 740	3 190	V_r 1 370	5 000	1 540	14 000	429
b = 300	3 000	2 510	2 410	2 200	3 370	4 030	6 610	2 920	L_u 3 990	6 000	1 390	16 000	356
t = 20	2 000	2 360	2 250	2 050	2 240	3 590	6 390	2 590	I_x 1 660	8 000	1 020	18 000	305
d = 700	1 000	2 100	2 000	1 870	1 120	2 910	5 970	2 180	S_x 4 760	10 000	711	20 000	266

$F_y = 350$ MPa

Note: Resistances are based on a concrete density of 2000 kg/m³.

Units: M_r - kN·m, V_r - kN, L_u - mm, I_x - 10^6 mm⁴, S_x - 10^3 mm³, b - mm, t - mm, d - mm

G40.21 350W
ASTM A992
A572 Grade 50
f'$_c$ = 25 MPa

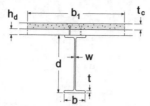

COMPOSITE BEAMS
Trial Selection Table
75 mm Deck with 85 mm Slab
$\phi = 0.90$, $\phi_c = 0.65$

Steel section	b$_1$	M$_{rc}$ (kN·m) for % shear connection			Q$_r$ (kN)	I$_t$ 10^6	S$_t$ 10^3	I$_{ts}$ 10^6	Steel section data	Unbraced condition			
	mm	100%	70%	40%	100%	mm^4	mm^3	mm^4		L' mm	M$_r$' kN·m	L' mm	M$_r$' kN·m
W760x185	5 000	3 450	3 270	2 970	5 610	5 970	8 540	4 390	M$_r$ 2 080	4 000	1 980	12 000	576
W30x124	4 000	3 300	3 150	2 830	4 490	5 660	8 410	4 100	V$_r$ 2 340	5 000	1 780	14 000	470
b = 267	3 000	3 140	2 970	2 670	3 370	5 230	8 210	3 750	L$_u$ 3 450	6 000	1 550	16 000	397
t = 23.6	2 000	2 920	2 730	2 480	2 240	4 640	7 900	3 340	I$_x$ 2 230	8 000	1 040	18 000	344
d = 766	1 000	2 550	2 420	2 280	1 120	3 740	7 320	2 840	S$_x$ 5 820	10 000	743	20 000	304
W760x173	5 000	3 270	3 100	2 810	5 610	5 630	8 010	4 160	M$_r$ 1 930	4 000	1 830	12 000	506
W30x116	4 000	3 120	2 980	2 680	4 490	5 340	7 890	3 880	V$_r$ 2 250	5 000	1 630	14 000	411
b = 267	3 000	2 970	2 820	2 520	3 370	4 940	7 710	3 540	L$_u$ 3 410	6 000	1 410	16 000	346
t = 21.6	2 000	2 760	2 580	2 340	2 240	4 390	7 420	3 150	I$_x$ 2 060	8 000	924	18 000	299
d = 762	1 000	2 400	2 280	2 130	1 120	3 530	6 870	2 660	S$_x$ 5 400	10 000	657	20 000	264
W760x161	5 000	3 060	2 890	2 630	5 610	5 220	7 370	3 880	M$_r$ 1 760	4 000	1 650	12 000	429
W30x108	4 000	2 920	2 780	2 490	4 490	4 960	7 260	3 610	V$_r$ 2 140	5 000	1 460	14 000	347
b = 266	3 000	2 770	2 630	2 340	3 370	4 600	7 100	3 300	L$_u$ 3 330	6 000	1 250	16 000	291
t = 19.3	2 000	2 570	2 400	2 160	2 240	4 090	6 840	2 920	I$_x$ 1 860	8 000	793	18 000	251
d = 758	1 000	2 220	2 100	1 960	1 120	3 290	6 330	2 450	S$_x$ 4 900	10 000	560	20 000	220
W760x147	5 000	2 850	2 690	2 430	5 610	4 800	6 730	3 590	M$_r$ 1 580	4 000	1 470	12 000	358
W30x99	4 000	2 710	2 570	2 310	4 490	4 570	6 630	3 340	V$_r$ 2 040	5 000	1 290	14 000	288
b = 265	3 000	2 560	2 430	2 160	3 370	4 250	6 480	3 050	L$_u$ 3 260	6 000	1 090	16 000	241
t = 17	2 000	2 380	2 220	1 980	2 240	3 780	6 250	2 690	I$_x$ 1 660	8 000	671	18 000	207
d = 753	1 000	2 050	1 930	1 780	1 120	3 040	5 790	2 240	S$_x$ 4 410	10 000	470	20 000	181
W760x134	5 000	2 610	2 460	2 230	5 280	4 420	6 130	3 340	M$_r$ 1 440	4 000	1 330	12 000	308
W30x90	4 000	2 510	2 370	2 140	4 490	4 220	6 050	3 110	V$_r$ 1 650	5 000	1 160	14 000	246
b = 264	3 000	2 360	2 250	2 000	3 370	3 940	5 930	2 840	L$_u$ 3 230	6 000	967	16 000	205
t = 15.5	2 000	2 200	2 050	1 830	2 240	3 520	5 720	2 500	I$_x$ 1 500	8 000	587	18 000	175
d = 750	1 000	1 890	1 770	1 630	1 120	2 830	5 310	2 070	S$_x$ 4 010	10 000	408	20 000	153
W690x192	5 000	3 310	3 130	2 850	5 610	5 340	8 310	3 900	M$_r$ 2 010	4 000	1 910	12 000	635
W27x129	4 000	3 160	3 010	2 720	4 490	5 050	8 170	3 640	V$_r$ 2 230	5 000	1 730	14 000	526
b = 254	3 000	3 000	2 850	2 570	3 370	4 660	7 980	3 320	L$_u$ 3 440	6 000	1 540	16 000	449
t = 27.9	2 000	2 790	2 620	2 390	2 240	4 120	7 670	2 960	I$_x$ 1 980	8 000	1 090	18 000	393
d = 702	1 000	2 450	2 340	2 200	1 120	3 320	7 090	2 520	S$_x$ 5 640	10 000	802	20 000	349
W690x170	5 000	2 980	2 810	2 560	5 610	4 750	7 330	3 500	M$_r$ 1 750	4 000	1 650	12 000	497
W27x114	4 000	2 840	2 690	2 430	4 490	4 500	7 210	3 260	V$_r$ 2 060	5 000	1 480	14 000	409
b = 256	3 000	2 680	2 550	2 290	3 370	4 170	7 050	2 980	L$_u$ 3 380	6 000	1 290	16 000	347
t = 23.6	2 000	2 500	2 350	2 120	2 240	3 700	6 790	2 640	I$_x$ 1 700	8 000	875	18 000	302
d = 693	1 000	2 180	2 070	1 940	1 120	2 970	6 280	2 220	S$_x$ 4 910	10 000	635	20 000	268
W690x152	5 000	2 730	2 570	2 340	5 610	4 320	6 600	3 220	M$_r$ 1 550	4 000	1 460	12 000	406
W27x102	4 000	2 590	2 460	2 230	4 490	4 110	6 500	3 000	V$_r$ 1 850	5 000	1 290	14 000	332
b = 254	3 000	2 450	2 330	2 090	3 370	3 820	6 360	2 740	L$_u$ 3 320	6 000	1 110	16 000	281
t = 21.1	2 000	2 280	2 140	1 930	2 240	3 400	6 130	2 420	I$_x$ 1 510	8 000	728	18 000	244
d = 688	1 000	1 980	1 870	1 740	1 120	2 730	5 690	2 020	S$_x$ 4 380	10 000	523	20 000	216

Note: Resistances are based on a concrete density of 2000 kg/m^3.

Units: M$_r$ - kN·m, V$_r$ - kN, L$_u$ - mm, I$_x$ - 10^6 mm^4, S$_x$ - 10^3 mm^3, b - mm, t - mm, d - mm

F$_y$ = 345 MPa

COMPOSITE BEAMS
Trial Selection Table
75 mm Deck with 85 mm Slab
$\phi = 0.90$, $\phi_c = 0.65$

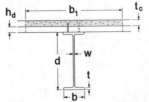

G40.21 350W
ASTM A992
A572 Grade 50
$f'_c = 25$ MPa

Steel section	b_1	M_{rc} (kN·m) for % shear connection			Q_r (kN)	I_t 10^6	S_t 10^3	I_{ts} 10^6	Steel section data	Unbraced condition			
		100%	70%	40%	100%					L'	M_r'	L'	M_r'
	mm					mm⁴	mm³	mm⁴		mm	kN·m	mm	kN·m
W690x140	5 000	2 540	2 390	2 170	5 530	3 990	6 040	2 990	M_r 1 410	4 000	1 320	10 000	447
W27x94	4 000	2 410	2 280	2 070	4 490	3 800	5 960	2 790	V_r 1 740	5 000	1 160	12 000	345
b = 254	3 000	2 270	2 160	1 940	3 370	3 540	5 830	2 540	L_u 3 270	6 000	987	14 000	280
t = 18.9	2 000	2 110	1 990	1 780	2 240	3 160	5 630	2 240	I_x 1 360	7 000	778	16 000	236
d = 684	1 000	1 840	1 730	1 600	1 120	2 540	5 230	1 860	S_x 3 980	8 000	628	18 000	204
W690x125	5 000	2 290	2 140	1 930	4 970	3 600	5 410	2 730	M_r 1 250	4 000	1 140	10 000	362
W27x84	4 000	2 210	2 080	1 880	4 490	3 440	5 340	2 540	V_r 1 610	5 000	999	12 000	277
b = 253	3 000	2 070	1 970	1 760	3 370	3 210	5 230	2 320	L_u 3 190	6 000	834	14 000	224
t = 16.3	2 000	1 920	1 810	1 610	2 240	2 870	5 060	2 040	I_x 1 190	7 000	641	16 000	188
d = 678	1 000	1 660	1 560	1 430	1 120	2 310	4 700	1 680	S_x 3 500	8 000	514	18 000	162
W610x174	5 000	2 780	2 610	2 390	5 610	4 090	7 020	3 000	M_r 1 660	4 500	1 660	10 000	924
W24x117	4 000	2 640	2 500	2 290	4 490	3 870	6 910	2 800	V_r 1 770	5 000	1 610	12 000	709
b = 325	3 000	2 490	2 380	2 160	3 370	3 580	6 760	2 550	L_u 4 480	6 000	1 490	14 000	574
t = 21.6	2 000	2 330	2 210	2 020	2 240	3 170	6 510	2 260	I_x 1 470	7 000	1 370	16 000	482
d = 616	1 000	2 060	1 960	1 850	1 120	2 550	6 040	1 910	S_x 4 780	8 000	1 230	18 000	415
W610x155	5 000	2 530	2 370	2 150	5 610	3 680	6 240	2 740	M_r 1 470	4 500	1 460	10 000	762
W24x104	4 000	2 390	2 260	2 060	4 490	3 500	6 160	2 550	V_r 1 590	5 000	1 410	12 000	579
b = 324	3 000	2 250	2 140	1 950	3 370	3 250	6 030	2 330	L_u 4 400	6 000	1 300	14 000	465
t = 19	2 000	2 100	1 990	1 810	2 240	2 890	5 820	2 050	I_x 1 290	7 000	1 180	16 000	388
d = 611	1 000	1 850	1 760	1 650	1 120	2 320	5 410	1 720	S_x 4 220	8 000	1 050	18 000	333
W610x140	5 000	2 370	2 210	1 990	5 560	3 390	5 620	2 530	M_r 1 290	4 000	1 170	10 000	422
W24x94	4 000	2 240	2 100	1 900	4 490	3 230	5 540	2 350	V_r 1 660	5 000	1 030	12 000	334
b = 230	3 000	2 090	1 990	1 780	3 370	3 000	5 420	2 140	L_u 3 070	6 000	874	14 000	277
t = 22.2	2 000	1 940	1 830	1 640	2 240	2 670	5 230	1 880	I_x 1 120	7 000	695	16 000	237
d = 617	1 000	1 680	1 590	1 470	1 120	2 130	4 840	1 550	S_x 3 630	8 000	573	18 000	207
W610x125	5 000	2 120	1 970	1 760	4 940	3 050	5 010	2 310	M_r 1 140	4 000	1 020	10 000	342
W24x84	4 000	2 040	1 910	1 720	4 490	2 910	4 940	2 150	V_r 1 490	5 000	889	12 000	269
b = 229	3 000	1 900	1 790	1 620	3 370	2 720	4 840	1 960	L_u 3 020	6 000	733	14 000	222
t = 19.6	2 000	1 750	1 650	1 480	2 240	2 430	4 680	1 710	I_x 985	7 000	575	16 000	189
d = 612	1 000	1 520	1 430	1 320	1 120	1 950	4 350	1 400	S_x 3 220	8 000	470	18 000	165
W610x113	5 000	1 920	1 780	1 590	4 470	2 780	4 530	2 120	M_r 1 020	4 000	906	10 000	282
W24x76	4 000	1 890	1 760	1 590	4 470	2 660	4 470	1 980	V_r 1 400	5 000	775	12 000	220
b = 228	3 000	1 750	1 650	1 490	3 370	2 490	4 390	1 800	L_u 2 950	6 000	617	14 000	180
t = 17.3	2 000	1 610	1 520	1 360	2 240	2 240	4 250	1 580	I_x 875	7 000	481	16 000	153
d = 608	1 000	1 400	1 310	1 200	1 120	1 800	3 950	1 280	S_x 2 880	8 000	391	18 000	133
W610x101	5 000	1 740	1 600	1 430	4 040	2 510	4 070	1 940	M_r 900	4 000	787	10 000	228
W24x68	4 000	1 710	1 590	1 420	4 040	2 410	4 020	1 810	V_r 1 300	5 000	664	12 000	176
b = 228	3 000	1 610	1 510	1 360	3 370	2 260	3 940	1 650	L_u 2 890	6 000	512	14 000	144
t = 14.9	2 000	1 470	1 390	1 230	2 240	2 040	3 820	1 440	I_x 764	7 000	396	16 000	121
d = 603	1 000	1 270	1 190	1 080	1 120	1 640	3 560	1 160	S_x 2 530	8 000	320	18 000	105

Note: Resistances are based on a concrete density of 2000 kg/m³.

Units: M_r - kN·m, V_r - kN, L_u - mm, I_x - 10^6 mm⁴, S_x - 10^3 mm³, b - mm, t - mm, d - mm

$F_y = 345$ MPa

G40.21 350W
ASTM A992
A572 Grade 50
f′_c = 25 MPa

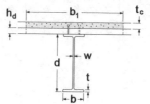

COMPOSITE BEAMS
Trial Selection Table
75 mm Deck with 85 mm Slab
$\phi = 0.90$, $\phi_c = 0.65$

Steel section	b₁	M_rc (kN·m) for % shear connection			Q_r (kN)	I_t 10⁶	S_t 10³	I_ts 10⁶	Steel section data	Unbraced condition			
	mm	100%	70%	40%	100%	mm⁴	mm³	mm⁴		L′ mm	M_r′ kN·m	L′ mm	M_r′ kN·m
W610x91	4 000	1 520	1 400	1 250	3 570	2 150	3 540	1 630	M_r 782	3 000	768	8 000	257
W24x61	3 000	1 460	1 370	1 230	3 370	2 020	3 480	1 490	V_r 1 100	4 000	672	10 000	181
b = 227	2 000	1 330	1 250	1 110	2 240	1 830	3 380	1 300	L_u 2 820	5 000	557	12 000	139
t = 12.7	1 000	1 140	1 060	956	1 120	1 480	3 150	1 040	I_x 657	6 000	416	14 000	112
d = 598	500	983	930	868	561	1 180	2 890	868	S_x 2 200	7 000	320	16 000	94.2
W610x82	4 000	1 400	1 290	1 130	3 260	1 960	3 190	1 500	M_r 686	3 000	589	8 000	147
W24x55	3 000	1 360	1 270	1 120	3 260	1 850	3 140	1 370	V_r 1 170	4 000	450	10 000	108
b = 178	2 000	1 240	1 160	1 010	2 240	1 680	3 040	1 190	L_u 2 110	5 000	306	12 000	84.8
t = 12.8	1 000	1 050	966	857	1 120	1 360	2 840	942	I_x 565	6 000	227	14 000	70.1
d = 599	500	884	830	767	561	1 070	2 590	775	S_x 1 880	7 000	179	16 000	59.8
W530x138	4 000	2 020	1 890	1 690	4 490	2 630	4 980	1 900	M_r 1 120	3 000	1 110	8 000	515
W21x93	3 000	1 880	1 770	1 580	3 370	2 440	4 870	1 720	V_r 1 650	4 000	1 000	10 000	390
b = 214	2 000	1 720	1 620	1 450	2 240	2 160	4 680	1 500	L_u 2 930	5 000	884	12 000	314
t = 23.6	1 000	1 490	1 400	1 290	1 120	1 720	4 310	1 220	I_x 861	6 000	759	14 000	263
d = 549	500	1 320	1 260	1 200	561	1 370	3 930	1 060	S_x 3 140	7 000	616	16 000	227
W530x123	4 000	1 850	1 720	1 540	4 490	2 380	4 460	1 740	M_r 997	3 000	984	8 000	421
W21x83	3 000	1 710	1 610	1 440	3 370	2 220	4 370	1 580	V_r 1 460	4 000	879	10 000	316
b = 212	2 000	1 560	1 470	1 310	2 240	1 980	4 210	1 380	L_u 2 860	5 000	762	12 000	253
t = 21.2	1 000	1 350	1 270	1 160	1 120	1 570	3 890	1 110	I_x 761	6 000	631	14 000	211
d = 544	500	1 190	1 140	1 080	561	1 250	3 560	951	S_x 2 800	7 000	505	16 000	182
W530x109	4 000	1 680	1 550	1 380	4 320	2 140	3 970	1 590	M_r 879	3 000	862	8 000	342
W21x73	3 000	1 560	1 460	1 310	3 370	2 000	3 890	1 440	V_r 1 280	4 000	764	10 000	254
b = 211	2 000	1 410	1 330	1 190	2 240	1 790	3 760	1 250	L_u 2 810	5 000	652	12 000	202
t = 18.8	1 000	1 220	1 140	1 040	1 120	1 440	3 490	1 010	I_x 667	6 000	520	14 000	168
d = 539	500	1 070	1 020	957	561	1 140	3 190	853	S_x 2 480	7 000	413	16 000	144
W530x101	4 000	1 560	1 440	1 280	4 010	2 010	3 690	1 500	M_r 814	3 000	794	8 000	301
W21x68	3 000	1 470	1 370	1 230	3 370	1 890	3 620	1 370	V_r 1 200	4 000	699	10 000	222
b = 210	2 000	1 330	1 260	1 120	2 240	1 690	3 510	1 190	L_u 2 770	5 000	591	12 000	176
t = 17.4	1 000	1 150	1 070	975	1 120	1 360	3 260	953	I_x 617	6 000	462	14 000	146
d = 537	500	999	950	893	561	1 080	2 990	801	S_x 2 300	7 000	365	16 000	125
W530x92	4 000	1 440	1 320	1 170	3 660	1 850	3 370	1 390	M_r 733	3 000	711	8 000	253
W21x62	3 000	1 370	1 280	1 140	3 370	1 740	3 310	1 270	V_r 1 110	4 000	621	9 000	214
b = 209	2 000	1 230	1 160	1 030	2 240	1 570	3 210	1 100	L_u 2 720	5 000	516	10 000	185
t = 15.6	1 000	1 060	992	894	1 120	1 260	2 990	879	I_x 552	6 000	393	12 000	146
d = 533	500	918	870	813	561	998	2 740	732	S_x 2 070	7 000	309	14 000	120
W530x82	4 000	1 280	1 170	1 030	3 260	1 650	2 990	1 260	M_r 640	3 000	616	8 000	203
W21x55	3 000	1 250	1 160	1 030	3 260	1 560	2 940	1 150	V_r 1 030	4 000	531	9 000	170
b = 209	2 000	1 120	1 050	935	2 240	1 410	2 850	1 000	L_u 2 660	5 000	433	10 000	147
t = 13.3	1 000	961	894	799	1 120	1 150	2 670	793	I_x 477	6 000	320	12 000	115
d = 528	500	822	775	719	561	903	2 440	653	S_x 1 810	7 000	249	14 000	94.0

Note: Resistances are based on a concrete density of 2000 kg/m³.

Units: M_r – kN·m, V_r – kN, L_u – mm, I_x – 10⁶ mm⁴, S_x – 10³ mm³, b – mm, t – mm, d – mm

F_y = 345 MPa

COMPOSITE BEAMS
Trial Selection Table
75 mm Deck with 85 mm Slab
$\phi = 0.90$, $\phi_c = 0.65$

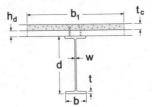

G40.21 350W
ASTM A992
A572 Grade 50
$f'_c = 25$ MPa

Steel section	b_1	M_{rc} (kN·m) for % shear connection			Q_r (kN)	I_t 10^6	S_t 10^3	I_{ts} 10^6	Steel section data		Unbraced condition			
		100%	70%	40%	100%	mm^4	mm^3	mm^4			L' mm	M_r' kN·m	L' mm	M_r' kN·m
	mm													
W530x74	4 000	1 170	1 070	932	2 960	1 500	2 690	1 160	M_r 562		3 000	474	8 000	123
W21x50	3 000	1 140	1 060	927	2 960	1 420	2 640	1 060	V_r 1 050		4 000	357	9 000	105
b = 166	2 000	1 040	977	856	2 240	1 290	2 560	919	L_u 2 040		5 000	247	10 000	91.7
t = 13.6	1 000	883	815	720	1 120	1 050	2 390	721	I_x 411		6 000	186	12 000	73.2
d = 529	500	743	696	640	561	827	2 190	585	S_x 1 550		7 000	148	14 000	61.0
W530x66	4 000	1 030	939	813	2 600	1 330	2 360	1 040	M_r 484		3 000	398	8 000	94.9
W21x44	3 000	1 010	929	810	2 600	1 260	2 320	952	V_r 927		4 000	284	9 000	80.6
b = 165	2 000	945	882	772	2 240	1 160	2 260	830	L_u 1 980		5 000	195	10 000	70.0
t = 11.4	1 000	795	733	641	1 120	949	2 110	649	I_x 351		6 000	145	12 000	55.5
d = 525	500	663	617	562	561	746	1 930	520	S_x 1 340		7 000	115	14 000	46.0
W460x158	4 000	2 000	1 870	1 680	4 490	2 380	5 210	1 690	M_r 1 170		4 500	1 150	9 000	795
W18x106	3 000	1 860	1 750	1 590	3 370	2 200	5 090	1 530	V_r 1 460		5 000	1 110	10 000	697
b = 284	2 000	1 700	1 620	1 470	2 240	1 940	4 890	1 340	L_u 4 190		6 000	1 040	11 000	618
t = 23.9	1 000	1 500	1 430	1 330	1 120	1 530	4 500	1 100	I_x 796		7 000	957	12 000	556
d = 476	500	1 350	1 300	1 250	561	1 220	4 110	957	S_x 3 350		8 000	876	14 000	463
W460x144	4 000	1 870	1 740	1 560	4 490	2 210	4 790	1 590	M_r 1 070		4 500	1 050	9 000	693
W18x97	3 000	1 730	1 620	1 470	3 370	2 050	4 690	1 440	V_r 1 320		5 000	1 010	10 000	602
b = 283	2 000	1 580	1 500	1 360	2 240	1 810	4 510	1 250	L_u 4 130		6 000	936	11 000	533
t = 22.1	1 000	1 390	1 320	1 230	1 120	1 430	4 160	1 020	I_x 726		7 000	858	12 000	478
d = 472	500	1 250	1 200	1 150	561	1 140	3 810	885	S_x 3 080		8 000	779	14 000	396
W460x128	4 000	1 720	1 590	1 410	4 490	2 000	4 280	1 450	M_r 947		4 500	918	9 000	567
W18x86	3 000	1 580	1 470	1 340	3 370	1 860	4 190	1 310	V_r 1 170		5 000	884	10 000	490
b = 282	2 000	1 430	1 360	1 230	2 240	1 650	4 050	1 140	L_u 4 040		6 000	812	11 000	432
t = 19.6	1 000	1 260	1 190	1 100	1 120	1 310	3 750	926	I_x 637		7 000	736	12 000	386
d = 467	500	1 120	1 080	1 020	561	1 040	3 430	792	S_x 2 730		8 000	658	14 000	318
W460x113	4 000	1 560	1 440	1 270	4 470	1 790	3 780	1 320	M_r 829		4 500	796	9 000	458
W18x76	3 000	1 430	1 330	1 200	3 370	1 670	3 710	1 190	V_r 1 020		5 000	765	10 000	394
b = 280	2 000	1 280	1 220	1 100	2 240	1 490	3 590	1 040	L_u 3 950		6 000	696	11 000	345
t = 17.3	1 000	1 130	1 070	979	1 120	1 190	3 340	836	I_x 556		7 000	623	12 000	307
d = 463	500	999	956	905	561	942	3 060	708	S_x 2 400		8 000	545	14 000	252
W460x106	3 000	1 380	1 280	1 130	3 370	1 580	3 420	1 120	M_r 742		3 000	719	8 000	308
W18x71	2 000	1 230	1 160	1 030	2 240	1 410	3 300	971	V_r 1 210		4 000	637	9 000	266
b = 194	1 500	1 150	1 080	964	1 680	1 290	3 210	878	L_u 2 690		5 000	549	10 000	235
t = 20.6	1 000	1 060	986	894	1 120	1 120	3 050	770	I_x 488		6 000	450	11 000	210
d = 469	500	915	871	818	561	875	2 770	642	S_x 2 080		7 000	366	12 000	190
W460x97	3 000	1 280	1 190	1 050	3 370	1 460	3 140	1 050	M_r 677		3 000	652	8 000	264
W18x65	2 000	1 140	1 070	955	2 240	1 310	3 040	911	V_r 1 090		4 000	574	9 000	227
b = 193	1 500	1 070	1 010	895	1 680	1 200	2 950	823	L_u 2 650		5 000	488	10 000	200
t = 19	1 000	980	916	827	1 120	1 050	2 820	720	I_x 445		6 000	389	11 000	178
d = 466	500	848	804	753	561	820	2 570	596	S_x 1 910		7 000	314	12 000	161

Note: Resistances are based on a concrete density of 2000 kg/m³.

Units: M_r - kN·m, V_r - kN, L_u - mm, I_x - 10^6 mm⁴, S_x - 10^3 mm³, b - mm, t - mm, d - mm

$F_y = 345$ MPa

G40.21 350W
ASTM A992
A572 Grade 50
f'$_c$ = 25 MPa

COMPOSITE BEAMS
Trial Selection Table
75 mm Deck with 85 mm Slab
$\phi = 0.90$, $\phi_c = 0.65$

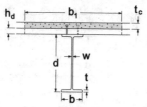

Steel section	b$_1$ mm	M$_{rc}$ (kN·m) for % shear connection 100%	70%	40%	Q$_r$ (kN) 100%	I$_t$ 10^6 mm^4	S$_t$ 10^3 mm^3	I$_{ts}$ 10^6 mm^4	Steel section data		Unbraced condition L' mm	M$_r$' kN·m	L' mm	M$_r$' kN·m
W460x89	3 000	1 210	1 120	991	3 370	1 370	2 920	993	M$_r$	624	3 000	598	8 000	231
W18x60	2 000	1 080	1 010	898	2 240	1 230	2 830	861	V$_r$	996	4 000	523	9 000	198
b = 192	1 500	1 000	945	840	1 680	1 130	2 750	778	L$_u$	2 620	5 000	439	10 000	174
t = 17.7	1 000	920	860	774	1 120	990	2 630	679	I$_x$	410	6 000	343	11 000	155
d = 463	500	794	751	700	561	775	2 400	559	S$_x$	1 770	7 000	276	12 000	140
W460x82	3 000	1 130	1 040	912	3 230	1 260	2 670	926	M$_r$	568	3 000	540	8 000	195
W18x55	2 000	1 000	936	834	2 240	1 140	2 590	804	V$_r$	933	4 000	467	9 000	167
b = 191	1 500	930	877	778	1 680	1 050	2 530	726	L$_u$	2 560	5 000	385	10 000	146
t = 16	1 000	852	797	714	1 120	923	2 420	632	I$_x$	370	6 000	292	11 000	129
d = 460	500	733	692	642	561	723	2 210	516	S$_x$	1 610	7 000	234	12 000	117
W460x74	3 000	1 030	943	828	2 930	1 160	2 430	862	M$_r$	512	3 000	484	8 000	164
W18x50	2 000	932	867	772	2 240	1 060	2 360	749	V$_r$	843	4 000	414	9 000	140
b = 190	1 500	862	811	719	1 680	975	2 310	676	L$_u$	2 530	5 000	332	10 000	122
t = 14.5	1 000	788	737	657	1 120	859	2 210	587	I$_x$	333	6 000	249	11 000	108
d = 457	500	675	635	586	561	674	2 030	476	S$_x$	1 460	7 000	198	12 000	96.9
W460x67	3 000	939	855	748	2 660	1 060	2 200	795	M$_r$	456	3 000	427	8 000	135
W18x45	2 000	866	803	712	2 240	968	2 140	693	V$_r$	791	4 000	361	9 000	115
b = 190	1 500	797	748	662	1 680	897	2 090	625	L$_u$	2 480	5 000	280	10 000	99.4
t = 12.7	1 000	725	678	601	1 120	793	2 010	541	I$_x$	295	6 000	208	11 000	87.8
d = 454	500	618	580	531	561	623	1 850	435	S$_x$	1 300	7 000	164	12 000	78.6
W460x61	3 000	842	762	663	2 370	950	1 960	721	M$_r$	401	3 000	370	8 000	107
W18x41	2 000	797	736	649	2 240	872	1 910	630	V$_r$	747	4 000	306	9 000	90.5
b = 189	1 500	730	681	600	1 680	811	1 860	568	L$_u$	2 410	5 000	227	10 000	78.1
t = 10.8	1 000	659	616	541	1 120	719	1 790	491	I$_x$	254	6 000	168	11 000	68.7
d = 450	500	558	520	472	561	566	1 650	390	S$_x$	1 130	7 000	131	12 000	61.3
W460x52	3 000	739	666	574	2 060	837	1 690	646	M$_r$	338	3 000	269	8 000	63.7
W18x35	2 000	712	652	569	2 060	773	1 650	565	V$_r$	680	4 000	185	9 000	54.4
b = 152	1 500	660	613	536	1 680	722	1 620	510	L$_u$	1 890	5 000	128	10 000	47.4
t = 10.8	1 000	590	550	479	1 120	644	1 560	440	I$_x$	212	6 000	96.3	11 000	42.1
d = 450	500	494	458	411	561	509	1 430	345	S$_x$	943	7 000	76.8	12 000	37.9
W410x149	3 000	1 660	1 550	1 400	3 370	1 830	4 550	1 260	M$_r$	1 020	4 500	993	8 000	773
W16x100	2 000	1 510	1 430	1 290	2 240	1 610	4 370	1 100	V$_r$	1 320	5 000	963	9 000	710
b = 265	1 500	1 430	1 350	1 230	1 680	1 460	4 230	1 000	L$_u$	4 080	5 500	931	10 000	637
t = 25	1 000	1 320	1 250	1 160	1 120	1 260	4 010	890	I$_x$	625	6 000	900	11 000	569
d = 431	500	1 180	1 130	1 080	561	997	3 650	766	S$_x$	2 900	7 000	836	12 000	515
W410x132	3 000	1 510	1 400	1 260	3 370	1 650	4 050	1 150	M$_r$	897	4 500	865	8 000	647
W16x89	2 000	1 360	1 280	1 160	2 240	1 460	3 900	996	V$_r$	1 160	5 000	835	9 000	579
b = 263	1 500	1 280	1 210	1 100	1 680	1 320	3 780	905	L$_u$	3 940	5 500	804	10 000	508
t = 22.2	1 000	1 180	1 120	1 030	1 120	1 150	3 590	802	I$_x$	545	6 000	773	11 000	453
d = 425	500	1 050	1 010	958	561	902	3 270	683	S$_x$	2 560	7 000	710	12 000	409

Note: Resistances are based on a concrete density of 2000 kg/m^3.

Units: M$_r$ - kN·m, V$_r$ - kN, L$_u$ - mm, I$_x$ - 10^6 mm^4, S$_x$ - 10^3 mm^3, b - mm, t - mm, d - mm

F$_y$ = 345 MPa

COMPOSITE BEAMS
Trial Selection Table
75 mm Deck with 85 mm Slab
$\phi = 0.90$, $\phi_c = 0.65$

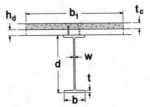

G40.21 350W
ASTM A992
A572 Grade 50
f'$_c$ = 25 MPa

Steel section	b₁	Composite							Non-composite					
		Mrc (kN·m) for % shear connection			Qr (kN)	It 10⁶	St 10³	Its 10⁶	Steel section data		Unbraced condition			
											L'	Mr'	L'	Mr'
	mm	100%	70%	40%	100%	mm⁴	mm³	mm⁴			mm	kN·m	mm	kN·m
W410x114	3 000	1 360	1 260	1 120	3 370	1 470	3 550	1 040	Mr 773		4 500	736	8 000	525
W16x77	2 000	1 210	1 140	1 030	2 240	1 310	3 430	897	Vr 998		5 000	707	9 000	451
b = 261	1 500	1 140	1 080	972	1 680	1 190	3 330	813	Lu 3 810		5 500	678	10 000	394
t = 19.3	1 000	1 050	992	907	1 120	1 030	3 170	716	Ix 468		6 000	648	11 000	350
d = 420	500	926	885	836	561	810	2 890	602	Sx 2 230		7 000	587	12 000	315
W410x100	3 000	1 230	1 130	1 000	3 370	1 310	3 120	936	Mr 671		4 500	632	8 000	423
W16x67	2 000	1 090	1 020	918	2 240	1 170	3 020	811	Vr 850		5 000	605	9 000	359
b = 260	1 500	1 010	959	865	1 680	1 070	2 940	733	Lu 3 730		5 500	577	10 000	312
t = 16.9	1 000	935	883	803	1 120	933	2 810	642	Ix 404		6 000	548	11 000	276
d = 415	500	821	781	733	561	731	2 570	535	Sx 1 950		7 000	489	12 000	247
W410x85	3 000	1 090	1 000	873	3 350	1 120	2 590	813	Mr 537		3 000	509	8 000	205
W16x57	2 000	957	890	789	2 240	1 010	2 510	702	Vr 931		4 000	444	9 000	178
b = 181	1 500	885	830	736	1 680	929	2 440	632	Lu 2 520		5 000	376	10 000	157
t = 18.2	1 000	807	753	675	1 120	811	2 330	547	Ix 315		6 000	297	11 000	141
d = 417	500	692	653	606	561	629	2 120	444	Sx 1 510		7 000	243	12 000	127
W410x74	3 000	976	887	770	2 970	1 010	2 300	741	Mr 469		3 000	440	8 000	163
W16x50	2 000	874	808	715	2 240	914	2 230	642	Vr 821		4 000	379	9 000	140
b = 180	1 500	803	752	665	1 680	843	2 170	577	Lu 2 470		5 000	312	10 000	124
t = 16	1 000	729	681	607	1 120	739	2 080	499	Ix 275		6 000	239	11 000	110
d = 413	500	623	586	540	561	575	1 900	401	Sx 1 330		7 000	194	12 000	99.8
W410x67	3 000	885	799	692	2 670	920	2 080	686	Mr 422		3 000	392	8 000	135
W16x45	2 000	810	747	659	2 240	839	2 020	595	Vr 739		4 000	333	9 000	116
b = 179	1 500	741	691	612	1 680	776	1 970	536	Lu 2 420		5 000	264	10 000	102
t = 14.4	1 000	668	627	556	1 120	684	1 890	462	Ix 246		6 000	201	11 000	90.5
d = 410	500	571	535	490	561	534	1 730	369	Sx 1 200		7 000	161	12 000	81.7
W410x60	3 000	786	706	609	2 350	825	1 840	625	Mr 369		3 000	341	8 000	109
W16x40	2 000	743	681	598	2 240	757	1 790	545	Vr 642		4 000	286	9 000	93.2
b = 178	1 500	675	626	555	1 680	703	1 750	491	Lu 2 390		5 000	218	10 000	81.4
t = 12.8	1 000	604	568	503	1 120	623	1 690	424	Ix 216		6 000	165	11 000	72.2
d = 407	500	516	483	440	561	490	1 550	335	Sx 1 060		7 000	131	12 000	65.0
W410x54	3 000	708	633	545	2 110	741	1 650	568	Mr 326		3 000	295	8 000	86.1
W16x36	2 000	680	620	540	2 110	683	1 600	497	Vr 619		4 000	242	9 000	73.2
b = 177	1 500	623	576	507	1 680	637	1 570	448	Lu 2 310		5 000	176	10 000	63.6
t = 10.9	1 000	553	519	455	1 120	567	1 510	385	Ix 186		6 000	132	11 000	56.3
d = 403	500	468	436	393	561	446	1 390	302	Sx 924		7 000	104	12 000	50.5
W410x46	3 000	619	551	470	1 830	653	1 420	509	Mr 275		2 000	265	7 000	61.7
W16x31	2 000	598	541	467	1 830	605	1 390	447	Vr 578		3 000	210	8 000	51.8
b = 140	1 500	566	520	454	1 680	566	1 360	403	Lu 1 790		4 000	142	9 000	44.6
t = 11.2	1 000	498	464	404	1 120	507	1 310	347	Ix 156		5 000	99.9	10 000	39.2
d = 403	500	416	384	342	561	402	1 210	269	Sx 773		6 000	76.4	11 000	35.0

Note: Resistances are based on a concrete density of 2000 kg/m³.

Units: Mr - kN·m, Vr - kN, Lu - mm, Ix - 10⁶ mm⁴, Sx - 10³ mm³, b - mm, t - mm, d - mm

Fy = 345 MPa

G40.21 350W
ASTM A992
A572 Grade 50
f′c = 25 MPa

COMPOSITE BEAMS
Trial Selection Table
75 mm Deck with 85 mm Slab
φ = 0.90, φc = 0.65

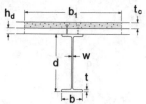

Steel section	b_1	M_{rc} (kN·m) for % shear connection			Q_r	I_t	S_t	I_{ts}	Steel section data		Unbraced condition			
											L′	M_r'	L′	M_r'
	mm	100%	70%	40%	100% (kN)	10^6 mm⁴	10^3 mm³	10^6 mm⁴			mm	kN·m	mm	kN·m
W410x39	3 000	527	467	395	1 550	557	1 210	443	M_r	227	2 000	216	7 000	44.1
W16x26	2 000	512	459	393	1 550	520	1 180	392	V_r	480	3 000	166	8 000	36.6
b = 140	1 500	496	452	390	1 550	489	1 150	355	L_u	1 730	4 000	105	9 000	31.3
t = 8.8	1 000	440	408	353	1 120	442	1 120	305	I_x	127	5 000	73.1	10 000	27.4
d = 399	500	363	334	293	561	354	1 040	235	S_x	634	6 000	55.2	11 000	24.3
W360x79	3 000	933	842	722	3 140	859	2 230	622	M_r	444	3 500	425	7 000	267
W14x53	2 000	816	750	663	2 240	774	2 160	535	V_r	682	4 000	404	8 000	225
b = 205	1 500	745	694	619	1 680	711	2 110	480	L_u	3 010	4 500	383	9 000	194
t = 16.8	1 000	671	632	566	1 120	620	2 010	413	I_x	226	5 000	361	10 000	171
d = 354	500	579	547	505	561	478	1 830	331	S_x	1 280	6 000	317	11 000	153
W360x72	3 000	846	759	648	2 830	781	2 020	574	M_r	397	3 500	377	7 000	222
W14x48	2 000	757	693	608	2 240	708	1 960	495	V_r	617	4 000	357	8 000	186
b = 204	1 500	687	637	567	1 680	653	1 910	444	L_u	2 940	4 500	336	9 000	160
t = 15.1	1 000	615	579	517	1 120	572	1 830	382	I_x	201	5 000	315	10 000	141
d = 350	500	529	498	457	561	442	1 670	303	S_x	1 150	6 000	272	11 000	126
W360x64	3 000	762	680	578	2 530	708	1 810	528	M_r	354	3 500	332	7 000	183
W14x43	2 000	702	640	556	2 240	646	1 760	457	V_r	548	4 000	313	8 000	153
b = 203	1 500	633	585	519	1 680	597	1 720	410	L_u	2 870	4 500	293	9 000	131
t = 13.5	1 000	563	529	471	1 120	526	1 650	352	I_x	178	5 000	273	10 000	115
d = 347	500	482	453	413	561	409	1 510	277	S_x	1 030	6 000	228	11 000	102
W360x57	3 000	697	619	526	2 240	664	1 630	502	M_r	314	3 000	289	7 000	119
W14x38	2 000	665	604	521	2 240	609	1 590	437	V_r	580	3 500	267	8 000	99.8
b = 172	1 500	598	549	483	1 680	566	1 550	392	L_u	2 360	4 000	244	9 000	86.0
t = 13.1	1 000	527	493	435	1 120	501	1 490	336	I_x	161	5 000	192	10 000	75.7
d = 358	500	446	417	377	561	391	1 370	262	S_x	897	6 000	147	11 000	67.6
W360x51	3 000	625	553	469	2 000	599	1 460	459	M_r	278	3 000	253	7 000	97.0
W14x34	2 000	600	541	465	2 000	552	1 420	401	V_r	524	3 500	232	8 000	81.0
b = 171	1 500	553	506	442	1 680	514	1 390	361	L_u	2 320	4 000	210	9 000	69.5
t = 11.6	1 000	484	451	397	1 120	458	1 340	309	I_x	141	5 000	159	10 000	60.9
d = 355	500	407	379	341	561	359	1 230	239	S_x	796	6 000	121	11 000	54.2
W360x45	3 000	558	491	415	1 780	536	1 300	417	M_r	242	3 000	217	7 000	76.5
W14x30	2 000	538	482	412	1 780	496	1 260	365	V_r	498	3 500	197	8 000	63.4
b = 171	1 500	511	465	403	1 680	464	1 240	329	L_u	2 260	4 000	176	9 000	54.1
t = 9.8	1 000	443	411	360	1 120	415	1 200	282	I_x	122	5 000	128	10 000	47.2
d = 352	500	369	342	304	561	328	1 100	217	S_x	691	6 000	96.1	11 000	41.9
W360x39	2 500	484	427	360	1 550	459	1 110	354	M_r	206	2 000	193	6 000	54.2
W14x26	2 000	475	423	359	1 550	441	1 100	330	V_r	470	2 500	172	7 000	44.3
b = 128	1 500	460	415	356	1 550	414	1 080	298	L_u	1 660	3 000	148	8 000	37.5
t = 10.7	1 000	404	372	322	1 120	373	1 040	255	I_x	102	4 000	97.2	9 000	32.5
d = 353	500	331	305	268	561	297	964	195	S_x	580	5 000	69.8	10 000	28.8

Note: Resistances are based on a concrete density of 2000 kg/m³. F_y = 345 MPa

Units: M_r - kN·m, V_r - kN, L_u - mm, I_x - 10^6 mm⁴, S_x - 10^3 mm³, b - mm, t - mm, d - mm

COMPOSITE BEAMS
Trial Selection Table
75 mm Deck with 85 mm Slab
$\phi = 0.90$, $\phi_c = 0.65$

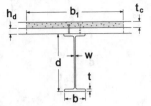

G40.21 350W
ASTM A992
A572 Grade 50
$f'_c = 25$ MPa

Steel section	b_1	M_{rc} (kN·m) for % shear connection			Q_r (kN)	I_t 10^6	S_t 10^3	I_{ts} 10^6	Steel section data		Unbraced condition			
											L'	M_r'	L'	M_r'
	mm	100%	70%	40%	100%	mm⁴	mm³	mm⁴			mm	kN·m	mm	kN·m
W360x33	2 500	408	358	299	1 290	389	935	307	M_r	168	2 000	155	6 000	38.1
W14x22	2 000	401	354	298	1 290	375	922	287	V_r	396	2 500	136	7 000	30.8
b = 127	1 500	391	349	297	1 290	354	905	261	L_u	1 600	3 000	113	8 000	25.9
t = 8.5	1 000	358	327	282	1 120	322	877	225	I_x	82.7	4 000	70.3	9 000	22.3
d = 349	500	288	265	230	561	260	817	171	S_x	474	5 000	49.7	10 000	19.6
W310x74	2 500	783	706	602	2 810	653	1 920	461	M_r	366	3 500	354	6 000	274
W12x50	2 000	716	651	566	2 240	616	1 880	423	V_r	597	4 000	339	7 000	240
b = 205	1 500	646	595	528	1 680	565	1 830	378	L_u	3 100	4 500	323	8 000	204
t = 16.3	1 000	573	538	481	1 120	492	1 750	322	I_x	164	5 000	307	9 000	177
d = 310	500	491	462	425	561	376	1 590	253	S_x	1 060	5 500	291	10 000	156
W310x67	2 500	717	642	543	2 620	592	1 720	423	M_r	326	3 500	312	6 000	234
W12x45	2 000	665	602	518	2 240	559	1 690	389	V_r	533	4 000	297	7 000	198
b = 204	1 500	596	547	482	1 680	515	1 650	347	L_u	3 020	4 500	282	8 000	167
t = 14.6	1 000	524	490	437	1 120	451	1 580	296	I_x	144	5 000	266	9 000	144
d = 306	500	446	420	383	561	346	1 440	230	S_x	942	5 500	250	10 000	127
W310x60	2 500	646	574	483	2 340	537	1 550	390	M_r	290	3 500	275	6 000	199
W12x40	2 000	618	557	474	2 240	509	1 520	360	V_r	466	4 000	261	7 000	163
b = 203	1 500	550	502	439	1 680	471	1 480	322	L_u	2 960	4 500	246	8 000	137
t = 13.1	1 000	480	447	398	1 120	415	1 430	274	I_x	128	5 000	231	9 000	118
d = 303	500	406	381	347	561	320	1 310	212	S_x	842	5 500	215	10 000	104
W310x52	2 500	596	528	444	2 070	514	1 400	380	M_r	261	3 000	241	6 000	130
W12x35	2 000	579	520	441	2 070	489	1 380	351	V_r	495	3 500	224	7 000	106
b = 167	1 500	526	479	416	1 680	455	1 350	315	L_u	2 370	4 000	206	8 000	89.4
t = 13.2	1 000	457	424	374	1 120	403	1 300	268	I_x	119	4 500	188	9 000	77.5
d = 318	500	382	357	322	561	314	1 190	206	S_x	750	5 000	167	10 000	68.4
W310x45	2 500	512	450	377	1 770	444	1 200	336	M_r	220	3 000	200	6 000	98.2
W12x30	2 000	500	444	375	1 770	425	1 180	311	V_r	423	3 500	184	7 000	79.3
b = 166	1 500	474	428	367	1 680	397	1 160	280	L_u	2 310	4 000	167	8 000	66.5
t = 11.2	1 000	406	374	329	1 120	355	1 120	239	I_x	99.2	4 500	150	9 000	57.3
d = 313	500	335	313	279	561	279	1 030	182	S_x	634	5 000	128	10 000	50.4
W310x39	2 500	448	391	326	1 530	392	1 050	301	M_r	189	3 000	170	6 000	77.7
W12x26	2 000	439	387	325	1 530	376	1 030	280	V_r	368	3 500	155	7 000	62.2
b = 165	1 500	424	379	322	1 530	353	1 010	253	L_u	2 260	4 000	139	8 000	51.8
t = 9.7	1 000	369	337	295	1 120	317	980	217	I_x	85.1	4 500	121	9 000	44.3
d = 310	500	299	280	248	561	252	910	165	S_x	549	5 000	103	10 000	38.8
W250x67	2 500	659	584	484	2 650	479	1 590	337	M_r	280	3 500	275	6 000	223
W10x45	2 000	604	541	457	2 240	452	1 560	308	V_r	469	4 000	265	6 500	212
b = 204	1 500	535	486	422	1 680	414	1 520	273	L_u	3 260	4 500	254	7 000	202
t = 15.7	1 000	464	430	382	1 120	360	1 450	230	I_x	104	5 000	244	7 500	192
d = 257	500	389	366	333	561	272	1 310	176	S_x	806	5 500	233	8 000	180

Note: Resistances are based on a concrete density of 2000 kg/m³.

Units: M_r - kN·m, V_r - kN, L_u - mm, I_x - 10^6 mm⁴, S_x - 10^3 mm³, b - mm, t - mm, d - mm

$F_y = 345$ MPa

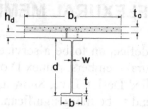

COMPOSITE BEAMS
Trial Selection Table
75 mm Deck with 85 mm Slab

G40.21 350W
ASTM A992
A572 Grade 50
$f'_c = 25$ MPa

$\phi = 0.90$, $\phi_c = 0.65$

Steel section	b_1	M_{rc} (kN·m) for % shear connection			Q_r	I_t	S_t	I_{ts}	Steel section data		Unbraced condition			
											L'	M_r'	L'	M_r'
	mm	100%	70%	40%	100% (kN)	10^6 mm⁴	10^3 mm³	10^6 mm⁴			mm	kN·m	mm	kN·m
W250x58	2 500	579	507	417	2 300	421	1 380	302	M_r	239	3 500	232	6 000	181
W10x39	2 000	554	493	411	2 240	398	1 360	276	V_r	413	4 000	222	6 500	171
b = 203	1 500	487	439	376	1 680	367	1 330	246	L_u	3 130	4 500	212	7 000	161
t = 13.5	1 000	417	383	339	1 120	321	1 270	207	I_x	87.3	5 000	202	7 500	148
d = 252	500	344	323	291	561	245	1 160	156	S_x	693	5 500	192	8 000	137
W250x45	2 500	473	410	336	1 780	363	1 110	270	M_r	187	3 000	167	5 500	101
W10x30	2 000	461	404	334	1 780	346	1 090	249	V_r	414	3 500	155	6 000	90.6
b = 148	1 500	434	388	326	1 680	322	1 060	223	L_u	2 170	4 000	142	6 500	82.2
t = 13	1 000	366	333	289	1 120	286	1 020	188	I_x	71.1	4 500	129	7 000	75.2
d = 266	500	294	273	242	561	222	938	141	S_x	534	5 000	114	7 500	69.3
W250x39	2 500	409	353	288	1 530	316	957	240	M_r	159	3 000	140	5 500	77.5
W10x26	2 000	400	348	286	1 530	303	942	223	V_r	354	3 500	128	6 000	69.2
b = 147	1 500	386	341	284	1 530	283	921	200	L_u	2 110	4 000	115	6 500	62.5
t = 11.2	1 000	331	299	258	1 120	254	889	170	I_x	60.1	4 500	102	7 000	57.0
d = 262	500	261	243	214	561	199	821	127	S_x	459	5 000	88.0	7 500	52.4
W250x33	2 500	349	299	243	1 290	271	813	210	M_r	132	3 000	112	5 500	55.6
W10x22	2 000	342	296	241	1 290	260	800	195	V_r	323	3 500	100	6 000	49.4
b = 146	1 500	332	290	240	1 290	245	783	177	L_u	2 020	4 000	88.4	6 500	44.4
t = 9.1	1 000	299	268	227	1 120	221	757	150	I_x	48.9	4 500	74.1	7 000	40.3
d = 258	500	230	213	185	561	176	703	112	S_x	379	5 000	63.6	7 500	36.9
W200x42	2 500	392	332	263	1 650	256	927	189	M_r	138	3 000	133	5 500	99.6
W8x28	2 000	381	327	262	1 650	244	910	174	V_r	302	3 500	126	6 000	92.9
b = 166	1 500	364	319	259	1 650	227	888	155	L_u	2 610	4 000	120	6 500	84.6
t = 11.8	1 000	300	268	226	1 120	201	854	129	I_x	40.9	4 500	113	7 000	77.5
d = 205	500	229	212	187	561	154	781	94.0	S_x	399	5 000	106	7 500	71.6
W200x36	2 500	339	286	225	1 420	224	804	168	M_r	118	3 000	112	5 500	79.3
W8x24	2 000	332	282	224	1 420	213	789	156	V_r	255	3 500	105	6 000	71.3
b = 165	1 500	319	276	222	1 420	199	770	139	L_u	2 510	4 000	99.0	6 500	64.6
t = 10.2	1 000	274	243	202	1 120	178	742	117	I_x	34.4	4 500	92.5	7 000	59.0
d = 201	500	205	189	165	561	139	684	84.9	S_x	342	5 000	85.9	7 500	54.4
W200x31	2 500	306	257	203	1 240	209	718	160	M_r	104	2 000	104	4 500	65.2
W8x21	2 000	300	254	202	1 240	200	705	149	V_r	275	2 500	96.7	5 000	57.0
b = 134	1 500	290	250	200	1 240	187	689	134	L_u	1 980	3 000	89.3	5 500	50.6
t = 10.2	1 000	262	231	191	1 120	169	665	113	I_x	31.4	3 500	81.7	6 000	45.6
d = 210	500	194	177	153	561	133	615	82.4	S_x	299	4 000	74.0	6 500	41.5
W200x27	2 500	261	218	171	1 050	180	612	140	M_r	86.6	2 000	85.3	4 500	47.5
W8x18	2 000	256	216	171	1 050	172	602	131	V_r	246	2 500	78.7	5 000	41.2
b = 133	1 500	249	213	169	1 050	162	588	119	L_u	1 890	3 000	71.5	5 500	36.4
t = 8.4	1 000	235	206	167	1 050	147	568	101	I_x	25.8	3 500	64.1	6 000	32.6
d = 207	500	173	157	134	561	118	529	74.0	S_x	249	4 000	56.0	6 500	29.6

Note: Resistances are based on a concrete density of 2000 kg/m³.

Units: M_r - kN·m, V_r - kN, L_u - mm, I_x - 10^6 mm⁴, S_x - 10^3 mm³, b - mm, t - mm, d - mm

$F_y = 345$ MPa

DEFLECTION OF FLEXURAL MEMBERS

The CSA S16-09 Standard considers deflection to be a serviceability limit state which must be accounted for in the design of flexural members. Annex D of S16-09, Recommended Maximum Values for Deflection for Specified Design Live, Snow and Wind Loads, provides some guidance to designers. Deflections tend to be more significant with longer clear spans, shallower members and with the use of high-strength steels. Deflection calculations are based on specified loads.

Three methods for dealing with deflection of prismatic beams are summarized below:

1. Compute the required minimum moment of inertia to satisfy the deflection constraint, prior to selection of the beam size.

   $I_{reqd} = W C_d B_d$, where

   I_{reqd} = required value of moment of inertia (10^6 mm^4)

   W = specified load value as described in Table 5-5 (kN)

   For distributed loading, W is the total applied load in kN. If there are multiple spans, W is the total applied load on a *single* span.

   For point loads, W is the value of a *single* point load in kN. For example, if point loads are applied at the quarter points (number of spaces, $n = 4$), the total load applied on a given span is $(n-1) W = 3 W$.

   C_d = value of deflection constant obtained from Figure 5-1 for the appropriate span L and span/deflection limit L / Δ (10^6 mm^4 / kN)

   B_d = a number to relate the actual load and support condition to a uniformly distributed load (UDL) on a simply-supported beam, Table 5-5. Values of B_d are computed for the maximum deflection within the span. For a uniformly distributed load, $B_d = 1.0$.

   The actual deflection of a beam can be computed as:

   $\Delta = (I_{reqd} / I) \Delta_m$, where

   Δ = actual deflection (mm)

   I = moment of inertia of beam (10^6 mm^4)

   Δ_m = maximum deflection permitted (mm)

   I_{reqd} = moment of inertia required to meet Δ_m (10^6 mm^4).

2. Compute deflections using the formulae for deflection of beams included with the Beam Diagrams and Formulae provided on pages 5-146 to 5-158.

3. The Beam Load Tables for WWF shapes, W shapes and rectangular HSS on pages 5-104 through 5-145 list approximate deflections for the various steel sections and spans, based on the tabulated uniformly distributed total factored loads at an assumed stress of 215 MPa for 300W steel, and 240 MPa for 350W steel. (See "Vertical Deflection" on page 5-82.) One can determine deflections (for live load only or for total load) caused by stress levels that are different from those assumed, by multiplying the tabulated deflection with the ratio of actual stress to assumed stress (either 215 or 240 MPa).

Examples

Given:

W410x85 section has been chosen for a simply supported non-composite beam spanning 10 m and subjected to a uniformly distributed specified load of 15 kN/m live and 7 kN/m dead. Check for live load deflection assuming the beam is laterally supported, 350W steel and deflection is limited to L/300 = 33 mm.

Solutions:

Method 1

From Table 5-5 on page 5-79:

$B_d = 1.0$ (simple-span UDL)

Using the graph (Figure 5-1, upper left) on page 5-78:

$C_d = 1.95 \times 10^6$ mm^4/kN (for $L/\Delta = 300$ and $L = 10$ m)

Or using the formula given on the same figure:

$C_d = \gamma L^2 / 15\,360 = 300 \times 10^2 / 15\,360 = 1.95 \times 10^6$ mm^4/kN

$I_{reqd} = W C_d B_d = (15 \times 10) \times 1.95 \times 10^6 \times 1.0 = 293 \times 10^6$ mm^4

For W410x85, $I_x = 315 \times 10^6$ mm^4

Actual deflection, $\Delta = (I_{reqd}/I)\Delta_m = (293/315)\,33 = 31$ mm

Method 2

From Beam Diagrams and Formulae, page 5-146:

$$\Delta = \frac{5wL^4}{384EI}, \text{ where}$$

$I = 315 \times 10^6$ mm^4, $E = 200\,000$ MPa

Therefore $\Delta = \dfrac{5 \times 15 \times (10 \times 10^3)^4}{384 \times 200\,000 \times 315 \times 10^6} = 31$ mm

Method 3

From Beam Load Tables, page 5-128, approximate deflection for W410x85 beam, span 10 m, loaded to a stress of 240 MPa = 61 mm

Stress due to live load is:

$$\frac{M}{S} = \frac{WL}{8S} = \frac{(15 \times 10 \times 10^3)(10 \times 10^3)}{8 \times 1510 \times 10^3} = 124 \text{ MPa}$$

Live load deflection is $(124/240)\,61 = 32$ mm

DEFLECTION CONSTANT C_d

Figure 5-1

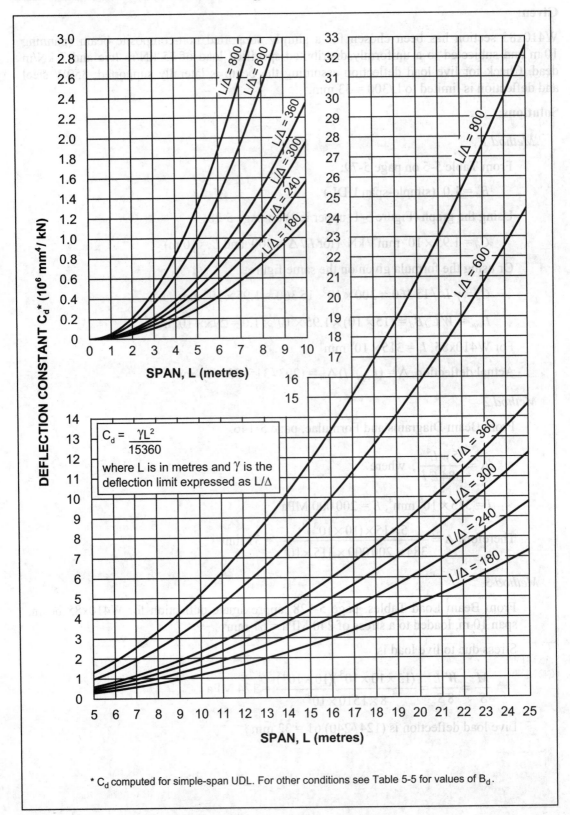

$$C_d = \frac{\gamma L^2}{15360}$$

where L is in metres and γ is the deflection limit expressed as L/Δ

* C_d computed for simple-span UDL. For other conditions see Table 5-5 for values of B_d.

Table 5-5

Values of B_d for Various Loadings & Support Conditions

LOADING CONDITION	a/L	B_d	LOADING CONDITION	a/L	B_d	LOADING CONDITION	B_d	LOADING CONDITION	B_d
(W at a, simply supported)	1.0	0.000	(W at a, fixed-fixed)	1.0	0.000	(W, fixed-fixed UDL)	1.00	(W, UDL)	0.200
	0.8	0.927		0.8	0.155				
	0.6	1.52		0.6	0.366				
	0.5	1.60		0.5	0.400				
	0.4	1.52		0.4	0.366	(W)	0.415	(W)	9.60
	0.2	0.927		0.2	0.155				
(W at a, cantilever)	1.0	1.00	(W at a, fixed)	1.0	0.200	(W, L/4 spacing)	1.43	(W, L/4 spacing)	2.24
	0.8	1.13		0.8	0.237				
	0.6	1.10		0.6	0.233				
	0.5	1.01		0.5	0.206				
	0.4	0.869		0.4	0.163	(W, triangular)	1.00	(W, triangular peak)	1.28
	0.2	0.477		0.2	0.0576				
(W at a)	1.0	0.415	(W at a)	1.0	0.415	(W W)	0.716	(W)	1.15
	0.8	0.456		0.8	0.503				
	0.6	0.393		0.6	0.539				
	0.5	0.325		0.5	0.520				
	0.4	0.243		0.4	0.467	(w w w)	1.17	(w w w)	1.93
	0.2	0.0794		0.2	0.271				
(W at a)	1.0	0.000	(W at a)	1.0	25.6	(www www)	1.60	(www)	2.69
	0.8	0.517		0.8	18.0				
	0.6	0.752		0.6	11.1				
	0.5	0.716		0.5	8.00	(W W)	0.416	(W)	0.703
	0.4	0.590		0.4	5.32				
	0.2	0.219		0.2	1.43				

$I_{required} = W \, C_d \, B_d$

Where: $I \quad 10^6 \text{ mm}^4$

$W \quad$ kN

C_d from graph (Figure 5-1)

B_d from this table = 1.0 for single span, UDL

(W W W)	0.529	(W W)	0.760
(w w w)	0.886	(w w)	1.24

LOADING CONDITION	n	B_d	LOADING CONDITION	n	B_d	LOADING CONDITION	B_d	LOADING CONDITION	B_d
(n-1)W, n = no. of equal spaces	2	1.60	(n-1)W, n = no. of equal spaces	2	0.400	(6W)	1.47	(2W 2W)	2.09
	3	2.73		3	0.593				
	4	3.80		4	0.800				
	5	4.84		5	0.998	(9W)	2.04	(3W 3W)	2.91
	6	5.87		6	1.20				
	7	6.89		7	1.40				

B_d is calculated at the position of maximum deflection. For multiple spans, each span length is L.

FACTORED RESISTANCE OF BEAMS

General

The following pages contain tables which can be used to select flexural members and tables for estimating maximum beam reactions. These tables include Beam Selection Tables on pages 5-86 to 5-103 and Beam Load Tables on pages 5-104 to 5-145. The Beam Selection Tables facilitate the proportioning of flexural members subject to forces and moments determined by elastic analysis. Some values in these tables may also be used for the selection of Class 1 flexural members for which the moments and forces have been determined by plastic analysis. The Beam Load Tables list total uniformly distributed factored loads for laterally supported beams.

When using these tables, factored moments or forces must be equal to or less than the appropriate factored resistances, V_r, M_r or M_r' given in the tables.

Beam Selection Tables

Tables

The Beam Selection Tables list beam sizes in descending order of their factored moment resistance M_r (shown in bold) based on full lateral support (Clause 13.5, CSA S16-09). Listed beams include all WWF 2000 to WWF 700 sizes, W shapes normally used as beams, and all Canadian C shapes. Tables for WWF sizes are based on $F_y = 350$ MPa for G40.21 grade 350W, while those for W shapes are based on $F_y = 345$ MPa, corresponding to the least value among the 3 grades represented (G40.21-350W, ASTM A992 and A572 grade 50). Tables for C shapes are based on G40.21-300W with $F_y = 300$ MPa. A table for S shapes based on ASTM A572 grade 50 steel with $F_y = 345$ MPa is also included.

Shapes shown in bold type are generally the economy sections, based on both M_r and mass. Other shapes listed below a bold-type section are heavier sections, but may be economy sections when depth limitations require a shallower beam, or when the shear resistance of a coped beam influences the beam selection.

For each beam size, the tables list the maximum unsupported length L_u for which the factored moment resistance M_r is applicable. In addition the tables list the factored moment resistance M_r' for laterally unsupported beams (Clause 13.6, S16-09) for selected values of the unbraced beam length greater than L_u. For other values of unbraced length greater than L_u, M_r' can be interpolated.

In place of a more accurate analysis, the destabilizing effect of beams loaded above the shear centre can be taken into account by increasing the effective unbraced length by a factor of 1.2 or 1.4 (depending on the end conditions), as specified in Clause 13.6.

The following items are included in the table:

V_r = factored shear resistance (kN)

= $\phi A_w F_s$ (Clause 13.4.1.1, S16-09)

I_x = moment of inertia about X-X axis (10^6 mm^4)

b = flange width (mm)

L_u = maximum unsupported beam length for which M_r is applicable (mm)

M_r = factored moment resistance for laterally supported members (kN·m)

   = $\phi Z_x F_y$ for Class 1 and Class 2 sections

   = $\phi S_x F_y$ for Class 3 sections (Clause 13.5, S16-09)

M_r' = factored moment resistance for tabulated unbraced beam length
     when greater than L_u (kN·m)

(M_r' is computed according to Clause 13.6 of S16-09 using $\omega_2 = 1.0$ in the expression for M_u.)

Design

Compute the maximum bending moment in the beam under factored loads M_f and the required moment of inertia I_{reqd} to meet the deflection limit using the specified loads. (For I_{reqd}, see "Deflection of Flexural Members", page 5-76.)

For a laterally supported beam, proceed up the M_r column until a value of $M_r > M_f$ is obtained. Any beam above will satisfy the factored moment requirement. Check to ensure that $V_r > V_f$, the maximum factored beam shear, that $I_x > I_{reqd}$, and that L_u is greater than the maximum unsupported beam length.

For a laterally unsupported beam, proceed up the M_r column until a value of $M_r > M_f$ is reached. Then move to the right across the table to the column headed by the unsupported length (or the first listed unsupported length greater than that required) to obtain a value of M_r'. Proceed up this column comparing a few beams that have an $M_r' > M_f$ and choose the lightest section. Check $V_r > V_f$ and $I_x > I_{reqd}$ if a deflection check is necessary.

Other Steel Grades

For steel grades where F_y is less than that used in the table, reduce the tabulated values by the ratio of the yield values. For steel grades with F_y greater than that used in the table, the tabulated values are conservative.

Plastic Analysis

For beams analysed plastically (Clause 8.3.2, S16-09), the Beam Selection Tables may be used to facilitate selection of a beam size as follows:

Proceed up the M_r column until a value of $M_r > M_f$ is obtained.

Any beam above will satisfy the factored moment requirement, provided the beam is a Class 1 section. (See Table 5-1 on pages 5-5 to 5-8 for the Class of Sections in Bending for various steel grades.)

Check to ensure that $0.8 V_r > V_f$, the maximum factored beam shear. (Clause 13.4.2)

Provide suitable lateral bracing. (Clause 13.7)

Beam Load Tables — WWF Beams and W Shapes

Loads

The Beam Load Tables list total uniformly distributed factored loads for simply supported beams with the top flange fully supported (i.e., the unsupported length of beam is less than or equal to L_u). Tables for WWF sizes are based on $F_y = 350$ MPa for G40.21 grade 350W, while those for W shapes are based on $F_y = 345$ MPa, corresponding to the least value among the 3 grades represented (G40.21 350W, ASTM A992 and A572 grade 50). Beam sizes listed include the same sections listed in the Beam Selection Tables. To obtain the net supported load (factored), the beam factored dead load should be deducted from the total tabulated load.

For laterally supported beams, the Beam Load Tables may also be used to estimate loads for other loading conditions by dividing the tabulated values by the coefficient of the "Equivalent Tabular Load" value for the particular loading condition. (See "Beam Diagrams and Formulae", pages 5-146 to 5-158.) Thus, for a simple beam, laterally supported and carrying equal concentrated loads at the third points (loading condition 9), each factored concentrated load is 3/8 of the tabulated uniformly distributed factored load, and the total load is 3/4 of the tabulated load for the same span.

For steel grades where F_y is less than that used in the table, reduce the tabulated values by the ratio of the yield values. For steel grades with F_y greater than that used in the table, the tabulated values are conservative.

The Beam Load Tables (sometimes referred to as "book loads") are frequently used to obtain maximum reactions for the design of connections, when beam reactions are not provided on the structural design drawings. It should be noted that reactions computed from Beam Load Tables are generally lower than beam reactions for compositely designed beams.

Vertical Deflection

The column headed "Approximate Deflection" lists the approximate theoretical mid-span deflection, at assumed bending stress levels of 215 MPa for 300W steel and 240 MPa for 350W, ASTM A992 and A572 grade 50 steels, for beams of various spans designed to support the tabulated factored loads.

The listed deflections are based on the nominal depth of the beam, and are calculated using the formula:

$$\Delta = \frac{5}{384} \frac{W L^3}{E I}$$

For $E = 200\ 000$ MPa and an assumed bending unit stress of 215 MPa this formula reduces to:

$$\Delta = \frac{224 \times 10^{-6} \times L^2}{d} \quad \text{where:}$$

Δ = deflection (mm)

W = total uniform load including the dead load of the beam (kN)

L = beam span (mm)

E = modulus of elasticity (MPa)

I = moment of inertia of beam (mm^4)

d = depth of beam (mm)

More accurate deflections can be determined by multiplying the approximate deflection values listed by the ratio of actual bending stress to the assumed unit bending stress of 215 MPa for 300W steel or 240 MPa for 350W, ASTM A992 and A527 grade 50 steels. (See also "Deflection of Flexural Members", page 5-76.)

Web Shear

For beams with very short spans and high end shear, and with flanges coped at the supports, the loads for beams may be limited by the shear capacity of the web rather than by the bending capacity of the section. The designer should consider the effect of copes on the load-carrying capacity of beams when selecting appropriate member sizes.

Both the depth and length of copes can vary considerably depending on the relative size and elevation of intersecting beams. For rolled shapes and for welded wide-flange sections, the Beam Load Tables list the factored shear resistance V_r for uncoped beams (Clause 13.4.1.1, S16-09). The factored shear resistance of singly and doubly coped beams should be adjusted for the depth and length of the copes, to account for possible non-uniform shear distribution across the effective web depth (see Clauses 13.4.3 and 13.11) and to account for local web buckling.

Web Crippling & Yielding

Bearing stiffeners are required when the factored compressive resistance (Clause 14.3.2, S16-09) of the web is exceeded. For most common beam sizes the bearing resistance is governed by web crippling, except for very short bearing lengths when web yielding may govern.

The Beam Load Tables for W shapes list values of R (kN), the maximum factored end reaction for 100 mm of bearing based on web yielding per Clause 14.3.2(b)(i), and values of the increment in bearing resistance, G (kN), per 10 millimetres of bearing length. For steels with a minimum specified yield stress other than $F_y = 345$ MPa, values of R and G can be computed by multiplying the values listed by the ratio $F_y / 345$. Also listed is the value of B_r' (kN), the factored bearing resistance based on web crippling per Clause 14.3.2(b)(ii).

For WWF shapes, values of R, G and B_r' are not listed, since the web slenderness of WWF shapes generally exceeds $1100 / \sqrt{F_y}$ and bearing stiffeners would be required (Clause 14.4).

Proper lateral support must be provided for the top flanges of beams at the reaction point to ensure that the web crippling strength is not decreased.

Properties and Dimensions

The properties and dimensions listed on the Beam Load Tables for rolled shapes include the beam depth d, the flange width b, the flange thickness t, and the web thickness w (all in millimetres). Dimensions t and w are required for calculating the compressive resistance of the web (yielding or crippling) per Clause 14.3.2, S16-09.

Beam Load Tables — Rectangular HSS

The Beam Load Tables for rectangular Hollow Structural Sections (HSS) on pages 5-134 to 5-145 list the total uniformly distributed factored loads for laterally supported rectangular HSS in strong-axis bending. As with the Beam Load Tables for W shapes, the "Equivalent Tabular Load" values for other loading conditions may be used. Two sets of tables are provided: one set based on CSA G40.21-350W steel and another based on ASTM A500 Grade C steel. See page 6-97 for more information on HSS produced to ASTM A500.

Approximate deflections listed are based on an assumed bending stress of 240 MPa.

Examples

1. Given:

Design a simply-supported beam spanning 8 m to carry a uniformly distributed load of 15 kN/m specified live load and 7 kN/m specified dead load. The dead load includes an assumed beam dead load of 0.7 kN/m. Live load deflection is limited to L/300. Assume that the beam frames into supporting members and that the beam is laterally supported. Use ASTM A992 steel.

Solutions:

(a) Using Beam Selection Tables — Elastic Analysis:

Factored load $= \alpha_D D + \alpha_L L = (1.25 \times 7) + (1.50 \times 15) = 31.3$ kN/m

M_f (factored load moment) $= wL^2/8 = 31.3 \times 8^2/8 = 250$ kN·m

V_f (factored end shear) $= wL/2 = 31.3 \times 8/2 = 125$ kN

Compute I_{reqd} to meet deflection limit, see page 5-76

For UDL, $B_d = 1.0$; from Figure 5-1, for $L/\Delta = 300$, $C_d = 1.25 \times 10^6$

$I_{reqd} = W C_d B_d = 15 \times 8 \times 1.25 \times 10^6 \times 1.0 = 150 \times 10^6$ mm^4

From table page 5-96, select a W410x46

$M_r = 275$ kN·m > 250 kN·m $V_r = 578$ kN > 125 kN

$I_x = 156 \times 10^6$ mm$^4 > 150 \times 10^6$ mm^4 The W410x46 beam is adequate

(b) Using Beam Load Tables:

Total factored load, $W_f = 31.3 \times 8 = 250$ kN

End reaction is $V_f = 250/2 = 125$ kN

From tables page 5-128, select a W410x46

$W_r (8\,000) = 275$ kN > 250 kN

$V_r = 578$ kN > 125 kN (uncoped)

(If the beam were load bearing rather than framing into a girder, it would be necessary to check that the factored bearing resistance is greater than or equal to the factored end reaction.)

Approximate deflection listed at assumed stress of 240 MPa = 39 mm

$$\text{Stress at specified live load} = \frac{M_{Live}}{S_x} = \frac{15}{31.3} \times \frac{250 \times 10^6}{773 \times 10^3} = 155 \text{ MPa}$$

Live load deflection = $39 \times 155 / 240 = 25$ mm

$L / 300 = 8\,000 / 300 = 27$ mm > 25 mm

The W410x46 beam is adequate.

2. Given:

Same as in Example (1), except that the beam is laterally supported at mid-span and at the ends of the beam only. It is assumed that the gravity loading is applied on the top flange.

Solution:

The point of application of the loading is located above the shear centre. In the absence of a more accurate analysis and in accordance with S16-09 Clause 13.6, the effective length is taken equal to 1.2 times the unbraced length (assuming pin-ended segments between the bracing points):

Effective unbraced length = $1.2 (8\,000 / 2) = 4\,800$ mm.

As in Example (1), consider a W410x46 on the basis of M_r and check M_r' for an unbraced length of 4 800 mm $\approx 5\,000$ mm:

$M_r' (5\,000) = 99.9$ kN·m < 250 kN·m

Thus the W410x46 is not adequate; therefore, check further up the table for the lightest section with $M_r' > 250$ kN·m for an unbraced length of 5 000 mm.

For W360x64, $M_r' (5\,000) = 273$ kN·m

A more accurate value could be obtained by linear interpolation between 4 500 and 5 000 mm, if desired:

$M_r' (4\,800) = 281$ kN·m > 250 kN·m

$V_r = 548$ kN > 125 kN (uncoped)

$I_x = 178 \times 10^6$ mm$^4 > 150 \times 10^6$

The W360x64 beam is adequate.

BEAM SELECTION TABLE
WWF and W Shapes

CSA G40.21 350W
ASTM A992, A572 Grade 50

Designation	V_r	I_x	b	L_u	M_r	Factored moment resistance M_r' (kN·m) Unbraced length (mm)					
	kN	10^6 mm^4	mm	mm	$\leq L_u$	5 000	5 500	6 000	6 500	7 000	7 500
†WWF2000x732	3 640	63 900	550	7 620	20 100	—	—	—	—	—	—
WWF1800x700	4 070	50 400	550	7 300	19 800	—	—	—	—	—	19 600
WWF1800x659	4 050	46 600	550	7 170	18 300	—	—	—	—	—	18 100
†WWF2000x648	3 600	54 200	550	7 370	17 100	—	—	—	—	—	17 000
WWF1800x617	4 020	42 700	550	7 020	16 900	—	—	—	—	—	16 600
†WWF2000x607	3 590	49 300	550	7 210	15 500	—	—	—	—	—	15 300
WWF1800x575	4 000	38 800	550	6 860	15 500	—	—	—	—	15 400	15 000
†WWF1600x622	2 360	37 600	550	8 010	14 800	—	—	—	—	—	—
W1000x883	10 200	21 000	424	6 850	14 100	—	—	—	—	14 000	13 800
WWF1400x597	2 730	28 100	550	7 790	13 900	—	—	—	—	—	—
†WWF1600x580	2 350	34 600	550	7 890	13 600	—	—	—	—	—	—
WWF1800x510	3 980	32 400	500	5 960	13 200	—	—	13 100	12 800	12 400	12 000
†WWF2000x542	3 570	41 400	500	6 310	13 000	—	—	—	12 900	12 600	12 300
†WWF1600x538	2 330	31 600	550	7 750	12 400	—	—	—	—	—	—
W1000x748	8 540	17 300	417	6 390	11 800	—	—	—	11 700	11 500	11 300
WWF1400x513	2 680	23 500	550	7 510	11 700	—	—	—	—	—	—
†WWF1600x496	2 320	28 400	550	7 620	11 200	—	—	—	—	—	—
WWF1400x471	2 660	21 100	550	7 360	10 500	—	—	—	—	—	—
W1000x642	7 300	14 500	412	6 060	9 970	—	—	—	9 790	9 580	9 370
W920x656	6 980	13 400	431	6 590	9 750	—	—	—	—	9 610	9 430
WWF1200x487	2 890	16 700	550	7 710	9 640	—	—	—	—	—	—
†WWF1600x431	2 300	23 400	500	6 720	9 230	—	—	—	—	9 110	8 900
W1000x591	6 610	13 300	409	5 920	9 160	—	—	—	9 130	8 930	8 730	8 530
WWF1400x405	2 640	17 300	500	6 450	8 760	—	—	—	8 740	8 530	8 310
W1000x584	7 790	12 500	314	4 530	8 690	8 480	8 240	8 000	7 760	7 520	7 270
W920x588	6 190	11 800	427	6 370	8 660	—	—	—	8 620	8 450	8 280
W1000x554	6 240	12 300	408	5 810	8 540	—	—	8 470	8 280	8 080	7 880
WWF1100x458	2 210	13 600	550	7 890	8 540	—	—	—	—	—	—
W1000x539	5 990	12 000	407	5 790	8 320	—	—	8 240	8 050	7 860	7 660
W1100x499	5 960	12 900	405	5 490	8 260	—	8 250	8 050	7 830	7 600	7 360
WWF1200x418	2 890	13 800	500	6 790	8 060	—	—	—	—	7 990	7 810
W840x576	5 990	10 100	411	6 320	7 950	—	—	—	7 900	7 750	7 600
W920x537	5 620	10 700	425	6 220	7 860	—	—	—	7 770	7 600	7 440
WWF1000x447	2 210	11 100	550	8 030	7 620	—	—	—	—	—	—

Note: For unbraced beam segments loaded above the shear centre, see CSA S16-09 Clause 13.6.

† Class 3 section

Nominal mass	Factored moment resistance M_r' (kN·m)									Imperial designation
	Unbraced length (mm)									
kg/m	8 000	9 000	10 000	11 000	12 000	14 000	16 000	18 000	20 000	
732	19 800	19 000	18 100	17 100	16 100	13 800	11 100	9 060	7 610	**WWF79x490**
700	19 200	18 300	17 400	16 300	15 300	12 800	10 200	8 420	7 120	**WWF71x470**
659	17 700	16 800	15 900	14 900	13 800	11 300	8 990	7 360	6 190	**WWF71x442**
648	16 600	15 900	15 000	14 100	13 100	10 800	8 510	6 910	5 760	**WWF79x436**
617	16 200	15 400	14 500	13 500	12 400	9 900	7 810	6 370	5 330	**WWF71x415**
607	15 000	14 300	13 500	12 600	11 600	9 360	7 330	5 930	4 920	**WWF79x408**
575	14 700	13 900	13 000	12 000	11 000	8 530	6 700	5 440	4 540	**WWF71x388**
622	—	14 300	13 700	13 100	12 400	11 000	9 370	7 750	6 580	WWF63x419
883	13 600	13 100	12 700	12 200	11 800	10 900	10 000	9 070	8 080	W40x593
597	13 800	13 200	12 700	12 100	11 500	10 100	8 610	7 180	6 140	WWF55x402
580	—	13 100	12 500	11 900	11 200	9 850	8 170	6 730	5 680	WWF63x388
510	11 600	10 700	9 750	8 650	7 350	5 530	4 340	3 530	2 940	**WWF71x344**
542	11 900	11 100	10 200	9 260	8 100	6 070	4 750	3 850	3 200	WWF79x364
538	12 300	11 800	11 300	10 700	10 100	8 710	7 050	5 770	4 850	WWF63x361
748	11 100	10 600	10 200	9 760	9 320	8 450	7 490	6 550	5 830	W40x503
513	11 400	10 900	10 400	9 850	9 250	7 950	6 400	5 270	4 460	WWF55x344
496	11 000	10 600	10 000	9 480	8 890	7 590	6 010	4 890	4 090	**WWF63x333**
471	10 200	9 780	9 280	8 730	8 150	6 840	5 410	4 430	3 730	**WWF55x316**
642	9 160	8 730	8 300	7 860	7 420	6 520	5 550	4 830	4 280	W40x431
656	9 250	8 890	8 520	8 150	7 790	7 060	6 270	5 470	4 850	W36x441
487	9 530	9 160	8 750	8 320	7 870	6 910	5 770	4 800	4 090	WWF47x326
431	8 670	8 180	7 630	7 040	6 410	4 920	3 870	3 140	2 630	**WWF63x289**
591	8 320	7 900	7 470	7 040	6 610	5 650	4 790	4 160	3 680	W40x397
405	8 080	7 580	7 030	6 440	5 800	4 390	3 470	2 840	2 390	**WWF55x272**
584	7 030	6 540	6 050	5 500	4 960	4 150	3 580	3 150	2 810	W40x392
588	8 100	7 750	7 390	7 030	6 670	5 950	5 100	4 440	3 930	W36x395
554	7 670	7 250	6 830	6 400	5 970	4 980	4 220	3 660	3 230	W40x372
458	8 500	8 190	7 850	7 500	7 120	6 340	5 450	4 550	3 890	WWF43x307
539	7 460	7 040	6 620	6 200	5 770	4 790	4 050	3 510	3 100	W40x362
499	7 120	6 620	6 100	5 570	4 920	3 960	3 310	2 840	2 490	**W44x335**
418	7 630	7 230	6 790	6 330	5 850	4 700	3 780	3 130	2 670	WWF47x281
576	7 440	7 130	6 820	6 510	6 210	5 590	4 890	4 270	3 790	W33x387
537	7 270	6 920	6 570	6 210	5 860	5 100	4 310	3 740	3 300	W36x361
447	—	7 360	7 080	6 780	6 470	5 820	5 140	4 340	3 730	WWF39x300

F_y taken as 350 MPa for WWF shapes and 345 MPa for W shapes. $\phi = 0.90$

BEAM SELECTION TABLE
WWF and W Shapes

CSA G40.21 350W
ASTM A992, A572 Grade 50

Designation	V_r	I_x	b	L_u	M_r ≤ L_u	Factored moment resistance M_r' (kN·m) — Unbraced length (mm)					
	kN	10^6 mm^4	mm	mm		4 500	5 000	5 500	6 000	6 500	7 000
WWF1400x358	2 640	14 500	400	5 000	**7 470**	—	—	7 240	6 990	6 730	6 450
W1000x483	5 310	10 700	404	5 650	7 420	—	—	—	7 300	7 120	6 930
W760x582	5 960	8 620	396	6 460	7 390	—	—	—	—	7 380	7 260
W1000x494	6 580	10 300	309	4 280	7 270	7 170	6 950	6 720	6 480	6 250	6 010
W840x527	5 460	9 150	409	6 150	7 230	—	—	—	—	7 140	6 990
W1100x433	5 000	11 300	402	5 400	**7 200**	—	—	7 170	6 970	6 770	6 560
W1000x486	6 370	10 200	308	4 270	7 200	7 100	6 880	6 660	6 420	6 190	5 950
WWF1200x380	2 890	12 300	500	6 630	7 180	—	—	—	—	—	7 060
W920x491	5 080	9 700	422	6 070	7 170	—	—	—	—	7 040	6 880
WWF1100x388	2 210	11 200	500	6 970	7 060	—	—	—	—	—	7 050
W1000x443	4 890	9 670	402	5 530	6 770	—	—	—	6 610	6 440	6 250
W760x531	5 380	7 770	393	6 230	6 710	—	—	—	—	6 640	6 520
WWF900x417	1 370	8 680	550	8 310	6 550	—	—	—	—	—	—
W920x449	4 660	8 780	423	6 000	6 520	—	—	—	—	6 370	6 220
W1100x390	4 510	10 100	400	5 310	**6 460**	—	—	6 390	6 210	6 020	5 820
W840x473	4 830	8 130	406	5 980	6 460	—	—	—	6 450	6 320	6 170
W1000x438	5 660	9 090	305	4 160	6 430	6 290	6 080	5 860	5 630	5 400	5 170
W1000x412	4 360	9 100	402	5 530	6 370	—	—	—	6 220	6 050	5 880
W690x548	5 550	6 730	372	6 400	6 330	—	—	—	—	6 310	6 210
WWF1000x377	2 210	9 120	500	7 080	6 300	—	—	—	—	—	—
WWF1100x351	2 210	9 930	500	6 810	6 270	—	—	—	—	—	6 220
W1000x415	5 430	8 530	304	4 080	6 090	5 920	5 710	5 490	5 260	5 030	4 800
W920x420	4 350	8 170	422	5 910	6 090	—	—	—	6 060	5 920	5 770
WWF1200x333	2 890	10 200	400	5 150	6 080	—	—	5 960	5 770	5 570	5 360
W760x484	4 890	6 990	390	6 040	6 050	—	—	—	—	5 950	5 830
W840x433	4 430	7 360	404	5 850	5 870	—	—	—	5 830	5 700	5 560
W610x551	5 620	5 570	347	6 620	5 780	—	—	—	—	—	5 710
W1000x393	5 080	8 080	303	4 050	5 740	5 570	5 370	5 160	4 940	4 710	4 480
W690x500	5 000	6 060	369	6 140	5 740	—	—	—	—	5 670	5 570
W1000x371	3 890	8 140	400	5 440	**5 710**	—	—	5 700	5 550	5 390	5 220
W1100x343	3 850	8 670	400	5 230	**5 620**	—	—	5 530	5 370	5 190	5 010
W920x390	4 090	7 450	420	5 810	5 590	—	—	—	5 540	5 400	5 260
WWF1000x340	2 210	8 060	500	6 910	5 580	—	—	—	—	—	5 550
W760x434	4 320	6 190	387	5 830	5 400	—	—	—	5 360	5 250	5 130
WWF1200x302	2 890	8 970	400	4 980	5 390	—	5 380	5 220	5 040	4 850	4 640
WWF900x347	1 370	7 100	500	7 320	5 390	—	—	—	—	—	—
W920x381	4 760	6 970	310	4 250	5 280	5 200	5 020	4 850	4 660	4 470	4 280
W840x392	3 970	6 600	401	5 720	5 280	—	—	—	5 210	5 080	4 950
WWF1100x304	2 210	8 220	400	5 310	5 260	—	—	—	5 060	4 890	4 720
W920x368	3 870	6 960	419	5 730	5 250	—	—	—	5 180	5 050	4 910
W690x457	4 550	5 470	367	5 920	5 220	—	—	—	5 200	5 100	5 000
W610x498	5 030	4 950	343	6 230	5 190	—	—	—	—	5 140	5 060
W1000x350	4 360	7 230	302	4 010	5 150	4 980	4 780	4 580	4 370	4 160	3 940

CHECK WWF AVAILABILITY

See page 6-29

Note: For unbraced beam segments loaded above the shear centre, see CSA S16-09 Clause 13.6.

Nominal mass	Factored moment resistance M_r' (kN·m)									Imperial designation
	Unbraced length (mm)									
kg/m	8 000	9 000	10 000	11 000	12 000	14 000	16 000	18 000	20 000	
358	5 830	5 160	4 330	3 650	3 130	2 400	1 920	1 590	1 360	**WWF55x240**
483	6 540	6 140	5 730	5 310	4 860	3 940	3 320	2 860	2 520	W40x324
582	7 000	6 750	6 500	6 250	6 000	5 500	5 010	4 420	3 940	W30x391
494	5 520	5 040	4 470	3 970	3 570	2 970	2 550	2 240	1 990	W40x331
527	6 690	6 390	6 080	5 780	5 470	4 860	4 140	3 610	3 200	W33x354
433	6 110	5 640	5 140	4 580	4 010	3 190	2 650	2 260	1 970	**W44x290**
486	5 460	4 980	4 410	3 910	3 510	2 930	2 510	2 200	1 960	W40x327
380	6 720	6 330	5 920	5 470	5 000	3 890	3 100	2 560	2 160	WWF47x255
491	6 550	6 210	5 860	5 510	5 150	4 350	3 660	3 170	2 790	W36x330
388	6 750	6 420	6 070	5 690	5 300	4 400	3 550	2 960	2 530	WWF43x260
443	5 880	5 480	5 070	4 660	4 160	3 360	2 810	2 420	2 130	W40x297
531	6 270	6 020	5 770	5 520	5 270	4 780	4 230	3 700	3 300	W30x357
417	—	6 400	6 180	5 950	5 710	5 210	4 690	4 110	3 550	WWF35x279
449	5 910	5 580	5 240	4 890	4 550	3 740	3 140	2 700	2 370	W36x302
390	5 400	4 950	4 470	3 890	3 390	2 690	2 220	1 880	1 640	**W44x262**
473	5 890	5 590	5 290	4 990	4 680	4 010	3 400	2 950	2 610	W33x318
438	4 700	4 190	3 640	3 220	2 890	2 400	2 050	1 790	1 600	W40x294
412	5 510	5 130	4 730	4 330	3 830	3 080	2 570	2 200	1 930	W40x277
548	6 010	5 800	5 600	5 400	5 200	4 810	4 410	3 960	3 540	W27x368
377	6 060	5 780	5 480	5 170	4 840	4 130	3 360	2 810	2 420	WWF39x253
351	5 930	5 620	5 280	4 920	4 530	3 620	2 890	2 390	2 030	WWF43x236
415	4 320	3 780	3 280	2 890	2 590	2 140	1 830	1 600	1 420	W40x278
420	5 470	5 140	4 810	4 470	4 120	3 330	2 790	2 390	2 100	W36x282
333	4 900	4 410	3 820	3 230	2 780	2 160	1 740	1 460	1 250	WWF47x224
484	5 580	5 340	5 090	4 850	4 600	4 110	3 540	3 100	2 760	W30x326
433	5 280	4 990	4 690	4 400	4 100	3 410	2 880	2 490	2 200	W33x291
551	5 550	5 390	5 230	5 070	4 910	4 590	4 280	3 970	3 600	W24x370
393	4 020	3 470	3 000	2 650	2 370	1 950	1 670	1 450	1 290	W40x264
500	5 370	5 170	4 970	4 770	4 570	4 180	3 770	3 310	2 960	W27x336
371	4 880	4 510	4 120	3 700	3 240	2 590	2 150	1 840	1 600	**W40x249**
343	4 610	4 190	3 730	3 180	2 760	2 160	1 770	1 490	1 290	**W44x230**
390	4 960	4 650	4 320	3 980	3 610	2 890	2 400	2 060	1 800	W36x262
340	5 310	5 040	4 760	4 450	4 130	3 380	2 720	2 260	1 930	WWF39x228
434	4 890	4 650	4 410	4 160	3 920	3 380	2 880	2 520	2 230	W30x292
302	4 200	3 710	3 110	2 620	2 250	1 730	1 390	1 150	978	WWF47x203
347	5 250	5 030	4 790	4 550	4 300	3 770	3 150	2 660	2 290	WWF35x233
381	3 890	3 470	3 010	2 650	2 370	1 960	1 670	1 460	1 300	W36x256
392	4 680	4 400	4 110	3 820	3 520	2 850	2 400	2 070	1 820	W33x263
304	4 350	3 950	3 530	3 000	2 590	2 010	1 630	1 370	1 180	WWF43x204
368	4 620	4 310	3 990	3 660	3 260	2 600	2 160	1 840	1 610	W36x247
457	4 800	4 610	4 410	4 210	4 010	3 620	3 170	2 790	2 490	W27x307
498	4 900	4 740	4 580	4 420	4 260	3 950	3 640	3 280	2 940	W24x335
350	3 490	2 950	2 540	2 230	1 980	1 630	1 380	1 200	1 070	W40x235

F_y taken as 350 MPa for WWF shapes and 345 MPa for W shapes. $\phi = 0.90$

Designation	V_r kN	I_x 10^6 mm^4	b mm	L_u mm	M_r $\leq L_u$	Factored moment resistance M_r' (kN·m) Unbraced length (mm)					
						4 000	4 500	5 000	5 500	6 000	6 500
W1000x321	3 250	6 960	400	5 360	**4 910**	—	—	—	4 870	4 730	4 590
W920x344	3 670	6 480	418	5 670	4 910	—	—	—	—	4 830	4 700
W760x389	3 880	5 450	385	5 640	4 810	—	—	—	—	4 730	4 620
W840x359	3 750	5 920	403	5 630	4 780	—	—	—	—	4 700	4 570
W920x345	4 270	6 260	308	4 170	4 750	—	4 650	4 480	4 310	4 130	3 950
W690x419	4 100	4 950	364	5 730	4 750	—	—	—	—	4 700	4 600
WWF900x309	1 370	6 240	500	7 160	4 730	—	—	—	—	—	—
WWF800x339	1 370	5 500	500	7 490	4 690	—	—	—	—	—	—
W610x455	4 520	4 440	340	5 940	4 690	—	—	—	—	4 680	4 600
WWF1000x293	2 210	6 640	400	5 400	4 660	—	—	—	4 640	4 510	4 370
WWF1100x273	2 210	7 160	400	5 150	4 630	—	—	—	4 540	4 390	4 240
W1000x314	3 910	6 440	300	3 910	**4 630**	4 600	4 430	4 240	4 050	3 850	3 640
WWF1200x263	2 890	7 250	300	3 560	4 470	4 300	4 090	3 850	3 600	3 330	3 040
W1000x296	3 230	6 200	400	5 230	**4 440**	—	—	—	4 370	4 240	4 110
W840x329	3 480	5 360	401	5 530	4 350	—	—	—	—	4 240	4 130
W690x384	3 760	4 490	362	5 550	4 350	—	—	—	—	4 260	4 170
W760x350	3 440	4 870	382	5 510	4 320	—	—	—	—	4 220	4 110
W610x415	4 100	4 000	338	5 700	4 250	—	—	—	—	4 210	4 130
W920x313	4 030	5 480	309	4 060	4 220	—	4 090	3 940	3 770	3 600	3 420
WWF800x300	1 370	4 840	500	7 280	4 130	—	—	—	—	—	—
WWF1000x262	2 210	5 780	400	5 230	4 100	—	—	—	4 030	3 910	3 780
W1000x272	3 250	5 540	300	3 870	**3 970**	3 940	3 780	3 620	3 440	3 260	3 060
W840x299	3 190	4 800	400	5 430	3 940	—	—	—	3 930	3 820	3 710
W920x289	3 690	5 050	308	4 010	3 910	—	3 780	3 620	3 460	3 300	3 120
W690x350	3 450	4 030	360	5 410	3 910	—	—	—	3 900	3 810	3 710
WWF900x262	1 370	5 110	400	5 630	3 910	—	—	—	—	3 830	3 730
W460x464	4 490	2 900	305	7 060	3 850	—	—	—	—	—	—
W760x314	3 170	4 290	384	5 420	3 820	—	—	—	3 800	3 710	3 610
W610x372	3 620	3 530	335	5 450	3 790	—	—	—	3 780	3 700	3 620
WWF1100x234	2 210	5 720	300	3 710	3 780	3 690	3 520	3 340	3 140	2 930	2 710
W920x271	3 480	4 720	307	3 970	**3 660**	—	3 520	3 380	3 220	3 060	2 890
W690x323	3 120	3 710	359	5 300	3 630	—	—	—	3 600	3 510	3 420
W1000x249	3 220	4 810	300	3 740	**3 510**	3 440	3 290	3 130	2 960	2 780	2 590
W760x284	2 870	3 830	382	5 300	3 450	—	—	—	3 410	3 320	3 220
W610x341	3 310	3 180	333	5 250	3 450	—	—	—	3 410	3 330	3 260
W460x421	4 050	2 570	302	6 600	3 450	—	—	—	—	—	—
W920x253	3 260	4 380	306	3 930	3 420	3 400	3 270	3 130	2 980	2 820	2 660
WWF900x231	1 350	4 410	400	5 460	3 400	—	—	—	—	3 300	3 200
WWF800x253	1 370	3 950	400	5 730	3 400	—	—	—	—	3 360	3 270
WWF1000x223	2 210	4 590	300	3 790	3 310	3 250	3 110	2 960	2 800	2 620	2 440
W840x251	2 990	3 860	292	3 890	3 200	3 170	3 050	2 920	2 790	2 650	2 500
W690x289	2 780	3 260	356	5 160	3 200	—	—	—	3 140	3 060	2 970
W920x238	3 090	4 060	305	3 890	**3 170**	3 140	3 020	2 890	2 740	2 590	2 430
W460x384	3 630	2 290	299	6 190	3 110	—	—	—	—	—	3 080
W760x257	2 630	3 430	381	5 230	3 100	—	—	—	3 050	2 960	2 870
W610x307	2 960	2 840	330	5 080	3 080	—	—	—	3 020	2 950	2 870

Note: For unbraced beam segments loaded above the shear centre, see CSA S16-09 Clause 13.6.

Nominal mass	Factored moment resistance M$_r$' (kN·m)									Imperial designation
	Unbraced length (mm)									
kg/m	7 000	8 000	9 000	10 000	11 000	12 000	14 000	16 000	18 000	
321	4 440	4 120	3 780	3 420	2 980	2 600	2 050	1 690	1 430	**W40x215**
344	4 560	4 280	3 980	3 660	3 340	2 930	2 330	1 920	1 640	W36x231
389	4 510	4 270	4 040	3 790	3 550	3 300	2 740	2 330	2 030	W30x261
359	4 450	4 190	3 910	3 630	3 340	3 000	2 420	2 020	1 740	W33x241
345	3 760	3 380	2 940	2 530	2 220	1 980	1 630	1 390	1 210	W36x232
419	4 510	4 310	4 110	3 910	3 720	3 520	3 120	2 680	2 350	W27x281
309	—	4 560	4 350	4 130	3 900	3 650	3 120	2 520	2 110	WWF35x208
339	—	4 610	4 430	4 240	4 050	3 850	3 440	2 980	2 530	WWF31x228
455	4 520	4 360	4 200	4 040	3 880	3 730	3 420	3 100	2 740	W24x306
293	4 230	3 920	3 580	3 230	2 800	2 420	1 900	1 550	1 310	WWF39x197
273	4 070	3 720	3 330	2 860	2 410	2 070	1 600	1 280	1 070	WWF43x184
314	3 420	2 940	2 460	2 110	1 840	1 640	1 340	1 130	979	**W40x211**
263	2 670	2 100	1 710	1 430	1 220	1 060	834	684	578	WWF47x176
296	3 960	3 650	3 320	2 960	2 530	2 190	1 720	1 410	1 190	**W40x199**
329	4 010	3 760	3 490	3 210	2 930	2 580	2 060	1 720	1 470	W33x221
384	4 070	3 880	3 680	3 480	3 290	3 090	2 650	2 270	1 990	W27x258
350	4 000	3 770	3 540	3 300	3 060	2 800	2 290	1 930	1 680	W30x235
415	4 050	3 890	3 730	3 570	3 420	3 260	2 960	2 600	2 290	W24x279
313	3 240	2 860	2 410	2 070	1 810	1 600	1 310	1 110	962	W36x210
300	—	4 010	3 840	3 660	3 470	3 270	2 860	2 370	1 990	WWF31x202
262	3 640	3 340	3 020	2 650	2 240	1 930	1 500	1 210	1 010	WWF39x176
272	2 860	2 390	1 990	1 690	1 470	1 300	1 050	883	761	**W40x183**
299	3 600	3 350	3 090	2 820	2 520	2 200	1 750	1 450	1 240	W33x201
289	2 940	2 560	2 130	1 820	1 590	1 410	1 140	963	833	W36x194
350	3 620	3 430	3 240	3 040	2 850	2 660	2 210	1 890	1 650	W27x235
262	3 620	3 380	3 130	2 860	2 580	2 240	1 760	1 450	1 230	WWF35x176
464	—	3 760	3 670	3 580	3 490	3 400	3 230	3 050	2 870	W18x311
314	3 500	3 290	3 060	2 830	2 600	2 310	1 870	1 570	1 360	W30x211
372	3 550	3 390	3 230	3 080	2 920	2 770	2 440	2 110	1 860	W24x250
234	2 450	1 930	1 570	1 320	1 120	978	770	632	535	WWF43x157
271	2 710	2 320	1 930	1 640	1 430	1 260	1 020	860	742	**W36x182**
323	3 330	3 140	2 940	2 750	2 560	2 340	1 930	1 650	1 430	W27x217
249	2 400	1 940	1 600	1 360	1 170	1 030	831	694	596	**W40x167**
284	3 120	2 910	2 690	2 460	2 210	1 940	1 560	1 310	1 120	W30x191
341	3 180	3 020	2 870	2 710	2 560	2 400	2 050	1 760	1 550	W24x229
421	3 410	3 320	3 230	3 140	3 050	2 970	2 790	2 620	2 450	W18x283
253	2 490	2 090	1 730	1 470	1 270	1 120	905	758	653	W36x170
231	3 100	2 870	2 630	2 360	2 040	1 760	1 370	1 110	933	WWF35x156
253	3 180	2 990	2 790	2 570	2 350	2 090	1 660	1 370	1 170	WWF31x170
223	2 250	1 790	1 460	1 230	1 050	920	729	602	512	WWF39x150
251	2 350	2 010	1 680	1 440	1 260	1 120	911	770	668	W33x169
289	2 880	2 700	2 510	2 320	2 130	1 900	1 560	1 320	1 150	W27x194
238	2 270	1 880	1 550	1 310	1 140	998	802	670	575	**W36x160**
384	3 030	2 940	2 860	2 770	2 680	2 600	2 420	2 250	2 080	W18x258
257	2 780	2 580	2 360	2 140	1 880	1 650	1 320	1 100	938	W30x173
307	2 800	2 640	2 490	2 340	2 180	2 020	1 690	1 450	1 270	W24x207

F$_y$ taken as 350 MPa for WWF shapes and 345 MPa for W shapes. $\phi = 0.90$

Designation	V_r	I_x	b	L_u	M_r ≤ L_u	Factored moment resistance M_r' (kN·m) Unbraced length (mm)					
	kN	10^6 mm^4	mm	mm		3 500	4 000	4 500	5 000	5 500	6 000
W1000x222	3 000	4 080	300	3 590	3 040	—	2 940	2 800	2 650	2 480	2 310
W920x223	2 970	3 770	304	3 830	2 960	—	2 920	2 800	2 670	2 530	2 380
WWF800x223	1 370	3 410	400	5 570	2 940	—	—	—	—	—	2 880
WWF700x245	1 370	2 950	400	5 880	2 900	—	—	—	—	—	2 890
W690x265	2 660	2 920	358	5 060	2 900	—	—	—	—	2 830	2 750
WWF1000x200	2 210	3 940	300	3 610	2 890	—	2 790	2 660	2 510	2 350	2 180
W610x285	2 730	2 610	329	4 980	2 850	—	—	—	2 840	2 770	2 700
W840x226	2 810	3 400	294	3 830	2 840	—	2 810	2 700	2 570	2 450	2 310
W460x349	3 230	2 040	296	5 840	2 800	—	—	—	—	—	2 780
WWF900x192	1 350	3 460	300	3 980	2 710	—	2 700	2 600	2 490	2 370	2 240
W530x300	2 770	2 210	319	5 210	2 690	—	—	—	—	2 660	2 600
W840x210	2 670	3 110	293	3 770	2 620	—	2 570	2 460	2 350	2 220	2 090
W690x240	2 410	2 630	356	4 960	2 620	—	—	—	2 610	2 540	2 460
W920x201	2 710	3 250	304	3 720	2 600	—	2 540	2 430	2 300	2 170	2 030
W610x262	2 500	2 360	327	4 850	2 590	—	—	—	2 570	2 500	2 430
W760x220	2 630	2 780	266	3 570	2 540	—	2 460	2 350	2 230	2 120	1 990
WWF700x214	1 370	2 540	400	5 690	2 500	—	—	—	—	—	2 470
W460x315	2 890	1 800	293	5 480	2 490	—	—	—	—	—	2 440
W530x272	2 490	1 970	318	5 040	2 430	—	—	—	—	2 370	2 320
W610x241	2 330	2 150	329	4 790	2 380	—	—	—	2 350	2 290	2 220
W840x193	2 530	2 780	292	3 690	2 370	—	2 310	2 200	2 090	1 970	1 850
W690x217	2 190	2 360	355	4 890	2 360	—	—	—	2 350	2 280	2 210
WWF800x184	1 370	2 660	300	4 060	2 330	—	—	2 260	2 170	2 070	1 970
WWF900x169	1 340	2 930	300	3 820	2 320	—	2 290	2 190	2 080	1 970	1 850
W460x286	2 590	1 610	291	5 220	2 250	—	—	—	—	2 220	2 180
W760x196	2 460	2 400	268	3 500	2 230	—	2 130	2 030	1 920	1 810	1 690
W530x248	2 220	1 770	315	4 880	2 190	—	—	—	2 180	2 120	2 070
W610x217	2 120	1 910	328	4 680	2 130	—	—	—	2 090	2 030	1 960
W840x176	2 300	2 460	292	3 610	2 110	—	2 050	1 950	1 840	1 730	1 610
W760x185	2 340	2 230	267	3 450	2 080	2 070	1 980	1 880	1 780	1 670	1 550
†WWF700x196	1 370	2 300	400	5 860	2 070	—	—	—	—	—	2 050
W460x260	2 360	1 440	289	4 980	2 030	—	—	—	—	1 980	1 940
W690x192	2 230	1 980	254	3 440	2 010	2 000	1 910	1 830	1 730	1 640	1 540
WWF800x161	1 370	2 250	300	3 900	1 990	—	1 980	1 900	1 810	1 720	1 620
WWF700x175	1 370	1 970	300	4 160	1 970	—	—	1 930	1 850	1 780	1 700
W760x173	2 250	2 060	267	3 410	1 930	1 910	1 830	1 730	1 630	1 520	1 410
W530x219	2 100	1 510	318	4 720	1 900	—	—	—	1 870	1 820	1 760
W610x195	1 960	1 680	327	4 570	1 880	—	—	—	1 840	1 780	1 710
W460x235	2 120	1 270	287	4 770	1 810	—	—	—	1 790	1 750	1 710
W760x161	2 140	1 860	266	3 330	1 760	1 730	1 650	1 560	1 460	1 360	1 250
W690x170	2 060	1 700	256	3 380	1 750	1 730	1 650	1 570	1 480	1 390	1 290
W530x196	1 870	1 340	316	4 600	1 700	—	—	—	1 660	1 610	1 550
WWF700x152	1 370	1 660	300	3 990	1 680	—	—	1 610	1 540	1 470	1 390
W610x174	1 770	1 470	325	4 480	1 660	—	—	—	1 610	1 550	1 490
W460x213	1 880	1 140	285	4 590	1 640	—	—	—	1 600	1 560	1 520

Note: For unbraced beam segments loaded above the shear centre, see CSA S16-09 Clause 13.6.

† Class 3 section

| Nominal mass | Factored moment resistance M_r' (kN·m) | | | | | | | | | Imperial designation |
| | Unbraced length (mm) | | | | | | | | | |
kg/m	7 000	8 000	9 000	10 000	11 000	12 000	14 000	16 000	18 000	
222	1 910	1 520	1 250	1 050	906	794	634	527	451	**W40x149**
223	2 070	1 680	1 380	1 170	1 010	884	707	589	504	W36x150
223	2 710	2 530	2 330	2 120	1 880	1 630	1 280	1 050	882	WWF31x150
245	2 750	2 600	2 440	2 280	2 110	1 950	1 560	1 310	1 120	WWF28x164
265	2 580	2 400	2 220	2 030	1 810	1 600	1 310	1 100	957	W27x178
200	1 770	1 390	1 130	945	806	699	549	449	379	WWF39x134
285	2 550	2 400	2 250	2 100	1 940	1 760	1 470	1 260	1 100	W24x192
226	2 020	1 680	1 400	1 190	1 030	914	741	623	537	W33x152
349	2 700	2 610	2 520	2 440	2 350	2 270	2 100	1 930	1 730	W18x234
192	1 960	1 630	1 330	1 120	964	842	670	555	473	WWF35x128
300	2 480	2 370	2 250	2 130	2 020	1 900	1 650	1 420	1 250	W21x201
210	1 810	1 470	1 220	1 040	899	792	639	535	461	**W33x141**
240	2 300	2 120	1 940	1 760	1 530	1 360	1 100	924	797	W27x161
201	1 720	1 370	1 120	941	809	707	561	464	396	**W36x135**
262	2 290	2 140	1 990	1 830	1 670	1 490	1 240	1 060	924	W24x176
220	1 740	1 430	1 210	1 050	922	823	679	579	504	W30x148
214	2 330	2 190	2 040	1 870	1 710	1 500	1 190	982	835	WWF28x144
315	2 360	2 270	2 190	2 100	2 020	1 930	1 770	1 580	1 400	W18x211
272	2 200	2 090	1 970	1 860	1 740	1 630	1 370	1 180	1 040	W21x182
241	2 080	1 930	1 780	1 630	1 450	1 300	1 070	911	795	W24x162
193	1 580	1 260	1 040	877	758	666	534	445	382	**W33x130**
217	2 050	1 880	1 710	1 510	1 310	1 150	930	778	669	W27x146
184	1 750	1 490	1 230	1 040	900	791	634	529	454	WWF31x123
169	1 570	1 250	1 010	845	721	625	491	402	339	WWF35x113
286	2 090	2 010	1 920	1 840	1 760	1 670	1 510	1 310	1 160	W18x192
196	1 430	1 160	973	835	731	650	532	451	391	W30x132
248	1 960	1 840	1 730	1 610	1 500	1 360	1 140	979	859	W21x166
217	1 820	1 680	1 530	1 370	1 200	1 070	878	745	647	W24x146
176	1 330	1 060	868	731	629	551	439	364	311	**W33x118**
185	1 280	1 040	867	743	649	576	470	397	344	W30x124
196	1 950	1 830	1 700	1 570	1 430	1 260	992	812	686	WWF28x132
260	1 850	1 770	1 690	1 600	1 520	1 440	1 250	1 080	958	W18x175
192	1 330	1 090	925	802	709	635	526	449	393	W27x129
161	1 400	1 130	927	778	666	581	460	379	322	WWF31x108
175	1 530	1 350	1 130	965	839	741	601	505	436	WWF28x117
173	1 150	924	770	657	572	506	411	346	299	**W30x116**
219	1 650	1 540	1 430	1 310	1 180	1 060	880	754	659	W21x147
195	1 580	1 440	1 300	1 120	981	870	709	598	518	W24x131
235	1 630	1 540	1 460	1 380	1 290	1 210	1 020	887	783	W18x158
161	988	793	658	560	486	429	347	291	251	**W30x108**
170	1 070	875	737	635	558	497	409	347	302	W27x114
196	1 450	1 340	1 230	1 110	977	873	721	615	537	W21x132
152	1 230	1 020	842	711	613	537	429	356	305	WWF28x102
174	1 370	1 230	1 090	924	803	709	574	482	415	W24x117
213	1 440	1 350	1 270	1 190	1 110	1 010	848	733	646	W18x143

F_y taken as 350 MPa for WWF shapes and 345 MPa for W shapes. $\phi = 0.90$

BEAM SELECTION TABLE
WWF and W Shapes

CSA G40.21 350W
ASTM A992, A572 Grade 50

| Designation | V_r | I_x | b | L_u | M_r | Factored moment resistance M_r' (kN·m) | | | | | |
| | | | | | | Unbraced length (mm) | | | | | |
	kN	$10^6\,mm^4$	mm	mm	$\leq L_u$	2 500	3 000	3 500	4 000	4 500	5 000
W760x147	2 040	1 660	265	3 260	**1 580**	—	—	1 550	1 470	1 380	1 290
W530x182	1 720	1 240	315	4 530	1 560	—	—	—	—	—	1 520
W690x152	1 850	1 510	254	3 320	1 550	—	—	1 530	1 460	1 380	1 290
W460x193	1 700	1 020	283	4 440	1 470	—	—	—	—	—	1 430
W610x155	1 590	1 290	324	4 400	1 470	—	—	—	—	1 460	1 410
W760x134	1 650	1 500	264	3 230	**1 440**	—	—	1 400	1 330	1 250	1 160
W610x153	1 790	1 250	229	3 110	1 430	—	—	1 380	1 310	1 240	1 160
W690x140	1 740	1 360	254	3 270	1 410	—	—	1 380	1 320	1 240	1 160
W530x165	1 570	1 110	313	4 440	1 410	—	—	—	—	—	1 360
W460x177	1 640	910	286	4 330	1 330	—	—	—	—	1 320	1 280
W610x140	1 660	1 120	230	3 070	1 290	—	—	1 240	1 170	1 100	1 030
W530x150	1 410	1 010	312	4 380	1 290	—	—	—	—	1 280	1 240
W690x125	1 610	1 190	253	3 190	**1 250**	—	—	1 210	1 140	1 070	999
W460x158	1 460	796	284	4 190	1 170	—	—	—	—	1 150	1 110
W610x125	1 490	985	229	3 020	1 140	—	—	1 090	1 020	959	889
W530x138	1 650	861	214	2 930	1 120	—	1 110	1 060	1 000	945	884
W460x144	1 320	726	283	4 130	1 070	—	—	—	—	1 050	1 010
W610x113	1 400	875	228	2 950	**1 020**	—	—	964	906	843	775
W410x149	1 320	619	265	4 080	1 010	—	—	—	—	984	953
W530x123	1 460	761	212	2 860	997	—	984	933	879	822	762
W360x162	992	516	371	5 980	975	—	—	—	—	—	—
W460x128	1 170	637	282	4 040	947	—	—	—	—	918	884
W610x101	1 300	764	228	2 890	**900**	—	891	842	787	728	664
W410x132	1 160	538	263	3 940	885	—	—	—	882	853	823
W530x109	1 280	667	211	2 810	879	—	862	815	764	709	652
W460x113	1 020	556	280	3 950	829	—	—	—	826	796	765
W530x101	1 200	617	210	2 770	814	—	794	749	699	647	591
†W360x147	907	463	370	6 190	798	—	—	—	—	—	—
W610x91	1 100	657	227	2 820	782	—	768	723	672	617	557
W610x92	1 350	646	179	2 180	779	744	683	614	540	448	376
W410x114	998	462	261	3 810	764	—	—	—	754	727	698
W460x106	1 210	488	194	2 690	742	—	719	679	637	594	549
W530x92	1 110	552	209	2 720	733	—	711	668	621	570	516
†W360x134	817	415	369	6 030	723	—	—	—	—	—	—
W360x122	967	365	257	4 040	705	—	—	—	—	686	664
W610x82	1 170	560	178	2 110	**683**	644	587	522	448	364	304
W460x97	1 090	445	193	2 650	677	—	652	614	574	531	488
W310x129	854	308	308	5 080	671	—	—	—	—	—	—
W410x100	850	398	260	3 730	661	—	—	—	648	623	596
W530x85	1 130	485	166	2 110	652	616	564	507	446	373	316
W530x82	1 030	477	209	2 660	640	—	616	576	531	484	433
W360x110	841	331	256	3 940	640	—	—	—	637	617	596
†W610x84	944	603	226	3 000	627	—	—	595	559	519	476
W460x89	996	410	192	2 620	624	—	598	562	523	482	439
W310x118	766	275	307	4 920	605	—	—	—	—	—	603
W360x101	768	301	255	3 860	584	—	—	—	578	559	538
W460x82	933	370	191	2 560	568	—	540	505	467	426	385

Note: For unbraced beam segments loaded above the shear centre, see CSA S16-09 Clause 13.6.

† Class 3 section

Nominal mass	Factored moment resistance M_r' (kN·m)									Imperial designation
	Unbraced length (mm)									
kg/m	6 000	7 000	8 000	9 000	10 000	11 000	12 000	14 000	16 000	
147	1 090	840	671	555	470	407	358	288	241	**W30x99**
182	1 420	1 320	1 210	1 100	969	851	759	625	531	W21x122
152	1 110	898	728	610	523	458	406	332	281	W27x102
193	1 350	1 270	1 180	1 100	1 020	925	836	702	606	W18x130
155	1 300	1 180	1 050	901	762	659	579	465	388	W24x104
134	967	738	587	483	408	351	308	246	205	**W30x90**
153	1 000	815	675	576	502	445	400	333	286	W24x103
140	987	778	628	523	447	389	345	280	236	W27x94
165	1 270	1 170	1 060	954	823	721	641	525	445	W21x111
177	1 200	1 120	1 040	953	866	771	695	581	500	W18x119
140	874	695	573	486	422	373	334	277	237	W24x94
150	1 150	1 050	943	829	709	618	548	446	377	W21x101
125	834	641	514	426	362	314	277	224	188	**W27x84**
158	1 040	957	876	795	697	618	556	463	397	W18x106
125	733	575	470	396	342	301	269	222	189	W24x84
138	759	616	515	444	390	347	314	263	227	W21x93
144	936	858	779	693	602	533	478	396	339	W18x97
113	617	481	391	328	282	247	220	180	153	**W24x76**
149	889	825	761	697	622	555	502	421	364	W16x100
123	631	505	421	361	316	281	253	211	182	W21x83
162	974	935	895	855	814	773	733	653	558	W14x109
128	812	736	658	567	490	432	386	318	271	W18x86
101	512	396	320	267	228	199	176	144	121	**W24x68**
132	762	699	635	566	496	441	398	333	287	W16x89
109	520	413	342	291	254	225	202	168	144	W21x73
113	696	623	545	458	394	345	307	252	213	W18x76
101	462	365	301	255	222	196	176	146	125	W21x68
147	—	773	740	708	675	642	609	544	467	W14x99
91	416	320	257	213	181	157	139	112	94.2	W24x61
92	281	222	183	156	135	120	107	88.9	76.1	W24x62
114	638	576	514	439	383	339	305	254	218	W16x77
106	450	366	308	266	235	210	190	160	138	W18x71
92	393	309	253	214	185	163	146	120	103	W21x62
134	—	694	663	630	598	565	532	461	392	W14x90
122	621	577	534	491	441	395	357	301	260	W14x82
82	225	177	145	123	106	93.4	83.4	68.9	58.7	**W24x55**
97	389	314	264	227	200	178	161	135	117	W18x65
129	643	612	581	551	520	490	460	390	336	W12x87
100	539	480	412	349	302	266	238	197	168	W16x67
85	240	193	162	139	122	108	97.8	81.9	70.6	W21x57
82	320	249	203	170	147	129	115	94.0	79.8	W21x55
110	553	510	467	423	372	332	300	252	217	W14x74
84	372	284	227	188	159	138	121	97.6	81.6	W24x56
89	343	276	231	198	174	155	140	117	101	W18x60
118	574	543	513	482	452	422	388	324	279	W12x79
101	497	454	411	363	318	283	255	214	184	W14x68
82	292	234	195	167	146	129	117	97.3	83.7	W18x55

F_y taken as 350 MPa for WWF shapes and 345 MPa for W shapes. $\phi = 0.90$

BEAM SELECTION TABLE
WWF and W Shapes

Designation	V_r	I_x	b	L_u	M_r	Factored moment resistance M_r' (kN·m)					
						Unbraced length (mm)					
	kN	10^6 mm^4	mm	mm	$\leq L_u$	2 000	2 500	3 000	3 500	4 000	4 500
W530x74	1 050	411	166	2 040	**562**	—	523	474	420	357	293
W310x107	695	248	306	4 790	550	—	—	—	—	—	—
W410x85	931	315	181	2 520	537	—	—	509	478	444	410
W360x91	687	267	254	3 760	522	—	—	—	—	513	494
W460x74	843	333	190	2 530	512	—	—	484	450	414	375
W530x66	927	351	165	1 980	**484**	483	444	398	347	284	232
†W530x72	926	400	207	2 760	472	—	—	460	431	400	366
W410x74	821	275	180	2 470	469	—	467	440	410	379	346
W460x68	856	297	154	2 010	463	—	429	390	348	301	250
W460x67	791	295	190	2 480	456	—	—	427	396	361	324
†W310x97	625	222	305	4 970	447	—	—	—	—	—	—
W360x79	682	226	205	3 010	444	—	—	425	404	383	
W310x86	578	199	254	3 900	441	—	—	—	438	424	
W250x101	644	164	257	4 470	435	—	—	—	—	434	
W410x67	739	246	179	2 420	422	—	418	392	364	333	301
W460x61	747	254	189	2 410	401	—	396	370	340	306	271
W460x60	746	255	153	1 970	**397**	396	365	329	289	242	200
W360x72	617	201	204	2 940	397	—	—	395	377	357	336
W310x79	552	177	254	3 810	397	—	—	—	—	392	379
W250x89	570	143	256	4 260	382	—	—	—	—	—	377
W410x60	642	216	178	2 390	369	—	365	341	314	286	255
W310x74	597	164	205	3 100	366	—	—	—	354	339	323
W200x100	680	113	210	4 460	357	—	—	—	—	—	356
W360x64	548	178	203	2 870	354	—	—	350	332	313	293
W460x52	680	212	152	1 890	**338**	333	303	269	231	185	152
W250x80	493	126	255	4 130	338	—	—	—	—	—	331
W410x54	619	186	177	2 310	326	—	318	295	269	242	210
W310x67	533	144	204	3 020	326	—	—	—	312	297	282
W360x57	580	161	172	2 360	314	—	309	289	267	244	220
W250x73	446	113	254	4 010	306	—	—	—	—	—	297
W200x86	591	94.7	209	4 110	305	—	—	—	—	—	299
W310x60	466	128	203	2 960	290	—	—	289	275	261	246
W250x67	469	104	204	3 260	280	—	—	—	275	265	254
W360x51	524	141	171	2 320	**278**	—	271	253	232	210	187
W410x46	578	156	140	1 790	**275**	265	240	210	177	142	117
W310x52	495	119	167	2 370	261	—	257	241	224	206	188
W200x71	452	76.6	206	3 730	249	—	—	—	—	246	239
W360x45	498	122	171	2 260	**242**	—	234	217	197	176	152
W250x58	413	87.3	203	3 130	239	—	—	—	232	222	212

Note: For unbraced beam segments loaded above the shear centre, see CSA S16-09 Clause 13.6.

† Class 3 section

Nominal mass	Factored moment resistance M_r' (kN·m)									Imperial designation
	Unbraced length (mm)									
kg/m	5 000	6 000	7 000	8 000	9 000	10 000	12 000	14 000	16 000	
74	247	186	148	123	105	91.7	73.2	61.0	52.4	**W21x50**
107	544	515	485	455	424	394	326	272	234	W12x72
85	376	297	243	205	178	157	127	107	92.9	W16x57
91	475	434	392	350	299	261	209	174	150	W14x61
74	332	249	198	164	140	122	96.9	80.6	69.1	W18x50
66	195	145	115	94.9	80.6	70.0	55.5	46.0	39.4	**W21x44**
72	330	246	190	154	128	110	85.1	69.4	58.6	W21x48
74	312	239	194	163	140	124	99.8	83.8	72.4	W16x50
68	214	164	133	112	96.8	85.3	69.0	58.0	50.1	W18x46
67	280	208	164	135	115	99.4	78.6	65.1	55.6	W18x45
97	446	424	400	376	351	327	272	226	194	W12x65
79	361	317	267	225	194	171	139	117	101	W14x53
86	409	379	348	317	283	248	200	167	144	W12x58
101	424	403	382	362	342	322	279	236	205	W10x68
67	264	201	161	135	116	102	81.7	68.4	58.9	W16x45
61	227	168	131	107	90.5	78.1	61.3	50.5	43.0	W18x41
60	169	129	104	86.7	74.4	65.3	52.4	43.9	37.8	**W18x40**
72	315	272	222	186	160	141	114	95.6	82.5	W14x48
79	364	334	304	273	237	207	166	139	119	W12x53
89	367	346	326	306	285	265	220	186	161	W10x60
60	218	165	131	109	93.2	81.4	65.0	54.2	46.5	W16x40
74	307	274	240	204	177	156	127	107	93.0	W12x50
100	349	335	321	307	294	280	253	222	194	W8x67
64	273	228	183	153	131	115	92.2	77.2	66.5	W14x43
52	128	96.3	76.8	63.7	54.4	47.4	37.9	31.6	27.1	**W18x35**
80	321	302	282	262	242	221	179	151	130	W10x54
54	176	132	104	86.1	73.2	63.6	50.5	41.9	35.9	W16x36
67	266	234	198	167	144	127	103	86.8	75.1	W12x45
57	192	147	119	99.8	86.0	75.7	61.1	51.3	44.3	W14x38
73	287	268	248	228	209	185	149	126	108	W10x49
86	292	279	265	252	238	225	197	168	147	W8x58
60	231	199	163	137	118	104	83.6	70.2	60.5	W12x40
67	244	223	202	180	157	139	114	96.5	83.8	W10x45
51	159	121	97.0	81.0	69.5	60.9	48.9	40.9	35.2	**W14x34**
46	99.9	76.4	61.7	51.8	44.6	39.2	31.6	26.5	22.9	**W16x31**
52	167	130	106	89.4	77.5	68.4	55.5	46.8	40.5	W12x35
71	232	219	205	192	179	166	137	116	101	W8x48
45	128	96.1	76.5	63.4	54.1	47.2	37.6	31.3	26.9	**W14x30**
58	202	181	161	137	119	105	85.7	72.4	62.8	W10x39

F_y taken as 350 MPa for WWF shapes and 345 MPa for W shapes. $\phi = 0.90$

Designation	V_r	I_x	b	L_u	M_r	Factored moment resistance M_r' (kN·m) Unbraced length (mm)					
	kN	$10^6\,mm^4$	mm	mm	$\leq L_u$	1 500	2 000	2 500	3 000	3 500	4 000
W410x39	480	127	140	1 730	**227**	—	216	193	166	133	105
W310x45	423	99.2	166	2 310	220	—	—	215	200	184	167
W360x39	470	102	128	1 660	206	—	193	172	148	120	97.2
W200x59	392	61.1	205	3 430	203	—	—	—	—	202	195
W310x39	368	85.1	165	2 260	189	—	—	184	170	155	139
W250x45	414	71.1	148	2 170	187	—	—	179	167	155	142
†W250x49	375	70.6	202	3 160	178	—	—	—	—	173	165
W200x52	334	52.7	204	3 300	177	—	—	—	—	174	168
W360x33	396	82.7	127	1 600	**168**	—	155	136	113	87.6	70.3
W250x39	354	60.1	147	2 110	159	—	—	151	140	128	115
W310x33	423	65.0	102	1 330	149	143	125	104	80.5	64.2	53.3
†W200x46	300	45.4	203	3 370	139	—	—	—	—	138	133
W200x42	302	40.9	166	2 610	138	—	—	—	133	126	120
W250x33	323	48.9	146	2 020	132	—	—	122	112	100	88.4
W310x28	380	54.3	102	1 290	**126**	120	103	83.1	61.9	48.8	40.2
W200x36	255	34.4	165	2 510	118	—	—	—	112	105	99.0
W250x28	341	40.0	102	1 370	110	107	94.5	81.0	65.4	52.6	44.0
W200x31	275	31.4	134	1 980	104	—	—	96.7	89.3	81.7	74.0
W310x24	350	42.7	101	1 210	**102**	94.2	78.3	58.1	42.8	33.5	27.3
W150x37	269	22.2	154	2 640	96.3	—	—	—	93.4	89.4	85.5
W250x25	321	34.2	102	1 330	95.3	91.7	80.0	66.9	51.6	41.2	34.2
W310x21	303	37.0	101	1 190	**89.1**	81.5	66.7	47.9	35.0	27.2	22.0
W200x27	246	25.8	133	1 890	86.6	—	85.3	78.7	71.5	64.1	56.0
W250x22	302	28.9	102	1 280	81.7	77.6	66.6	53.9	40.3	31.9	26.3
W150x30	212	17.2	153	2 440	75.8	—	—	75.4	71.6	67.8	64.0
W200x22	262	20.0	102	1 390	68.9	67.4	60.1	52.1	43.2	35.0	29.4
W150x24	216	13.4	102	1 630	59.6	—	56.4	52.1	47.9	43.6	39.3
W200x19	241	16.6	102	1 340	**58.1**	56.0	49.2	41.5	32.7	26.2	21.9
†W250x18	247	22.4	101	1 330	**55.6**	53.4	46.1	37.5	27.8	21.7	17.7
‡W150x22	181	12.1	152	2 470	46.6	—	—	46.5	44.0	41.4	38.8
W150x18	182	9.17	102	1 480	42.2	42.1	38.3	34.3	30.2	25.5	21.6
†W200x15	176	12.7	100	1 380	**39.4**	38.5	33.8	28.5	22.1	17.4	14.4
W150x14	132	6.87	100	1 390	**32.0**	31.3	27.8	24.0	19.6	15.8	13.2
†W150x13	130	6.13	100	1 460	**25.7**	25.5	22.9	20.0	16.9	13.6	11.3

Note: For unbraced beam segments loaded above the shear centre, see CSA S16-09 Clause 13.6.

† Class 3 section   ‡ Class 4 section

Nominal mass	Factored moment resistance M_r' (kN·m)									Imperial designation
	Unbraced length (mm)									
kg/m	5 000	6 000	7 000	8 000	9 000	10 000	11 000	12 000	14 000	
39	73.1	55.2	44.1	36.6	31.3	27.4	24.3	21.9	18.2	**W16x26**
45	128	98.2	79.3	66.5	57.3	50.4	45.0	40.6	34.1	W12x30
39	69.8	54.2	44.3	37.5	32.5	28.8	25.8	23.4	19.7	W14x26
59	182	169	155	142	128	114	102	93.2	79.1	W8x40
39	103	77.7	62.2	51.8	44.3	38.8	34.5	31.1	25.9	W12x26
45	114	90.6	75.2	64.4	56.3	50.1	45.1	41.1	34.9	W10x30
49	149	133	115	97.2	84.0	74.1	66.3	60.0	50.5	W10x33
52	155	142	129	116	101	89.5	80.6	73.3	62.1	W8x35
33	49.7	38.1	30.8	25.9	22.3	19.6	17.5	15.8	13.3	**W14x22**
39	88.0	69.2	57.0	48.6	42.3	37.6	33.8	30.7	26.0	W10x26
33	39.7	31.7	26.4	22.7	19.9	17.7	16.0	14.6	12.4	W12x22
46	122	112	101	90.2	78.4	69.5	62.4	56.6	47.9	W8x31
42	106	92.9	77.5	66.5	58.3	51.9	46.9	42.7	36.3	W8x28
33	63.6	49.4	40.3	34.1	29.6	26.1	23.4	21.2	17.9	W10x22
28	29.5	23.4	19.4	16.5	14.5	12.8	11.6	10.5	8.93	**W12x19**
36	85.9	71.3	59.0	50.4	44.0	39.1	35.2	32.1	27.2	W8x24
28	33.1	26.6	22.3	19.2	16.9	15.1	13.6	12.4	10.6	W10x19
31	57.0	45.6	38.0	32.7	28.7	25.6	23.1	21.0	17.9	W8x21
24	19.8	15.5	12.8	10.9	9.45	8.37	7.52	6.83	5.78	**W12x16**
37	77.6	69.9	61.6	53.3	47.0	42.1	38.1	34.8	29.7	W6x25
25	25.5	20.4	17.0	14.6	12.8	11.4	10.3	9.40	7.99	W10x17
21	15.8	12.3	10.0	8.49	7.36	6.50	5.83	5.29	4.46	**W12x14**
27	41.2	32.6	27.1	23.1	20.2	18.0	16.2	14.7	12.5	W8x18
22	19.5	15.4	12.8	11.0	9.60	8.54	7.70	7.01	5.95	W10x15
30	56.4	48.3	40.4	34.8	30.6	27.3	24.7	22.5	19.1	W6x20
22	22.3	18.0	15.1	13.0	11.5	10.3	9.28	8.47	7.22	W8x15
24	30.5	25.1	21.3	18.5	16.4	14.7	13.3	12.2	10.4	W6x16
19	16.4	13.2	11.0	9.48	8.33	7.44	6.72	6.13	5.22	**W8x13**
18	12.8	10.0	8.24	7.00	6.09	5.40	4.85	4.40	3.73	**W10x12**
22	33.4	27.4	22.6	19.3	16.9	15.0	13.5	12.3	10.4	W6x15
18	16.6	13.5	11.4	9.86	8.70	7.79	7.05	6.45	5.50	W6x12
15	10.6	8.35	6.92	5.91	5.17	4.59	4.14	3.76	3.19	**W8x10**
14	9.98	8.02	6.72	5.80	5.10	4.55	4.11	3.75	3.20	**W6x9**
13	8.49	6.81	5.70	4.90	4.31	3.84	3.47	3.17	2.70	**W6x8.5**

F_y taken as 350 MPa for WWF shapes and 345 MPa for W shapes. $\phi = 0.90$

Designation	V_r	I_x	b	L_u	M_r	Factored moment resistance M_r' (kN·m)					
						Unbraced length (mm)					
	kN	10^6 mm^4	mm	mm	≤ L_u	1 500	2 000	2 500	3 000	3 500	4 000
†C250x37	607	37.9	73	1 630	**80.7**	—	77.0	71.9	66.9	61.9	57.0
†C250x30	435	32.7	69	1 460	**69.4**	69.0	63.4	57.7	52.0	46.4	39.8
†C250x23	276	27.8	65	1 340	**59.1**	57.3	51.3	45.2	38.8	32.0	27.3
†C230x22	294	21.3	63	1 330	**50.2**	48.7	44.0	39.2	34.5	29.0	24.9
†C200x28	449	18.2	64	1 540	48.6	—	45.8	42.9	39.9	37.0	34.1
†C230x20	241	19.8	61	1 270	**46.7**	44.6	39.8	35.0	29.7	24.7	21.1
†C200x21	279	14.9	59	1 280	39.7	38.2	34.6	31.0	27.5	23.5	20.3
†C200x17	203	13.5	57	1 210	**35.9**	33.8	30.1	26.3	22.2	18.5	15.9
†C180x22	336	11.3	58	1 410	34.3	33.9	31.6	29.3	27.0	24.8	22.5
†C180x18	254	10.0	55	1 250	30.5	29.2	26.6	24.1	21.5	18.7	16.2
†C180x15	168	8.86	53	1 150	**26.9**	25.0	22.2	19.4	16.4	13.7	11.9
†C150x19	301	7.11	54	1 470	25.3	25.2	23.7	22.2	20.7	19.2	17.8
†C150x16	217	6.21	51	1 230	22.1	21.1	19.4	17.7	16.0	14.1	12.3
†C150x12	138	5.36	48	1 080	**19.0**	17.4	15.4	13.5	11.4	9.62	8.34
†C130x13	188	3.66	47	1 260	15.6	15.0	13.9	12.8	11.8	10.7	9.46
†C130x10	109	3.09	44	1 040	**13.1**	11.9	10.7	9.42	8.03	6.82	5.93
†C100x11	149	1.91	43	1 330	10.1	9.88	9.25	8.63	8.02	7.40	6.79
†C100x9	115	1.77	42	1 170	**9.34**	8.88	8.19	7.51	6.84	6.14	5.35
†C100x8	85.4	1.61	40	1 040	**8.53**	7.83	7.08	6.35	5.59	4.76	4.15
†C100x7	58.2	1.53	40	984	**8.10**	7.27	6.48	5.71	4.83	4.11	3.58
†C75x9	122	0.847	40	1 670	6.02	—	5.84	5.56	5.28	5.01	4.73
†C75x7	89.4	0.749	37	1 310	**5.32**	5.19	4.87	4.55	4.23	3.91	3.59
†C75x6	58.2	0.670	35	1 070	**4.75**	4.43	4.07	3.70	3.34	2.93	2.56
†C75x5	46.0	0.635	34	993	**4.51**	4.11	3.73	3.35	2.96	2.53	2.21

Note: The designation comprises the nominal depth in millimetres and the mass in kilograms per metre.

† Class 3 section

| Nominal mass | Factored moment resistance M_r' (kN·m) | | | | | | | | | Imperial designation |
| | Unbraced length (mm) | | | | | | | | | |
kg/m	4 500	5 000	6 000	7 000	8 000	9 000	10 000	11 000	12 000	
37	51.5	46.1	38.0	32.4	28.2	25.0	22.5	20.4	18.7	**C10x25**
30	34.8	31.0	25.5	21.7	18.8	16.7	15.0	13.6	12.4	**C10x20**
23	23.8	21.1	17.3	14.6	12.7	11.2	10.1	9.12	8.34	**C10x15.3**
22	21.8	19.4	16.0	13.6	11.8	10.4	9.38	8.51	7.79	**C9x15**
28	30.9	27.7	23.0	19.6	17.1	15.2	13.7	12.4	11.4	C8x18.75
20	18.5	16.5	13.5	11.5	9.98	8.83	7.93	7.19	6.58	**C9x13.4**
21	17.8	15.9	13.1	11.2	9.76	8.65	7.77	7.06	6.46	C8x13.75
17	14.0	12.5	10.3	8.75	7.62	6.75	6.06	5.50	5.03	**C8x11.5**
22	19.9	17.8	14.8	12.6	11.0	9.79	8.81	8.00	7.33	C7x14.75
18	14.3	12.8	10.6	9.04	7.89	7.00	6.29	5.71	5.23	C7x12.25
15	10.5	9.35	7.72	6.58	5.74	5.09	4.57	4.15	3.80	**C7x9.8**
19	16.2	14.5	12.1	10.3	9.03	8.02	7.21	6.55	6.00	C6x13
16	10.9	9.75	8.09	6.91	6.04	5.36	4.82	4.38	4.01	C6x10.5
12	7.37	6.60	5.47	4.67	4.08	3.62	3.25	2.95	2.71	**C6x8.2**
13	8.39	7.54	6.26	5.36	4.69	4.16	3.74	3.40	3.12	C5x9
10	5.25	4.71	3.91	3.34	2.92	2.59	2.33	2.12	1.94	**C5x6.7**
11	6.04	5.43	4.52	3.87	3.38	3.01	2.71	2.46	2.25	C4x7.25
9	4.75	4.27	3.55	3.04	2.66	2.36	2.12	1.93	1.77	**C4x6.25**
8	3.68	3.31	2.75	2.36	2.06	1.83	1.65	1.50	1.37	**C4x5.4**
7	3.18	2.85	2.37	2.03	1.77	1.57	1.42	1.29	1.18	**C4x4.5**
9	4.45	4.18	3.54	3.03	2.65	2.36	2.12	1.93	1.77	C3x6
7	3.21	2.88	2.40	2.06	1.80	1.60	1.44	1.31	1.20	**C3x5**
6	2.27	2.04	1.70	1.46	1.27	1.13	1.02	0.926	0.849	**C3x4.1**
5	1.96	1.76	1.47	1.26	1.10	0.978	0.880	0.800	0.733	**C3x3.5**

BEAM SELECTION TABLE
S Shapes

ASTM A992, A572 Gr. 50

$\phi = 0.90$

Designation	V_r	I_x	b	L_u	M_r	Factored moment resistance M_r' (kN·m)					
						Unbraced length (mm)					
	kN	10^6 mm^4	mm	mm	≤ L_u	1 500	2 000	2 500	3 000	3 500	4 000
S610x180	2 590	1 310	204	2 540	1 560	—	—	—	1 480	1 400	1 310
S610x158	2 000	1 220	200	2 530	1 420	—	—	—	1 350	1 270	1 190
S610x149	2 360	997	184	2 120	1 220	—	—	1 160	1 080	989	897
S610x134	1 990	940	181	2 120	1 140	—	—	1 080	997	910	820
S610x119	1 590	880	178	2 130	1 040	—	—	992	915	833	747
S510x143	2 150	700	183	2 290	1 010	—	—	986	929	870	811
S510x128	1 780	658	179	2 250	935	—	—	908	852	794	735
S510x112	1 680	532	162	1 940	776	—	770	715	656	595	533
S510x98.2	1 330	497	159	1 940	711	—	705	653	596	538	477
S460x104	1 700	387	159	1 880	637	—	626	581	534	485	437
S460x81.4	1 100	335	152	1 840	531	—	518	476	431	384	331
S380x74	1 090	203	143	1 740	394	—	379	348	316	284	248
S380x64	812	187	140	1 730	354	—	339	310	279	248	211
S310x74	1 090	127	139	1 930	311	—	308	291	273	256	239
S310x60.7	731	113	133	1 820	270	—	263	245	227	209	191
S310x52	681	95.9	129	1 640	229	—	216	197	178	159	137
S310x47	556	91.2	127	1 630	214	—	201	183	164	145	123
S250x52	786	61.5	126	1 690	181	—	174	162	150	138	127
S250x38	411	51.4	118	1 560	144	—	134	122	109	97.0	82.5
S200x34	466	27.0	106	1 460	98.1	97.5	90.0	82.5	75.1	67.8	59.3
S200x27	287	24.0	102	1 390	84.5	82.9	75.4	67.8	60.2	51.6	44.2
S150x26	368	10.9	91	1 400	53.7	52.9	49.2	45.6	42.0	38.4	34.5
S150x19	184	9.16	85	1 230	42.8	40.7	36.7	32.7	28.8	24.3	21.0
S130x15	141	5.11	76	1 150	28.8	26.9	24.2	21.6	18.9	16.0	13.9
S100x14.1	173	2.85	71	1 230	20.7	19.8	18.3	16.9	15.4	13.9	12.2
S100x11	102	2.56	68	1 100	18.0	16.7	15.1	13.5	12.0	10.2	8.9
S75x11	139	1.22	64	1 380	12.0	11.9	11.1	10.5	9.8	9.1	8.4
S75x8	67.0	1.04	59	1 090	9.9	9.2	8.4	7.6	6.8	5.9	5.2

Note: The designation comprises the nominal depth in millimetres and the mass in kilograms per metre.

$F_y = 345$ MPa

Nominal mass	Factored moment resistance M_r' (kN·m)									Imperial designation
	Unbraced length (mm)									
kg/m	5 000	6 000	7 000	8 000	9 000	10 000	12 000	14 000	16 000	
180	1 130	930	766	652	569	504	412	349	303	**S24x121**
158	1 010	818	671	569	495	438	357	301	261	**S24x106**
149	690	543	448	382	333	295	241	205	178	**S24x100**
134	618	483	397	337	293	259	212	179	155	**S24x90**
119	556	432	353	298	259	229	186	157	136	**S24x80**
143	691	558	465	399	350	312	257	218	190	S20x96
128	613	487	404	346	303	270	221	188	164	S20x86
112	401	320	266	228	200	178	146	124	108	**S20x75**
98.2	352	279	231	198	173	154	126	107	92.8	**S20x66**
104	334	268	225	194	171	152	126	107	93.2	S18x70
81.4	245	194	161	138	121	108	88.3	74.9	65.2	**S18x54.7**
74	188	152	128	110	96.9	86.6	71.5	61.0	53.2	**S15x50**
64	158	127	106	91.3	80.2	71.6	59.0	50.2	43.7	**S15x42.9**
74	204	167	142	123	109	97.6	81.0	69.2	60.5	S12x50
60.7	152	124	105	90.7	80.1	71.7	59.4	50.7	44.3	**S12x40.8**
52	105	84.9	71.6	62.0	54.7	48.9	40.5	34.5	30.1	**S12x35**
47	93.8	75.9	63.9	55.2	48.7	43.6	36.0	30.7	26.8	**S12x31.8**
52	101	83.1	70.6	61.5	54.4	48.8	40.6	34.7	30.3	S10x35
38	63.4	51.7	43.7	37.9	33.5	30.0	24.8	21.2	18.5	**S10x25.4**
34	46.6	38.4	32.7	28.5	25.2	22.7	18.8	16.1	14.1	**S8x23**
27	34.5	28.3	24.0	20.9	18.5	16.6	13.8	11.8	10.3	**S8x18.4**
26	27.4	22.7	19.4	16.9	15.0	13.5	11.3	9.64	8.43	**S6x17.25**
19	16.5	13.7	11.6	10.2	9.00	8.09	6.73	5.76	5.03	**S6x12.5**
15	11.0	9.09	7.77	6.78	6.02	5.41	4.50	3.86	3.37	**S5x10**
14.1	9.7	8.07	6.91	6.04	5.36	4.82	4.02	3.44	3.01	**S4x9.5**
11	7.0	5.84	5.00	4.37	3.88	3.49	2.90	2.49	2.18	**S4x7.7**
11	6.8	5.68	4.86	4.25	3.78	3.40	2.83	2.43	2.12	S3x7.5
8	4.1	3.43	2.93	2.57	2.28	2.05	1.71	1.46	1.28	**S3x5.7**

Total Uniformly Distributed Factored Loads for Laterally Supported Beams (kN)

Designation	WWF2000				Approx. Deflect. (mm)	WWF1800					Approx. Deflect. (mm)
Mass (kg/m)	732†	648†	607†	542†		700	659	617	575	510	
13 000					21					7 960	23
13 500					23					7 800	25
14 000					25					7 520	27
14 500				7 140	26					7 260	29
15 000				6 960	28				8 000	7 020	31
15 500				6 730	30				7 980	6 800	33
16 000				6 520	32				7 730	6 580	36
16 500				6 320	34			8 040	7 500	6 380	38
17 000			7 180	6 140	36			7 960	7 280	6 200	40
17 500			7 100	5 960	38			7 730	7 070	6 020	43
18 000			6 900	5 800	41		8 100	7 520	6 870	5 850	45
18 500		7 200	6 720	5 640	43		7 930	7 310	6 690	5 690	48
19 000		7 190	6 540	5 490	45	8 140	7 720	7 120	6 510	5 540	50
19 500		7 000	6 370	5 350	48	8 100	7 520	6 940	6 350	5 400	53
20 000		6 830	6 210	5 220	50	7 900	7 330	6 770	6 190	5 270	56
20 500		6 660	6 060	5 090	53	7 710	7 150	6 600	6 040	5 140	58
21 000		6 500	5 920	4 970	55	7 520	6 980	6 440	5 890	5 020	61
21 500		6 350	5 780	4 850	58	7 350	6 820	6 290	5 750	4 900	64
22 000	7 280	6 210	5 650	4 740	61	7 180	6 670	6 150	5 620	4 790	67
22 500	7 160	6 070	5 520	4 640	63	7 020	6 520	6 010	5 500	4 680	70
23 000	7 000	5 940	5 400	4 540	66	6 870	6 380	5 880	5 380	4 580	73
23 500	6 850	5 810	5 290	4 440	69	6 720	6 240	5 760	5 270	4 480	77
24 000	6 710	5 690	5 180	4 350	72	6 580	6 110	5 640	5 160	4 390	80
24 500	6 570	5 570	5 070	4 260	75	6 450	5 990	5 520	5 050	4 300	83
25 000	6 440	5 460	4 970	4 170	78	6 320	5 870	5 410	4 950	4 210	87
25 500	6 310	5 360	4 870	4 090	81	6 200	5 750	5 310	4 850	4 130	90
26 000	6 190	5 250	4 780	4 010	85	6 080	5 640	5 200	4 760	4 050	94
26 500	6 080	5 150	4 690	3 940	88	5 960	5 530	5 110	4 670	3 970	98
27 000	5 960	5 060	4 600	3 860	91	5 850	5 430	5 010	4 580	3 900	101
27 500	5 860	4 970	4 520	3 790	95	5 750	5 330	4 920	4 500	3 830	105
28 000	5 750	4 880	4 440	3 730	98	5 640	5 240	4 830	4 420	3 760	109
28 500	5 650	4 790	4 360	3 660	102	5 540	5 150	4 750	4 340	3 700	113
29 000	5 550	4 710	4 280	3 600	105	5 450	5 060	4 670	4 270	3 630	117
29 500	5 460	4 630	4 210	3 540	109	5 360	4 970	4 590	4 190	3 570	121
30 000	5 370	4 550	4 140	3 480	113	5 270	4 890	4 510	4 120	3 510	125

DESIGN DATA AND PROPERTIES

	732†	648†	607†	542†		700	659	617	575	510	
V_r (kN)	3 640	3 600	3 590	3 570		4 070	4 050	4 020	4 000	3 980	
L_u (mm)	7 620	7 370	7 210	6 310		7 300	7 170	7 020	6 860	5 960	
d (mm)	2 000	2 000	2 000	2 000		1 800	1 800	1 800	1 800	1 800	
b (mm)	550	550	550	500		550	550	550	550	500	
t (mm)	50.0	40.0	35.0	30.0		50.0	45.0	40.0	35.0	30.0	
w (mm)	20.0	20.0	20.0	20.0		20.0	20.0	20.0	20.0	20.0	
k (mm)	61	51	46	41		61	56	51	46	41	

IMPERIAL SIZE AND MASS

	732†	648†	607†	542†		700	659	617	575	510	
Mass (lb./ft.)	490	436	408	364		470	442	415	388	344	
Nominal Depth (in.)			79					71			

Note: F_y = 350 MPa and ϕ = 0.90

† Class 3

Total Uniformly Distributed Factored Loads for Laterally Supported Beams (kN)

Designation	WWF1600					Approx. Deflect. (mm)	WWF1400					Approx. Deflect. (mm)
Mass (kg/m)	622†	580†	538†	496†	431†		597	513	471	405	358	
11 000						19					5 280	22
11 500						21					5 190	24
12 000						23					4 980	26
12 500						24					4 780	28
13 000						26				5 280	4 590	30
13 500						28				5 190	4 420	33
14 000						31				5 000	4 270	35
14 500						33				4 830	4 120	38
15 000						35				4 670	3 980	40
15 500						38			5 320	4 520	3 850	43
16 000					4 600	40			5 260	4 380	3 730	46
16 500					4 470	43			5 100	4 250	3 620	49
17 000					4 340	45		5 360	4 950	4 120	3 510	52
17 500					4 220	48		5 330	4 810	4 000	3 410	55
18 000					4 100	51		5 180	4 680	3 890	3 320	58
18 500					3 990	53		5 040	4 550	3 790	3 230	61
19 000				4 640	3 890	56		4 910	4 430	3 690	3 140	64
19 500				4 590	3 790	59		4 780	4 320	3 590	3 060	68
20 000				4 470	3 690	63	5 460	4 660	4 210	3 500	2 990	71
20 500				4 360	3 600	66	5 410	4 550	4 110	3 420	2 910	75
21 000			4 660	4 260	3 520	69	5 280	4 440	4 010	3 340	2 840	79
21 500			4 630	4 160	3 430	72	5 160	4 340	3 910	3 260	2 780	83
22 000			4 520	4 070	3 360	76	5 040	4 240	3 830	3 180	2 710	86
22 500			4 420	3 980	3 280	79	4 930	4 140	3 740	3 110	2 650	90
23 000		4 700	4 330	3 890	3 210	83	4 820	4 050	3 660	3 050	2 600	94
23 500		4 640	4 240	3 810	3 140	86	4 720	3 970	3 580	2 980	2 540	99
24 000		4 550	4 150	3 730	3 080	90	4 620	3 890	3 510	2 920	2 490	103
24 500		4 450	4 060	3 650	3 010	94	4 530	3 810	3 440	2 860	2 440	107
25 000	4 720	4 360	3 980	3 580	2 950	98	4 440	3 730	3 370	2 800	2 390	112
25 500	4 650	4 280	3 900	3 510	2 900	102	4 350	3 660	3 300	2 750	2 340	116
26 000	4 570	4 200	3 830	3 440	2 840	106	4 260	3 590	3 240	2 690	2 300	121
26 500	4 480	4 120	3 760	3 380	2 790	110	4 180	3 520	3 180	2 640	2 250	125
27 000	4 400	4 040	3 690	3 310	2 730	114	4 110	3 450	3 120	2 590	2 210	130
27 500	4 320	3 970	3 620	3 250	2 680	118	4 030	3 390	3 060	2 550	2 170	135
28 000	4 240	3 900	3 560	3 200	2 640	123	3 960	3 330	3 010	2 500	2 130	140

DESIGN DATA AND PROPERTIES

	622†	580†	538†	496†	431†		597	513	471	405	358	
V_r (kN)	2 360	2 350	2 330	2 320	2 300		2 730	2 680	2 660	2 640	2 640	
L_u (mm)	8 010	7 890	7 750	7 620	6 720		7 790	7 510	7 360	6 450	5 000	
d (mm)	1 600	1 600	1 600	1 600	1 600		1 400	1 400	1 400	1 400	1 400	
b (mm)	550	550	550	550	500		550	550	550	500	400	
t (mm)	50.0	45.0	40.0	35.0	30.0		50.0	40.0	35.0	30.0	30.0	
w (mm)	16.0	16.0	16.0	16.0	16.0		16.0	16.0	16.0	16.0	16.0	
k (mm)	61	56	51	44	39		61	51	44	39	39	

IMPERIAL SIZE AND MASS

	622†	580†	538†	496†	431†		597	513	471	405	358	
Mass (lb./ft.)	419	388	361	333	289		402	344	316	272	240	
Nominal Depth (in.)			63						55			

Note: F_y = 350 MPa and ϕ = 0.90

† Class 3

5-105

Total Uniformly Distributed Factored Loads for Laterally Supported Beams (kN)

Designation	WWF1200						Approx. Deflect. (mm)
Mass (kg/m)	487	418	380	333	302	263	
6 000						5 780	8
6 500						5 510	9
7 000					5 780	5 110	10
7 500					5 750	4 770	12
8 000				5 780	5 390	4 470	13
8 500				5 720	5 070	4 210	15
9 000				5 400	4 790	3 980	17
9 500			5 780	5 120	4 540	3 770	19
10 000			5 750	4 860	4 310	3 580	21
10 500			5 470	4 630	4 100	3 410	23
11 000		5 780	5 220	4 420	3 920	3 250	25
11 500		5 610	5 000	4 230	3 750	3 110	28
12 000		5 380	4 790	4 050	3 590	2 980	30
12 500		5 160	4 600	3 890	3 450	2 860	33
13 000	5 780	4 960	4 420	3 740	3 310	2 750	35
13 500	5 710	4 780	4 260	3 600	3 190	2 650	38
14 000	5 510	4 610	4 100	3 470	3 080	2 560	41
14 500	5 320	4 450	3 960	3 350	2 970	2 470	44
15 000	5 140	4 300	3 830	3 240	2 870	2 390	47
15 500	4 970	4 160	3 710	3 140	2 780	2 310	50
16 000	4 820	4 030	3 590	3 040	2 690	2 240	53
16 500	4 670	3 910	3 480	2 950	2 610	2 170	57
17 000	4 540	3 790	3 380	2 860	2 530	2 100	60
17 500	4 410	3 690	3 280	2 780	2 460	2 040	64
18 000	4 280	3 580	3 190	2 700	2 390	1 990	68
18 500	4 170	3 490	3 110	2 630	2 330	1 930	71
19 000	4 060	3 400	3 020	2 560	2 270	1 880	75
19 500	3 950	3 310	2 950	2 490	2 210	1 840	79
20 000	3 860	3 230	2 870	2 430	2 150	1 790	83
20 500	3 760	3 150	2 800	2 370	2 100	1 750	88
21 000	3 670	3 070	2 740	2 320	2 050	1 700	92
21 500	3 590	3 000	2 670	2 260	2 000	1 660	96
22 000	3 510	2 930	2 610	2 210	1 960	1 630	101
22 500	3 430	2 870	2 550	2 160	1 920	1 590	105
23 000	3 350	2 800	2 500	2 110	1 870	1 560	110
DESIGN DATA AND PROPERTIES							
V_r (kN)	2 890	2 890	2 890	2 890	2 890	2 890	
L_u (mm)	7 710	6 790	6 630	5 150	4 980	3 560	
d (mm)	1 200	1 200	1 200	1 200	1 200	1 200	
b (mm)	550	500	500	400	400	300	
t (mm)	40.0	35.0	30.0	30.0	25.0	25.0	
w (mm)	16.0	16.0	16.0	16.0	16.0	16.0	
k (mm)	51	44	39	39	34	34	
IMPERIAL SIZE AND MASS							
Mass (lb./ft.)	326	281	255	224	203	176	
Nominal Depth (in.)	47						

Span in Millimetres

Note: F_y = 350 MPa and ϕ = 0.90

BEAM LOAD TABLES
WWF Shapes

Total Uniformly Distributed Factored Loads for Laterally Supported Beams (kN)

Designation				WWF1100				Approx. Deflect. (mm)
Mass (kg/m)		458	388	351	304	273	234	
Span in Millimetres	6 000							8
	6 500						4 420	10
	7 000						4 320	11
	7 500						4 030	13
	8 000					4 420	3 780	15
	8 500					4 360	3 560	16
	9 000					4 120	3 360	18
	9 500				4 420	3 900	3 180	21
	10 000				4 210	3 700	3 020	23
	10 500				4 010	3 530	2 880	25
	11 000			4 420	3 830	3 370	2 750	28
	11 500			4 360	3 660	3 220	2 630	30
	12 000			4 180	3 510	3 090	2 520	33
	12 500		4 420	4 010	3 370	2 960	2 420	36
	13 000		4 340	3 860	3 240	2 850	2 330	38
	13 500		4 180	3 710	3 120	2 740	2 240	41
	14 000		4 030	3 580	3 010	2 650	2 160	45
	14 500		3 890	3 460	2 900	2 550	2 090	48
	15 000	4 420	3 760	3 340	2 810	2 470	2 020	51
	15 500	4 410	3 640	3 240	2 720	2 390	1 950	55
	16 000	4 270	3 530	3 130	2 630	2 320	1 890	58
	16 500	4 140	3 420	3 040	2 550	2 250	1 830	62
	17 000	4 020	3 320	2 950	2 480	2 180	1 780	66
	17 500	3 900	3 230	2 870	2 400	2 120	1 730	70
	18 000	3 790	3 140	2 790	2 340	2 060	1 680	74
	18 500	3 690	3 050	2 710	2 270	2 000	1 630	78
	19 000	3 590	2 970	2 640	2 210	1 950	1 590	82
	19 500	3 500	2 890	2 570	2 160	1 900	1 550	86
	20 000	3 410	2 820	2 510	2 100	1 850	1 510	91
	20 500	3 330	2 750	2 450	2 050	1 810	1 480	96
	21 000	3 250	2 690	2 390	2 000	1 760	1 440	100
	21 500	3 180	2 630	2 330	1 960	1 720	1 410	105
	22 000	3 100	2 570	2 280	1 910	1 680	1 370	110
	22 500	3 040	2 510	2 230	1 870	1 650	1 340	115
	23 000	2 970	2 450	2 180	1 830	1 610	1 310	120

DESIGN DATA AND PROPERTIES

	458	388	351	304	273	234	
V_r (kN)	2 210	2 210	2 210	2 210	2 210	2 210	
L_u (mm)	7 890	6 970	6 810	5 310	5 150	3 710	
d (mm)	1 100	1 100	1 100	1 100	1 100	1 100	
b (mm)	550	500	500	400	400	300	
t (mm)	40.0	35.0	30.0	30.0	25.0	25.0	
w (mm)	14.0	14.0	14.0	14.0	14.0	14.0	
k (mm)	51	44	39	39	34	34	

IMPERIAL SIZE AND MASS

	458	388	351	304	273	234	
Mass (lb./ft.)	307	260	236	204	184	157	
Nominal Depth (in.)				43			

Note: F_y = 350 MPa and ϕ = 0.90

Total Uniformly Distributed Factored Loads for Laterally Supported Beams (kN)

Designation	WWF1000							Approx. Deflect. (mm)
Mass (kg/m)	447	377	340	293	262	223	200	
Span in Millimetres								
5 000							4 420	6
5 500						4 420	4 200	8
6 000						4 410	3 850	9
6 500						4 070	3 560	11
7 000					4 420	3 780	3 300	12
7 500					4 370	3 530	3 080	14
8 000				4 420	4 100	3 310	2 890	16
8 500				4 390	3 850	3 110	2 720	18
9 000				4 140	3 640	2 940	2 570	20
9 500				3 930	3 450	2 790	2 430	23
10 000			4 420	3 730	3 280	2 650	2 310	25
10 500			4 250	3 550	3 120	2 520	2 200	28
11 000		4 420	4 050	3 390	2 980	2 410	2 100	30
11 500		4 380	3 880	3 240	2 850	2 300	2 010	33
12 000		4 200	3 720	3 110	2 730	2 210	1 930	36
12 500		4 030	3 570	2 980	2 620	2 120	1 850	39
13 000		3 880	3 430	2 870	2 520	2 040	1 780	42
13 500	4 420	3 730	3 300	2 760	2 430	1 960	1 710	46
14 000	4 360	3 600	3 190	2 660	2 340	1 890	1 650	49
14 500	4 210	3 480	3 080	2 570	2 260	1 820	1 590	53
15 000	4 070	3 360	2 970	2 490	2 180	1 760	1 540	56
15 500	3 930	3 250	2 880	2 410	2 110	1 710	1 490	60
16 000	3 810	3 150	2 790	2 330	2 050	1 650	1 440	64
16 500	3 700	3 050	2 700	2 260	1 990	1 600	1 400	68
17 000	3 590	2 960	2 620	2 190	1 930	1 560	1 360	72
17 500	3 480	2 880	2 550	2 130	1 870	1 510	1 320	77
18 000	3 390	2 800	2 480	2 070	1 820	1 470	1 280	81
18 500	3 300	2 720	2 410	2 020	1 770	1 430	1 250	86
19 000	3 210	2 650	2 350	1 960	1 720	1 390	1 220	90
19 500	3 130	2 580	2 290	1 910	1 680	1 360	1 190	95
20 000	3 050	2 520	2 230	1 860	1 640	1 320	1 160	100
20 500	2 970	2 460	2 180	1 820	1 600	1 290	1 130	105
21 000	2 900	2 400	2 120	1 780	1 560	1 260	1 100	110
21 500	2 840	2 340	2 070	1 730	1 520	1 230	1 070	116
22 000	2 770	2 290	2 030	1 700	1 490	1 200	1 050	121

DESIGN DATA AND PROPERTIES							
V_r (kN)	2 210	2 210	2 210	2 210	2 210	2 210	2 210
L_u (mm)	8 030	7 080	6 910	5 400	5 230	3 790	3 610
d (mm)	1 000	1 000	1 000	1 000	1 000	1 000	1 000
b (mm)	550	500	500	400	400	300	300
t (mm)	40.0	35.0	30.0	30.0	25.0	25.0	20.0
w (mm)	14.0	14.0	14.0	14.0	14.0	14.0	14.0
k (mm)	51	44	39	39	34	34	29

IMPERIAL SIZE AND MASS							
Mass (lb./ft.)	300	253	228	197	176	150	134
Nominal Depth (in.)				39			

Note: F_y = 350 MPa and ϕ = 0.90

Total Uniformly Distributed Factored Loads for Laterally Supported Beams (kN)

Designation				WWF900				Approx. Deflect. (mm)
Mass (kg/m)	417	347	309	262	231	192	169	
Span in Millimetres								
6 000								10
6 500							2 680	12
7 000							2 650	14
7 500							2 480	16
8 000						2 700	2 320	18
8 500						2 550	2 180	20
9 000						2 410	2 060	23
9 500						2 280	1 950	25
10 000					2 700	2 170	1 860	28
10 500					2 590	2 060	1 770	31
11 000				2 740	2 470	1 970	1 690	34
11 500				2 720	2 370	1 880	1 610	37
12 000				2 600	2 270	1 810	1 550	40
12 500				2 500	2 180	1 730	1 490	43
13 000				2 400	2 090	1 670	1 430	47
13 500			2 740	2 310	2 020	1 610	1 380	51
14 000			2 700	2 230	1 940	1 550	1 330	54
14 500			2 610	2 160	1 880	1 490	1 280	58
15 000			2 520	2 080	1 810	1 440	1 240	63
15 500		2 740	2 440	2 020	1 760	1 400	1 200	67
16 000		2 690	2 360	1 950	1 700	1 350	1 160	71
16 500		2 610	2 290	1 890	1 650	1 310	1 130	76
17 000		2 530	2 220	1 840	1 600	1 270	1 090	80
17 500		2 460	2 160	1 790	1 560	1 240	1 060	85
18 000		2 390	2 100	1 740	1 510	1 200	1 030	90
18 500		2 330	2 040	1 690	1 470	1 170	1 000	95
19 000	2 740	2 270	1 990	1 640	1 430	1 140	977	100
19 500	2 690	2 210	1 940	1 600	1 400	1 110	952	106
20 000	2 620	2 150	1 890	1 560	1 360	1 080	929	111
20 500	2 560	2 100	1 840	1 520	1 330	1 060	906	117
21 000	2 500	2 050	1 800	1 490	1 300	1 030	884	123
21 500	2 440	2 000	1 760	1 450	1 270	1 010	864	128
22 000	2 380	1 960	1 720	1 420	1 240	985	844	134
22 500	2 330	1 920	1 680	1 390	1 210	963	825	141
23 000	2 280	1 870	1 640	1 360	1 180	942	807	147

DESIGN DATA AND PROPERTIES								
V_r (kN)	1 370	1 370	1 370	1 370	1 350	1 350	1 340	
L_u (mm)	8 310	7 320	7 160	5 630	5 460	3 980	3 820	
d (mm)	900	900	900	900	900	900	900	
b (mm)	550	500	500	400	400	300	300	
t (mm)	40.0	35.0	30.0	30.0	25.0	25.0	20.0	
w (mm)	11.0	11.0	11.0	11.0	11.0	11.0	11.0	
k (mm)	51	44	39	39	34	34	29	

IMPERIAL SIZE AND MASS								
Mass (lb./ft.)	279	233	208	176	156	128	113	
Nominal Depth (in.)				35				

Note: F_y = 350 MPa and ϕ = 0.90

Total Uniformly Distributed Factored Loads for Laterally Supported Beams (kN)

Designation		WWF800						Approx. Deflect. (mm)
Mass (kg/m)		339	300	253	223	184	161	
Span in Millimetres	5 000							8
	5 500						2 740	9
	6 000						2 650	11
	6 500					2 740	2 450	13
	7 000					2 670	2 280	15
	7 500					2 490	2 120	18
	8 000					2 330	1 990	20
	8 500				2 740	2 200	1 870	23
	9 000				2 620	2 070	1 770	25
	9 500			2 740	2 480	1 970	1 680	28
	10 000			2 720	2 350	1 870	1 590	31
	10 500			2 590	2 240	1 780	1 520	34
	11 000			2 470	2 140	1 700	1 450	38
	11 500			2 370	2 050	1 620	1 380	41
	12 000		2 740	2 270	1 960	1 560	1 330	45
	12 500		2 640	2 180	1 880	1 490	1 270	49
	13 000		2 540	2 090	1 810	1 440	1 230	53
	13 500	2 740	2 450	2 020	1 740	1 380	1 180	57
	14 000	2 680	2 360	1 940	1 680	1 330	1 140	61
	14 500	2 590	2 280	1 880	1 620	1 290	1 100	66
	15 000	2 500	2 200	1 810	1 570	1 240	1 060	70
	15 500	2 420	2 130	1 760	1 520	1 200	1 030	75
	16 000	2 350	2 060	1 700	1 470	1 170	995	80
	16 500	2 280	2 000	1 650	1 430	1 130	965	85
	17 000	2 210	1 940	1 600	1 380	1 100	937	90
	17 500	2 150	1 890	1 560	1 340	1 070	910	96
	18 000	2 090	1 830	1 510	1 310	1 040	885	101
	18 500	2 030	1 780	1 470	1 270	1 010	861	107
	19 000	1 980	1 740	1 430	1 240	983	838	113
	19 500	1 930	1 690	1 400	1 210	958	817	119
	20 000	1 880	1 650	1 360	1 180	934	796	125
	20 500	1 830	1 610	1 330	1 150	911	777	131
	21 000	1 790	1 570	1 300	1 120	889	758	138
	21 500	1 750	1 540	1 270	1 090	869	741	144
	22 000	1 710	1 500	1 240	1 070	849	724	151

DESIGN DATA AND PROPERTIES							
V_r (kN)	1 370	1 370	1 370	1 370	1 370	1 370	
L_u (mm)	7 490	7 280	5 730	5 570	4 060	3 900	
d (mm)	800	800	800	800	800	800	
b (mm)	500	500	400	400	300	300	
t (mm)	35.0	30.0	30.0	25.0	25.0	20.0	
w (mm)	11.0	11.0	11.0	11.0	11.0	11.0	
k (mm)	44	39	39	34	34	29	

IMPERIAL SIZE AND MASS							
Mass (lb./ft.)	228	202	170	150	123	108	
Nominal Depth (in.)				31			

Note: F_y = 350 MPa and ϕ = 0.90

Total Uniformly Distributed Factored Loads for Laterally Supported Beams (kN)

Designation	WWF700					Approx. Deflect. (mm)
Mass (kg/m)	245	214	196†	175	152	
4 000						6
4 500					2 740	7
5 000					2 680	9
5 500				2 740	2 440	11
6 000			2 740	2 630	2 230	13
6 500			2 540	2 430	2 060	15
7 000		2 740	2 360	2 250	1 920	18
7 500		2 670	2 200	2 100	1 790	20
8 000	2 740	2 500	2 070	1 970	1 680	23
8 500	2 730	2 360	1 940	1 860	1 580	26
9 000	2 580	2 230	1 840	1 750	1 490	29
9 500	2 440	2 110	1 740	1 660	1 410	32
10 000	2 320	2 000	1 650	1 580	1 340	36
10 500	2 210	1 910	1 570	1 500	1 280	39
11 000	2 110	1 820	1 500	1 430	1 220	43
11 500	2 020	1 740	1 440	1 370	1 170	47
12 000	1 930	1 670	1 380	1 310	1 120	51
12 500	1 860	1 600	1 320	1 260	1 070	56
13 000	1 790	1 540	1 270	1 210	1 030	60
13 500	1 720	1 480	1 220	1 170	993	65
14 000	1 660	1 430	1 180	1 130	958	70
14 500	1 600	1 380	1 140	1 090	925	75
15 000	1 550	1 340	1 100	1 050	894	80
15 500	1 500	1 290	1 070	1 020	865	86
16 000	1 450	1 250	1 030	986	838	91
16 500	1 410	1 210	1 000	956	813	97
17 000	1 370	1 180	972	928	789	103
17 500	1 330	1 140	945	901	766	109
18 000	1 290	1 110	918	876	745	116
18 500	1 250	1 080	894	853	725	122
19 000	1 220	1 050	870	830	706	129
19 500	1 190	1 030	848	809	688	136
20 000	1 160	1 000	827	789	670	143
20 500	1 130	977	806	770	654	150
21 000	1 110	954	787	751	638	158

Span in Millimetres

DESIGN DATA AND PROPERTIES

	245	214	196†	175	152	
V_r (kN)	1 370	1 370	1 370	1 370	1 370	
L_u (mm)	5 880	5 690	5 860	4 160	3 990	
d (mm)	700	700	700	700	700	
b (mm)	400	400	400	300	300	
t (mm)	30.0	25.0	22.0	25.0	20.0	
w (mm)	11.0	11.0	11.0	11.0	11.0	
k (mm)	39	34	31	34	29	

IMPERIAL SIZE AND MASS

Mass (lb./ft.)	164	144	132	117	102	
Nominal Depth (in.)			28			

Note: F_y = 350 MPa and ϕ = 0.90

† Class 3

Total Uniformly Distributed Factored Loads for Laterally Supported Beams (kN)

Designation	W1100				Approx. Deflect. (mm)	W1000						Approx. Deflect. (mm)
Mass (kg/m)	499	433	390	343		883	748	642	591	554	539	
5 000					6			14 600		12 500		6
5 500	11 900	10 000	9 020	7 700	7	20 400	17 100	14 500	13 200	12 400	12 000	8
6 000	11 000	9 600	8 610	7 490	8	18 800	15 700	13 300	12 200	11 400	11 100	9
6 500	10 200	8 870	7 950	6 920	10	17 300	14 500	12 300	11 300	10 500	10 200	11
7 000	9 440	8 230	7 380	6 420	11	16 100	13 400	11 400	10 500	9 760	9 510	12
7 500	8 810	7 680	6 890	5 990	13	15 000	12 600	10 600	9 770	9 110	8 880	14
8 000	8 260	7 200	6 460	5 620	15	14 100	11 800	9 970	9 160	8 540	8 320	16
8 500	7 770	6 780	6 080	5 290	16	13 200	11 100	9 380	8 620	8 040	7 830	18
9 000	7 340	6 400	5 740	5 000	18	12 500	10 500	8 860	8 140	7 590	7 400	20
9 500	6 960	6 070	5 440	4 730	21	11 800	9 910	8 390	7 710	7 190	7 010	23
10 000	6 610	5 760	5 170	4 500	23	11 300	9 410	7 970	7 330	6 830	6 660	25
10 500	6 290	5 490	4 920	4 280	25	10 700	8 970	7 590	6 980	6 510	6 340	28
11 000	6 010	5 240	4 700	4 090	28	10 200	8 560	7 250	6 660	6 210	6 050	30
11 500	5 750	5 010	4 490	3 910	30	9 780	8 190	6 930	6 370	5 940	5 790	33
12 000	5 510	4 800	4 310	3 750	33	9 380	7 850	6 640	6 110	5 690	5 550	36
12 500	5 290	4 610	4 130	3 600	36	9 000	7 530	6 380	5 860	5 460	5 330	39
13 000	5 080	4 430	3 970	3 460	38	8 660	7 240	6 130	5 640	5 250	5 120	42
13 500	4 890	4 270	3 830	3 330	41	8 340	6 970	5 910	5 430	5 060	4 930	46
14 000	4 720	4 120	3 690	3 210	45	8 040	6 720	5 700	5 230	4 880	4 760	49
14 500	4 560	3 970	3 560	3 100	48	7 760	6 490	5 500	5 050	4 710	4 590	53
15 000	4 400	3 840	3 440	3 000	51	7 500	6 280	5 320	4 890	4 550	4 440	56
15 500	4 260	3 720	3 330	2 900	55	7 260	6 070	5 140	4 730	4 410	4 290	60
16 000	4 130	3 600	3 230	2 810	58	7 030	5 880	4 980	4 580	4 270	4 160	64
16 500	4 000	3 490	3 130	2 720	62	6 820	5 710	4 830	4 440	4 140	4 030	68
17 000	3 890	3 390	3 040	2 640	66	6 620	5 540	4 690	4 310	4 020	3 920	72
17 500	3 780	3 290	2 950	2 570	70	6 430	5 380	4 560	4 190	3 900	3 800	77
18 000	3 670	3 200	2 870	2 500	74	6 250	5 230	4 430	4 070	3 800	3 700	81
18 500	3 570	3 120	2 790	2 430	78	6 080	5 090	4 310	3 960	3 690	3 600	86
19 000	3 480	3 030	2 720	2 370	82	5 920	4 950	4 200	3 860	3 600	3 500	90
19 500	3 390	2 960	2 650	2 310	86	5 770	4 830	4 090	3 760	3 500	3 410	95
20 000	3 300	2 880	2 580	2 250	91	5 630	4 710	3 990	3 660	3 420	3 330	100
20 500	3 220	2 810	2 520	2 190	96	5 490	4 590	3 890	3 570	3 330	3 250	105
21 000	3 150	2 740	2 460	2 140	100	5 360	4 480	3 800	3 490	3 250	3 170	110
21 500	3 070	2 680	2 400	2 090	105	5 230	4 380	3 710	3 410	3 180	3 100	116
22 000	3 000	2 620	2 350	2 040	110	5 110	4 280	3 620	3 330	3 110	3 030	121

PROPERTIES AND DESIGN DATA

V_r (kN)	5 960	5 000	4 510	3 850		10 200	8 540	7 300	6 610	6 240	5 990	
R (kN)	1 880	1 480	1 260	1 040		5 040	3 830	2 990	2 600	2 350	2 240	
G (kN)	67.3	56.9	51.8	46.6		118	101	88.0	80.2	76.3	73.5	
B_r' (kN)	2 530	1 810	1 500	1 210		7 740	5 690	4 320	3 590	3 250	3 010	
L_u (mm)	5 490	5 400	5 310	5 230		6 850	6 390	6 060	5 920	5 810	5 790	
d (mm)	1 118	1 108	1 100	1 090		1 092	1 068	1 048	1 040	1 032	1 030	
b (mm)	405	402	400	400		424	417	412	409	408	407	
t (mm)	45.0	40.0	36.0	31.0		82.0	70.0	60.0	55.9	52.0	51.1	
w (mm)	26.0	22.0	20.0	18.0		45.5	39.0	34.0	31.0	29.5	28.4	

IMPERIAL SIZE AND WEIGHT

Weight (lb/ft)	335	290	262	230		593	503	431	397	372	362	
Nominal Depth (in.)		44					40					

Note: F_y taken as 345 MPa. $\phi = 0.90$

Total Uniformly Distributed Factored Loads for Laterally Supported Beams (kN)

Designation	W1000											Approx. Deflect. (mm)
Mass (kg/m)	483	443	412	371	321	296	584	494	486	438	415	
4 000							15 600	13 200			10 900	4
4 500							15 500	12 900	12 700	11 300	10 800	5
5 000							13 900	11 600	11 500	10 300	9 740	6
5 500	10 600	9 780	8 720	7 780		6 460	12 600	10 600	10 500	9 350	8 850	8
6 000	9 890	9 030	8 490	7 620	6 500	5 920	11 600	9 690	9 600	8 570	8 110	9
6 500	9 130	8 330	7 830	7 030	6 040	5 460	10 700	8 940	8 870	7 910	7 490	11
7 000	8 480	7 740	7 270	6 530	5 610	5 070	9 940	8 300	8 230	7 350	6 960	12
7 500	7 920	7 220	6 790	6 090	5 230	4 740	9 270	7 750	7 680	6 860	6 490	14
8 000	7 420	6 770	6 370	5 710	4 910	4 440	8 690	7 270	7 200	6 430	6 090	16
8 500	6 980	6 370	5 990	5 380	4 620	4 180	8 180	6 840	6 780	6 050	5 730	18
9 000	6 600	6 020	5 660	5 080	4 360	3 950	7 730	6 460	6 400	5 710	5 410	20
9 500	6 250	5 700	5 360	4 810	4 130	3 740	7 320	6 120	6 070	5 410	5 120	23
10 000	5 940	5 420	5 090	4 570	3 920	3 550	6 960	5 810	5 760	5 140	4 870	25
10 500	5 650	5 160	4 850	4 350	3 740	3 380	6 620	5 540	5 490	4 900	4 640	28
11 000	5 400	4 920	4 630	4 160	3 570	3 230	6 320	5 280	5 240	4 670	4 430	30
11 500	5 160	4 710	4 430	3 970	3 410	3 090	6 050	5 050	5 010	4 470	4 230	33
12 000	4 950	4 510	4 240	3 810	3 270	2 960	5 800	4 840	4 800	4 280	4 060	36
12 500	4 750	4 330	4 070	3 660	3 140	2 840	5 560	4 650	4 610	4 110	3 890	39
13 000	4 570	4 170	3 920	3 520	3 020	2 730	5 350	4 470	4 430	3 960	3 750	42
13 500	4 400	4 010	3 770	3 390	2 910	2 630	5 150	4 310	4 270	3 810	3 610	46
14 000	4 240	3 870	3 640	3 260	2 800	2 540	4 970	4 150	4 120	3 670	3 480	49
14 500	4 090	3 730	3 510	3 150	2 710	2 450	4 800	4 010	3 970	3 550	3 360	53
15 000	3 960	3 610	3 390	3 050	2 620	2 370	4 640	3 880	3 840	3 430	3 250	56
15 500	3 830	3 490	3 290	2 950	2 530	2 290	4 490	3 750	3 720	3 320	3 140	60
16 000	3 710	3 380	3 180	2 860	2 450	2 220	4 350	3 630	3 600	3 210	3 040	64
16 500	3 600	3 280	3 090	2 770	2 380	2 150	4 220	3 520	3 490	3 120	2 950	68
17 000	3 490	3 190	3 000	2 690	2 310	2 090	4 090	3 420	3 390	3 020	2 860	72
17 500	3 390	3 090	2 910	2 610	2 240	2 030	3 970	3 320	3 290	2 940	2 780	77
18 000	3 300	3 010	2 830	2 540	2 180	1 970	3 860	3 230	3 200	2 860	2 700	81
18 500	3 210	2 930	2 750	2 470	2 120	1 920	3 760	3 140	3 120	2 780	2 630	86
19 000	3 120	2 850	2 680	2 410	2 070	1 870	3 660	3 060	3 030	2 710	2 560	90
19 500	3 040	2 780	2 610	2 340	2 010	1 820	3 570	2 980	2 960	2 640	2 500	95
20 000	2 970	2 710	2 550	2 290	1 960	1 780	3 480	2 910	2 880	2 570	2 430	100
20 500	2 900	2 640	2 480	2 230	1 910	1 730	3 390	2 840	2 810	2 510	2 370	105
21 000	2 830	2 580	2 420	2 180	1 870	1 690	3 310	2 770	2 740	2 450	2 320	110

Span in Millimetres

PROPERTIES AND DESIGN DATA

Vr (kN)	5 310	4 890	4 360	3 890	3 250	3 230	7 790	6 580	6 370	5 660	5 430
R (kN)	1 870	1 630	1 420	1 200	956	890	3 320	2 530	2 460	2 060	1 910
G (kN)	65.7	61.1	54.6	49.2	42.7	42.7	93.2	80.2	77.6	69.6	67.3
Br′ (kN)	2 410	2 080	1 660	1 350	1 020	1 020	4 840	3 590	3 360	2 700	2 530
Lu (mm)	5 650	5 530	5 530	5 440	5 360	5 230	4 530	4 280	4 270	4 160	4 080
d (mm)	1 020	1 012	1 008	1 000	990	982	1 056	1 036	1 036	1 026	1 020
b (mm)	404	402	402	400	400	400	314	309	308	305	304
t (mm)	46.0	41.9	40.0	36.1	31.0	27.1	64.0	54.0	54.1	49.0	46.0
w (mm)	25.4	23.6	21.1	19.0	16.5	16.5	36.0	31.0	30.0	26.9	26.0

IMPERIAL SIZE AND WEIGHT

Weight (lb/ft)	324	297	277	249	215	199	392	331	327	294	278
Nominal Depth (in.)	40										

Note: F_y taken as 345 MPa. $\phi = 0.90$

Total Uniformly Distributed Factored Loads for Laterally Supported Beams (kN)

Designation Mass (kg/m)	W1000 393	350	314	272	249	222	Approx. Deflect. (mm)	W920 656	588	Approx. Deflect. (mm)
4 000					6 440	6 000	4			4
4 500	10 200	8 720	7 820	6 500	6 240	5 410	5			6
5 000	9 190	8 250	7 400	6 360	5 610	4 870	6			7
5 500	8 360	7 500	6 730	5 780	5 100	4 430	8	14 000	12 400	8
6 000	7 660	6 870	6 170	5 300	4 680	4 060	9	13 000	11 600	10
6 500	7 070	6 340	5 690	4 890	4 320	3 750	11	12 000	10 700	11
7 000	6 560	5 890	5 290	4 540	4 010	3 480	12	11 100	9 900	13
7 500	6 130	5 500	4 930	4 240	3 740	3 250	14	10 400	9 240	15
8 000	5 740	5 150	4 630	3 970	3 510	3 040	16	9 750	8 660	17
8 500	5 410	4 850	4 350	3 740	3 300	2 860	18	9 180	8 150	20
9 000	5 110	4 580	4 110	3 530	3 120	2 700	20	8 670	7 700	22
9 500	4 840	4 340	3 900	3 350	2 950	2 560	23	8 210	7 300	25
10 000	4 600	4 120	3 700	3 180	2 810	2 430	25	7 800	6 930	27
10 500	4 380	3 930	3 520	3 030	2 670	2 320	28	7 430	6 600	30
11 000	4 180	3 750	3 360	2 890	2 550	2 210	30	7 090	6 300	33
11 500	4 000	3 590	3 220	2 760	2 440	2 120	33	6 780	6 030	36
12 000	3 830	3 440	3 080	2 650	2 340	2 030	36	6 500	5 780	39
12 500	3 680	3 300	2 960	2 540	2 250	1 950	39	6 240	5 540	42
13 000	3 530	3 170	2 850	2 450	2 160	1 870	42	6 000	5 330	46
13 500	3 400	3 050	2 740	2 360	2 080	1 800	46	5 780	5 130	50
14 000	3 280	2 950	2 640	2 270	2 000	1 740	49	5 570	4 950	53
14 500	3 170	2 840	2 550	2 190	1 940	1 680	53	5 380	4 780	57
15 000	3 060	2 750	2 470	2 120	1 870	1 620	56	5 200	4 620	61
15 500	2 960	2 660	2 390	2 050	1 810	1 570	60	5 030	4 470	65
16 000	2 870	2 580	2 310	1 990	1 750	1 520	64	4 870	4 330	70
16 500	2 790	2 500	2 240	1 930	1 700	1 480	68	4 730	4 200	74
17 000	2 700	2 430	2 180	1 870	1 650	1 430	72	4 590	4 080	79
17 500	2 630	2 360	2 110	1 820	1 600	1 390	77	4 460	3 960	83
18 000	2 550	2 290	2 060	1 770	1 560	1 350	81	4 330	3 850	88
18 500	2 480	2 230	2 000	1 720	1 520	1 320	86	4 220	3 750	93
19 000	2 420	2 170	1 950	1 670	1 480	1 280	90	4 110	3 650	98
19 500	2 360	2 110	1 900	1 630	1 440	1 250	95	4 000	3 550	103
20 000	2 300	2 060	1 850	1 590	1 400	1 220	100	3 900	3 470	109
20 500	2 240	2 010	1 810	1 550	1 370	1 190	105	3 800	3 380	114
21 000	2 190	1 960	1 760	1 510	1 340	1 160	110	3 710	3 300	120

Span in Millimetres

PROPERTIES AND DESIGN DATA

V_r (kN)	5 080	4 360	3 910	3 250	3 220	3 000		6 980	6 190	
R (kN)	1 740	1 420	1 200	956	871	763		3 110	2 600	
G (kN)	63.1	54.6	49.4	42.7	42.7	41.4		89.3	80.2	
B_r' (kN)	2 230	1 660	1 360	1 020	1 020	957		4 450	3 590	
L_u (mm)	4 050	4 010	3 910	3 870	3 740	3 590		6 590	6 370	
d (mm)	1 016	1 008	1 000	990	980	970		987	975	
b (mm)	303	302	300	300	300	300		431	427	
t (mm)	43.9	40.0	35.9	31.0	26.0	21.1		62.0	55.9	
w (mm)	24.4	21.1	19.1	16.5	16.5	16.0		34.5	31.0	

IMPERIAL SIZE AND WEIGHT

Weight (lb/ft)	264	235	211	183	167	149		441	395
Nominal Depth (in.)			40					36	

Note: F_y taken as 345 MPa. $\phi = 0.90$

Total Uniformly Distributed Factored Loads for Laterally Supported Beams (kN)

Designation				W920					Approx. Deflect. (mm)
Mass (kg/m)		537	491	449	420	390	368	344	
Span in Millimetres	5 000					8 180	7 740	7 340	7
	5 500	11 200	10 200	9 320	8 700	8 130	7 630	7 140	8
	6 000	10 500	9 560	8 690	8 110	7 450	7 000	6 540	10
	6 500	9 670	8 830	8 030	7 490	6 880	6 460	6 040	11
	7 000	8 980	8 200	7 450	6 960	6 390	6 000	5 610	13
	7 500	8 380	7 650	6 960	6 490	5 960	5 600	5 230	15
	8 000	7 860	7 170	6 520	6 090	5 590	5 250	4 910	17
	8 500	7 390	6 750	6 140	5 730	5 260	4 940	4 620	20
	9 000	6 980	6 380	5 800	5 410	4 970	4 660	4 360	22
	9 500	6 620	6 040	5 490	5 120	4 710	4 420	4 130	25
	10 000	6 280	5 740	5 220	4 870	4 470	4 200	3 920	27
	10 500	5 990	5 460	4 970	4 640	4 260	4 000	3 740	30
	11 000	5 710	5 220	4 740	4 430	4 060	3 820	3 570	33
	11 500	5 460	4 990	4 540	4 230	3 890	3 650	3 410	36
	12 000	5 240	4 780	4 350	4 060	3 730	3 500	3 270	39
	12 500	5 030	4 590	4 170	3 890	3 580	3 360	3 140	42
	13 000	4 830	4 410	4 010	3 750	3 440	3 230	3 020	46
	13 500	4 660	4 250	3 860	3 610	3 310	3 110	2 910	50
	14 000	4 490	4 100	3 730	3 480	3 190	3 000	2 800	53
	14 500	4 330	3 960	3 600	3 360	3 080	2 900	2 710	57
	15 000	4 190	3 830	3 480	3 250	2 980	2 800	2 620	61
	15 500	4 050	3 700	3 370	3 140	2 880	2 710	2 530	65
	16 000	3 930	3 590	3 260	3 040	2 790	2 620	2 450	70
	16 500	3 810	3 480	3 160	2 950	2 710	2 540	2 380	74
	17 000	3 700	3 380	3 070	2 860	2 630	2 470	2 310	79
	17 500	3 590	3 280	2 980	2 780	2 550	2 400	2 240	83
	18 000	3 490	3 190	2 900	2 700	2 480	2 330	2 180	88
	18 500	3 400	3 100	2 820	2 630	2 420	2 270	2 120	93
	19 000	3 310	3 020	2 750	2 560	2 350	2 210	2 070	98
	19 500	3 220	2 940	2 680	2 500	2 290	2 150	2 010	103
	20 000	3 140	2 870	2 610	2 430	2 240	2 100	1 960	109
	20 500	3 070	2 800	2 540	2 370	2 180	2 050	1 910	114
	21 000	2 990	2 730	2 480	2 320	2 130	2 000	1 870	120
	21 500	2 920	2 670	2 430	2 260	2 080	1 950	1 830	126
	22 000	2 860	2 610	2 370	2 210	2 030	1 910	1 780	132

PROPERTIES AND DESIGN DATA								
V_r (kN)	5 620	5 080	4 660	4 350	4 090	3 870	3 670
R (kN)	2 240	1 930	1 680	1 510	1 360	1 250	1 140
G (kN)	73.5	67.0	62.1	58.2	55.1	52.5	49.9
B_r' (kN)	3 010	2 510	2 150	1 890	1 700	1 540	1 390
L_u (mm)	6 220	6 070	6 000	5 910	5 810	5 730	5 670
d (mm)	965	957	948	943	936	931	927
b (mm)	425	422	423	422	420	419	418
t (mm)	51.1	47.0	42.7	39.9	36.6	34.3	32.0
w (mm)	28.4	25.9	24.0	22.5	21.3	20.3	19.3

IMPERIAL SIZE AND WEIGHT								
Weight (lb/ft)	361	330	302	282	262	247	231
Nominal Depth (in.)				36			

Note: F_y taken as 345 MPa. $\phi = 0.90$

Total Uniformly Distributed Factored Loads for Laterally Supported Beams (kN)

Designation					W920						Approx. Deflect. (mm)
Mass (kg/m)	381	345	313	289	271	253	238	223	201		
Span in Millimetres											
3 000											2
3 500								5 940	5 420		3
4 000	9 520	8 540	8 060	7 380	6 960	6 520	6 180	5 920	5 190		4
4 500	9 380	8 450	7 510	6 960	6 510	6 070	5 630	5 270	4 610		6
5 000	8 450	7 600	6 760	6 260	5 860	5 460	5 070	4 740	4 150		7
5 500	7 680	6 910	6 140	5 690	5 330	4 970	4 610	4 310	3 780		8
6 000	7 040	6 330	5 630	5 220	4 890	4 550	4 220	3 950	3 460		10
6 500	6 500	5 850	5 200	4 820	4 510	4 200	3 900	3 650	3 190		11
7 000	6 030	5 430	4 830	4 470	4 190	3 900	3 620	3 390	2 970		13
7 500	5 630	5 070	4 500	4 170	3 910	3 640	3 380	3 160	2 770		15
8 000	5 280	4 750	4 220	3 910	3 660	3 420	3 170	2 960	2 600		17
8 500	4 970	4 470	3 970	3 680	3 450	3 210	2 980	2 790	2 440		20
9 000	4 690	4 220	3 750	3 480	3 260	3 040	2 820	2 630	2 310		22
9 500	4 450	4 000	3 560	3 290	3 090	2 880	2 670	2 490	2 190		25
10 000	4 220	3 800	3 380	3 130	2 930	2 730	2 530	2 370	2 080		27
10 500	4 020	3 620	3 220	2 980	2 790	2 600	2 410	2 260	1 980		30
11 000	3 840	3 460	3 070	2 850	2 660	2 480	2 300	2 150	1 890		33
11 500	3 670	3 300	2 940	2 720	2 550	2 380	2 200	2 060	1 810		36
12 000	3 520	3 170	2 820	2 610	2 440	2 280	2 110	1 970	1 730		39
12 500	3 380	3 040	2 700	2 500	2 340	2 190	2 030	1 900	1 660		42
13 000	3 250	2 920	2 600	2 410	2 250	2 100	1 950	1 820	1 600		46
13 500	3 130	2 820	2 500	2 320	2 170	2 020	1 880	1 760	1 540		50
14 000	3 020	2 710	2 410	2 240	2 090	1 950	1 810	1 690	1 480		53
14 500	2 910	2 620	2 330	2 160	2 020	1 880	1 750	1 630	1 430		57
15 000	2 820	2 530	2 250	2 090	1 950	1 820	1 690	1 580	1 380		61
15 500	2 720	2 450	2 180	2 020	1 890	1 760	1 630	1 530	1 340		65
16 000	2 640	2 380	2 110	1 960	1 830	1 710	1 580	1 480	1 300		70
16 500	2 560	2 300	2 050	1 900	1 780	1 660	1 540	1 440	1 260		74
17 000	2 480	2 240	1 990	1 840	1 720	1 610	1 490	1 390	1 220		79
17 500	2 410	2 170	1 930	1 790	1 670	1 560	1 450	1 350	1 190		83
18 000	2 350	2 110	1 880	1 740	1 630	1 520	1 410	1 320	1 150		88
18 500	2 280	2 050	1 830	1 690	1 580	1 480	1 370	1 280	1 120		93
19 000	2 220	2 000	1 780	1 650	1 540	1 440	1 330	1 250	1 090		98
19 500	2 170	1 950	1 730	1 610	1 500	1 400	1 300	1 220	1 060		103
20 000	2 110	1 900	1 690	1 560	1 470	1 370	1 270	1 180	1 040		109

PROPERTIES AND DESIGN DATA

	381	345	313	289	271	253	238	223	201
V_r (kN)	4 760	4 270	4 030	3 690	3 480	3 260	3 090	2 970	2 710
R (kN)	1 740	1 480	1 300	1 140	1 050	947	869	805	710
G (kN)	63.1	57.2	54.6	50.2	47.6	44.8	42.7	41.1	39.3
B_r' (kN)	2 230	1 830	1 660	1 410	1 270	1 120	1 020	945	864
L_u (mm)	4 250	4 170	4 060	4 010	3 970	3 930	3 890	3 830	3 720
d (mm)	951	943	932	927	923	919	915	911	903
b (mm)	310	308	309	308	307	306	305	304	304
t (mm)	43.9	39.9	34.5	32.0	30.0	27.9	25.9	23.9	20.1
w (mm)	24.4	22.1	21.1	19.4	18.4	17.3	16.5	15.9	15.2

IMPERIAL SIZE AND WEIGHT

	381	345	313	289	271	253	238	223	201
Weight (lb/ft)	256	232	210	194	182	170	160	150	135
Nominal Depth (in.)					36				

Note: F_y taken as 345 MPa. $\phi = 0.90$

Total Uniformly Distributed Factored Loads for Laterally Supported Beams (kN)

Designation				W840					Approx. Deflect. (mm)
Mass (kg/m)	576	527	473	433	392	359	329	299	
4 000									5
4 500								6 380	6
5 000	12 000	10 900	9 660	8 860	7 940	7 500	6 960	6 310	7
5 500	11 600	10 500	9 390	8 540	7 680	6 960	6 320	5 740	9
6 000	10 600	9 650	8 610	7 820	7 040	6 380	5 800	5 260	11
6 500	9 780	8 900	7 950	7 220	6 500	5 890	5 350	4 850	13
7 000	9 080	8 270	7 380	6 710	6 030	5 460	4 970	4 510	15
7 500	8 480	7 720	6 890	6 260	5 630	5 100	4 640	4 210	17
8 000	7 950	7 230	6 460	5 870	5 280	4 780	4 350	3 940	19
8 500	7 480	6 810	6 080	5 520	4 970	4 500	4 090	3 710	22
9 000	7 070	6 430	5 740	5 220	4 690	4 250	3 860	3 510	24
9 500	6 690	6 090	5 440	4 940	4 450	4 030	3 660	3 320	27
10 000	6 360	5 790	5 170	4 690	4 220	3 830	3 480	3 150	30
10 500	6 060	5 510	4 920	4 470	4 020	3 640	3 310	3 000	33
11 000	5 780	5 260	4 700	4 270	3 840	3 480	3 160	2 870	36
11 500	5 530	5 030	4 490	4 080	3 670	3 330	3 020	2 740	39
12 000	5 300	4 820	4 310	3 910	3 520	3 190	2 900	2 630	43
12 500	5 090	4 630	4 130	3 760	3 380	3 060	2 780	2 520	47
13 000	4 890	4 450	3 970	3 610	3 250	2 940	2 680	2 430	50
13 500	4 710	4 290	3 830	3 480	3 130	2 830	2 580	2 340	54
14 000	4 540	4 130	3 690	3 350	3 020	2 730	2 480	2 250	58
14 500	4 390	3 990	3 560	3 240	2 910	2 640	2 400	2 180	63
15 000	4 240	3 860	3 440	3 130	2 820	2 550	2 320	2 100	67
15 500	4 100	3 730	3 330	3 030	2 720	2 470	2 240	2 040	72
16 000	3 970	3 620	3 230	2 930	2 640	2 390	2 170	1 970	76
16 500	3 850	3 510	3 130	2 850	2 560	2 320	2 110	1 910	81
17 000	3 740	3 400	3 040	2 760	2 480	2 250	2 050	1 860	86
17 500	3 630	3 310	2 950	2 680	2 410	2 190	1 990	1 800	91
18 000	3 530	3 220	2 870	2 610	2 350	2 130	1 930	1 750	96
18 500	3 440	3 130	2 790	2 540	2 280	2 070	1 880	1 710	102
19 000	3 350	3 050	2 720	2 470	2 220	2 010	1 830	1 660	107
19 500	3 260	2 970	2 650	2 410	2 170	1 960	1 780	1 620	113
20 000	3 180	2 890	2 580	2 350	2 110	1 910	1 740	1 580	119
20 500	3 100	2 820	2 520	2 290	2 060	1 870	1 700	1 540	125
21 000	3 030	2 760	2 460	2 240	2 010	1 820	1 660	1 500	131

PROPERTIES AND DESIGN DATA

Vr (kN)	5 990	5 460	4 830	4 430	3 970	3 750	3 480	3 190	
R (kN)	2 750	2 380	1 990	1 740	1 480	1 320	1 170	1 020	
G (kN)	82.8	76.3	68.3	63.1	57.2	54.6	51.0	47.1	
Br′ (kN)	3 830	3 250	2 610	2 230	1 830	1 660	1 450	1 240	
Lu (mm)	6 320	6 150	5 980	5 850	5 720	5 630	5 530	5 430	
d (mm)	913	903	893	885	877	868	862	855	
b (mm)	411	409	406	404	401	403	401	400	
t (mm)	57.9	53.1	48.0	43.9	39.9	35.6	32.4	29.2	
w (mm)	32.0	29.5	26.4	24.4	22.1	21.1	19.7	18.2	

IMPERIAL SIZE AND WEIGHT

Weight (lb/ft)	387	354	318	291	263	241	221	201	
Nominal Depth (in.)				33					

Note: F_y taken as 345 MPa. $\phi = 0.90$

Total Uniformly Distributed Factored Loads for Laterally Supported Beams (kN)

Designation	W840					Approx. Deflect. (mm)	W760					Approx. Deflect. (mm)
Mass (kg/m)	251	226	210	193	176		582	531	484	434	389	
Span in Millimetres												
3 000						3						3
3 500			5 340	5 060	4 600	4						4
4 000	5 980	5 620	5 240	4 730	4 230	5						5
4 500	5 690	5 060	4 650	4 210	3 760	6	11 900	10 800	9 780		7 760	7
5 000	5 120	4 550	4 190	3 790	3 380	7	11 800	10 700	9 690	8 640	7 700	8
5 500	4 650	4 140	3 810	3 440	3 080	9	10 700	9 760	8 810	7 860	7 000	10
6 000	4 260	3 790	3 490	3 150	2 820	11	9 850	8 940	8 070	7 200	6 420	12
6 500	3 940	3 500	3 220	2 910	2 600	13	9 100	8 250	7 450	6 650	5 920	14
7 000	3 660	3 250	2 990	2 700	2 420	15	8 450	7 660	6 920	6 170	5 500	16
7 500	3 410	3 030	2 790	2 520	2 260	17	7 880	7 150	6 460	5 760	5 130	19
8 000	3 200	2 840	2 620	2 370	2 110	19	7 390	6 710	6 050	5 400	4 810	21
8 500	3 010	2 680	2 460	2 230	1 990	22	6 960	6 310	5 700	5 080	4 530	24
9 000	2 840	2 530	2 330	2 100	1 880	24	6 570	5 960	5 380	4 800	4 280	27
9 500	2 690	2 400	2 200	1 990	1 780	27	6 220	5 650	5 100	4 550	4 050	30
10 000	2 560	2 280	2 090	1 890	1 690	30	5 910	5 370	4 840	4 320	3 850	33
10 500	2 440	2 170	1 990	1 800	1 610	33	5 630	5 110	4 610	4 120	3 670	36
11 000	2 330	2 070	1 900	1 720	1 540	36	5 370	4 880	4 400	3 930	3 500	40
11 500	2 220	1 980	1 820	1 650	1 470	39	5 140	4 670	4 210	3 760	3 350	44
12 000	2 130	1 900	1 750	1 580	1 410	43	4 930	4 470	4 040	3 600	3 210	47
12 500	2 050	1 820	1 680	1 510	1 350	47	4 730	4 290	3 880	3 460	3 080	51
13 000	1 970	1 750	1 610	1 460	1 300	50	4 550	4 130	3 730	3 320	2 960	56
13 500	1 900	1 690	1 550	1 400	1 250	54	4 380	3 970	3 590	3 200	2 850	60
14 000	1 830	1 630	1 500	1 350	1 210	58	4 220	3 830	3 460	3 090	2 750	64
14 500	1 760	1 570	1 440	1 310	1 170	63	4 080	3 700	3 340	2 980	2 660	69
15 000	1 710	1 520	1 400	1 260	1 130	67	3 940	3 580	3 230	2 880	2 570	74
15 500	1 650	1 470	1 350	1 220	1 090	72	3 810	3 460	3 130	2 790	2 480	79
16 000	1 600	1 420	1 310	1 180	1 060	76	3 690	3 350	3 030	2 700	2 410	84
16 500	1 550	1 380	1 270	1 150	1 030	81	3 580	3 250	2 940	2 620	2 330	90
17 000	1 510	1 340	1 230	1 110	995	86	3 480	3 160	2 850	2 540	2 260	95
17 500	1 460	1 300	1 200	1 080	967	91	3 380	3 070	2 770	2 470	2 200	101
18 000	1 420	1 260	1 160	1 050	940	96	3 280	2 980	2 690	2 400	2 140	107
18 500	1 380	1 230	1 130	1 020	914	102	3 200	2 900	2 620	2 340	2 080	113
19 000	1 350	1 200	1 100	996	890	107	3 110	2 820	2 550	2 270	2 030	119
19 500	1 310	1 170	1 070	971	867	113	3 030	2 750	2 480	2 220	1 970	125
20 000	1 280	1 140	1 050	946	846	119	2 960	2 680	2 420	2 160	1 930	132

PROPERTIES AND DESIGN DATA

	251	226	210	193	176		582	531	484	434	389	
V_r (kN)	2 990	2 810	2 670	2 530	2 300		5 960	5 380	4 890	4 320	3 880	
R (kN)	985	863	787	711	635		3 110	2 670	2 310	1 930	1 630	
G (kN)	44.0	41.7	39.8	38.0	36.2		89.3	81.5	75.0	67.0	61.1	
B_r' (kN)	1 080	969	886	808	733		4 450	3 710	3 140	2 510	2 080	
L_u (mm)	3 890	3 830	3 770	3 690	3 610		6 460	6 230	6 040	5 830	5 640	
d (mm)	859	851	846	840	835		843	833	823	813	803	
b (mm)	292	294	293	292	292		396	393	390	387	385	
t (mm)	31.0	26.8	24.4	21.7	18.8		62.0	56.9	52.1	47.0	41.9	
w (mm)	17.0	16.1	15.4	14.7	14.0		34.5	31.5	29.0	25.9	23.6	

IMPERIAL SIZE AND WEIGHT

	251	226	210	193	176		582	531	484	434	389	
Weight (lb/ft)	169	152	141	130	118		391	357	326	292	261	
Nominal Depth (in.)			33						30			

Note: F_y taken as 345 MPa. ϕ = 0.90

Total Uniformly Distributed Factored Loads for Laterally Supported Beams (kN)

Designation	W760											Approx. Deflect. (mm)
Mass (kg/m)	350	314	284	257	220	196	185	173	161	147	134	
3 000								4 500	4 280	4 080	3 300	3
3 500					5 260	4 920	4 680	4 410	4 020	3 620	3 290	4
4 000					5 090	4 450	4 150	3 860	3 510	3 170	2 880	5
4 500		6 340	5 740	5 260	4 520	3 960	3 690	3 430	3 120	2 820	2 560	7
5 000	6 880	6 110	5 510	4 950	4 070	3 560	3 320	3 090	2 810	2 530	2 300	8
5 500	6 280	5 560	5 010	4 500	3 700	3 240	3 020	2 800	2 560	2 300	2 090	10
6 000	5 750	5 090	4 600	4 130	3 390	2 970	2 770	2 570	2 340	2 110	1 920	12
6 500	5 310	4 700	4 240	3 810	3 130	2 740	2 560	2 370	2 160	1 950	1 770	14
7 000	4 930	4 360	3 940	3 540	2 910	2 540	2 370	2 200	2 010	1 810	1 640	16
7 500	4 600	4 070	3 680	3 300	2 710	2 370	2 220	2 060	1 870	1 690	1 530	19
8 000	4 320	3 820	3 450	3 100	2 540	2 230	2 080	1 930	1 760	1 580	1 440	21
8 500	4 060	3 590	3 240	2 910	2 390	2 100	1 960	1 810	1 650	1 490	1 350	24
9 000	3 840	3 390	3 060	2 750	2 260	1 980	1 850	1 710	1 560	1 410	1 280	27
9 500	3 630	3 220	2 900	2 610	2 140	1 870	1 750	1 620	1 480	1 330	1 210	30
10 000	3 450	3 060	2 760	2 480	2 030	1 780	1 660	1 540	1 410	1 270	1 150	33
10 500	3 290	2 910	2 630	2 360	1 940	1 700	1 580	1 470	1 340	1 210	1 100	36
11 000	3 140	2 780	2 510	2 250	1 850	1 620	1 510	1 400	1 280	1 150	1 050	40
11 500	3 000	2 660	2 400	2 150	1 770	1 550	1 450	1 340	1 220	1 100	1 000	44
12 000	2 880	2 550	2 300	2 060	1 700	1 480	1 380	1 290	1 170	1 060	958	47
12 500	2 760	2 440	2 210	1 980	1 630	1 420	1 330	1 230	1 120	1 010	920	51
13 000	2 660	2 350	2 120	1 910	1 560	1 370	1 280	1 190	1 080	974	885	56
13 500	2 560	2 260	2 040	1 830	1 510	1 320	1 230	1 140	1 040	938	852	60
14 000	2 470	2 180	1 970	1 770	1 450	1 270	1 190	1 100	1 000	905	821	64
14 500	2 380	2 110	1 900	1 710	1 400	1 230	1 150	1 060	970	874	793	69
15 000	2 300	2 040	1 840	1 650	1 360	1 190	1 110	1 030	937	845	767	74
15 500	2 230	1 970	1 780	1 600	1 310	1 150	1 070	995	907	817	742	79
16 000	2 160	1 910	1 720	1 550	1 270	1 110	1 040	964	879	792	719	84
16 500	2 090	1 850	1 670	1 500	1 230	1 080	1 010	935	852	768	697	90
17 000	2 030	1 800	1 620	1 460	1 200	1 050	978	907	827	745	677	95
17 500	1 970	1 750	1 580	1 420	1 160	1 020	950	881	803	724	657	101
18 000	1 920	1 700	1 530	1 380	1 130	989	923	857	781	704	639	107
18 500	1 870	1 650	1 490	1 340	1 100	963	898	834	760	685	622	113
19 000	1 820	1 610	1 450	1 300	1 070	937	875	812	740	667	605	119
19 500	1 770	1 570	1 410	1 270	1 040	913	852	791	721	650	590	125
20 000	1 730	1 530	1 380	1 240	1 020	891	831	771	703	633	575	132

Span in Millimetres

PROPERTIES AND DESIGN DATA

V_r (kN)	3 440	3 170	2 870	2 630	2 630	2 460	2 340	2 250	2 140	2 040	1 650
R (kN)	1 380	1 190	1 030	895	939	814	749	695	633	574	499
G (kN)	54.6	51.0	46.6	43.0	42.7	40.4	38.6	37.3	35.7	34.2	30.8
B_r' (kN)	1 660	1 450	1 210	1 030	1 020	910	830	775	712	651	529
L_u (mm)	5 510	5 420	5 300	5 230	3 570	3 500	3 450	3 410	3 330	3 260	3 230
d (mm)	795	786	779	773	779	770	766	762	758	753	750
b (mm)	382	384	382	381	266	268	267	267	266	265	264
t (mm)	38.1	33.4	30.1	27.1	30.0	25.4	23.6	21.6	19.3	17.0	15.5
w (mm)	21.1	19.7	18.0	16.6	16.5	15.6	14.9	14.4	13.8	13.2	11.9

IMPERIAL SIZE AND WEIGHT

Weight (lb/ft)	235	211	191	173	148	132	124	116	108	99	90
Nominal Depth (in.)	30										

Note: F_y taken as 345 MPa. $\phi = 0.90$

Total Uniformly Distributed Factored Loads for Laterally Supported Beams (kN)

Designation	W690								Approx. Deflect. (mm)
Mass (kg/m)	548	500	457	419	384	350	323	289	
4 000									6
4 500	11 100	10 000	9 100	8 200	7 520	6 900	6 240	5 560	7
5 000	10 100	9 190	8 350	7 600	6 960	6 260	5 810	5 120	9
5 500	9 210	8 360	7 590	6 910	6 320	5 690	5 280	4 650	11
6 000	8 450	7 660	6 960	6 330	5 800	5 220	4 840	4 260	13
6 500	7 800	7 070	6 420	5 850	5 350	4 820	4 470	3 940	15
7 000	7 240	6 560	5 960	5 430	4 970	4 470	4 150	3 660	18
7 500	6 760	6 130	5 560	5 070	4 640	4 170	3 880	3 410	20
8 000	6 330	5 740	5 220	4 750	4 350	3 910	3 630	3 200	23
8 500	5 960	5 410	4 910	4 470	4 090	3 680	3 420	3 010	26
9 000	5 630	5 110	4 640	4 220	3 860	3 480	3 230	2 840	29
9 500	5 330	4 840	4 390	4 000	3 660	3 290	3 060	2 690	33
10 000	5 070	4 600	4 170	3 800	3 480	3 130	2 910	2 560	36
10 500	4 830	4 380	3 970	3 620	3 310	2 980	2 770	2 440	40
11 000	4 610	4 180	3 790	3 460	3 160	2 850	2 640	2 330	44
11 500	4 410	4 000	3 630	3 300	3 020	2 720	2 530	2 220	48
12 000	4 220	3 830	3 480	3 170	2 900	2 610	2 420	2 130	52
12 500	4 050	3 680	3 340	3 040	2 780	2 500	2 330	2 050	57
13 000	3 900	3 530	3 210	2 920	2 680	2 410	2 240	1 970	61
13 500	3 750	3 400	3 090	2 820	2 580	2 320	2 150	1 900	66
14 000	3 620	3 280	2 980	2 710	2 480	2 240	2 080	1 830	71
14 500	3 490	3 170	2 880	2 620	2 400	2 160	2 000	1 760	76
15 000	3 380	3 060	2 780	2 530	2 320	2 090	1 940	1 710	82
15 500	3 270	2 960	2 690	2 450	2 240	2 020	1 880	1 650	87
16 000	3 170	2 870	2 610	2 380	2 170	1 960	1 820	1 600	93
16 500	3 070	2 790	2 530	2 300	2 110	1 900	1 760	1 550	99
17 000	2 980	2 700	2 450	2 240	2 050	1 840	1 710	1 510	105
17 500	2 900	2 630	2 380	2 170	1 990	1 790	1 660	1 460	111
18 000	2 820	2 550	2 320	2 110	1 930	1 740	1 610	1 420	117
18 500	2 740	2 480	2 260	2 050	1 880	1 690	1 570	1 380	124
19 000	2 670	2 420	2 200	2 000	1 830	1 650	1 530	1 350	131
19 500	2 600	2 360	2 140	1 950	1 780	1 610	1 490	1 310	138
20 000	2 530	2 300	2 090	1 900	1 740	1 560	1 450	1 280	145
20 500	2 470	2 240	2 040	1 850	1 700	1 530	1 420	1 250	152
21 000	2 410	2 190	1 990	1 810	1 660	1 490	1 380	1 220	160

Span in Millimetres

PROPERTIES AND DESIGN DATA

	548	500	457	419	384	350	323	289
V_r (kN)	5 550	5 000	4 550	4 100	3 760	3 450	3 120	2 780
R (kN)	3 200	2 750	2 380	2 060	1 800	1 580	1 380	1 160
G (kN)	90.8	82.8	76.3	69.6	64.4	59.8	54.6	49.2
B_r' (kN)	4 610	3 830	3 250	2 700	2 320	1 990	1 660	1 350
L_u (mm)	6 400	6 140	5 920	5 730	5 550	5 410	5 300	5 160
d (mm)	772	762	752	744	736	728	722	714
b (mm)	372	369	367	364	362	360	359	356
t (mm)	63.0	57.9	53.1	49.0	45.0	40.9	38.1	34.0
w (mm)	35.1	32.0	29.5	26.9	24.9	23.1	21.1	19.0

IMPERIAL SIZE AND WEIGHT

	548	500	457	419	384	350	323	289
Weight (lb/ft)	368	336	307	281	258	235	217	194
Nominal Depth (in.)	27							

Note: F_y taken as 345 MPa. $\phi = 0.90$

Total Uniformly Distributed Factored Loads for Laterally Supported Beams (kN)

Designation	W690								Approx. Deflect. (mm)	W610		Approx. Deflect. (mm)
Mass (kg/m)	265	240	217	192	170	152	140	125		551	498	
Span in Millimetres												
3 000					4 120	3 700	3 480	3 220	3			4
3 500				4 460	3 990	3 550	3 230	2 850	4			5
4 000	5 320	4 820	4 380	4 010	3 490	3 110	2 830	2 490	6	11 200	10 100	7
4 500	5 150	4 650	4 200	3 570	3 100	2 760	2 510	2 210	7	10 300	9 220	8
5 000	4 640	4 190	3 780	3 210	2 790	2 480	2 260	1 990	9	9 240	8 300	10
5 500	4 210	3 810	3 440	2 920	2 540	2 260	2 050	1 810	11	8 400	7 540	12
6 000	3 860	3 490	3 150	2 670	2 330	2 070	1 880	1 660	13	7 700	6 910	15
6 500	3 570	3 220	2 910	2 470	2 150	1 910	1 740	1 530	15	7 110	6 380	17
7 000	3 310	2 990	2 700	2 290	1 990	1 770	1 610	1 420	18	6 600	5 930	20
7 500	3 090	2 790	2 520	2 140	1 860	1 660	1 510	1 330	20	6 160	5 530	23
8 000	2 900	2 620	2 360	2 010	1 750	1 550	1 410	1 250	23	5 780	5 190	26
8 500	2 730	2 460	2 220	1 890	1 640	1 460	1 330	1 170	26	5 440	4 880	30
9 000	2 580	2 330	2 100	1 780	1 550	1 380	1 260	1 110	29	5 130	4 610	33
9 500	2 440	2 200	1 990	1 690	1 470	1 310	1 190	1 050	33	4 860	4 370	37
10 000	2 320	2 090	1 890	1 600	1 400	1 240	1 130	996	36	4 620	4 150	41
10 500	2 210	1 990	1 800	1 530	1 330	1 180	1 080	949	40	4 400	3 950	45
11 000	2 110	1 900	1 720	1 460	1 270	1 130	1 030	906	44	4 200	3 770	50
11 500	2 020	1 820	1 640	1 400	1 210	1 080	983	866	48	4 020	3 610	54
12 000	1 930	1 750	1 580	1 340	1 160	1 040	942	830	52	3 850	3 460	59
12 500	1 850	1 680	1 510	1 280	1 120	994	904	797	57	3 700	3 320	64
13 000	1 780	1 610	1 450	1 230	1 070	955	869	766	61	3 550	3 190	69
13 500	1 720	1 550	1 400	1 190	1 030	920	837	738	66	3 420	3 070	75
14 000	1 660	1 500	1 350	1 150	997	887	807	711	71	3 300	2 960	80
14 500	1 600	1 440	1 300	1 110	963	857	779	687	76	3 190	2 860	86
15 000	1 550	1 400	1 260	1 070	931	828	753	664	82	3 080	2 770	92
15 500	1 500	1 350	1 220	1 040	901	801	729	643	87	2 980	2 680	98
16 000	1 450	1 310	1 180	1 000	873	776	706	623	93	2 890	2 590	105
16 500	1 400	1 270	1 150	973	846	753	685	604	99	2 800	2 510	112
17 000	1 360	1 230	1 110	944	821	731	665	586	105	2 720	2 440	118
17 500	1 320	1 200	1 080	917	798	710	646	569	111	2 640	2 370	126
18 000	1 290	1 160	1 050	891	776	690	628	553	117	2 570	2 300	133
18 500	1 250	1 130	1 020	867	755	671	611	538	124	2 500	2 240	140
19 000	1 220	1 100	995	845	735	654	595	524	131	2 430	2 180	148
19 500	1 190	1 070	969	823	716	637	580	511	138	2 370	2 130	156
20 000	1 160	1 050	945	802	698	621	565	498	145	2 310	2 070	164
PROPERTIES AND DESIGN DATA												
V_r (kN)	2 660	2 410	2 190	2 230	2 060	1 850	1 740	1 610		5 620	5 030	
R (kN)	1 050	911	794	849	729	625	563	500		3 760	3 200	
G (kN)	47.6	43.5	39.8	40.1	37.5	33.9	32.1	30.3		99.9	90.8	
B_r' (kN)	1 270	1 060	886	898	786	641	575	512		5 570	4 610	
L_u (mm)	5 060	4 960	4 890	3 440	3 380	3 320	3 270	3 190		6 620	6 230	
d (mm)	706	701	695	702	693	688	684	678		711	699	
b (mm)	358	356	355	254	256	254	254	253		347	343	
t (mm)	30.2	27.4	24.8	27.9	23.6	21.1	18.9	16.3		69.1	63.0	
w (mm)	18.4	16.8	15.4	15.5	14.5	13.1	12.4	11.7		38.6	35.1	
IMPERIAL SIZE AND WEIGHT												
Weight (lb/ft)	178	161	146	129	114	102	94	84		370	335	
Nominal Depth (in.)	27									24		

Note: F_y taken as 345 MPa. $\phi = 0.90$

BEAM LOAD TABLES
W Shapes

Total Uniformly Distributed Factored Loads for Laterally Supported Beams (kN)

Designation	W610										Approx. Deflect. (mm)
Mass (kg/m)	455	415	372	341	307	285	262	241	217	195	
Span in Millimetres											
3 000											4
3 500										3 920	5
4 000	9 040	8 200	7 240	6 620	5 920	5 460	5 000	4 660	4 240	3 770	7
4 500	8 340	7 560	6 730	6 130	5 480	5 060	4 610	4 230	3 780	3 350	8
5 000	7 500	6 810	6 060	5 510	4 930	4 560	4 150	3 810	3 400	3 020	10
5 500	6 820	6 190	5 510	5 010	4 480	4 140	3 770	3 460	3 090	2 740	12
6 000	6 250	5 670	5 050	4 600	4 110	3 800	3 460	3 180	2 840	2 510	15
6 500	5 770	5 240	4 660	4 240	3 790	3 500	3 190	2 930	2 620	2 320	17
7 000	5 360	4 860	4 330	3 940	3 520	3 250	2 960	2 720	2 430	2 150	20
7 500	5 000	4 540	4 040	3 680	3 290	3 040	2 770	2 540	2 270	2 010	23
8 000	4 690	4 250	3 790	3 450	3 080	2 850	2 590	2 380	2 130	1 880	26
8 500	4 410	4 000	3 570	3 240	2 900	2 680	2 440	2 240	2 000	1 770	30
9 000	4 170	3 780	3 370	3 060	2 740	2 530	2 300	2 120	1 890	1 680	33
9 500	3 950	3 580	3 190	2 900	2 600	2 400	2 180	2 010	1 790	1 590	37
10 000	3 750	3 400	3 030	2 760	2 470	2 280	2 070	1 910	1 700	1 510	41
10 500	3 570	3 240	2 890	2 630	2 350	2 170	1 980	1 810	1 620	1 440	45
11 000	3 410	3 090	2 750	2 510	2 240	2 070	1 890	1 730	1 550	1 370	50
11 500	3 260	2 960	2 640	2 400	2 140	1 980	1 800	1 660	1 480	1 310	54
12 000	3 130	2 840	2 530	2 300	2 060	1 900	1 730	1 590	1 420	1 260	59
12 500	3 000	2 720	2 420	2 210	1 970	1 820	1 660	1 520	1 360	1 210	64
13 000	2 890	2 620	2 330	2 120	1 900	1 750	1 600	1 470	1 310	1 160	69
13 500	2 780	2 520	2 240	2 040	1 830	1 690	1 540	1 410	1 260	1 120	75
14 000	2 680	2 430	2 160	1 970	1 760	1 630	1 480	1 360	1 220	1 080	80
14 500	2 590	2 350	2 090	1 900	1 700	1 570	1 430	1 310	1 170	1 040	86
15 000	2 500	2 270	2 020	1 840	1 640	1 520	1 380	1 270	1 130	1 010	92
15 500	2 420	2 200	1 960	1 780	1 590	1 470	1 340	1 230	1 100	973	98
16 000	2 340	2 130	1 890	1 720	1 540	1 420	1 300	1 190	1 060	942	105
16 500	2 270	2 060	1 840	1 670	1 490	1 380	1 260	1 150	1 030	914	112
17 000	2 210	2 000	1 780	1 620	1 450	1 340	1 220	1 120	1 000	887	118
17 500	2 140	1 940	1 730	1 580	1 410	1 300	1 190	1 090	972	862	126
18 000	2 080	1 890	1 680	1 530	1 370	1 270	1 150	1 060	945	838	133
18 500	2 030	1 840	1 640	1 490	1 330	1 230	1 120	1 030	920	815	140
19 000	1 970	1 790	1 590	1 450	1 300	1 200	1 090	1 000	896	794	148

PROPERTIES AND DESIGN DATA

V_r (kN)	4 520	4 100	3 620	3 310	2 960	2 730	2 500	2 330	2 120	1 960	
R (kN)	2 750	2 380	1 990	1 740	1 480	1 320	1 160	1 040	900	787	
G (kN)	82.8	76.3	68.3	63.1	57.2	53.3	49.2	46.3	42.7	39.8	
B_r' (kN)	3 830	3 250	2 610	2 230	1 830	1 590	1 350	1 200	1 020	886	
L_u (mm)	5 940	5 700	5 450	5 250	5 080	4 980	4 850	4 790	4 680	4 570	
d (mm)	689	679	669	661	653	647	641	635	628	622	
b (mm)	340	338	335	333	330	329	327	329	328	327	
t (mm)	57.9	53.1	48.0	43.9	39.9	37.1	34.0	31.0	27.7	24.4	
w (mm)	32.0	29.5	26.4	24.4	22.1	20.6	19.0	17.9	16.5	15.4	

IMPERIAL SIZE AND WEIGHT

Weight (lb/ft)	306	279	250	229	207	192	176	162	146	131	
Nominal Depth (in.)	24										

Note: F_y taken as 345 MPa. $\phi = 0.90$

Total Uniformly Distributed Factored Loads for Laterally Supported Beams (kN)

Designation	W610											Approx. Deflect. (mm)
Mass (kg/m)	174	155	153	140	125	113	101	91	84*	92	82	
2 000										2 700	2 340	2
2 500						2 800	2 600	2 200	1 890	2 490	2 190	3
3 000			3 580	3 320	2 980	2 720	2 400	2 090	1 670	2 080	1 820	4
3 500	3 540	3 180	3 260	2 950	2 600	2 330	2 060	1 790	1 430	1 780	1 560	5
4 000	3 330	2 940	2 860	2 580	2 280	2 040	1 800	1 560	1 250	1 560	1 370	7
4 500	2 960	2 610	2 540	2 290	2 030	1 820	1 600	1 390	1 120	1 390	1 210	8
5 000	2 660	2 350	2 290	2 060	1 820	1 630	1 440	1 250	1 000	1 250	1 090	10
5 500	2 420	2 140	2 080	1 870	1 660	1 490	1 310	1 140	912	1 130	994	12
6 000	2 220	1 960	1 900	1 720	1 520	1 360	1 200	1 040	836	1 040	911	15
6 500	2 050	1 810	1 760	1 590	1 400	1 260	1 110	963	772	959	841	17
7 000	1 900	1 680	1 630	1 470	1 300	1 170	1 030	894	717	891	781	20
7 500	1 780	1 570	1 520	1 370	1 220	1 090	960	835	669	831	729	23
8 000	1 660	1 470	1 430	1 290	1 140	1 020	900	782	627	779	683	26
8 500	1 570	1 380	1 340	1 210	1 070	961	847	736	590	734	643	30
9 000	1 480	1 310	1 270	1 150	1 010	908	800	696	558	693	607	33
9 500	1 400	1 240	1 200	1 090	960	860	758	659	528	656	575	37
10 000	1 330	1 170	1 140	1 030	912	817	720	626	502	623	546	41
10 500	1 270	1 120	1 090	982	868	778	686	596	478	594	520	45
11 000	1 210	1 070	1 040	937	829	743	655	569	456	567	497	50
11 500	1 160	1 020	994	896	793	711	626	544	436	542	475	54
12 000	1 110	979	952	859	760	681	600	522	418	520	455	59
12 500	1 070	940	914	825	729	654	576	501	401	499	437	64
13 000	1 020	904	879	793	701	629	554	482	386	480	420	69
13 500	986	870	846	764	675	605	534	464	372	462	405	75
14 000	951	839	816	736	651	584	515	447	358	445	390	80
14 500	918	810	788	711	629	564	497	432	346	430	377	86
15 000	888	783	762	687	608	545	480	417	335	416	364	92
15 500	859	758	737	665	588	527	465	404	324	402	353	98
16 000	832	734	714	644	570	511	450	391	314	390	342	105
16 500	807	712	693	625	553	495	437	379	304	378	331	112
17 000	783	691	672	606	536	481	424	368	295	367	321	118
17 500	761	671	653	589	521	467	412	358	287	356	312	126
18 000	740	653	635	573	506	454	400	348	279	346	304	133
18 500	720	635	618	557	493	442	389	338	271	337	295	140
19 000	701	618	601	543	480	430	379	329	264	328	288	148

Span in Millimetres

PROPERTIES AND DESIGN DATA

Vr (kN)	1 770	1 590	1 790	1 660	1 490	1 400	1 300	1 100	944	1 350	1 170
R (kN)	675	578	723	640	549	490	434	378	342	451	391
G (kN)	36.2	32.9	36.2	33.9	30.8	29.0	27.2	25.1	23.3	28.2	25.9
Br' (kN)	733	603	733	641	529	469	412	352	303	444	374
Lu (mm)	4 480	4 400	3 110	3 070	3 020	2 950	2 890	2 820	3 000	2 180	2 110
d (mm)	616	611	623	617	612	608	603	598	596	603	599
b (mm)	325	324	229	230	229	228	228	227	226	179	178
t (mm)	21.6	19.0	24.9	22.2	19.6	17.3	14.9	12.7	11.7	15.0	12.8
w (mm)	14.0	12.7	14.0	13.1	11.9	11.2	10.5	9.7	9.0	10.9	10.0

IMPERIAL SIZE AND WEIGHT

Weight (lb/ft)	117	104	103	94	84	76	68	61	56	62	55
Nominal Depth (in.)	24										

Note: F_y taken as 345 MPa. $\phi = 0.90$

* Class 3

Total Uniformly Distributed Factored Loads for Laterally Supported Beams (kN)

Designation	W530										Approx. Deflect. (mm)
Mass (kg/m)	300	272	248	219	196	182	165	150	138	123	
2 000											2
2 500									3 300	2 920	3
3 000									2 990	2 660	4
3 500	5 540	4 980	4 440	4 200	3 740	3 440	3 140	2 820	2 560	2 280	6
4 000	5 380	4 850	4 380	3 790	3 390	3 130	2 830	2 580	2 240	1 990	8
4 500	4 790	4 310	3 900	3 370	3 010	2 780	2 510	2 290	1 990	1 770	10
5 000	4 310	3 880	3 510	3 040	2 710	2 500	2 260	2 060	1 790	1 590	12
5 500	3 920	3 530	3 190	2 760	2 470	2 280	2 050	1 870	1 630	1 450	14
6 000	3 590	3 230	2 920	2 530	2 260	2 090	1 880	1 720	1 490	1 330	17
6 500	3 310	2 980	2 700	2 330	2 090	1 930	1 740	1 590	1 380	1 230	20
7 000	3 080	2 770	2 510	2 170	1 940	1 790	1 610	1 470	1 280	1 140	23
7 500	2 870	2 590	2 340	2 020	1 810	1 670	1 510	1 370	1 200	1 060	27
8 000	2 690	2 430	2 190	1 900	1 700	1 560	1 410	1 290	1 120	997	30
8 500	2 530	2 280	2 060	1 790	1 600	1 470	1 330	1 210	1 050	938	34
9 000	2 390	2 160	1 950	1 690	1 510	1 390	1 260	1 150	996	886	38
9 500	2 270	2 040	1 850	1 600	1 430	1 320	1 190	1 090	944	839	43
10 000	2 150	1 940	1 750	1 520	1 360	1 250	1 130	1 030	897	797	47
10 500	2 050	1 850	1 670	1 450	1 290	1 190	1 080	982	854	759	52
11 000	1 960	1 760	1 590	1 380	1 230	1 140	1 030	937	815	725	57
11 500	1 870	1 690	1 520	1 320	1 180	1 090	983	896	780	693	62
12 000	1 790	1 620	1 460	1 260	1 130	1 040	942	859	747	664	68
12 500	1 720	1 550	1 400	1 210	1 090	1 000	904	825	717	638	74
13 000	1 660	1 490	1 350	1 170	1 040	963	869	793	690	613	80
13 500	1 600	1 440	1 300	1 120	1 000	927	837	764	664	591	86
14 000	1 540	1 390	1 250	1 080	969	894	807	736	641	570	92
14 500	1 490	1 340	1 210	1 050	935	863	779	711	618	550	99
15 000	1 440	1 290	1 170	1 010	904	835	753	687	598	532	106
15 500	1 390	1 250	1 130	979	875	808	729	665	579	514	113
16 000	1 350	1 210	1 100	949	848	782	706	644	560	498	121

PROPERTIES AND DESIGN DATA

Vr (kN)	2 770	2 490	2 220	2 100	1 870	1 720	1 570	1 410	1 650	1 460	
R (kN)	1 590	1 370	1 170	1 030	876	777	684	595	739	626	
G (kN)	59.8	54.6	49.2	47.4	42.7	39.3	36.2	32.9	38.0	33.9	
Br' (kN)	1 990	1 660	1 350	1 250	1 020	864	733	603	808	641	
Lu (mm)	5 210	5 040	4 880	4 720	4 600	4 530	4 440	4 380	2 930	2 860	
d (mm)	585	577	571	560	554	551	546	543	549	544	
b (mm)	319	318	315	318	316	315	313	312	214	212	
t (mm)	41.4	37.6	34.5	29.2	26.3	24.4	22.2	20.3	23.6	21.2	
w (mm)	23.1	21.1	19.0	18.3	16.5	15.2	14.0	12.7	14.7	13.1	

IMPERIAL SIZE AND WEIGHT

Weight (lb/ft)	201	182	166	147	132	122	111	101	93	83	
Nominal Depth (in.)	21										

Note: Fy taken as 345 MPa. $\phi = 0.90$

Total Uniformly Distributed Factored Loads for Laterally Supported Beams (kN)

Designation					W530					Approx. Deflect. (mm)
Mass (kg/m)		109	101	92	82	72*	85	74	66	
Span in Millimetres	2 000					2 060	1 850	2 260	2 100	1 850	2
	2 500	2 560	2 400	2 220	2 050	1 510	2 090	1 800	1 550	3
	3 000	2 340	2 170	1 950	1 710	1 260	1 740	1 500	1 290	4
	3 500	2 010	1 860	1 670	1 460	1 080	1 490	1 280	1 110	6
	4 000	1 760	1 630	1 470	1 280	944	1 300	1 120	969	8
	4 500	1 560	1 450	1 300	1 140	839	1 160	999	861	10
	5 000	1 410	1 300	1 170	1 020	755	1 040	899	775	12
	5 500	1 280	1 180	1 070	930	686	948	817	705	14
	6 000	1 170	1 080	977	853	629	869	749	646	17
	6 500	1 080	1 000	902	787	581	803	692	596	20
	7 000	1 000	930	837	731	539	745	642	554	23
	7 500	937	868	782	682	503	696	599	517	27
	8 000	879	814	733	640	472	652	562	484	30
	8 500	827	766	690	602	444	614	529	456	34
	9 000	781	723	651	569	420	580	500	431	38
	9 500	740	685	617	539	397	549	473	408	43
	10 000	703	651	586	512	378	522	450	388	47
	10 500	669	620	558	487	360	497	428	369	52
	11 000	639	592	533	465	343	474	409	352	57
	11 500	611	566	510	445	328	454	391	337	62
	12 000	586	542	489	426	315	435	375	323	68
	12 500	562	521	469	409	302	417	360	310	74
	13 000	541	501	451	394	290	401	346	298	80
	13 500	521	482	434	379	280	386	333	287	86
	14 000	502	465	419	366	270	373	321	277	92
	14 500	485	449	404	353	260	360	310	267	99
	15 000	469	434	391	341	252	348	300	258	106
	15 500	454	420	378	330	244	337	290	250	113
	16 000	439	407	366	320	236	326	281	242	121

PROPERTIES AND DESIGN DATA									
V_r (kN)	1 280	1 200	1 110	1 030	926	1 130	1 050	927	
R (kN)	526	478	429	377	331	442	388	335	
G (kN)	30.0	28.2	26.4	24.6	23.0	26.7	25.1	23.0	
B_r' (kN)	503	444	389	337	296	397	352	296	
L_u (mm)	2 810	2 770	2 720	2 660	2 760	2 110	2 040	1 980	
d (mm)	539	537	533	528	524	535	529	525	
b (mm)	211	210	209	209	207	166	166	165	
t (mm)	18.8	17.4	15.6	13.3	10.9	16.5	13.6	11.4	
w (mm)	11.6	10.9	10.2	9.5	8.9	10.3	9.7	8.9	

IMPERIAL SIZE AND WEIGHT								
Weight (lb/ft)	73	68	62	55	48	57	50	44
Nominal Depth (in.)				21				

Note: F_y taken as 345 MPa. $\phi = 0.90$

* Class 3

BEAM LOAD TABLES
W Shapes

CSA G40.21 350W
ASTM A992, A572 grade 50

Total Uniformly Distributed Factored Loads for Laterally Supported Beams (kN)

Designation Mass (kg/m)	W460									Approx. Deflect. (mm)
	260	235	213	193	177	158	144	128	113	
3 000	4 720	4 240	3 760	3 400	3 280	2 920	2 640	2 340	2 040	5
3 500	4 630	4 140	3 740	3 370	3 040	2 680	2 450	2 160	1 890	7
4 000	4 060	3 630	3 270	2 950	2 660	2 350	2 140	1 890	1 660	9
4 500	3 600	3 220	2 910	2 620	2 360	2 090	1 900	1 680	1 470	11
5 000	3 240	2 900	2 620	2 360	2 130	1 880	1 710	1 520	1 330	14
5 500	2 950	2 640	2 380	2 150	1 930	1 710	1 560	1 380	1 210	16
6 000	2 700	2 420	2 180	1 970	1 770	1 560	1 430	1 260	1 110	20
6 500	2 500	2 230	2 010	1 820	1 640	1 440	1 320	1 170	1 020	23
7 000	2 320	2 070	1 870	1 690	1 520	1 340	1 220	1 080	947	27
7 500	2 160	1 930	1 750	1 570	1 420	1 250	1 140	1 010	884	31
8 000	2 030	1 810	1 640	1 470	1 330	1 170	1 070	947	829	35
8 500	1 910	1 710	1 540	1 390	1 250	1 100	1 010	891	780	39
9 000	1 800	1 610	1 450	1 310	1 180	1 040	952	842	737	44
9 500	1 710	1 530	1 380	1 240	1 120	988	902	797	698	49
10 000	1 620	1 450	1 310	1 180	1 060	939	857	758	663	54
10 500	1 540	1 380	1 250	1 120	1 010	894	816	722	632	60
11 000	1 470	1 320	1 190	1 070	967	854	779	689	603	66
11 500	1 410	1 260	1 140	1 030	924	816	745	659	577	72
12 000	1 350	1 210	1 090	983	886	782	714	631	553	78
12 500	1 300	1 160	1 050	944	851	751	686	606	531	85
13 000	1 250	1 120	1 010	908	818	722	659	583	510	92
13 500	1 200	1 070	970	874	788	696	635	561	491	99
14 000	1 160	1 040	935	843	759	671	612	541	474	107

Span in Millimetres

PROPERTIES AND DESIGN DATA

Vr (kN)	2 360	2 120	1 880	1 700	1 640	1 460	1 320	1 170	1 020
R (kN)	1 530	1 310	1 120	977	892	759	663	563	473
G (kN)	58.5	53.3	47.9	44.0	43.0	38.8	35.2	31.6	27.9
Br' (kN)	1 910	1 590	1 280	1 080	1 030	841	691	556	436
Lu (mm)	4 980	4 770	4 590	4 440	4 330	4 190	4 130	4 040	3 950
d (mm)	509	501	495	489	482	476	472	467	463
b (mm)	289	287	285	283	286	284	283	282	280
t (mm)	40.4	36.6	33.5	30.5	26.9	23.9	22.1	19.6	17.3
w (mm)	22.6	20.6	18.5	17.0	16.6	15.0	13.6	12.2	10.8

IMPERIAL SIZE AND WEIGHT

Weight (lb/ft)	175	158	143	130	119	106	97	86	76	
Nominal Depth (in.)	18									

Note: F_y taken as 345 MPa. $\phi = 0.90$

Total Uniformly Distributed Factored Loads for Laterally Supported Beams (kN)

Designation					W460						Approx. Deflect. (mm)
Mass (kg/m)	106	97	89	82	74	67	61	68	60	52	
2 000	2 420	2 180		1 870	1 690	1 580	1 490	1 710	1 490	1 350	2
2 500	2 370	2 170	1 990	1 820	1 640	1 460	1 280	1 480	1 270	1 080	3
3 000	1 980	1 810	1 660	1 520	1 370	1 220	1 070	1 230	1 060	903	5
3 500	1 700	1 550	1 430	1 300	1 170	1 040	916	1 060	908	774	7
4 000	1 480	1 350	1 250	1 140	1 020	913	801	925	795	677	9
4 500	1 320	1 200	1 110	1 010	911	811	712	822	707	602	11
5 000	1 190	1 080	999	909	820	730	641	740	636	542	14
5 500	1 080	985	908	826	745	664	583	673	578	492	16
6 000	989	903	832	758	683	609	534	617	530	451	20
6 500	913	833	768	699	631	562	493	569	489	417	23
7 000	848	774	713	649	586	522	458	529	454	387	27
7 500	792	722	666	606	546	487	427	493	424	361	31
8 000	742	677	624	568	512	456	401	463	397	338	35
8 500	698	637	587	535	482	430	377	435	374	319	39
9 000	660	602	555	505	455	406	356	411	353	301	44
9 500	625	570	526	478	431	384	337	390	335	285	49
10 000	594	542	499	455	410	365	320	370	318	271	54
10 500	565	516	476	433	390	348	305	352	303	258	60
11 000	540	492	454	413	373	332	291	336	289	246	66
11 500	516	471	434	395	356	318	279	322	276	235	72
12 000	495	451	416	379	342	304	267	308	265	226	78
12 500	475	433	399	364	328	292	256	296	254	217	85
13 000	457	417	384	350	315	281	246	285	245	208	92
13 500	440	401	370	337	304	270	237	274	236	201	99
14 000	424	387	357	325	293	261	229	264	227	193	107

PROPERTIES AND DESIGN DATA

V_r (kN)	1 210	1 090	996	933	843	791	747	856	746	680	
R (kN)	595	519	464	420	368	332	300	381	317	282	
G (kN)	32.6	29.5	27.2	25.6	23.3	22.0	21.0	23.5	20.7	19.7	
B_r' (kN)	593	486	412	366	303	270	245	310	239	216	
L_u (mm)	2 690	2 650	2 620	2 560	2 530	2 480	2 410	2 010	1 970	1 890	
d (mm)	469	466	463	460	457	454	450	459	455	450	
b (mm)	194	193	192	191	190	190	189	154	153	152	
t (mm)	20.6	19.0	17.7	16.0	14.5	12.7	10.8	15.4	13.3	10.8	
w (mm)	12.6	11.4	10.5	9.9	9.0	8.5	8.1	9.1	8.0	7.6	

IMPERIAL SIZE AND WEIGHT

Weight (lb/ft)	71	65	60	55	50	45	41	46	40	35	
Nominal Depth (in.)						18					

Note: F_y taken as 345 MPa. $\phi = 0.90$

Total Uniformly Distributed Factored Loads for Laterally Supported Beams (kN)

Designation	W410											Approx. Deflect. (mm)
Mass (kg/m)	149	132	114	100	85	74	67	60	54	46	39	
1 000												1
1 500										1 160	960	1
2 000					1 860	1 640	1 480	1 280	1 240	1 100	907	2
2 500					1 720	1 500	1 350	1 180	1 040	879	725	4
3 000	2 640	2 320	2 000	1 700	1 430	1 250	1 130	985	869	733	604	5
3 500	2 310	2 020	1 750	1 510	1 230	1 070	965	845	745	628	518	7
4 000	2 020	1 770	1 530	1 320	1 070	938	845	739	652	550	453	10
4 500	1 790	1 570	1 360	1 180	955	834	751	657	580	489	403	12
5 000	1 610	1 420	1 220	1 060	859	750	676	591	522	440	363	15
5 500	1 470	1 290	1 110	962	781	682	614	537	474	400	330	18
6 000	1 350	1 180	1 020	882	716	625	563	493	435	366	302	22
6 500	1 240	1 090	940	814	661	577	520	455	401	338	279	26
7 000	1 150	1 010	873	756	614	536	483	422	373	314	259	30
7 500	1 080	944	815	705	573	500	450	394	348	293	242	34
8 000	1 010	885	764	661	537	469	422	369	326	275	227	39
8 500	950	833	719	622	506	441	397	348	307	259	213	44
9 000	897	787	679	588	477	417	375	328	290	244	201	49
9 500	850	745	643	557	452	395	356	311	275	231	191	55
10 000	807	708	611	529	430	375	338	296	261	220	181	61
10 500	769	674	582	504	409	357	322	282	248	209	173	67
11 000	734	644	556	481	391	341	307	269	237	200	165	74
11 500	702	616	531	460	374	326	294	257	227	191	158	81
12 000	673	590	509	441	358	313	282	246	217	183	151	88
12 500	646	566	489	423	344	300	270	236	209	176	145	95
13 000	621	545	470	407	331	289	260	227	201	169	139	103

PROPERTIES AND DESIGN DATA												
V_r (kN)	1 320	1 160	998	850	931	821	739	642	619	578	480	
R (kN)	771	650	532	434	487	412	359	301	279	262	224	
G (kN)	38.6	34.4	30.0	25.9	28.2	25.1	22.8	19.9	19.4	18.1	16.6	
B_r' (kN)	830	661	503	374	444	352	289	222	210	183	153	
L_u (mm)	4 080	3 940	3 810	3 730	2 520	2 470	2 420	2 390	2 310	1 790	1 730	
d (mm)	431	425	420	415	417	413	410	407	403	403	399	
b (mm)	265	263	261	260	181	180	179	178	177	140	140	
t (mm)	25.0	22.2	19.3	16.9	18.2	16.0	14.4	12.8	10.9	11.2	8.8	
w (mm)	14.9	13.3	11.6	10.0	10.9	9.7	8.8	7.7	7.5	7.0	6.4	

IMPERIAL SIZE AND WEIGHT												
Weight (lb/ft)	100	89	77	67	57	50	45	40	36	31	26	
Nominal Depth (in.)	16											

Note: F_y taken as 345 MPa. $\phi = 0.90$

Total Uniformly Distributed Factored Loads for Laterally Supported Beams (kN)

Designation	W360								Approx. Deflect. (mm)
Mass (kg/m)	122	110	101	91	79	72	64	57	
2 000									3
2 500	1 930				1 360	1 230	1 100	1 160	3
3 000	1 880	1 680	1 540	1 370	1 180	1 060	944	1 000	4
3 500	1 610	1 460	1 330	1 190	1 010	908	809	836	6
4 000	1 410	1 280	1 170	1 040	888	795	708	717	9
								627	11
4 500	1 250	1 140	1 040	927	789	707	629	558	14
5 000	1 130	1 020	934	835	710	636	566	502	17
5 500	1 030	930	849	759	646	578	515	456	21
6 000	940	853	778	696	592	530	472	418	25
6 500	867	787	718	642	546	489	436	386	29
7 000	806	731	667	596	507	454	405	358	34
7 500	752	682	623	556	474	424	378	335	39
8 000	705	640	584	522	444	397	354	314	44
8 500	663	602	549	491	418	374	333	295	50
9 000	627	569	519	464	395	353	315	279	56
9 500	594	539	492	439	374	335	298	264	63
10 000	564	512	467	417	355	318	283	251	69
10 500	537	487	445	397	338	303	270	239	77
11 000	513	465	425	379	323	289	257	228	84

PROPERTIES AND DESIGN DATA

V_r (kN)	967	841	768	687	682	617	548	580
R (kN)	628	530	471	407	407	357	307	312
G (kN)	33.6	29.5	27.2	24.6	24.3	22.3	19.9	20.4
B_r' (kN)	632	486	412	337	330	276	222	233
L_u (mm)	4 040	3 940	3 860	3 760	3 010	2 940	2 870	2 360
d (mm)	363	360	357	353	354	350	347	358
b (mm)	257	256	255	254	205	204	203	172
t (mm)	21.7	19.9	18.3	16.4	16.8	15.1	13.5	13.1
w (mm)	13.0	11.4	10.5	9.5	9.4	8.6	7.7	7.9

IMPERIAL SIZE AND WEIGHT

Weight (lb/ft)	82	74	68	61	53	48	43	38
Nominal Depth (in.)				14				

Note: F_y taken as 345 MPa. $\phi = 0.90$

BEAM LOAD TABLES
W Shapes

CSA G40.21 350W
ASTM A992, A572 grade 50

Total Uniformly Distributed Factored Loads for Laterally Supported Beams (kN)

Designation	W360				Approx. Deflect. (mm)	W310					Approx. Deflect. (mm)
Mass (kg/m)	51	45	39	33		86	79	74	67	60	
1 000					1						1
1 500		996	940	792	2						2
2 000	1 050	968	822	673	3			1 190	1 070	932	3
2 500	888	774	658	539	4		1 100	1 170	1 040	927	5
3 000	740	645	548	449	6	1 160	1 060	977	869	773	7
3 500	634	553	470	385	9	1 010	908	837	745	662	10
4 000	555	484	411	337	11	882	795	733	652	579	13
4 500	493	430	365	299	14	784	707	651	580	515	16
5 000	444	387	329	269	17	705	636	586	522	464	20
5 500	404	352	299	245	21	641	578	533	474	421	24
6 000	370	323	274	224	25	588	530	489	435	386	29
6 500	342	298	253	207	29	543	489	451	401	357	34
7 000	317	276	235	192	34	504	454	419	373	331	40
7 500	296	258	219	180	39	470	424	391	348	309	45
8 000	278	242	206	168	44	441	397	366	326	290	52
8 500	261	228	193	158	50	415	374	345	307	273	58
9 000	247	215	183	150	56	392	353	326	290	258	65
9 500	234	204	173	142	63	371	335	309	275	244	73
10 000	222	194	164	135	69	353	318	293	261	232	81
10 500	211	184	157	128	77	336	303	279	248	221	89
11 000	202	176	149	122	84	321	289	266	237	211	98

Span in Millimetres

PROPERTIES AND DESIGN DATA

V_r (kN)	524	498	470	396		578	552	597	533	466	
R (kN)	273	249	240	201		389	361	402	348	296	
G (kN)	18.6	17.9	16.8	15.0		23.5	22.8	24.3	22.0	19.4	
B_r' (kN)	194	178	158	126		310	289	330	270	210	
L_u (mm)	2 320	2 260	1 660	1 600		3 900	3 810	3 100	3 020	2 960	
d (mm)	355	352	353	349		310	306	310	306	303	
b (mm)	171	171	128	127		254	254	205	204	203	
t (mm)	11.6	9.8	10.7	8.5		16.3	14.6	16.3	14.6	13.1	
w (mm)	7.2	6.9	6.5	5.8		9.1	8.8	9.4	8.5	7.5	

IMPERIAL SIZE AND WEIGHT

Weight (lb/ft)	34	30	26	22		58	53	50	45	40
Nominal Depth (in.)		14						12		

Note: F_y taken as 345 MPa. $\phi = 0.90$

Total Uniformly Distributed Factored Loads for Laterally Supported Beams (kN)

Designation				W310				Approx. Deflect. (mm)
Mass (kg/m)	52	45	39	33	28	24	21	
1 000				846	760	700	606	1
1 500				795	674	543	475	2
2 000	990	846	736	596	505	407	356	3
2 500	836	703	606	477	404	326	285	5
3 000	696	586	505	397	337	272	238	7
3 500	597	502	433	341	289	233	204	10
4 000	522	440	379	298	253	204	178	13
4 500	464	391	337	265	225	181	158	16
5 000	418	352	303	238	202	163	143	20
5 500	380	320	275	217	184	148	130	24
6 000	348	293	253	199	168	136	119	29
6 500	321	271	233	183	156	125	110	34
7 000	298	251	216	170	144	116	102	40
7 500	279	234	202	159	135	109	95	45
8 000	261	220	189	149	126	102	89	52
8 500	246	207	178	140	119	96	84	58
9 000	232	195	168	132	112	91	79	65
9 500	220	185	159	126	106	86	75	73
10 000	209	176	152	119	101	82	71	81

Span in Millimetres

PROPERTIES AND DESIGN DATA								
V_r (kN)	495	423	368	423	380	350	303	
R (kN)	300	247	208	245	211	184	162	
G (kN)	19.7	17.1	15.0	17.1	15.5	14.5	13.2	
B_r' (kN)	216	163	126	163	135	117	97.2	
L_u (mm)	2 370	2 310	2 260	1 330	1 290	1 210	1 190	
d (mm)	318	313	310	313	309	305	303	
b (mm)	167	166	165	102	102	101	101	
t (mm)	13.2	11.2	9.7	10.8	8.9	6.7	5.7	
w (mm)	7.6	6.6	5.8	6.6	6.0	5.6	5.1	

IMPERIAL SIZE AND WEIGHT								
Weight (lb/ft)	35	30	26	22	19	16	14	
Nominal Depth (in.)				12				

Note: F_y taken as 345 MPa. $\phi = 0.90$

Total Uniformly Distributed Factored Loads for Laterally Supported Beams (kN)

Designation					W250						Approx. Deflect. (mm)
Mass (kg/m)	67	58	49*	45	39	33	28	25	22	18*	
1 000							682	642	604	445	1
1 500			750	828	708	646	585	508	436	296	2
2 000	938	826	710	748	637	527	438	381	327	222	4
2 500	895	765	568	598	510	421	351	305	261	178	6
3 000	746	638	474	498	425	351	292	254	218	148	9
3 500	639	546	406	427	364	301	251	218	187	127	12
4 000	560	478	355	374	319	263	219	191	163	111	16
4 500	497	425	316	332	283	234	195	169	145	99	20
5 000	448	383	284	299	255	211	175	153	131	89	25
5 500	407	348	258	272	232	191	159	139	119	81	30
6 000	373	319	237	249	212	176	146	127	109	74	36
6 500	344	294	219	230	196	162	135	117	101	68	42
7 000	320	273	203	214	182	150	125	109	93	64	49
7 500	298	255	189	199	170	140	117	102	87	59	56
8 000	280	239	178	187	159	132	110	95	82	56	64

Span in Millimetres

PROPERTIES AND DESIGN DATA										
V_r (kN)	469	413	375	414	354	323	341	321	302	247
R (kN)	375	319	276	299	247	215	232	211	191	151
G (kN)	23.0	20.7	19.1	19.7	17.1	15.8	16.6	15.8	15.0	12.4
B_r' (kN)	296	239	205	216	163	139	153	139	126	86.1
L_u (mm)	3 260	3 130	3 160	2 170	2 110	2 020	1 370	1 330	1 280	1 330
d (mm)	257	252	247	266	262	258	260	257	254	251
b (mm)	204	203	202	148	147	146	102	102	102	101
t (mm)	15.7	13.5	11.0	13.0	11.2	9.1	10.0	8.4	6.9	5.3
w (mm)	8.9	8.0	7.4	7.6	6.6	6.1	6.4	6.1	5.8	4.8

IMPERIAL SIZE AND WEIGHT										
Weight (lb/ft)	45	39	33	30	26	22	19	17	15	12
Nominal Depth (in.)	10									

Note: F_y taken as 345 MPa. $\phi = 0.90$

* Class 3

Total Uniformly Distributed Factored Loads for Laterally Supported Beams (kN)

Designation	W200							Approx. Deflect. (mm)
Mass (kg/m)	42	36	31	27	22	19	15*	
1 000				492	524	465	315	1
1 500	604	510	550	462	368	310	210	3
2 000	553	471	416	347	276	232	158	5
2 500	442	377	333	277	221	186	126	8
3 000	368	314	277	231	184	155	105	11
3 500	316	269	238	198	158	133	90	15
4 000	276	235	208	173	138	116	79	20
4 500	246	209	185	154	123	103	70	25
5 000	221	188	166	139	110	93	63	31
5 500	201	171	151	126	100	85	57	38
6 000	184	157	139	116	92	77	53	45
6 500	170	145	128	107	85	72	49	53
7 000	158	134	119	99	79	66	45	61

Span in Millimetres

PROPERTIES AND DESIGN DATA

V_r (kN)	302	255	275	246	262	241	176	
R (kN)	274	226	233	201	212	189	134	
G (kN)	18.6	16.0	16.6	15.0	16.0	15.0	11.1	
B_r' (kN)	194	144	153	126	144	126	69.1	
L_u (mm)	2 610	2 510	1 980	1 890	1 390	1 340	1 380	
d (mm)	205	201	210	207	206	203	200	
b (mm)	166	165	134	133	102	102	100	
t (mm)	11.8	10.2	10.2	8.4	8.0	6.5	5.2	
w (mm)	7.2	6.2	6.4	5.8	6.2	5.8	4.3	

IMPERIAL SIZE AND WEIGHT

Weight (lb/ft)	28	24	21	18	15	13	10
Nominal Depth (in.)				8			

Note: F_y taken as 345 MPa. $\phi = 0.90$

* Class 3

BEAM LOAD TABLES[1]
Rectangular HSS

G40.21 350W
$\phi = 0.90$

Total Uniformly Distributed Factored Loads for Laterally Supported Beams (kN)

Designation mm x mm mm	HSS 356 x 254		Approx. Deflect. (mm)	HSS 305 x 203				Approx. Deflect. (mm)
	13	9.5		13	9.5	8.0	6.4	
Mass (kg/m)	113	86.5		93.0	71.3	60.1	48.6	
500								
1 000	3 220	2 520	1	2 680	2 110	1 800	1 480	1
1 500	2 910	2 250	2	2 000	1 560	1 320	1 080	2
2 000	2 180	1 690	3	1 500	1 170	992	806	3
2 500	1 740	1 350	4	1 200	933	793	645	5
3 000	1 450	1 130	6	1 000	778	661	538	7
3 500	1 250	965	9	857	667	567	461	10
4 000	1 090	844	11	750	583	496	403	13
4 500	969	750	14	666	519	441	358	17
5 000	872	675	18	600	467	397	323	21
5 500	793	614	21	545	424	361	293	25
6 000	727	563	25	500	389	331	269	30
6 500	671	520	30	461	359	305	248	35
7 000	623	482	34	428	333	283	230	40
7 500	581	450	40	400	311	264	215	46
8 000	545	422	45	375	292	248	202	52
8 500	513	397	51	353	275	233	190	59
9 000	484	375	57	333	259	220	179	66
9 500	459	355	63	316	246	209	170	74
10 000	436	338	70	300	233	198	161	82
10 500	415	322	78	286	222	189	154	90
11 000	396	307	85	273	212	180	147	99
11 500	379	294	93	261	203	172	140	108
12 000	363	281	101	250	194	165	134	118

Span in Millimetres

DESIGN DATA AND PROPERTIES

S_x (10^3 mm^3)	1 420	1 120		964	762	652	535
Z_x (10^3 mm^3)	1 730	1 340		1 190	926	787	640
I_x (10^6 mm^4)	253	198		147	116	99.4	81.5
C_{rt} (mm^2)	7 740	6 050		6 450	5 080	4 340	3 550
V_r (kN)	1 610	1 260		1 340	1 060	902	738

IMPERIAL SIZE AND MASS

Mass (lb./ft.)	76.1	58.1		62.5	47.9	40.4	32.6
Thickness (in.)	0.500	0.375		0.500	0.375	0.313	0.250
Size (in.)	14 x 10			12 x 8			

[1] For strong axis bending only

Total Uniformly Distributed Factored Loads for Laterally Supported Beams (kN)

Designation mm x mm mm	HSS 254 x 152				Approx. Deflect. (mm)	HSS 203 x 152					Approx. Deflect. (mm)
	13	9.5	8.0	6.4		13	9.5	8.0	6.4	4.8	
Mass (kg/m)	72.7	56.1	47.5	38.4		62.6	48.5	41.1	33.4	25.5	
500	2 150	1 710	1 470	1 210		1 610	1 310	1 130	939	732	
1 000	1 880	1 480	1 270	1 040	1	1 330	1 060	907	743	575	1
1 500	1 250	990	845	690	2	887	706	605	496	383	3
2 000	941	742	634	518	4	665	529	454	372	287	5
2 500	753	594	507	414	6	532	423	363	297	230	8
3 000	627	495	423	345	9	444	353	302	248	192	11
3 500	538	424	362	296	12	380	302	259	212	164	15
4 000	471	371	317	259	16	333	265	227	186	144	20
4 500	418	330	282	230	20	296	235	202	165	128	25
5 000	376	297	254	207	25	266	212	181	149	115	31
5 500	342	270	230	188	30	242	192	165	135	104	37
6 000	314	247	211	173	35	222	176	151	124	96	44
6 500	290	228	195	159	42	205	163	140	114	88	52
7 000	269	212	181	148	48	190	151	130	106	82	60
7 500	251	198	169	138	55	177	141	121	99	77	69
8 000	235	186	158	129	63	166	132	113	93	72	79

Span in Millimetres

DESIGN DATA AND PROPERTIES

S_x (10^3 mm^3)	592	475	410	338		423	343	297	246	192	
Z_x (10^3 mm^3)	747	589	503	411		528	420	360	295	228	
I_x (10^6 mm^4)	75.2	60.4	52.0	42.9		43.0	34.8	30.2	25.0	19.5	
C_{rt} (mm^2)	5 160	4 110	3 530	2 900		3 870	3 150	2 730	2 260	1 760	
V_r (kN)	1 070	855	735	604		805	654	567	469	366	

IMPERIAL SIZE AND MASS

Mass (lb./ft.)	48.9	37.7	31.9	25.8		42.1	32.6	27.6	22.4	17.1	
Thickness (in.)	0.500	0.375	0.313	0.250		0.500	0.375	0.313	0.250	0.188	
Size (in.)	10 x 6					8 x 6					

[1] For strong axis bending only

Total Uniformly Distributed Factored Loads for Laterally Supported Beams (kN)

Designation mm x mm mm	HSS 203 x 102					Approx. Deflect. (mm)	HSS 178 x 127					Approx. Deflect. (mm)
	13	9.5	8.0	6.4	4.8		13	9.5	8.0	6.4	4.8	
Mass (kg/m)	52.4	40.9	34.8	28.3	21.7		52.4	40.9	34.8	28.3	21.7	
500	1 610	1 310	1 130	939	732		1 340	1 110	965	805	631	
1 000	1 020	822	708	585	454	1	953	764	658	544	423	1
1 500	680	548	472	390	302	3	635	509	438	363	282	3
2 000	510	411	354	292	227	5	476	382	329	272	212	6
2 500	408	329	283	234	181	8	381	305	263	218	169	9
3 000	340	274	236	195	151	11	318	255	219	181	141	13
3 500	292	235	202	167	130	15	272	218	188	156	121	17
4 000	255	205	177	146	113	20	238	191	164	136	106	22
4 500	227	183	157	130	101	25	212	170	146	121	94	28
5 000	204	164	142	117	91	31	191	153	132	109	85	35
5 500	186	149	129	106	83	37	173	139	120	99	77	43
6 000	170	137	118	97	76	44	159	127	110	91	71	51
6 500	157	126	109	90	70	52	147	117	101	84	65	59
7 000	146	117	101	84	65	60	136	109	94	78	61	69

Span in Millimetres

DESIGN DATA AND PROPERTIES

S_x (10^3 mm^3)	308	254	221	185	145		297	244	213	178	140	
Z_x (10^3 mm^3)	405	326	281	232	180		378	303	261	216	168	
I_x (10^6 mm^4)	31.3	25.8	22.5	18.8	14.7		26.4	21.7	19.0	15.8	12.4	
C_{rt} (mm^2)	3 870	3 150	2 730	2 260	1 760		3 230	2 660	2 320	1 940	1 520	
V_r (kN)	805	654	567	469	366		671	553	483	402	315	

IMPERIAL SIZE AND MASS

Mass (lb./ft.)	35.2	27.5	23.4	19.0	14.6		35.2	27.5	23.4	19.0	14.6	
Thickness (in.)	0.500	0.375	0.313	0.250	0.188		0.500	0.375	0.313	0.250	0.188	
Size (in.)	8 x 4						7 x 5					

[1] For strong axis bending only

Designation mm x mm mm	HSS 152 x 102					HSS 152 x 76					Approx. Deflect. (mm)
	13	9.5	8.0	6.4	4.8	13	9.5	8.0	6.4	4.8	
Mass (kg/m)	42.3	33.3	28.4	23.2	17.9	37.3	29.5	25.3	20.7	16.0	
500	1 070	906	797	671	530	1 040	862	751	630	494	1
1 000	635	519	451	373	292	522	431	375	315	247	2
1 500	423	346	301	249	195	348	287	250	210	165	4
2 000	318	260	226	186	146	261	215	188	158	124	7
2 500	254	208	180	149	117	209	172	150	126	99	10
3 000	212	173	150	124	97	174	144	125	105	82	15
3 500	181	148	129	107	84	149	123	107	90	71	20
4 000	159	130	113	93	73	130	108	94	79	62	26
4 500	141	115	100	83	65	116	96	83	70	55	33
5 000	127	104	90	75	59	104	86	75	63	49	41
5 500	115	94	82	68	53	95	78	68	57	45	50
6 000	106	87	75	62	49	87	72	63	53	41	59

Span in Millimetres

DESIGN DATA AND PROPERTIES										
S_x (10^3 mm^3)	193	162	143	121	95.6	152	130	115	98.0	78.2
Z_x (10^3 mm^3)	252	206	179	148	116	207	171	149	125	98.1
I_x (10^6 mm^4)	14.7	12.4	10.9	9.19	7.28	11.5	9.89	8.79	7.47	5.96
C_{rt} (mm^2)	2 580	2 180	1 920	1 610	1 270	2 580	2 180	1 920	1 610	1 270
V_r (kN)	537	453	399	335	265	537	453	399	335	265

IMPERIAL SIZE AND MASS										
Mass (lb./ft.)	28.4	22.4	19.1	15.6	12.0	25.0	19.8	17.0	13.9	10.7
Thickness (in.)	0.500	0.375	0.313	0.250	0.188	0.500	0.375	0.313	0.250	0.188
Size (in.)	6 x 4					6 x 3				

[1] For strong axis bending only

Total Uniformly Distributed Factored Loads for Laterally Supported Beams (kN)

Designation mm x mm mm	HSS 127 x 76				Approx. Deflect. (mm)	HSS 102 x 76					Approx. Deflect. (mm)
	9.5	8.0	6.4	4.8		9.5	8.0	6.4	4.8	3.2	
Mass (kg/m)	25.7	22.1	18.2	14.1		21.9	18.9	15.6	12.2	8.35	
500	635	559	471	372	1	443	393	333	265	186	1
1 000	318	280	235	186	2	222	196	166	133	93	2
1 500	212	186	157	124	4	148	131	111	88	62	6
2 000	159	140	118	93	8	111	98	83	66	47	10
2 500	127	112	94	74	12	89	79	67	53	37	15
3 000	106	93	79	62	18	74	65	55	44	31	22
3 500	91	80	67	53	24	63	56	48	38	27	30
4 000	79	70	59	47	31	55	49	42	33	23	39

Span in Millimetres

DESIGN DATA AND PROPERTIES

S_x (10^3 mm^3)	96.5	86.5	74.1	59.6		67.4	61.1	52.9	43.0	30.8	
Z_x (10^3 mm^3)	126	111	93.4	73.8		87.9	77.9	66.0	52.6	37.0	
I_x (10^6 mm^4)	6.13	5.49	4.70	3.78		3.42	3.10	2.69	2.18	1.57	
C_{rt} (mm^2)	1 690	1 510	1 290	1 030		1 210	1 110	968	789	565	
V_r (kN)	352	315	268	214		252	231	201	164	118	

IMPERIAL SIZE AND MASS

Mass (lb./ft.)	17.3	14.9	12.2	9.46		14.7	12.7	10.5	8.17	5.61	
Thickness (in.)	0.375	0.313	0.250	0.188		0.375	0.313	0.250	0.188	0.125	
Size (in.)	5 x 3					4 x 3					

[1] For strong axis bending only

Designation mm x mm mm	HSS 102 x 51					Approx. Deflect. (mm)
	9.5	8.0	6.4	4.8	3.2	
Mass (kg/m)	18.1	15.8	13.1	10.3	7.09	
500	331	297	256	206	146	1
1 000	165	149	128	103	73	2
1 500	110	99	85	69	49	6
2 000	83	74	64	51	37	10
2 500	66	60	51	41	29	15
3 000	55	50	43	34	24	22
3 500	47	43	37	29	21	30
4 000	41	37	32	26	18	39

Span in Millimetres

DESIGN DATA AND PROPERTIES

S_x (10^3 mm^3)	47.1	43.6	38.5	31.8	23.1	
Z_x (10^3 mm^3)	65.6	59.0	50.7	40.8	29.0	
I_x (10^6 mm^4)	2.39	2.21	1.95	1.61	1.17	
C_{rt} (mm^2)	1 210	1 110	968	789	565	
V_r (kN)	252	231	201	164	118	

IMPERIAL SIZE AND MASS

Mass (lb./ft.)	12.2	10.6	8.81	6.89	4.76	
Thickness (in.)	0.375	0.313	0.250	0.188	0.125	
Size (in.)	4 x 2					

[1] For strong axis bending only

BEAM LOAD TABLES[1]
Rectangular HSS

ASTM A500 Grade C
$F_y = 345$ MPa
$\phi = 0.90$

Total Uniformly Distributed Factored Loads for Laterally Supported Beams (kN)

Designation mm x mm mm	HSS 356 x 254			Approx. Deflect. (mm)	HSS 305 x 203					Approx. Deflect. (mm)
	16	13	9.5		16	13	9.5	8.0	6.4	
Mass (kg/m)	139	113	86.5		114	93.0	71.3	60.1	48.6	
500									1 320	
1 000	3 500	2 900	2 260	1	2 900	2 430	1 900	1 620	1 210	1
1 500	3 160	2 600	2 000	2	2 170	1 810	1 400	1 180	805	2
2 000	2 370	1 950	1 500	3	1 630	1 350	1 050	888	604	3
2 500	1 900	1 560	1 200	4	1 300	1 080	838	710	483	5
3 000	1 580	1 300	1 000	6	1 080	903	698	592	402	7
3 500	1 360	1 110	859	9	930	774	598	507	345	10
4 000	1 190	975	751	11	814	677	524	444	302	13
4 500	1 050	867	668	14	723	602	465	395	268	17
5 000	949	780	601	18	651	542	419	355	241	21
5 500	863	709	546	21	592	492	381	323	219	25
6 000	791	650	501	25	542	451	349	296	201	30
6 500	730	600	462	30	501	417	322	273	186	35
7 000	678	557	429	34	465	387	299	254	172	40
7 500	633	520	401	40	434	361	279	237	161	46
8 000	593	487	376	45	407	338	262	222	151	52
8 500	558	459	354	51	383	319	246	209	142	59
9 000	527	433	334	57	362	301	233	197	134	66
9 500	499	411	316	63	343	285	220	187	127	74
10 000	474	390	301	70	325	271	209	178	121	82
10 500	452	371	286	78	310	258	199	169	115	90
11 000	431	355	273	85	296	246	190	161	110	99
11 500	413	339	261	93	283	235	182	154	105	108
12 000	395	325	250	101	271	226	175	148	101	118

(Span in Millimetres)

DESIGN DATA AND PROPERTIES										
S_x (10^3 mm^3)	1 570	1 300	1 020		1 060	886	697	595	486	
Z_x (10^3 mm^3)	1 910	1 570	1 210		1 310	1 090	843	715	581	
I_x (10^6 mm^4)	279	232	181		161	135	106	90.6	74.1	
C_{rt} (mm^2)	8 530	7 080	5 510		7 080	5 920	4 640	3 950	3 220	
V_r (kN)	1 750	1 450	1 130		1 450	1 210	951	810	661	

IMPERIAL SIZE AND MASS										
Mass (lb./ft.)	93.4	76.1	58.1		76.4	62.5	47.9	40.4	32.6	
Thickness[†] (in.)	0.563	0.450	0.338		0.563	0.450	0.338	0.282	0.225	
Size (in.)	14 x 10				12 x 8					

[1] For strong axis bending only

[†] Design wall thickness

Total Uniformly Distributed Factored Loads for Laterally Supported Beams (kN)

Designation mm x mm mm	HSS 254 x 152					Approx. Deflect. (mm)	HSS 203 x 152					Approx. Deflect. (mm)
	16	13	9.5	8.0	6.4		13	9.5	8.0	6.4	4.8	
Mass (kg/m)	88.3	72.7	56.1	47.5	38.4		62.6	48.5	41.1	33.4	25.5	
500	2 310	1 950	1 550	1 320	1 080		1 480	1 190	1 020	845	656	
1 000	2 040	1 700	1 340	1 140	929	1	1 210	954	815	668	435	1
1 500	1 360	1 140	891	758	619	2	805	636	543	445	290	3
2 000	1 020	852	668	569	465	4	604	477	407	334	217	5
2 500	815	682	535	455	372	6	483	382	326	267	174	8
3 000	679	568	445	379	310	9	402	318	272	223	145	11
3 500	582	487	382	325	265	12	345	273	233	191	124	15
4 000	509	426	334	284	232	16	302	238	204	167	109	20
4 500	453	379	297	253	206	20	268	212	181	148	97	25
5 000	407	341	267	228	186	25	241	191	163	134	87	31
5 500	370	310	243	207	169	30	219	173	148	121	79	37
6 000	339	284	223	190	155	35	201	159	136	111	73	44
6 500	313	262	206	175	143	42	186	147	125	103	67	52
7 000	291	243	191	163	133	48	172	136	116	96	62	60
7 500	272	227	178	152	124	55	161	127	109	89	58	69
8 000	255	213	167	142	116	63	151	119	102	84	54	79

Span in Millimetres

DESIGN DATA AND PROPERTIES

S_x (10^3 mm^3)	644	548	436	375	308		393	316	272	225	175	
Z_x (10^3 mm^3)	820	686	538	458	374		486	384	328	269	207	
I_x (10^6 mm^4)	81.8	69.6	55.4	47.6	39.1		39.9	32.1	27.7	22.9	17.8	
C_{rt} (mm^2)	5 630	4 760	3 770	3 230	2 640		3 600	2 900	2 500	2 060	1 600	
V_r (kN)	1 150	976	773	661	542		738	594	512	423	328	

IMPERIAL SIZE AND MASS

Mass (lb./ft.)	59.3	48.9	37.7	31.9	25.8		42.1	32.6	27.6	22.4	17.1	
Thickness[†] (in.)	0.563	0.450	0.338	0.282	0.225		0.450	0.338	0.282	0.225	0.169	
Size (in.)	10 x 6						8 x 6					

[1] For strong axis bending only

[†] Design wall thickness

BEAM LOAD TABLES[1]
Rectangular HSS

ASTM A500 Grade C
$F_y = 345$ MPa
$\phi = 0.90$

Total Uniformly Distributed Factored Loads for Laterally Supported Beams (kN)

Designation mm x mm mm	HSS 203 x 102					Approx. Deflect. (mm)	HSS 178 x 127					Approx. Deflect. (mm)
	13	9.5	8.0	6.4	4.8		13	9.5	8.0	6.4	4.8	
Mass (kg/m)	52.4	40.9	34.8	28.3	21.7		52.4	40.9	34.8	28.3	21.7	
500	1 480	1 190	1 020	845	656		1 240	1 010	875	726	566	
1 000	932	743	638	524	407	1	869	691	594	489	378	1
1 500	621	495	426	349	272	3	580	460	396	326	252	3
2 000	466	371	319	262	204	5	435	345	297	245	189	6
2 500	373	297	255	210	163	8	348	276	237	196	151	9
3 000	311	248	213	175	136	11	290	230	198	163	126	13
3 500	266	212	182	150	116	15	248	197	170	140	108	17
4 000	233	186	160	131	102	20	217	173	148	122	94	22
4 500	207	165	142	116	91	25	193	153	132	109	84	28
5 000	186	149	128	105	82	31	174	138	119	98	76	35
5 500	169	135	116	95	74	37	158	126	108	89	69	43
6 000	155	124	106	87	68	44	145	115	99	82	63	51
6 500	143	114	98	81	63	52	134	106	91	75	58	59
7 000	133	106	91	75	58	60	124	99	85	70	54	69

Span in Millimetres

DESIGN DATA AND PROPERTIES

S_x (10^3 mm^3)	288	235	204	169	132		278	226	196	163	127	
Z_x (10^3 mm^3)	375	299	257	211	164		350	278	239	197	152	
I_x (10^6 mm^4)	29.2	23.8	20.7	17.2	13.4		24.7	20.1	17.4	14.5	11.3	
C_{rt} (mm^2)	3 600	2 900	2 500	2 060	1 600		3 020	2 460	2 130	1 770	1 380	
V_r (kN)	738	594	512	423	328		619	505	438	363	283	

IMPERIAL SIZE AND MASS

Mass (lb./ft.)	35.2	27.5	23.4	19.0	14.6		35.2	27.5	23.4	19.0	14.6	
Thickness[†] (in.)	0.450	0.338	0.282	0.225	0.169		0.450	0.338	0.282	0.225	0.169	
Size (in.)	8 x 4						7 x 5					

[1] For strong axis bending only

[†] Design wall thickness

Designation mm x mm mm	HSS 152 x 102					HSS 152 x 76					Approx. Deflect. (mm)
	13	9.5	8.0	6.4	4.8	13	9.5	8.0	6.4	4.8	
Mass (kg/m)	42.3	33.3	28.4	23.2	17.9	37.3	29.5	25.3	20.7	16.0	
500	1 000	830	726	607	477	964	785	686	566	444	1
1 000	584	472	407	338	263	482	392	343	283	222	2
1 500	389	315	272	225	176	321	262	229	189	148	4
2 000	292	236	204	169	132	241	196	171	142	111	7
2 500	233	189	163	135	105	193	157	137	113	89	10
3 000	195	157	136	113	88	161	131	114	94	74	15
3 500	167	135	116	97	75	138	112	98	81	63	20
4 000	146	118	102	85	66	120	98	86	71	56	26
4 500	130	105	91	75	59	107	87	76	63	49	33
5 000	117	94	82	68	53	96	79	69	57	44	41
5 500	106	86	74	61	48	88	71	62	52	40	50
6 000	97	79	68	56	44	80	65	57	47	37	59

Span in Millimetres

DESIGN DATA AND PROPERTIES

S_x (10^3 mm^3)	182	151	132	111	87.3	144	121	107	90.3	71.6
Z_x (10^3 mm^3)	235	190	164	136	106	194	158	138	114	89.4
I_x (10^6 mm^4)	13.9	11.5	10.1	8.44	6.66	11.0	9.25	8.16	6.88	5.46
C_{rt} (mm^2)	2 440	2 030	1 770	1 480	1 160	2 440	2 030	1 770	1 480	1 160
V_r (kN)	500	415	363	304	238	500	415	363	304	238

IMPERIAL SIZE AND MASS

Mass (lb./ft.)	28.4	22.4	19.1	15.6	12.0	25.0	19.8	17.0	13.9	10.7
Thickness[†] (in.)	0.450	0.338	0.282	0.225	0.169	0.450	0.338	0.282	0.225	0.169
Size (in.)	6 x 4					6 x 3				

[1] For strong axis bending only

[†] Design wall thickness

BEAM LOAD TABLES[1]
Rectangular HSS

ASTM A500 Grade C
$F_y = 345$ MPa
$\phi = 0.90$

Total Uniformly Distributed Factored Loads for Laterally Supported Beams (kN)

Designation mm x mm mm	HSS 127 x 76				Approx. Deflect. (mm)	HSS 102 x 76					Approx. Deflect. (mm)
	9.5	8.0	6.4	4.8		9.5	8.0	6.4	4.8	3.2	
Mass (kg/m)	25.7	22.1	18.2	14.1		21.9	18.9	15.6	12.2	8.35	
500	581	512	426	335	1	408	359	302	239	167	1
1 000	291	256	213	167	2	204	179	151	119	84	2
1 500	194	171	142	112	4	136	120	101	80	56	6
2 000	145	128	106	84	8	102	90	76	60	42	10
2 500	116	102	85	67	12	82	72	60	48	33	15
3 000	97	85	71	56	18	68	60	50	40	28	22
3 500	83	73	61	48	24	58	51	43	34	24	30
4 000	73	64	53	42	31	51	45	38	30	21	39

Span in Millimetres

DESIGN DATA AND PROPERTIES

S_x (10^3 mm^3)	90.7	80.6	68.5	54.7		63.8	57.2	49.1	39.6	28.2
Z_x (10^3 mm^3)	117	103	85.7	67.4		82.1	72.2	60.8	48.1	33.6
I_x (10^6 mm^4)	5.76	5.12	4.35	3.47		3.24	2.91	2.49	2.01	1.43
C_{rt} (mm^2)	1 590	1 410	1 190	945		1 150	1 040	900	726	516
V_r (kN)	326	289	244	194		237	214	185	149	106

IMPERIAL SIZE AND MASS

Mass (lb./ft.)	17.3	14.9	12.2	9.46		14.7	12.7	10.5	8.17	5.61
Thickness[†] (in.)	0.338	0.282	0.225	0.169		0.338	0.282	0.225	0.169	0.113
Size (in.)	5 x 3					4 x 3				

[1] For strong axis bending only

[†] Design wall thickness

Designation mm x mm mm	HSS 102 x 51					Approx. Deflect. (mm)
	9.5	8.0	6.4	4.8	3.2	
Mass (kg/m)	18.1	15.8	13.1	10.3	7.09	
500	307	274	233	186	131	1
1 000	154	137	116	93	66	2
1 500	102	91	78	62	44	6
2 000	77	68	58	47	33	10
2 500	61	55	47	37	26	15
3 000	51	46	39	31	22	22
3 500	44	39	33	27	19	30
4 000	38	34	29	23	16	39

Span in Millimetres

DESIGN DATA AND PROPERTIES						
S_x (10^3 mm^3)	45.2	41.2	36.0	29.4	21.2	
Z_x (10^3 mm^3)	61.8	55.1	46.9	37.5	26.4	
I_x (10^6 mm^4)	2.29	2.10	1.83	1.49	1.08	
C_{rt} (mm^2)	1 150	1 040	900	726	516	
V_r (kN)	237	214	185	149	106	

IMPERIAL SIZE AND MASS						
Mass (lb./ft.)	12.2	10.6	8.81	6.89	4.76	
Thickness[†] (in.)	0.338	0.282	0.225	0.169	0.113	
Size (in.)	4 x 2					

[1] For strong axis bending only

[†] Design wall thickness

BEAM DIAGRAMS AND FORMULAE

Equivalent Tabular Load is the uniformly distributed factored load given in the Beam Load Tables

1. SIMPLE BEAM — UNIFORMLY DISTRIBUTED LOAD

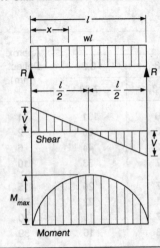

Equivalent Tabular Load .... $= wl$

$R = V$ .... $= \dfrac{wl}{2}$

V_x .... $= w\left(\dfrac{l}{2} - x\right)$

M max. (at center) .... $= \dfrac{wl^2}{8}$

M_x .... $= \dfrac{wx}{2}(l - x)$

Δ max. (at center) .... $= \dfrac{5wl^4}{384\,EI}$

Δ_x .... $= \dfrac{wx}{24\,EI}\left(l^3 - 2lx^2 + x^3\right)$

2. SIMPLE BEAM — LOAD INCREASING UNIFORMLY TO ONE END

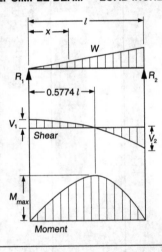

Equivalent Tabular Load .... $= \dfrac{16W}{9\sqrt{3}} = 1.0264\,W$

$R_1 = V_1$ .... $= \dfrac{W}{3}$

$R_2 = V_2 = V$ max. .... $= \dfrac{2W}{3}$

V_x .... $= \dfrac{W}{3} - \dfrac{Wx^2}{l^2}$

M max. $\left(\text{at } x = \dfrac{l}{\sqrt{3}} = 0.5774l\right)$ .... $= \dfrac{2Wl}{9\sqrt{3}} = .1283\,Wl$

M_x .... $= \dfrac{Wx}{3l^2}\left(l^2 - x^2\right)$

Δ max. $\left(\text{at } x = l\sqrt{1 - \sqrt{\dfrac{8}{15}}} = .5193\,l\right)$ .... $= .01304\dfrac{Wl^3}{EI}$

Δ_x .... $= \dfrac{Wx}{180\,EIl^2}\left(3x^4 - 10l^2x^2 + 7l^4\right)$

3. SIMPLE BEAM — LOAD INCREASING UNIFORMLY TO CENTER

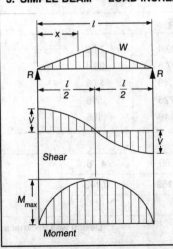

Equivalent Tabular Load .... $= \dfrac{4W}{3}$

$R = V$ .... $= \dfrac{W}{2}$

$V_x\left(\text{when } x < \dfrac{l}{2}\right)$ .... $= \dfrac{W}{2l^2}\left(l^2 - 4x^2\right)$

M max. (at center) .... $= \dfrac{Wl}{6}$

$M_x\left(\text{when } x < \dfrac{l}{2}\right)$ .... $= Wx\left(\dfrac{1}{2} - \dfrac{2x^2}{3l^2}\right)$

Δ max. (at center) .... $= \dfrac{Wl^3}{60\,EI}$

$\Delta_x\left(\text{when } x < \dfrac{l}{2}\right)$ .... $= \dfrac{Wx}{480\,EIl^2}\left(5l^2 - 4x^2\right)^2$

Note: For deflection calculations, use specified loads.

4. SIMPLE BEAM — UNIFORM LOAD PARTIALLY DISTRIBUTED

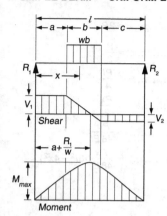

$$R_1 = V_1 \text{ (max. when } a < c) \ldots\ldots = \frac{wb}{2l}(2c + b)$$

$$R_2 = V_2 \text{ (max. when } a > c) \ldots\ldots = \frac{wb}{2l}(2a + b)$$

$$V_x \text{ (when } x > a \text{ and } < (a + b)) \ldots = R_1 - w(x - a)$$

$$M \text{ max. } \left(\text{at } x = a + \frac{R_1}{w}\right) \ldots\ldots = R_1\left(a + \frac{R_1}{2w}\right)$$

$$M_x \text{ (when } x < a) \ldots\ldots\ldots\ldots = R_1 x$$

$$M_x \text{ (when } x > a \text{ and } < (a + b)) \ldots = R_1 x - \frac{w}{2}(x - a)^2$$

$$M_x \text{ (when } x > (a + b)) \ldots\ldots\ldots = R_2 (l - x)$$

5. SIMPLE BEAM — UNIFORM LOAD PARTIALLY DISTRIBUTED AT ONE END

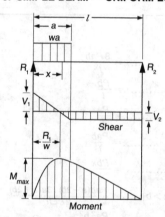

$$R_1 = V_1 \text{ max.} \ldots\ldots\ldots\ldots\ldots = \frac{wa}{2l}(2l - a)$$

$$R_2 = V_2 \ldots\ldots\ldots\ldots\ldots\ldots = \frac{wa^2}{2l}$$

$$V_x \text{ (when } x < a) \ldots\ldots\ldots\ldots = R_1 - wx$$

$$M \text{ max. } \left(\text{at } x = \frac{R_1}{w}\right) \ldots\ldots\ldots = \frac{R_1^2}{2w}$$

$$M_x \text{ (when } x < a) \ldots\ldots\ldots\ldots = R_1 x - \frac{wx^2}{2}$$

$$M_x \text{ (when } x > a) \ldots\ldots\ldots\ldots = R_2 (l - x)$$

$$\Delta_x \text{ (when } x < a) \ldots\ldots\ldots\ldots = \frac{wx}{24\,EIl}\left(a^2(2l - a)^2 - 2ax^2(2l - a) + lx^3\right)$$

$$\Delta_x \text{ (when } x > a) \ldots\ldots\ldots\ldots = \frac{wa^2(l - x)}{24\,EIl}(4xl - 2x^2 - a^2)$$

6. SIMPLE BEAM — UNIFORM LOADS PARTIALLY DISTRIBUTED AT EACH END

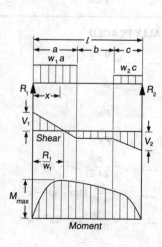

$$R_1 = V_1 \ldots\ldots\ldots\ldots\ldots\ldots = \frac{w_1 a(2l - a) + w_2 c^2}{2l}$$

$$R_2 = V_2 \ldots\ldots\ldots\ldots\ldots\ldots = \frac{w_2 c(2l - c) + w_1 a^2}{2l}$$

$$V_x \text{ (when } x < a) \ldots\ldots\ldots\ldots = R_1 - w_1 x$$

$$V_x \text{ (when } x > a \text{ and } < (a + b)) \ldots\ldots = R_1 - w_1 a$$

$$V_x \text{ (when } x > (a + b)) \ldots\ldots\ldots = R_2 - w_2 (l - x)$$

$$M \text{ max. } \left(\text{at } x = \frac{R_1}{w_1}, \text{ when } R_1 < w_1 a\right) \ldots = \frac{R_1^2}{2w_1}$$

$$M \text{ max. } \left(\text{at } x = l - \frac{R_2}{w_2}, \text{ when } R_2 < w_2 c\right) = \frac{R_2^2}{2w_2}$$

$$M_x \text{ (when } x < a) \ldots\ldots\ldots\ldots = R_1 x - \frac{w_1 x^2}{2}$$

$$M_x \text{ (when } x > a \text{ and } < (a + b)) \ldots\ldots = R_1 x - \frac{w_1 a}{2}(2x - a)$$

$$M_x \text{ (when } x > (a + b)) \ldots\ldots\ldots = R_2 (l - x) - w_2 \frac{(l - x)^2}{2}$$

Note: For deflection calculations, use specified loads.

BEAM DIAGRAMS AND FORMULAE

Equivalent Tabular Load is the uniformly distributed factored load given in the Beam Load Tables

7. SIMPLE BEAM — CONCENTRATED LOAD AT CENTER

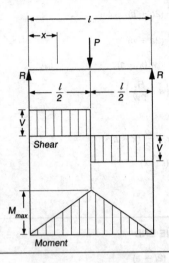

Equivalent Tabular Load .... $= 2P$

$R = V$ .... $= \dfrac{P}{2}$

M max. (at point of load) .... $= \dfrac{Pl}{4}$

M_x (when $x < \dfrac{l}{2}$) .... $= \dfrac{Px}{2}$

Δ max. (at point of load) .... $= \dfrac{Pl^3}{48\,EI}$

Δ_x (when $x < \dfrac{l}{2}$) .... $= \dfrac{Px}{48\,EI}\left(3l^2 - 4x^2\right)$

8. SIMPLE BEAM — CONCENTRATED LOAD AT ANY POINT

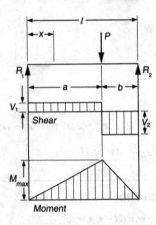

Equivalent Tabular Load .... $= \dfrac{8\,Pab}{l^2}$

$R_1 = V_1$ (max. when $a < b$) .... $= \dfrac{Pb}{l}$

$R_2 = V_2$ (max. when $a > b$) .... $= \dfrac{Pa}{l}$

M max. (at point of load) .... $= \dfrac{Pab}{l}$

M_x (when $x < a$) .... $= \dfrac{Pbx}{l}$

Δ max. $\left(\text{at } x = \sqrt{\dfrac{a(a+2b)}{3}} \text{ when } a > b\right)$ ..... $= \dfrac{Pab(a+2b)\,\sqrt{3a(a+2b)}}{27\,EIl}$

Δ_a (at point of load) .... $= \dfrac{Pa^2 b^2}{3\,EIl}$

Δ_x (when $x < a$) .... $= \dfrac{Pbx}{6\,EIl}\left(l^2 - b^2 - x^2\right)$

9. SIMPLE BEAM — TWO EQUAL CONCENTRATED LOADS SYMMETRICALLY PLACED

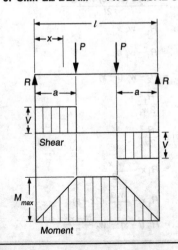

Equivalent Tabular Load .... $= \dfrac{8\,Pa}{l}$

$R = V$ .... $= P$

M max. (between loads) .... $= Pa$

M_x (when $x < a$) .... $= Px$

Δ max. (at center) .... $= \dfrac{Pa}{24\,EI}\left(3l^2 - 4a^2\right)$

Δ_x (when $x < a$) .... $= \dfrac{Px}{6\,EI}\left(3la - 3a^2 - x^2\right)$

Δ_x (when $x > a$ and $< (l-a)$) .... $= \dfrac{Pa}{6\,EI}\left(3lx - 3x^2 - a^2\right)$

Note: For deflection calculations, use specified loads.

Equivalent Tabular Load is the uniformly distributed factored load given in the Beam Load Tables

10. SIMPLE BEAM — TWO EQUAL CONCENTRATED LOADS UNSYMMETRICALLY PLACED

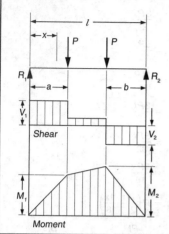

$$R_1 = V_1 \text{ (max. when } a < b) \dots\dots\dots\dots = \frac{P}{l}(l - a + b)$$

$$R_2 = V_2 \text{ (max. when } a > b) \dots\dots\dots\dots = \frac{P}{l}(l - b + a)$$

$$V_x \text{ (when } x > a \text{ and } < (l - b)) \dots\dots\dots = \frac{P}{l}(b - a)$$

$$M_1 \text{ (max. when } a > b) \dots\dots\dots\dots = R_1 a$$

$$M_2 \text{ (max. when } a < b) \dots\dots\dots\dots = R_2 b$$

$$M_x \text{ (when } x < a) \dots\dots\dots\dots = R_1 x$$

$$M_x \text{ (when } x > a \text{ and } < (l - b)) \dots\dots\dots = R_1 x - P(x - a)$$

11. SIMPLE BEAM — TWO UNEQUAL CONCENTRATED LOADS UNSYMMETRICALLY PLACED

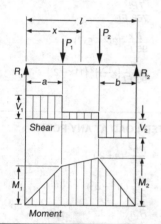

$$R_1 = V_1 \dots\dots\dots\dots\dots\dots\dots = \frac{P_1(l - a) + P_2 b}{l}$$

$$R_2 = V_2 \dots\dots\dots\dots\dots\dots\dots = \frac{P_1 a + P_2(l - b)}{l}$$

$$V_x \text{ (when } x > a \text{ and } < (l - b)) \dots\dots\dots = R_1 - P_1$$

$$M_1 \text{ (max. when } R_1 < P_1) \dots\dots\dots\dots = R_1 a$$

$$M_2 \text{ (max. when } R_2 < P_2) \dots\dots\dots\dots = R_2 b$$

$$M_x \text{ (when } x < a) \dots\dots\dots\dots = R_1 x$$

$$M_x \text{ (when } x > a \text{ and } < (l - b)) \dots\dots\dots = R_1 x - P_1(x - a)$$

12. BEAM FIXED AT ONE END, SUPPORTED AT OTHER — UNIFORMLY DISTRIBUTED LOAD

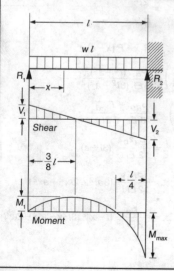

$$\text{Equivalent Tabular Load} \dots\dots\dots\dots = wl$$

$$R_1 = V_1 \dots\dots\dots\dots\dots\dots\dots = \frac{3wl}{8}$$

$$R_2 = V_2 \text{ max.} \dots\dots\dots\dots\dots\dots = \frac{5wl}{8}$$

$$V_x \dots\dots\dots\dots\dots\dots\dots\dots = R_1 - wx$$

$$M \text{ max.} \dots\dots\dots\dots\dots\dots\dots = \frac{wl^2}{8}$$

$$M_1 \left(\text{at } x = \frac{3}{8}l\right) \dots\dots\dots\dots = \frac{9}{128}wl^2$$

$$M_x \dots\dots\dots\dots\dots\dots\dots\dots = R_1 x - \frac{wx^2}{2}$$

$$\Delta \text{ max.} \left(\text{at } x = \frac{l}{16}(1 + \sqrt{33}) = .4215l\right) \dots\dots = \frac{wl^4}{185\,EI}$$

$$\Delta_x \dots\dots\dots\dots\dots\dots\dots\dots = \frac{wx}{48\,EI}(l^3 - 3lx^2 + 2x^3)$$

Note: For deflection calculations, use specified loads.

BEAM DIAGRAMS AND FORMULAE

Equivalent Tabular Load is the uniformly distributed factored load given in the Beam Load Tables

---

13. BEAM FIXED AT ONE END, SUPPORTED AT OTHER — CONCENTRATED LOAD AT CENTER

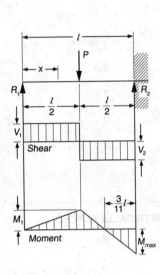

Equivalent Tabular Load $\ldots\ldots\ldots\ldots\ldots = \dfrac{3P}{2}$

$R_1 = V_1 \ldots\ldots\ldots\ldots\ldots\ldots = \dfrac{5P}{16}$

$R_2 = V_2 \text{ max.} \ldots\ldots\ldots\ldots\ldots = \dfrac{11P}{16}$

$M \text{ max. (at fixed end)} \ldots\ldots\ldots\ldots = \dfrac{3Pl}{16}$

$M_1 \text{ (at point of load)} \ldots\ldots\ldots\ldots = \dfrac{5Pl}{32}$

$M_x \left(\text{when } x < \dfrac{l}{2}\right) \ldots\ldots\ldots\ldots = \dfrac{5Px}{16}$

$M_x \left(\text{when } x > \dfrac{l}{2}\right) \ldots\ldots\ldots\ldots = P\left(\dfrac{l}{2} - \dfrac{11x}{16}\right)$

$\Delta \text{ max.} \left(\text{at } x = l\sqrt{\dfrac{1}{5}} = .4472l\right) \ldots\ldots\ldots = \dfrac{Pl^3}{48\,EI\,\sqrt{5}} = .009317\,\dfrac{Pl^3}{EI}$

$\Delta_x \text{ (at point of load)} \ldots\ldots\ldots\ldots = \dfrac{7Pl^3}{768\,EI}$

$\Delta_x \left(\text{when } x < \dfrac{l}{2}\right) \ldots\ldots\ldots\ldots = \dfrac{Px}{96\,EI}\left(3l^2 - 5x^2\right)$

$\Delta_x \left(\text{when } x > \dfrac{l}{2}\right) \ldots\ldots\ldots\ldots = \dfrac{P}{96\,EI}\left(x-l\right)^2\left(11x - 2l\right)$

---

14. BEAM FIXED AT ONE END, SUPPORTED AT OTHER — CONCENTRATED LOAD AT ANY POINT

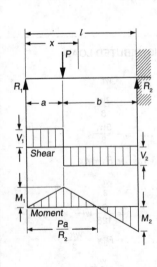

$R_1 = V_1 \ldots\ldots\ldots\ldots\ldots\ldots = \dfrac{Pb^2}{2l^3}\left(a + 2l\right)$

$R_2 = V_2 \ldots\ldots\ldots\ldots\ldots\ldots = \dfrac{Pa}{2l^3}\left(3l^2 - a^2\right)$

$M_1 \text{ (at point of load)} \ldots\ldots\ldots\ldots = R_1 a$

$M_2 \text{ (at fixed end)} \ldots\ldots\ldots\ldots = \dfrac{Pab}{2l^2}\left(a + l\right)$

$M_x \text{ (when } x < a) \ldots\ldots\ldots\ldots = R_1 x$

$M_x \text{ (when } x > a) \ldots\ldots\ldots\ldots = R_1 x - P\left(x - a\right)$

$\Delta \text{ max.} \left(\text{when } a < .414l \text{ at } x = l\sqrt{\dfrac{l^2 + a^2}{3l^2 - a^2}}\right) = \dfrac{Pa}{3\,EI}\dfrac{(l^2 - a^2)^3}{(3l^2 - a^2)^2}$

$\Delta \text{ max.} \left(\text{when } a > .414l \text{ at } x = l\sqrt{\dfrac{a}{2l + a}}\right) = \dfrac{Pab^2}{6\,EI}\sqrt{\dfrac{a}{2l + a}}$

$\Delta_a \text{ (at point of load)} \ldots\ldots\ldots\ldots = \dfrac{Pa^2 b^3}{12\,EI\,l^3}\left(3l + a\right)$

$\Delta_x \text{ (when } x < a) \ldots\ldots\ldots\ldots = \dfrac{Pb^2 x}{12\,EI\,l^3}\left(3al^2 - 2lx^2 - ax^2\right)$

$\Delta_x \text{ (when } x > a) \ldots\ldots\ldots\ldots = \dfrac{Pa}{12\,EI\,l^3}\left(l - x\right)^2\left(3l^2 x - a^2 x - 2a^2 l\right)$

Note: For deflection calculations, use specified loads.

15. BEAM FIXED AT BOTH ENDS — UNIFORMLY DISTRIBUTED LOADS

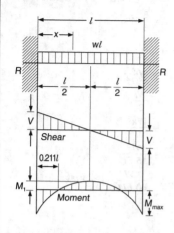

$$\text{Equivalent Tabular Load} = \frac{2wl}{3}$$

$$R = V = \frac{wl}{2}$$

$$V_x = w\left(\frac{l}{2} - x\right)$$

$$M \text{ max. (at ends)} = \frac{wl^2}{12}$$

$$M_1 \text{ (at center)} = \frac{wl^2}{24}$$

$$M_x = \frac{w}{12}\left(6lx - l^2 - 6x^2\right)$$

$$\Delta \text{ max. (at center)} = \frac{wl^4}{384\,EI}$$

$$\Delta_x = \frac{wx^2}{24\,EI}\left(l - x\right)^2$$

16. BEAM FIXED AT BOTH ENDS — CONCENTRATED LOAD AT CENTER

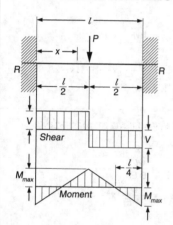

$$\text{Equivalent Tabular Load} = P$$

$$R = V = \frac{P}{2}$$

$$M \text{ max. (at center and ends)} = \frac{Pl}{8}$$

$$M_x\left(\text{when } x < \frac{l}{2}\right) = \frac{P}{8}\left(4x - l\right)$$

$$\Delta \text{ max. (at center)} = \frac{Pl^3}{192\,EI}$$

$$\Delta_x\left(\text{when } x < \frac{l}{2}\right) = \frac{Px^2}{48\,EI}\left(3l - 4x\right)$$

17. BEAM FIXED AT BOTH ENDS — CONCENTRATED LOAD AT ANY POINT

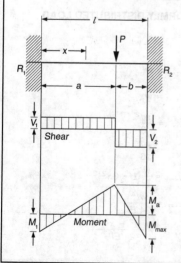

$$R_1 = V_1 \text{ (max. when } a < b) = \frac{Pb^2}{l^3}\left(3a + b\right)$$

$$R_2 = V_2 \text{ (max. when } a > b) = \frac{Pa^2}{l^3}\left(a + 3b\right)$$

$$M_1 \text{ (max. when } a < b) = \frac{Pab^2}{l^2}$$

$$M_2 \text{ (max. when } a > b) = \frac{Pa^2b}{l^2}$$

$$M_a \text{ (at point of load)} = \frac{2Pa^2b^2}{l^3}$$

$$M_x \text{ (when } x < a) = R_1 x - \frac{Pab^2}{l^2}$$

$$\Delta \text{ max. }\left(\text{when } a > b \text{ at } x = \frac{2al}{3a + b}\right) = \frac{2Pa^3b^2}{3\,EI\,(3a + b)^2}$$

$$\Delta_a \text{ (at point of load)} = \frac{Pa^3b^3}{3\,EI\,l^3}$$

$$\Delta_x \text{ (when } x < a) = \frac{Pb^2x^2}{6\,EI\,l^3}\left(3al - 3ax - bx\right)$$

Note: For deflection calculations, use specified loads.

BEAM DIAGRAMS AND FORMULAE

Equivalent Tabular Load is the uniformly distributed factored load given in the Beam Load Tables

18. CANTILEVER BEAM — LOAD INCREASING UNIFORMLY TO FIXED END

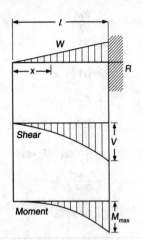

Equivalent Tabular Load $= \dfrac{8}{3} W$

$R = V$ $= W$

V_x $= W \dfrac{x^2}{l^2}$

M max. (at fixed end) $= \dfrac{Wl}{3}$

M_x $= \dfrac{Wx^3}{3l^2}$

Δ max. (at free end) $= \dfrac{Wl^3}{15\,EI}$

Δ_x $= \dfrac{W}{60\,EI\,l^2}\left(x^5 - 5l^4x + 4l^5\right)$

19. CANTILEVER BEAM — UNIFORMLY DISTRIBUTED LOAD

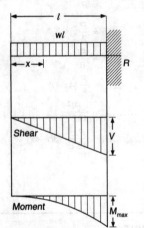

Equivalent Tabular Load $= 4wl$

$R = V$ $= wl$

V_x $= wx$

M max. (at fixed end) $= \dfrac{wl^2}{2}$

M_x $= \dfrac{wx^2}{2}$

Δ max. (at free end) $= \dfrac{wl^4}{8\,EI}$

Δ_x $= \dfrac{w}{24\,EI}\left(x^4 - 4l^3x + 3l^4\right)$

20. BEAM FIXED AT ONE END, FREE BUT GUIDED AT OTHER — UNIFORMLY DISTRIBUTED LOAD

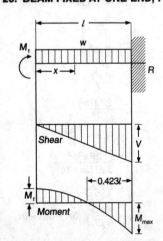

Equivalent Tabular Load $= \dfrac{8}{3} wl$

$R = V$ $= wl$

V_x $= wx$

M max. (at fixed end) $= \dfrac{wl^2}{3}$

M_1 (at deflected end) $= \dfrac{wl^2}{6}$

M_x $= \dfrac{w}{6}\left(l^2 - 3x^2\right)$

Δ max. (at deflected end) $= \dfrac{wl^4}{24\,EI}$

Δ_x $= \dfrac{w\,(l^2 - x^2)^2}{24\,EI}$

Note: For deflection calculations, use specified loads.

21. CANTILEVER BEAM — CONCENTRATED LOAD AT ANY POINT

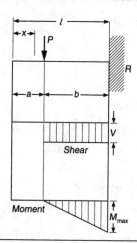

Equivalent Tabular Load $\dots\dots\dots\dots = \dfrac{8Pb}{l}$

$R = V$ (when $x < a$) $\dots\dots\dots\dots = P$

M max. (at fixed end) $\dots\dots\dots\dots = Pb$

M_x (when $x > a$) $\dots\dots\dots\dots = P(x - a)$

Δ max. (at free end) $\dots\dots\dots\dots = \dfrac{Pb^2}{6\,EI}(3l - b)$

Δ_a (at point of load) $\dots\dots\dots\dots = \dfrac{Pb^3}{3\,EI}$

Δ_x (when $x < a$) $\dots\dots\dots\dots = \dfrac{Pb^2}{6\,EI}(3l - 3x - b)$

Δ_x (when $x > a$) $\dots\dots\dots\dots = \dfrac{P(l - x)^2}{6\,EI}(3b - l + x)$

22. CANTILEVER BEAM — CONCENTRATED LOAD AT FREE END

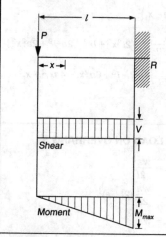

Equivalent Tabular Load $\dots\dots\dots\dots = 8P$

$R = V \dots\dots\dots\dots = P$

M max. (at fixed end) $\dots\dots\dots\dots = Pl$

$M_x \dots\dots\dots\dots = Px$

Δ max. (at free end) $\dots\dots\dots\dots = \dfrac{Pl^3}{3\,EI}$

$\Delta_x \dots\dots\dots\dots = \dfrac{P}{6\,EI}\left(2l^3 - 3l^2 x + x^3\right)$

23. BEAM FIXED AT ONE END, FREE BUT GUIDED AT OTHER — CONCENTRATED LOAD AT GUIDED END

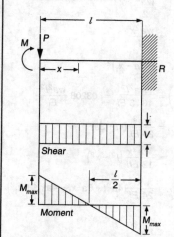

Equivalent Tabular Load $\dots\dots\dots\dots = 4P$

$R = V \dots\dots\dots\dots = P$

M max. (at both ends) $\dots\dots\dots\dots = \dfrac{Pl}{2}$

$M_x \dots\dots\dots\dots = P\left(\dfrac{l}{2} - x\right)$

Δ max. (at deflected end) $\dots\dots\dots\dots = \dfrac{Pl^3}{12\,EI}$

$\Delta_x \dots\dots\dots\dots = \dfrac{P(l - x)^2}{12\,EI}(l + 2x)$

Note: For deflection calculations, use specified loads.

BEAM DIAGRAMS AND FORMULAE

Equivalent Tabular Load is the uniformly distributed factored load given in the Beam Load Tables

---

24. BEAM OVERHANGING ONE SUPPORT — UNIFORMLY DISTRIBUTED LOAD

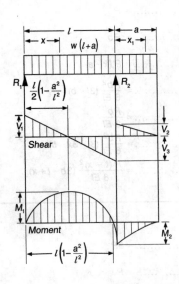

$$R_1 = V_1 \dots = \frac{w}{2l}\left(l^2 - a^2\right)$$

$$R_2 = V_2 + V_3 \dots = \frac{w}{2l}\left(l + a\right)^2$$

$$V_2 \dots = wa$$

$$V_3 \dots = \frac{w}{2l}\left(l^2 + a^2\right)$$

$$V_x \text{ (between supports)} \dots = R_1 - wx$$

$$V_{x_1} \text{ (for overhang)} \dots = w\left(a - x_1\right)$$

$$M_1 \left(\text{at } x = \frac{l}{2}\left[1 - \frac{a^2}{l^2}\right]\right) \dots = \frac{w}{8l^2}\left(l + a\right)^2\left(l - a\right)^2$$

$$M_2 \left(\text{at } R_2\right) \dots = \frac{wa^2}{2}$$

$$M_x \text{ (between supports)} \dots = \frac{wx}{2l}\left(l^2 - a^2 - xl\right)$$

$$M_{x_1} \text{ (for overhang)} \dots = \frac{w}{2}\left(a - x_1\right)^2$$

$$\Delta_x \text{ (between supports)} \dots = \frac{wx}{24\,EIl}\left(l^4 - 2l^2x^2 + lx^3 - 2a^2l^2 + 2a^2x^2\right)$$

$$\Delta_{x_1} \text{ (for overhang)} \dots = \frac{wx_1}{24\,EI}\left(4a^2l - l^3 + 6a^2x_1 - 4ax_1^2 + x_1^3\right)$$

---

25. BEAM OVERHANGING ONE SUPPORT — UNIFORMLY DISTRIBUTED LOAD ON OVERHANG

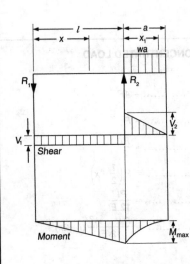

$$R_1 = V_1 \dots = \frac{wa^2}{2l}$$

$$R_2 = V_1 + V_2 \dots = \frac{wa}{2l}\left(2l + a\right)$$

$$V_2 \dots = wa$$

$$V_{x_1} \text{ (for overhang)} \dots = w\left(a - x_1\right)$$

$$M \text{ max. } \left(\text{at } R_2\right) \dots = \frac{wa^2}{2}$$

$$M_x \text{ (between supports)} \dots = \frac{wa^2x}{2l}$$

$$M_{x_1} \text{ (for overhang)} \dots = \frac{w}{2}\left(a - x_1\right)^2$$

$$\Delta \text{ max. } \left(\text{between supports at } x = \frac{l}{\sqrt{3}}\right) = \frac{wa^2l^2}{18\sqrt{3}\,EI} = .03208\,\frac{wa^2l^2}{EI}$$

$$\Delta \text{ max. } \left(\text{for overhang at } x_1 = a\right) \dots = \frac{wa^3}{24\,EI}\left(4l + 3a\right)$$

$$\Delta_x \text{ (between supports)} \dots = \frac{wa^2x}{12\,EIl}\left(l^2 - x^2\right)$$

$$\Delta_{x_1} \text{ (for overhang)} \dots = \frac{wx_1}{24\,EI}\left(4a^2l + 6a^2x_1 - 4ax_1^2 + x_1^3\right)$$

Note: For deflection calculations, use specified loads.

Equivalent Tabular Load is the uniformly distributed factored load given in the Beam Load Tables

26. BEAM OVERHANGING ONE SUPPORT — CONCENTRATED LOAD AT END OF OVERHANG

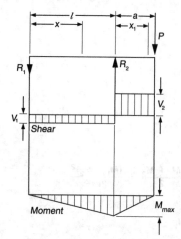

$$R_1 = V_1 \dots\dots\dots\dots\dots\dots = \frac{Pa}{l}$$

$$R_2 = V_1 + V_2 \dots\dots\dots\dots\dots = \frac{P}{l}(l + a)$$

$$V_2 \dots\dots\dots\dots\dots\dots\dots\dots = P$$

$$M \text{ max. (at } R_2) \dots\dots\dots\dots\dots = Pa$$

$$M_x \text{ (between supports)} \dots\dots\dots = \frac{Pax}{l}$$

$$M_{x_1} \text{ (for overhang)} \dots\dots\dots = P(a - x_1)$$

$$\Delta \text{ max. }\left(\text{between supports at } x = \frac{l}{\sqrt{3}}\right) \dots = \frac{Pal^2}{9\sqrt{3}\,EI} = .06415\frac{Pal^2}{EI}$$

$$\Delta \text{ max. (for overhang at } x_1 = a) \dots\dots = \frac{Pa^2}{3EI}(l + a)$$

$$\Delta_x \text{ (between supports)} \dots\dots\dots = \frac{Pax}{6EIl}(l^2 - x^2)$$

$$\Delta_{x_1} \text{ (for overhang)} \dots\dots\dots = \frac{Px_1}{6EI}(2al + 3ax_1 - x_1^2)$$

27. BEAM OVERHANGING ONE SUPPORT — UNIFORMLY DISTRIBUTED LOAD BETWEEN SUPPORTS

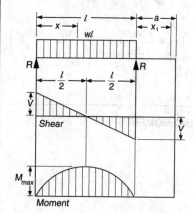

$$\text{Equivalent Tabular Load} \dots\dots\dots = wl$$

$$R = V \dots\dots\dots\dots\dots\dots\dots = \frac{wl}{2}$$

$$V_x \dots\dots\dots\dots\dots\dots\dots\dots = w\left(\frac{l}{2} - x\right)$$

$$M \text{ max. (at center)} \dots\dots\dots = \frac{wl^2}{8}$$

$$M_x \dots\dots\dots\dots\dots\dots\dots\dots = \frac{wx}{2}(l - x)$$

$$\Delta \text{ max. (at center)} \dots\dots\dots = \frac{5wl^4}{384EI}$$

$$\Delta_x \dots\dots\dots\dots\dots\dots\dots\dots = \frac{wx}{24EI}(l^3 - 2lx^2 + x^3)$$

$$\Delta_{x_1} \dots\dots\dots\dots\dots\dots\dots\dots = \frac{wl^3 x_1}{24EI}$$

28. BEAM OVERHANGING ONE SUPPORT — CONCENTRATED LOAD ANY POINT BETWEEN SUPPORTS

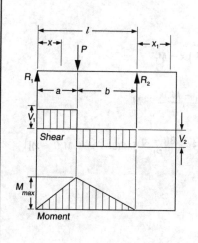

$$\text{Equivalent Tabular Load} \dots\dots\dots = \frac{8Pab}{l^2}$$

$$R_1 = V_1 \text{ (max. when } a < b) \dots\dots = \frac{Pb}{l}$$

$$R_2 = V_2 \text{ (max. when } a > b) \dots\dots = \frac{Pa}{l}$$

$$M \text{ max. (at point of load)} \dots\dots\dots = \frac{Pab}{l}$$

$$M_x \text{ (when } x < a) \dots\dots\dots\dots = \frac{Pbx}{l}$$

$$\Delta \text{ max. }\left(\text{at } x = \sqrt{\frac{a(a+2b)}{3}} \text{ when } a > b\right) = \frac{Pab(a+2b)\sqrt{3a(a+2b)}}{27\,EIl}$$

$$\Delta_a \text{ (at point of load)} \dots\dots\dots = \frac{Pa^2 b^2}{3EIl}$$

$$\Delta_x \text{ (when } x < a) \dots\dots\dots = \frac{Pbx}{6EIl}(l^2 - b^2 - x^2)$$

$$\Delta_x \text{ (when } x > a) \dots\dots\dots = \frac{Pa(l-x)}{6EIl}(2lx - x^2 - a^2)$$

$$\Delta_{x_1} \dots\dots\dots\dots\dots\dots\dots\dots = \frac{Pabx_1}{6EIl}(l + a)$$

Note: For deflection calculations, use specified loads.

BEAM DIAGRAMS AND FORMULAE

Equivalent Tabular Load is the uniformly distributed factored load given in the Beam Load Tables

---

29. BEAM — UNIFORMLY DISTRIBUTED LOAD AND VARIABLE END MOMENTS

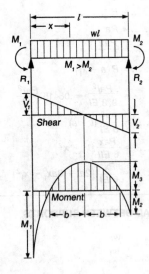

$$R_1 = V_1 = \frac{wl}{2} + \frac{M_1 - M_2}{l}$$

$$R_2 = V_2 = \frac{wl}{2} - \frac{M_1 - M_2}{l}$$

$$V_x = w\left(\frac{l}{2} - x\right) + \frac{M_1 - M_2}{l}$$

$$M_3\left(\text{at } x = \frac{l}{2} + \frac{M_1 - M_2}{wl}\right) = \frac{wl^2}{8} - \frac{M_1 + M_2}{2} + \frac{(M_1 - M_2)^2}{2wl^2}$$

$$M_x = \frac{wx}{2}(l - x) + \left(\frac{M_1 - M_2}{l}\right)x - M_1$$

$$b \text{ (To locate infection points)} = \sqrt{\frac{l^2}{4} - \left(\frac{M_1 + M_2}{w}\right) + \left(\frac{M_1 - M_2}{wl}\right)^2}$$

$$\Delta_x = \frac{wx}{24\,EI}\left[x^3 - \left(2l + \frac{4M_1}{wl} - \frac{4M_2}{wl}\right)x^2 + \frac{12M_1}{w}x + l^3 - \frac{8M_1 l}{w} - \frac{4M_2 l}{w}\right]$$

---

30. BEAM — CONCENTRATED LOAD AT CENTER AND VARIABLE END MOMENTS

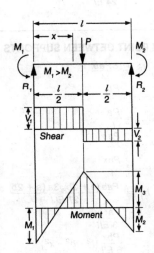

$$R_1 = V_1 = \frac{P}{2} + \frac{M_1 - M_2}{l}$$

$$R_2 = V_2 = \frac{P}{2} - \frac{M_1 - M_2}{l}$$

$$M_3 \text{ (at center)} = \frac{Pl}{4} - \frac{M_1 + M_2}{2}$$

$$M_x\left(\text{when } x < \frac{l}{2}\right) = \left(\frac{P}{2} + \frac{M_1 - M_2}{l}\right)x - M_1$$

$$M_x\left(\text{when } x > \frac{l}{2}\right) = \frac{P}{2}(l - x) + \frac{(M_1 - M_2)x}{l} - M_1$$

$$\Delta_x\left(\text{when } x < \frac{l}{2}\right) = \frac{Px}{48\,EI}\left(3l^2 - 4x^2 - \frac{8(l - x)}{Pl}\,[M_1(2l - x) + M_2(l + x)]\right)$$

Note: For deflection calculations, use specified loads.

31. SIMPLE BEAM — ONE CONCENTRATED MOVING LOAD

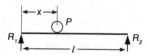

$$R_1 \text{ max.} = V_1 \text{ max. (at } x = 0) \ldots\ldots\ldots\ldots\ldots\ldots = P$$

$$M \text{ max.} \left(\text{at point of load, when } x = \frac{l}{2} \right) \ldots\ldots\ldots = \frac{Pl}{4}$$

32. SIMPLE BEAM — TWO EQUAL CONCENTRATED MOVING LOADS

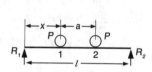

$$R_1 \text{ max.} = V_1 \text{ max. (at } x = 0) \ldots\ldots\ldots\ldots\ldots\ldots = P\left(2 - \frac{a}{l}\right)$$

$$M \text{ max.} \begin{cases} \left[\begin{array}{l} \text{when } a < \left(2 - \sqrt{2}\right) l = .586l \\ \text{under load 1 at } x = \frac{1}{2}\left(l - \frac{a}{2}\right) \end{array}\right] \ldots\ldots = \frac{P}{2l}\left(l - \frac{a}{2}\right)^2 \\[2em] \left[\begin{array}{l} \text{when } a > \left(2 - \sqrt{2}\right) l = .586l \\ \text{with one load at center of span} \\ \text{(case 31)} \end{array}\right] \ldots\ldots = \frac{Pl}{4} \end{cases}$$

33. SIMPLE BEAM — TWO UNEQUAL CONCENTRATED MOVING LOADS

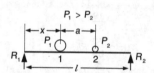

$$R_1 \text{ max.} = V_1 \text{ max. (at } x = 0) \ldots\ldots\ldots\ldots\ldots\ldots = P_1 + P_2\frac{l - a}{l}$$

$$M \text{ max.} \begin{cases} \left[\text{under } P_1, \text{ at } x = \frac{1}{2}\left(l - \frac{P_2 a}{P_1 + P_2}\right)\right] = \left(P_1 + P_2\right)\frac{x^2}{l} \\[1.5em] \left[\begin{array}{l} M \text{ max. may occur with larger} \\ \text{load at center of span and other} \\ \text{load off span (case 31)]} \end{array}\right] \ldots\ldots = \frac{P_1 l}{4} \end{cases}$$

GENERAL RULES FOR SIMPLE BEAMS CARRYING MOVING CONCENTRATED LOADS

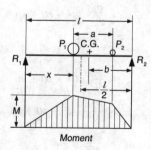

Moment

The maximum shear due to moving concentrated loads occurs at one support when one of the loads is at that support. With several moving loads, the location that will produce maximum shear must be determined by trial.

The maximum bending moment produced by moving concentrated loads occurs under one of the loads when that load is as far from one support as the center of gravity of all the moving loads on the beam is from the other support.

In the accompanying diagram, the maximum bending moment occurs under load P_1 when $x = b$. It should also be noted that this condition occurs when the center line of the span is midway between the center of gravity of loads and the nearest concentrated load.

Note: For deflection calculations, use specified loads.

BEAM DIAGRAMS AND FORMULAE

Equivalent Tabular Load is the uniformly distributed factored load given in the Beam Load Tables

---

34. CONTINUOUS BEAM — TWO EQUAL SPANS — UNIFORM LOAD ON ONE SPAN

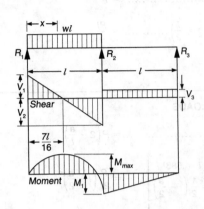

$$\text{Equivalent Tabular Load} = \frac{49}{64} wl$$

$$R_1 = V_1 = \frac{7}{16} wl$$

$$R_2 = V_2 + V_3 = \frac{5}{8} wl$$

$$R_3 = V_3 = -\frac{1}{16} wl$$

$$V_2 = \frac{9}{16} wl$$

$$M \text{ max.} \left(\text{at } x = \frac{7}{16} l \right) = \frac{49}{512} wl^2$$

$$M_1 \text{ (at support } R_2) = \frac{1}{16} wl^2$$

$$M_x \text{ (when } x < l) = \frac{wx}{16} (7l - 8x)$$

$$\Delta \text{ max.} \left(0.472 \, l \text{ from } R_1 \right) = 0.0092 \, wl^4/EI$$

---

35. CONTINUOUS BEAM — TWO EQUAL SPANS — CONCENTRATED LOAD AT CENTER OF ONE SPAN

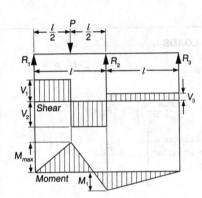

$$\text{Equivalent Tabular Load} = \frac{13}{8} P$$

$$R_1 = V_1 = \frac{13}{32} P$$

$$R_2 = V_2 + V_3 = \frac{11}{16} P$$

$$R_3 = V_3 = -\frac{3}{32} P$$

$$V_2 = \frac{19}{32} P$$

$$M \text{ max. (at point of load)} = \frac{13}{64} Pl$$

$$M_1 \text{ (at support } R_2) = \frac{3}{32} Pl$$

$$\Delta \text{ max.} \left(0.480 \, l \text{ from } R_1 \right) = 0.015 \, Pl^3/EI$$

---

36. CONTINUOUS BEAM — TWO EQUAL SPANS — CONCENTRATED LOAD AT ANY POINT

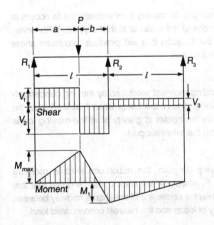

$$R_1 = V_1 = \frac{Pb}{4l^3} \left(4l^2 - a(l + a) \right)$$

$$R_2 = V_2 + V_3 = \frac{Pa}{2l^3} \left(2l^2 + b(l + a) \right)$$

$$R_3 = V_3 = -\frac{Pab}{4l^3} (l + a)$$

$$V_2 = \frac{Pa}{4l^3} \left(4l^2 + b(l + a) \right)$$

$$M \text{ max. (at point of load)} = \frac{Pab}{4l^3} \left(4l^2 - a(l + a) \right)$$

$$M_1 \text{ (at support } R_2) = \frac{Pab}{4l^2} (l + a)$$

Note: For deflection calculations, use specified loads.

UNIFORMLY DISTRIBUTED LOADS

Moment = Coefficient × W × L
Reaction = Coefficient × W
Where: W = Total uniformly distributed load on one span
L = Length of one span

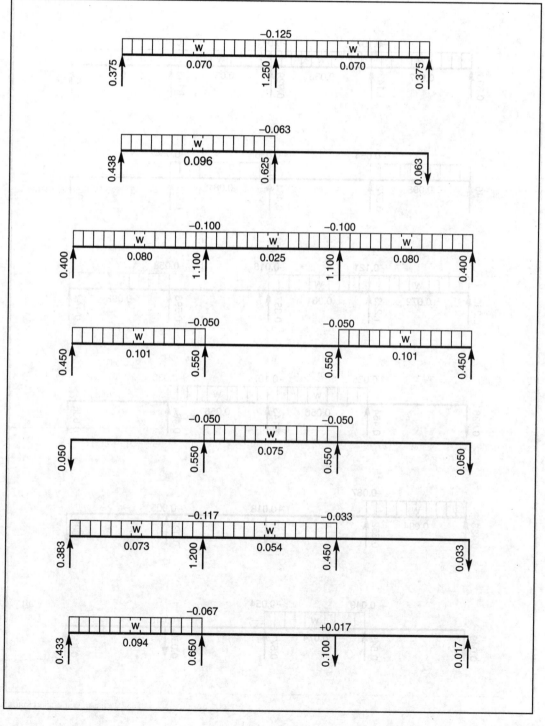

MOMENTS, REACTIONS
Equal Span Continuous Beams

UNIFORMLY DISTRIBUTED LOADS

Moment = Coefficient × W × L
Reaction = Coefficient × W
Where: W = Total uniformly distributed load on one span
L = Length of one span

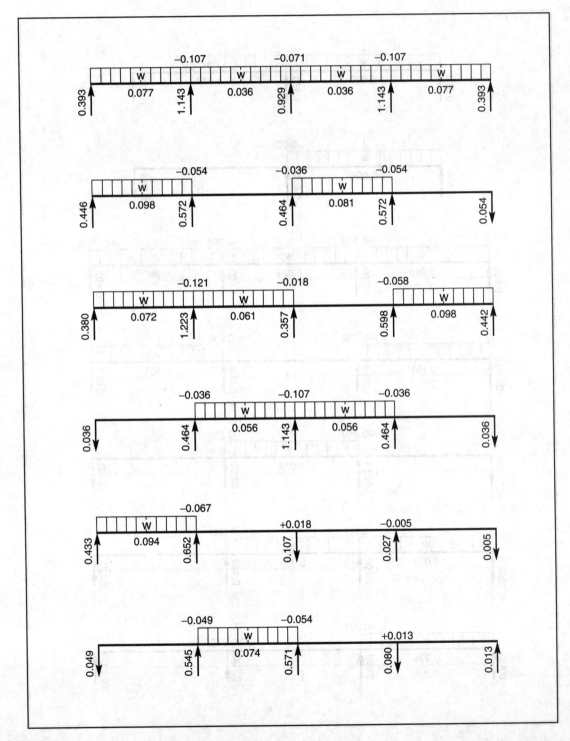

CENTRAL POINT LOADS

Moment = Coefficient × W × L
Reaction = Coefficient × W
Where: W = The concentrated load on one span
L = Length of one span

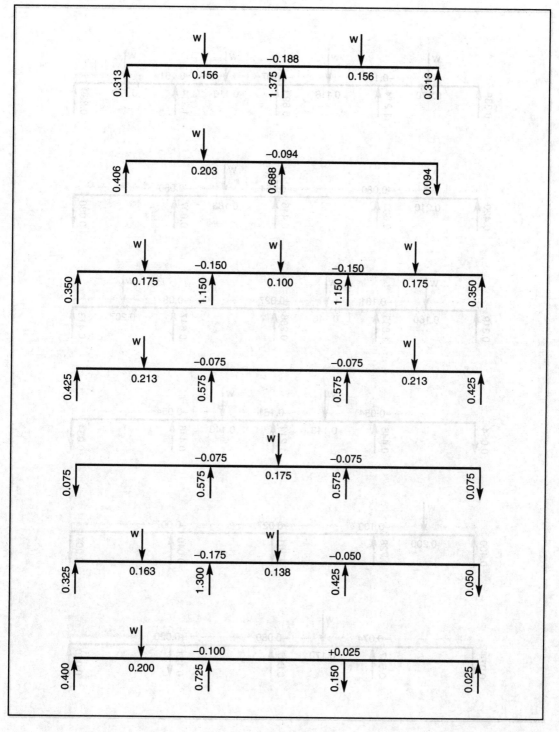

MOMENTS, REACTIONS
Equal Span Continuous Beams

CENTRAL POINT LOADS

Moment = Coefficient × W × L
Reaction = Coefficient × W
Where: W = The concentrated load on one span
L = Length of one span

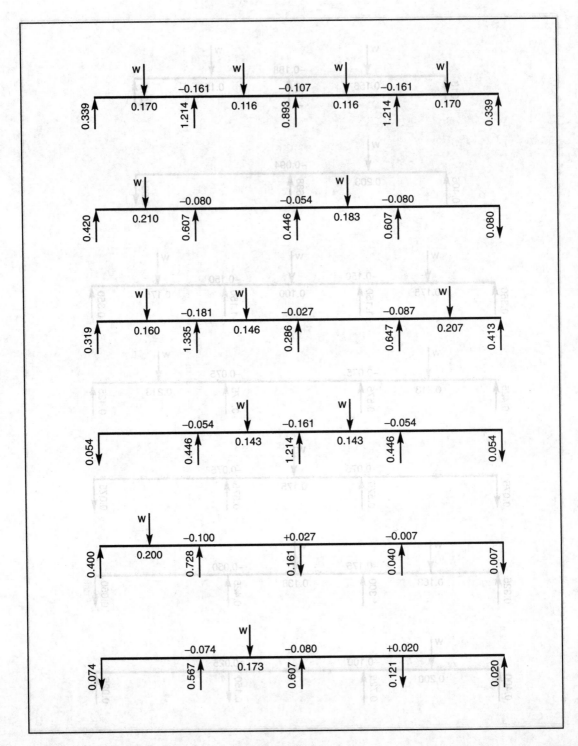

MOMENTS, REACTIONS
Equal Span Continuous Beams

POINT LOADS AT THIRD POINTS OF SPAN

Moment = Coefficient $\times$ W $\times$ L
Reaction = Coefficient $\times$ W
Where: W = The total load on one span
L = Length of one span

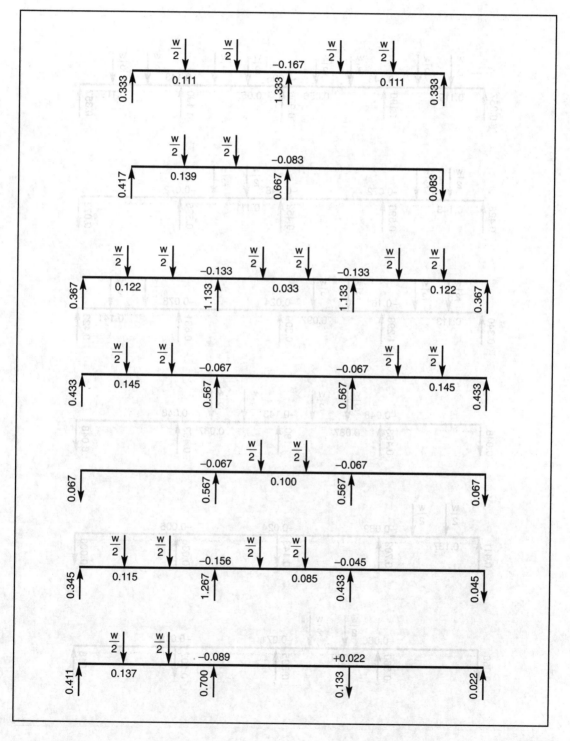

MOMENTS, REACTIONS
Equal Span Continuous Beams

POINT LOADS AT THIRD POINTS OF SPAN

Moment = Coefficient × W × L
Reaction = Coefficient × W
Where: W = The total load on one span
L = Length of one span

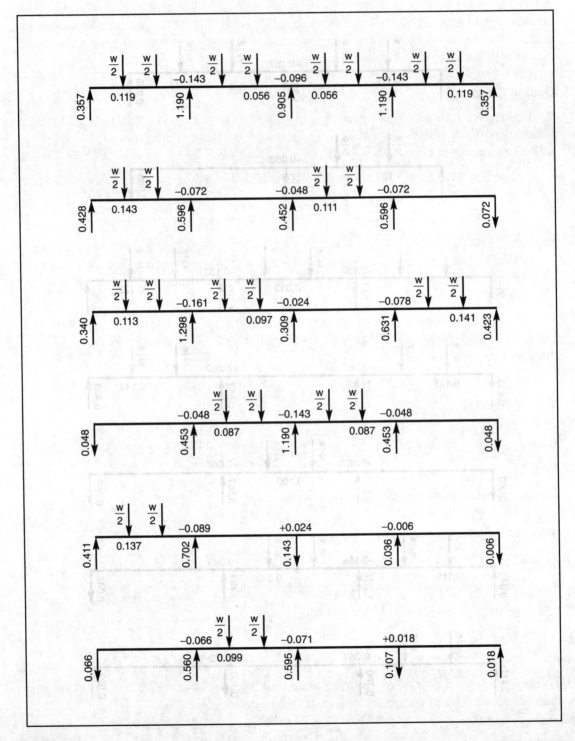

BEAM BEARING PLATES

General

When a flexural member is supported by a masonry wall or pier, the beam reaction must be distributed over sufficient area to avoid exceeding the bearing capacity of the masonry or concrete. Steel bearing plates may be used for this purpose.

Bearing plates are usually set in place and grouted level at the required elevation before positioning the beam. Thus, even though the beam flange may be able to distribute the reaction to supporting masonry or concrete, a bearing plate can be useful to facilitate erection. Some form of anchorage is required to ensure that the beam is connected to the pier or wall either longitudinally or for uplift forces.

Design Chart

Figure 5-2 on page 5-167 provides a graph to determine the thickness of bearing plates using CSA G40.21-300W steel, for beams without bearing stiffeners, based on the following assumptions:

- The beam reaction P_f is uniformly distributed to the bearing plate over an effective area of width $2k$ and length C.

- The bearing pressure between the effective area of the bearing plate and the concrete or masonry support is uniform over the area of the plate.

- The bearing pressure under the portion of plate projecting beyond the k-distance from the centre line of the beam is ignored, since in practice the flange may be slightly "curled".

Equating the factored moment acting on the portion of the bearing plate, taken as a cantilever, to the factored moment resistance of the plate, $(M_r = \phi Z F_y)$, the bearing plate thickness is calculated as:

$$t_p = \sqrt{\frac{2 P_f\, n^2}{A \phi F_y}}$$

where:

P_f = factored end reaction

F_y = specified minimum yield strength of the bearing plate steel (MPa)

A = $B \times C$ = area of plate (mm^2)

t_p = required thickness of bearing plate (mm)

k = beam k-distance = distance from web toe of fillet to outer face of flange (mm)

n = $B/2 - k$, (mm)

b = width of beam flange (mm)

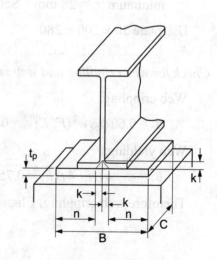

To minimize deflection of the bearing plate, the thickness generally should not be less than about one fifth of the overhang, i.e., $t_p \geq (B - b) / 10$.

Use of chart

1. Required area, A = beam reaction due to factored loads divided by the unit factored concrete bearing resistance, $(0.85\,\phi_c\,f'_c)$, where $\phi_c = 0.65$

2. Determine C and solve for B. (C, the length of bearing, is usually governed by the available wall thickness or other structural considerations.)

3. Determine n and enter Figure 5-2 to determine t_p.

Example

Given:

A W610x140 of ASTM A992 steel beam has a factored end reaction of 600 kN and is supported on a concrete pier with 28-day compressive strength of 20 MPa. Design the bearing plate assuming G40.21-300W steel and a concrete bearing length of 200 mm.

Solution:

Unit factored bearing resistance of concrete is:

$$0.85 \times 0.65 \times 20 = 11.1 \text{ MPa}$$

Area required is $(600 \times 10^3)\,/\,11.1 = 54\,100 \text{ mm}^2$

Therefore, required B is: $54\,100\,/\,200 = 271 \text{ mm}$

For W610x140, $b = 230$ mm, $t = 22.2$ mm, $w = 13.1$ mm, $k = 44$ mm

Select $B = 280$ mm (greater than flange width, $b = 230$ mm)

$n = (B/2) - k = (280/2) - 44 = 96 \text{ mm}$

From Figure 5-2, for unit factored bearing resistance of 11.1 MPa and n of 96 mm,

minimum $t_p \approx 28$ mm   Select $t_p = 30$ mm

Use plate 30 × 200 × 280

Check for web crippling and web yielding   (Clause 14.3.2(b), S16-09)

Web crippling:

$$B_r = 0.60\,\phi_{be}\,w^2\,(F_y\,E)^{0.5} = 0.60 \times 0.75 \times 13.1^2\,(345 \times 2 \times 10^5)^{0.5} = 641 \text{ kN}$$

Web yielding:

$$B_r = \phi_{be}\,w\,(N + 4\,t)\,F_y = 0.75 \times 13.1\,(200 + 4 \times 22.2)\,345 = 979 \text{ kN}$$

Therefore web crippling, Clause 14.3.2(b)(ii), governs and $B_r = 641$ kN > 600 kN.

FIGURE 5-2
BEAM BEARING PLATE THICKNESS, t_p

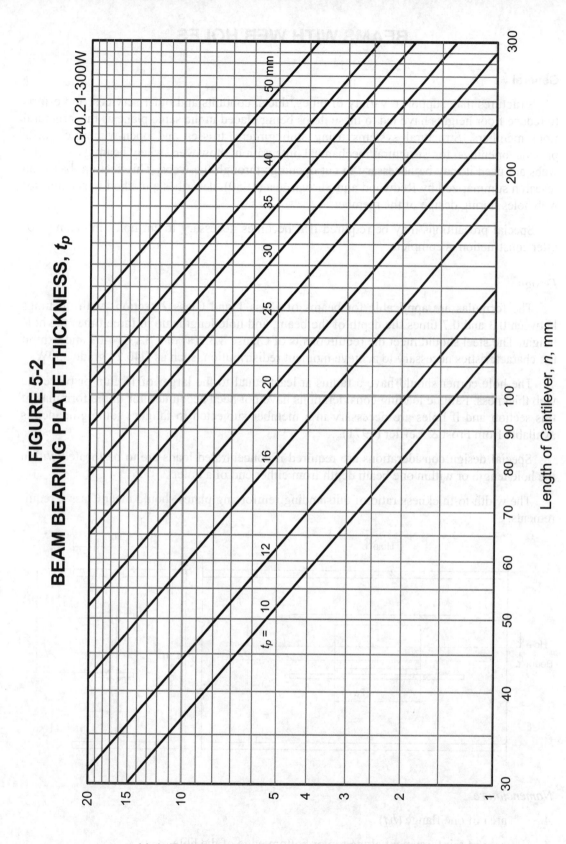

G40.21-300W

Length of Cantilever, n, mm

Unit Factored Bearing Resistance, B_r, MPa

BEAMS WITH WEB HOLES

General

Structures may support a variety of pipes, ducts, conduits and other services, and efforts to reduce floor heights have led to these items being placed in the same plane as the structural floor members. Structural systems using stub girders, trusses and open-web steel joists provide openings for structural/mechanical integration; however, when beams with solid webs are used it may be necessary to cut openings through the webs. This section, based on research summarized by Redwood and Shrivastava (1980), describes a method to account for web holes during design of the member.

Special precautions may be required if it becomes necessary to cut holes in beam webs after construction is complete.

Design

The formulas are applicable for beams of Class 1 and Class 2 sections with openings between 0.3 and 0.7 times the depth of the beam, and hole lengths up to three times the hole height. The steel should meet the requirements of Clause 8.3.2(a) of CSA S16-09 and exhibit the characteristics necessary to achieve moment redistribution, such as G40.21 grade 350W.

The hole corner should have a radius at least equal to the larger of 16 mm or twice the web thickness. Fatigue loading considerations have not been accounted for in the formulas of this section and if holes are necessary in a member subjected to fatigue, some guidance is available from Frost & Leffler (1971).

Special design considerations are required if concentrated loads are to be located within the hole length or within one beam depth from either end of a hole.

The width-to-thickness ratio of outstanding reinforcing plates should meet Class 1 requirements.

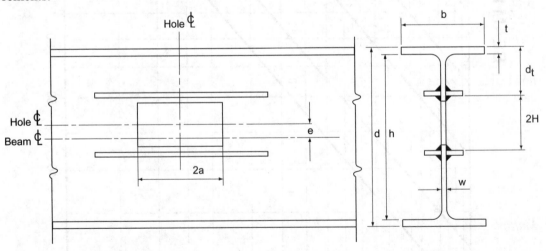

Nomenclature

A_f area of one flange ($b\,t$)

A_r area of reinforcement along top or bottom edge of the hole

A_w area of web (dw)

e eccentricity of centreline of the hole above or below beam centreline (*always positive*)

M_f bending moment due to factored loads at centreline of hole

M_r factored moment resistance of an unperforated beam

M_o, M_l values of moment resistance defined in web hole formulas

R radius of a circular hole

s length of web between adjacent holes

V_f shear force at centreline of hole due to factored loads

V_r' factored shear resistance based on plastic analysis of an unperforated beam = $0.8\phi A_w F_s$ (S16-09 Clause 13.4.2)

V_o, V_l values of shear resistance defined in web hole formulas

Web Stability

This section of the Handbook is valid for the following range of values:

For Class 1 Sections	For Class 2 Sections
$V_f \leq 0.67\,V_r'$	$V_f \leq 0.45\,V_r'$
and in addition, for rectangular holes	and in addition, for rectangular holes
$a/H \leq 3.0$	$a/H \leq 2.2$
$(a/H) + 6(2H/d) \leq 5.6$	$(a/H) + 6(2H/d) \leq 5.6$

If these values are exceeded, refer to Redwood and Shrivastava (1980).

Deflections

One or two small circular holes normally result in negligible additional deflections; however, deflections of beams with large holes will increase because of local deformations caused by:

(a) effect of rotation produced by change in length of the tee sections above and below the hole

(b) local bending over the length of the hole

(c) shear deformations.

Multiple Holes

To avoid effects of interaction between two adjacent holes which may occur with high shear, the length of the web between the holes should satisfy the following, where s = clear length of solid web between the holes:

Rectangular holes

$$s \geq 2H, \qquad s \geq 2a \left[\frac{V_f/V_r'}{1-(V_f/V_r')} \right]$$

Circular holes

$$s \geq 3R, \qquad s \geq 2R \left[\frac{V_f/V_r'}{1-(V_f/V_r')} \right]$$

where in each case the length, height or radius refers to that of the larger of the two holes.

Lateral Stability

The presence of a web hole has only a minor effect on the lateral stability of a beam, when the strength of the beam is governed by the resistance of a section remote from the hole. For members that may be susceptible to lateral buckling, refer to the paper by Redwood and Shrivastava (1980).

Unreinforced Holes

According to Clause 14.3.3.2 of S16-09 (see Part Two), unreinforced circular openings may be used under stipulated conditions. Round holes that are not covered by Clause 14.3.3.2 may be checked using the unreinforced hole formulas below by equating a and H to hole radius R as follows:

$$2a = 0.9R \quad \text{and} \quad 2H = 1.8R$$

Beam Resistance — Unreinforced Holes

Web stability must always be confirmed (page 5-169), and compression zone stability of the tee section must be checked when $2a > 4\,d_t$.

The factored shear force V_f and factored moment M_f applied at the web hole centreline must satisfy:

$$V_f \leq V_l \tag{1}$$

$$M_f \leq M_o - (M_o - M_l)\, V_f/V_l \tag{2}$$

in which

$$\frac{M_o}{M_r} = 1 - \frac{\dfrac{A_w}{4A_f}\left[\left(\dfrac{2H}{d}\right)^2 + \left(\dfrac{4e}{d}\right)\left(\dfrac{2H}{d}\right) \right]}{1 + \dfrac{A_w}{4A_f}} \tag{3}$$

$$\frac{M_l}{M_r} = \frac{1 - \dfrac{2}{\sqrt{3}}\left(\dfrac{A_w}{A_f}\right)\left(\dfrac{a}{d}\right)\sqrt{\dfrac{\alpha_2}{1+\alpha_2}}}{1 + \dfrac{A_w}{4A_f}} \tag{4}$$

$$\frac{V_l}{V_r'} = \frac{2}{\sqrt{3}}\left(\dfrac{a}{d}\right)\left(\frac{\alpha_1}{\sqrt{1+\alpha_1}} + \frac{\alpha_2}{\sqrt{1+\alpha_2}} \right) \tag{5}$$

where

$$\alpha_1 = \frac{3}{16}\left(\frac{d}{a}\right)^2\left(1 - \frac{2H}{d} - \frac{2e}{d}\right)^2 \qquad [6]$$

$$\alpha_2 = \frac{3}{16}\left(\frac{d}{a}\right)^2\left(1 - \frac{2H}{d} + \frac{2e}{d}\right)^2 \qquad [7]$$

Table 5-6, page 5-178, and Table 5-7, page 5-179, provide a means of evaluating [1] and [2]. For further explanation of these tables, see page 5-174.

Reinforced Holes

Horizontal Bars Only

Equal areas of reinforcement should be placed above and below the opening, with the reinforcement as close as possible to the edges of the hole. Welds attaching the reinforcement to the beam web should be continuous and may be placed on only one side of the reinforcing bar (with a short weld at each end on the opposite side of the bar to maintain alignment). Within the length of the hole, the welds should develop twice the factored tensile resistance of the reinforcement except that the weld capacity need not exceed $1.15 \, a \, w \, F_y$. The reinforcement should extend past the hole far enough for the weld to develop the factored tensile resistance of the reinforcement but not less than a distance of $a/2$.

Reinforcement may be placed on only one side of the web of Class 1 sections (for economy) providing the following conditions are satisfied:

$$A_r \le 0.333 A_f, \qquad M_f \le 20 V_f d \text{ (at the hole centreline)}$$

$$a/H \le 2.5, \qquad d_t/w \le 370/\sqrt{F_y}$$

Round holes may be checked using the reinforced hole formulas by relating a and H to R as follows:

$$2a = 0.9R \text{ and } 2H = 2R$$

Once it is established that hole reinforcement is required, Table 5-8 provides a means of checking the resistance of a beam with a reinforced hole for an assumed area of reinforcement. To determine minimum reinforcement requirements, a flow chart for writing computer programs is shown on page 5-173.

Vertical Bars

The compression zone stability of the reinforced tee should be checked by treating it as an axially loaded column with effective length equal to $2a$.

If it is determined that web instability could be a problem, vertical reinforcing at the ends of the hole will be required. Attachment of both vertical and horizontal bars is generally more economical when the horizontal bars are placed on one side of the web with the vertical bars on the other side.

Beam Resistance — Holes with Horizontal Reinforcing Bars

Web stability and compression zone stability must be checked in addition to the following strength criteria. The factored shear force V_f and factored moment M_f at the web hole centreline must satisfy the following, where A_r is less than A_f:

$$V_f \le V_l \qquad\qquad\qquad [8a]$$

$$V_f / V_r' \le 1 - \frac{2H}{d} \qquad\qquad\qquad [8b]$$

$$M_f \le M_o - (M_o - M_l) V_f / V_l \qquad\qquad\qquad [9a]$$

$$M_f \le M_r \qquad\qquad\qquad [9b]$$

in which

$$\left(\frac{M_o}{M_r}\right)_a = 1 + \frac{\dfrac{A_r}{A_f}\left(\dfrac{2H}{d}\right) - \dfrac{A_w}{4A_f}\left[\left(\dfrac{2H}{d}\right)^2 + 4\left(\dfrac{2H}{d}\right)\left(\dfrac{e}{d}\right) - 4\left(\dfrac{e}{d}\right)^2\right]}{1 + \dfrac{A_w}{4A_f}} \quad \text{for } \frac{e}{d} \le \frac{A_r}{A_w} \quad [10a]$$

$$\text{or} \quad \left(\frac{M_o}{M_r}\right)_b = \left(\frac{M_o}{M_r}\right)_a - \frac{\dfrac{A_w}{A_f}\left(\dfrac{e}{d} - \dfrac{A_r}{A_w}\right)^2}{1 + \dfrac{A_w}{4A_f}} \quad \text{for } \frac{e}{d} > \frac{A_r}{A_w} \quad [10b]$$

$$\left(\frac{M_l}{M_r}\right) = \frac{1 - \dfrac{A_r}{A_f}}{1 + \dfrac{A_w}{4A_f}} \qquad\qquad\qquad [11]$$

$$\frac{V_l}{V_r'} = \sqrt{3}\left(\frac{d}{a}\right)\frac{A_r}{A_w}\left(1 - \frac{2H}{d}\right) \qquad\qquad\qquad [12]$$

Flow Chart

The flow chart on page 5-173 is provided as a guide in developing computer programs. The logic provided determines the minimum A_r which will satisfy [9a]. It is anticipated that the individuals implementing the program will modify it to their own needs.

References

FROST, R.W., and LEFFLER, R.E. 1971. Fatigue tests of beams with rectangular web holes. Journal of the Structural Division, ASCE, **97**(ST2): 509-527.

PART TWO of this Handbook.

REDWOOD, R.G. 1974. The influence of web holes on the design of steel beams. Proceedings, Canadian Structural Engineering Conference, Canadian Steel Construction Council, Willowdale, Ontario.

REDWOOD, R.G. 1971. Simplified plastic analysis for reinforced web holes. Engineering Journal, AISC, **8**(3): 128-131.

REDWOOD, R.G., and SHRIVASTAVA, S.C. 1980. Design recommendations for steel beams with web holes. Canadian Journal of Civil Engineering, **7**(4), December.

REDWOOD, R.G., and WONG, P. 1982. Web holes in composite beams with steel deck. Proceedings, Canadian Structural Engineering Conference, Canadian Steel Construction Council, Willowdale, Ontario.

REINFORCED HOLE PROGRAM FLOWCHART

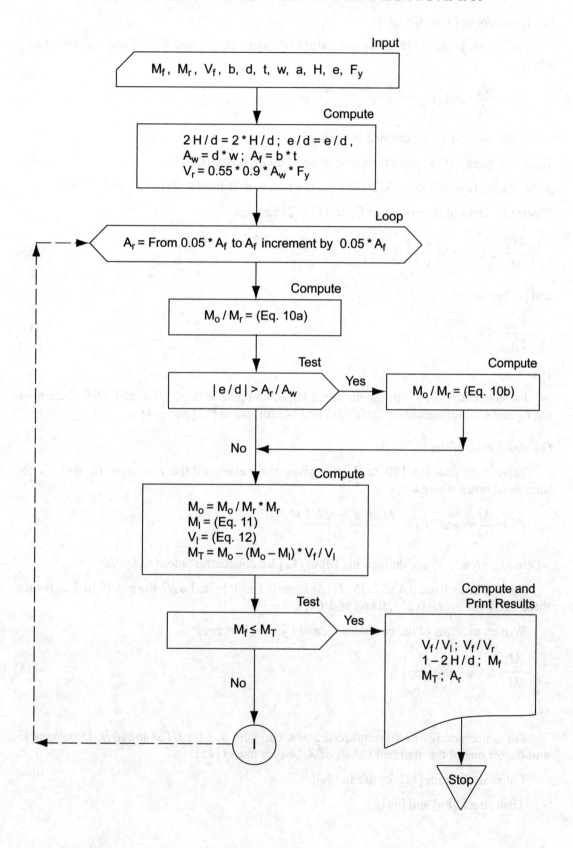

Input

M_f, M_r, V_f, b, d, t, w, a, H, e, F_y

Compute

$2H/d = 2*H/d$; $e/d = e/d$,
$A_w = d*w$; $A_f = b*t$
$V_r = 0.55*0.9*A_w*F_y$

Loop

A_r = From $0.05*A_f$ to A_f increment by $0.05*A_f$

Compute

M_o/M_r = (Eq. 10a)

Test

$|e/d| > A_r/A_w$ — Yes → Compute M_o/M_r = (Eq. 10b)

No

Compute

$M_o = M_o/M_r*M_r$
M_l = (Eq. 11)
V_l = (Eq. 12)
$M_T = M_o - (M_o - M_l)*V_f/V_l$

Test

$M_f \leq M_T$ — Yes → Compute and Print Results

V_f/V_l; V_f/V_r
$1-2H/d$; M_f
M_T; A_r

No

1

Stop

Tables

(a) *Unreinforced Holes*

Table 5-6, page 5-178 gives the values of constants C_1 and C_2 for unreinforced holes where

$$C_1 = \frac{M_o}{M_r} \quad \text{and} \quad C_2 = \frac{M_o/M_r - M_l/M_r}{V_l/V_r'}$$

where M_o, M_l and V_l are defined in [3] to [5].

Table 5-7, page 5-179, gives the value of constant C_3 taken as V_l/V_r'.

A_w/A_f varies from 0.5 to 2.25, $2H/d$ from 0.3 to 0.6, a/H from 0.50 to 2.2, and $e/d = 0$.

Written in terms of the constants C_1 and C_2, [2] becomes

$$\frac{M_f}{M_r} \le C_1 - C_2\left(\frac{V_f}{V_r'}\right) \tag{13}$$

and [1] becomes

$$\frac{V_f}{V_r'} \le C_3 \tag{14}$$

Use

For concentric ($e/d = 0$) unreinforced holes, compute A_w/A_f, $2H/d$ and a/H. Determine C_1, C_2 and C_3 with the aid of Tables 5-6 and 5-7 for use in [13] and [14].

(b) *Reinforced Holes*

Table 5-8, pages 5-180 to 5-182, gives the values of the constants C_4 and C_5 for reinforced holes where

$$C_4 = \frac{M_o}{M_r} \quad \text{and} \quad C_5 = \frac{M_o/M_r - M_l/M_r}{V_l/V_r'}$$

where M_o, M_l and V_l are defined in [10] to [12] for concentric holes ($e/d = 0$).

A_w/A_f varies from 0.5 to 2.25, $2H/d$ from 0.3 to 0.6, and a/H from 0.45 to 2.2, for the three values of A_r/A_f, 0.333, 0.667 and 1.0.

Written in terms of the constants C_4 and C_5, [9a] becomes

$$\frac{M_f}{M_r} \le C_4 - C_5\left(\frac{V_f}{V_r'}\right) \tag{15}$$

Use

For concentric ($e/d = 0$) reinforced holes, compute A_w/A_f, $2H/d$ and a/H. Determine C_4 and C_5, for one of the assumed values of A_r/A_f, for use in [15].

Calculate V_l from [12] for use in [8a].

Then check [8b] and [9b].

Example

Given:

A simple-span W610x101 beam spanning 12 m supports a factored total uniformly distributed load of 480 kN (40 kN/m). Check the adequacy of the section for two rectangular holes located as shown. Use F_y = 345 MPa (lowest value among G40.21-350W, ASTM A992 and A572 Grade 50). Lateral support to the compression flange is provided.

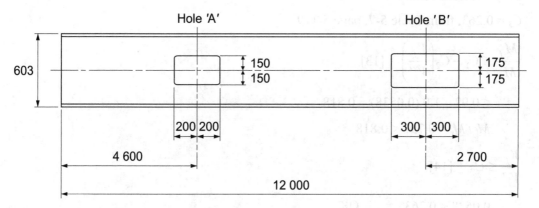

Solution for Hole 'A':

Class of beam: From page 5-7, W610x101 is a Class 1

From page 5-94, M_r = 900 kN·m

$V_r' = 0.8\,\phi\,A_w F_s = 0.8 \times 0.9 \times (603 \times 10.5) \times 0.66 \times 345 = 1040$ kN

At centreline of hole

$M_f = 40$ kN/m $\times 4.6$ m $\times (12 - 4.6)/2 = 681$ kN·m

$V_f = 40$ kN/m $\times ((12/2) - 4.6) = 56.0$ kN

$\dfrac{M_f}{M_r} = \dfrac{681}{900} = 0.757$ and $\dfrac{V_f}{V_r'} = \dfrac{56.0}{1\,040} = 0.0538$

Check web stability (refer to page 5-169)

$\dfrac{V_f}{V_r'} = 0.0538 < 0.67$

$a/H = 1.33 < 3.0$ (limit for Class 1 beam)

$a/H + 6\,(2\,H/d) = 200/150 + 6\,(300/603) = 1.33 + 6\,(0.498) = 4.32 < 5.6$

Check compression zone stability

OK, if $2a \le 4\,d_t = 4\,((603/2) - 150) = 606$ mm

$2a = 400$ mm < 606 mm

Check for unreinforced hole

$$\frac{A_w}{A_f} = \frac{10.5 \times 603}{228 \times 14.9} = 1.86 \quad \text{and} \quad \frac{2H}{d} = 0.50$$

$C_1 = 0.92$, from Table 5-6, page 5-178

For $a/H = 1.33$ Use 1.4

$C_2 = 1.9$, from Table 5-6

$C_3 = 0.263$, from Table 5-7, page 5-179

$$\frac{M_f}{M_r} \leq C_1 - C_2\left(\frac{V_f}{V_r'}\right) \quad [13]$$

$$\leq 0.92 - 1.9\,(0.0538) = 0.818$$

$$M_f / M_r = 0.757 < 0.818$$

$$\frac{V_f}{V_r'} \leq C_3 \quad [14]$$

$$0.0538 < 0.263 \quad\quad\quad \text{OK}$$

Therefore, reinforcement is not required.

Solution for Hole 'B'

At centreline of hole

$M_f = 40$ kN/m $\times$ 2.7 m $\times$ (12 − 2.7) / 2 = 502 kN·m

$V_f = 40$ kN/m $\times$ ((12 / 2) − 2.7) = 132 kN

$$\frac{M_f}{M_r} = \frac{502}{900} = 0.558 \quad \text{and} \quad \frac{V_f}{V_r'} = \frac{132}{1040} = 0.127$$

Check spacing between holes

Use $2H$ of larger hole.

OK, if $s \geq 2H = 350$

$$s = 12\,000 - (2\,700 + 4\,600) = 4\,700 \text{ mm} > 350 \text{ mm}$$

Check web stability (refer to page 5-169)

$$\frac{V_f}{V_r'} = 0.127 < 0.67$$

$a/H = 1.71 < 3.0$ (limit for Class 1 beam)

$a/H + 6\,(2H/d) = 300/175 + 6\,(350/603) = 1.71 + 6\,(0.580) = 5.19 < 5.6$

Check compression zone stability

OK, if $2a \leq 4\,d_t$ (unreinforced tee)

$$\leq 4\,((603\,/\,2) - 175) = 506 \text{ mm}$$

$2a = 600 \text{ mm} > 506$ (not adequate)

Check for unreinforced hole

From Table 5-6, page 5-178, for $A_w\,/\,A_f = 1.86$ (use 2.0)

and $2H\,/\,d = 0.58$ (use 0.60), $C_1 = 0.88$

For $a\,/\,H = 1.71$ (use 1.8), $C_2 = 3.83$

$$\frac{M_f}{M_r} \leq C_1 - C_2\!\left(\frac{V_f}{V_r{}'}\right) \quad [13]$$

$$\leq 0.88 - 3.83\,(0.127) = 0.394$$

$M_f\,/\,M_r = 0.558 > 0.394$ (reinforcement required)

Reinforcement

Assume $A_r\,/\,A_f = 0.333$ (maximum permitted for one-sided reinforcement)

From Table 5-8, page 5-180,

for $\dfrac{A_r}{A_f} = 0.333$, $\dfrac{A_w}{A_f} = 2.0$, $\dfrac{2H}{d} \approx 0.60$

$C_4 = 1.013$

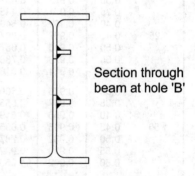

Section through beam at hole 'B'

For $a\,/\,H = 1.71$, $C_5 = 2.53$ (by interpolation)

$$\frac{M_f}{M_r} \leq C_4 - C_5\!\left(\frac{V_f}{V_r{}'}\right) \quad [15]$$

$$\leq 1.013 - 2.53\,(0.127) = 0.692$$

$M_f\,/\,M_r = 0.558 < 0.692$

Further refinement of $A_r\,/\,A_f$ can be accomplished by using the expressions previously given.

Check one-sided reinforcement

$M_f \leq 20\,V_f\,d$ at hole centreline (see page 5-171)

$$\leq 20 \times 132 \times 603 = 1\,590 \text{ kN·m}$$

$M_f = 502 \text{ kN·m} < 1\,590 \text{ kN·m}$

$a\,/\,H = 1.71 < 2.5$

For Unreinforced Concentric Holes in Beam Webs

$\dfrac{A_w}{A_f}$	$\dfrac{2H}{d}$	C_1	C_2 For following a/H values							
			0.50	1.0	1.2	1.4	1.6	1.8	2.0	2.2
0.50	0.30	0.990	0.204	0.271	0.300	0.330	0.360	0.391	0.423	0.455
	0.35	0.986	0.226	0.315	0.353	0.392	0.433	0.474	0.516	0.558
	0.40	0.982	0.252	0.367	0.417	0.468	0.520	0.574	0.628	0.682
	0.45	0.978	0.283	0.432	0.495	0.561	0.628	0.696	0.764	0.833
	0.50	0.972	0.321	0.511	0.593	0.676	0.761	0.846	0.933	1.020
	0.55	0.966	0.368	0.612	0.715	0.820	0.927	1.035	1.143	1.252
	0.60	0.960	0.428	0.740	0.872	1.005	1.140	1.275	1.411	*
0.75	0.30	0.986	0.290	0.385	0.426	0.468	0.512	0.556	0.601	0.647
	0.35	0.981	0.321	0.447	0.502	0.557	0.615	0.673	0.733	0.793
	0.40	0.975	0.358	0.522	0.593	0.665	0.740	0.815	0.892	0.970
	0.45	0.968	0.402	0.613	0.704	0.797	0.892	0.989	1.086	1.184
	0.50	0.961	0.456	0.726	0.842	0.961	1.081	1.203	1.325	1.449
	0.55	0.952	0.522	0.869	1.016	1.166	1.317	1.470	1.624	1.779
	0.60	0.943	0.608	1.052	1.239	1.428	1.619	1.812	2.005	*
1.00	0.30	0.982	0.367	0.488	0.540	0.593	0.648	0.705	0.762	0.820
	0.35	0.976	0.407	0.567	0.635	0.706	0.779	0.853	0.928	1.005
	0.40	0.968	0.454	0.661	0.751	0.843	0.937	1.033	1.130	1.228
	0.45	0.960	0.510	0.777	0.892	1.010	1.130	1.252	1.376	1.500
	0.50	0.950	0.577	0.920	1.067	1.217	1.369	1.523	1.679	1.835
	0.55	0.940	0.662	1.101	1.287	1.477	1.669	1.862	2.057	2.253
	0.60	0.928	0.770	1.333	1.569	1.809	2.051	2.295	2.539	*
1.25	0.30	0.979	0.437	0.581	0.643	0.706	0.772	0.839	0.907	0.976
	0.35	0.971	0.485	0.675	0.756	0.841	0.927	1.015	1.105	1.196
	0.40	0.962	0.540	0.787	0.894	1.003	1.115	1.229	1.345	1.462
	0.45	0.952	0.607	0.925	1.062	1.202	1.346	1.491	1.638	1.786
	0.50	0.940	0.687	1.095	1.270	1.449	1.630	1.813	1.999	2.185
	0.55	0.928	0.788	1.310	1.532	1.758	1.987	2.217	2.449	2.682
	0.60	0.914	0.916	1.587	1.868	2.154	2.442	2.732	3.023	*
1.50	0.30	0.975	0.500	0.666	0.736	0.809	0.884	0.961	1.039	1.118
	0.35	0.967	0.555	0.773	0.866	0.963	1.062	1.163	1.266	1.370
	0.40	0.956	0.619	0.902	1.024	1.149	1.278	1.408	1.541	1.675
	0.45	0.945	0.695	1.059	1.216	1.377	1.541	1.708	1.876	2.046
	0.50	0.932	0.787	1.255	1.455	1.659	1.867	2.077	2.289	2.502
	0.55	0.918	0.902	1.501	1.755	2.014	2.276	2.540	2.805	3.072
	0.60	0.902	1.050	1.817	2.140	2.467	2.797	3.129	3.463	*
1.75	0.30	0.973	0.558	0.743	0.822	0.903	0.987	1.072	1.159	1.248
	0.35	0.963	0.619	0.862	0.967	1.075	1.185	1.298	1.413	1.529
	0.40	0.951	0.691	1.006	1.142	1.282	1.426	1.572	1.719	1.869
	0.45	0.938	0.776	1.182	1.357	1.537	1.720	1.906	2.094	2.283
	0.50	0.924	0.879	1.400	1.624	1.852	2.084	2.318	2.555	2.793
	0.55	0.908	1.007	1.675	1.959	2.247	2.539	2.834	3.131	3.429
	0.60	0.890	1.171	2.028	2.388	2.753	3.122	3.492	3.864	*
2.00	0.30	0.970	0.611	0.813	0.900	0.989	1.081	1.174	1.270	1.366
	0.35	0.959	0.678	0.944	1.059	1.177	1.298	1.421	1.547	1.674
	0.40	0.947	0.757	1.102	1.251	1.405	1.561	1.721	1.883	2.047
	0.45	0.933	0.849	1.295	1.486	1.683	1.884	2.087	2.293	2.500
	0.50	0.917	0.962	1.534	1.778	2.028	2.282	2.539	2.798	3.059
	0.55	0.899	1.103	1.835	2.145	2.461	2.781	3.104	3.429	3.755
	0.60	0.880	1.283	2.221	2.616	3.016	3.419	3.825	4.232	*
2.25	0.30	0.968	0.660	0.878	0.972	1.068	1.167	1.268	1.371	1.476
	0.35	0.956	0.733	1.020	1.144	1.271	1.402	1.535	1.671	1.808
	0.40	0.942	0.817	1.190	1.351	1.517	1.686	1.859	2.034	2.211
	0.45	0.927	0.917	1.398	1.605	1.818	2.034	2.254	2.476	2.700
	0.50	0.910	1.039	1.656	1.920	2.190	2.465	2.742	3.022	3.303
	0.55	0.891	1.191	1.981	2.317	2.658	3.004	3.352	3.703	4.056
	0.60	0.870	1.386	2.399	2.825	3.257	3.692	4.131	4.571	*

* a/H plus 6 (2H/d) exceeds 5.6.

$$\frac{d_t}{w} = \frac{(603/2) - 175}{10.5} = 12.0 \le \frac{370}{\sqrt{F_y}} = 19.9$$

Therefore, one-sided reinforcement is adequate.

$$A_r = 0.33 \times A_f = 0.33\,(228 \times 14.9) = 1\,120 \text{ mm}^2$$

Check shear

$$V_l = \sqrt{3}\left(\frac{d}{a}\right)\left(\frac{A_r}{A_w}\right)\left(1 - \frac{2H}{d}\right)V_r{}' \quad [12]$$

$$= \sqrt{3}\left(\frac{603}{300}\right)\left(\frac{1120}{10.5 \times 603}\right)(1 - 0.58)\,1\,040 = 269$$

$$V_f \le V_l \quad [8a]$$

$$132 < 269$$

$$V_f / V_r{}' \le 1 - 2H/d \quad [8b]$$

$$\le 1 - 0.58 = 0.42$$

$$V_f / V_r{}' = 0.127 < 0.42$$

Try 16 × 70 reinforcement

$$\frac{b}{t} \le \frac{145}{\sqrt{F_y}} \quad \text{(for Class 1)}$$

$$\le 7.81$$

$$b / t = 70 / 16 = 4.38 < 7.81$$

Therefore, use 16 × 70 one-sided reinforcement.

VALUES OF C_3

Table 5-7

For Unreinforced Concentric Holes in Beam Webs

2H/d	a/H							
	0.5	1.0	1.2	1.4	1.6	1.8	2.0	2.2
.30	.680	.627	.602	.575	.549	.523	.498	.474
.35	.621	.552	.521	.490	.461	.433	.407	.384
.40	.560	.475	.441	.408	.378	.351	.327	.305
.45	.497	.400	.364	.332	.303	.279	.257	.238
.50	.433	.327	.293	.263	.238	.217	.199	.183
.55	.368	.260	.229	.203	.182	.165	.150	.138
.60	.302	.200	.173	.152	.136	.122	.111	.102

VALUES OF C_4 AND C_5

For Reinforced Concentric Holes in Beam Webs

Table 5-8

$A_r/A_f = 0.333$

$\frac{A_w}{A_f}$	$\frac{2H}{d}$	C_4	C_5 For following a/H values							
			0.45	1.0	1.2	1.4	1.6	1.8	2.0	2.2
0.50	0.30	1.079	0.041	0.090	0.108	0.126	0.144	0.162	0.181	0.199
	0.35	1.090	0.052	0.116	0.139	0.162	0.186	0.209	0.232	0.255
	0.40	1.101	0.066	0.147	0.176	0.205	0.235	0.264	0.293	0.323
	0.45	1.111	0.083	0.184	0.220	0.257	0.294	0.331	0.367	0.404
	0.50	1.120	0.103	0.229	0.274	0.320	0.366	0.411	0.457	0.503
	0.55	1.129	0.128	0.284	0.341	0.398	0.455	0.511	0.568	0.625
	0.60	1.138	0.159	0.354	0.425	0.496	0.567	0.637	0.708	*
0.75	0.30	1.070	0.064	0.142	0.170	0.198	0.227	0.255	0.283	0.312
	0.35	1.079	0.081	0.181	0.217	0.253	0.290	0.326	0.362	0.398
	0.40	1.087	0.102	0.228	0.273	0.319	0.364	0.410	0.455	0.501
	0.45	1.094	0.127	0.283	0.340	0.397	0.453	0.510	0.567	0.623
	0.50	1.101	0.158	0.350	0.421	0.491	0.561	0.631	0.701	0.771
	0.55	1.106	0.195	0.433	0.519	0.606	0.693	0.779	0.866	0.952
	0.60	1.111	0.241	0.536	0.643	0.751	0.858	0.965	1.072	*
1.00	0.30	1.062	0.088	0.196	0.236	0.275	0.314	0.353	0.393	0.432
	0.35	1.069	0.112	0.250	0.300	0.350	0.400	0.450	0.500	0.550
	0.40	1.075	0.141	0.313	0.375	0.438	0.500	0.563	0.625	0.688
	0.45	1.079	0.174	0.387	0.465	0.542	0.619	0.697	0.774	0.852
	0.50	1.083	0.214	0.476	0.572	0.667	0.762	0.858	0.953	1.048
	0.55	1.086	0.263	0.585	0.702	0.819	0.936	1.054	1.171	1.288
	0.60	1.088	0.324	0.721	0.865	1.009	1.153	1.297	1.441	*
1.25	0.30	1.055	0.114	0.254	0.305	0.355	0.406	0.457	0.508	0.558
	0.35	1.060	0.145	0.322	0.386	0.450	0.515	0.579	0.644	0.708
	0.40	1.063	0.180	0.401	0.481	0.562	0.642	0.722	0.802	0.882
	0.45	1.066	0.223	0.495	0.593	0.692	0.791	0.890	0.989	1.088
	0.50	1.067	0.273	0.606	0.727	0.848	0.969	1.091	1.212	1.333
	0.55	1.068	0.333	0.741	0.889	1.037	1.185	1.333	1.482	1.630
	0.60	1.067	0.408	0.908	1.089	1.271	1.452	1.634	1.815	*
1.50	0.30	1.048	0.141	0.314	0.377	0.439	0.502	0.565	0.628	0.690
	0.35	1.051	0.178	0.396	0.476	0.555	0.634	0.714	0.793	0.872
	0.40	1.053	0.222	0.493	0.591	0.690	0.788	0.887	0.985	1.084
	0.45	1.054	0.272	0.605	0.726	0.847	0.968	1.089	1.210	1.331
	0.50	1.053	0.332	0.738	0.886	1.034	1.181	1.329	1.477	1.624
	0.55	1.051	0.405	0.899	1.079	1.258	1.438	1.618	1.798	1.978
	0.60	1.047	0.493	1.096	1.316	1.535	1.754	1.973	2.193	*
1.75	0.30	1.042	0.169	0.376	0.451	0.526	0.601	0.677	0.752	0.827
	0.35	1.044	0.213	0.474	0.568	0.663	0.758	0.853	0.947	1.042
	0.40	1.044	0.264	0.587	0.704	0.821	0.938	1.056	1.173	1.290
	0.45	1.043	0.323	0.718	0.862	1.005	1.149	1.293	1.436	1.580
	0.50	1.040	0.393	0.873	1.048	1.223	1.397	1.572	1.747	1.922
	0.55	1.035	0.477	1.059	1.271	1.483	1.695	1.907	2.119	2.331
	0.60	1.029	0.579	1.287	1.544	1.801	2.059	2.316	2.573	*
2.00	0.30	1.037	0.198	0.440	0.528	0.616	0.704	0.792	0.880	0.968
	0.35	1.037	0.249	0.553	0.663	0.774	0.885	0.995	1.106	1.216
	0.40	1.035	0.307	0.683	0.819	0.956	1.093	1.229	1.366	1.502
	0.45	1.032	0.375	0.834	1.000	1.167	1.334	1.501	1.667	1.834
	0.50	1.028	0.455	1.011	1.213	1.415	1.617	1.819	2.022	2.224
	0.55	1.021	0.550	1.222	1.466	1.711	1.955	2.199	2.444	2.688
	0.60	1.013	0.665	1.479	1.774	2.070	2.366	2.661	2.957	*
2.25	0.30	1.032	0.227	0.505	0.607	0.708	0.809	0.910	1.011	1.112
	0.35	1.030	0.285	0.634	0.761	0.888	1.014	1.141	1.268	1.395
	0.40	1.028	0.352	0.781	0.937	1.094	1.250	1.406	1.562	1.719
	0.45	1.023	0.428	0.951	1.142	1.332	1.522	1.712	1.903	2.093
	0.50	1.017	0.518	1.150	1.380	1.610	1.840	2.070	2.300	2.530
	0.55	1.008	0.624	1.386	1.663	1.941	2.218	2.495	2.772	3.049
	0.60	0.998	0.752	1.672	2.006	2.340	2.675	3.009	3.344	*

* a/H plus 6 (2H/d) exceeds 5.6.

VALUES OF C_4 AND C_5

For Reinforced Concentric Holes in Beam Webs

Table 5-8

$A_r/A_f = 0.667$

$\dfrac{A_w}{A_f}$	$\dfrac{2H}{d}$	C_4	C_5 For following a/H values							
			0.45	1.0	1.2	1.4	1.6	1.8	2.0	2.2
0.50	0.30	1.168	0.036	0.081	0.097	0.113	0.129	0.146	0.162	0.178
	0.35	1.194	0.047	0.105	0.126	0.146	0.167	0.188	0.209	0.230
	0.40	1.219	0.060	0.133	0.160	0.186	0.213	0.240	0.266	0.293
	0.45	1.244	0.076	0.168	0.201	0.235	0.269	0.302	0.336	0.369
	0.50	1.269	0.095	0.210	0.253	0.295	0.337	0.379	0.421	0.463
	0.55	1.292	0.119	0.264	0.316	0.369	0.422	0.474	0.527	0.580
	0.60	1.316	0.149	0.331	0.397	0.463	0.530	0.596	0.662	*
0.75	0.30	1.154	0.055	0.122	0.146	0.170	0.195	0.219	0.243	0.267
	0.35	1.177	0.071	0.157	0.188	0.219	0.251	0.282	0.314	0.345
	0.40	1.199	0.089	0.199	0.239	0.278	0.318	0.358	0.398	0.438
	0.45	1.221	0.112	0.250	0.300	0.350	0.400	0.450	0.499	0.549
	0.50	1.241	0.140	0.312	0.374	0.437	0.499	0.561	0.624	0.686
	0.55	1.261	0.175	0.389	0.467	0.545	0.623	0.700	0.778	0.856
	0.60	1.280	0.219	0.487	0.584	0.681	0.779	0.876	0.974	*
1.00	0.30	1.142	0.073	0.162	0.195	0.227	0.260	0.292	0.325	0.357
	0.35	1.162	0.094	0.209	0.251	0.292	0.334	0.376	0.418	0.459
	0.40	1.181	0.119	0.264	0.317	0.370	0.422	0.475	0.528	0.581
	0.45	1.200	0.149	0.330	0.397	0.463	0.529	0.595	0.661	0.727
	0.50	1.217	0.185	0.411	0.494	0.576	0.658	0.740	0.823	0.905
	0.55	1.233	0.230	0.511	0.614	0.716	0.818	0.920	1.023	1.125
	0.60	1.248	0.287	0.637	0.765	0.892	1.020	1.147	1.275	*
1.25	0.30	1.131	0.092	0.203	0.244	0.285	0.325	0.366	0.407	0.448
	0.35	1.149	0.117	0.261	0.313	0.365	0.417	0.469	0.521	0.574
	0.40	1.165	0.148	0.329	0.394	0.460	0.526	0.592	0.657	0.723
	0.45	1.180	0.185	0.410	0.492	0.574	0.656	0.738	0.820	0.902
	0.50	1.195	0.229	0.509	0.611	0.713	0.814	0.916	1.018	1.120
	0.55	1.207	0.284	0.631	0.757	0.883	1.009	1.135	1.261	1.387
	0.60	1.219	0.353	0.783	0.940	1.097	1.254	1.410	1.567	*
1.50	0.30	1.121	0.110	0.245	0.293	0.342	0.391	0.440	0.489	0.538
	0.35	1.136	0.141	0.313	0.375	0.438	0.500	0.563	0.625	0.688
	0.40	1.150	0.177	0.393	0.472	0.550	0.629	0.708	0.786	0.865
	0.45	1.163	0.220	0.489	0.587	0.685	0.783	0.880	0.978	1.076
	0.50	1.174	0.272	0.605	0.726	0.847	0.968	1.089	1.210	1.331
	0.55	1.184	0.336	0.748	0.897	1.047	1.196	1.346	1.495	1.645
	0.60	1.193	0.417	0.926	1.111	1.296	1.481	1.666	1.852	*
1.75	0.30	1.112	0.129	0.286	0.343	0.400	0.457	0.514	0.571	0.629
	0.35	1.125	0.164	0.364	0.437	0.510	0.583	0.656	0.729	0.802
	0.40	1.137	0.206	0.457	0.549	0.640	0.731	0.823	0.914	1.006
	0.45	1.147	0.255	0.567	0.681	0.794	0.908	1.021	1.135	1.248
	0.50	1.156	0.315	0.700	0.840	0.980	1.120	1.260	1.400	1.540
	0.55	1.163	0.388	0.862	1.035	1.207	1.380	1.552	1.725	1.897
	0.60	1.169	0.479	1.065	1.278	1.491	1.704	1.917	2.129	*
2.00	0.30	1.103	0.147	0.327	0.392	0.458	0.523	0.589	0.654	0.719
	0.35	1.115	0.187	0.416	0.499	0.583	0.666	0.749	0.832	0.915
	0.40	1.125	0.234	0.521	0.625	0.729	0.833	0.937	1.042	1.146
	0.45	1.133	0.290	0.645	0.774	0.903	1.032	1.161	1.290	1.419
	0.50	1.139	0.357	0.794	0.952	1.111	1.270	1.429	1.587	1.746
	0.55	1.144	0.439	0.975	1.170	1.365	1.560	1.755	1.950	2.145
	0.60	1.147	0.540	1.201	1.441	1.681	1.921	2.161	2.402	*
2.25	0.30	1.096	0.166	0.368	0.442	0.516	0.589	0.663	0.737	0.810
	0.35	1.105	0.211	0.468	0.561	0.655	0.749	0.842	0.936	1.029
	0.40	1.113	0.263	0.584	0.701	0.818	0.935	1.052	1.169	1.285
	0.45	1.119	0.325	0.722	0.866	1.011	1.155	1.299	1.444	1.588
	0.50	1.123	0.399	0.886	1.064	1.241	1.418	1.596	1.773	1.950
	0.55	1.126	0.489	1.086	1.304	1.521	1.738	1.955	2.173	2.390
	0.60	1.127	0.600	1.334	1.601	1.868	2.135	2.402	2.668	*

* a/H plus 6 (2H/d) exceeds 5.6.

VALUES OF C_4 AND C_5

For Reinforced Concentric Holes in Beam Webs

Table 5-8

$A_r/A_f = 1.00$

$\dfrac{A_w}{A_f}$	$\dfrac{2H}{d}$	C_4	C_5 For following a/H values							
			0.45	1.0	1.2	1.4	1.6	1.8	2.0	2.2
0.50	0.30	1.257	0.035	0.078	0.093	0.109	0.124	0.140	0.155	0.171
	0.35	1.298	0.045	0.101	0.121	0.141	0.161	0.182	0.202	0.222
	0.40	1.338	0.058	0.129	0.154	0.180	0.206	0.232	0.257	0.283
	0.45	1.378	0.073	0.163	0.195	0.228	0.260	0.293	0.325	0.358
	0.50	1.417	0.092	0.204	0.245	0.286	0.327	0.368	0.409	0.450
	0.55	1.455	0.116	0.257	0.308	0.359	0.411	0.462	0.513	0.565
	0.60	1.493	0.145	0.323	0.388	0.453	0.517	0.582	0.647	*
0.75	0.30	1.238	0.052	0.115	0.138	0.161	0.184	0.207	0.230	0.253
	0.35	1.275	0.067	0.149	0.178	0.208	0.238	0.268	0.297	0.327
	0.40	1.312	0.085	0.189	0.227	0.265	0.303	0.341	0.379	0.416
	0.45	1.347	0.107	0.239	0.286	0.334	0.382	0.429	0.477	0.525
	0.50	1.382	0.135	0.299	0.359	0.419	0.479	0.538	0.598	0.658
	0.55	1.415	0.169	0.375	0.449	0.524	0.599	0.674	0.749	0.824
	0.60	1.448	0.212	0.470	0.564	0.659	0.753	0.847	0.941	*
1.00	0.30	1.222	0.068	0.151	0.181	0.212	0.242	0.272	0.302	0.333
	0.35	1.256	0.088	0.195	0.234	0.273	0.312	0.351	0.390	0.429
	0.40	1.288	0.112	0.248	0.297	0.347	0.397	0.446	0.496	0.545
	0.45	1.320	0.140	0.312	0.374	0.436	0.499	0.561	0.623	0.686
	0.50	1.350	0.175	0.390	0.468	0.546	0.624	0.701	0.779	0.857
	0.55	1.380	0.219	0.487	0.584	0.681	0.779	0.876	0.973	1.071
	0.60	1.408	0.274	0.610	0.732	0.854	0.975	1.097	1.219	*
1.25	0.30	1.207	0.084	0.187	0.224	0.261	0.299	0.336	0.373	0.411
	0.35	1.238	0.108	0.240	0.289	0.337	0.385	0.433	0.481	0.529
	0.40	1.267	0.137	0.305	0.366	0.427	0.488	0.548	0.609	0.670
	0.45	1.295	0.172	0.382	0.459	0.535	0.612	0.688	0.764	0.841
	0.50	1.321	0.215	0.477	0.572	0.668	0.763	0.858	0.954	1.049
	0.55	1.347	0.267	0.594	0.713	0.832	0.951	1.069	1.188	1.307
	0.60	1.371	0.334	0.742	0.891	1.039	1.188	1.336	1.485	*
1.50	0.30	1.194	0.100	0.222	0.266	0.310	0.354	0.399	0.443	0.487
	0.35	1.221	0.128	0.285	0.342	0.399	0.456	0.512	0.569	0.626
	0.40	1.247	0.162	0.360	0.432	0.504	0.576	0.648	0.720	0.792
	0.45	1.272	0.203	0.451	0.541	0.631	0.721	0.811	0.901	0.991
	0.50	1.295	0.252	0.561	0.673	0.785	0.898	1.010	1.122	1.234
	0.55	1.318	0.314	0.697	0.837	0.976	1.116	1.255	1.395	1.534
	0.60	1.338	0.391	0.869	1.043	1.217	1.391	1.565	1.738	*
1.75	0.30	1.181	0.115	0.256	0.307	0.358	0.409	0.460	0.512	0.563
	0.35	1.206	0.148	0.328	0.394	0.459	0.525	0.591	0.656	0.722
	0.40	1.230	0.186	0.414	0.497	0.580	0.663	0.745	0.828	0.911
	0.45	1.251	0.233	0.517	0.621	0.724	0.828	0.931	1.034	1.138
	0.50	1.272	0.289	0.642	0.771	0.899	1.028	1.156	1.285	1.413
	0.55	1.291	0.359	0.797	0.956	1.116	1.275	1.434	1.594	1.753
	0.60	1.308	0.446	0.991	1.189	1.387	1.586	1.784	1.982	*
2.00	0.30	1.170	0.130	0.289	0.347	0.405	0.463	0.521	0.579	0.637
	0.35	1.193	0.167	0.371	0.445	0.519	0.593	0.667	0.741	0.816
	0.40	1.213	0.210	0.467	0.560	0.654	0.747	0.841	0.934	1.027
	0.45	1.233	0.262	0.582	0.699	0.815	0.932	1.048	1.164	1.281
	0.50	1.250	0.325	0.722	0.866	1.010	1.155	1.299	1.443	1.588
	0.55	1.266	0.402	0.893	1.072	1.251	1.429	1.608	1.786	1.965
	0.60	1.280	0.499	1.109	1.330	1.552	1.774	1.995	2.217	*
2.25	0.30	1.160	0.145	0.323	0.387	0.452	0.516	0.581	0.646	0.710
	0.35	1.180	0.186	0.413	0.495	0.578	0.660	0.743	0.825	0.908
	0.40	1.198	0.234	0.519	0.623	0.726	0.830	0.934	1.038	1.142
	0.45	1.215	0.291	0.646	0.775	0.904	1.033	1.162	1.291	1.421
	0.50	1.230	0.360	0.799	0.959	1.118	1.278	1.438	1.598	1.758
	0.55	1.243	0.444	0.987	1.184	1.382	1.579	1.776	1.974	2.171
	0.60	1.254	0.550	1.222	1.467	1.711	1.955	2.200	2.444	*

* a/H plus 6(2H/d) exceeds 5.6.

PART SIX
PROPERTIES AND DIMENSIONS

STRUCTURAL STEELS

General

Canadian structural steels are covered by two standards prepared by the Canadian Standards Association Technical Committee on Structural Steel, G40. These are CSA G40.20 and CSA G40.21. The information provided in this section is based on the current 2004 editions of both standards, and on the SI metric values, in keeping with Canadian design standards for steel structures.

CSA G40.20, "General Requirements for Rolled or Welded Structural Quality Steel" sets out the general requirements governing the delivery of structural quality steels. These requirements include: Definitions, Chemical Composition, Variations in Dimensions, Methods of Testing, Frequency of Testing, Heat Treatment, Repairs of Defects, Marking, etc.

CSA G40.21, "Structural Quality Steel" governs the chemical and mechanical properties of 7 types and 8 strength levels of structural steels for general construction and engineering purposes. All strength levels are not available in all types, and selection of the proper grade (type and strength level) is important for a particular application. CSA G40.21 350A and CSA G40.21 350AT are atmospheric corrosion-resistant steels normally used in bridge construction. For HSS sections, 350W is the normal grade used when produced to CSA G40.21.

The 7 types covered in CSA G40.21 are:

(a) **Type W – Weldable Steel.** Steels of this type meet specified strength requirements and are suitable for general welded construction where notch toughness at low temperatures is not a design requirement. Applications include buildings, compression members of bridges, etc.

(b) **Type WT – Weldable Notch-Tough Steel.** Steels of this type meet specified strength and Charpy V-notch impact requirements and are suitable for welded construction where notch toughness at low temperature is a design requirement. The purchaser, in addition to specifying the grade, specifies the required category of steel that establishes the Charpy V-notch test temperature and energy level. Applications include primary tension members in bridges and similar elements.

(c) **Type R – Atmospheric Corrosion-Resistant Steel.** Steels of this type meet specified strength requirements. The atmospheric corrosion resistance of these steels in most environments is substantially better than that of carbon structural steels with or without a copper addition*. These steels are welded readily up to the maximum thickness covered by the G40.21 standard. Applications include unpainted siding, unpainted light structural members, etc., where notch toughness at low temperature is not a design requirement.

(d) **Type A – Atmospheric Corrosion-Resistant Weldable Steel.** Steels of this type meet specified strength requirements. The atmospheric corrosion resistance of these steels in most environments is substantially better than that of carbon structural steels with or without a copper addition*. These steels are suitable for welded construction where notch toughness at low temperature is not a design requirement. Applications include those similar to type W steel.

(e) **Type AT – Atmospheric Corrosion-Resistant Weldable Notch-Tough Steel.** Steels of this type meet specified strength and Charpy V-notch impact requirements. The atmospheric corrosion resistance of these steels in most environments is substantially better than that of carbon structural steels with or without a copper addition*. These steels are suitable for welded construction where notch toughness at low temperature is a design requirement. The purchaser, in addition to specifying the grade, specifies the required category of steel that establishes the Charpy V-notch test temperature and energy level. Applications include primary tension members in bridges and similar elements.

(f) **Type Q – Quenched and Tempered Low-Alloy Steel Plate.** Steels of this type meet specified strength requirements. While these steels are weldable, the welding and fabrication techniques are of fundamental importance to the properties of the plate, especially the heat-affected zone. Applications include bridges and similar structures.

(g) **Type QT – Quenched and Tempered Low-Alloy Notch-Tough Steel Plate.** Steels of this type meet specified strength and Charpy V-Notch impact requirements. They provide good resistance to brittle fracture and are suitable for structures where notch toughness at low temperature is a design requirement. The purchaser, in addition to specifying the grade, specifies the required category of steel that establishes the Charpy V-notch test temperature and energy level. While these steels are weldable, the welding and fabrication techniques are of fundamental importance to the properties of the plate, especially the heat-affected zone. Applications include primary tension members in bridges and similar elements.

* For methods of estimating the atmospheric corrosion resistance of low-alloy steels, see CSA G40.21 Clause 7.6. When properly exposed to the atmosphere, these steels can be used bare (unpainted) for many applications.

Tables

Table 6-1, "Grades, Types, Strength Levels", gives the grade designation of the various types and strength levels of structural steels according to the requirements of CSA G40.21.

Availability of any grade and shape combination should be kept in mind when designing to ensure overall economy, since a specified product may not always be available in the tonnage and time frame contemplated. Local availability should always be checked.

Table 6-2, "Shape Size Groupings for Tensile Property Classification", summarizes the size groupings for SLB, C, MC and L shapes. Table 6-3, "Mechanical Properties Summary", provides a summary of the various grades, tensile strengths and yield strengths for plates, bars, welded shapes, rolled shapes, sheet piling, and hollow structural sections based on CSA G40.21.

Table 6-4, "Chemical Composition", summarizes the chemical requirements of various grades of steel covered by CSA G40.21.

The particular standards, CSA G40.20 and CSA G40.21, should be consulted for more details. Similar information about steel covered by ASTM standards should be consulted when appropriate.

Historical Remarks

When confronted with an unidentified structural steel, Clause 5.2.2 of CSA S16-09 requires that F_y be taken as 210 MPa and F_u as 380 MPa. This provides a minimum in the place of more precise information, such as coupon testing. The following tables list selected dates of publication and data from various CSA and ASTM structural steel standards and specifications, many of which preceded current standards.

For more information on ASTM specifications and properties and dimensions of iron and steel beams previously produced in the U.S.A., consult the "AISC Rehabilitation and Retrofit Guide: A Reference for Historic Shapes and Specifications" published by the American Institute of Steel Construction. In that publication, the first date listed for both ASTM A7 and A9 is the year 1900. Between 1900 and 1909, medium steel in A7 and A9 had a tensile strength 5 ksi higher than that adopted in 1914. For CSA standards, consult original documents.

Historical Listing of Selected Structural Steels

CSA Standards

Designation	Date Published	Yield Strength		Tensile Strength (F$_u$)	
		ksi	MPa	ksi	MPa
A16	1924	½ F$_u$	½ F$_u$	55-65	380-450
S39	1935	30	210	55-65	380-450
S40	1935	33	230	60-72	410-500
G40.4	1950	33	230	60-72	410-500
G40.5	1950	33	230	60-72	410-500
G40.6	1950	45[1]	310	80-95	550-650
G40.8	1960	40[3]	280	65-85	450-590
G40.12	1964*	44[2]	300	65	450
G40.21	1973**	Replaced all previous Standards, see CISC Handbook			

* Introduced in May 1962 by the Algoma Steel Corporation as 'Algoma 44'
** In May 1997, grade 350W became the only grade for W and HP shapes produced by Algoma Steel Inc.
[1] Silicon steel
[2] Yield reduces when thickness exceeds 1½ inches (40 mm).
[3] Yield reduces when thickness exceeds ⅝ inches (16 mm).

Rivet Steel

Designation	Date Published	Yield Strength		Tensile Strength (F$_u$)	
		ksi	MPa	ksi	MPa
G40.2	1950	28	190	52 - 62	360 - 430

ASTM Specifications

Designation	Date Published	Yield Strength		Tensile Strength (F$_u$)	
		ksi	MPa	ksi	MPa
A7 (bridges) A9 (buildings)	1914*	½ F$_u$	½ F$_u$	55-65	380-450
	1924	½ F$_u$ ≥ 30	½ F$_u$ ≥ 210	55-65	380-450
	1934	½ F$_u$ ≥ 33	½ F$_u$ ≥ 230	60-72	410-500
A373	1954	32	220	58-75	400-520
A242	1955	50[1]	350	70[1]	480
A36	1960	36	250	60-80	410-550
A440	1959	50[1]	350	70[1]	480
A441	1960	50[1]	350	70[1]	480
A572 grade 50	1966	50	345	65	450
A588	1968	50[1]	345	70[1]	485
A992	1998	50 min. to 65 max.	345 min. to 450 max.	65	450

* See text, Historical Remarks, above.   [1] Reduces with increasing thickness

GRADES, TYPES, STRENGTH LEVELS*   Table 6-1

Type	Yield Strength, MPa							
	260	300	350	380	400	480	550	700
W	260W	300W	350W	380W**	400W	480W	550W	—
WT	260WT	300WT	350WT	380WT***	400WT	480WT	550WT	—
R	—	—	350R	—	—	—	—	—
A	—	—	350A	—	400A	480A	550A	—
AT	—	—	350AT	—	400AT	480AT	550AT	—
Q	—	—	—	—	—	—	—	700Q
QT	—	—	—	—	—	—	—	700QT

* See CSA-G40.20/G40.21

** This grade is available in Hollow Structural Sections, angles and bars only.

*** This grade is available in Hollow Structural Sections only.

SHAPE SIZE GROUPINGS FOR TENSILE PROPERTY CLASSIFICATION*   Table 6-2

Shape Type	Group 1	Group 2	Group 3
Super-Light Beams (SLB)	To 28.1 kg/m	—	—
C Shapes	To 30.8 kg/m	Over 30.8 kg/m	—
MC Shapes	To 42.4 kg/m	Over 42.4 kg/m	—
L Shapes	To 13 mm	Over 13 to 19 mm	Over 19 mm

* See CSA-G40.20/G40.21

Table 6-3 — MECHANICAL PROPERTIES SUMMARY

CSA G40.21* Type	Grade	Tensile Strength F_u (MPa)	Plates, Floor Plates, Bars, Sheet and Welded Shapes F_y (MPa) min. Thickness *t ≤ 65 mm	Plates, Floor Plates, Bars, Sheet and Welded Shapes F_y (MPa) min. Thickness[4] t > 65 mm	Rolled Shapes and Sheet Piling Common Available Shape Size Group	Rolled Shapes and Sheet Piling F_y (MPa) min. Groups 1 to 3	Hollow Structural Sections F_y (MPa) min.
W	260W	410-590	260	250	3	260	
	300W	450-620[1]	300	280	3	300	300
	350W	450-650[2]	350	320	2	350	350
	380W	480-650	380		2[3]	380	380
	400W	520-690	400		1	400	400
	480W	590-790	480		1	480	480
	550W	620-860	550				550
WT	260WT	410-590	260	250	3	260	
	300WT	450-620	300	280	3	300	
	350WT	480-650[2]	350	320	3	350	350
	380WT	480-650					380
	400WT	520-690	400		2	400	400
	480WT	590-790	480		1	480	480
	550WT	620-860	550				550
R	350R	480-650	350		1	350	
A	350A	480-650	350	350	3	350	350
	400A	520-690	400		2	400	400
	480A	590-790	480				480
	550A	620-860	550				550
AT	350AT	480-650	350	350	3	350	350
	400AT	520-690	400		2	400	400
	480AT	590-790	480				480
	550AT	620-860	550				550
Q	700Q	760-895	700	620			
QT	700QT	760-895	700	620			

[1] 410-590 MPa for HSS
[2] 450-620 MPa for HSS
[3] For angles only
[4] For thickness t > 100 mm, see CSA G40.21
* See CSA G40.20/G40.21

CHEMICAL COMPOSITION[1]

Table 6-4

CSA G40.21 Grade	Chemical Composition (Heat Analysis) Percent[2] All percentages are maxima unless otherwise indicated.								
	C	Mn[3]	P	S	Si[4,5]	Other[6]	Cr	Ni	Cu[7]
260W	0.20[10]	0.50-1.50	0.04	0.05	0.40	0.10	—	—	—
300W[8]	0.22[10]	0.50-1.50	0.04	0.05	0.40	0.10	—	—	—
350W	0.23	0.50-1.50	0.04	0.05	0.40	0.10	—	—	—
380W[9]	0.23	0.50-1.50	0.04	0.05	0.40	0.10	—	—	—
400W	0.23[11]	0.50-1.50	0.04	0.05	0.40	0.10	—	—	—
480W	0.26[11]	0.50-1.50	0.04	0.05	0.40	0.10[15]	—	—	—
550W	0.15	1.75[12]	0.04	0.05	0.40	0.15	—	—	—
260WT	0.20[10]	0.80-1.50	0.03	0.04	0.15-0.40	0.10	—	—	—
300WT	0.22[10]	0.80-1.50	0.03	0.04	0.15-0.40	0.10	—	—	—
350WT	0.22[10]	0.80-1.50[12]	0.03	0.04	0.15-0.40	0.10[16]	—	—	—
380WT[9]	0.22	0.80-1.50	0.03	0.04	0.15-0.40	0.10	—	—	—
400WT	0.22[11]	0.80-1.50[12]	0.03	0.04[14]	0.15-0.40	0.10[16]	—	—	—
480WT	0.26[11]	0.80-1.50[12]	0.03	0.04[14]	0.15-0.40	0.10[15,16]	—	—	—
550WT	0.15	1.75[12]	0.03	0.04[14]	0.15-0.40	0.15	—	—	—
350R	0.16	0.75	0.05-0.15	0.04	0.75	0.10	0.30-1.25[17]	0.90[17]	0.20-0.60[17]
350A	0.20	0.75-1.35[12]	0.03	0.04	0.15-0.50	0.10	0.70[18]	0.90[18]	0.20-0.60
400A	0.20	0.75-1.35[12]	0.03	0.04[14]	0.15-0.50	0.10	0.70[18]	0.90[18]	0.20-0.60
480A	0.20	1.00-1.60	0.025[13]	0.035[14]	0.15-0.50	0.12	0.70[18]	0.25-0.50[18]	0.20-0.60
550A	0.15	1.75[12]	0.025[13]	0.035[14]	0.15-0.50	0.15	0.70[18]	0.25-0.50[18]	0.20-0.60
350AT	0.20	0.75-1.35[12]	0.03	0.04	0.15-0.50	0.10	0.70[18]	0.90[18]	0.20-0.60
400AT	0.20	0.75-1.35[12]	0.03	0.04[14]	0.15-0.50	0.10	0.70[18]	0.90[18]	0.20-0.60
480AT	0.20	1.00-1.60	0.025[13]	0.035[14]	0.15-0.50	0.12	0.70[18]	0.25-0.50[18]	0.20-0.60
550AT	0.15	1.75[12]	0.025[13]	0.035[14]	0.15-0.50	0.15	0.70[18]	0.25-0.50[18]	0.20-0.60
700Q	0.20	1.50	0.03	0.04	0.15-0.40	—	Boron 0.0005-0.005		—
700QT	0.20	1.50	0.03	0.04	0.15-0.40	—	Boron 0.0005-0.005		—

Notes:

1. For full details, consult CSA Standard G40.20/G40.21. Usual deoxidation for all grades is fully killed.
2. Additional alloying elements may be used when approved.
3. For HSS Mn 0.50 - 1.50% for 350WT and 380WT, 1.65% for 400 yield, 1.75% for 480 yield and 1.85% for 550 yield steels. For HSS mininum limit for Mn shall be 0.30% provided that the ratio of Mn to C is not less than 2 to 1 and the ratio of Mn to S is not less than 20 to 1.
4. Si content of 0.15% to 0.40% is required for type W steel over 40 mm thickness, HSS of A or AT steel, or bar diameter except as required by Note 5.
5. By purchaser's request or producer's option, no minimum Si content is required provided that 0.015% acid-soluble Al or 0.02% total Al is used.
6. Includes grain-refining elements Cb, V, Al. Elements Cb and V may be used singly or in combination. See G40.20/G40.21 for qualifications. Al, when used, is not included in the summation.
7. Copper content of 0.20% minimum may be specified.
8. For HSS 0.26% C and 0.30-1.20% Mn.
9. Only angles, bars, and HSS in 380W grade, and only HSS in 380WT grade.
10. For thicknesses over 100 mm, C may be 0.22% for 260W and 260WT grades, and 0.23% for 300W, 300WT and 350WT grades.
11. For HSS 0.20% C.
12. Mn may be increased. See G40.20/G40.21 for qualifications.
13. For HSS 0.03% P.
14. For HSS 0.03% S.
15. For HSS 0.12%
16. 0.01-0.02% N may be used but N ≤ ¼ V.
17. Cr + Ni + Cu ≥ 1.00%
18. Cr + Ni ≥ 0.40% and for HSS, 0.90% Ni max.

Table 6-5   STEEL MARKING COLOUR CODE

Steel Grade	Primary Colour	Secondary Colour
260W	White	Green
300W	Green	Green
350W	Blue	Green
380W	Brown	Green
400W	Black	Green
480W	Yellow	Green
550W	Pink	Green
260WT	White	White
300WT	Green	White
350WT	Blue	White
380WT	Brown	White
400WT	Black	White
480WT	Yellow	White
550WT	Pink	White
350R	Blue	Blue
350A	Blue	Yellow
400A	Black	Yellow
480A	Yellow	Yellow
550A	Pink	Yellow
350AT	Blue	Brown
400AT	Black	Brown
480AT	Yellow	Brown
550AT	Pink	Brown
700Q	Red	Red
700QT	Red	Purple

In this Code, the following colour system applies:

Strength Level	Primary Colour	Type	Secondary Colour
260	White	W	Green
300	Green	WT	White
350	Blue	R	Blue
380	Brown	A	Yellow
400	Black	AT	Brown
480	Yellow	Q	Red
550	Pink	QT	Purple
700	Red		

STANDARD IMPACT ENERGY AND TEST TEMPERATURE FOR SPECIFIED TYPE, GRADE AND CATEGORY

Type	Grade	Category				
		1	2	3	4	5
WT	260, 300	20 J, 0° C	20 J, -20° C	20 J, -30° C	20 J, -45° C	Both energy and test temperature are specified by the purchaser.
	350, 380, 400, 480, 550	27 J, 0° C	27 J, -20° C	27 J, -30° C	27 J, -45° C	
AT	350, 400, 480, 550	27 J, 0° C	27 J, -20° C	27 J, -30° C	27 J, -45° C	
QT	700	34 J, 0° C	34 J, -20° C	34 J, -30° C	34 J, -45° C	

Units: Impact energy in Joules (1 J ≈ 0.738 ft·lb) and test temperature in degrees Celsius.

Notes: Charpy V-Notch, longitudinal specimens. See CSA G40.21-04 Clause 8.2.2.

See CSA S16-09 Annex L "Design to Prevent Brittle Fracture" for information on test and service temperatures.

STANDARD MILL PRACTICE

General

Rolled structural shapes are produced by passing hot blooms, billets or slabs of steel through a series of grooved rolls. Wear on the rolls can cause the dimensions of the finished product to vary slightly from the theoretical, published dimensions. Standard rolling tolerances have been established to make allowance for roll wear and other factors. These tolerances are contained in CSA G40.20 for shapes supplied according to CSA material standards, and in ASTM Standard A6 for shapes supplied according to ASTM material standards.

Letter symbols for dimensions on sketches shown in this section are in accordance with CSA G40.20, ASTM A6, and mill catalogs.

Methods of increasing area and mass by spreading rolls

Most nominal size groups of rolled shapes contain several specific shapes, each of which is slightly different in mass, area and properties from other shapes in the same size group. Methods used to increase the area and mass, from the minimum nominal size, by spreading the rolls are described below:

For W Shapes (Fig. 1), the thickness of both flange and web is increased, resulting in an increase to the overall beam depth and flange width, with the distance between inside faces of flanges being unchanged.

For S Shapes and Channels (Fig. 2 and 3), the web thickness and flange width are increased by equal amounts, all other dimensions remaining unchanged.

For angles (Fig. 4) the thickness of each leg is increased an equal amount, resulting in a corresponding increase in leg length.

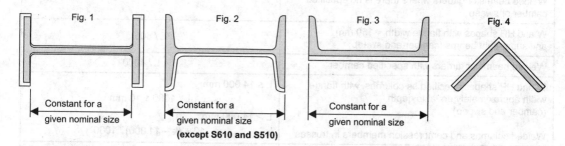

Fig. 1 — Constant for a given nominal size

Fig. 2 — Constant for a given nominal size (except S610 and S510)

Fig. 3 — Constant for a given nominal size

Fig. 4

Tolerances

Tolerances are the permissible variations in the mass, cross-sectional area, length, depth, flange width, camber, sweep and other geometric properties of a rolled or welded section. A summary of the basic manufacturing tolerances, taken from CSA G40.20, are provided in the following tables. While these tables are provided for convenience, the actual Standard should be referred to for complete information.

Camber and Sweep

After a section is rolled, it is cold-straightened to meet the specified sweep and camber tolerances.

Camber is a deflection, approximating a simple regular curve, measured along the depth of a section. It is usually measured halfway between two specified points. The length for purposes of determining the "maximum permissible variation" is the distance between the two specified points.

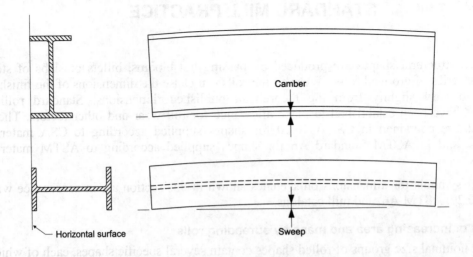

Camber

Horizontal surface

Sweep

Positions for measuring camber and sweep

Sweep is a deflection, similar to camber, measured along the width of the section.

The following table lists Permissible Variations in Straightness.

PERMISSIBLE VARIATIONS IN STRAIGHTNESS

Shape	Maximum Permissible Variation in Straightness, mm
W and HP shapes with flange width ≥ 150 mm [1] (camber and sweep) Welded beams or girders where there is no specified camber or sweep	L / 1000
W and HP shapes with flange width < 150 mm [1] and super-light beams (camber and sweep)	L / 500
Welded beams or girders with specified camber	6 + L / 4000
W and HP shapes specified as columns, with flange width approximately equal to depth [1, 2] (camber and sweep) Welded columns and compression members in trusses	L ≤ 14 000 mm: L / 1000 ≤ 10 mm L > 14 000 mm: 10 + (L − 14 000) / 1000
S, M, C, MC, L, T shapes [1] (greatest cross-sectional dimension ≥ 75 mm)	Camber: L / 500 Sweep: Negotiable
Bars [1, 3]	L / 250 [4]
S, M, C, MC, L, T bar-size shapes [1] (greatest cross-sectional dimension < 75 mm)	Camber: L / 250 Sweep: Negotiable

Notes:

[1] See ASTM A6 / A6M

[2] Applies only to: 200 mm-deep sections − 46 kg/m and heavier, 250 mm-deep sections − 73 kg/m and heavier, 310 mm-deep sections − 97 kg/m and heavier, and 360 mm-deep sections − 116 kg/m and heavier. For other sections specified as columns, tolerances are negotiable.

[3] Permitted variations do not apply to hot-rolled bars if any subsequent heating operation has been performed.

[4] Round to the nearest whole millimetre.

Sectional Dimensions

The permissible variations in sectional dimensions for welded shapes and rolled shapes are given in the following tables.

PERMISSIBLE VARIATIONS IN SECTIONAL DIMENSIONS OF WELDED STRUCTURAL SHAPES

Nominal Depth, mm	Depth, A, mm		Width of flange, B, mm		Combined warpage and tilt,* mm	Web off-centre, E, mm	Web flatness **	Diagram
	Over	Under	Over	Under	Maximum	Maximum	Maximum	
900 and under	5	3	6	5	Greater of B / 100 or 6	6	A / 150	
Over 900 to 2000 incl.	5	5	6	5		6	A / 150	

* The combined warpage and tilt of the flange is measured from the toe of the flange to a line normal to the plane of the web through the intersection of the centreline of the web with the outside surface of the flange plate.

** The deviation from flatness of the web is measured in any length of the web equal to the total depth of the beam.

PERMISSIBLE VARIATIONS IN SECTIONAL DIMENSIONS OF W AND HP SHAPES

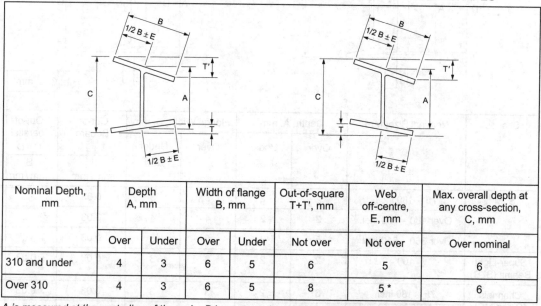

Nominal Depth, mm	Depth A, mm		Width of flange B, mm		Out-of-square T+T', mm	Web off-centre, E, mm	Max. overall depth at any cross-section, C, mm
	Over	Under	Over	Under	Not over	Not over	Over nominal
310 and under	4	3	6	5	6	5	6
Over 310	4	3	6	5	8	5 *	6

A is measured at the centreline of the web. B is measured parallel to the flange. C is measured parallel to the web.
* Web off-centre tolerance is 8 mm for sections over 634 kg/m. See ASTM A6 / A6M.

PERMISSIBLE VARIATIONS IN LENGTH FOR W AND HP SHAPES

Nominal Depth, mm	Variations from Specified Length for Lengths Given, mm			
	9000 and under		Over 9000	
	Over	Under	Over	Under
Beams 610 mm and under	10	10	10 plus 1 for each additional 1000 mm or fraction thereof	10
Beams over 610 mm and all columns	13	13	13 plus 1 for each additional 1000 mm or fraction thereof	13

Notes: For W and HP shapes used as bearing piles, the length tolerance is +125 mm, -0 mm.
The permitted variations in end out-of-square for W and HP shapes shall be 0.016 mm per mm of depth, or per mm of flange width if the flange width is larger than the depth, rounded to the nearest mm. See ASTM A6 / A6M.

PERMISSIBLE VARIATIONS IN LENGTH FOR S, M, C, MC, L, AND T SHAPES

Nominal Size, mm	Variations from Specified Length for Lengths Given, mm											
(Greatest Cross-sectional Dimension)	1500 to 3000 excl.		3000 to 6000 excl.		6000 to 9000 incl.		Over 9000 to 12 000 incl.		Over 12 000 to 20 000 incl.		Over 20 000	
	Over	Under	Over	Under	Over	Under	Over	Under	Over	Under	Over	Under
Under 75	16	0	25	0	38	0	51	0	64	0	...	...
75 and over	25	0	38	0	45	0	57	0	70	0	...	...

Note: Where "..." appears in this table, there is no requirement. See ASTM A6 /A6M.

PERMISSIBLE VARIATIONS IN SECTION DIMENSIONS FOR S, M, SLB, C AND MC SHAPES

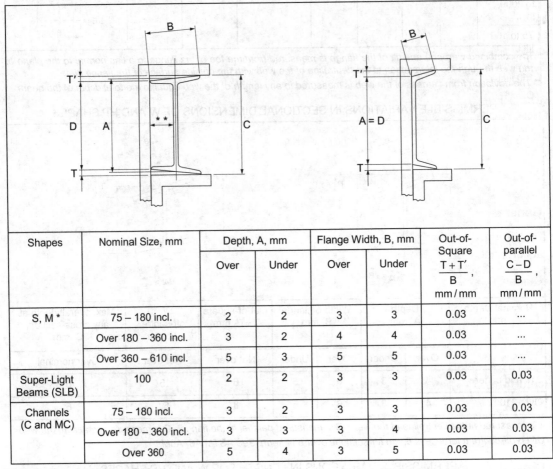

Shapes	Nominal Size, mm	Depth, A, mm		Flange Width, B, mm		Out-of-Square $\dfrac{T+T'}{B}$, mm / mm	Out-of-parallel $\dfrac{C-D}{B}$, mm / mm
		Over	Under	Over	Under		
S, M *	75 – 180 incl.	2	2	3	3	0.03	...
	Over 180 – 360 incl.	3	2	4	4	0.03	...
	Over 360 – 610 incl.	5	3	5	5	0.03	...
Super-Light Beams (SLB)	100	2	2	3	3	0.03	0.03
Channels (C and MC)	75 – 180 incl.	3	2	3	3	0.03	0.03
	Over 180 – 360 incl.	3	3	3	4	0.03	0.03
	Over 360	5	4	3	5	0.03	0.03

* Web off-centre tolerance is 5 mm.

** Back of square and centreline of web to be parallel when measuring out-of-square.

A is measured at centreline of web for beams and at back of web for channels.

Mass and Area Tolerances

Structural-size shapes – cross-sectional area or mass: ±2.5% from theoretical.

Super-light beams – cross-sectional area or mass: -2.5% or +7.5% from theoretical.

Web Thickness Tolerances for SLB Shapes

For super-light beams (SLB) under 150 mm specified size, the permissible variation given in CSA Standard G40.20 is ±15%.

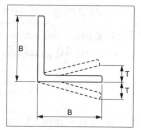

Tolerances for Angles

Permissible variations for cross-sectional dimemsions of bar-size angles (defined as rolled angles having maximum cross-sectional dimensions less than 75 mm), differ from structural size angles, and both variations are given in the following table (see ASTM A6 / A6M).

Structural Size Angles				Bar-Size Angles**				
Specified Size*, mm	Length of Leg, B, mm		Out-of-Square T / B	Specified Length of Leg*, mm	Variations from Thickness Given, mm			Variations from Length of Leg Over and Under, mm
	Over	Under			5 and under	Over 5 to 10 incl.	Over 10	
75 to 100 incl.	3	2	0.026	25 and Under	0.2	0.2	...	1
Over 100 to 150 incl.	3	3	0.026	Over 25 to 50 incl.	0.2	0.2	0.3	1
Over 150	5	3	0.026	Over 50	0.3	0.4	0.4	2

Note: Where "..." appears in this table, there is no requirement.
* For unequal-leg angles, longer leg determines classification.
** Permissible out-of-square in either direction is 1.5 degrees.

HOLLOW STRUCTURAL SECTIONS (HSS)

General

Production information and tolerances given below correspond to HSS produced in accordance with CSA G40.20/G40.21, unless noted otherwise.

Class of Section

Class H means hollow sections made by:

(i) A seamless or furnace-buttwelded (continuous-welded) or automatic electric welding process hot-formed to final shape; or

(ii) A seamless or automatic electric welding process producing a continuous weld, and cold-formed to final shape, subsequently stress-relieved by heating to a temperature of 450°C or higher, followed by cooling in air.

Class C means HSS that are cold-formed from a section produced by a seamless process or by an automatic electric welding process producing a continuous weld.

Cross-Sectional Dimensions

Outside dimensions measured across the flats or diameter at least 50 mm from either end of a piece, including an allowance for convexity or concavity, shall not vary from the specified dimensions of the section by more than the prescribed tolerances.

Largest Outside Dimension Across Flats or Diameter, mm	Tolerance*, mm
To 65	± 0.5
Over 65 - 90 incl.	± 0.8
Over 90 - 140 incl.	± 1.0
Over 140	± 1%

* Tolerance includes allowance for convexity or concavity. Tolerance may be increased by 50 percent when applied to the smaller dimension of rectangular sections whose ratio of cross-sectional dimensions is between 1.5 and 3, and by 100 percent when this ratio exceeds 3.

Mass Variation – CSA G40.20 and ASTM A500

For HSS produced to CSA G40.20 and based on a mass density of 7850 kg/m^3, the actual mass shall not deviate from the published mass by more than minus 3.5 or plus 10 percent. For HSS produced to ASTM A500, there is no required mass tolerance.

Wall Thickness – CSA G40.20 and ASTM A500

For HSS produced to CSA G40.20, the tolerance on the wall thickness is not more than plus 10 or minus 5 percent from the nominal specified wall thickness, except for the weld seam. For HSS produced to ASTM A500, the tolerance is not more than plus or minus 10 percent from the nominal wall thickness, except for the weld seam.

Maximum Outside Corner radius

Wall Thickness mm	Maximum Outside Corner Radii, mm	
	Perimeter to 700 mm Incl.	Perimeter Over 700 mm
To 3 incl.	6	–
Over 3 - 4 incl.	8	–
Over 4 - 5 incl.	15	–
Over 5 - 6 incl.	18	18
Over 6 - 8 incl.	21	24
Over 8 - 10 incl.	27	30
Over 10 - 13 incl.	36	39
Over 13	–	3 x wall thickness

Corner squareness

For rectangular sections, corners shall be square (90°) within plus or minus 1° for hot-formed sections and plus or minus 2° for cold-formed sections, with the average slope of the sides being the basis for determination.

Straightness Variation

Deviation from straightness in millimetres shall not exceed the total length in millimetres divided by 500.

Permissible Twist

Twist of a rectangular section measured by holding down the side of one end of the section on a flat surface and noting the height above the surface of either corner at the opposite end of that side shall not exceed the prescribed tolerances.

Largest Outside Dimension, mm	Maximum Twist per 1000 mm of Length, mm
To 40 incl.	1.3
Over 40 - 65 incl.	1.7
Over 65 - 105 incl.	2.1
Over 105 - 155 incl.	2.4
Over 155 - 205 incl.	2.8
Over 205	3.1

Cutting Tolerances

Tolerances on ordered cold-cut lengths are:
    plus 12 and minus 6 millimetres for lengths 7500 mm and under;
    plus 18 and minus 6 millimetres for lengths over 7500 mm.

Tolerances on ordered hot-cut lengths of hot rolled sections are:
    plus or minus 25 millimetres for lengths 7500 mm and under;
    plus or minus 50 millimetres for lengths over 7500 mm.

PRINCIPAL SOURCES OF STRUCTURAL STEEL SECTIONS

General

Standard Canadian and North American sections can be supplied by a number of steel mills in Canada and elsewhere. Principal sources for the various section sizes listed in this Handbook are indicated below.

In 1999, Algoma Steel Inc., the sole Canadian producer of W and HP shapes for 30 years, announced its withdrawal from the rolled shape market.

Canadian Sections

Structural sections available from Canadian mills are listed below. Canadian sizes should be specified to the CSA G40.20/G40.21 material standards. When Canadian sizes are obtained from non-Canadian sources, the material should be supplied to the CSA G40.20/G40.21 Standards. If material substitutions are offered, the sections must be designed using the minimum specified strength levels of the substitute material.

STRUCTURAL SECTIONS AVAILABLE FROM CANADIAN MILLS

WRF – All sizes listed

WWF – All sizes listed

CHANNELS – See Tables of Properties and Dimensions

ANGLES – See Tables of Properties and Dimensions.

HSS – All sizes listed

PIPE – All Standard sizes

Non-Canadian Sections

Channels and angles not available from Canadian mills are identified by an asterisk (*) in the Tables of Section Properties. When non-Canadian sizes are required, generally the material should also be specified to the CSA G40.20/G40.21 Standards, and if material substitutions are offered, the sections must be designed using the minimum specified strength levels applicable to the substitute material.

W-shapes most commonly produced to ASTM Standards by North American mills will be to ASTM A572 grade 50 and A992 (a more restrictive version of A572 grade 50). See page 6-5 for mechanical properties.

Principal Sources

Some of the more common sources (for Canada) of structural sections and other products are listed below. Producers' catalogs should be consulted for more information and details about particular sections and other products produced. This list is a general guide and is not necessarily complete.

ArcelorMittal Canada - Contrecoeur (bars, coil)
ArcelorMittal Dofasco (sheet steel in coils and cut lengths)
ArcelorMittal International Canada * (shapes, plate, bars, HSS)
Atlas Tube Canada ULC (HSS)
Barzel Industries Canada Inc. (HSS)
Corus International Americas * (shapes, plate, bars)
Essar Steel Algoma Inc. (WWF, WRF shapes, plate, checkered floor plate, coil)
Evraz Inc. NA * (HSS, pipe, plate, coil)
Gerdau Ameristeel - Cambridge (angles, channels, bars)
Gerdau Ameristeel - Texas Steel Mill * (W-shapes, channels)
Gerdau Ameristeel - Whitby (angles, channels, bars)
Nucor-Yamato Steel Company * (shapes)
SSAB Central Inc. (sheet steel in cut lengths, plate)
Steel Dynamics Inc. * (shapes, coil)
U.S. Steel Canada - Hamilton Works (bar, sheet steel in coil, pipe)
Welded Tube of Canada (HSS, pipe)

non-Canadian sources

Note: Since not all of the above are members of CISC, please visit the CISC website (www.cisc-icca.ca) to view the current list of CISC mill and steel service centre members.

Availability of Rolled Shapes

Section sizes are generally produced by steel mills according to rolling schedules. Steel mills and service centres carry various inventories, usually of the more commonly used sections, and serve as a buffer between rolling cycles to provide ready availability of material. The designer should consider material availability when specifying section sizes, particularly for the heavier mass per metre sizes in a nominal size range and for small quantities of the less commonly used sizes. Guidance as to the availability of particular sizes can be obtained from local steel fabricators and from steel mill and service centre sources.

Availability of Angles

Tables of properties and dimensions of angles listed in this Part are based on the imperial series. There are two Canadian producers of angles.

METRIC AND IMPERIAL DESIGNATIONS

General

In Canada, the official designation for structural steel sections for purposes of design, detailing and ordering material is the metric (SI) designation. For WWF, W and HP shapes, angles, cold-formed channels, and hollow structural sections (HSS), this is described in the CAN/CSA-G312.3-M92 Standard. Canadian and North American sections may also be defined using imperial designations; however, all tables of properties and dimensions, and all design tables included elsewhere in this Handbook generally provide only metric properties and metric design information. Tables on pages 6-21 to 6-28 list Canadian (SI) Designations and corresponding Imperial Designations.

WWF Shapes

Canadian WWF shapes, page 6-21, are hard metric shapes, and the Canadian (SI) designation is the total depth in millimetres times the mass in kilograms per metre. The corresponding imperial designation is expressed in inches × lb/ft.

W Shapes

Canadian (SI) designations and imperial designations for W shapes are given on pages 6-22 and 6-23. The Canadian (SI) designation is the nominal depth in millimetres times the mass in kilograms per metre. The corresponding imperial designation is generally the ASTM A6 designation and is expressed in inches × lb/ft.

HP Shapes, S Shapes, M shapes

Canadian (SI) designations and imperial designations for HP, S and M shapes are given on page 6-24. The Canadian (SI) designation is the nominal depth in millimetres times the mass in kilograms per metre and is generally soft-converted from the corresponding imperial designation expressed as inches × lb/ft.

C Shapes, MC Shapes

Canadian (SI) designations and imperial designations for C and MC shapes are given on page 6-24. The Canadian (SI) designation is the nominal depth in millimetres times the mass in kilograms per metre and is soft-converted from the corresponding imperial designation expressed in inches × lb/ft.

Angles (L)

While the G312.3 Standard includes a metric angle series and an imperial angle series, only the imperial series is included herein as it is the only series currently produced in Canada. The designation for the imperial series is a soft conversion of the imperial size, expressed as leg lengths in millimetres and thickness in millimetres to two significant figures. Designations for angles are given on page 6-25.

Hollow Structural Sections (HSS)

Revisions to the G312.3 Standard for square, rectangular and round hollow structural sections provide for Canadian (SI) designations to be expressed as the nominal outside dimensions in millimetres times the thickness in millimetres to two significant figures. The imperial designation (size) is the outside dimensions times the thickness, both in inches. Designations for rectangular HSS, square HSS and round HSS are given on pages 6-26, 6-27 and 6-28, respectively.

CSA G312.3 AND ASTM A6/A6M DESIGNATIONS

Metric (SI) designations for rolled shapes in this Handbook generally conform to the CSA G312.3-M92 Standard "Metric Dimensions for Structural Steel Shapes and Hollow Structural Sections". For a number of section sizes, the metric designation according to this standard is slightly different from that of ASTM A6/A6M. In many cases, the principal difference involves a decimal digit in the nominal mass based on A6. These sections are listed in the comparison table below, with the Imperial designation also provided for reference purposes. For other sections not listed, metric designations according to G312.3 and A6 are the same.

In the case of angles, the only difference between the respective designations involves a decimal digit in the nominal leg thickness based on A6 for thicknesses greater than 9.5 mm. Since the leg widths are identical according to both standards, only the thicknesses are listed.

G312.3 (Handbook)	A6/A6M		G312.3 (Handbook)	A6/A6M	
Metric	Metric	Imperial	Metric	Metric	Imperial
W Shapes			**S Shapes**		
W410x74	W410x75	W16x50	S510x98.2	S510x98	S20x66
W410x54	W410x53	W16x36	S310x47	S310x47.3	S12x31.8
W410x46	W410x46.1	W16x31	S250x38	S250x37.8	S10x25.4
W410x39	W410x38.8	W16x26	S200x27	S200x27.4	S8x18.4
W360x57	W360x58	W14x38	S150x26	S150x25.7	S6x17.25
W360x45	W360x44.6	W14x30	S150x19	S150x18.6	S6x12.5
W360x33	W360x32.9	W14x22	S100x11	S100x11.5	S4x7.7
W310x118	W310x117	W12x79	S75x11	S75x11.2	S3x7.5
W310x45	W310x44.5	W12x30	S75x8	S75x8.5	S3x5.7
W310x39	W310x38.7	W12x26	**C Shapes**		
W310x33	W310x32.7	W12x22	C380x50	C380x50.4	C15x33.9
W310x28	W310x28.3	W12x19	C310x31	C310x30.8	C12x20.7
W310x24	W310x23.8	W12x16	C250x23	C250x22.8	C10x15.3
W250x49	W250x49.1	W10x33	C230x20	C230x19.9	C9x13.4
W250x45	W250x44.8	W10x30	C200x28	C200x27.9	C8x18.75
W250x39	W250x38.5	W10x26	C200x21	C200x20.5	C8x13.75
W250x33	W250x32.7	W10x22	C200x17	C200x17.1	C8x11.5
W250x28	W250x28.4	W10x19	C180x18	C180x18.2	C7x12.25
W250x25	W250x25.3	W10x17	C180x15	C180x14.6	C7x9.8
W250x22	W250x22.3	W10x15	C150x19	C150x19.3	C6x13
W250x18	W250x17.9	W10x12	C150x16	C150x15.6	C6x10.5
W200x46	W200x46.1	W8x31	C150x12	C150x12.2	C6x8.2
W200x42	W200x41.7	W8x28	C130x10	C130x10.4	C5x6.7
W200x36	W200x35.9	W8x24	C100x11	C100x10.8	C4x7.25
W200x31	W200x31.3	W8x21	C100x7	C100x6.7	C4x4.5
W200x27	W200x26.6	W8x18	C75x9	C75x8.9	C3x6
W200x22	W200x22.5	W8x15	C75x7	C75x7.4	C3x5
W200x19	W200x19.3	W8x13	C75x6	C75x6.1	C3x4.1
W150x37	W150x37.1	W6x25	C75x5	C75x5.2	C3x3.5
W150x30	W150x29.8	W6x20	**L Shapes - Leg Thicknesses > 9.5 mm**		

G312.3 (Handbook)	A6/A6M	
mm	mm	in.
29	28.6	1 1/8
25	25.4	1
22	22.2	7/8
19	19	3/4
16	15.9	5/8
14	14.3	9/16
13	12.7	1/2
11	11.1	7/16

G312.3 (Handbook)	A6/A6M	
Metric	Metric	Imperial
W150x22	W150x22.5	W6x15
W150x14	W150x13.5	W6x9
W130x28	W130x28.1	W5x19
W130x24	W130x23.8	W5x16
W100x19	W100x19.3	W4x13
HP Shapes		
HP310x94	HP310x93	HP12x63
HP200x54	HP200x53	HP8x36

DESIGNATION TABLE FOR WWF SHAPES

Canadian (SI) Designation (mm x kg/m)	Imperial Designation (in. x lb./ft.)	Canadian (SI) Designation (mm x kg/m)	Imperial Designation (in. x lb./ft.)
WWF2000x732	WWF79x490	WWF700x245	WWF28x164
x648	x436	x214	x144
x607	x408	x196	x132
x542	x364	x175	x117
		x152	x102
WWF1800x700	WWF71x470		
x659	x442	WWF650x864	WWF26x580
x617	x415	x739	x497
x575	x388	x598	x402
x510	x344	x499	x336
		x400	x269
WWF1600x622	WWF63x419		
x580	x388	WWF600x793	WWF24x531
x538	x361	x680	x456
x496	x333	x551	x371
x431	x289	x460	x309
		x369	x248
WWF1400x597	WWF55x402		
x513	x344	WWF550x721	WWF22x484
x471	x316	x620	x416
x405	x272	x503	x338
x358	x240	x420	x282
		x280	x188
WWF1200x487	WWF47x326		
x418	x281	WWF500x651	WWF20x437
x380	x255	x561	x377
x333	x224	x456	x306
x302	x203	x381	x256
x263	x176	x343	x230
		x306	x205
WWF1100x458	WWF43x307	x276	x185
x388	x260	x254	x170
x351	x236	x223	x150
x304	x204	x197	x132
x273	x184		
x234	x157	WWF450x503	WWF18x337
		x409	x275
WWF1000x447	WWF39x300	x342	x229
x377	x253	x308	x207
x340	x228	x274	x184
x293	x197	x248	x166
x262	x176	x228	x152
x223	x150	x201	x134
x200	x134	x177	x119
WWF900x417	WWF35x279	WWF400x444	WWF16x298
x347	x233	x362	x243
x309	x208	x303	x203
x262	x176	x273	x183
x231	x156	x243	x163
x192	x128	x220	x147
x169	x113	x202	x135
		x178	x119
WWF800x339	WWF31x228	x157	x105
x300	x202		
x253	x170	WWF350x315	WWF14x211
x223	x150	x263	x177
x184	x123	x238	x159
x161	x108	x212	x142
		x192	x128
		x176	x118
		x155	x104
		x137	x92

Canadian (SI) Designation (mm x kg/m)	Imperial Designation (in. x lb./ft.)	Canadian (SI) Designation (mm x kg/m)	Imperial Designation (in. x lb./ft.)	Canadian (SI) Designation (mm x kg/m)	Imperial Designation (in. x lb./ft.)
W1100x499	W44x335	W840x251	W33x169	W610x153	W24x103
x433	x290	x226	x152	x140	x94
x390	x262	x210	x141	x125	x84
x343	x230	x193	x130	x113	x76
		x176	x118	x101	x68
W1000x883	W40x593			x91	x61
x748	x503	W760x582	W30x391	x84	x56
x642	x431	x531	x357		
x591	x397	x484	x326	W610x92	W24x62
x554	x372	x434	x292	x82	x55
x539	x362	x389	x261		
x483	x324	x350	x235	W530x300	W21x201
x443	x297	x314	x211	x272	x182
x412	x277	x284	x191	x248	x166
x371	x249	x257	x173	x219	x147
x321	x215			x196	x132
x296	x199	W760x220	W30x148	x182	x122
		x196	x132	x165	x111
W1000x584	W40x392	x185	x124	x150	x101
x494	x331	x173	x116		
x486	x327	x161	x108	W530x138	W21x93
x438	x294	x147	x99	x123	x83
x415	x278	x134	x90	x109	x73
x393	x264			x101	x68
x350	x235	W690x548	W27x368	x92	x62
x314	x211	x500	x336	x82	x55
x272	x183	x457	x307	x72	x48
x249	x167	x419	x281		
x222	x149	x384	x258	W530x85	W21x57
		x350	x235	x74	x50
W920x656	W36x441	x323	x217	x66	x44
x588	x395	x289	x194		
x537	x361	x265	x178	W460x464	W18x311
x491	x330	x240	x161	x421	x283
x449	x302	x217	x146	x384	x258
x420	x282			x349	x234
x390	x262	W690x192	W27x129	x315	x211
x368	x247	x170	x114	x286	x192
x344	x231	x152	x102	x260	x175
		x140	x94	x235	x158
W920x381	W36x256	x125	x84	x213	x143
x345	x232			x193	x130
x313	x210	W610x551	W24x370	x177	x119
x289	x194	x498	x335	x158	x106
x271	x182	x455	x306	x144	x97
x253	x170	x415	x279	x128	x86
x238	x160	x372	x250	x113	x76
x223	x150	x341	x229		
x201	x135	x307	x207	W460x106	W18x71
		x285	x192	x97	x65
W840x576	W33x387	x262	x176	x89	x60
x527	x354	x241	x162	x82	x55
x473	x318	x217	x146	x74	x50
x433	x291	x195	x131	x67	x45
x392	x263	x174	x117	x61	x41
x359	x241	x155	x104		
x329	x221			W460x68	W18x46
x299	x201			x60	x40
				x52	x35

DESIGNATION TABLE FOR W SHAPES

Canadian (SI) Designation (mm x kg/m)	Imperial Designation (in. x lb./ft.)	Canadian (SI) Designation (mm x kg/m)	Imperial Designation (in. x lb./ft.)	Canadian (SI) Designation (mm x kg/m)	Imperial Designation (in. x lb./ft.)
W410x149	W16x100	W310x283	W12x190	W200x31	W8x21
x132	x89	x253	x170	x27	x18
x114	x77	x226	x152		
x100	x67	x202	x136	W200x22	W8x15
		x179	x120	x19	x13
W410x85	W16x57	x158	x106	x15	x10
x74	x50	x143	x96		
x67	x45	x129	x87	W150x37	W6x25
x60	x40	x118	x79	x30	x20
x54	x36	x107	x72	x22	x15
		x97	x65		
W410x46	W16x31			W150x24	W6x16
x39	x26	W310x86	W12x58	x18	x12
		x79	x53	x14	x9
W360x1086	W14x730			x13	x8.5
x990	x665	W310x74	W12x50		
x900	x605	x67	x45	W130x28	W5x19
x818	x550	x60	x40	x24	x16
x744	x500				
x677	x455	W310x52	W12x35	W100x19	W4x13
		x45	x30		
W360x634	W14x426	x39	x26		
x592	x398				
x551	x370	W310x33	W12x22		
x509	x342	x28	x19		
x463	x311	x24	x16		
x421	x283	x21	x14		
x382	x257				
x347	x233	W250x167	W10x112		
x314	x211	x149	x100		
x287	x193	x131	x88		
x262	x176	x115	x77		
x237	x159	x101	x68		
x216	x145	x89	x60		
		x80	x54		
W360x196	W14x132	x73	x49		
x179	x120				
x162	x109	W250x67	W10x45		
x147	x99	x58	x39		
x134	x90	x49	x33		
W360x122	W14x82	W250x45	W10x30		
x110	x74	x39	x26		
x101	x68	x33	x22		
x91	x61				
		W250x28	W10x19		
W360x79	W14x53	x25	x17		
x72	x48	x22	x15		
x64	x43	x18	x12		
W360x57	W14x38	W200x100	W8x67		
x51	x34	x86	x58		
x45	x30	x71	x48		
		x59	x40		
W360x39	W14x26	x52	x35		
x33	x22	x46	x31		
W310x500	W12x336	W200x42	W8x28		
x454	x305	x36	x24		
x415	x279				
x375	x252				
x342	x230				
x313	x210				

DESIGNATION TABLE FOR HP, M, S, C, MC SHAPES

Canadian (SI) Designation (mm x kg/m)	Imperial Designation (in. x lb./ft.)	Canadian (SI) Designation (mm x kg/m)	Imperial Designation (in. x lb./ft.)	Canadian (SI) Designation (mm x kg/m)	Imperial Designation (in. x lb./ft.)
HP360x174	HP14x117	S250x52	S10x35	C75x9	C3x6
x152	x102	x38	x25.4	x7	x5
x132	x89			x6	x4.1
x108	x73	S200x34	S8x23	x5	x3.5
		x27	x18.4		
HP310x125	HP12x84			MC460x86	MC18x58
x110	x74	S150x26	S6x17.25	x77.2	x51.9
x94	x63	x19	x12.5	x68.2	x45.8
x79	x53			x63.5	x42.7
		S130x15	S5x10		
HP250x85	HP10x57			MC330x74	MC13x50
x62	x42	S100x14.1	S4x9.5	x60	x40
		x11	x7.7	x52	x35
HP200x54	HP8x36			x47.3	x31.8
		S75x11	S3x7.5		
		x8	x5.7	MC310x74	MC12x50
M310x17.6	M12x11.8			x67	x45
x16.1	x10.8			x60	x40
x14.9	x10	C380x74	C15x50	x52	x35
		x60	x40	x46	x31
M250x13.4	M10x9	x50	x33.9		
x11.9	x8			MC310x15.8	MC12x10.6
x11.2	x7.5	C310x45	C12x30		
		x37	x25	MC250x61.2	MC10x41.1
M200x9.7	M8x6.5	x31	x20.7	x50	x33.6
				x42.4	x28.5
M150x6.6	M6x4.4	C250x45	C10x30		
		x37	x25	MC250x37	MC10x25
M100x8.9	M4x6	x30	x20	x33	x22
		x23	x15.3		
				MC250x12.5	MC10x8.4
S610x180	S24x121	C230x30	C9x20		
x158	x106	x22	x15	MC230x37.8	MC9x25.4
		x20	x13.4	x35.6	x23.9
S610x149	S24x100				
x134	x90	C200x28	C8x18.75	MC200x33.9	MC8x22.8
x119	x80	x21	x13.75	x31.8	x21.4
		x17	x11.5		
S510x143	S20x96			MC200x29.8	MC8x20
x128	x86	C180x22	C7x14.75	x27.8	x18.7
		x18	x12.25		
S510x112	S20x75	x15	x9.8	MC200x12.6	MC8x8.5
x98.2	x66				
		C150x19	C6x13	MC180x33.8	MC7x22.7
S460x104	S18x70	x16	x10.5	x28.4	x19.1
x81.4	x54.7	x12	x8.2		
				MC150x26.8	MC6x18
S380x74	S15x50	C130x13	C5x9	x22.8	x15.3
x64	x42.9	x10	x6.7		
				MC150x24.3	MC6x16.3
S310x74	S12x50	C100x11	C4x7.25	x22.5	x15.1
x60.7	x40.8	x9	x6.25		
		x8	x5.4	MC150x17.9	MC6x12
S310x52	S12x35	x7	x4.5		
x47	x31.8				

DESIGNATION TABLE FOR ANGLES

Canadian (SI) Designation (mm x mm x mm)	Imperial Designation (in. x in. x in.)
L203x 203x 29	L8x 8x $1\frac{1}{8}$
x 25	x 1
x 22	x $\frac{7}{8}$
x 19	x $\frac{3}{4}$
x 16	x $\frac{5}{8}$
x 14	x $\frac{9}{16}$
x 13	x $\frac{1}{2}$
L203x 152x 25	L8x 6x 1
x 22	x $\frac{7}{8}$
x 19	x $\frac{3}{4}$
x 16	x $\frac{5}{8}$
x 14	x $\frac{9}{16}$
x 13	x $\frac{1}{2}$
L203x 102x 25	L8x 4x 1
x 19	x $\frac{3}{4}$
x 13	x $\frac{1}{2}$
L178x 102x 19	L7x 4x $\frac{3}{4}$
x 16	x $\frac{5}{8}$
x 13	x $\frac{1}{2}$
x 11	x $\frac{7}{16}$
x 9.5	x $\frac{3}{8}$
L152x 152x 25	L6x 6x 1
x 22	x $\frac{7}{8}$
x 19	x $\frac{3}{4}$
x 16	x $\frac{5}{8}$
x 14	x $\frac{9}{16}$
x 13	x $\frac{1}{2}$
x 11	x $\frac{7}{16}$
x 9.5	x $\frac{3}{8}$
x 7.9	x $\frac{5}{16}$
x 6.4	x $\frac{1}{4}$
L152x 102x 22	L6x 4x $\frac{7}{8}$
x 19	x $\frac{3}{4}$
x 16	x $\frac{5}{8}$
x 14	x $\frac{9}{16}$
x 13	x $\frac{1}{2}$
x 11	x $\frac{7}{16}$
x 9.5	x $\frac{3}{8}$
x 7.9	x $\frac{5}{16}$
L152x 89x 16	L6x $3\frac{1}{2}$x $\frac{5}{8}$
x 13	x $\frac{1}{2}$
x 9.5	x $\frac{3}{8}$
x 7.9	x $\frac{5}{16}$
L127x 127x 22	L5x 5x $\frac{7}{8}$
x 19	x $\frac{3}{4}$
x 16	x $\frac{5}{8}$
x 13	x $\frac{1}{2}$
x 11	x $\frac{7}{16}$
x 9.5	x $\frac{3}{8}$
x 7.9	x $\frac{5}{16}$
x 6.4	x $\frac{1}{4}$

Canadian (SI) Designation (mm x mm x mm)	Imperial Designation (in. x in. x in.)
L127x 89x 19	L5x $3\frac{1}{2}$x $\frac{3}{4}$
x 16	x $\frac{5}{8}$
x 13	x $\frac{1}{2}$
x 9.5	x $\frac{3}{8}$
x 7.9	x $\frac{5}{16}$
x 6.4	x $\frac{1}{4}$
L127x 76x 13	L5x 3x $\frac{1}{2}$
x 11	x $\frac{7}{16}$
x 9.5	x $\frac{3}{8}$
x 7.9	x $\frac{5}{16}$
x 6.4	x $\frac{1}{4}$
L102x 102x 19	L4x 4x $\frac{3}{4}$
x 16	x $\frac{5}{8}$
x 13	x $\frac{1}{2}$
x 11	x $\frac{7}{16}$
x 9.5	x $\frac{3}{8}$
x 7.9	x $\frac{5}{16}$
x 6.4	x $\frac{1}{4}$
L102x 89x 13	L4x $3\frac{1}{2}$x $\frac{1}{2}$
x 11	x $\frac{7}{16}$
x 9.5	x $\frac{3}{8}$
x 7.9	x $\frac{5}{16}$
x 6.4	x $\frac{1}{4}$
L102x 76x 16	L4x 3x $\frac{5}{8}$
x 13	x $\frac{1}{2}$
x 11	x $\frac{7}{16}$
x 9.5	x $\frac{3}{8}$
x 7.9	x $\frac{5}{16}$
x 6.4	x $\frac{1}{4}$
L89x 89x 13	L$3\frac{1}{2}$x $3\frac{1}{2}$x $\frac{1}{2}$
x 11	x $\frac{7}{16}$
x 9.5	x $\frac{3}{8}$
x 7.9	x $\frac{5}{16}$
x 6.4	x $\frac{1}{4}$
L89x 76x 13	L$3\frac{1}{2}$x 3x $\frac{1}{2}$
x 9.5	x $\frac{3}{8}$
x 7.9	x $\frac{5}{16}$
x 6.4	x $\frac{1}{4}$
L89x 64x 13	L$3\frac{1}{2}$x $2\frac{1}{2}$x $\frac{1}{2}$
x 9.5	x $\frac{3}{8}$
x 7.9	x $\frac{5}{16}$
x 6.4	x $\frac{1}{4}$
L76x 76x 13	L3x 3x $\frac{1}{2}$
x 11	x $\frac{7}{16}$
x 9.5	x $\frac{3}{8}$
x 7.9	x $\frac{5}{16}$
x 6.4	x $\frac{1}{4}$
x 4.8	x $\frac{3}{16}$
L76x 64x 13	L3x $2\frac{1}{2}$x $\frac{1}{2}$
x 9.5	x $\frac{3}{8}$
x 7.9	x $\frac{5}{16}$
x 6.4	x $\frac{1}{4}$
x 4.8	x $\frac{3}{16}$

Canadian (SI) Designation (mm x mm x mm)	Imperial Designation (in. x in. x in.)
L76x 51x 13	L3x 2x $\frac{1}{2}$
x 9.5	x $\frac{3}{8}$
x 7.9	x $\frac{5}{16}$
x 6.4	x $\frac{1}{4}$
x 4.8	x $\frac{3}{16}$
L64x 64x 13	L$2\frac{1}{2}$x $2\frac{1}{2}$x $\frac{1}{2}$
x 9.5	x $\frac{3}{8}$
x 7.9	x $\frac{5}{16}$
x 6.4	x $\frac{1}{4}$
x 4.8	x $\frac{3}{16}$
L64x 51x 9.5	L$2\frac{1}{2}$x 2x $\frac{3}{8}$
x 7.9	x $\frac{5}{16}$
x 6.4	x $\frac{1}{4}$
x 4.8	x $\frac{3}{16}$
L51x 51x 9.5	L2x 2x $\frac{3}{8}$
x 7.9	x $\frac{5}{16}$
x 6.4	x $\frac{1}{4}$
x 4.8	x $\frac{3}{16}$
x 3.2	x $\frac{1}{8}$
L51x 38x 6.4	L2x $1\frac{1}{2}$x $\frac{1}{4}$
x 4.8	x $\frac{3}{16}$
x 3.2	x $\frac{1}{8}$
L44x 44x 6.4	L$1\frac{3}{4}$x $1\frac{3}{4}$x $\frac{1}{4}$
x 4.8	x $\frac{3}{16}$
x 3.2	x $\frac{1}{8}$
L38x 38x 6.4	L$1\frac{1}{2}$x $1\frac{1}{2}$x $\frac{1}{4}$
x 4.8	x $\frac{3}{16}$
x 3.2	x $\frac{1}{8}$
L32x 32x 6.4	L$1\frac{1}{4}$x $1\frac{1}{4}$x $\frac{1}{4}$
x 4.8	x $\frac{3}{16}$
x 3.2	x $\frac{1}{8}$
L25x 25x 6.4	L1x 1x $\frac{1}{4}$
x 4.8	x $\frac{3}{16}$
x 3.2	x $\frac{1}{8}$
L19x 19x 3.2	L$\frac{3}{4}$x $\frac{3}{4}$x $\frac{1}{8}$

DESIGNATION TABLE FOR RECTANGULAR HSS

Canadian (SI) Designation (mm x mm x mm)	Imperial Designation (in. x in. x in.)	CSA G40.20/21	ASTM A500
356x 254x 16	14x 10x 0.625		X
x 13	x 0.500	(X)	X
x 9.5	x 0.375	(X)	X
305x 203x 16	12x 8x 0.625		X
x 13	x 0.500	X	X
x 9.5	x 0.375	X	X
x 8.0	x 0.313	X	X
x 6.4	x 0.250	X	X
254x 152x 16	10x 6x 0.625		X
x 13	x 0.500	X	X
x 9.5	x 0.375	X	X
x 8.0	x 0.313	X	X
x 6.4	x 0.250	X	X
203x 152x 13	8x 6x 0.500	X	X
x 9.5	x 0.375	X	X
x 8.0	x 0.313	X	X
x 6.4	x 0.250	X	X
x 4.8	x 0.188	X	X
203x 102x 13	8x 4x 0.500	X	X
x 9.5	x 0.375	X	X
x 8.0	x 0.313	X	X
x 6.4	x 0.250	X	X
x 4.8	x 0.188	X	X
178x 127x 13	7x 5x 0.500	X	X
x 9.5	x 0.375	X	X
x 8.0	x 0.313	X	X
x 6.4	x 0.250	X	X
x 4.8	x 0.188	X	X
152x 102x 13	6x 4x 0.500	(X)	X
x 9.5	x 0.375	(X)	X
x 8.0	x 0.313	(X)	X
x 6.4	x 0.250	(X)	X
x 4.8	x 0.188	(X)	X
152x 76x 13	6x 3x 0.500	X	X
x 9.5	x 0.375	X	X
x 8.0	x 0.313	X	X
x 6.4	x 0.250	X	X
x 4.8	x 0.188	X	X
127x 76x 9.5	5x 3x 0.375	X	X
x 8.0	x 0.313	X	X
x 6.4	x 0.250	X	X
x 4.8	x 0.188	X	X
102x 76x 9.5	4x 3x 0.375	X	X
x 8.0	x 0.313	X	X
x 6.4	x 0.250	X	X
x 4.8	x 0.188	X	X
x 3.2	x 0.125	X	X
102x 51x 9.5	4x 2x 0.375	X	X
x 8.0	x 0.313	X	X
x 6.4	x 0.250	X	X
x 4.8	x 0.188	X	X
x 3.2	x 0.125	X	X
89x 64x 8.0	$3\frac{1}{2}$ x $2\frac{1}{2}$ x 0.313	X	X
x 6.4	x 0.250	X	X
x 4.8	x 0.188	X	X
x 3.2	x 0.125	X	X
76x 51x 8.0	3x 2x 0.313		X
x 6.4	x 0.250	X	X
x 4.8	x 0.188	X	X
x 3.2	x 0.125	X	X
51x 25x 4.8	2x 1x 0.188	(X)	X
x 3.2	x 0.125	X	X

X - Available in the indicated grade

(X) - Available in grade G40.21-350W but not listed in the CSA G40.20/21 Standard

DESIGNATION TABLE FOR SQUARE HSS

Canadian (SI) Designation (mm x mm x mm)	Imperial Designation (in. x in. x in.)	CSA G40.20/21	ASTM A500
305x 305x 16	12x 12x 0.625		X
x 13	x 0.500	X	X
x 9.5	x 0.375	X	X
x 8.0	x 0.313	X	X
x 6.4	x 0.250	X	X
254x 254x 16	10x 10x 0.625		X
x 13	x 0.500	X	X
x 9.5	x 0.375	X	X
x 8.0	x 0.313	X	X
x 6.4	x 0.250	X	X
203x 203x 16	8x 8x 0.625		X
x 13	x 0.500	X	X
x 9.5	x 0.375	X	X
x 8.0	x 0.313	X	X
x 6.4	x 0.250	X	X
178x 178x 16	7x 7x 0.625		X
x 13	x 0.500	X	X
x 9.5	x 0.375	X	X
x 8.0	x 0.313	X	X
x 6.4	x 0.250	X	X
x 4.8	x 0.188	X	X
152x 152x 13	6x 6x 0.500	X	X
x 9.5	x 0.375	X	X
x 8.0	x 0.313	X	X
x 6.4	x 0.250	X	X
x 4.8	x 0.188	X	X
127x 127x 13	5x 5x 0.500	X	X
x 9.5	x 0.375	X	X
x 8.0	x 0.313	X	X
x 6.4	x 0.250	X	X
x 4.8	x 0.188	X	X
114x 114x 13	4¹/₂ x 4¹/₂ x 0.500	X	X
x 9.5	x 0.375	X	X
x 8.0	x 0.313	X	X
x 6.4	x 0.250	X	X
x 4.8	x 0.188	X	X
x 3.2	x 0.125	X	X
102x 102x 13	4x 4x 0.500	X	X
x 9.5	x 0.375	X	X
x 8.0	x 0.313	X	X
x 6.4	x 0.250	X	X
x 4.8	x 0.188	X	X
x 3.2	x 0.125	X	X
89x 89x 9.5	3¹/₂ x 3¹/₂ x 0.375	X	X
x 8.0	x 0.313	X	X
x 6.4	x 0.250	X	X
x 4.8	x 0.188	X	X
x 3.2	x 0.125	(X)	X
76x 76x 9.5	3x 3x 0.375	X	X
x 8.0	x 0.313	X	X
x 6.4	x 0.250	X	X
x 4.8	x 0.188	X	X
x 3.2	x 0.125	X	X

Canadian (SI) Designation (mm x mm x mm)	Imperial Designation (in. x in. x in.)	CSA G40.20/21	ASTM A500
64x 64x 8.0	2¹/₂ x 2¹/₂ x 0.313		X
x 6.4	x 0.250	X	X
x 4.8	x 0.188	X	X
x 3.2	x 0.125	X	X
51x 51x 6.4	2x 2x 0.250	X	X
x 4.8	x 0.188	X	X
x 3.2	x 0.125	X	X
38x 38x 4.8	1¹/₂ x 1¹/₂ x 0.188	X	X
x 3.2	x 0.125	X	X

X - Available in the indicated grade

(X) - Available in grade G40.21-350W but not listed in the CSA G40.20/21 Standard

DESIGNATION TABLE FOR ROUND HSS

Canadian (SI) Designation (mm x mm)	Imperial Designation (in. x in.)	CSA G40.20/21	ASTM A500
406x 13	16x 0.500	X	X
x 9.5	x 0.375	X	X
x 6.4	x 0.250	X	X
356x 16	14x 0.625		X
x 13	x 0.500	X	X
x 9.5	x 0.375	X	X
x 6.4	x 0.250	X	X
324x 13	12.75x 0.500	X	X
x 9.5	x 0.375	X	X
x 6.4	x 0.250	X	X
273x 13	10.75x 0.500	X	X
x 6.4	x 0.250	X	X
x 4.8	x 0.188	X	X
219x 16	8.625x 0.625		X
x 13	x 0.500	X	X
x 9.5	x 0.375	X	X
x 6.4	x 0.250	X	X
x 4.8	x 0.188	X	X
178x 13	7x 0.500	(X)	X
x 9.5	x 0.375	(X)	X
x 8.0	x 0.313	(X)	X
x 6.4	x 0.250	(X)	X
x 4.8	x 0.188	(X)	X
168x 13	6.625x 0.500	X	X
x 9.5	x 0.375	X	X
x 8.0	x 0.313	X	X
x 6.4	x 0.250	X	X
x 4.8	x 0.188	X	X
x 3.2	x 0.125	X	X
152x 9.5	6x 0.375	X	X
x 8.0	x 0.313	X	X
x 6.4	x 0.250	X	X
x 4.8	x 0.188	X	X
x 3.2	x 0.125	X	X
141x 9.5	5.563x 0.375	X	X
x 6.4	x 0.250	X	X
x 4.8	x 0.188	X	X
127x 13	5x 0.500	X	X
x 9.5	x 0.375	X	X
x 8.0	x 0.313	X	X
x 6.4	x 0.250	(X)	X
x 4.8	x 0.188	X	X
x 3.2	x 0.125	X	X
114x 9.5	4.5x 0.375	(X)	X
x 4.8	x 0.188	X	X
x 3.2	x 0.125	X	X
102x 8.0	4x 0.313	(X)	X
x 6.4	x 0.250	X	X
x 4.8	x 0.188	X	X
x 3.2	x 0.125	X	X

Canadian (SI) Designation (mm x mm)	Imperial Designation (in. x in.)	CSA G40.20/21	ASTM A500
89x 8.0	3.5x 0.313		X
x 6.4	x 0.250	X	X
x 4.8	x 0.188	X	X
x 3.2	x 0.125	X	X
76x 6.4	3x 0.250	X	X
x 4.8	x 0.188	X	X
73x 6.4	2.875x 0.250	X	X
x 4.8	x 0.188	X	X
x 3.2	x 0.125	X	X
64x 6.4	2.5x 0.250	X	X
x 4.8	x 0.188	X	X
x 3.2	x 0.125	X	X
60x 6.4	2.375x 0.250	(X)	X
x 4.8	x 0.188	X	X
x 3.2	x 0.125	X	X
48x 4.8	1.9x 0.188	(X)	X
x 3.2	x 0.125	(X)	X

X - Available in the indicated grade

(X) - Available in grade G40.21-350W but not listed in the CSA G40.20/21 Standard

WELDED SHAPES

General

Welded shapes are produced to the requirements of the CSA G40.20 Standard, using plate meeting the material requirements of CSA G40.21. Properties and dimensions of WWF (welded wide flange) shapes and WRF (welded reduced flange) shapes are provided on the following pages.

Manufacture

The G40.20 Standard defines welded shapes as I-type sections produced by automatic welding processes from three individual components. Hot-rolled plates are flame-cut to the required width, then assembled together on a special jig where pressure rolls hold the flange and web plates in contact for automatic submerged arc welding. Welds are made simultaneously along both flange-to-web joints in the horizontal fillet position.

For web thicknesses up to and including 20 mm, the flange-to-web welds develop the full capacity of the flange-to-web joint. For web thicknesses greater than 20 mm, which occur in the heavier WWF column shapes, the full strength of the web is not developed by the web-to-flange welds, so that additional welding by the purchaser may be required at major connection points. Column WWF shapes with partial-strength web welds are identified by asterisks (**), and the note "welding does not fully develop the web strength for these sections".

Products

WWF beams range in depth from 700 mm to 2000 mm and have equal-width flanges which range in width between 300 mm and 550 mm. Flange thickness varies while the overall depth of beams in each size range is constant. The Class in bending for WWF beams for G40.21 grade 350W steel is given in Table 5-1.

WWF column shapes range in depth and width from 350 mm to 650 mm in increments of 50 mm. Overall depth and flange width in each size range is the same.

WRF shapes are asymmetrical beams in which one flange is narrower than the other. Overall depths vary from 1000 mm to 1800 mm and are constant for all beams in each range. Flange widths are 300 mm and 550 mm.

Availability of WWF and WRF Shapes

Important note: Essar Steel Algoma Inc. had been the prime producer until their production of welded shapes discontinued in late 2010. Accordingly, the availability of WWF and WRF shapes should be checked before specifying these sections.

WWF beam and column shapes, and WRF shapes are generally not carried in inventory.

A fabricator may request the approval of the designer to substitute a welded three-plate section, welded to the requirements of CSA Standard W59 for oxy-flame-cut plates of the same grade as that of the WWF section originally designed.

WELDED REDUCED-FLANGE SHAPES
WRF1800 - WRF1000

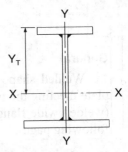

PROPERTIES

| Designation‡ | Dead Load | Area | Axis X-X | | | | | Axis Y-Y | | | Torsional Constant | Warping Constant |
| | | | I_X | S_{XT} | S_{XB} | r_X | Y_T | I_Y | S_Y | r_Y | J | C_W |
	kN/m	mm²	10^6 mm⁴	10^3 mm³	10^3 mm³	mm	mm	10^6 mm⁴	10^3 mm³	mm	10^3 mm⁴	10^9 mm⁶
WRF1800												
x543	5.33	69 200	35 700	34 200	47 100	718	1 040	726	2 640	102	29 100	268 000
x480	4.70	61 100	30 100	29 300	38 900	702	1 030	565	2 050	96.2	15 500	211 000
x416	4.08	52 900	24 300	24 200	30 600	678	1 000	404	1 470	87.3	7 830	152 000
WRF1600												
x491	4.82	62 500	26 600	28 300	40 200	652	940	726	2 640	108	27 900	211 000
x427	4.19	54 400	22 200	24 000	32 900	639	926	565	2 050	102	14 200	166 000
x362	3.56	46 200	17 700	19 500	25 500	619	907	403	1 470	93.5	6 540	120 000
WRF1400												
x413	4.05	52 600	17 600	21 200	30 800	578	829	645	2 350	111	19 300	143 000
x348	3.42	44 400	14 200	17 500	24 400	566	816	484	1 760	104	8 880	109 000
x284	2.78	36 200	10 800	13 500	17 800	545	795	323	1 170	94.4	3 510	73 700
WRF1200												
x373	3.66	47 600	12 200	16 900	25 500	506	722	645	2 340	116	18 800	104 000
x309	3.03	39 300	9 760	13 700	20 000	498	712	484	1 760	111	8 310	79 500
x244	2.39	31 000	7 240	10 400	14 300	483	695	322	1 170	102	2 930	53 900
WRF1000												
x340	3.34	43 300	7 980	13 100	20 500	429	611	645	2 340	122	18 400	71 400
x275	2.70	35 000	6 340	10 500	16 000	426	604	484	1 760	117	7 960	54 600
x210	2.06	26 700	4 620	7 810	11 300	416	592	322	1 170	110	2 590	37 200

‡ Nominal depth in millimetres and mass in kilograms per metre

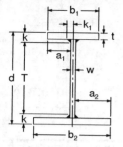

WELDED REDUCED-FLANGE SHAPES
WRF1800 - WRF1000

DIMENSIONS AND SURFACE AREAS

Nominal Mass	Depth	Flange Width	Flange Width	Flange Thickness	Web Thickness	Distances						Surface Area (m²) per metre of length	
	d	b_1	b_2	t	w	a_1	a_2	T	k	k_1	d-2t	Total	Minus Top of Top Flange
kg/m	mm	mm	mm	mm	mm	mm	mm	mm	mm	mm	mm		
543	1 800	300	550	45.0	18.0	141	266	1 688	56	19	1 710	5.26	4.96
480	1 800	300	550	35.0	18.0	141	266	1 708	46	19	1 730	5.26	4.96
416	1 800	300	550	25.0	18.0	141	266	1 728	36	19	1 750	5.26	4.96
491	1 600	300	550	45.0	16.0	142	267	1 492	54	16	1 510	4.87	4.57
427	1 600	300	550	35.0	16.0	142	267	1 512	44	16	1 530	4.87	4.57
362	1 600	300	550	25.0	16.0	142	267	1 532	34	16	1 550	4.87	4.57
413	1 400	300	550	40.0	14.0	143	268	1 302	49	15	1 320	4.47	4.17
348	1 400	300	550	30.0	14.0	143	268	1 322	39	15	1 340	4.47	4.17
284	1 400	300	550	20.0	14.0	143	268	1 342	29	15	1 360	4.47	4.17
373	1 200	300	550	40.0	12.0	144	269	1 102	49	14	1 120	4.08	3.78
309	1 200	300	550	30.0	12.0	144	269	1 122	39	14	1 140	4.08	3.78
244	1 200	300	550	20.0	12.0	144	269	1 142	29	14	1 160	4.08	3.78
340	1 000	300	550	40.0	10.0	145	270	902	49	13	920	3.68	3.38
275	1 000	300	550	30.0	10.0	145	270	922	39	13	940	3.68	3.38
210	1 000	300	550	20.0	10.0	145	270	942	29	13	960	3.68	3.38

CHECK WRF AVAILABILITY See page 6-29

WELDED WIDE-FLANGE SHAPES
WWF2000 - WWF1100

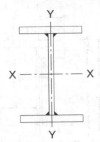

PROPERTIES

Designation‡	Dead Load	Area	Axis X-X				Axis Y-Y				Torsional Constant	Warping Constant
			I_x	S_x	r_x	Z_x	I_y	S_y	r_y	Z_y	J	C_w
	kN/m	mm²	10^6 mm⁴	10^3 mm³	mm	10^3 mm³	10^6 mm⁴	10^3 mm³	mm	10^3 mm³	10^3 mm⁴	10^9 mm⁶
WWF2000												
◆x732	7.18	93 200	63 900	63 900	828	71 800	1 390	5 050	122	7 750	50 900	1 320 000
◆x648	6.36	82 600	54 200	54 200	810	61 700	1 110	4 040	116	6 240	28 600	1 070 000
◆x607	5.95	77 300	49 300	49 300	799	56 600	972	3 530	112	5 490	20 900	938 000
x542	5.31	69 000	41 400	41 400	775	48 500	626	2 510	95.3	3 950	14 200	608 000
WWF1800												
◆x700	6.87	89 200	50 400	56 000	752	62 700	1 390	5 050	125	7 730	50 400	1 060 000
◆x659	6.46	83 900	46 600	51 800	745	58 200	1 250	4 540	122	6 980	38 000	962 000
◆x617	6.05	78 600	42 700	47 400	737	53 700	1 110	4 040	119	6 220	28 100	860 000
◆x575	5.64	73 300	38 800	43 100	727	49 100	972	3 530	115	5 470	20 300	757 000
x510	5.00	65 000	32 400	36 000	706	41 800	626	2 500	98.2	3 930	13 600	490 000
WWF1600												
◆x622	6.10	79 200	37 600	47 100	690	51 800	1 390	5 040	132	7 660	47 900	833 000
◆x580	5.69	73 800	34 600	43 300	685	47 700	1 250	4 540	130	6 900	35 500	755 000
x538	5.28	68 500	31 600	39 500	679	43 700	1 110	4 040	127	6 150	25 500	675 000
x496	4.86	63 100	28 400	35 500	671	39 600	971	3 530	124	5 390	17 800	595 000
x431	4.22	54 800	23 400	29 300	654	33 100	626	2 500	107	3 850	11 100	385 000
WWF1400												
◆x597	5.85	76 000	28 100	40 100	608	44 000	1 390	5 040	135	7 650	47 600	632 000
x513	5.03	65 300	23 500	33 600	600	37 000	1 110	4 040	130	6 140	25 300	513 000
x471	4.61	59 900	21 100	30 200	594	33 400	971	3 530	127	5 380	17 500	452 000
x405	3.97	51 600	17 300	24 800	580	27 800	625	2 500	110	3 840	10 800	293 000
x358	3.51	45 600	14 500	20 800	565	23 700	320	1 600	83.9	2 490	9 030	150 000
WWF1200												
x487	4.78	62 100	16 700	27 900	519	30 600	1 110	4 030	134	6 120	25 000	373 000
x418	4.10	53 200	13 800	23 100	510	25 600	730	2 920	117	4 450	15 800	248 000
x380	3.72	48 400	12 300	20 500	504	22 800	625	2 500	114	3 820	10 600	214 000
x333	3.26	42 400	10 200	17 100	491	19 300	320	1 600	87.0	2 470	8 760	110 000
x302	2.97	38 500	8 970	15 000	483	17 100	267	1 340	83.3	2 070	5 740	92 200
x263	2.58	33 500	7 250	12 100	465	14 200	113	753	58.0	1 200	4 700	39 000
WWF1100												
x458	4.50	58 500	13 600	24 800	483	27 100	1 110	4 030	138	6 100	24 400	312 000
x388	3.82	49 500	11 200	20 400	476	22 400	729	2 920	121	4 430	15 200	207 000
x351	3.44	44 700	9 930	18 100	472	19 900	625	2 500	118	3 800	9 950	179 000
x304	2.98	38 700	8 220	14 900	461	16 700	320	1 600	91.0	2 450	8 150	91 700
x273	2.68	34 800	7 160	13 000	454	14 700	267	1 330	87.5	2 050	5 130	77 100
x234	2.30	29 800	5 720	10 400	438	12 000	113	752	61.5	1 180	4 090	32 600

‡ Nominal depth in millimetres and mass in kilograms per metre
♦ Maximum piece weight may limit length.

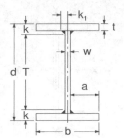

DIMENSIONS AND SURFACE AREAS

Nominal Mass	Depth d	Flange Width b	Flange Thickness t	Web Thickness w	Distances a	T	k	k₁	d-2t	Surface Area (m²) per metre of length Total	Minus Top of Top Flange	Imperial Designation
kg/m	mm	mm	mm	mm	mm	mm	mm	mm	mm			
732	2 000	550	50.0	20.0	265	1 878	61	20	1 900	6.16	5.61	WWF79x490
648	2 000	550	40.0	20.0	265	1 898	51	20	1 920	6.16	5.61	WWF79x436
607	2 000	550	35.0	20.0	265	1 908	46	20	1 930	6.16	5.61	WWF79x408
542	2 000	500	30.0	20.0	240	1 918	41	20	1 940	5.96	5.46	WWF79x364
700	1 800	550	50.0	20.0	265	1 678	61	20	1 700	5.76	5.21	WWF71x470
659	1 800	550	45.0	20.0	265	1 688	56	20	1 710	5.76	5.21	WWF71x442
617	1 800	550	40.0	20.0	265	1 698	51	20	1 720	5.76	5.21	WWF71x415
575	1 800	550	35.0	20.0	265	1 708	46	20	1 730	5.76	5.21	WWF71x388
510	1 800	500	30.0	20.0	240	1 718	41	20	1 740	5.56	5.06	WWF71x344
622	1 600	550	50.0	16.0	267	1 478	61	18	1 500	5.37	4.82	WWF63x419
580	1 600	550	45.0	16.0	267	1 488	56	18	1 510	5.37	4.82	WWF63x388
538	1 600	550	40.0	16.0	267	1 498	51	18	1 520	5.37	4.82	WWF63x361
496	1 600	550	35.0	16.0	267	1 512	44	16	1 530	5.37	4.82	WWF63x333
431	1 600	500	30.0	16.0	242	1 522	39	16	1 540	5.17	4.67	WWF63x289
597	1 400	550	50.0	16.0	267	1 278	61	18	1 300	4.97	4.42	WWF55x402
513	1 400	550	40.0	16.0	267	1 298	51	18	1 320	4.97	4.42	WWF55x344
471	1 400	550	35.0	16.0	267	1 312	44	16	1 330	4.97	4.42	WWF55x316
405	1 400	500	30.0	16.0	242	1 322	39	16	1 340	4.77	4.27	WWF55x272
358	1 400	400	30.0	16.0	192	1 322	39	16	1 340	4.37	3.97	WWF55x240
487	1 200	550	40.0	16.0	267	1 098	51	18	1 120	4.57	4.02	WWF47x326
418	1 200	500	35.0	16.0	242	1 112	44	16	1 130	4.37	3.87	WWF47x281
380	1 200	500	30.0	16.0	242	1 122	39	16	1 140	4.37	3.87	WWF47x255
333	1 200	400	30.0	16.0	192	1 122	39	16	1 140	3.97	3.57	WWF47x224
302	1 200	400	25.0	16.0	192	1 132	34	16	1 150	3.97	3.57	WWF47x203
263	1 200	300	25.0	16.0	142	1 132	34	16	1 150	3.57	3.27	WWF47x176
458	1 100	550	40.0	14.0	268	998	51	17	1 020	4.37	3.82	WWF43x307
388	1 100	500	35.0	14.0	243	1 012	44	15	1 030	4.17	3.67	WWF43x260
351	1 100	500	30.0	14.0	243	1 022	39	15	1 040	4.17	3.67	WWF43x236
304	1 100	400	30.0	14.0	193	1 022	39	15	1 040	3.77	3.37	WWF43x204
273	1 100	400	25.0	14.0	193	1 032	34	15	1 050	3.77	3.37	WWF43x184
234	1 100	300	25.0	14.0	143	1 032	34	15	1 050	3.37	3.07	WWF43x157

WELDED WIDE-FLANGE SHAPES
WWF1000 - WWF600

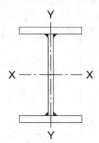

PROPERTIES

Designation‡	Dead Load	Area	Axis X-X				Axis Y-Y				Torsional Constant	Warping Constant
			I_x	S_x	r_x	Z_x	I_y	S_y	r_y	Z_y	J	C_w
	kN/m	mm²	10^6 mm⁴	10^3 mm³	mm	10^3 mm³	10^6 mm⁴	10^3 mm³	mm	10^3 mm³	10^3 mm⁴	10^9 mm⁶
WWF1000												
x447	4.39	57 100	11 100	22 200	441	24 200	1 110	4 030	139	6 100	24 300	256 000
x377	3.71	48 100	9 120	18 200	435	20 000	729	2 920	123	4 420	15 100	170 000
x340	3.33	43 300	8 060	16 100	431	17 700	625	2 500	120	3 800	9 860	147 000
x293	2.87	37 300	6 640	13 300	422	14 800	320	1 600	92.7	2 450	8 060	75 300
x262	2.57	33 400	5 780	11 600	416	13 000	267	1 330	89.4	2 050	5 040	63 400
x223	2.19	28 400	4 590	9 190	402	10 500	113	752	63.0	1 170	3 990	26 800
x200	1.97	25 600	3 940	7 880	393	9 170	90.2	602	59.4	948	2 480	21 700
WWF900												
x417	4.10	53 200	8 680	19 300	404	20 800	1 110	4 030	144	6 080	23 800	205 000
x347	3.41	44 300	7 100	15 800	400	17 100	729	2 920	128	4 400	14 700	136 000
x309	3.03	39 400	6 240	13 900	398	15 000	625	2 500	126	3 780	9 370	118 000
x262	2.57	33 400	5 110	11 400	391	12 400	320	1 600	97.9	2 430	7 570	60 600
x231	2.27	29 500	4 410	9 810	387	10 800	267	1 330	95.1	2 030	4 540	51 100
x192	1.88	24 500	3 460	7 680	376	8 600	113	751	67.8	1 150	3 500	21 600
x169	1.66	21 600	2 930	6 510	368	7 370	90.1	601	64.6	927	1 980	17 400
WWF800												
x339	3.32	43 200	5 500	13 700	357	14 900	729	2 920	130	4 400	14 600	107 000
x300	2.95	38 300	4 840	12 100	356	13 100	625	2 500	128	3 770	9 330	92 700
x253	2.48	32 300	3 950	9 870	350	10 800	320	1 600	99.6	2 420	7 530	47 400
x223	2.19	28 400	3 410	8 520	347	9 340	267	1 330	97.0	2 020	4 500	40 100
x184	1.80	23 400	2 660	6 640	337	7 410	113	751	69.4	1 150	3 460	16 900
x161	1.58	20 500	2 250	5 610	331	6 320	90.1	601	66.3	924	1 940	13 700
WWF700												
x245	2.40	31 200	2 950	8 420	308	9 210	320	1 600	101	2 420	7 480	35 900
x214	2.10	27 300	2 540	7 270	305	7 950	267	1 330	98.9	2 020	4 460	30 400
x196	1.92	24 900	2 300	6 560	303	7 190	235	1 170	97.0	1 780	3 130	27 000
x175	1.72	22 300	1 970	5 640	298	6 260	113	751	71.1	1 150	3 410	12 800
x152	1.49	19 400	1 660	4 760	293	5 320	90.1	601	68.2	921	1 890	10 400
WWF650												
♦x864**	8.47	110 000	7 570	23 300	262	27 300	2 760	8 480	158	13 200	132 000	240 000
♦x739**	7.24	94 100	7 200	22 100	277	25 200	2 750	8 450	171	12 800	98 400	239 000
♦x598**	5.87	76 200	6 150	18 900	284	21 100	2 290	7 040	173	10 600	55 600	206 000
x499	4.90	63 600	5 170	15 900	285	17 500	1 830	5 630	170	8 510	29 300	170 000
x400	3.93	51 000	4 110	12 600	284	13 900	1 370	4 230	164	6 400	13 300	132 000
WWF600												
♦x793**	7.78	101 000	5 830	19 400	240	22 900	2 170	7 230	147	11 200	121 000	158 000
♦x680**	6.67	86 600	5 560	18 500	253	21 200	2 160	7 200	158	10 900	90 700	158 000
x551	5.40	70 200	4 770	15 900	261	17 800	1 800	6 000	160	9 050	51 300	136 000
x460	4.51	58 600	4 020	13 400	262	14 800	1 440	4 800	157	7 250	27 000	113 000
x369	3.62	47 000	3 200	10 700	261	11 800	1 080	3 600	152	5 460	12 200	87 800

‡ Nominal depth in millimetres and mass in kilograms per metre

** Welding does not fully develop the web strength for these sections.

♦ Maximum piece weight may limit length.

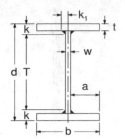

DIMENSIONS AND SURFACE AREAS

Nominal Mass	Depth	Flange Width	Flange Thickness	Web Thickness	Distances					Surface Area (m²) per metre of length		Imperial Designation
	d	b	t	w	a	T	k	k_1	d-2t	Total	Minus Top of Top Flange	
kg/m	mm	mm	mm	mm	mm	mm	mm	mm	mm			
447	1 000	550	40.0	14.0	268	898	51	17	920	4.17	3.62	WWF39x300
377	1 000	500	35.0	14.0	243	912	44	15	930	3.97	3.47	WWF39x253
340	1 000	500	30.0	14.0	243	922	39	15	940	3.97	3.47	WWF39x228
293	1 000	400	30.0	14.0	193	922	39	15	940	3.57	3.17	WWF39x197
262	1 000	400	25.0	14.0	193	932	34	15	950	3.57	3.17	WWF39x176
223	1 000	300	25.0	14.0	143	932	34	15	950	3.17	2.87	WWF39x150
200	1 000	300	20.0	14.0	143	942	29	15	960	3.17	2.87	WWF39x134
417	900	550	40.0	11.0	270	798	51	16	820	3.98	3.43	WWF35x279
347	900	500	35.0	11.0	245	812	44	14	830	3.78	3.28	WWF35x233
309	900	500	30.0	11.0	245	822	39	14	840	3.78	3.28	WWF35x208
262	900	400	30.0	11.0	195	822	39	14	840	3.38	2.98	WWF35x176
231	900	400	25.0	11.0	195	832	34	14	850	3.38	2.98	WWF35x156
192	900	300	25.0	11.0	145	832	34	14	850	2.98	2.68	WWF35x128
169	900	300	20.0	11.0	145	842	29	14	860	2.98	2.68	WWF35x113
339	800	500	35.0	11.0	245	712	44	14	730	3.58	3.08	WWF31x228
300	800	500	30.0	11.0	245	722	39	14	740	3.58	3.08	WWF31x202
253	800	400	30.0	11.0	195	722	39	14	740	3.18	2.78	WWF31x170
223	800	400	25.0	11.0	195	732	34	14	750	3.18	2.78	WWF31x150
184	800	300	25.0	11.0	145	732	34	14	750	2.78	2.48	WWF31x123
161	800	300	20.0	11.0	145	742	29	14	760	2.78	2.48	WWF31x108
245	700	400	30.0	11.0	195	622	39	14	640	2.98	2.58	WWF28x164
214	700	400	25.0	11.0	195	632	34	14	650	2.98	2.58	WWF28x144
196	700	400	22.0	11.0	195	638	31	14	656	2.98	2.58	WWF28x132
175	700	300	25.0	11.0	145	632	34	14	650	2.58	2.28	WWF28x117
152	700	300	20.0	11.0	145	642	29	14	660	2.58	2.28	WWF28x102
864	650	650	60.0	60.0	295	508	71	40	530	3.78	3.13	WWF26x580
739	650	650	60.0	30.0	310	508	71	25	530	3.84	3.19	WWF26x497
598	650	650	50.0	20.0	315	528	61	20	550	3.86	3.21	WWF26x402
499	650	650	40.0	20.0	315	548	51	20	570	3.86	3.21	WWF26x336
400	650	650	30.0	20.0	315	568	41	20	590	3.86	3.21	WWF26x269
793	600	600	60.0	60.0	270	458	71	40	480	3.48	2.88	WWF24x531
680	600	600	60.0	30.0	285	458	71	25	480	3.54	2.94	WWF24x456
551	600	600	50.0	20.0	290	478	61	20	500	3.56	2.96	WWF24x371
460	600	600	40.0	20.0	290	498	51	20	520	3.56	2.96	WWF24x309
369	600	600	30.0	20.0	290	518	41	20	540	3.56	2.96	WWF24x248

WELDED WIDE-FLANGE SHAPES
WWF550 - WWF350

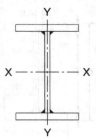

PROPERTIES

Designation[‡]	Dead Load	Area	Axis X-X				Axis Y-Y				Torsional Constant	Warping Constant
			I_x	S_x	r_x	Z_x	I_y	S_y	r_y	Z_y	J	C_w
	kN/m	mm²	10^6 mm⁴	10^3 mm³	mm	10^3 mm³	10^6 mm⁴	10^3 mm³	mm	10^3 mm³	10^3 mm⁴	10^9 mm⁶
WWF550												
♦x721**	7.08	92 000	4 390	16 000	218	19 000	1 670	6 080	135	9 470	110 000	100 000
♦x620**	6.09	79 100	4 190	15 200	230	17 600	1 660	6 050	145	9 180	83 100	99 900
x503	4.94	64 200	3 610	13 100	237	14 800	1 390	5 040	147	7 610	47 000	86 700
x420	4.13	53 600	3 050	11 100	239	12 400	1 110	4 030	144	6 100	24 700	72 100
x280	2.74	35 600	2 070	7 530	241	8 250	693	2 520	140	3 810	6 410	47 800
WWF500												
♦x651**	6.39	83 000	3 200	12 800	196	15 400	1 260	5 030	123	7 850	99 400	60 800
x561**	5.51	71 600	3 070	12 300	207	14 300	1 250	5 000	132	7 590	75 400	60 500
x456	4.48	58 200	2 660	10 600	214	12 100	1 040	4 170	134	6 290	42 700	52 700
x381	3.74	48 600	2 250	9 010	215	10 100	834	3 330	131	5 040	22 500	44 100
x343	3.37	43 800	2 040	8 140	216	9 100	729	2 920	129	4 420	15 400	39 400
x306	3.00	39 000	1 810	7 240	215	8 060	625	2 500	127	3 800	10 200	34 500
x276	2.71	35 200	1 680	6 740	219	7 420	583	2 330	129	3 530	7 920	32 500
x254	2.49	32 300	1 540	6 160	218	6 780	521	2 080	127	3 160	5 820	29 400
x223	2.20	28 500	1 370	5 500	220	6 010	458	1 830	127	2 770	3 970	26 200
x197	1.94	25 200	1 250	4 990	223	5 410	417	1 670	129	2 510	2 870	24 000
WWF450												
x503**	4.93	64 100	2 160	9 620	184	11 400	912	4 050	119	6 150	67 800	34 700
x409	4.02	52 200	1 890	8 380	190	9 640	760	3 380	121	5 100	38 400	30 400
x342	3.36	43 600	1 610	7 150	192	8 100	608	2 700	118	4 090	20 200	25 500
x308	3.02	39 300	1 460	6 480	193	7 290	532	2 360	116	3 580	13 900	22 900
x274	2.69	35 000	1 300	5 770	193	6 470	456	2 030	114	3 080	9 140	20 100
x248	2.44	31 600	1 210	5 380	196	5 960	425	1 890	116	2 860	7 120	18 900
x228	2.24	29 000	1 110	4 920	195	5 450	380	1 690	114	2 560	5 230	17 200
x201	1.97	25 600	991	4 400	197	4 840	334	1 490	114	2 250	3 570	15 300
x177	1.74	22 600	901	4 000	200	4 360	304	1 350	116	2 040	2 580	14 000
WWF400												
x444**	4.36	56 600	1 460	7 300	161	8 770	641	3 200	106	4 870	60 100	18 500
x362	3.56	46 200	1 280	6 410	167	7 480	534	2 670	107	4 030	34 100	16 300
x303	2.97	38 600	1 100	5 500	169	6 300	427	2 130	105	3 230	17 900	13 800
x273	2.68	34 800	1 000	5 000	170	5 680	374	1 870	104	2 840	12 300	12 400
x243	2.39	31 000	894	4 470	170	5 050	320	1 600	102	2 440	8 110	11 000
x220	2.16	28 000	834	4 170	173	4 660	299	1 490	103	2 260	6 320	10 300
x202	1.98	25 700	765	3 830	172	4 260	267	1 330	102	2 020	4 640	9 380
x178	1.75	22 700	686	3 430	174	3 790	235	1 170	102	1 780	3 170	8 390
x157	1.55	20 100	625	3 120	176	3 420	213	1 070	103	1 610	2 290	7 700
WWF350												
x315	3.09	40 200	824	4 710	143	5 580	357	2 040	94.3	3 090	29 800	8 040
x263	2.59	33 600	712	4 070	146	4 730	286	1 630	92.3	2 480	15 700	6 870
x238	2.33	30 300	650	3 720	147	4 280	250	1 430	90.9	2 170	10 800	6 210
x212	2.08	27 000	583	3 330	147	3 810	215	1 230	89.2	1 870	7 070	5 490
x192	1.88	24 400	546	3 120	149	3 520	200	1 140	90.5	1 740	5 520	5 190
x176	1.73	22 400	502	2 870	150	3 220	179	1 020	89.3	1 550	4 060	4 720
x155	1.53	19 800	451	2 580	151	2 870	157	899	89.1	1 360	2 760	4 230
x137	1.35	17 500	412	2 350	153	2 590	143	817	90.3	1 240	2 000	3 890

‡ Nominal depth in millimetres and mass in kilograms per metre
** Welding does not fully develop the web strength for these sections.
♦ Maximum piece weight may limit length.

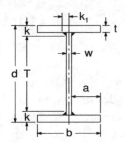

DIMENSIONS AND SURFACE AREAS

Nominal Mass	Depth d	Flange Width b	Flange Thick-ness t	Web Thick-ness w	Distances a	T	k	k₁	d-2t	Surface Area (m²) per metre of length Total	Minus Top of Top Flange	Imperial Designation
kg/m	mm	mm	mm	mm	mm	mm	mm	mm	mm			
721	550	550	60.0	60.0	245	408	71	40	430	3.18	2.63	WWF22x484
620	550	550	60.0	30.0	260	408	71	25	430	3.24	2.69	WWF22x416
503	550	550	50.0	20.0	265	428	61	20	450	3.26	2.71	WWF22x338
420	550	550	40.0	20.0	265	448	51	20	470	3.26	2.71	WWF22x282
280	550	550	25.0	16.0	267	482	34	16	500	3.27	2.72	WWF22x188
651	500	500	60.0	60.0	220	358	71	40	380	2.88	2.38	WWF20x437
561	500	500	60.0	30.0	235	358	71	25	380	2.94	2.44	WWF20x377
456	500	500	50.0	20.0	240	378	61	20	400	2.96	2.46	WWF20x306
381	500	500	40.0	20.0	240	398	51	20	420	2.96	2.46	WWF20x256
343	500	500	35.0	20.0	240	408	46	20	430	2.96	2.46	WWF20x230
306	500	500	30.0	20.0	240	418	41	20	440	2.96	2.46	WWF20x205
276	500	500	28.0	16.0	242	426	37	16	444	2.97	2.47	WWF20x185
254	500	500	25.0	16.0	242	432	34	16	450	2.97	2.47	WWF20x170
223	500	500	22.0	14.0	243	438	31	15	456	2.97	2.47	WWF20x150
197	500	500	20.0	11.0	245	442	29	14	460	2.98	2.48	WWF20x132
503	450	450	60.0	30.0	210	308	71	25	330	2.64	2.19	WWF18x337
409	450	450	50.0	20.0	215	328	61	20	350	2.66	2.21	WWF18x275
342	450	450	40.0	20.0	215	348	51	20	370	2.66	2.21	WWF18x229
308	450	450	35.0	20.0	215	358	46	20	380	2.66	2.21	WWF18x207
274	450	450	30.0	20.0	215	368	41	20	390	2.66	2.21	WWF18x184
248	450	450	28.0	16.0	217	376	37	16	394	2.67	2.22	WWF18x166
228	450	450	25.0	16.0	217	382	34	16	400	2.67	2.22	WWF18x152
201	450	450	22.0	14.0	218	388	31	15	406	2.67	2.22	WWF18x134
177	450	450	20.0	11.0	220	392	29	14	410	2.68	2.23	WWF18x119
444	400	400	60.0	30.0	185	258	71	25	280	2.34	1.94	WWF16x298
362	400	400	50.0	20.0	190	278	61	20	300	2.36	1.96	WWF16x243
303	400	400	40.0	20.0	190	298	51	20	320	2.36	1.96	WWF16x203
273	400	400	35.0	20.0	190	308	46	20	330	2.36	1.96	WWF16x183
243	400	400	30.0	20.0	190	318	41	20	340	2.36	1.96	WWF16x163
220	400	400	28.0	16.0	192	326	37	16	344	2.37	1.97	WWF16x147
202	400	400	25.0	16.0	192	332	34	16	350	2.37	1.97	WWF16x135
178	400	400	22.0	14.0	193	338	31	15	356	2.37	1.97	WWF16x119
157	400	400	20.0	11.0	195	342	29	14	360	2.38	1.98	WWF16x105
315	350	350	50.0	20.0	165	228	61	20	250	2.06	1.71	WWF14x211
263	350	350	40.0	20.0	165	248	51	20	270	2.06	1.71	WWF14x177
238	350	350	35.0	20.0	165	258	46	20	280	2.06	1.71	WWF14x159
212	350	350	30.0	20.0	165	268	41	20	290	2.06	1.71	WWF14x142
192	350	350	28.0	16.0	167	276	37	16	294	2.07	1.72	WWF14x128
176	350	350	25.0	16.0	167	282	34	16	300	2.07	1.72	WWF14x118
155	350	350	22.0	14.0	168	288	31	15	306	2.07	1.72	WWF14x104
137	350	350	20.0	11.0	170	292	29	14	310	2.08	1.73	WWF14x92

ROLLED STRUCTURAL SHAPES

General

The majority of rolled shapes available in Canada are produced either to CSA Standard G40.21 350W, to ASTM A572 grade 50, or to ASTM A992. All of these grades have similar specified minimum values of yield. See pages 6-3 to 6-10 for more information on steel grades, and pages 6-11 to 6-16 for information on tolerances and mill practice.

The tables of properties and dimensions on pages 6-40 to 6-95 include most of the rolled shapes used in construction. Channels and angles not rolled in Canada are identified in the tables by an asterisk (*) and the note "not available from Canadian mills". (See "Principal sources of Structural Sections", page 6-17 for comments regarding Canadian and non-Canadian sections).

Special shapes, such as rolled Tees, Zees, Bulb Angles, Carbuilding and Shipbuilding Channels are produced by some mills. These shapes are generally rolled only at irregular intervals and usually by special arrangement. Their use should, therefore, be avoided unless the quantity of any one size can warrant a rolling. Properties and dimensions of these shapes may be obtained from the appropriate mill catalogs.

Properties and Dimensions

The basic metric dimensions used to compute properties of the rolled steel shapes are taken from the CAN/CSA-G312.3-M92 Standard "Metric Dimensions for Structural Steel Shapes and Hollow Structural Sections". For shapes not listed in this Standard, they are taken from the ASTM A6 Standard or information provided by the producer.

W shapes rolled by most mills supplying the Canadian market have essentially parallel flanges, although some mills offer W shapes with slightly tapered (approximately 3°) flanges. Also the web-to-flange fillet radius may vary slightly for different mills. Properties for W shapes are calculated using the smallest theoretical fillet radius while dimensions for detailing are adjusted for the largest theoretical fillet radius. W shapes are not produced in Canada.

HP shapes are essentially square (equal flange width and overall depth) with parallel flange surfaces and with flanges and web of equal thickness. They are not produced in Canada.

S shapes and Standard channels (C shapes) have tapered flanges with the inside face sloping at approximately 16⅔ % (2 in 12). The tabulated thickness is the mean thickness. S shapes are not available from any Canadian producer.

M and MC shapes are essentially shapes that cannot be classified as W, HP, S or C shapes. They are not rolled in Canada and are usually only produced by a single mill. Availability should be checked before specifying their use. These shapes may be produced with parallel flanges or with tapered flanges of various slopes. Dimensions and properties provided in this Handbook should be suitable for general use, in spite of possible variations in actual dimensions.

Availability of W Shapes

Currently structural steel is widely available and as such makes an excellent choice as a structural material. While there are thousands of sections listed at any one time, the availability of a specific section in a particular region of the country for a specific project and time frame may result in the fabricator requesting a substitution. Some sections are almost always available due to a constant demand for them. It is important to remember that the least-cost solution is not always the least-weight alternative.

When Algoma Steel stopped rolling structural shapes in 2000, the availability of those W shapes that were exclusively rolled by Algoma was thrown into question (a partial list is given below). Since then certain mills that regularly supplied to the Canadian market have produced these sections. Currently, the status of these sections is as follows:

- W610x91, W610x84, W460x67 and W460x61: produced by Nucor-Yamato

Even if produced, these sections may be subject to rolling schedules and may not necessarily be stocked by steel service centres or available to fabricators in your area. In the design tables throughout this Handbook, these sections are denoted by grey font so as to caution users regarding their restricted availability.

Angles

Properties and dimensions in metric units are provided for the imperial series hot-rolled angles for equal-leg angles and for unequal-leg angles. The tables include properties and dimensions for single angles and for two equal-leg angles back-to-back, two unequal-leg angles with short legs back-to-back, and two unequal-leg angles with long legs back-to-back. Section properties of hot-rolled angles are based on flat rectangular legs excluding the fillet and roundings.

The properties of angles produced by cold-forming may be up to 7 percent less than the properties of hot-rolled angles of similar size due to the absence of a heel. Designers encountering cold-formed angles should consult the manufacturer's catalog for the exact dimensions and properties.

For the definition of torsional properties x_o, y_o, $\bar{r}_o$ and Ω given in the tables, see CSA S16-09 Clause 13.3.2. The Y-Y axis of symmetry of equal-leg angles corresponds to X'-X' in the tables.

Tees cut from W shapes

Properties and dimensions of Tees are based on W shapes assuming a depth of the Tee equal to one-half the depth of the W shape. Tees are not rolled in Canada, and are usually fabricated from W shapes by splitting the web either using rotary shears or flame cutting and subsequently straightening to meet published tolerances.

For the definition of torsional properties y_o, $\bar{r}_o$ and Ω, see CSA S16-09 Clause 13.3.2.

Structural Section Tables (SST Database)

Properties and dimensions of welded and rolled steel shapes are available in the form of an electronic database from the Canadian Institute of Steel Construction (CISC). The SST database is in Excel spreadsheet format and contains additional information such as flange slopes, width-to-thickness ratios, and special torsional and buckling constants. Further details on the SST database may be found on CISC's website (*www.cisc-icca.ca*).

W SHAPES
W1100 - W920

PROPERTIES

Designation‡	Dead Load	Area	Axis X-X				Axis Y-Y				Torsional Constant	Warping Constant
			I_x	S_x	r_x	Z_x	I_y	S_y	r_y	Z_y	J	C_w
	kN/m	mm²	10^6 mm⁴	10^3 mm³	mm	10^3 mm³	10^6 mm⁴	10^3 mm³	mm	10^3 mm³	10^3 mm⁴	10^9 mm⁶
W1100												
x499	4.89	63 500	12 900	23 100	451	26 600	500	2 470	88.7	3 870	31 100	144 000
x433	4.24	55 100	11 300	20 300	452	23 200	434	2 160	88.7	3 360	21 200	124 000
x390	3.83	49 700	10 100	18 300	450	20 800	385	1 920	88.0	2 990	15 600	109 000
x343	3.36	43 600	8 670	15 900	446	18 100	331	1 660	87.1	2 570	10 300	92 900
W1000												
x883	8.67	113 000	21 000	38 400	432	45 300	1 050	4 950	96.6	7 870	185 000	268 000
x748	7.34	95 300	17 300	32 400	426	37 900	851	4 080	94.5	6 460	116 000	212 000
x642	6.30	81 800	14 500	27 700	421	32 100	703	3 410	92.7	5 380	73 800	172 000
x591	5.80	75 300	13 300	25 600	421	29 500	640	3 130	92.2	4 920	59 000	155 000
x554	5.44	70 600	12 300	23 900	418	27 500	591	2 900	91.5	4 550	48 300	142 000
x539	5.29	68 700	12 000	23 400	418	26 800	576	2 830	91.6	4 440	45 300	138 000
x483	4.74	61 500	10 700	20 900	417	23 900	507	2 510	90.8	3 920	33 100	120 000
x443	4.34	56 400	9 670	19 100	414	21 800	455	2 260	89.8	3 530	25 400	107 000
x412	4.04	52 500	9 100	18 100	416	20 500	434	2 160	90.9	3 350	21 400	102 000
x371	3.64	47 300	8 140	16 300	415	18 400	386	1 930	90.3	2 980	15 900	89 600
x321	3.15	40 900	6 960	14 100	413	15 800	331	1 660	90.0	2 550	10 300	76 100
x296	2.91	37 800	6 200	12 600	405	14 300	290	1 450	87.6	2 240	7 640	66 000
W1000												
x584	5.73	74 400	12 500	23 600	409	28 000	334	2 130	67.0	3 470	71 500	82 200
x494	4.84	62 900	10 300	19 800	404	23 400	268	1 740	65.3	2 820	44 000	64 700
x486	4.77	61 900	10 200	19 700	406	23 200	266	1 730	65.5	2 790	42 900	64 100
x438	4.28	55 600	9 090	17 700	404	20 700	234	1 530	64.8	2 460	31 800	55 700
x415	4.07	52 900	8 530	16 700	402	19 600	217	1 430	64.1	2 300	27 000	51 500
x393	3.85	50 000	8 080	15 900	402	18 500	205	1 350	64.0	2 170	23 300	48 400
x350	3.43	44 500	7 230	14 300	403	16 600	185	1 220	64.4	1 940	17 200	43 200
x314	3.08	40 000	6 440	12 900	401	14 900	162	1 080	63.7	1 710	12 600	37 700
x272	2.67	34 700	5 540	11 200	400	12 800	140	933	63.5	1 470	8 350	32 200
x249	2.44	31 700	4 810	9 820	390	11 300	118	783	60.9	1 240	5 820	26 700
x222	2.18	28 300	4 080	8 410	380	9 800	95.4	636	58.1	1 020	3 900	21 500
W920												
x656	6.45	83 700	13 400	27 100	400	31 400	831	3 850	99.6	6 030	80 700	178 000
x588	5.78	75 000	11 800	24 300	397	27 900	728	3 410	98.5	5 310	59 000	154 000
x537	5.27	68 400	10 700	22 200	395	25 300	656	3 090	97.9	4 800	45 300	137 000
x491	4.81	62 500	9 700	20 300	394	23 100	590	2 800	97.2	4 340	35 100	122 000
x449	4.41	57 300	8 780	18 500	391	21 000	540	2 550	97.0	3 950	26 800	111 000
x420	4.13	53 600	8 170	17 300	390	19 600	501	2 370	96.7	3 670	22 000	102 000
x390	3.82	49 600	7 450	15 900	388	18 000	453	2 160	95.5	3 330	17 300	91 600
x368	3.60	46 700	6 960	14 900	386	16 900	421	2 010	94.9	3 110	14 500	84 700
x344	3.38	43 900	6 480	14 000	384	15 800	390	1 870	94.3	2 880	11 900	78 100

‡ Nominal depth in millimetres and mass in kilograms per metre

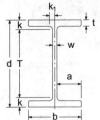

DIMENSIONS AND SURFACE AREAS

Nominal Mass	Theo-retical Mass	Depth	Flange Width	Flange Thick-ness	Web Thick-ness	Distances					Surface Area (m²) per metre of length		Imperial Designation
		d	b	t	w	a	T	k	k₁	d-2t	Total	Minus Top of Top Flange	
kg/m	kg/m	mm	mm	mm	mm	mm	mm	mm	mm	mm			
499	498.6	1 118	405	45.0	26.0	190	985	67	33	1 028	3.80	3.40	W44x335
433	432.7	1 108	402	40.0	22.0	190	985	62	31	1 028	3.78	3.38	W44x290
390	390.2	1 100	400	36.0	20.0	190	985	58	30	1 028	3.76	3.36	W44x262
343	342.6	1 090	400	31.0	18.0	191	985	53	29	1 028	3.74	3.34	W44x230
883	883.4	1 092	424	82.0	45.5	189	865	114	53	928	3.79	3.37	W40x593
748	748.5	1 068	417	70.0	39.0	189	865	102	50	928	3.73	3.31	W40x503
642	641.9	1 048	412	60.0	34.0	189	865	92	47	928	3.68	3.26	W40x431
591	590.9	1 040	409	55.9	31.0	189	865	87	46	928	3.65	3.25	W40x397
554	554.1	1 032	408	52.0	29.5	189	865	84	45	928	3.64	3.23	W40x372
539	539.4	1 030	407	51.1	28.4	189	865	83	44	928	3.63	3.22	W40x362
483	482.9	1 020	404	46.0	25.4	189	865	78	43	928	3.61	3.20	W40x324
443	442.5	1 012	402	41.9	23.6	189	865	73	42	928	3.58	3.18	W40x297
412	412.2	1 008	402	40.0	21.1	190	865	72	41	928	3.58	3.18	W40x277
371	371.2	1 000	400	36.1	19.0	191	865	68	40	928	3.56	3.16	W40x249
321	320.9	990	400	31.0	16.5	192	865	63	38	928	3.55	3.15	W40x215
296	296.4	982	400	27.1	16.5	192	865	59	38	928	3.53	3.13	W40x199
584	583.8	1 056	314	64.0	36.0	139	865	96	48	928	3.30	2.98	W40x392
494	493.9	1 036	309	54.0	31.0	139	865	86	46	928	3.25	2.94	W40x331
486	486.2	1 036	308	54.1	30.0	139	865	86	45	928	3.24	2.94	W40x327
438	436.7	1 026	305	49.0	26.9	139	865	81	43	928	3.22	2.91	W40x294
415	415.0	1 020	304	46.0	26.0	139	865	78	43	928	3.20	2.90	W40x278
393	392.7	1 016	303	43.9	24.4	139	865	75	42	928	3.20	2.89	W40x264
350	349.4	1 008	302	40.0	21.1	140	865	72	41	928	3.18	2.88	W40x235
314	314.3	1 000	300	35.9	19.1	140	865	67	40	928	3.16	2.86	W40x211
272	272.3	990	300	31.0	16.5	142	865	63	38	928	3.15	2.85	W40x183
249	248.7	980	300	26.0	16.5	142	865	58	38	928	3.13	2.83	W40x167
222	222.0	970	300	21.1	16.0	142	865	53	38	928	3.11	2.81	W40x149
656	657.2	987	431	62.0	34.5	198	800	94	47	863	3.63	3.20	W36x441
588	588.7	975	427	55.9	31.0	198	800	87	46	863	3.60	3.17	W36x395
537	537.2	965	425	51.1	28.4	198	800	83	44	863	3.57	3.15	W36x361
491	490.8	957	422	47.0	25.9	198	800	79	43	863	3.55	3.13	W36x330
449	450.0	948	423	42.7	24.0	200	800	74	42	863	3.54	3.12	W36x302
420	420.7	943	422	39.9	22.5	200	800	71	41	863	3.53	3.11	W36x282
390	389.5	936	420	36.6	21.3	199	800	68	41	863	3.51	3.09	W36x262
368	367.0	931	419	34.3	20.3	199	799	66	40	862	3.50	3.08	W36x247
344	344.7	927	418	32.0	19.3	199	800	64	40	863	3.49	3.07	W36x231

W SHAPES
W920 - W760

PROPERTIES

Designation‡	Dead Load	Area	Axis X-X				Axis Y-Y				Torsional Constant	Warping Constant
			I_x	S_x	r_x	Z_x	I_y	S_y	r_y	Z_y	J	C_w
	kN/m	mm²	10^6 mm⁴	10^3 mm³	mm	10^3 mm³	10^6 mm⁴	10^3 mm³	mm	10^3 mm³	10^3 mm⁴	10^9 mm⁶
W920												
x381	3.74	48 600	6 970	14 700	379	17 000	219	1 410	67.1	2 240	22 000	45 100
x345	3.39	44 000	6 260	13 300	377	15 300	195	1 270	66.6	2 000	16 500	39 800
x313	3.07	39 800	5 480	11 800	371	13 600	170	1 100	65.4	1 750	11 600	34 300
x289	2.83	36 800	5 050	10 900	370	12 600	156	1 020	65.2	1 600	9 230	31 300
x271	2.67	34 600	4 720	10 200	369	11 800	145	946	64.8	1 490	7 700	28 900
x253	2.49	32 300	4 380	9 520	368	11 000	134	874	64.3	1 370	6 270	26 500
x238	2.34	30 400	4 060	8 880	366	10 200	123	806	63.6	1 270	5 150	24 300
x223	2.20	28 600	3 770	8 270	363	9 540	112	738	62.7	1 160	4 220	22 100
x201	1.98	25 600	3 250	7 200	356	8 360	94.4	621	60.7	982	2 910	18 400
W840												
x576	5.66	73 400	10 100	22 200	371	25 600	672	3 270	95.7	5 100	61 700	123 000
x527	5.18	67 300	9 150	20 300	369	23 300	607	2 970	95.0	4 620	47 800	110 000
x473	4.65	60 400	8 130	18 200	367	20 800	537	2 640	94.3	4 100	35 100	95 800
x433	4.26	55 300	7 360	16 600	365	18 900	484	2 390	93.5	3 710	27 000	85 500
x392	3.85	50 000	6 600	15 000	363	17 000	430	2 140	92.7	3 310	20 300	75 300
x359	3.53	45 800	5 920	13 600	359	15 400	389	1 930	92.1	2 980	15 100	67 400
x329	3.24	42 000	5 360	12 400	357	14 000	349	1 740	91.1	2 690	11 600	60 000
x299	2.94	38 200	4 800	11 200	355	12 700	312	1 560	90.4	2 410	8 660	53 200
W840												
x251	2.46	31 900	3 860	9 000	348	10 300	129	884	63.6	1 380	7 350	22 100
x226	2.22	28 900	3 400	7 990	343	9 160	114	774	62.8	1 210	5 140	19 300
x210	2.07	26 800	3 110	7 340	340	8 430	103	700	61.8	1 100	4 050	17 300
x193	1.90	24 700	2 780	6 630	336	7 620	90.3	618	60.5	971	3 050	15 100
x176	1.73	22 400	2 460	5 900	331	6 810	78.2	536	59.1	844	2 220	13 000
W760												
x582	5.72	74 300	8 620	20 400	341	23 800	644	3 250	93.2	5 080	72 200	98 300
x531	5.22	67 700	7 770	18 600	339	21 600	578	2 940	92.4	4 580	55 600	87 000
x484	4.76	61 800	6 990	17 000	336	19 500	517	2 650	91.4	4 120	42 800	76 800
x434	4.26	55 300	6 190	15 200	334	17 400	455	2 350	90.7	3 650	31 300	66 800
x389	3.82	49 600	5 450	13 600	332	15 500	399	2 070	89.8	3 210	22 500	57 800
x350	3.44	44 600	4 870	12 200	330	13 900	355	1 860	89.1	2 870	16 800	50 800
x314	3.09	40 200	4 290	10 900	327	12 300	316	1 640	88.7	2 540	11 800	44 700
x284	2.79	36 300	3 830	9 820	325	11 100	280	1 470	87.9	2 260	8 750	39 300
x257	2.54	32 900	3 430	8 880	323	9 970	250	1 310	87.2	2 020	6 510	34 800
W760												
x220	2.16	28 100	2 780	7 140	315	8 190	94.4	710	58.0	1 110	6 050	13 200
x196	1.93	25 100	2 400	6 240	309	7 170	81.7	610	57.1	959	4 040	11 300
x185	1.81	23 500	2 230	5 820	308	6 690	75.1	563	56.5	884	3 330	10 300
x173	1.70	22 100	2 060	5 400	305	6 210	68.7	515	55.7	810	2 690	9 420
x161	1.57	20 400	1 860	4 900	302	5 660	60.7	457	54.5	720	2 070	8 280
x147	1.44	18 700	1 660	4 410	298	5 100	52.9	399	53.1	631	1 560	7 160
x134	1.31	17 000	1 500	4 010	297	4 630	47.7	361	53.0	568	1 180	6 430

‡ Nominal depth in millimetres and mass in kilograms per metre

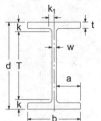

DIMENSIONS AND SURFACE AREAS

Nominal Mass	Theo-retical Mass	Depth d	Flange Width b	Flange Thick-ness t	Web Thick-ness w	Distances					Surface Area (m²) per metre of length		Imperial Designation
						a	T	k	k₁	d - 2t	Total	Minus Top of Top Flange	
kg/m	kg/m	mm	mm	mm	mm	mm	mm	mm	mm	mm			
381	381.5	951	310	43.9	24.4	143	820	66	33	863	3.09	2.78	W36x256
345	345.2	943	308	39.9	22.1	143	820	62	31	863	3.07	2.77	W36x232
313	312.8	932	309	34.5	21.1	144	819	56	31	863	3.06	2.75	W36x210
289	288.6	927	308	32.0	19.4	144	819	54	30	863	3.05	2.74	W36x194
271	271.7	923	307	30.0	18.4	144	819	52	30	863	3.04	2.73	W36x182
253	253.7	919	306	27.9	17.3	144	820	50	29	863	3.03	2.72	W36x170
238	238.3	915	305	25.9	16.5	144	820	48	29	863	3.02	2.71	W36x160
223	224.3	911	304	23.9	15.9	144	820	46	28	863	3.01	2.70	W36x150
201	201.3	903	304	20.1	15.2	144	819	42	28	863	2.99	2.69	W36x135
576	576.6	913	411	57.9	32.0	190	754	79	36	797	3.41	3.00	W33x387
527	528.2	903	409	53.1	29.5	190	754	75	35	797	3.38	2.97	W33x354
473	473.8	893	406	48.0	26.4	190	754	70	33	797	3.36	2.95	W33x318
433	433.8	885	404	43.9	24.4	190	754	65	32	797	3.34	2.93	W33x291
392	392.2	877	401	39.9	22.1	189	754	61	31	797	3.31	2.91	W33x263
359	359.9	868	403	35.6	21.1	191	754	57	31	797	3.31	2.90	W33x241
329	330.0	862	401	32.4	19.7	191	754	54	30	797	3.29	2.89	W33x221
299	299.9	855	400	29.2	18.2	191	754	51	29	797	3.27	2.87	W33x201
251	250.6	859	292	31.0	17.0	138	753	53	29	797	2.85	2.56	W33x169
226	226.6	851	294	26.8	16.1	139	754	49	28	797	2.85	2.55	W33x152
210	210.8	846	293	24.4	15.4	139	754	46	28	797	2.83	2.54	W33x141
193	193.5	840	292	21.7	14.7	139	753	44	28	797	2.82	2.53	W33x130
176	176.0	835	292	18.8	14.0	139	754	41	27	797	2.81	2.52	W33x118
582	582.9	843	396	62.0	34.5	181	676	84	37	719	3.20	2.81	W30x391
531	531.6	833	393	56.9	31.5	181	676	78	36	719	3.18	2.78	W30x357
484	485.3	823	390	52.1	29.0	181	676	74	35	719	3.15	2.76	W30x326
434	434.4	813	387	47.0	26.2	181	676	69	33	719	3.12	2.74	W30x292
389	389.2	803	385	41.9	23.6	181	676	63	32	719	3.10	2.71	W30x261
350	350.3	795	382	38.1	21.1	180	676	60	31	719	3.08	2.69	W30x235
314	315.3	786	384	33.4	19.7	182	676	55	30	719	3.07	2.68	W30x211
284	284.8	779	382	30.1	18.0	182	676	52	29	719	3.05	2.67	W30x191
257	258.5	773	381	27.1	16.6	182	676	49	28	719	3.04	2.66	W30x173
220	220.2	779	266	30.0	16.5	125	675	52	29	719	2.59	2.32	W30x148
196	196.8	770	268	25.4	15.6	126	676	47	28	719	2.58	2.31	W30x132
185	184.8	766	267	23.6	14.9	126	675	45	28	719	2.57	2.30	W30x124
173	173.6	762	267	21.6	14.4	126	675	43	28	719	2.56	2.30	W30x116
161	160.4	758	266	19.3	13.8	126	676	41	27	719	2.55	2.29	W30x108
147	147.1	753	265	17.0	13.2	126	675	39	27	719	2.54	2.27	W30x99
134	133.2	750	264	15.5	11.9	126	675	37	26	719	2.53	2.27	W30x90

PROPERTIES

Designation‡	Dead Load	Area	Axis X-X				Axis Y-Y				Torsional Constant	Warping Constant
			I_x	S_x	r_x	Z_x	I_y	S_y	r_y	Z_y	J	C_w
	kN/m	mm²	10^6 mm⁴	10^3 mm³	mm	10^3 mm³	10^6 mm⁴	10^3 mm³	mm	10^3 mm³	10^3 mm⁴	10^9 mm⁶
W690												
x548	5.38	69 900	6 730	17 400	310	20 400	543	2 920	88.1	4 570	70 700	68 200
x500	4.91	63 800	6 060	15 900	308	18 500	487	2 640	87.4	4 110	54 600	60 300
x457	4.49	58 400	5 470	14 500	306	16 800	439	2 390	86.7	3 720	42 300	53 600
x419	4.11	53 400	4 950	13 300	305	15 300	395	2 170	86.0	3 370	33 000	47 700
x384	3.77	49 000	4 490	12 200	303	14 000	357	1 970	85.3	3 050	25 700	42 600
x350	3.44	44 700	4 030	11 100	300	12 600	319	1 770	84.4	2 740	19 500	37 600
x323	3.18	41 300	3 710	10 300	300	11 700	294	1 640	84.4	2 530	15 700	34 400
x289	2.84	36 800	3 260	9 140	298	10 300	256	1 440	83.4	2 220	11 200	29 600
x265	2.61	33 800	2 920	8 270	294	9 330	231	1 290	82.7	1 990	8 340	26 400
x240	2.36	30 700	2 630	7 490	292	8 430	206	1 160	82.0	1 790	6 270	23 400
x217	2.15	27 900	2 360	6 790	291	7 610	185	1 040	81.5	1 610	4 720	20 800
W690												
x192	1.88	24 400	1 980	5 640	285	6 460	76.4	602	56.0	941	4 620	8 680
x170	1.67	21 600	1 700	4 910	280	5 620	66.2	517	55.3	809	3 050	7 410
x152	1.49	19 400	1 510	4 380	279	5 000	57.8	455	54.6	710	2 200	6 420
x140	1.37	17 800	1 360	3 980	276	4 550	51.7	407	53.9	636	1 670	5 720
x125	1.23	16 000	1 190	3 500	272	4 010	44.1	349	52.5	546	1 180	4 830
W610												
x551	5.41	70 200	5 570	15 700	282	18 600	484	2 790	83.0	4 380	83 800	49 900
x498	4.89	63 500	4 950	14 200	279	16 700	426	2 480	81.9	3 890	63 200	43 100
x455	4.46	57 900	4 440	12 900	277	15 100	381	2 240	81.1	3 500	48 800	37 900
x415	4.08	52 900	4 000	11 800	275	13 700	343	2 030	80.5	3 160	37 700	33 600
x372	3.65	47 400	3 530	10 600	273	12 200	302	1 800	79.8	2 800	27 700	29 100
x341	3.34	43 400	3 180	9 630	271	11 100	271	1 630	79.0	2 520	21 300	25 800
x307	3.01	39 100	2 840	8 690	269	9 930	240	1 450	78.2	2 240	15 900	22 500
x285	2.80	36 300	2 610	8 060	268	9 170	221	1 340	77.9	2 070	12 800	20 500
x262	2.56	33 300	2 360	7 360	266	8 350	198	1 210	77.2	1 870	9 900	18 300
x241	2.37	30 800	2 150	6 780	264	7 670	184	1 120	77.4	1 730	7 700	16 800
x217	2.14	27 800	1 910	6 070	262	6 850	163	995	76.7	1 530	5 600	14 700
x195	1.92	24 900	1 680	5 400	260	6 070	142	871	75.6	1 340	3 970	12 700
x174	1.71	22 200	1 470	4 780	257	5 360	124	761	74.7	1 170	2 800	10 900
x155	1.52	19 700	1 290	4 220	256	4 730	108	666	73.9	1 020	1 950	9 450
W610												
x153	1.51	19 600	1 250	4 020	253	4 600	50.0	437	50.5	682	2 950	4 470
x140	1.37	17 900	1 120	3 630	250	4 150	45.1	392	50.3	613	2 180	3 990
x125	1.23	15 900	985	3 220	249	3 670	39.3	343	49.7	535	1 540	3 450
x113	1.11	14 400	875	2 880	246	3 290	34.3	300	48.7	469	1 120	2 990
x101	0.997	13 000	764	2 530	243	2 900	29.5	259	47.7	404	781	2 550
x91†	0.882	11 500	657	2 200	239	2 520	24.8	219	46.5	342	531	2 120
x84†	0.815	10 600	603	2 020	239	2 320	22.6	200	46.2	311	420	1 920
W610												
x92	0.905	11 800	646	2 140	234	2 510	14.4	161	35.0	258	710	1 250
x82	0.803	10 400	560	1 870	232	2 200	12.1	136	34.0	218	488	1 040

‡ Nominal depth in millimetres and mass in kilograms per metre

† Check availability

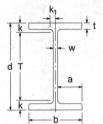

DIMENSIONS AND SURFACE AREAS

Nominal Mass	Theo-retical Mass	Depth d	Flange Width b	Flange Thick-ness t	Web Thick-ness w	Distances					Surface Area (m²) per metre of length		Imperial Designation
						a	T	k	k_1	d-2t	Total	Minus Top of Top Flange	
kg/m	kg/m	mm	mm	mm	mm	mm	mm	mm	mm	mm			
548	548.6	772	372	63.0	35.1	168	602	85	38	646	2.96	2.59	W27x368
500	500.5	762	369	57.9	32.0	169	603	80	36	646	2.94	2.57	W27x336
457	458.2	752	367	53.1	29.5	169	602	75	35	646	2.91	2.55	W27x307
419	419.1	744	364	49.0	26.9	169	602	71	34	646	2.89	2.53	W27x281
384	384.7	736	362	45.0	24.9	169	602	67	33	646	2.87	2.51	W27x258
350	351.0	728	360	40.9	23.1	168	603	63	32	646	2.85	2.49	W27x235
323	324.4	722	359	38.1	21.1	169	602	60	31	646	2.84	2.48	W27x217
289	289.1	714	356	34.0	19.0	169	602	56	30	646	2.81	2.46	W27x194
265	265.7	706	358	30.2	18.4	170	602	52	30	646	2.81	2.45	W27x178
240	241.1	701	356	27.4	16.8	170	603	49	29	646	2.79	2.44	W27x161
217	218.9	695	355	24.8	15.4	170	602	47	28	645	2.78	2.42	W27x146
192	191.4	702	254	27.9	15.5	119	603	50	28	646	2.39	2.14	W27x129
170	169.9	693	256	23.6	14.5	121	602	45	28	646	2.38	2.13	W27x114
152	152.1	688	254	21.1	13.1	120	602	43	27	646	2.37	2.11	W27x102
140	139.8	684	254	18.9	12.4	121	603	41	27	646	2.36	2.11	W27x94
125	125.6	678	253	16.3	11.7	121	602	38	26	645	2.34	2.09	W27x84
551	551.1	711	347	69.1	38.6	154	529	91	40	573	2.73	2.39	W24x370
498	498.2	699	343	63.0	35.1	154	529	85	38	573	2.70	2.36	W24x335
455	454.1	689	340	57.9	32.0	154	530	80	36	573	2.67	2.33	W24x306
415	415.5	679	338	53.1	29.5	154	529	75	35	573	2.65	2.31	W24x279
372	372.3	669	335	48.0	26.4	154	529	70	34	573	2.63	2.29	W24x250
341	340.4	661	333	43.9	24.4	154	530	66	33	573	2.61	2.27	W24x229
307	307.3	653	330	39.9	22.1	154	530	62	31	573	2.58	2.25	W24x207
285	285.3	647	329	37.1	20.6	154	529	59	31	573	2.57	2.24	W24x192
262	261.1	641	327	34.0	19.0	154	529	56	30	573	2.55	2.23	W24x176
241	241.7	635	329	31.0	17.9	156	529	53	29	573	2.55	2.22	W24x162
217	217.9	628	328	27.7	16.5	156	529	50	29	573	2.54	2.21	W24x146
195	195.6	622	327	24.4	15.4	156	530	46	28	573	2.52	2.19	W24x131
174	174.3	616	325	21.6	14.0	156	529	43	27	573	2.50	2.18	W24x117
155	154.9	611	324	19.0	12.7	156	529	41	27	573	2.49	2.17	W24x104
153	153.6	623	229	24.9	14.0	108	530	47	27	573	2.13	1.91	W24x103
140	140.1	617	230	22.2	13.1	108	529	44	27	573	2.13	1.90	W24x94
125	125.1	612	229	19.6	11.9	109	529	41	26	573	2.12	1.89	W24x84
113	113.4	608	228	17.3	11.2	108	530	39	26	573	2.11	1.88	W24x76
101	101.7	603	228	14.9	10.5	109	530	37	26	573	2.10	1.87	W24x68
91	89.9	598	227	12.7	9.7	109	529	35	25	573	2.08	1.86	W24x61
84	83.1	596	226	11.7	9.0	109	529	34	25	573	2.08	1.85	W24x56
92	92.3	603	179	15.0	10.9	84	530	37	25	573	1.90	1.72	W24x62
82	81.9	599	178	12.8	10.0	84	530	34	25	573	1.89	1.71	W24x55

W SHAPES
W530 - W460

PROPERTIES

Designation‡	Dead Load	Area	Axis X-X				Axis Y-Y				Torsional Constant	Warping Constant
			I_x	S_x	r_x	Z_x	I_y	S_y	r_y	Z_y	J	C_w
	kN/m	mm²	10^6 mm⁴	10^3 mm³	mm	10^3 mm³	10^6 mm⁴	10^3 mm³	mm	10^3 mm³	10^3 mm⁴	10^9 mm⁶
W530												
x300	2.94	38 200	2 210	7 550	241	8 670	225	1 410	76.7	2 180	17 000	16 600
x272	2.67	34 600	1 970	6 840	239	7 810	202	1 270	76.4	1 960	12 800	14 700
x248	2.42	31 400	1 770	6 220	238	7 060	180	1 140	75.7	1 760	9 770	13 000
x219	2.15	27 900	1 510	5 390	233	6 110	157	986	75.0	1 520	6 420	11 000
x196	1.93	25 000	1 340	4 840	231	5 460	139	877	74.4	1 350	4 700	9 640
x182	1.78	23 100	1 240	4 480	231	5 040	127	808	74.2	1 240	3 740	8 820
x165	1.62	21 100	1 110	4 060	230	4 550	114	726	73.4	1 110	2 830	7 790
x150	1.48	19 200	1 010	3 710	229	4 150	103	659	73.2	1 010	2 160	7 030
W530												
x138	1.36	17 600	861	3 140	221	3 610	38.7	362	46.9	569	2 500	2 670
x123	1.21	15 700	761	2 800	220	3 210	33.8	319	46.4	499	1 800	2 310
x109	1.07	13 900	667	2 480	219	2 830	29.5	280	46.1	437	1 260	2 000
x101	0.995	12 900	617	2 300	219	2 620	26.9	256	45.6	400	1 020	1 820
x92	0.907	11 800	552	2 070	217	2 360	23.8	228	44.9	355	762	1 590
x82	0.806	10 500	477	1 810	213	2 060	20.3	194	44.0	303	518	1 340
x72	0.702	9 120	400	1 520	209	1 750	16.2	156	42.1	244	334	1 060
W530												
x85	0.831	10 800	485	1 810	212	2 100	12.6	152	34.2	242	737	849
x74	0.733	9 520	411	1 550	208	1 810	10.4	125	33.1	200	480	692
x66	0.645	8 370	351	1 340	205	1 560	8.57	104	32.0	166	320	565
W460												
x464	4.55	59 100	2 900	10 200	222	12 400	331	2 170	74.9	3 400	73 100	20 500
x421	4.14	53 700	2 570	9 250	219	11 100	293	1 940	73.9	3 030	55 700	17 700
x384	3.77	48 900	2 290	8 420	217	10 000	261	1 750	73.1	2 730	42 700	15 500
x349	3.42	44 400	2 040	7 640	214	9 010	233	1 570	72.3	2 440	32 800	13 500
x315	3.08	40 000	1 800	6 850	212	8 020	204	1 390	71.4	2 160	24 300	11 600
x286	2.80	36 400	1 610	6 230	210	7 240	183	1 260	70.9	1 940	18 600	10 200
x260	2.55	33 100	1 440	5 650	208	6 530	163	1 130	70.1	1 740	14 100	8 950
x235	2.30	29 900	1 270	5 080	206	5 840	145	1 010	69.5	1 550	10 500	7 790
x213	2.09	27 100	1 140	4 620	205	5 270	129	909	69.1	1 400	7 970	6 890
x193	1.90	24 600	1 020	4 190	204	4 750	115	816	68.5	1 250	6 030	6 060
x177	1.74	22 600	910	3 780	201	4 280	105	735	68.2	1 130	4 410	5 440
x158	1.55	20 100	796	3 350	199	3 780	91.4	643	67.4	989	3 120	4 670
x144	1.42	18 400	726	3 080	199	3 450	83.6	591	67.4	906	2 440	4 230
x128	1.26	16 400	637	2 730	197	3 050	73.3	520	66.9	796	1 720	3 670
x113	1.11	14 400	556	2 400	196	2 670	63.3	452	66.3	691	1 180	3 150
W460												
x106	1.04	13 500	488	2 080	190	2 390	25.1	259	43.2	405	1 460	1 260
x97	0.947	12 300	445	1 910	190	2 180	22.8	237	43.1	368	1 130	1 140
x89	0.876	11 400	410	1 770	190	2 010	20.9	218	42.9	339	907	1 040
x82	0.804	10 400	370	1 610	188	1 830	18.6	195	42.2	303	691	918
x74	0.728	9 450	333	1 460	188	1 650	16.6	175	41.9	271	517	813
x67†	0.659	8 560	295	1 300	186	1 470	14.5	153	41.2	238	372	708
x61†	0.588	7 640	254	1 130	182	1 290	12.2	129	39.9	200	256	587

‡ Nominal depth in millimetres and mass in kilograms per metre

† Check availability

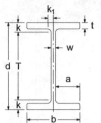

DIMENSIONS AND SURFACE AREAS

Nominal Mass	Theo-retical Mass	Depth	Flange Width	Flange Thick-ness	Web Thick-ness	Distances					Surface Area (m²) per metre of length		Imperial Designation
		d	b	t	w	a	T	k	k₁	d-2t	Total	Minus Top of Top Flange	
kg/m	kg/m	mm	mm	mm	mm	mm	mm	mm	mm	mm			
300	299.5	585	319	41.4	23.1	148	459	63	32	502	2.40	2.08	W21x201
272	271.9	577	318	37.6	21.1	148	458	59	31	502	2.38	2.07	W21x182
248	246.6	571	315	34.5	19.0	148	458	56	30	502	2.36	2.05	W21x166
219	218.9	560	318	29.2	18.3	150	458	51	29	502	2.36	2.04	W21x147
196	196.5	554	316	26.3	16.5	150	458	48	29	501	2.34	2.02	W21x132
182	181.7	551	315	24.4	15.2	150	459	46	28	502	2.33	2.02	W21x122
165	165.3	546	313	22.2	14.0	150	458	44	27	502	2.32	2.00	W21x111
150	150.6	543	312	20.3	12.7	150	459	42	27	502	2.31	2.00	W21x101
138	138.3	549	214	23.6	14.7	100	468	40	23	502	1.92	1.71	W21x93
123	123.2	544	212	21.2	13.1	99	468	38	22	502	1.91	1.70	W21x83
109	109.0	539	211	18.8	11.6	100	468	36	21	501	1.90	1.69	W21x73
101	101.4	537	210	17.4	10.9	100	469	34	21	502	1.89	1.68	W21x68
92	92.5	533	209	15.6	10.2	99	468	32	20	502	1.88	1.67	W21x62
82	82.1	528	209	13.3	9.5	100	468	30	20	501	1.87	1.66	W21x55
72	71.6	524	207	10.9	8.9	99	469	28	20	502	1.86	1.65	W21x48
85	84.7	535	166	16.5	10.3	78	469	33	20	502	1.71	1.55	W21x57
74	74.7	529	166	13.6	9.7	78	468	30	20	502	1.70	1.54	W21x50
66	65.7	525	165	11.4	8.9	78	469	28	20	502	1.69	1.53	W21x44
464	464.0	567	305	69.6	38.6	133	394	86	35	428	2.28	1.97	W18x311
421	421.8	555	302	63.5	35.6	133	395	80	33	428	2.25	1.94	W18x283
384	384.1	545	299	58.4	32.5	133	395	75	31	428	2.22	1.92	W18x258
349	348.9	535	296	53.6	29.5	133	394	70	30	428	2.20	1.90	W18x234
315	314.2	525	293	48.5	26.9	133	395	65	29	428	2.17	1.88	W18x211
286	285.6	517	291	44.4	24.4	133	395	61	27	428	2.15	1.86	W18x192
260	260.0	509	289	40.4	22.6	133	385	62	32	428	2.13	1.84	W18x175
235	234.8	501	287	36.6	20.6	133	384	58	31	428	2.11	1.82	W18x158
213	212.8	495	285	33.5	18.5	133	384	55	30	428	2.09	1.81	W18x143
193	193.3	489	283	30.5	17.0	133	384	52	29	428	2.08	1.79	W18x130
177	177.3	482	286	26.9	16.6	135	385	49	29	428	2.07	1.79	W18x119
158	157.7	476	284	23.9	15.0	135	385	46	28	428	2.06	1.77	W18x106
144	144.6	472	283	22.1	13.6	135	384	44	27	428	2.05	1.77	W18x97
128	128.4	467	282	19.6	12.2	135	384	41	26	428	2.04	1.76	W18x86
113	113.1	463	280	17.3	10.8	135	385	39	26	428	2.02	1.74	W18x76
106	105.8	469	194	20.6	12.6	91	394	37	22	428	1.69	1.49	W18x71
97	96.6	466	193	19.0	11.4	91	395	36	21	428	1.68	1.49	W18x65
89	89.3	463	192	17.7	10.5	91	394	34	20	428	1.67	1.48	W18x60
82	81.9	460	191	16.0	9.9	91	395	33	20	428	1.66	1.47	W18x55
74	74.2	457	190	14.5	9.0	91	395	31	20	428	1.66	1.47	W18x50
67	67.2	454	190	12.7	8.5	91	395	29	19	429	1.65	1.46	W18x45
61	60.0	450	189	10.8	8.1	90	395	28	19	428	1.64	1.45	W18x41

W SHAPES
W460 - W360

PROPERTIES

Designation‡	Dead Load	Area	Axis X-X				Axis Y-Y				Torsional Constant	Warping Constant
			I_x	S_x	r_x	Z_x	I_y	S_y	r_y	Z_y	J	C_w
	kN/m	mm^2	$10^6 mm^4$	$10^3 mm^3$	mm	$10^3 mm^3$	$10^6 mm^4$	$10^3 mm^3$	mm	$10^3 mm^3$	$10^3 mm^4$	$10^9 mm^6$
W460												
x68	0.672	8 730	297	1 290	184	1 490	9.41	122	32.8	192	509	463
x60	0.584	7 590	255	1 120	183	1 280	7.96	104	32.4	163	335	388
x52	0.510	6 630	212	943	179	1 090	6.34	83.4	30.9	131	210	306
W410												
x149	1.46	19 000	619	2 870	180	3 250	77.7	586	63.9	900	3 220	3 200
x132	1.30	16 800	538	2 530	179	2 850	67.4	512	63.3	785	2 260	2 730
x114	1.12	14 600	462	2 200	178	2 460	57.2	439	62.6	671	1 490	2 300
x100	0.977	12 700	398	1 920	177	2 130	49.5	381	62.5	581	994	1 960
W410												
x85	0.834	10 800	315	1 510	171	1 730	18.0	199	40.8	310	926	717
x74	0.735	9 550	275	1 330	170	1 510	15.6	173	40.4	269	637	614
x67	0.662	8 600	246	1 200	169	1 360	13.8	154	40.0	239	469	540
x60	0.584	7 580	216	1 060	169	1 190	12.0	135	39.9	209	328	468
x54	0.524	6 810	186	924	165	1 050	10.1	114	38.5	177	226	388
W410												
x46	0.454	5 890	156	773	163	885	5.14	73.4	29.5	115	192	197
x39	0.385	4 990	127	634	159	730	4.04	57.7	28.4	90.6	111	154
W360												
x1086	10.7	139 000	5 960	20 900	207	27 200	1 960	8 650	119	13 400	605 000	96 700
x990	9.72	126 000	5 190	18 900	203	24 300	1 730	7 740	117	12 000	469 000	82 000
x900	8.85	115 000	4 500	17 000	198	21 600	1 530	6 940	116	10 700	364 000	69 200
x818	8.03	104 000	3 920	15 300	194	19 300	1 360	6 200	114	9 560	279 000	58 900
x744	7.30	94 800	3 420	13 700	190	17 200	1 200	5 550	112	8 550	214 000	50 200
x677	6.65	86 300	2 990	12 400	186	15 300	1 070	4 990	111	7 680	165 000	43 100
W360												
x634	6.22	80 800	2 740	11 600	184	14 200	983	4 630	110	7 120	138 000	38 700
x592	5.81	75 500	2 500	10 800	182	13 100	902	4 280	109	6 570	114 000	34 800
x551	5.40	70 100	2 260	9 940	180	12 100	825	3 950	108	6 050	92 500	31 000
x509	5.00	64 900	2 050	9 170	178	11 000	754	3 630	108	5 550	74 000	27 700
x463	4.54	59 000	1 800	8 280	175	9 880	670	3 250	107	4 980	56 500	23 900
x421	4.14	53 700	1 600	7 510	172	8 880	601	2 940	106	4 490	43 400	20 800
x382	3.75	48 700	1 410	6 790	170	7 970	536	2 640	105	4 030	32 900	18 200
x347	3.40	44 200	1 250	6 140	168	7 140	481	2 380	104	3 630	24 800	15 900
x314	3.07	39 900	1 100	5 530	166	6 370	426	2 120	103	3 240	18 500	13 800
x287	2.82	36 600	997	5 070	165	5 810	388	1 940	103	2 960	14 500	12 300
x262	2.58	33 500	894	4 620	163	5 260	350	1 760	102	2 680	11 100	11 000
x237	2.32	30 100	788	4 150	162	4 690	310	1 570	102	2 390	8 190	9 500
x216	2.12	27 600	712	3 790	161	4 260	283	1 430	101	2 180	6 330	8 520

‡ Nominal depth in millimetres and mass in kilograms per metre

When subject to tension, bolted connections are preferred for these sections.

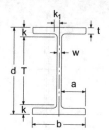

DIMENSIONS AND SURFACE AREAS

Nominal Mass	Theo-retical Mass	Depth d	Flange Width b	Flange Thick-ness t	Web Thick-ness w	Distances a	T	k	k_1	d-2t	Surface Area (m²) per metre of length Total	Minus Top of Top Flange	Imperial Designation
kg/m	kg/m	mm	mm	mm	mm	mm	mm	mm	mm	mm			
68	68.5	459	154	15.4	9.1	72	395	32	20	428	1.52	1.36	W18x46
60	59.6	455	153	13.3	8.0	73	395	30	19	428	1.51	1.35	W18x40
52	52.0	450	152	10.8	7.6	72	395	28	19	428	1.49	1.34	W18x35
149	149.3	431	265	25.0	14.9	125	337	47	28	381	1.89	1.63	W16x100
132	132.1	425	263	22.2	13.3	125	337	44	27	381	1.88	1.61	W16x89
114	114.5	420	261	19.3	11.6	125	338	41	26	381	1.86	1.60	W16x77
100	99.6	415	260	16.9	10.0	125	338	39	25	381	1.85	1.59	W16x67
85	85.0	417	181	18.2	10.9	85	347	35	21	381	1.54	1.36	W16x57
74	74.9	413	180	16.0	9.7	85	348	33	20	381	1.53	1.35	W16x50
67	67.5	410	179	14.4	8.8	85	348	31	20	381	1.52	1.34	W16x45
60	59.5	407	178	12.8	7.7	85	348	30	19	381	1.51	1.33	W16x40
54	53.4	403	177	10.9	7.5	85	348	28	19	381	1.50	1.32	W16x36
46	46.2	403	140	11.2	7.0	67	347	28	19	381	1.35	1.21	W16x31
39	39.2	399	140	8.8	6.4	67	348	26	18	381	1.35	1.21	W16x26
1 086	1 087.9	569	454	125	78.0	188	256	157	69	319	2.80	2.34	W14x730
990	991.0	550	448	115	71.9	188	257	147	66	320	2.75	2.30	W14x665
900	902.2	531	442	106	65.9	188	256	138	63	319	2.70	2.26	W14x605
818	819.0	514	437	97.0	60.5	188	257	129	60	320	2.66	2.22	W14x550
744	744.3	498	432	88.9	55.6	188	257	120	58	320	2.61	2.18	W14x500
677	677.8	483	428	81.5	51.2	188	257	113	56	320	2.58	2.15	W14x455
634	634.3	474	424	77.1	47.6	188	257	109	54	320	2.55	2.12	W14x426
592	592.6	465	421	72.3	45.0	188	257	104	53	320	2.52	2.10	W14x398
551	550.6	455	418	67.6	42.0	188	257	99	51	320	2.50	2.08	W14x370
509	509.5	446	416	62.7	39.1	188	258	94	50	321	2.48	2.06	W14x342
463	462.8	435	412	57.4	35.8	188	257	89	48	320	2.45	2.03	W14x311
421	421.7	425	409	52.6	32.8	188	257	84	46	320	2.42	2.01	W14x283
382	382.4	416	406	48.0	29.8	188	257	80	45	320	2.40	1.99	W14x257
347	347.0	407	404	43.7	27.2	188	257	75	44	320	2.38	1.97	W14x233
314	313.4	399	401	39.6	24.9	188	257	71	42	320	2.35	1.95	W14x211
287	287.6	393	399	36.6	22.6	188	257	68	41	320	2.34	1.94	W14x193
262	262.7	387	398	33.3	21.1	188	257	65	41	320	2.32	1.93	W14x176
237	236.3	380	395	30.2	18.9	188	257	62	39	320	2.30	1.91	W14x159
216	216.3	375	394	27.7	17.3	188	257	59	39	320	2.29	1.90	W14x145

W SHAPES
W360 - W310

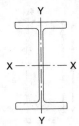

PROPERTIES

Designation‡	Dead Load	Area	Axis X-X				Axis Y-Y				Torsional Constant	Warping Constant
			I_x	S_x	r_x	Z_x	I_y	S_y	r_y	Z_y	J	C_w
	kN/m	mm²	10^6 mm⁴	10^3 mm³	mm	10^3 mm³	10^6 mm⁴	10^3 mm³	mm	10^3 mm³	10^3 mm⁴	10^9 mm⁶
W360												
x196	1.93	25 000	636	3 420	159	3 840	229	1 220	95.5	1 860	5 140	6 830
x179	1.76	22 800	575	3 120	159	3 480	207	1 110	95.2	1 680	3 910	6 120
x162	1.59	20 600	516	2 830	158	3 140	186	1 000	94.8	1 520	2 940	5 430
x147	1.45	18 800	463	2 570	157	2 840	167	904	94.3	1 370	2 230	4 840
x134	1.31	17 100	415	2 330	156	2 560	151	817	94.0	1 240	1 680	4 310
W360												
x122	1.19	15 500	365	2 010	154	2 270	61.5	478	63.0	732	2 110	1 790
x110	1.08	14 000	331	1 840	154	2 060	55.7	435	63.0	664	1 600	1 610
x101	0.993	12 900	301	1 690	153	1 880	50.6	397	62.7	605	1 250	1 450
x91	0.891	11 600	267	1 510	152	1 680	44.8	353	62.3	538	914	1 270
W360												
x79	0.777	10 100	226	1 280	150	1 430	24.2	236	48.9	362	811	687
x72	0.701	9 100	201	1 150	149	1 280	21.4	210	48.5	322	601	600
x64	0.627	8 140	178	1 030	148	1 140	18.8	186	48.1	284	436	524
W360												
x57	0.556	7 220	161	897	149	1 010	11.1	129	39.3	200	334	331
x51	0.496	6 450	141	796	148	894	9.68	113	38.8	174	238	285
x45	0.442	5 730	122	691	146	779	8.18	95.7	37.8	148	160	239
W360												
x39	0.384	4 980	102	580	143	662	3.75	58.6	27.4	91.7	151	110
x33	0.321	4 170	82.7	474	141	542	2.91	45.8	26.4	71.8	85.9	84.3
W310												
x500	4.91	63 800	1 690	7 910	163	9 880	494	2 910	88.0	4 490	101 000	15 300
x454	4.45	57 800	1 480	7 130	160	8 820	436	2 600	86.8	4 000	77 200	13 100
x415	4.07	52 900	1 300	6 450	157	7 900	391	2 340	86.0	3 610	59 500	11 300
x375	3.68	47 700	1 130	5 770	154	7 000	344	2 080	84.8	3 210	44 900	9 570
x342	3.37	43 700	1 010	5 260	152	6 330	310	1 890	84.2	2 910	34 900	8 420
x313	3.07	39 900	896	4 790	150	5 720	277	1 700	83.3	2 620	27 000	7 350
W310												
x283	2.78	36 000	787	4 310	148	5 100	246	1 530	82.6	2 340	20 400	6 330
x253	2.48	32 200	682	3 830	146	4 490	215	1 350	81.6	2 060	14 800	5 370
x226	2.22	28 900	596	3 420	144	3 980	189	1 190	81.0	1 830	10 800	4 620
x202	1.99	25 800	520	3 050	142	3 510	166	1 050	80.2	1 610	7 740	3 960
x179	1.75	22 800	445	2 680	140	3 050	144	919	79.5	1 400	5 380	3 340
x158	1.54	20 100	386	2 360	139	2 670	125	805	78.9	1 220	3 780	2 840
x143	1.40	18 200	348	2 150	138	2 420	113	729	78.6	1 110	2 870	2 540
x129	1.27	16 500	308	1 940	137	2 160	100	652	78.0	991	2 130	2 220
x118	1.15	15 000	275	1 750	136	1 950	90.2	588	77.6	893	1 600	1 970
x107	1.05	13 600	248	1 590	135	1 770	81.2	531	77.2	806	1 220	1 760
x97	0.950	12 300	222	1 440	134	1 590	72.9	478	76.9	725	912	1 560

‡ Nominal depth in millimetres and mass in kilograms per metre

When subject to tension, bolted connections are preferred for these sections.

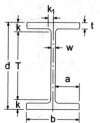

DIMENSIONS AND SURFACE AREAS

Nominal Mass	Theo-retical Mass	Depth d	Flange Width b	Flange Thick-ness t	Web Thick-ness w	Distances					Surface Area (m²) per metre of length		Imperial Designation
						a	T	k	k_1	d-2t	Total	Minus Top of Top Flange	
kg/m	kg/m	mm	mm	mm	mm	mm	mm	mm	mm	mm			
196	196.5	372	374	26.2	16.4	179	257	58	38	320	2.21	1.83	W14x132
179	179.2	368	373	23.9	15.0	179	257	55	38	320	2.20	1.83	W14x120
162	162.0	364	371	21.8	13.3	179	257	53	37	320	2.19	1.81	W14x109
147	147.5	360	370	19.8	12.3	179	257	51	36	320	2.18	1.81	W14x99
134	134.0	356	369	18.0	11.2	179	257	50	36	320	2.17	1.80	W14x90
122	121.7	363	257	21.7	13.0	122	276	44	27	320	1.73	1.47	W14x82
110	110.2	360	256	19.9	11.4	122	277	42	26	320	1.72	1.47	W14x74
101	101.2	357	255	18.3	10.5	122	277	40	26	320	1.71	1.46	W14x68
91	90.8	353	254	16.4	9.5	122	277	38	25	320	1.70	1.45	W14x61
79	79.2	354	205	16.8	9.4	98	277	39	25	320	1.51	1.30	W14x53
72	71.5	350	204	15.1	8.6	98	276	37	25	320	1.50	1.29	W14x48
64	63.9	347	203	13.5	7.7	98	276	35	24	320	1.49	1.29	W14x43
57	56.7	358	172	13.1	7.9	82	298	30	19	332	1.39	1.22	W14x38
51	50.6	355	171	11.6	7.2	82	298	28	19	332	1.38	1.21	W14x34
45	45.0	352	171	9.8	6.9	82	299	27	19	332	1.37	1.20	W14x30
39	39.1	353	128	10.7	6.5	61	298	27	18	332	1.21	1.08	W14x26
33	32.8	349	127	8.5	5.8	61	299	25	18	332	1.19	1.07	W14x22
500	500.4	427	340	75.1	45.1	147	233	97	43	277	2.12	1.78	W12x336
454	454.0	415	336	68.7	41.3	147	234	91	41	278	2.09	1.76	W12x305
415	415.1	403	334	62.7	38.9	148	234	85	40	278	2.06	1.73	W12x279
375	374.8	391	330	57.2	35.4	147	233	79	38	277	2.03	1.70	W12x252
342	343.3	382	328	52.6	32.6	148	233	74	37	277	2.01	1.68	W12x230
313	313.3	374	325	48.3	30.0	148	234	70	35	277	1.99	1.66	W12x210
283	283.0	365	322	44.1	26.9	148	233	66	34	277	1.96	1.64	W12x190
253	252.9	356	319	39.6	24.4	147	233	61	33	277	1.94	1.62	W12x170
226	226.8	348	317	35.6	22.1	147	233	57	31	277	1.92	1.60	W12x152
202	202.6	341	315	31.8	20.1	147	234	54	30	277	1.90	1.59	W12x136
179	178.8	333	313	28.1	18.0	148	233	50	29	277	1.88	1.57	W12x120
158	157.4	327	310	25.1	15.5	147	233	47	28	277	1.86	1.55	W12x106
143	143.1	323	309	22.9	14.0	148	234	45	27	277	1.85	1.55	W12x96
129	129.6	318	308	20.6	13.1	147	233	42	27	277	1.84	1.53	W12x87
118	117.5	314	307	18.7	11.9	148	233	41	26	277	1.83	1.53	W12x79
107	106.9	311	306	17.0	10.9	148	233	39	26	277	1.82	1.52	W12x72
97	96.8	308	305	15.4	9.9	148	234	37	25	277	1.82	1.51	W12x65

PROPERTIES

Designation[‡]	Dead Load	Area	Axis X-X				Axis Y-Y				Torsional Constant	Warping Constant
			I_x	S_x	r_x	Z_x	I_y	S_y	r_y	Z_y	J	C_w
	kN/m	mm²	10^6 mm⁴	10^3 mm³	mm	10^3 mm³	10^6 mm⁴	10^3 mm³	mm	10^3 mm³	10^3 mm⁴	10^9 mm⁶
W310												
x86	0.847	11 000	199	1 280	134	1 420	44.5	351	63.6	533	877	961
x79	0.774	10 100	177	1 160	133	1 280	39.9	314	63.0	478	657	847
W310												
x74	0.726	9 430	164	1 060	132	1 180	23.4	229	49.9	350	718	505
x67	0.651	8 450	144	942	131	1 050	20.7	203	49.5	310	522	439
x60	0.580	7 530	128	842	130	933	18.3	180	49.3	275	378	384
W310												
x52	0.514	6 670	119	750	134	841	10.3	123	39.2	189	308	238
x45	0.438	5 690	99.2	634	132	708	8.55	103	38.8	158	191	195
x39	0.380	4 940	85.1	549	131	610	7.27	88.1	38.4	135	126	164
W310												
x33	0.322	4 180	65.0	415	125	480	1.92	37.6	21.4	59.6	122	43.8
x28	0.278	3 610	54.3	351	123	407	1.58	31.0	20.9	49.2	75.7	35.6
x24	0.234	3 040	42.7	280	119	328	1.16	22.9	19.5	36.7	42.5	25.7
x21	0.207	2 690	37.0	244	117	287	0.983	19.5	19.1	31.2	29.4	21.7
W250												
x167	1.64	21 300	300	2 080	119	2 430	98.8	746	68.1	1 140	6 310	1 630
x149	1.46	19 000	259	1 840	117	2 130	86.2	656	67.4	1 000	4 510	1 390
x131	1.29	16 700	221	1 610	115	1 850	74.5	571	66.8	870	3 120	1 160
x115	1.13	14 600	189	1 410	114	1 600	64.1	495	66.2	753	2 130	976
x101	0.992	12 900	164	1 240	113	1 400	55.5	432	65.6	656	1 490	829
x89	0.879	11 400	143	1 100	112	1 230	48.4	378	65.1	574	1 040	713
x80	0.786	10 200	126	982	111	1 090	43.1	338	65.0	513	757	623
x73	0.715	9 280	113	891	110	985	38.8	306	64.6	463	575	553
W250												
x67	0.659	8 550	104	806	110	901	22.2	218	51.0	332	625	324
x58	0.571	7 420	87.3	693	108	770	18.8	186	50.4	283	409	268
x49	0.481	6 250	70.6	572	106	633	15.1	150	49.2	228	241	211
W250												
x45	0.441	5 720	71.1	534	111	602	7.03	95.1	35.1	146	261	113
x39	0.379	4 920	60.1	459	110	513	5.94	80.8	34.7	124	169	93.4
x33	0.321	4 170	48.9	379	108	424	4.73	64.7	33.7	99.5	98.5	73.2
W250												
x28	0.279	3 630	40.0	307	105	353	1.78	34.8	22.1	54.7	96.7	27.7
x25	0.249	3 230	34.2	266	103	307	1.49	29.2	21.5	46.2	65.2	23.0
x22	0.220	2 850	28.9	227	101	263	1.23	24.0	20.7	38.1	43.4	18.7
x18	0.175	2 270	22.4	179	99.3	207	0.913	18.1	20.0	28.6	22.4	13.8

‡ Nominal depth in millimetres and mass in kilograms per metre

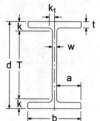

DIMENSIONS AND SURFACE AREAS

Nominal Mass	Theo-retical Mass	Depth	Flange Width	Flange Thick-ness	Web Thick-ness	Distances					Surface Area (m²) per metre of length		Imperial Designation
		d	b	t	w	a	T	k	k₁	d-2t	Total	Minus Top of Top Flange	
kg/m	kg/m	mm	mm	mm	mm	mm	mm	mm	mm	mm			
86	86.4	310	254	16.3	9.1	122	238	36	23	277	1.62	1.36	W12x58
79	78.9	306	254	14.6	8.8	123	238	34	22	277	1.61	1.36	W12x53
74	74.0	310	205	16.3	9.4	98	238	36	23	277	1.42	1.22	W12x50
67	66.3	306	204	14.6	8.5	98	238	34	22	277	1.41	1.21	W12x45
60	59.1	303	203	13.1	7.5	98	238	33	22	277	1.40	1.20	W12x40
52	52.4	318	167	13.2	7.6	80	258	30	19	292	1.29	1.12	W12x35
45	44.6	313	166	11.2	6.6	80	257	28	19	291	1.28	1.11	W12x30
39	38.7	310	165	9.7	5.8	80	257	26	18	291	1.27	1.10	W12x26
33	32.8	313	102	10.8	6.6	48	266	23	14	291	1.02	0.919	W12x22
28	28.4	309	102	8.9	6.0	48	266	22	14	291	1.01	0.912	W12x19
24	23.8	305	101	6.7	5.6	48	266	19	14	292	1.00	0.902	W12x16
21	21.1	303	101	5.7	5.1	48	266	18	14	292	1.00	0.899	W12x14
167	167.4	289	265	31.8	19.2	123	192	49	25	225	1.60	1.33	W10x112
149	148.9	282	263	28.4	17.3	123	192	45	24	225	1.58	1.32	W10x100
131	131.1	275	261	25.1	15.4	123	191	42	23	225	1.56	1.30	W10x88
115	114.8	269	259	22.1	13.5	123	191	39	22	225	1.55	1.29	W10x77
101	101.2	264	257	19.6	11.9	123	191	36	21	225	1.53	1.28	W10x68
89	89.6	260	256	17.3	10.7	123	192	34	21	225	1.52	1.27	W10x60
80	80.1	256	255	15.6	9.4	123	191	32	20	225	1.51	1.26	W10x54
73	72.9	253	254	14.2	8.6	123	191	31	20	225	1.50	1.25	W10x49
67	67.1	257	204	15.7	8.9	98	192	32	20	226	1.31	1.11	W10x45
58	58.2	252	203	13.5	8.0	98	192	30	19	225	1.30	1.10	W10x39
49	49.0	247	202	11.0	7.4	97	192	28	19	225	1.29	1.09	W10x33
45	44.9	266	148	13.0	7.6	70	212	27	17	240	1.11	0.961	W10x30
39	38.7	262	147	11.2	6.6	70	211	25	16	240	1.10	0.952	W10x26
33	32.7	258	146	9.1	6.1	70	211	23	16	240	1.09	0.942	W10x22
28	28.5	260	102	10.0	6.4	48	215	23	14	240	0.915	0.813	W10x19
25	25.3	257	102	8.4	6.1	48	215	21	14	240	0.910	0.808	W10x17
22	22.4	254	102	6.9	5.8	48	215	20	14	240	0.904	0.802	W10x15
18	17.9	251	101	5.3	4.8	48	215	18	14	240	0.896	0.795	W10x12

PROPERTIES

Designation‡	Dead Load	Area	Axis X-X				Axis Y-Y				Torsional Constant	Warping Constant
			I_x	S_x	r_x	Z_x	I_y	S_y	r_y	Z_y	J	C_w
	kN/m	mm²	10^6 mm⁴	10^3 mm³	mm	10^3 mm³	10^6 mm⁴	10^3 mm³	mm	10^3 mm³	10^3 mm⁴	10^9 mm⁶
W200												
x100	0.976	12 700	113	989	94.5	1 150	36.6	349	53.8	533	2 090	386
x86	0.851	11 000	94.7	853	92.6	981	31.4	300	53.3	458	1 390	318
x71	0.701	9 100	76.6	709	91.7	803	25.4	246	52.8	375	817	250
x59	0.582	7 560	61.1	582	89.9	653	20.4	199	52.0	303	463	196
x52	0.512	6 650	52.7	512	89.0	569	17.8	175	51.8	266	323	167
x46	0.451	5 860	45.4	448	88.1	495	15.3	151	51.2	229	220	141
W200												
x42	0.409	5 310	40.9	399	87.7	445	9.00	108	41.2	165	222	84.0
x36	0.352	4 570	34.4	342	86.7	379	7.64	92.6	40.9	141	145	69.6
W200												
x31	0.308	4 000	31.4	299	88.6	335	4.10	61.1	32.0	93.8	119	40.9
x27	0.261	3 390	25.8	249	87.3	279	3.30	49.6	31.2	76.1	71.3	32.5
W200												
x22	0.220	2 860	20.0	194	83.6	222	1.42	27.8	22.3	43.7	56.6	13.9
x19	0.191	2 480	16.6	163	81.7	187	1.15	22.6	21.6	35.6	36.2	11.1
x15	0.147	1 900	12.7	127	81.8	145	0.869	17.4	21.4	27.1	17.6	8.24
W150												
x37	0.364	4 730	22.2	274	68.5	310	7.07	91.8	38.6	140	193	40.0
x30	0.292	3 790	17.2	219	67.3	244	5.56	72.6	38.3	111	101	30.3
x22	0.219	2 850	12.1	159	65.1	176	3.87	50.9	36.9	77.6	42.0	20.4
W150												
x24	0.235	3 060	13.4	168	66.3	192	1.83	35.8	24.4	55.3	93.1	10.2
x18	0.176	2 290	9.17	120	63.3	136	1.26	24.7	23.5	38.3	37.4	6.70
x14	0.133	1 730	6.87	91.6	63.0	103	0.918	18.4	23.0	28.3	17.1	4.79
x13	0.124	1 610	6.13	82.8	61.7	93.0	0.818	16.4	22.5	25.3	13.6	4.19
W130												
x28	0.277	3 590	11.0	168	55.3	191	3.81	59.6	32.6	90.8	131	13.8
x24	0.233	3 020	8.84	139	54.1	157	3.11	49.0	32.1	74.6	79.1	10.8
W100												
x19	0.191	2 480	4.77	89.9	43.9	103	1.61	31.2	25.5	48.0	63.6	3.79

‡ Nominal depth in millimetres and mass in kilograms per metre

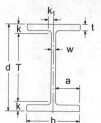

DIMENSIONS AND SURFACE AREAS

Nominal Mass	Theo-retical Mass	Depth	Flange Width	Flange Thick-ness	Web Thick-ness	Distances					Surface Area (m²) per metre of length		Imperial Designation
		d	b	t	w	a	T	k	k₁	d - 2t	Total	Minus Top of Top Flange	
kg/m	kg/m	mm	mm	mm	mm	mm	mm	mm	mm	mm			
100	99.5	229	210	23.7	14.5	98	148	40	22	182	1.27	1.06	W8x67
86	86.7	222	209	20.6	13.0	98	147	37	22	181	1.25	1.04	W8x58
71	71.5	216	206	17.4	10.2	98	148	34	20	181	1.24	1.03	W8x48
59	59.3	210	205	14.2	9.1	98	148	31	20	182	1.22	1.02	W8x40
52	52.2	206	204	12.6	7.9	98	147	29	19	181	1.21	1.01	W8x35
46	46.0	203	203	11.0	7.2	98	148	28	19	181	1.20	1.00	W8x31
42	41.7	205	166	11.8	7.2	79	158	23	14	181	1.06	0.894	W8x28
36	35.9	201	165	10.2	6.2	79	158	22	13	181	1.05	0.885	W8x24
31	31.4	210	134	10.2	6.4	64	167	22	13	190	0.943	0.809	W8x21
27	26.6	207	133	8.4	5.8	64	167	20	13	190	0.934	0.801	W8x18
22	22.4	206	102	8.0	6.2	48	167	20	13	190	0.808	0.706	W8x15
19	19.4	203	102	6.5	5.8	48	167	18	13	190	0.802	0.700	W8x13
15	15.0	200	100	5.2	4.3	48	167	17	12	190	0.791	0.691	W8x10
37	37.1	162	154	11.6	8.1	73	116	23	14	139	0.924	0.770	W6x25
30	29.8	157	153	9.3	6.6	73	115	21	13	138	0.913	0.760	W6x20
22	22.3	152	152	6.6	5.8	73	116	18	13	139	0.900	0.748	W6x15
24	24.0	160	102	10.3	6.6	48	116	22	13	139	0.715	0.613	W6x16
18	18.0	153	102	7.1	5.8	48	116	19	13	139	0.702	0.600	W6x12
14	13.6	150	100	5.5	4.3	48	116	17	12	139	0.691	0.591	W6x9
13	12.6	148	100	4.9	4.3	48	115	16	12	138	0.687	0.587	W6x8.5
28	28.2	131	128	10.9	6.9	61	91	20	11	109	0.760	0.632	W5x19
24	23.7	127	127	9.1	6.1	60	91	18	11	109	0.750	0.623	W5x16
19	19.4	106	103	8.8	7.1	48	69	18	12	88	0.610	0.507	W4x13

HP SHAPES

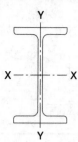

PROPERTIES

Designation[‡]	Dead Load	Area	Axis X-X				Axis Y-Y				Torsional Constant	Warping Constant
			I_x	S_x	r_x	Z_x	I_y	S_y	r_y	Z_y	J	C_w
	kN/m	mm²	10^6 mm⁴	10^3 mm³	mm	10^3 mm³	10^6 mm⁴	10^3 mm³	mm	10^3 mm³	10^3 mm⁴	10^9 mm⁶
HP360												
x174	1.71	22 200	508	2 820	152	3 180	184	973	91.1	1 490	3 310	5 330
x152	1.49	19 400	439	2 470	150	2 770	159	845	90.5	1 290	2 240	4 540
x132	1.30	16 800	375	2 140	149	2 380	135	724	89.6	1 110	1 490	3 800
x108	1.06	13 800	303	1 750	148	1 940	108	585	88.6	891	832	3 000
HP310												
x125	1.22	15 900	270	1 730	130	1 960	88.2	566	74.5	870	1 760	1 910
x110	1.08	14 100	237	1 540	130	1 730	77.1	497	74.0	763	1 240	1 650
x94	0.916	11 900	196	1 300	129	1 450	63.9	415	73.3	635	764	1 340
x79	0.768	9 980	163	1 090	128	1 210	52.6	344	72.6	525	460	1 090
HP250												
x85	0.837	10 900	123	968	106	1 090	42.3	325	62.3	500	829	606
x62	0.614	7 980	87.5	711	105	792	30.0	234	61.3	358	339	415
HP200												
x54	0.525	6 820	49.8	488	85.5	552	16.7	162	49.5	249	321	155

‡ Nominal depth in millimetres and mass in kilograms per metre

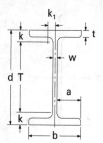

HP SHAPES

DIMENSIONS AND SURFACE AREAS

Nominal Mass	Theo-retical Mass	Depth	Flange Width	Flange Thick-ness	Web Thick-ness	Distances					Surface Area (m²) per metre of length		Imperial Designation
		d	b	t	w	a	T	k	k₁	d-2t	Total	Minus Top of Top Flange	
kg/m	kg/m	mm	mm	mm	mm	mm	mm	mm	mm	mm			
174	173.9	361	378	20.4	20.4	179	288	37	25	320	2.19	1.82	HP14x117
152	152.2	356	376	17.9	17.9	179	288	34	24	320	2.18	1.80	HP14x102
132	132.1	351	373	15.6	15.6	179	287	32	23	320	2.16	1.79	HP14x89
108	108.1	346	370	12.8	12.8	179	288	29	22	320	2.15	1.78	HP14x73
125	124.7	312	312	17.4	17.4	147	245	34	24	277	1.84	1.53	HP12x84
110	110.5	308	310	15.5	15.4	147	245	32	23	277	1.83	1.52	HP12x74
94	93.4	303	308	13.1	13.1	147	244	29	22	277	1.81	1.50	HP12x63
79	78.3	299	306	11.0	11.0	148	245	27	21	277	1.80	1.49	HP12x53
85	85.3	254	260	14.4	14.4	123	193	31	22	225	1.52	1.26	HP10x57
62	62.6	246	256	10.7	10.5	123	192	27	20	225	1.50	1.24	HP10x42
54	53.5	204	207	11.3	11.3	98	149	28	21	181	1.21	1.01	HP8x36

M SHAPES

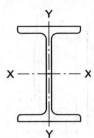

PROPERTIES

Designation‡	Dead Load	Area	Axis X-X				Axis Y-Y				Torsional Constant	Warping Constant
			I_x	S_x	r_x	Z_x	I_y	S_y	r_y	Z_y	J	C_w
	kN/m	mm²	10^6 mm⁴	10^3 mm³	mm	10^3 mm³	10^6 mm⁴	10^3 mm³	mm	10^3 mm³	10^3 mm⁴	10^9 mm⁶
M310												
x17.6	0.173	2 240	30.1	197	116	235	0.453	11.6	14.2	18.8	20.8	10.1
x16.1	0.159	2 060	27.7	182	116	216	0.421	10.8	14.3	17.4	16.3	9.39
x14.9	0.147	1 910	25.8	170	116	201	0.440	10.6	15.2	16.9	12.1	9.85
M250												
x13.4	0.132	1 710	16.2	127	97.2	151	0.274	8.05	12.7	13.0	13.1	4.24
x11.9	0.118	1 530	14.4	114	96.9	134	0.242	7.12	12.6	11.4	9.35	3.73
x11.2	0.110	1 430	13.7	108	97.9	127	0.231	6.80	12.7	10.8	7.77	3.60
M200												
x9.7	0.095 0	1 230	7.70	75.9	79.0	88.9	0.157	5.40	11.3	8.63	7.67	1.54
M150												
x6.6	0.064 2	834	2.99	39.3	59.8	45.7	0.074 7	3.18	9.47	5.05	4.10	0.407
M100												
x8.9	0.087 6	1 140	2.00	41.2	41.9	45.6	0.624	12.9	23.4	19.5	7.63	1.35

‡ Nominal depth in millimetres and mass in kilograms per metre
Note: These shapes are not available from Canadian mills.

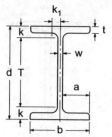

DIMENSIONS AND SURFACE AREAS

Nominal Mass	Theo-retical Mass	Depth	Flange Width	Flange Thick-ness	Web Thick-ness	Distances				Surface Area (m²) per metre of length		Imperial Designation
		d	b	t	w	a	T	k	k₁	Total	Minus Top of Top Flange	
kg/m	kg/m	mm	mm	mm	mm	mm	mm	mm	mm			
17.6	17.6	305	78	5.7	4.5	37	277	14	9	0.913	0.835	M12x11.8
16.1	16.2	304	78	5.3	4.1	37	276	14	9	0.912	0.834	M12x10.8
14.9	15.0	304	83	4.6	3.8	40	280	12	8	0.932	0.849	M12x10
13.4	13.4	254	68	5.2	4.0	32	226	14	9	0.772	0.704	M10x9
11.9	12.0	253	68	4.6	3.6	32	227	13	9	0.771	0.703	M10x8
11.2	11.2	254	68	4.4	3.3	32	232	11	7	0.773	0.705	M10x7.5
9.7	9.7	203	58	4.8	3.4	27	175	14	9	0.631	0.573	M8x6.5
6.6	6.5	152	47	4.3	2.9	22	134	9	5	0.486	0.439	M6x4.4
8.9	8.9	97	97	4.1	3.3	47	71	13	9	0.575	0.478	M4x6

SUPER-LIGHT BEAMS
SLB100 - SLB55

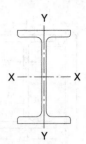

PROPERTIES

Designation‡	Dead Load	Area	Axis X-X				Axis Y-Y				Torsional Constant	Warping Constant
			I_x	S_x	r_x	Z_x	I_y	S_y	r_y	Z_y	J	C_w
	kN/m	mm²	10^6 mm⁴	10^3 mm³	mm	10^3 mm³	10^6 mm⁴	10^3 mm³	mm	10^3 mm³	10^3 mm⁴	10^9 mm⁶
SLB100												
x5.4	0.053 5	695	1.17	23.1	41.1	26.4	0.099 1	3.46	11.9	5.49	2.86	0.239
x5.1	0.050 3	653	1.17	23.0	42.3	25.9	0.104	3.64	12.6	5.68	2.50	0.251
x4.8	0.047 4	615	1.11	21.9	42.5	24.5	0.098 8	3.46	12.7	5.37	2.12	0.239
SLB75												
x5.6	0.054 9	713	0.757	19.7	32.6	22.1	0.131	4.59	13.6	7.08	4.44	0.173
x4.5	0.044 5	577	0.614	16.1	32.6	17.9	0.107	3.73	13.6	5.74	2.28	0.141
x4.3	0.042 1	547	0.581	15.3	32.6	16.9	0.099 4	3.48	13.5	5.36	1.92	0.132
x3.8	0.037 1	482	0.498	13.1	32.1	14.6	0.064 9	2.56	11.6	3.96	1.51	0.086 8
SLB55												
x6.4	0.063 0	818	0.498	17.4	24.7	19.6	0.268	7.67	18.1	11.7	6.12	0.184

‡ Nominal depth in millimetres and mass in kilograms per metre. The availability of SLB sections should be checked.

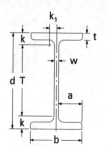

DIMENSIONS AND SURFACE AREAS

Nominal Mass	Theo-retical Mass	Depth	Flange Width	Flange Thick-ness	Web Thick-ness	Distances				Surface Area (m²) per metre of length		Imperial Designation
		d	b	t	w	a	T	k	k₁	Total	Minus Top of Top Flange	
kg/m	kg/m	mm	mm	mm	mm	mm	mm	mm	mm			
5.4	5.45	101.6	57.2	3.28	3.18	27	81	10	6	0.426	0.368	SLB4x3.64
5.1	5.12	101.6	57.2	3.45	2.54	27	80	11	6	0.427	0.370	SLB4x3.45
4.8	4.83	101.6	57.2	3.28	2.34	27	81	10	6	0.427	0.370	SLB4x3.20
5.6	5.59	77.0	57.2	4.32	2.79	27	52	12	7	0.377	0.320	SLB3x3.75
4.5	4.53	76.2	57.2	3.53	2.29	27	55	10	5	0.377	0.319	SLB3x3.05
4.3	4.29	76.2	57.2	3.30	2.21	27	56	10	5	0.377	0.320	SLB3x2.90
3.8	3.78	76.2	50.8	3.07	2.21	24	57	10	5	0.351	0.300	SLB3x2.54
6.4	6.42	57.2	69.9	4.85	2.54	34	32	13	6	0.389	0.319	SLB2.25x4.30

S SHAPES
S610 - S200

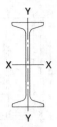

PROPERTIES

Designation[‡]	Dead Load	Area	Axis X-X				Axis Y-Y				Torsional Constant	Warping Constant
			I_x	S_x	r_x	Z_x	I_y	S_y	r_y	Z_y	J	C_w
	kN/m	mm²	10^6 mm⁴	10^3 mm³	mm	10^3 mm³	10^6 mm⁴	10^3 mm³	mm	10^3 mm³	10^3 mm⁴	10^9 mm⁶
S610												
x180	1.77	22 900	1 310	4 220	239	5 020	33.9	332	38.5	592	5 330	2 990
x158	1.55	20 100	1 220	3 940	247	4 580	31.6	316	39.7	545	4 210	2 790
S610												
x149	1.46	19 000	997	3 270	229	3 940	19.7	214	32.2	393	3 160	1 700
x134	1.32	17 100	940	3 080	234	3 660	18.6	205	32.9	367	2 530	1 600
x119	1.17	15 200	880	2 890	241	3 360	17.5	197	34.0	342	2 040	1 510
S510												
x143	1.40	18 200	700	2 710	196	3 250	20.7	226	33.7	410	3 500	1 260
x128	1.26	16 400	658	2 550	200	3 010	19.2	214	34.2	378	2 780	1 160
S510												
x112	1.09	14 200	532	2 090	194	2 500	12.3	152	29.4	274	1 910	731
x98.2	0.965	12 500	497	1 960	199	2 290	11.5	145	30.3	253	1 490	684
S460												
x104	1.03	13 300	387	1 690	170	2 050	10.1	127	27.5	238	1 740	487
x81.4	0.800	10 400	335	1 470	180	1 710	8.62	113	28.8	199	983	416
S380												
x74	0.732	9 500	203	1 060	146	1 270	6.49	90.8	26.1	164	884	217
x64	0.627	8 150	187	980	151	1 140	6.01	85.9	27.2	149	641	200
S310												
x74	0.729	9 470	127	833	116	1 000	6.48	93.3	26.2	169	1 160	135
x60.7	0.595	7 720	113	744	121	868	5.56	83.7	26.8	145	722	116
S310												
x52	0.513	6 660	95.9	629	120	737	4.10	63.5	24.8	112	452	86.9
x47	0.466	6 050	91.2	598	123	690	3.88	61.2	25.3	105	376	82.3
S250												
x52	0.513	6 660	61.5	484	96.1	583	3.51	55.8	23.0	103	539	51.2
x38	0.371	4 810	51.4	405	103	465	2.80	47.5	24.1	81.3	250	40.9
S200												
x34	0.336	4 370	27.0	266	78.6	316	1.79	33.8	20.2	60.4	229	16.5
x27	0.270	3 500	24.0	237	82.9	272	1.56	30.7	21.1	52.4	140	14.4

‡ Designation consists of nominal depth in millimetres and nominal mass in kilograms per metre.
   For sections formerly available from Canadian mills, the nominal mass has been rounded to the nearest kg/m.
Note: These shapes have been soft-converted from Imperial to SI dimensions.

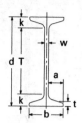

DIMENSIONS AND SURFACE AREAS

Nominal Mass	Theo-retical Mass	Depth	Flange Width	Mean Flange Thickness	Web Thickness	Distances			Surface Area (m²) per metre of length		Imperial Designation
		d	b	t	w	a	T	k	Total	Minus Top of Top Flange	
kg/m	kg/m	mm	mm	mm	mm	mm	mm	mm			
180	180.0	622	204	27.7	20.3	92	522	50	2.02	1.82	S24x121
158	157.8	622	200	27.7	15.7	92	522	50	2.01	1.81	S24x106
149	148.8	610	184	22.1	18.9	83	522	44	1.92	1.73	S24x100
134	134.4	610	181	22.1	15.9	83	522	44	1.91	1.73	S24x90
119	119.2	610	178	22.1	12.7	83	522	44	1.91	1.73	S24x80
143	143.0	516	183	23.4	20.3	81	426	45	1.72	1.54	S20x96
128	128.6	516	179	23.4	16.8	81	426	45	1.71	1.54	S20x86
112	111.4	508	162	20.2	16.1	73	426	41	1.63	1.47	S20x75
98.2	98.4	508	159	20.2	12.8	73	426	41	1.63	1.47	S20x66
104	104.7	457	159	17.6	18.1	70	383	37	1.51	1.35	S18x70
81.4	81.5	457	152	17.6	11.7	70	383	37	1.50	1.35	S18x54.7
74	74.6	381	143	15.8	14.0	65	313	34	1.31	1.16	S15x50
64	64.0	381	140	15.8	10.4	65	313	34	1.30	1.16	S15x42.9
74	74.4	305	139	16.7	17.4	61	235	35	1.13	0.992	S12x50
60.7	60.6	305	133	16.7	11.7	61	235	35	1.12	0.986	S12x40.8
52	52.3	305	129	13.8	10.9	59	245	30	1.10	0.975	S12x35
47	47.5	305	127	13.8	8.9	59	245	30	1.10	0.973	S12x31.8
52	52.3	254	126	12.5	15.1	55	200	27	0.982	0.856	S10x35
38	37.8	254	118	12.5	7.9	55	200	27	0.964	0.846	S10x25.4
34	34.3	203	106	10.8	11.2	47	155	24	0.808	0.702	S8x23
27	27.5	203	102	10.8	6.9	48	155	24	0.800	0.698	S8x18.4

S SHAPES
S150 - S75

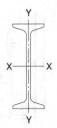

PROPERTIES

Designation[‡]	Dead Load	Area	Axis X-X				Axis Y-Y				Torsional Constant	Warping Constant
			I_x	S_x	r_x	Z_x	I_y	S_y	r_y	Z_y	J	C_w
	kN/m	mm²	10^6 mm⁴	10^3 mm³	mm	10^3 mm³	10^6 mm⁴	10^3 mm³	mm	10^3 mm³	10^3 mm⁴	10^9 mm⁶
S150												
x26	0.251	3 260	10.9	143	57.8	173	0.969	21.3	17.2	38.9	152	4.95
x19	0.182	2 370	9.16	121	62.2	138	0.765	18.0	18.0	30.6	68.5	3.90
S130												
x15	0.145	1 890	5.11	80.5	52.0	92.7	0.501	13.2	16.3	22.3	47.0	1.76
S100												
x14.1	0.139	1 810	2.85	55.9	39.7	66.6	0.372	10.5	14.3	18.4	50.6	0.832
x11	0.113	1 470	2.56	50.3	41.8	58.0	0.320	9.40	14.8	15.9	30.7	0.715
S75												
x11	0.110	1 430	1.22	32.0	29.2	38.7	0.246	7.68	13.1	13.6	38.1	0.296
x8	0.083	1 070	1.04	27.4	31.2	31.8	0.187	6.34	13.2	10.6	18.2	0.225

‡ Designation consists of nominal depth in millimetres and nominal mass in kilograms per metre.
  For sections formerly available from Canadian mills, the nominal mass has been rounded to the nearest kg/m.
Note: These shapes have been soft-converted from Imperial to SI dimensions.

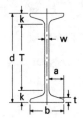

DIMENSIONS AND SURFACE AREAS

| Nominal Mass | Theo-retical Mass | Depth | Flange Width | Mean Flange Thickness | Web Thickness | Distances | | | Surface Area (m²) per metre of length | | Imperial Designation |
| | | d | b | t | w | a | T | k | Total | Minus Top of Top Flange | |
kg/m	kg/m	mm	mm	mm	mm	mm	mm	mm			
26	25.6	152	91	9.1	11.8	40	112	20	0.644	0.553	S6x17.25
19	18.6	152	85	9.1	5.9	40	112	20	0.632	0.547	S6x12.5
15	14.8	127	76	8.3	5.4	35	89	19	0.547	0.471	S5x10
14.1	14.2	102	71	7.4	8.3	31	66	18	0.471	0.400	S4x9.5
11	11.5	102	68	7.4	4.9	32	66	18	0.466	0.398	S4x7.7
11	11.2	76	64	6.6	8.9	28	44	16	0.390	0.326	S3x7.5
8	8.4	76	59	6.6	4.3	27	44	16	0.379	0.320	S3x5.7

STANDARD CHANNELS (C SHAPES)

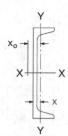

PROPERTIES

Designation	Dead Load	Area	Axis X-X			Axis Y-Y				Shear Centre	Torsional Constant	Warping Constant
			I_x	S_x	r_x	I_y	S_y	r_y	x	x_o	J	C_w
	kN/m	mm²	10^6 mm⁴	10^3 mm³	mm	10^6 mm⁴	10^3 mm³	mm	mm	mm	10^3 mm⁴	10^9 mm⁶
C380												
x74*	0.730	9 480	168	881	133	4.60	62.4	22.0	20.3	34.9	1 100	131
x60*	0.583	7 570	145	760	138	3.84	55.5	22.5	19.8	39.1	603	109
x50*	0.495	6 430	131	687	143	3.39	51.4	23.0	20.0	42.6	421	95.2
C310												
x45	0.438	5 690	67.3	442	109	2.12	33.6	19.3	17.0	32.4	360	39.9
x37	0.363	4 720	59.9	393	113	1.85	30.9	19.8	17.1	35.9	222	34.6
x31	0.302	3 920	53.5	351	117	1.59	28.1	20.1	17.6	39.3	152	29.3
C250												
x45	0.437	5 670	42.8	337	86.9	1.60	26.8	16.8	16.3	25.3	508	20.5
x37	0.365	4 750	37.9	299	89.4	1.40	24.3	17.1	15.7	28.1	289	18.2
x30	0.291	3 780	32.7	257	93.0	1.16	21.5	17.5	15.4	31.3	153	15.0
x23	0.222	2 880	27.8	219	98.2	0.920	18.8	17.9	15.9	35.7	86.4	11.7
C230												
x30*	0.292	3 800	25.5	222	81.9	1.01	19.3	16.3	14.8	27.7	179	10.5
x22	0.219	2 840	21.3	186	86.6	0.805	16.8	16.8	15.0	32.3	86.6	8.33
x20	0.195	2 530	19.8	173	88.6	0.715	15.6	16.8	15.2	33.7	69.5	7.35
C200												
x28	0.274	3 560	18.2	180	71.6	0.825	16.6	15.2	14.4	25.2	182	6.67
x21	0.200	2 600	14.9	147	75.8	0.627	13.9	15.5	14.0	29.1	77.0	5.04
x17	0.167	2 170	13.5	133	78.7	0.543	12.8	15.8	14.5	32.0	53.8	4.34
C180												
x22	0.214	2 780	11.3	127	63.7	0.568	12.8	14.3	13.5	24.6	110	3.47
x18	0.178	2 310	10.0	113	65.9	0.476	11.4	14.3	13.2	26.5	66.8	2.90
x15	0.142	1 850	8.86	99.6	69.3	0.404	10.3	14.8	13.8	30.3	41.4	2.46
C150												
x19	0.188	2 450	7.11	93.6	53.9	0.425	10.3	13.2	12.9	22.3	98.9	1.84
x16	0.152	1 980	6.21	81.8	56.1	0.351	9.13	13.3	12.6	24.6	53.4	1.53
x12	0.118	1 530	5.36	70.5	59.1	0.278	7.93	13.5	12.9	27.7	30.6	1.21
C130												
x13	0.130	1 690	3.66	57.6	46.5	0.252	7.20	12.2	12.0	22.3	45.0	0.746
x10	0.097	1 260	3.09	48.6	49.5	0.195	6.14	12.4	12.3	26.1	22.5	0.579
C100												
x11	0.106	1 370	1.91	37.4	37.3	0.174	5.52	11.3	11.5	20.9	34.1	0.320
x9	0.092	1 190	1.77	34.6	38.5	0.158	5.18	11.5	11.6	23.0	23.1	0.293
x8	0.079	1 020	1.61	31.6	39.7	0.132	4.65	11.4	11.6	24.2	16.6	0.246
x7	0.069	892	1.53	30.0	41.4	0.122	4.45	11.7	12.6	27.3	13.3	0.233
C75												
x9	0.087	1 120	0.847	22.3	27.4	0.123	4.31	10.5	11.5	19.4	29.7	0.118
x7	0.072	934	0.749	19.7	28.3	0.095 9	3.67	10.1	10.9	20.3	17.5	0.093 4
x6	0.059	763	0.670	17.6	29.6	0.077 2	3.21	10.1	11.0	22.3	10.9	0.076 8
x5	0.053	693	0.635	16.7	30.3	0.068 3	2.98	9.93	11.1	23.1	9.19	0.068 9

* Not available from Canadian mills

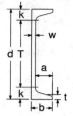

STANDARD CHANNELS (C SHAPES)

DIMENSIONS AND SURFACE AREAS

Nominal Mass	Theo-retical Mass	Depth	Flange Width	Flange Thick-ness	Web Thick-ness	Distances			Surface Area (m²) per metre of length		Imperial Designation
		d	b	t	w	a	T	k	Total	Minus Top of Top Flange	
kg/m	kg/m	mm	mm	mm	mm	mm	mm	mm			
74	74.4	381	94	16.5	18.2	76	311	35	1.10	1.01	C15x50
60	59.4	381	89	16.5	13.2	76	311	35	1.09	1.00	C15x40
50	50.5	381	86	16.5	10.2	76	311	35	1.09	1.00	C15x33.9
45	44.7	305	80	12.7	13.0	67	250	27	0.904	0.824	C12x30
37	37.0	305	77	12.7	9.8	67	250	27	0.898	0.821	C12x25
31	30.7	305	74	12.7	7.2	67	250	27	0.892	0.818	C12x20.7
45	44.5	254	76	11.1	17.1	59	205	24	0.778	0.702	C10x30
37	37.3	254	73	11.1	13.4	60	205	24	0.773	0.700	C10x25
30	29.6	254	69	11.1	9.6	59	205	24	0.765	0.696	C10x20
23	22.6	254	65	11.1	6.1	59	205	24	0.756	0.691	C10x15.3
30	29.8	229	67	10.5	11.4	56	182	23	0.703	0.636	C9x20
22	22.3	229	63	10.5	7.2	56	182	23	0.696	0.633	C9x15
20	19.8	229	61	10.5	5.9	55	182	23	0.690	0.629	C9x13.4
28	27.9	203	64	9.9	12.4	52	159	22	0.637	0.573	C8x18.75
21	20.4	203	59	9.9	7.7	51	159	22	0.627	0.568	C8x13.75
17	17.0	203	57	9.9	5.6	51	159	22	0.623	0.566	C8x11.5
22	21.9	178	58	9.3	10.6	47	136	21	0.567	0.509	C7x14.75
18	18.2	178	55	9.3	8.0	47	136	21	0.560	0.505	C7x12.25
15	14.5	178	53	9.3	5.3	48	136	21	0.557	0.504	C7x9.8
19	19.2	152	54	8.7	11.1	43	113	20	0.498	0.444	C6x13
16	15.5	152	51	8.7	8.0	43	113	20	0.492	0.441	C6x10.5
12	12.0	152	48	8.7	5.1	43	113	20	0.486	0.438	C6x8.2
13	13.3	127	47	8.1	8.3	39	90	18	0.425	0.378	C5x9
10	9.9	127	44	8.1	4.8	39	90	19	0.420	0.376	C5x6.7
11	10.8	102	43	7.5	8.2	35	67	17	0.360	0.317	C4x7.25
9	9.4	102	42	7.5	6.3	36	67	17	0.359	0.317	C4x6.25
8	8.0	102	40	7.5	4.7	35	67	17	0.355	0.315	C4x5.4
7	7.0	102	40	7.5	3.2	37	67	17	0.358	0.318	C4x4.5
9	8.8	76	40	6.9	9.0	31	43	16	0.294	0.254	C3x6
7	7.3	76	37	6.9	6.6	30	43	16	0.287	0.250	C3x5
6	6.0	76	35	6.9	4.3	31	43	16	0.283	0.248	C3x4.1
5	5.4	76	34	6.9	3.4	31	43	16	0.281	0.247	C3x3.5

MISCELLANEOUS CHANNELS
MC460 - MC200

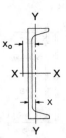

PROPERTIES

Designation ‡	Dead Load	Area	Axis X-X			Axis Y-Y				Shear Centre	Torsional Constant	Warping Constant
			I_x	S_x	r_x	I_y	S_y	r_y	x	x_o	J	C_w
	kN/m	mm²	10^6 mm⁴	10^3 mm³	mm	10^6 mm⁴	10^3 mm³	mm	mm	mm	10^3 mm⁴	10^9 mm⁶
MC460												
x86	0.849	11 000	282	1230	160	7.36	86.4	25.8	21.9	39.6	1 170	290
x77.2	0.758	9 840	261	1140	163	6.81	82.8	26.3	21.8	42.1	842	264
x68.2	0.669	8 680	241	1050	166	6.18	77.1	26.7	21.9	45.2	605	243
x63.5	0.624	8 100	231	1010	169	5.94	76.3	27.1	22.2	46.8	513	227
MC330												
x74	0.730	9 480	131	792	117	6.81	78.0	26.8	24.7	45.4	1 240	149
x60	0.582	7 560	113	685	122	5.63	69.0	27.3	24.4	50.6	643	123
x52	0.511	6 640	105	635	126	5.13	65.8	27.8	24.9	54.1	472	110
x47.3	0.464	6 020	99.3	602	128	4.69	61.1	27.9	25.4	57.2	393	103
MC310												
x74	0.731	9 500	112	738	109	7.26	92.7	27.7	26.7	45.5	1 340	111
x67	0.658	8 540	105	689	111	6.55	86.5	27.7	26.3	47.7	976	101
x60	0.585	7 600	97.8	641	113	5.92	81.4	27.9	26.3	50.5	708	90.9
x52	0.512	6 650	90.4	593	117	5.27	76.1	28.1	26.7	54.0	519	80.7
x46	0.454	5 890	84.4	554	120	4.69	71.6	28.2	27.6	57.2	418	71.5
MC310												
x15.8	0.154	1 990	23.0	151	107	0.157	5.04	8.88	6.81	14.0	24.8	3.11
MC250												
x61.2	0.601	7 800	65.7	518	91.8	6.56	79.6	29.0	27.6	49.7	942	72.7
x50	0.491	6 370	57.9	456	95.3	5.43	70.9	29.2	27.5	54.4	500	60.0
x42.4	0.416	5 400	52.6	414	98.7	4.66	64.9	29.4	28.2	58.9	329	51.5
MC250												
x37	0.365	4 740	45.8	360	98.2	3.02	48.9	25.2	24.2	49.9	264	33.1
x33	0.321	4 170	42.7	336	101	2.67	45.2	25.3	25.1	53.4	213	29.6
MC250												
x12.5	0.122	1 580	13.3	104	91.6	0.136	4.41	9.28	7.21	15.6	17.2	1.87
MC230												
x37.8	0.372	4 830	36.9	322	87.4	3.16	49.0	25.6	24.6	49.8	289	28.2
x35.6	0.349	4 540	35.6	310	88.5	2.97	46.9	25.6	24.8	51.2	249	26.7
MC200												
x33.9	0.332	4 310	26.5	261	78.4	2.89	45.6	25.9	25.6	52.2	236	20.2
x31.8	0.312	4 050	25.6	253	79.5	2.74	44.3	26.0	26.0	54.0	205	19.2
MC200												
x29.8	0.292	3 790	22.7	223	77.3	1.84	32.9	22.0	21.3	42.7	184	12.9
x27.8	0.273	3 550	21.8	215	78.4	1.72	31.4	22.0	21.4	44.1	159	12.2

‡ Designation consists of nominal depth in millimetres and nominal mass in kilograms per metre.

For sections formerly available from Canadian mills, the nominal mass has been rounded to the nearest kg/m.

Note: These shapes have been soft-converted from Imperial to SI dimensions.

DIMENSIONS AND SURFACE AREAS

Nominal Mass	Theoretical Mass	Depth	Flange Width	Flange Thickness	Web Thickness	Distances			Surface Area (m²) per metre of length		Imperial Designation
		d	b	t	w	a	T	k	Total	Minus Top of Top Flange	
kg/m	kg/m	mm	mm	mm	mm	mm	mm	mm			
86	86.5	457	107	15.9	17.8	89	385	36	1.31	1.20	MC18x58
77.2	77.2	457	104	15.9	15.2	89	385	36	1.30	1.20	MC18x51.9
68.2	68.2	457	102	15.9	12.7	89	385	36	1.30	1.19	MC18x45.8
63.5	63.6	457	100	15.9	11.4	89	385	36	1.29	1.19	MC18x42.7
74	74.5	330	112	15.5	20.0	92	258	36	1.07	0.956	MC13x50
60	59.3	330	106	15.5	14.2	92	258	36	1.06	0.950	MC13x40
52	52.1	330	103	15.5	11.4	92	258	36	1.05	0.946	MC13x35
47.3	47.3	330	102	15.5	9.5	93	258	36	1.05	0.947	MC13x31.8
74	74.5	305	105	17.8	21.2	84	237	34	0.988	0.883	MC12x50
67	67.1	305	102	17.8	18.1	84	237	34	0.982	0.880	MC12x45
60	59.7	305	99	17.8	15.0	84	237	34	0.976	0.877	MC12x40
52	52.2	305	96	17.8	11.9	84	237	34	0.970	0.874	MC12x35
46	46.2	305	93	17.8	9.4	84	237	34	0.963	0.870	MC12x31
15.8	15.7	305	38	7.8	4.8	33	267	19	0.752	0.714	MC12x10.6
61.2	61.3	254	110	14.6	20.2	90	188	33	0.908	0.798	MC10x41.1
50	50.0	254	104	14.6	14.6	89	188	33	0.895	0.791	MC10x33.6
42.4	42.4	254	100	14.6	10.8	89	188	33	0.886	0.786	MC10x28.5
37	37.2	254	86	14.6	9.7	76	188	33	0.833	0.747	MC10x25
33	32.7	254	84	14.6	7.4	77	188	33	0.829	0.745	MC10x22
12.5	12.4	254	38	7.1	4.3	34	218	18	0.651	0.613	MC10x8.4
37.8	37.9	229	89	14.0	11.4	78	167	31	0.791	0.702	MC9x25.4
35.6	35.6	229	88	14.0	10.2	78	167	31	0.790	0.702	MC9x23.9
33.9	33.8	203	89	13.3	10.8	78	143	30	0.740	0.651	MC8x22.8
31.8	31.8	203	88	13.3	9.5	79	143	30	0.739	0.651	MC8x21.4
29.8	29.8	203	77	12.7	10.2	67	147	28	0.694	0.617	MC8x20
27.8	27.9	203	76	12.7	9.0	67	147	28	0.692	0.616	MC8x18.7

MISCELLANEOUS CHANNELS
MC200 - MC150

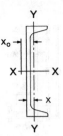

PROPERTIES

Designation ‡	Dead Load	Area	Axis X-X			Axis Y-Y				Shear Centre	Torsional Constant	Warping Constant
			I_x	S_x	r_x	I_y	S_y	r_y	x	x_o	J	C_w
	kN/m	mm²	10^6 mm⁴	10^3 mm³	mm	10^6 mm⁴	10^3 mm³	mm	mm	mm	10^3 mm⁴	10^9 mm⁶
MC200												
x12.6	0.124	1 600	9.66	95.2	77.6	0.260	7.02	12.7	10.9	25.0	24.3	2.24
MC180												
x33.8	0.332	4 310	19.9	223	67.9	3.01	45.9	26.4	26.4	52.3	259	15.9
x28.4	0.279	3 620	18.0	203	70.6	2.50	41.2	26.3	27.2	56.7	170	13.4
MC150												
x26.8	0.263	3 410	12.3	162	60.1	2.43	40.1	26.7	28.4	58.1	158	9.25
x22.8	0.223	2 900	10.5	139	60.3	2.05	33.0	26.6	26.8	56.5	92.8	8.09
MC150												
x24.3	0.238	3 090	10.8	142	59.1	1.56	29.7	22.5	23.5	47.1	141	5.90
x22.5	0.220	2 860	10.3	136	60.2	1.44	28.1	22.4	23.8	49.0	119	5.52
MC150												
x17.9	0.175	2 280	7.75	102	58.3	0.769	17.0	18.4	17.9	36.1	64.5	2.97

‡ Designation consists of nominal depth in millimetres and nominal mass in kilograms per metre.
  For sections formerly available from Canadian mills, the nominal mass has been rounded to the nearest kg/m.
Note: These shapes have been soft-converted from Imperial to SI dimensions.

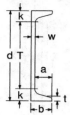

DIMENSIONS AND SURFACE AREAS

Nominal Mass	Theo-retical Mass	Depth	Flange Width	Flange Thick-ness	Web Thick-ness	Distances			Surface Area (m²) per metre of length		Imperial Designation
		d	b	t	w	a	T	k	Total	Minus Top of Top Flange	
kg/m	kg/m	mm	mm	mm	mm	mm	mm	mm			
12.6	12.6	203	48	7.9	4.5	44	165	19	0.589	0.541	MC8x8.5
33.8	33.9	178	92	12.7	12.8	79	122	28	0.698	0.606	MC7x22.7
28.4	28.4	178	88	12.7	8.9	79	122	28	0.690	0.602	MC7x19.1
26.8	26.8	152	89	12.1	9.6	79	98	27	0.641	0.552	MC6x18
22.8	22.8	152	89	9.8	8.6	80	108	22	0.643	0.554	MC6x15.3
24.3	24.2	152	76	12.1	9.5	67	98	27	0.589	0.513	MC6x16.3
22.5	22.4	152	75	12.1	8.0	67	98	27	0.588	0.513	MC6x15.1
17.9	17.9	152	63	9.5	7.9	55	110	21	0.540	0.477	MC6x12

ANGLES
L203 - L152

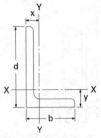

PROPERTIES ABOUT GEOMETRIC AXES

Designation	Dead Load	Area	Axis X-X				Axis Y-Y				Torsional Constant	Warping Constant
			I_x	S_x	r_x	y	I_y	S_y	r_y	x	J	C_w
	kN/m	mm²	10^6 mm⁴	10^3 mm³	mm	mm	10^6 mm⁴	10^3 mm³	mm	mm	10^3 mm⁴	10^9 mm⁶
L203x203												
x29*	0.831	10 800	40.7	287	61.4	61.2	40.7	287	61.4	61.2	2 940	8.73
x25*	0.744	9 670	36.9	258	61.8	60.1	36.9	258	61.8	60.1	2 080	6.27
x22*	0.656	8 520	33.0	229	62.2	58.9	33.0	229	62.2	58.9	1 400	4.30
x19*	0.569	7 390	29.0	200	62.6	57.8	29.0	200	62.6	57.8	899	2.80
x16*	0.478	6 200	24.7	169	63.1	56.6	24.7	169	63.1	56.6	523	1.66
x14*	0.431	5 600	22.5	153	63.3	56.0	22.5	153	63.3	56.0	382	1.22
x13	0.385	4 990	20.2	137	63.6	55.5	20.2	137	63.6	55.5	269	0.865
L203x152												
x25*	0.645	8 370	33.5	247	63.3	67.4	16.0	145	43.7	41.9	1 800	4.37
x22*	0.569	7 390	30.0	219	63.7	66.2	14.4	129	44.1	40.7	1 210	3.00
x19*	0.494	6 420	26.4	191	64.1	65.1	12.7	113	44.5	39.6	780	1.96
x16*	0.415	5 390	22.5	162	64.6	64.0	10.9	95.9	44.9	38.5	454	1.16
x14*	0.375	4 870	20.4	146	64.8	63.4	9.94	87.1	45.2	37.9	332	0.857
x13*	0.335	4 350	18.4	131	65.0	62.8	8.96	78.1	45.4	37.3	234	0.609
L203x102												
x25*	0.547	7 100	29.0	230	63.8	77.2	4.90	65.1	26.3	26.7	1 530	3.46
x19*	0.421	5 460	22.9	178	64.7	74.8	3.95	50.8	26.9	24.3	664	1.55
x13*	0.286	3 710	16.0	123	65.7	72.4	2.84	35.4	27.6	21.9	200	0.482
L178x102												
x19*	0.384	4 980	15.8	139	56.4	63.8	3.82	50.1	27.7	25.8	606	1.08
x16*	0.323	4 200	13.6	118	56.8	62.6	3.31	42.7	28.1	24.6	354	0.642
x13	0.261	3 390	11.1	95.6	57.3	61.4	2.75	35.0	28.5	23.4	183	0.338
x11*	0.230	2 980	9.88	84.3	57.5	60.8	2.45	31.0	28.7	22.8	123	0.229
x9.5	0.198	2 580	8.60	73.0	57.8	60.2	2.15	26.9	28.9	22.2	78.0	0.147
L152x152												
x25*	0.545	7 080	14.6	140	45.5	47.2	14.6	140	45.5	47.2	1 520	2.46
x22*	0.482	6 260	13.2	124	45.9	46.1	13.2	124	45.9	46.1	1 030	1.70
x19	0.419	5 440	11.6	109	46.3	45.0	11.6	109	46.3	45.0	662	1.12
x16	0.353	4 580	9.99	92.3	46.7	43.9	9.99	92.3	46.7	43.9	386	0.668
x14*	0.319	4 140	9.12	83.8	46.9	43.3	9.12	83.8	46.9	43.3	282	0.494
x13	0.285	3 700	8.22	75.2	47.1	42.7	8.22	75.2	47.1	42.7	199	0.352
x11*	0.250	3 250	7.29	66.4	47.4	42.1	7.29	66.4	47.4	42.1	134	0.239
x9.5	0.216	2 810	6.36	57.5	47.6	41.5	6.36	57.5	47.6	41.5	85.0	0.153
x7.9*	0.181	2 350	5.38	48.4	47.8	41.0	5.38	48.4	47.8	41.0	49.4	0.090 2
x6.4*	0.146	1 890	4.37	39.1	48.1	40.4	4.37	39.1	48.1	40.4	25.4	0.046 9

See page 6-39 for qualification of properties of angles produced by cold-forming.

* Not available from Canadian mills

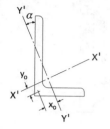

DIMENSIONS AND PROPERTIES ABOUT PRINCIPAL AXES

Mass	d	b	t	Axis X'-X'		Axis Y'-Y'		$\bar{r}_o$	Ω	tan α
				r_x	y_o	r_y	x_o			
kg/m	mm	mm	mm	mm	mm	mm	mm	mm		
84.7	203	203	28.6	77.3	0.00	39.6	66.3	109	0.631	1.00
75.9	203	203	25.4	77.9	0.00	39.7	67.0	110	0.630	1.00
66.9	203	203	22.2	78.5	0.00	39.8	67.6	111	0.629	1.00
58.0	203	203	19.1	79.1	0.00	40.0	68.2	112	0.628	1.00
48.7	203	203	15.9	79.7	0.00	40.1	68.8	113	0.627	1.00
44.0	203	203	14.3	80.0	0.00	40.2	69.2	113	0.626	1.00
39.2	203	203	12.7	80.3	0.00	40.3	69.5	114	0.626	1.00
65.7	203	152	25.4	69.7	34.2	32.4	51.7	98.8	0.606	0.541
58.0	203	152	22.2	70.3	34.2	32.5	52.4	99.6	0.605	0.545
50.4	203	152	19.1	70.9	34.2	32.6	53.1	100	0.604	0.549
42.3	203	152	15.9	71.5	34.3	32.8	53.8	101	0.603	0.553
38.2	203	152	14.3	71.8	34.3	32.9	54.1	102	0.603	0.554
34.1	203	152	12.7	72.1	34.3	33.0	54.5	102	0.603	0.556
55.7	203	102	25.4	65.6	59.2	21.6	29.2	95.5	0.523	0.249
42.9	203	102	19.1	66.6	59.5	21.7	30.7	96.9	0.523	0.260
29.1	203	102	12.7	67.7	59.8	22.1	32.2	98.4	0.524	0.269
39.1	178	102	19.1	58.9	46.5	21.9	32.2	84.5	0.552	0.325
33.0	178	102	15.9	59.4	46.6	22.1	33.0	85.3	0.552	0.331
26.6	178	102	12.7	60.0	46.7	22.2	33.7	86.1	0.552	0.336
23.4	178	102	11.1	60.3	46.8	22.3	34.1	86.5	0.552	0.339
20.2	178	102	9.53	60.6	46.8	22.4	34.4	86.9	0.553	0.341
55.6	152	152	25.4	57.1	0.00	29.6	48.8	80.8	0.634	1.00
49.1	152	152	22.2	57.7	0.00	29.6	49.5	81.6	0.632	1.00
42.7	152	152	19.1	58.3	0.00	29.7	50.1	82.4	0.630	1.00
36.0	152	152	15.9	58.9	0.00	29.8	50.8	83.3	0.628	1.00
32.5	152	152	14.3	59.2	0.00	29.9	51.1	83.7	0.628	1.00
29.0	152	152	12.7	59.5	0.00	30.0	51.4	84.2	0.627	1.00
25.5	152	152	11.1	59.8	0.00	30.1	51.7	84.6	0.627	1.00
22.0	152	152	9.53	60.1	0.00	30.2	52.0	85.1	0.626	1.00
18.5	152	152	7.94	60.5	0.00	30.3	52.3	85.5	0.626	1.00
14.8	152	152	6.35	60.8	0.00	30.4	52.6	85.9	0.626	1.00

See CSA S16-09 Clause 13.3.2 for the definition of x_o, y_o, $\bar{r}_o$ and Ω.
The Y-Y axis of symmetry of equal-leg (singly-symmetric) angles corresponds to X'-X' in the above table.

ANGLES
L152 - L127

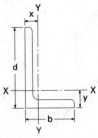

PROPERTIES ABOUT GEOMETRIC AXES

Designation	Dead Load	Area	Axis X-X				Axis Y-Y				Torsional Constant	Warping Constant
			I_x	S_x	r_x	y	I_y	S_y	r_y	x	J	C_w
	kN/m	mm²	10^6 mm⁴	10^3 mm³	mm	mm	10^6 mm⁴	10^3 mm³	mm	mm	10^3 mm⁴	10^9 mm⁶
L152x102												
x22*	0.396	5 150	11.5	117	47.2	53.7	4.10	55.9	28.2	28.7	845	1.08
x19	0.346	4 490	10.2	102	47.6	52.5	3.66	49.2	28.6	27.5	546	0.712
x16	0.292	3 790	8.73	86.8	48.0	51.4	3.17	41.9	28.9	26.4	319	0.427
x14*	0.264	3 430	7.98	78.8	48.2	50.8	2.91	38.2	29.1	25.8	234	0.316
x13	0.236	3 060	7.20	70.7	48.5	50.2	2.64	34.4	29.3	25.2	165	0.226
x11*	0.208	2 700	6.39	62.4	48.7	49.6	2.35	30.4	29.6	24.6	111	0.153
x9.5	0.179	2 330	5.58	54.2	48.9	49.1	2.06	26.5	29.8	24.1	70.5	0.098 8
x7.9	0.150	1 950	4.72	45.6	49.2	48.5	1.76	22.4	30.0	23.5	41.1	0.058 2
L152x89												
x16	0.275	3 580	8.31	84.7	48.2	53.9	2.12	31.8	24.3	22.4	301	0.393
x13	0.223	2 900	6.86	69.1	48.6	52.7	1.77	26.1	24.7	21.2	156	0.208
x9.5	0.170	2 200	5.32	52.9	49.1	51.6	1.39	20.2	25.1	20.0	66.8	0.091 1
x7.9	0.142	1 850	4.50	44.6	49.3	51.0	1.19	17.1	25.3	19.4	38.9	0.053 6
L127x127												
x22*	0.396	5 150	7.39	84.7	37.9	39.8	7.39	84.7	37.9	39.8	845	0.946
x19	0.346	4 490	6.57	74.4	38.3	38.7	6.57	74.4	38.3	38.7	546	0.627
x16	0.292	3 790	5.66	63.3	38.7	37.6	5.66	63.3	38.7	37.6	319	0.377
x13	0.236	3 060	4.68	51.7	39.1	36.4	4.68	51.7	39.1	36.4	165	0.200
x11*	0.208	2 700	4.17	45.7	39.3	35.8	4.17	45.7	39.3	35.8	111	0.136
x9.5	0.179	2 330	3.64	39.7	39.5	35.3	3.64	39.7	39.5	35.3	70.5	0.087 8
x7.9	0.150	1 950	3.09	33.5	39.8	34.7	3.09	33.5	39.8	34.7	41.1	0.051 8
x6.4*	0.121	1 570	2.52	27.1	40.0	34.1	2.52	27.1	40.0	34.1	21.1	0.027 0
L127x89												
x19*	0.289	3 760	5.80	70.2	39.3	44.4	2.31	36.4	24.8	25.3	457	0.410
x16*	0.245	3 180	5.01	59.8	39.7	43.2	2.01	31.1	25.2	24.2	268	0.248
x13	0.199	2 580	4.16	48.9	40.1	42.1	1.68	25.6	25.6	23.0	139	0.132
x9.5	0.151	1 970	3.24	37.6	40.6	40.9	1.33	19.8	26.0	21.9	59.5	0.058 2
x7.9	0.127	1 650	2.75	31.7	40.8	40.3	1.13	16.7	26.2	21.3	34.7	0.034 4
x6.4	0.102	1 330	2.24	25.7	41.0	39.7	0.928	13.6	26.4	20.7	17.9	0.018 0
L127x76												
x13	0.186	2 420	3.93	47.7	40.3	44.5	1.07	18.8	21.1	19.1	130	0.119
x11*	0.164	2 130	3.51	42.2	40.6	43.9	0.963	16.7	21.3	18.5	87.6	0.081 5
x9.5	0.142	1 850	3.07	36.7	40.8	43.3	0.849	14.6	21.5	17.9	55.9	0.052 7
x7.9	0.119	1 550	2.61	30.9	41.0	42.7	0.727	12.3	21.7	17.3	32.6	0.031 1
x6.4	0.096 3	1 250	2.13	25.0	41.2	42.1	0.598	10.1	21.9	16.7	16.8	0.016 3

See page 6-39 for qualification of properties of angles produced by cold-forming.

* Not available from Canadian mills

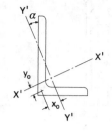

DIMENSIONS AND PROPERTIES ABOUT PRINCIPAL AXES

Mass	d	b	t	Axis X'-X'		Axis Y'-Y'		$\bar{r}_o$	Ω	tan α
				r_x	y_o	r_y	x_o			
kg/m	mm	mm	mm	mm	mm	mm	mm	mm		
40.4	152	102	22.2	50.5	32.2	21.9	32.9	71.7	0.588	0.427
35.2	152	102	19.1	51.0	32.3	21.9	33.6	72.5	0.586	0.434
29.7	152	102	15.9	51.6	32.3	22.0	34.4	73.3	0.585	0.440
26.9	152	102	14.3	51.8	32.4	22.1	34.7	73.7	0.585	0.443
24.1	152	102	12.7	52.1	32.4	22.2	35.1	74.1	0.585	0.446
21.2	152	102	11.1	52.4	32.4	22.3	35.5	74.5	0.584	0.449
18.3	152	102	9.53	52.7	32.4	22.4	35.8	74.9	0.584	0.451
15.3	152	102	7.94	53.0	32.5	22.5	36.1	75.3	0.584	0.454
28.1	152	88.9	15.9	50.5	38.9	19.1	28.4	72.4	0.557	0.339
22.8	152	88.9	12.7	51.0	39.0	19.3	29.2	73.1	0.556	0.345
17.3	152	88.9	9.53	51.6	39.1	19.5	29.9	73.9	0.557	0.351
14.5	152	88.9	7.94	51.9	39.1	19.6	30.2	74.3	0.557	0.354
40.4	127	127	22.2	47.5	0.00	24.7	40.6	67.2	0.635	1.00
35.2	127	127	19.1	48.1	0.00	24.8	41.3	68.0	0.632	1.00
29.7	127	127	15.9	48.7	0.00	24.8	41.9	68.9	0.630	1.00
24.1	127	127	12.7	49.3	0.00	25.0	42.5	69.8	0.628	1.00
21.2	127	127	11.1	49.6	0.00	25.0	42.8	70.2	0.627	1.00
18.3	127	127	9.53	49.9	0.00	25.1	43.2	70.6	0.627	1.00
15.3	127	127	7.94	50.3	0.00	25.2	43.5	71.1	0.626	1.00
12.3	127	127	6.35	50.6	0.00	25.4	43.7	71.5	0.626	1.00
29.5	127	88.9	19.1	42.4	24.9	19.0	29.0	60.2	0.597	0.464
25.0	127	88.9	15.9	43.0	25.0	19.1	29.7	61.0	0.594	0.472
20.3	127	88.9	12.7	43.5	25.0	19.2	30.5	61.8	0.593	0.479
15.4	127	88.9	9.53	44.1	25.0	19.3	31.2	62.6	0.592	0.486
13.0	127	88.9	7.94	44.4	25.1	19.4	31.5	63.0	0.592	0.489
10.4	127	88.9	6.35	44.7	25.1	19.6	31.8	63.4	0.592	0.492
19.0	127	76.2	12.7	42.4	31.6	16.5	24.8	60.7	0.562	0.357
16.7	127	76.2	11.1	42.7	31.7	16.5	25.1	61.1	0.562	0.361
14.5	127	76.2	9.53	43.0	31.7	16.6	25.5	61.5	0.562	0.364
12.2	127	76.2	7.94	43.3	31.7	16.7	25.9	61.9	0.562	0.368
9.81	127	76.2	6.35	43.6	31.8	16.8	26.2	62.3	0.562	0.371

See CSA S16-09 Clause 13.3.2 for the definition of x_o, y_o, $\bar{r}_o$ and Ω.
The Y-Y axis of symmetry of equal-leg (singly-symmetric) angles corresponds to X'-X' in the above table.

ANGLES
L102 - L89

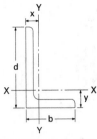

PROPERTIES ABOUT GEOMETRIC AXES

Designation	Dead Load	Area	Axis X-X				Axis Y-Y				Torsional Constant	Warping Constant
			I_x	S_x	r_x	y	I_y	S_y	r_y	x	J	C_w
	kN/m	mm²	10^6 mm⁴	10^3 mm³	mm	mm	10^6 mm⁴	10^3 mm³	mm	mm	10^3 mm⁴	10^9 mm⁶
L102x102												
x19	0.272	3 530	3.24	46.5	30.3	32.4	3.24	46.5	30.3	32.4	429	0.306
x16*	0.230	2 990	2.81	39.8	30.7	31.3	2.81	39.8	30.7	31.3	252	0.186
x13	0.187	2 430	2.34	32.6	31.1	30.2	2.34	32.6	31.1	30.2	131	0.099 6
x11*	0.165	2 140	2.09	28.9	31.3	29.6	2.09	28.9	31.3	29.6	87.9	0.068 2
x9.5	0.143	1 850	1.84	25.2	31.5	29.0	1.84	25.2	31.5	29.0	56.1	0.044 2
x7.9	0.120	1 560	1.57	21.3	31.7	28.4	1.57	21.3	31.7	28.4	32.7	0.026 2
x6.4	0.096 7	1 260	1.28	17.3	31.9	27.9	1.28	17.3	31.9	27.9	16.9	0.013 7
L102x89												
x13	0.174	2 260	2.24	32.0	31.5	31.9	1.58	24.9	26.4	25.4	122	0.081 8
x11*	0.154	2 000	2.00	28.3	31.7	31.3	1.42	22.1	26.6	24.8	82.0	0.056 1
x9.5	0.133	1 730	1.76	24.7	31.9	30.8	1.24	19.2	26.8	24.2	52.3	0.036 4
x7.9	0.112	1 450	1.50	20.9	32.1	30.2	1.06	16.3	27.1	23.6	30.5	0.021 6
x6.4	0.090 2	1 170	1.23	16.9	32.3	29.6	0.872	13.2	27.3	23.1	15.8	0.011 3
L102x76												
x16*	0.199	2 580	2.54	38.0	31.4	35.0	1.20	22.2	21.6	22.1	217	0.128
x13	0.162	2 100	2.12	31.2	31.8	33.9	1.01	18.3	21.9	21.0	113	0.069 2
x11*	0.143	1 850	1.90	27.7	32.0	33.3	0.907	16.3	22.1	20.4	76.2	0.047 5
x9.5	0.124	1 610	1.67	24.1	32.2	32.7	0.800	14.2	22.3	19.8	48.7	0.030 9
x7.9	0.104	1 350	1.42	20.4	32.4	32.1	0.686	12.0	22.5	19.2	28.4	0.018 3
x6.4	0.084 0	1 090	1.17	16.5	32.7	31.6	0.565	9.81	22.7	18.7	14.7	0.009 63
L89x89												
x13	0.161	2 100	1.51	24.4	26.9	26.9	1.51	24.4	26.9	26.9	113	0.064 0
x11*	0.142	1 850	1.36	21.7	27.1	26.3	1.36	21.7	27.1	26.3	76.0	0.044 0
x9.5	0.123	1 600	1.19	18.9	27.3	25.7	1.19	18.9	27.3	25.7	48.5	0.028 6
x7.9	0.104	1 350	1.02	16.0	27.5	25.2	1.02	16.0	27.5	25.2	28.3	0.017 0
x6.4	0.083 8	1 090	0.837	13.0	27.7	24.6	0.837	13.0	27.7	24.6	14.6	0.008 96
L89x76												
x13	0.149	1 940	1.44	23.8	27.3	28.6	0.969	18.0	22.4	22.2	104	0.051 4
x9.5	0.114	1 480	1.13	18.5	27.7	27.4	0.769	14.0	22.8	21.1	44.9	0.023 1
x7.9	0.096 1	1 250	0.970	15.6	27.9	26.9	0.659	11.8	23.0	20.5	26.2	0.013 8
x6.4	0.077 6	1 010	0.796	12.7	28.1	26.3	0.543	9.65	23.2	19.9	13.5	0.007 25
L89x64												
x13	0.137	1 770	1.35	23.1	27.6	30.6	0.568	12.5	17.9	17.9	95.4	0.042 6
x9.5	0.105	1 360	1.07	17.9	28.0	29.5	0.454	9.71	18.3	16.8	41.2	0.019 2
x7.9	0.088 3	1 150	0.912	15.2	28.2	28.9	0.391	8.26	18.5	16.2	24.1	0.011 5
x6.4	0.071 4	927	0.749	12.4	28.4	28.3	0.323	6.75	18.7	15.6	12.5	0.006 04

See page 6-39 for qualification of properties of angles produced by cold-forming.

* Not available from Canadian mills

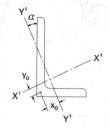

DIMENSIONS AND PROPERTIES ABOUT PRINCIPAL AXES

Mass	d	b	t	Axis X'-X'		Axis Y'-Y'		$\bar{r}_o$	Ω	tan α
				r_x	y_o	r_y	x_o			
kg/m	mm	mm	mm	mm	mm	mm	mm	mm		
27.7	102	102	19.1	37.9	0.00	19.8	32.3	53.7	0.637	1.00
23.5	102	102	15.9	38.5	0.00	19.9	33.0	54.5	0.633	1.00
19.1	102	102	12.7	39.1	0.00	19.9	33.7	55.3	0.630	1.00
16.8	102	102	11.1	39.4	0.00	20.0	34.0	55.8	0.629	1.00
14.5	102	102	9.53	39.7	0.00	20.1	34.3	56.2	0.628	1.00
12.2	102	102	7.94	40.1	0.00	20.2	34.6	56.6	0.627	1.00
9.85	102	102	6.35	40.4	0.00	20.3	34.9	57.1	0.626	1.00
17.8	102	88.9	12.7	36.8	9.16	18.4	30.5	52.0	0.625	0.744
15.7	102	88.9	11.1	37.1	9.16	18.4	30.8	52.4	0.623	0.746
13.6	102	88.9	9.53	37.4	9.15	18.5	31.2	52.8	0.622	0.749
11.4	102	88.9	7.94	37.7	9.15	18.6	31.5	53.3	0.621	0.751
9.20	102	88.9	6.35	38.0	9.15	18.7	31.8	53.7	0.621	0.753
20.3	102	76.2	15.9	34.5	17.3	16.2	25.2	48.8	0.609	0.529
16.5	102	76.2	12.7	35.0	17.3	16.2	25.9	49.6	0.606	0.538
14.6	102	76.2	11.1	35.3	17.3	16.3	26.3	50.0	0.605	0.543
12.6	102	76.2	9.53	35.6	17.3	16.4	26.6	50.4	0.604	0.547
10.6	102	76.2	7.94	35.9	17.3	16.5	27.0	50.9	0.603	0.550
8.57	102	76.2	6.35	36.2	17.3	16.6	27.3	51.3	0.603	0.554
16.5	88.9	88.9	12.7	33.8	0.00	17.3	29.0	47.8	0.632	1.00
14.5	88.9	88.9	11.1	34.1	0.00	17.4	29.3	48.2	0.630	1.00
12.6	88.9	88.9	9.53	34.4	0.00	17.4	29.7	48.7	0.629	1.00
10.6	88.9	88.9	7.94	34.7	0.00	17.5	30.0	49.1	0.627	1.00
8.55	88.9	88.9	6.35	35.0	0.00	17.6	30.3	49.5	0.627	1.00
15.2	88.9	76.2	12.7	31.5	8.86	15.8	25.8	44.6	0.625	0.714
11.6	88.9	76.2	9.53	32.1	8.85	15.9	26.5	45.4	0.622	0.721
9.80	88.9	76.2	7.94	32.4	8.84	15.9	26.8	45.9	0.621	0.724
7.91	88.9	76.2	6.35	32.7	8.84	16.0	27.1	46.3	0.620	0.727
13.9	88.9	63.5	12.7	29.9	16.8	13.6	21.0	42.4	0.600	0.486
10.7	88.9	63.5	9.53	30.5	16.8	13.6	21.7	43.2	0.597	0.496
9.00	88.9	63.5	7.94	30.8	16.8	13.7	22.1	43.7	0.596	0.501
7.28	88.9	63.5	6.35	31.1	16.8	13.8	22.4	44.1	0.596	0.506

See CSA S16-09 Clause 13.3.2 for the definition of x_o, y_o, $\bar{r}_o$ and Ω.
The Y-Y axis of symmetry of equal-leg (singly-symmetric) angles corresponds to X'-X' in the above table.

ANGLES
L76 - L51

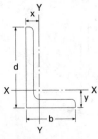

PROPERTIES ABOUT GEOMETRIC AXES

Designation	Dead Load	Area	Axis X-X				Axis Y-Y				Torsional Constant	Warping Constant
			I_x	S_x	r_x	y	I_y	S_y	r_y	x	J	C_w
	kN/m	mm²	10^6 mm⁴	10^3 mm³	mm	mm	10^6 mm⁴	10^3 mm³	mm	mm	10^3 mm⁴	10^9 mm⁶
L76x76												
x13	0.137	1 770	0.923	17.6	22.8	23.7	0.923	17.6	22.8	23.7	95.4	0.038 8
x11*	0.121	1 570	0.830	15.6	23.0	23.1	0.830	15.6	23.0	23.1	64.4	0.026 8
x9.5	0.105	1 360	0.733	13.7	23.2	22.5	0.733	13.7	23.2	22.5	41.2	0.017 5
x7.9	0.088 3	1 150	0.629	11.6	23.4	22.0	0.629	11.6	23.4	22.0	24.1	0.010 5
x6.4	0.071 4	927	0.518	9.45	23.6	21.4	0.518	9.45	23.6	21.4	12.5	0.005 54
x4.8	0.054 1	703	0.400	7.22	23.9	20.8	0.400	7.22	23.9	20.8	5.31	0.002 41
L76x64												
x13*	0.124	1 610	0.867	17.1	23.2	25.4	0.542	12.2	18.3	19.1	86.7	0.030 0
x9.5	0.095 5	1 240	0.690	13.3	23.6	24.3	0.434	9.52	18.7	17.9	37.6	0.013 6
x7.9	0.080 6	1 050	0.592	11.3	23.8	23.7	0.374	8.10	18.9	17.4	22.0	0.008 17
x6.4	0.065 2	847	0.488	9.20	24.0	23.1	0.309	6.62	19.1	16.8	11.4	0.004 33
x4.8*	0.049 5	642	0.377	7.04	24.2	22.6	0.240	5.08	19.3	16.2	4.85	0.001 89
L76x51												
x13	0.112	1 450	0.800	16.4	23.5	27.5	0.280	7.77	13.9	14.8	78.0	0.024 4
x9.5	0.086 2	1 120	0.638	12.8	23.9	26.4	0.226	6.09	14.2	13.7	33.9	0.011 1
x7.9	0.072 8	945	0.548	10.9	24.1	25.8	0.196	5.20	14.4	13.1	19.9	0.006 67
x6.4	0.059 0	766	0.453	8.88	24.3	25.2	0.163	4.26	14.6	12.5	10.3	0.003 54
x4.8	0.044 8	582	0.350	6.79	24.5	24.6	0.128	3.28	14.8	11.9	4.39	0.001 55
L64x64												
x13	0.112	1 450	0.511	11.9	18.8	20.5	0.511	11.9	18.8	20.5	78.0	0.021 2
x9.5	0.086 2	1 120	0.410	9.28	19.1	19.4	0.410	9.28	19.1	19.4	33.9	0.009 74
x7.9	0.072 8	945	0.353	7.90	19.3	18.8	0.353	7.90	19.3	18.8	19.9	0.005 87
x6.4	0.059 0	766	0.293	6.46	19.5	18.2	0.293	6.46	19.5	18.2	10.3	0.003 12
x4.8	0.044 8	582	0.227	4.96	19.8	17.6	0.227	4.96	19.8	17.6	4.39	0.001 37
L64x51												
x9.5	0.076 9	998	0.380	8.96	19.5	21.1	0.214	5.94	14.6	14.8	30.2	0.007 22
x7.9	0.065 0	844	0.328	7.64	19.7	20.6	0.186	5.08	14.8	14.2	17.7	0.004 36
x6.4	0.052 8	685	0.272	6.25	19.9	20.0	0.155	4.17	15.0	13.6	9.21	0.002 33
x4.8	0.040 2	521	0.212	4.80	20.1	19.4	0.121	3.21	15.2	13.1	3.94	0.001 02
L51x51												
x9.5	0.067 6	877	0.199	5.76	15.1	16.2	0.199	5.76	15.1	16.2	26.6	0.004 69
x7.9	0.057 3	744	0.173	4.92	15.3	15.6	0.173	4.92	15.3	15.6	15.6	0.002 86
x6.4	0.046 6	605	0.145	4.04	15.5	15.0	0.145	4.04	15.5	15.0	8.13	0.001 54
x4.8	0.035 5	461	0.113	3.12	15.7	14.5	0.113	3.12	15.7	14.5	3.48	0.000 680
x3.2	0.024 1	313	0.079 2	2.14	15.9	13.9	0.079 2	2.14	15.9	13.9	1.05	0.000 213

See page 6-39 for qualification of properties of angles produced by cold-forming.

* Not available from Canadian mills

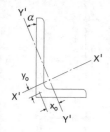

ANGLES
L76 - L51

DIMENSIONS AND PROPERTIES ABOUT PRINCIPAL AXES

Mass	d	b	t	Axis X'-X'		Axis Y'-Y'		$\bar{r}_o$	Ω	tan α
				r_x	y_o	r_y	x_o			
kg/m	mm	mm	mm	mm	mm	mm	mm	mm		
13.9	76.2	76.2	12.7	28.6	0.00	14.8	24.5	40.5	0.634	1.00
12.3	76.2	76.2	11.1	28.9	0.00	14.9	24.8	40.9	0.632	1.00
10.7	76.2	76.2	9.53	29.2	0.00	14.9	25.1	41.3	0.630	1.00
9.00	76.2	76.2	7.94	29.5	0.00	15.0	25.5	41.8	0.628	1.00
7.28	76.2	76.2	6.35	29.8	0.00	15.0	25.8	42.2	0.627	1.00
5.52	76.2	76.2	4.76	30.2	0.00	15.1	26.1	42.6	0.626	1.00
12.7	76.2	63.5	12.7	26.4	8.81	13.2	21.1	37.4	0.625	0.667
9.74	76.2	63.5	9.53	27.0	8.79	13.3	21.8	38.2	0.620	0.676
8.21	76.2	63.5	7.94	27.3	8.79	13.3	22.2	38.6	0.619	0.680
6.65	76.2	63.5	6.35	27.6	8.79	13.4	22.5	39.1	0.618	0.684
5.04	76.2	63.5	4.76	27.9	8.79	13.5	22.8	39.5	0.617	0.688
11.4	76.2	50.8	12.7	25.0	16.3	10.9	15.9	35.5	0.589	0.414
8.79	76.2	50.8	9.53	25.5	16.4	10.9	16.7	36.3	0.585	0.428
7.42	76.2	50.8	7.94	25.8	16.4	11.0	17.1	36.7	0.584	0.435
6.01	76.2	50.8	6.35	26.1	16.4	11.0	17.5	37.1	0.583	0.440
4.57	76.2	50.8	4.76	26.4	16.4	11.1	17.8	37.5	0.583	0.446
11.4	63.5	63.5	12.7	23.5	0.00	12.4	20.0	33.2	0.639	1.00
8.79	63.5	63.5	9.53	24.1	0.00	12.4	20.6	34.0	0.632	1.00
7.42	63.5	63.5	7.94	24.4	0.00	12.4	21.0	34.4	0.630	1.00
6.01	63.5	63.5	6.35	24.7	0.00	12.5	21.3	34.9	0.628	1.00
4.57	63.5	63.5	4.76	25.0	0.00	12.6	21.6	35.3	0.627	1.00
7.84	63.5	50.8	9.53	21.9	8.70	10.7	17.1	31.0	0.618	0.614
6.63	63.5	50.8	7.94	22.2	8.70	10.7	17.4	31.4	0.616	0.620
5.38	63.5	50.8	6.35	22.5	8.70	10.8	17.8	31.9	0.614	0.626
4.09	63.5	50.8	4.76	22.8	8.70	10.9	18.1	32.3	0.612	0.631
6.89	50.8	50.8	9.53	18.9	0.00	9.89	16.1	26.7	0.637	1.00
5.84	50.8	50.8	7.94	19.2	0.00	9.90	16.4	27.1	0.633	1.00
4.75	50.8	50.8	6.35	19.5	0.00	9.93	16.8	27.6	0.630	1.00
3.62	50.8	50.8	4.76	19.8	0.00	10.0	17.1	28.0	0.628	1.00
2.46	50.8	50.8	3.18	20.1	0.00	10.1	17.4	28.4	0.626	1.00

See CSA S16-09 Clause 13.3.2 for the definition of x_o, y_o, $\bar{r}_o$ and Ω.
The Y-Y axis of symmetry of equal-leg (singly-symmetric) angles corresponds to X'-X' in the above table.

ANGLES
L51 - L19

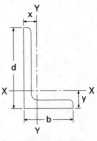

PROPERTIES ABOUT GEOMETRIC AXES

Designation	Dead Load	Area	Axis X-X				Axis Y-Y				Torsional Constant	Warping Constant
			I_x	S_x	r_x	y	I_y	S_y	r_y	x	J	C_w
	kN/m	mm^2	$10^6\ mm^4$	$10^3\ mm^3$	mm	mm	$10^6\ mm^4$	$10^3\ mm^3$	mm	mm	$10^3\ mm^4$	$10^9\ mm^6$
L51x38												
x6.4	0.040 4	524	0.131	3.87	15.8	16.9	0.063 0	2.28	11.0	10.5	7.05	0.001 07
x4.8	0.030 8	401	0.103	2.99	16.0	16.3	0.049 9	1.77	11.2	9.93	3.02	0.000 477
x3.2	0.021 0	273	0.072 1	2.06	16.3	15.7	0.035 3	1.23	11.4	9.35	0.919	0.000 150
L44x44												
x6.4	0.040 4	525	0.094 9	3.06	13.4	13.4	0.094 9	3.06	13.4	13.4	7.05	0.001 00
x4.8	0.030 9	401	0.074 8	2.36	13.7	12.9	0.074 8	2.36	13.7	12.9	3.03	0.000 448
x3.2	0.021 0	273	0.052 5	1.63	13.9	12.3	0.052 5	1.63	13.9	12.3	0.920	0.000 141
L38x38												
x6.4	0.034 2	444	0.057 7	2.20	11.4	11.8	0.057 7	2.20	11.4	11.8	5.96	0.000 606
x4.8	0.026 2	340	0.045 8	1.71	11.6	11.3	0.045 8	1.71	11.6	11.3	2.57	0.000 273
x3.2	0.017 9	232	0.032 4	1.18	11.8	10.7	0.032 4	1.18	11.8	10.7	0.783	0.000 087
L32x32												
x6.4	0.028 0	364	0.032 1	1.49	9.40	10.2	0.032 1	1.49	9.40	10.2	4.89	0.000 334
x4.8	0.021 6	280	0.025 7	1.16	9.58	9.69	0.025 7	1.16	9.58	9.69	2.12	0.000 153
x3.2	0.014 8	192	0.018 4	0.812	9.79	9.12	0.018 4	0.812	9.79	9.12	0.648	0.000 049
L25x25												
x6.4	0.021 7	282	0.015 3	0.915	7.37	8.62	0.015 3	0.915	7.37	8.62	3.79	0.000 156
x4.8	0.016 9	219	0.012 5	0.719	7.54	8.07	0.012 5	0.719	7.54	8.07	1.66	0.000 073
x3.2	0.011 7	151	0.009 05	0.506	7.73	7.52	0.009 05	0.506	7.73	7.52	0.510	0.000 024
L19x19												
x3.2	0.008 6	111	0.003 64	0.276	5.72	5.93	0.003 64	0.276	5.72	5.93	0.375	0.000 010

See page 6-39 for qualification of properties of angles produced by cold-forming.

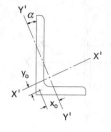

DIMENSIONS AND PROPERTIES ABOUT PRINCIPAL AXES

| Mass | d | b | t | Axis X'-X' | | Axis Y'-Y' | | $\bar{r}_o$ | Ω | tan α |
				r_x	y_o	r_y	x_o			
kg/m	mm	mm	mm	mm	mm	mm	mm	mm		
4.11	50.8	38.1	6.35	17.5	8.53	8.12	13.0	24.7	0.606	0.543
3.14	50.8	38.1	4.76	17.8	8.53	8.18	13.3	25.1	0.604	0.551
2.14	50.8	38.1	3.18	18.0	8.54	8.27	13.7	25.6	0.603	0.558
4.12	44.5	44.5	6.35	16.9	0.00	8.68	14.5	23.9	0.632	1.00
3.15	44.5	44.5	4.76	17.2	0.00	8.73	14.8	24.4	0.629	1.00
2.14	44.5	44.5	3.18	17.5	0.00	8.82	15.2	24.8	0.627	1.00
3.48	38.1	38.1	6.35	14.3	0.00	7.42	12.2	20.2	0.634	1.00
2.67	38.1	38.1	4.76	14.6	0.00	7.45	12.6	20.7	0.630	1.00
1.82	38.1	38.1	3.18	14.9	0.00	7.52	12.9	21.1	0.627	1.00
2.85	31.8	31.8	6.35	11.8	0.00	6.19	10.0	16.6	0.639	1.00
2.20	31.8	31.8	4.76	12.0	0.00	6.20	10.3	17.0	0.632	1.00
1.51	31.8	31.8	3.18	12.4	0.00	6.25	10.7	17.5	0.628	1.00
2.22	25.4	25.4	6.35	9.17	0.00	4.98	7.70	13.0	0.647	1.00
1.72	25.4	25.4	4.76	9.45	0.00	4.94	8.05	13.4	0.637	1.00
1.19	25.4	25.4	3.18	9.74	0.00	4.97	8.38	13.8	0.630	1.00
0.874	19.1	19.1	3.18	7.18	0.00	3.72	6.14	10.2	0.634	1.00

See CSA S16-09 Clause 13.3.2 for the definition of x_o, y_o, $\bar{r}_o$ and Ω.
The Y-Y axis of symmetry of equal-leg (singly-symmetric) angles corresponds to X'-X' in the above table.

STRUCTURAL TEES
Cut from W Shapes
WT460 - WT345

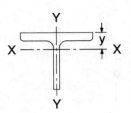

PROPERTIES

Designation	Dead Load	Area	Axis X-X				Axis Y-Y			Torsional Constant	Warping Constant
			I_x	S_x	r_x	y	I_y	S_y	r_y	J	C_w
	kN/m	mm^2	10^6 mm^4	10^3 mm^3	mm	mm	10^6 mm^4	10^3 mm^3	mm	10^3 mm^4	10^9 mm^6
WT460											
x224.5	2.21	28 700	534	1 450	136	107	270	1 280	97.0	13 400	76.5
x210	2.06	26 800	498	1 360	136	106	250	1 190	96.6	11 000	62.4
x195	1.91	24 800	460	1 270	136	105	226	1 080	95.5	8 640	49.6
x184	1.80	23 400	434	1 200	136	105	211	1 010	94.9	7 210	41.6
x172	1.69	22 000	408	1 140	136	104	195	933	94.2	5 950	34.6
WT460											
x156.5	1.53	19 900	410	1 200	143	124	85.2	551	65.4	5 790	32.0
x144.5	1.42	18 400	376	1 100	143	122	78.2	508	65.2	4 600	24.9
x135.5	1.33	17 300	353	1 040	143	121	72.6	473	64.7	3 840	20.9
x126.5	1.25	16 200	329	969	143	120	66.8	437	64.3	3 120	17.1
x119	1.17	15 200	309	916	143	121	61.4	403	63.6	2 570	14.4
x111.5	1.10	14 300	292	874	143	122	56.1	369	62.7	2 110	12.4
x100.5	0.988	12 800	266	814	144	126	47.2	311	60.7	1 450	10.0
WT420											
x179.5	1.77	22 900	363	1 080	126	97.5	195	965	92.1	7 530	39.3
x164.5	1.62	21 000	333	997	126	96.9	174	870	91.1	5 780	30.4
x149.5	1.47	19 100	303	912	126	96.1	156	780	90.3	4 320	22.9
WT420											
x113	1.11	14 400	247	778	131	108	56.9	387	62.8	2 560	11.5
x105	1.03	13 400	230	733	131	109	51.3	350	61.8	2 020	9.57
x96.5	0.949	12 300	213	688	131	111	45.1	309	60.5	1 520	7.81
x88	0.864	11 200	196	646	132	114	39.1	268	59.1	1 100	6.35
WT380											
x157	1.55	20 100	254	828	112	86.2	158	822	88.7	5 900	26.0
x142	1.40	18 100	229	750	112	84.8	140	733	87.8	4 360	19.1
x128.5	1.27	16 500	207	684	112	83.9	125	657	87.1	3 250	14.3
WT380											
x98	0.965	12 500	175	613	118	99.0	40.9	305	57.1	2 020	7.63
x92.5	0.907	11 800	165	580	118	99.1	37.5	281	56.5	1 660	6.44
x86.5	0.852	11 100	156	554	119	100	34.4	257	55.7	1 340	5.54
x80.5	0.787	10 200	145	523	119	102	30.4	228	54.5	1 030	4.62
x73.5	0.722	9 370	134	493	120	104	26.4	200	53.1	778	3.83
WT345											
x132.5	1.30	16 900	172	624	101	77.2	116	646	82.7	4 160	15.5
x120	1.18	15 400	156	567	101	76.0	103	580	82.0	3 130	11.5
x108.5	1.07	14 000	140	514	100	74.7	92.6	522	81.5	2 350	8.57

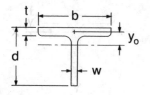

PROPERTIES AND DIMENSIONS

Nominal Mass	Theoretical Mass	Depth d	Flange Width b	Flange Thickness t	Stem Thickness w	y_o	$\bar{r}_o$	Ω
kg/m	kg/m	mm	mm	mm	mm	mm	mm	
224.5	225.0	474	423	42.7	24.0	85.8	188	0.792
210	210.5	472	422	39.9	22.5	85.8	188	0.791
195	194.8	468	420	36.6	21.3	86.9	188	0.786
184	183.6	466	419	34.3	20.3	87.6	188	0.782
172	172.4	464	418	32.0	19.3	88.3	188	0.779
156.5	156.4	466	309	34.5	21.1	107	190	0.686
144.5	144.4	464	308	32.0	19.4	106	190	0.688
135.5	135.9	462	307	30.0	18.4	106	189	0.685
126.5	126.9	460	306	27.9	17.3	107	189	0.683
119	119.2	458	305	25.9	16.5	108	190	0.678
111.5	112.2	456	304	23.9	15.9	110	191	0.669
100.5	100.7	452	304	20.1	15.2	116	194	0.645
179.5	180.0	434	403	35.6	21.1	79.7	175	0.793
164.5	165.0	431	401	32.4	19.7	80.7	175	0.788
149.5	150.0	428	400	29.2	18.2	81.5	175	0.783
113	113.4	426	294	26.8	16.1	95.0	173	0.700
105	105.4	423	293	24.4	15.4	96.9	174	0.691
96.5	96.8	420	292	21.7	14.7	99.9	176	0.677
88	88.0	418	292	18.8	14.0	104	179	0.659
157	157.6	393	384	33.4	19.7	69.5	159	0.809
142	142.5	390	382	30.1	18.0	69.8	159	0.807
128.5	129.3	387	381	27.1	16.6	70.4	159	0.803
98	98.4	385	268	25.4	15.6	86.3	157	0.698
92.5	92.4	383	267	23.6	14.9	87.3	157	0.693
86.5	86.8	381	267	21.6	14.4	89.3	159	0.683
80.5	80.2	379	266	19.3	13.8	92.2	160	0.669
73.5	73.6	377	265	17.0	13.2	95.7	162	0.652
132.5	132.8	353	358	30.2	18.4	62.1	144	0.815
120	120.6	351	356	27.4	16.8	62.3	144	0.813
108.5	109.5	348	355	24.8	15.4	62.3	143	0.812

STRUCTURAL TEES
Cut from W Shapes
WT345 - WT265

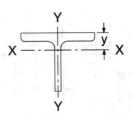

PROPERTIES

Designation	Dead Load	Area	Axis X-X				Axis Y-Y			Torsional Constant	Warping Constant
			I_x	S_x	r_x	y	I_y	S_y	r_y	J	C_w
	kN/m	mm²	10^6 mm⁴	10^3 mm³	mm	mm	10^6 mm⁴	10^3 mm³	mm	10^3 mm⁴	10^9 mm⁶
WT345											
x85	0.834	10 800	121	465	106	87.1	33.1	259	55.3	1 520	4.72
x76	0.746	9 690	107	415	105	85.8	28.9	227	54.6	1 100	3.38
x70	0.686	8 910	99.3	389	106	86.5	25.9	204	53.9	833	2.72
x62.5	0.616	8 000	90.0	359	106	88.3	22.0	174	52.5	586	2.10
WT305											
x120.5	1.19	15 400	123	491	89.2	68.6	92.1	560	77.3	3 840	11.8
x108.5	1.07	13 900	110	444	88.8	67.4	81.6	497	76.7	2 790	8.58
x97.5	0.960	12 500	99.4	408	89.3	67.4	71.2	435	75.6	1 980	6.23
x87	0.855	11 100	88.3	366	89.2	66.5	61.9	381	74.7	1 400	4.40
x77.5	0.760	9 870	78.9	329	89.4	66.1	53.9	333	73.9	975	3.10
WT305											
x70	0.688	8 930	77.8	334	93.3	76.2	22.6	196	50.3	1 090	2.58
x62.5	0.613	7 970	69.0	299	93.1	75.4	19.7	172	49.7	769	1.84
x56.5	0.556	7 220	63.2	278	93.5	76.3	17.1	150	48.7	559	1.43
x50.5	0.499	6 480	57.4	256	94.1	77.8	14.7	129	47.7	389	1.09
WT305											
x46	0.455	5 910	55.0	256	96.4	87.6	7.21	80.5	34.9	367	1.05
x41	0.404	5 250	48.9	231	96.5	88.6	6.05	67.9	33.9	254	0.785
WT265											
x109.5	1.07	13 900	85.0	388	78.1	60.8	78.4	493	75.0	3 200	8.74
x98	0.964	12 500	75.2	345	77.5	59.0	69.3	438	74.4	2 340	6.28
x91	0.892	11 600	69.3	317	77.3	57.9	63.6	404	74.1	1 860	4.94
x82.5	0.811	10 500	62.2	288	76.9	56.7	56.8	363	73.4	1 410	3.70
x75	0.739	9 600	56.5	261	76.7	55.5	51.4	330	73.2	1 080	2.79
WT265											
x69	0.679	8 820	60.2	293	82.6	69.6	19.3	181	46.8	1 250	2.50
x61.5	0.604	7 850	52.6	258	81.9	67.6	16.9	159	46.4	899	1.75
x54.5	0.535	6 950	46.2	227	81.5	66.1	14.8	140	46.1	630	1.20
x50.5	0.498	6 470	43.0	212	81.6	65.9	13.5	128	45.6	507	0.973
x46	0.454	5 890	39.3	196	81.7	66.0	11.9	114	44.9	380	0.754
x41	0.403	5 230	35.0	178	81.9	66.9	10.1	97.0	44.0	258	0.555
WT265											
x42.5	0.416	5 400	37.8	194	83.7	72.7	6.32	76.1	34.2	367	0.675
x37	0.367	4 770	33.7	177	84.1	74.7	5.21	62.7	33.1	239	0.516
x33	0.323	4 190	29.8	159	84.3	76.1	4.29	52.0	32.0	159	0.380

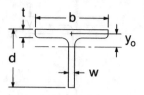

PROPERTIES AND DIMENSIONS

Nominal Mass	Theoretical Mass	Depth	Flange Width	Flange Thickness	Stem Thickness	y_o	$\bar{r}_o$	Ω
		d	b	t	w			
kg/m	kg/m	mm	mm	mm	mm	mm	mm	
85	85.0	347	256	23.6	14.5	75.3	141	0.715
76	76.1	344	254	21.1	13.1	75.2	140	0.713
70	69.9	342	254	18.9	12.4	77.1	141	0.703
62.5	62.8	339	253	16.3	11.7	80.2	143	0.686
120.5	120.9	318	329	31.0	17.9	53.1	129	0.832
108.5	108.9	314	328	27.7	16.5	53.5	129	0.828
97.5	97.8	311	327	24.4	15.4	55.2	129	0.818
87	87.1	308	325	21.6	14.0	55.7	129	0.813
77.5	77.5	306	324	19.0	12.7	56.6	129	0.808
70	70.1	309	230	22.2	13.1	65.1	124	0.726
62.5	62.5	306	229	19.6	11.9	65.6	124	0.721
56.5	56.7	304	228	17.3	11.2	67.7	125	0.708
50.5	50.9	302	228	14.9	10.5	70.3	127	0.692
46	46.4	302	179	15.0	10.9	80.1	130	0.621
41	41.2	300	178	12.8	10.0	82.2	131	0.607
109.5	109.5	280	318	29.2	18.3	46.2	118	0.846
98	98.3	277	316	26.3	16.5	45.9	117	0.846
91	90.9	276	315	24.4	15.2	45.7	116	0.846
82.5	82.7	273	313	22.2	14.0	45.6	116	0.845
75	75.4	272	312	20.3	12.7	45.4	115	0.845
69	69.2	275	214	23.6	14.7	57.8	111	0.730
61.5	61.6	272	212	21.2	13.1	57.0	110	0.731
54.5	54.6	270	211	18.8	11.6	56.7	109	0.732
50.5	50.8	269	210	17.4	10.9	57.2	110	0.728
46	46.3	267	209	15.6	10.2	58.2	110	0.719
41	41.1	264	209	13.3	9.5	60.2	111	0.704
42.5	42.4	268	166	16.5	10.3	64.4	111	0.663
37	37.4	265	166	13.6	9.7	67.9	113	0.639
33	32.9	263	165	11.4	8.9	70.4	114	0.621

STRUCTURAL TEES
Cut from W Shapes
WT230 - WT205

PROPERTIES

Designation	Dead Load	Area	Axis X-X				Axis Y-Y			Torsional Constant	Warping Constant
			I_x	S_x	r_x	y	I_y	S_y	r_y	J	C_w
	kN/m	mm²	10^6 mm⁴	10^3 mm³	mm	mm	10^6 mm⁴	10^3 mm³	mm	10^3 mm⁴	10^9 mm⁶
WT230											
x88.5	0.870	11 300	49.4	260	66.1	51.4	52.5	367	68.2	2 200	4.66
x79	0.773	10 000	43.5	231	65.8	50.1	45.7	322	67.4	1 550	3.25
x72	0.709	9 210	39.0	208	65.1	48.4	41.8	295	67.4	1 220	2.49
x64	0.631	8 190	34.5	185	64.9	47.2	36.7	260	66.9	856	1.74
x56.5	0.555	7 210	30.2	162	64.7	46.0	31.7	226	66.3	590	1.18
WT230											
x53	0.519	6 740	32.8	185	69.7	57.5	12.6	130	43.2	726	1.07
x48.5	0.474	6 150	29.4	166	69.1	55.8	11.4	118	43.1	563	0.802
x44.5	0.438	5 690	27.0	152	68.8	54.8	10.5	109	42.9	453	0.630
x41	0.402	5 220	24.8	141	68.9	54.8	9.31	97.5	42.2	345	0.493
x37	0.364	4 730	22.4	128	68.8	54.1	8.30	87.4	41.9	258	0.366
WT230											
x34	0.336	4 370	21.8	128	70.6	59.2	4.70	61.1	32.8	254	0.323
x30	0.292	3 800	18.8	111	70.4	58.3	3.98	52.0	32.4	167	0.213
x26	0.255	3 310	16.7	102	71.0	60.8	3.17	41.7	30.9	105	0.160
WT205											
x74.5	0.740	9 610	32.3	188	57.9	44.7	38.8	293	63.6	1 700	2.79
x66	0.656	8 520	28.0	165	57.4	43.1	33.7	256	62.9	1 200	1.92
x57	0.569	7 390	23.9	141	56.8	41.3	28.6	219	62.3	802	1.24
x50	0.496	6 440	20.4	121	56.2	39.6	24.8	191	62.0	544	0.810
WT205											
x42.5	0.417	5 420	20.4	127	61.3	49.3	9.02	99.6	40.8	462	0.536
x37	0.368	4 780	17.8	112	61.1	48.2	7.79	86.6	40.4	318	0.366
x33.5	0.331	4 300	15.8	100	60.7	47.3	6.90	77.0	40.0	234	0.265
x30	0.292	3 800	13.9	87.8	60.4	46.1	6.02	67.7	39.8	164	0.180
x27	0.262	3 410	12.8	83.3	61.4	48.0	5.05	57.0	38.5	113	0.139
WT205											
x23	0.227	2 950	11.5	76.3	62.4	51.5	2.57	36.7	29.5	96.0	0.099 0
x19.5	0.193	2 500	9.96	67.9	63.1	53.5	2.02	28.8	28.4	55.3	0.067 5

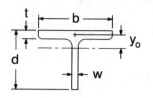

PROPERTIES AND DIMENSIONS

Nominal Mass	Theoretical Mass	Depth	Flange Width	Flange Thickness	Stem Thickness	y_o	$\bar{r}_o$	Ω
		d	b	t	w			
kg/m	kg/m	mm	mm	mm	mm	mm	mm	
88.5	88.6	241	286	26.9	16.6	38.0	102	0.862
79	78.8	238	284	23.9	15.0	38.1	102	0.859
72	72.3	236	283	22.1	13.6	37.3	101	0.863
64	64.3	234	282	19.6	12.2	37.4	100	0.861
56.5	56.6	232	280	17.3	10.8	37.4	99.9	0.860
53	52.9	235	194	20.6	12.6	47.2	94.6	0.752
48.5	48.3	233	193	19.0	11.4	46.3	93.7	0.756
44.5	44.7	232	192	17.7	10.5	45.9	93.2	0.757
41	41.0	230	191	16.0	9.9	46.8	93.4	0.749
37	37.1	229	190	14.5	9.0	46.8	93.2	0.748
34	34.3	230	154	15.4	9.1	51.5	93.4	0.696
30	29.8	228	153	13.3	8.0	51.7	93.1	0.692
26	26.0	225	152	10.8	7.6	55.4	95.2	0.662
74.5	75.4	216	265	25.0	14.9	32.2	91.8	0.877
66	66.8	213	263	22.2	13.3	32.0	91.0	0.876
57	58.0	210	261	19.3	11.6	31.7	90.0	0.876
50	50.6	208	260	16.9	10.0	31.1	89.3	0.879
42.5	42.5	209	181	18.2	10.9	40.2	83.9	0.770
37	37.5	207	180	16.0	9.7	40.2	83.5	0.768
33.5	33.8	205	179	14.4	8.8	40.1	83.0	0.767
30	29.8	204	178	12.8	7.7	39.7	82.5	0.769
27	26.7	202	177	10.9	7.5	42.6	84.0	0.743
23	23.1	202	140	11.2	7.0	45.9	82.9	0.694
19.5	19.6	200	140	8.8	6.4	49.1	84.8	0.666

STRUCTURAL TEES
Cut from W Shapes
WT180

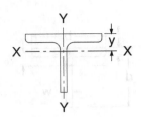

PROPERTIES

Designation	Dead Load	Area	Axis X-X				Axis Y-Y			Torsional Constant	Warping Constant
			I_x	S_x	r_x	y	I_y	S_y	r_y	J	C_w
	kN/m	mm²	10^6 mm⁴	10^3 mm³	mm	mm	10^6 mm⁴	10^3 mm³	mm	10^3 mm⁴	10^9 mm⁶
WT180											
x543	5.34	69 300	308	1 570	66.7	88.2	981	4 320	119	299 000	1 410
x495	4.86	63 100	259	1 350	64.1	82.7	867	3 870	117	232 000	1 060
x450	4.43	57 500	219	1 160	61.7	77.5	767	3 470	115	180 000	791
x409	4.02	52 200	184	997	59.4	72.4	678	3 100	114	138 000	585
x372	3.65	47 400	156	864	57.4	67.9	600	2 780	112	106 000	434
x338.5	3.33	43 200	134	754	55.8	63.9	534	2 500	111	81 600	325
WT180											
x317	3.11	40 400	119	677	54.3	61.0	491	2 320	110	68 300	266
x296	2.91	37 800	108	620	53.5	58.6	451	2 140	109	56 400	215
x275.5	2.70	35 100	95.9	557	52.3	55.8	412	1 970	108	46 000	172
x254.5	2.50	32 500	84.8	499	51.1	53.0	377	1 810	108	36 700	135
x231.5	2.27	29 500	73.8	439	50.0	50.1	335	1 630	107	28 100	100
x210.5	2.07	26 900	64.2	387	48.9	47.3	300	1 470	106	21 600	75.5
x191	1.88	24 400	55.4	338	47.7	44.5	268	1 320	105	16 300	56.0
x173.5	1.70	22 100	48.5	300	46.8	42.1	240	1 190	104	12 400	41.6
x157	1.54	20 000	42.6	266	46.2	39.9	213	1 060	103	9 210	30.3
x143.5	1.41	18 300	37.6	236	45.3	37.9	194	972	103	7 230	23.5
x131	1.29	16 700	33.9	215	45.0	36.4	175	880	102	5 510	17.6
x118.5	1.16	15 000	29.1	187	44.0	34.3	155	786	102	4 080	12.8
x108	1.06	13 800	26.2	169	43.6	32.9	141	717	101	3 160	9.79
WT180											
x98	0.964	12 500	24.0	157	43.8	32.7	114	611	95.5	2 560	7.17
x89.5	0.879	11 400	21.6	141	43.5	31.4	103	555	95.2	1 950	5.40
x81	0.795	10 300	18.8	124	42.7	29.8	92.8	500	94.8	1 470	4.00
x73.5	0.724	9 400	17.0	113	42.6	28.9	83.6	452	94.3	1 110	2.98
x67	0.657	8 530	15.2	101	42.2	27.8	75.4	409	94.0	840	2.22
WT180											
x61	0.597	7 760	17.3	118	47.2	35.5	30.7	239	62.9	1 050	1.51
x55	0.540	7 020	15.0	102	46.2	33.5	27.8	218	63.0	799	1.12
x50.5	0.497	6 450	13.7	93.7	46.1	32.7	25.3	199	62.6	626	0.863
x45.5	0.446	5 790	12.1	83.5	45.8	31.7	22.4	176	62.2	456	0.617
WT180											
x39.5	0.389	5 050	11.5	81.2	47.8	35.0	12.1	118	48.9	405	0.394
x36	0.351	4 550	10.3	73.1	47.5	34.2	10.7	105	48.5	300	0.286
x32	0.314	4 070	9.17	65.2	47.4	33.4	9.42	92.8	48.1	218	0.202

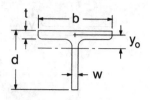

PROPERTIES AND DIMENSIONS

Nominal Mass	Theoretical Mass	Depth	Flange Width	Flange Thickness	Stem Thickness	y_o	$\bar{r}_o$	Ω
		d	b	t	w			
kg/m	kg/m	mm	mm	mm	mm	mm	mm	
543	544.2	285	454	125	78.0	25.7	139	0.966
495	495.5	275	448	115	71.9	25.2	136	0.966
450	451.3	266	442	106	65.9	24.5	133	0.966
409	409.5	257	437	97.0	60.5	23.9	131	0.966
372	372.1	249	432	88.9	55.6	23.5	128	0.967
338.5	339.1	242	428	81.5	51.2	23.1	127	0.967
317	317.1	237	424	77.1	47.6	22.4	125	0.968
296	296.5	233	421	72.3	45.0	22.4	124	0.967
275.5	275.5	228	418	67.6	42.0	22.0	122	0.968
254.5	254.7	223	416	62.7	39.1	21.6	121	0.968
231.5	231.6	218	412	57.4	35.8	21.4	120	0.968
210.5	211.0	213	409	52.6	32.8	21.0	118	0.969
191	191.2	208	406	48.0	29.8	20.5	117	0.969
173.5	173.6	204	404	43.7	27.2	20.2	116	0.970
157	156.8	200	401	39.6	24.9	20.1	115	0.969
143.5	143.9	197	399	36.6	22.6	19.6	114	0.970
131	131.4	194	398	33.3	21.1	19.8	113	0.970
118.5	118.1	190	395	30.2	18.9	19.2	112	0.971
108	108.2	188	394	27.7	17.3	19.0	112	0.971
98	98.3	186	374	26.2	16.4	19.6	107	0.966
89.5	89.6	184	373	23.9	15.0	19.5	106	0.966
81	81.0	182	371	21.8	13.3	18.9	106	0.968
73.5	73.8	180	370	19.8	12.3	19.0	105	0.967
67	67.0	178	369	18.0	11.2	18.8	105	0.968
61	60.9	182	257	21.7	13.0	24.6	82.4	0.911
55	55.1	180	256	19.9	11.4	23.6	81.6	0.916
50.5	50.6	179	255	18.3	10.5	23.6	81.3	0.916
45.5	45.4	177	254	16.4	9.5	23.5	80.8	0.915
39.5	39.6	177	205	16.8	9.4	26.6	73.4	0.868
36	35.7	175	204	15.1	8.6	26.7	73.0	0.866
32	32.0	174	203	13.5	7.7	26.6	72.6	0.865

STRUCTURAL TEES
Cut from W Shapes
WT180 - WT155

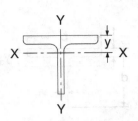

PROPERTIES

Designation	Dead Load	Area	Axis X-X				Axis Y-Y			Torsional Constant	Warping Constant
			I_x	S_x	r_x	y	I_y	S_y	r_y	J	C_w
	kN/m	mm²	10^6 mm⁴	10^3 mm³	mm	mm	10^6 mm⁴	10^3 mm³	mm	10^3 mm⁴	10^9 mm⁶
WT180											
x28.5	0.278	3 610	9.70	69.4	51.9	39.2	5.56	64.7	39.3	167	0.150
x25.5	0.248	3 230	8.73	62.8	52.0	39.0	4.84	56.6	38.7	119	0.107
x22.5	0.221	2 870	7.96	58.6	52.7	40.2	4.09	47.8	37.8	79.7	0.078 4
WT180											
x19.5	0.192	2 500	7.28	54.7	54.0	43.8	1.88	29.3	27.4	75.3	0.056 4
x16.5	0.161	2 090	6.19	47.6	54.4	44.8	1.45	22.9	26.4	42.8	0.035 7
WT155											
x250	2.46	31 900	79.7	513	50.0	58.7	247	1 450	88.0	50 100	130
x227	2.23	28 900	68.2	446	48.6	55.2	218	1 300	86.8	38 300	95.7
x207.5	2.04	26 500	59.6	397	47.4	52.2	195	1 170	85.9	29 500	71.9
x187.5	1.84	23 900	50.5	343	46.0	48.9	172	1 040	84.8	22 300	52.5
x171	1.68	21 900	43.8	302	44.8	46.1	155	946	84.2	17 400	40.0
x156.5	1.54	20 000	38.5	269	43.9	43.8	139	852	83.3	13 400	30.1
WT155											
x141.5	1.39	18 000	33.1	233	42.8	41.1	123	764	82.6	10 100	22.1
x126.5	1.24	16 100	28.1	202	41.8	38.6	107	673	81.6	7 350	15.6
x113	1.11	14 400	24.3	176	41.0	36.4	94.6	597	81.0	5 360	11.1
x101	0.994	12 900	21.3	156	40.7	34.6	82.9	527	80.1	3 860	7.82
x89.5	0.877	11 400	18.2	135	39.9	32.5	71.9	459	79.4	2 680	5.30
x79	0.773	10 000	15.2	114	38.9	30.3	62.4	402	78.8	1 880	3.63
x71.5	0.703	9 120	13.5	101	38.4	28.9	56.3	365	78.6	1 430	2.72
x64.5	0.636	8 260	12.0	91.8	38.2	27.9	50.2	326	78.0	1 060	1.98
x59	0.576	7 490	10.7	82.0	37.8	26.8	45.1	294	77.6	799	1.46
x53.5	0.525	6 820	9.71	74.7	37.7	26.0	40.6	265	77.2	607	1.09
x48.5	0.475	6 170	8.59	66.6	37.3	25.0	36.4	239	76.9	455	0.804
WT155											
x43	0.424	5 500	7.93	61.5	38.0	26.1	22.3	175	63.6	438	0.559
x39.5	0.387	5 030	7.38	58.1	38.3	26.1	20.0	157	63.0	328	0.413
WT155											
x37	0.363	4 710	7.80	62.3	40.7	29.7	11.7	114	49.9	358	0.332
x33.5	0.325	4 220	6.88	55.3	40.3	28.8	10.3	101	49.5	260	0.236
x30	0.290	3 770	6.05	48.7	40.0	27.7	9.14	90.1	49.2	189	0.167
WT155											
x26	0.257	3 340	6.66	52.9	44.7	33.1	5.13	61.4	39.2	154	0.118
x22.5	0.219	2 850	5.64	45.2	44.5	32.2	4.27	51.5	38.7	95.5	0.072 3
x19.5	0.190	2 470	4.82	39.0	44.2	31.4	3.63	44.0	38.4	62.8	0.046 8

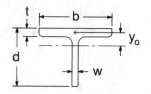

PROPERTIES AND DIMENSIONS

Nominal Mass	Theoretical Mass	Depth d	Flange Width b	Flange Thickness t	Stem Thickness w	y_o	$\bar{r}_o$	Ω
kg/m	kg/m	mm	mm	mm	mm	mm	mm	
28.5	28.3	179	172	13.1	7.9	32.6	72.8	0.799
25.5	25.3	178	171	11.6	7.2	33.2	72.8	0.793
22.5	22.5	176	171	9.8	6.9	35.3	73.8	0.771
19.5	19.6	177	128	10.7	6.5	38.5	71.8	0.713
16.5	16.4	175	127	8.5	5.8	40.6	72.8	0.690
250	250.4	214	340	75.1	45.1	21.1	103	0.958
227	227.1	208	336	68.7	41.3	20.8	102	0.958
207.5	207.7	202	334	62.7	38.9	20.8	100	0.957
187.5	187.5	196	330	57.2	35.4	20.3	98.6	0.958
171	171.6	191	328	52.6	32.6	19.8	97.4	0.959
156.5	156.7	187	325	48.3	30.0	19.6	96.2	0.958
141.5	141.6	183	322	44.1	26.9	19.1	95.0	0.960
126.5	126.5	178	319	39.6	24.4	18.8	93.6	0.960
113	113.4	174	317	35.6	22.1	18.6	92.6	0.960
101	101.4	171	315	31.8	20.1	18.7	91.8	0.959
89.5	89.4	167	313	28.1	18.0	18.5	90.8	0.959
79	78.8	164	310	25.1	15.5	17.8	89.7	0.961
71.5	71.6	162	309	22.9	14.0	17.5	89.2	0.962
64.5	64.8	159	308	20.6	13.1	17.6	88.6	0.960
59	58.8	157	307	18.7	11.9	17.4	88.1	0.961
53.5	53.5	156	306	17.0	10.9	17.5	87.7	0.960
48.5	48.4	154	305	15.4	9.9	17.3	87.2	0.961
43	43.2	155	254	16.3	9.1	18.0	76.2	0.944
39.5	39.5	153	254	14.6	8.8	18.8	76.1	0.939
37	37.0	155	205	16.3	9.4	21.6	67.9	0.899
33.5	33.2	153	204	14.6	8.5	21.5	67.4	0.898
30	29.6	152	203	13.1	7.5	21.2	66.9	0.900
26	26.2	159	167	13.2	7.6	26.5	65.1	0.835
22.5	22.3	157	166	11.2	6.6	26.6	64.7	0.831
19.5	19.4	155	165	9.7	5.8	26.5	64.3	0.830

STRUCTURAL TEES
Cut from W Shapes
WT155 - WT100

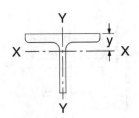

PROPERTIES

Designation	Dead Load	Area	Axis X-X				Axis Y-Y			Torsional Constant	Warping Constant
			I_x	S_x	r_x	y	I_y	S_y	r_y	J	C_w
	kN/m	mm²	10^6 mm⁴	10^3 mm³	mm	mm	10^6 mm⁴	10^3 mm³	mm	10^3 mm⁴	10^9 mm⁶
WT155											
x16.5	0.161	2 090	4.92	42.7	48.5	41.7	0.959	18.8	21.4	60.7	0.037 1
x14	0.139	1 810	4.27	37.8	48.6	42.1	0.790	15.5	20.9	37.8	0.025 7
x12	0.117	1 520	3.67	33.8	49.1	44.6	0.578	11.4	19.5	21.2	0.018 5
x10.5	0.104	1 350	3.25	30.3	49.1	45.0	0.491	9.73	19.1	14.6	0.013 6
WT125											
x83.5	0.822	10 700	12.1	106	33.7	30.8	49.4	373	68.0	3 140	4.58
x74.5	0.731	9 490	10.2	91.3	32.9	28.8	43.1	328	67.4	2 250	3.19
x65.5	0.644	8 360	8.73	78.7	32.3	27.0	37.2	285	66.7	1 560	2.15
x57.5	0.563	7 320	7.34	66.8	31.7	25.2	32.0	247	66.2	1 060	1.43
x50.5	0.496	6 440	6.17	57.0	31.0	23.6	27.7	216	65.6	741	0.973
x44.5	0.439	5 700	5.39	50.2	30.7	22.5	24.2	189	65.1	517	0.664
x40	0.393	5 100	4.61	43.2	30.1	21.2	21.6	169	65.0	377	0.477
x36.5	0.358	4 650	4.17	39.2	30.0	20.5	19.4	153	64.6	287	0.356
WT125											
x33.5	0.330	4 280	4.34	41.0	31.8	23.2	11.1	109	51.0	312	0.263
x29	0.286	3 710	3.68	35.5	31.5	22.2	9.42	92.8	50.4	204	0.167
x24.5	0.241	3 130	3.25	32.0	32.2	22.3	7.56	74.9	49.2	120	0.094 9
WT125											
x22.5	0.220	2 860	3.86	36.7	36.7	27.8	3.52	47.5	35.1	130	0.074 1
x19.5	0.190	2 460	3.26	31.3	36.4	26.7	2.97	40.4	34.7	84.1	0.046 7
x16.5	0.161	2 080	2.85	28.1	37.0	27.3	2.36	32.4	33.7	49.1	0.028 4
WT125											
x14	0.140	1 810	2.79	28.7	39.2	32.6	0.888	17.4	22.1	48.2	0.021 6
x12.5	0.125	1 620	2.56	26.8	39.8	33.6	0.746	14.6	21.5	32.5	0.016 6
x11	0.110	1 430	2.27	24.5	39.9	34.6	0.613	12.0	20.7	21.6	0.012 6
x9	0.087 7	1 140	1.83	20.0	40.1	34.8	0.457	9.04	20.0	11.2	0.006 8
WT100											
x50	0.489	6 340	4.61	50.6	27.0	23.9	18.3	174	53.7	1 040	0.949
x43	0.425	5 520	3.80	42.8	26.2	22.2	15.7	150	53.3	694	0.617
x35.5	0.350	4 550	2.86	32.5	25.1	19.8	12.7	123	52.8	407	0.349
x29.5	0.291	3 780	2.39	27.7	25.1	18.7	10.2	99.5	52.0	231	0.191
x26	0.256	3 330	2.00	23.4	24.5	17.5	8.92	87.4	51.8	161	0.130
x23	0.226	2 930	1.79	21.1	24.7	17.0	7.67	75.6	51.2	110	0.086 6
WT100											
x21	0.205	2 660	1.78	21.2	25.9	18.8	4.50	54.2	41.2	111	0.061 7
x18	0.176	2 290	1.48	17.7	25.4	17.7	3.82	46.3	40.9	72.5	0.038 9
WT100											
x15.5	0.154	2 000	1.63	19.4	28.5	21.1	2.05	30.6	32.0	59.4	0.025 0
x13.5	0.131	1 700	1.43	17.3	29.1	21.3	1.65	24.8	31.2	35.5	0.015 1

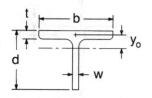

PROPERTIES AND DIMENSIONS

Nominal Mass	Theoretical Mass	Depth	Flange Width	Flange Thickness	Stem Thickness	y_o	$\bar{r}_o$	Ω
		d	b	t	w			
kg/m	kg/m	mm	mm	mm	mm	mm	mm	
16.5	16.4	157	102	10.8	6.6	36.3	64.3	0.681
14	14.2	155	102	8.9	6.0	37.6	64.9	0.664
12	11.9	153	101	6.7	5.6	41.3	67.1	0.621
10.5	10.6	152	101	5.7	5.1	42.2	67.5	0.609
83.5	83.8	145	265	31.8	19.2	14.9	77.4	0.963
74.5	74.5	141	263	28.4	17.3	14.6	76.4	0.963
65.5	65.6	138	261	25.1	15.4	14.5	75.6	0.963
57.5	57.4	135	259	22.1	13.5	14.2	74.7	0.964
50.5	50.6	132	257	19.6	11.9	13.8	73.9	0.965
44.5	44.8	130	256	17.3	10.7	13.9	73.4	0.964
40	40.1	128	255	15.6	9.4	13.4	72.9	0.966
36.5	36.5	127	254	14.2	8.6	13.4	72.5	0.966
33.5	33.6	129	204	15.7	8.9	15.4	62.0	0.939
29	29.1	126	203	13.5	8.0	15.5	61.4	0.937
24.5	24.6	124	202	11.0	7.4	16.8	61.1	0.925
22.5	22.5	133	148	13.0	7.6	21.3	55.1	0.851
19.5	19.3	131	147	11.2	6.6	21.1	54.5	0.850
16.5	16.4	129	146	9.1	6.1	22.7	54.9	0.829
14	14.2	130	102	10.0	6.4	27.6	52.9	0.727
12.5	12.7	129	102	8.4	6.1	29.4	53.9	0.702
11	11.2	127	102	6.9	5.8	31.1	54.7	0.676
9	8.9	126	101	5.3	4.8	32.1	55.1	0.660
50	49.8	115	210	23.7	14.5	12.1	61.3	0.961
43	43.4	111	209	20.6	13.0	11.9	60.6	0.961
35.5	35.7	108	206	17.4	10.2	11.1	59.5	0.965
29.5	29.7	105	205	14.2	9.1	11.6	58.9	0.961
26	26.1	103	204	12.6	7.9	11.2	58.4	0.963
23	23.0	102	203	11.0	7.2	11.5	58.0	0.961
21	20.9	103	166	11.8	7.2	12.9	50.3	0.935
18	18.0	101	165	10.2	6.2	12.6	49.7	0.936
15.5	15.7	105	134	10.2	6.4	16.0	45.8	0.877
13.5	13.3	104	133	8.4	5.8	17.1	45.9	0.862

STRUCTURAL TEES
Cut from W Shapes
WT100 - WT50

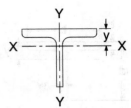

PROPERTIES

Designation	Dead Load	Area	Axis X-X				Axis Y-Y			Torsional Constant	Warping Constant
			I_x	S_x	r_x	y	I_y	S_y	r_y	J	C_w
	kN/m	mm²	10^6 mm⁴	10^3 mm³	mm	mm	10^6 mm⁴	10^3 mm³	mm	10^3 mm⁴	10^9 mm⁶
WT100											
x11	0.110	1 430	1.36	17.5	30.9	25.3	0.710	13.9	22.3	28.1	0.010 2
x9.5	0.095 6	1 240	1.22	16.0	31.3	26.1	0.577	11.3	21.6	18.0	0.007 2
x7.5	0.073 3	952	0.885	11.7	30.5	24.1	0.434	8.69	21.4	8.75	0.003 0
WT75											
x18.5	0.183	2 370	0.947	14.5	20.0	15.5	3.53	45.9	38.6	97.9	0.045 9
x15	0.147	1 900	0.725	11.3	19.5	14.1	2.78	36.3	38.2	51.4	0.023 2
x11	0.110	1 430	0.581	9.38	20.2	14.1	1.93	25.4	36.8	21.6	0.009 1
WT75											
x12	0.118	1 530	0.708	11.3	21.5	17.3	0.913	17.9	24.4	46.4	0.011 4
x9	0.088 1	1 140	0.544	9.16	21.8	17.1	0.629	12.3	23.5	18.6	0.004 7
x7	0.066 7	866	0.395	6.68	21.4	15.8	0.459	9.18	23.0	8.50	0.002 0
WT65											
x14	0.138	1 800	0.426	8.02	15.4	12.4	1.91	29.8	32.6	65.4	0.020 8
x12	0.116	1 510	0.350	6.74	15.2	11.6	1.55	24.5	32.1	39.4	0.012 0
WT50											
x9.5	0.095 3	1 240	0.221	5.28	13.4	11.2	0.803	15.6	25.5	31.5	0.006 3

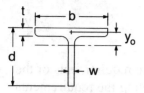

PROPERTIES AND DIMENSIONS

Nominal Mass	Theoretical Mass	Depth	Flange Width	Flange Thickness	Stem Thickness	y_o	$\bar{r}_o$	Ω
		d	b	t	w			
kg/m	kg/m	mm	mm	mm	mm	mm	mm	
11	11.2	103	102	8.0	6.2	21.3	43.6	0.761
9.5	9.7	102	102	6.5	5.8	22.8	44.3	0.734
7.5	7.5	100	100	5.2	4.3	21.5	43.0	0.750
18.5	18.6	81.0	154	11.6	8.1	9.67	44.5	0.953
15	14.9	78.5	153	9.3	6.6	9.50	43.9	0.953
11	11.2	76.0	152	6.6	5.8	10.8	43.3	0.938
12	12.0	80.0	102	10.3	6.6	12.1	34.7	0.878
9	9.0	76.5	102	7.1	5.8	13.5	34.8	0.849
7	6.8	75.0	100	5.5	4.3	13.0	34.0	0.853
14	14.1	65.5	128	10.9	6.9	6.97	36.7	0.964
12	11.9	63.5	127	9.1	6.1	7.07	36.2	0.962
9.5	9.7	53.0	103	8.8	7.1	6.80	29.6	0.947

HOLLOW STRUCTURAL SECTIONS
PRODUCED TO CSA G40.20

General

Hollow Structural Sections (HSS) are produced in Canada to the requirements of the CSA G40.20 Standard to either Class C or Class H, from steel meeting the requirements of the CSA G40.21 material Standard. The normal grade of steel used is G40.21 350W. See pages 6-15 and 6-16 for descriptions of the class of HSS and for data on manufacturing tolerances. Round sections produced in accordance with common pipe specifications may sometimes be used as structural members, but are not classified as HSS (see page 6-99).

Properties and Dimensions

The tables of properties and dimensions on pages 6-100 to 6-105 include rectangular, square and round HSS currently produced in Canada. The designations (e.g. HSS 127 x 76 x 6.4 Class C) used throughout this Handbook should be used by designers and detailers when calling up HSS, as non-Canadian HSS may differ in name, size, designation, tolerances and material grade from those produced in Canada.

Section properties given in the following tables for square and rectangular sections are based on an interior corner radius taken equal to the wall thickness, and on an exterior corner radius taken equal to twice the wall thickness.

Manufacture

HSS produced to the CSA G40.20 Standard may be manufactured using either a seamless or a welding process. Seamless products are produced by piercing solid material to form a tube or by an extrusion-type process. Welded products are manufactured from flat-rolled steel which is formed and joined by various welding processes into a tubular shape. The tubular shape is then either cold-formed or hot-formed to the final shape and, if cold-formed, may be subsequently stress relieved. Class H sections are either hot-formed to final shape, or are cold-formed to final shape and then stress relieved. Class C sections are generally more readily available than class H sections, though Class H sections have greater resistance in direct compression. Outside dimensions for HSS are constant for all sizes in the same size range, with the inside dimensions changing with material thickness.

Availability

Since the sections listed in this Handbook are those best suited for structural applications, designers may wish to consult the catalogues of HSS producers supplying HSS to their region of the country for sections not listed herein.

A number of Hollow Structural Sections in CSA G40.21 grade 350W were found to be unavailable or of limited availability as of press time. These shapes have been removed from design tables in Parts 4, 5 and 6 by leaving the appropriate rows or columns blank. For more information on the standards (CSA G40.20/21 and ASTM A500) to which the listed HSS are produced, please refer to pages 6-26 to 6-28.

HOLLOW STRUCTURAL SECTIONS
PRODUCED TO ASTM A500

Manufacture

Manufacturers of Hollow Structural Sections (HSS) may produce HSS to meet the requirements of either the CAN/CSA Standard G40.20/G40.21, usually grade 350W, or ASTM Specification A500 Grade C. The availability of HSS to either standard or specification varies across the different regions of Canada.

While designs using CAN/CSA Standard G40.20/G40.21 Grade 350W will generally result in a lighter overall steel structure than those using ASTM A500 grade C, CAN/CSA G40.21 350W may not be available in the quantities and time frame envisaged for a specific project in some regions of Canada.

HSS manufactured to ASTM Standard A500 Grade C are not equivalent to HSS meeting the requirements of CSA G40.21 grade 350W. If HSS produced to A500 are offered as a substitute, it would be prudent to assess the influence of the differences that arise from a possible difference in wall thickness and material strengths. Information on design issues related to this substitution may be found on CISC's Internet website, *www.cisc-icca.ca.*

Properties and Dimensions

The tables of properties and dimensions on pages 6-106 to 6-111 have been prepared assuming that the thickness of the HSS produced to ASTM A500 Grade C will be at the lower end of the wall thickness tolerance permitted by that specification. Unlike CAN/CSA Standard G40.20/G40.21, the ASTM A500 specification has no tolerance for mass and has a tolerance of ± 10% on the wall thickness. This difference has been the subject of two letters from CISC's President, Mr. H. A. Krentz, in 1995 and 1996. These letters are posted on CISC's website, *www.cisc-icca.ca.*

Therefore, these tables include a new quantity termed the "Design Wall Thickness". This Design Wall Thickness is taken as 0.90 times the nominal wall thickness. The nominal wall thickness is the thickness that has been published in previous tables as the "wall thickness" and, when rounded, forms the third term of the HSS designation.

With the exception of the Mass and the Dead Load, the values of Properties and Dimensions published in the following tables were computed based on the value of the "Design Wall Thickness".

Information on ASTM A500 Grade C

The following information is taken from ASTM A500 - 03, Standard Specification for Cold-Formed Welded and Seamless Carbon Steel Structural Tubing in Rounds and Shapes. For complete information on HSS produced to ASTM A500 Grade C, please refer to the actual specification.

Mechanical Properties of ASTM A500 Grade C Steel *

HSS Shape	** F_y (min)	F_u (min)
Round HSS	317 MPa	427 MPa
Square and Rectangular HSS	345 MPa	427 MPa

* Clause 1.2 Note 1: Products manufactured to this specification may not be suitable for those applications such as dynamically loaded elements in welded structures, etc., where low-temperature notch-toughness properties may be important.

** Clause 15.3 The yield strength corresponding to an offset of 0.2% of the gage length or to a total extension under load of 0.5% of the gage length shall be determined.

Chemical Composition of ASTM A500 Grade C Steel

Element	Composition, %	
	Heat Analysis	Product Analysis
Carbon, max	0.23	0.27
Manganese, max	1.35	1.40
Phosphorus, max	0.035	0.045
Sulphur, max	0.035	0.045
Copper (when specified)	0.20	0.18

Manufacturing Tolerances of ASTM A500 Steel

Wall Thickness: ± 10%

Mass: none required

PIPE

Properties and dimensions for pipe provided in the table on page 6-112 have been soft-converted to metric from the ASTM A53 "Standard Specification for Pipe, Steel, Black and Hot-Dipped, Zinc-Coated, Welded and Seamless". Although not a normal structural quality steel, pipe produced in accordance with the ASTM A53 Standard is available in three types and two grades, with specified minimum yield strengths of 205 or 240 MPa. These are considerably lower than 350 MPa generally used for Hollow Structural Sections.

Size and wall thickness of seamless and welded mill pipe up to 323.9 mm outside diameter permit threading the ends for joining lengths with couplings or other connectors. The wall thickness of mill pipe has been expressed in terms of "standard wall" (STD), "extra strong" (XS), "double extra strong" (XXS), and in terms of "schedule numbers" (Sch). STD is the same as Sch 40 for all sizes up to and including 273.1 mm outside diameter; XS is the same as Sch 80 for all sizes up to and including 219.1 mm outside diameter; and XXS is the next heavier pipe to the Sch 160 pipe for all sizes up to and including 168.3 mm outside diameter.

HOLLOW STRUCTURAL SECTIONS
CSA G40.20
Rectangular

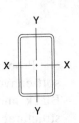

PROPERTIES AND DIMENSIONS

Designation*	Wall Thick-ness	Mass	Dead Load	Area	Axis X-X				Axis Y-Y				Torsional Constant	Shear Constant
					I_x	S_x	r_x	Z_x	I_y	S_y	r_y	Z_y	J	C_{rt}
mm x mm x mm	mm	kg/m	kN/m	mm²	10^6 mm⁴	10^3 mm³	mm	10^3 mm³	10^6 mm⁴	10^3 mm³	mm	10^3 mm³	10^3 mm⁴	mm²
HSS 356x254														
x13	12.70	113	1.11	14 400	253	1 420	132	1 730	150	1 180	102	1 370	304 000	7 740
x9.5	9.53	86.5	0.849	11 000	198	1 120	134	1 340	118	931	104	1 060	235 000	6 050
HSS 305x203														
x13	12.70	93.0	0.912	11 800	147	964	111	1 190	78.2	769	81.2	897	167 000	6 450
x9.5	9.53	71.3	0.700	9 090	116	762	113	926	62.1	611	82.7	701	130 000	5 080
x8.0	7.95	60.1	0.590	7 660	99.4	652	114	787	53.3	525	83.4	596	110 000	4 340
x6.4	6.35	48.6	0.476	6 190	81.5	535	115	640	43.8	431	84.1	486	89 700	3 550
HSS 254x152														
x13	12.70	72.7	0.713	9 260	75.2	592	90.1	747	33.6	442	60.3	522	77 700	5 160
x9.5	9.53	56.1	0.551	7 150	60.4	475	91.9	589	27.2	357	61.7	413	61 400	4 110
x8.0	7.95	47.5	0.466	6 050	52.0	410	92.7	503	23.6	309	62.4	354	52 500	3 530
x6.4	6.35	38.4	0.377	4 900	42.9	338	93.6	411	19.5	256	63.1	290	42 900	2 900
HSS 203x152														
x13	12.70	62.6	0.614	7 970	43.0	423	73.4	528	27.3	359	58.6	432	56 000	3 870
x9.5	9.53	48.5	0.476	6 180	34.8	343	75.1	420	22.3	292	60.0	344	44 400	3 150
x8.0	7.95	41.1	0.403	5 240	30.2	297	75.9	360	19.3	254	60.8	295	38 100	2 730
x6.4	6.35	33.4	0.327	4 250	25.0	246	76.7	295	16.1	211	61.5	243	31 200	2 260
x4.8	4.78	25.5	0.250	3 250	19.5	192	77.5	228	12.6	165	62.2	188	24 100	1 760
HSS 203x102														
x13	12.70	52.4	0.515	6 680	31.3	308	68.4	405	10.2	201	39.1	246	26 700	3 870
x9.5	9.53	40.9	0.401	5 210	25.8	254	70.3	326	8.57	169	40.5	199	21 700	3 150
x8.0	7.95	34.8	0.341	4 430	22.5	221	71.2	281	7.54	148	41.3	172	18 800	2 730
x6.4	6.35	28.3	0.278	3 610	18.8	185	72.2	232	6.35	125	42.0	143	15 600	2 260
x4.8	4.78	21.7	0.213	2 760	14.7	145	73.1	180	5.03	99.0	42.7	111	12 100	1 760
HSS 178x127														
x13	12.70	52.4	0.515	6 680	26.4	297	62.9	378	15.5	244	48.1	298	33 300	3 230
x9.5	9.53	40.9	0.401	5 210	21.7	244	64.6	303	12.8	202	49.6	240	26 800	2 660
x8.0	7.95	34.8	0.341	4 430	19.0	213	65.4	261	11.2	177	50.3	207	23 000	2 320
x6.4	6.35	28.3	0.278	3 610	15.8	178	66.2	216	9.40	148	51.1	171	19 000	1 940
x4.8	4.78	21.7	0.213	2 760	12.4	140	67.1	168	7.41	117	51.8	133	14 700	1 520
HSS 152x102														
x13	12.70	42.3	0.415	5 390	14.7	193	52.2	252	7.67	151	37.7	189	17 500	2 580
x9.5	9.53	33.3	0.327	4 240	12.4	162	54.0	206	6.51	128	39.2	155	14 400	2 180
x8.0	7.95	28.4	0.279	3 620	10.9	143	54.8	179	5.76	113	39.9	135	12 500	1 920
x6.4	6.35	23.2	0.228	2 960	9.19	121	55.7	148	4.88	96.2	40.6	112	10 400	1 610
x4.8	4.78	17.9	0.175	2 280	7.28	95.6	56.5	116	3.89	76.6	41.3	87.8	8 150	1 270

* Depth x Width x Thickness, see page 6-19.
Note: C_{rt} is the ratio of applied shear force to maximum shear stress for the strong bending axis.

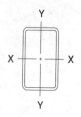

PROPERTIES AND DIMENSIONS

Designation*	Wall Thickness	Mass	Dead Load	Area	Axis X-X				Axis Y-Y				Torsional Constant	Shear Constant
					I_x	S_x	r_x	Z_x	I_y	S_y	r_y	Z_y	J	C_{rt}
mm x mm x mm	mm	kg/m	kN/m	mm^2	$10^6\ mm^4$	$10^3\ mm^3$	mm	$10^3\ mm^3$	$10^6\ mm^4$	$10^3\ mm^3$	mm	$10^3\ mm^3$	$10^3\ mm^4$	mm^2
HSS 152x76														
x13	12.70	37.3	0.365	4 750	11.5	152	49.3	207	3.71	97.3	28.0	124	9 960	2 580
x9.5	9.53	29.5	0.290	3 760	9.89	130	51.3	171	3.24	85.0	29.4	104	8 450	2 180
x8.0	7.95	25.3	0.248	3 220	8.79	115	52.3	149	2.91	76.3	30.1	91.2	7 450	1 920
x6.4	6.35	20.7	0.203	2 640	7.47	98.0	53.2	125	2.50	65.5	30.8	76.6	6 270	1 610
x4.8	4.78	16.0	0.157	2 040	5.96	78.2	54.1	98.1	2.02	52.9	31.5	60.5	4 950	1 270
HSS 127x76														
x9.5	9.53	25.7	0.252	3 280	6.13	96.5	43.3	126	2.70	70.8	28.7	87.8	6 500	1 690
x8.0	7.95	22.1	0.217	2 820	5.49	86.5	44.2	111	2.44	63.9	29.4	77.4	5 750	1 510
x6.4	6.35	18.2	0.178	2 320	4.70	74.1	45.1	93.4	2.10	55.2	30.1	65.3	4 860	1 290
x4.8	4.78	14.1	0.138	1 790	3.78	59.6	45.9	73.8	1.71	44.8	30.8	51.8	3 850	1 030
HSS 102x76														
x9.5	9.53	21.9	0.215	2 790	3.42	67.4	35.0	87.9	2.16	56.6	27.8	71.6	4 630	1 210
x8.0	7.95	18.9	0.186	2 410	3.10	61.1	35.9	77.9	1.96	51.5	28.5	63.6	4 120	1 110
x6.4	6.35	15.6	0.153	1 990	2.69	52.9	36.7	66.0	1.71	44.8	29.3	54.0	3 500	968
x4.8	4.78	12.2	0.119	1 550	2.18	43.0	37.5	52.6	1.39	36.6	30.0	43.1	2 780	789
x3.2	3.18	8.35	0.082	1 060	1.57	30.8	38.4	37.0	1.01	26.4	30.7	30.4	1 950	565
HSS 102x51														
x9.5	9.53	18.1	0.178	2 310	2.39	47.1	32.2	65.6	0.762	30.0	18.2	39.2	2 070	1 210
x8.0	7.95	15.8	0.155	2 010	2.21	43.6	33.2	59.0	0.714	28.1	18.9	35.6	1 910	1 110
x6.4	6.35	13.1	0.129	1 670	1.95	38.5	34.2	50.7	0.640	25.2	19.6	30.8	1 670	968
x4.8	4.78	10.3	0.101	1 310	1.61	31.8	35.1	40.8	0.537	21.1	20.3	25.0	1 360	789
x3.2	3.18	7.09	0.070	903	1.17	23.1	36.1	29.0	0.397	15.6	21.0	17.9	976	565
HSS 89x64														
x8.0	7.95	15.8	0.155	2 010	1.88	42.2	30.6	55.1	1.09	34.4	23.3	43.3	2 410	908
x6.4	6.35	13.1	0.129	1 670	1.65	37.1	31.4	47.2	0.968	30.5	24.1	37.3	2 080	806
x4.8	4.78	10.3	0.101	1 310	1.36	30.6	32.3	38.0	0.803	25.3	24.8	30.1	1 680	667
x3.2	3.18	7.09	0.070	903	0.990	22.3	33.1	27.0	0.588	18.5	25.5	21.4	1 190	485
HSS 76x51														
x6.4	6.35	10.6	0.104	1 350	0.919	24.1	26.1	31.5	0.479	18.9	18.9	23.6	1 100	645
x4.8	4.78	8.35	0.082	1 060	0.775	20.3	27.0	25.8	0.408	16.1	19.6	19.4	903	546
x3.2	3.18	5.82	0.057	741	0.575	15.1	27.8	18.6	0.306	12.0	20.3	14.0	652	404
HSS 51x25														
x4.8	4.78	4.54	0.045	578	0.150	5.89	16.1	8.21	0.047 6	3.75	9.08	4.91	129	303
x3.2	3.18	3.28	0.032	418	0.122	4.81	17.1	6.34	0.040 0	3.15	9.78	3.85	104	242

* Depth x Width x Thickness, see page 6-19.

Note: C_{rt} is the ratio of applied shear force to maximum shear stress for the strong bending axis.

HOLLOW STRUCTURAL SECTIONS
CSA G40.20
Square

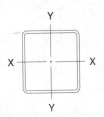

PROPERTIES AND DIMENSIONS

Designation*	Wall Thick-ness	Mass	Dead Load	Area	I	S	r	Z	Torsional Constant J	Shear Constant C_{rt}	Surface Area
mm x mm x mm	mm	kg/m	kN/m	mm²	10⁶ mm⁴	10³ mm³	mm	10³ mm³	10³ mm⁴	mm²	m²/m
HSS 305x305											
x13	12.70	113	1.11	14 400	202	1 330	118	1 560	323 000	6 450	1.18
x9.5	9.53	86.5	0.849	11 000	158	1 040	120	1 210	250 000	5 080	1.19
x8.0	7.95	72.8	0.714	9 280	135	886	121	1 030	211 000	4 340	1.19
x6.4	6.35	58.7	0.576	7 480	110	723	121	833	171 000	3 550	1.20
HSS 254x254											
x13	12.70	93.0	0.912	11 800	113	889	97.6	1 060	183 000	5 160	0.972
x9.5	9.53	71.3	0.700	9 090	89.3	703	99.1	825	142 000	4 110	0.983
x8.0	7.95	60.1	0.590	7 660	76.5	602	99.9	702	120 000	3 530	0.989
x6.4	6.35	48.6	0.476	6 190	62.7	494	101	571	97 800	2 900	0.994
HSS 203x203											
x13	12.70	72.7	0.713	9 260	54.7	538	76.9	651	90 200	3 870	0.769
x9.5	9.53	56.1	0.551	7 150	43.9	432	78.4	513	70 800	3 150	0.780
x8.0	7.95	47.5	0.466	6 050	37.9	373	79.2	439	60 400	2 730	0.786
x6.4	6.35	38.4	0.377	4 900	31.3	308	79.9	359	49 300	2 260	0.791
HSS 178x178											
x13	12.70	62.6	0.614	7 970	35.2	396	66.5	484	58 800	3 230	0.668
x9.5	9.53	48.5	0.476	6 180	28.6	322	68.0	385	46 500	2 660	0.678
x8.0	7.95	41.1	0.403	5 240	24.8	279	68.8	330	39 800	2 320	0.684
x6.4	6.35	33.4	0.327	4 250	20.6	231	69.6	271	32 600	1 940	0.689
x4.8	4.78	25.5	0.250	3 250	16.1	181	70.3	210	25 100	1 520	0.695
HSS 152x152											
x13	12.70	52.4	0.515	6 680	21.0	276	56.1	342	35 600	2 580	0.566
x9.5	9.53	40.9	0.401	5 210	17.3	227	57.6	275	28 500	2 180	0.577
x8.0	7.95	34.8	0.341	4 430	15.1	198	58.4	237	24 600	1 920	0.582
x6.4	6.35	28.3	0.278	3 610	12.6	166	59.2	196	20 200	1 610	0.588
x4.8	4.78	21.7	0.213	2 760	9.93	130	59.9	152	15 600	1 270	0.593
HSS 127x127											
x13	12.70	42.3	0.415	5 390	11.3	177	45.7	225	19 500	1 940	0.464
x9.5	9.53	33.3	0.327	4 240	9.48	149	47.3	183	15 900	1 690	0.475
x8.0	7.95	28.4	0.279	3 620	8.36	132	48.0	159	13 800	1 510	0.481
x6.4	6.35	23.2	0.228	2 960	7.05	111	48.8	132	11 400	1 290	0.486
x4.8	4.78	17.9	0.175	2 280	5.60	88.1	49.6	103	8 900	1 030	0.492

* Depth x Width x Thickness, see page 6-19.
Note: C_{rt} is the ratio of applied shear force to maximum shear stress.

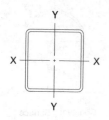

PROPERTIES AND DIMENSIONS

Designation*	Wall Thick-ness	Mass	Dead Load	Area	I	S	r	Z	Torsional Constant J	Shear Constant C_{rt}	Surface Area
mm x mm x mm	mm	kg/m	kN/m	mm^2	10^6 mm^4	10^3 mm^3	mm	10^3 mm^3	10^3 mm^4	mm^2	m^2/m
HSS 114x114											
x13	12.70	37.3	0.365	4 750	7.78	136	40.5	175	13 600	1 610	0.414
x9.5	9.53	29.5	0.290	3 760	6.65	116	42.1	144	11 300	1 450	0.424
x8.0	7.95	25.3	0.248	3 220	5.91	103	42.8	126	9 830	1 310	0.430
x6.4	6.35	20.7	0.203	2 640	5.02	87.8	43.6	105	8 190	1 130	0.435
x4.8	4.78	16.0	0.157	2 040	4.01	70.1	44.4	82.7	6 410	910	0.441
x3.2	3.18	10.9	0.107	1 390	2.83	49.5	45.1	57.4	4 430	646	0.446
HSS 102x102											
x13	12.70	32.2	0.316	4 100	5.10	100	35.3	131	9 070	1 290	0.363
x9.5	9.53	25.7	0.252	3 280	4.45	87.6	36.9	110	7 640	1 210	0.374
x8.0	7.95	22.1	0.217	2 820	3.99	78.5	37.6	96.8	6 720	1 110	0.379
x6.4	6.35	18.2	0.178	2 320	3.42	67.3	38.4	81.4	5 640	968	0.385
x4.8	4.78	14.1	0.138	1 790	2.75	54.2	39.2	64.3	4 440	789	0.390
x3.2	3.18	9.62	0.094	1 230	1.96	38.5	40.0	44.9	3 080	565	0.395
HSS 89x89											
x9.5	9.53	21.9	0.215	2 790	2.80	63.0	31.7	80.5	4 880	968	0.323
x8.0	7.95	18.9	0.186	2 410	2.54	57.1	32.4	71.4	4 340	908	0.328
x6.4	6.35	15.6	0.153	1 990	2.20	49.5	33.2	60.5	3 670	806	0.334
x4.8	4.78	12.2	0.119	1 550	1.79	40.3	34.0	48.2	2 920	667	0.339
x3.2	3.18	8.35	0.082	1 060	1.29	29.0	34.8	33.9	2 040	485	0.345
HSS 76x76											
x9.5	9.53	18.1	0.178	2 310	1.61	42.4	26.5	55.5	2 870	726	0.272
x8.0	7.95	15.8	0.155	2 010	1.49	39.1	27.2	49.8	2 590	706	0.278
x6.4	6.35	13.1	0.129	1 670	1.31	34.5	28.0	42.8	2 230	645	0.283
x4.8	4.78	10.3	0.101	1 310	1.08	28.5	28.8	34.4	1 790	546	0.288
x3.2	3.18	7.09	0.070	903	0.790	20.7	29.6	24.5	1 260	404	0.294
HSS 64x64											
x6.4	6.35	10.6	0.104	1 350	0.703	22.2	22.8	28.1	1 220	484	0.232
x4.8	4.78	8.35	0.082	1 060	0.594	18.7	23.6	23.0	995	424	0.238
x3.2	3.18	5.82	0.057	741	0.441	13.9	24.4	16.6	715	323	0.243
HSS 51x51											
x6.4	6.35	8.05	0.079	1 030	0.319	12.6	17.6	16.4	567	323	0.181
x4.8	4.78	6.45	0.063	821	0.279	11.0	18.4	13.8	479	303	0.187
x3.2	3.18	4.55	0.045	580	0.214	8.42	19.2	10.2	353	242	0.192
HSS 38x38											
x4.8	4.78	4.54	0.045	578	0.101	5.30	13.2	6.95	180	181	0.136
x3.2	3.18	3.28	0.032	418	0.082 2	4.31	14.0	5.35	139	161	0.141

* Depth x Width x Thickness, see page 6-19.

Note: C_{rt} is the ratio of applied shear force to maximum shear stress.

HOLLOW STRUCTURAL SECTIONS
G40.20 - Round

PROPERTIES AND DIMENSIONS

Designation*	Wall Thick-ness	Mass	Dead Load	Area	I	S	r	Z	Torsional Constant J	Shear Constant C_{rt}	Surface Area
mm x mm	mm	kg/m	kN/m	mm²	10^6 mm⁴	10^3 mm³	mm	10^3 mm³	10^3 mm⁴	mm²	m²/m
HSS 406											
x13	12.70	123	1.21	15 700	305	1 500	139	1 970	609 000	7 860	1.28
x9.5	9.53	93.3	0.915	11 900	234	1 150	140	1 500	468 000	5 940	1.28
x6.4†	6.35	62.6	0.615	7 980	160	786	141	1 020	319 000	3 990	1.28
HSS 356											
x13	12.70	107	1.05	13 700	201	1 130	121	1 490	403 000	6 850	1.12
x9.5	9.53	81.3	0.798	10 400	155	873	122	1 140	310 000	5 180	1.12
x6.4†	6.35	54.7	0.537	6 970	106	598	123	775	213 000	3 480	1.12
HSS 324											
x13	12.70	97.5	0.956	12 400	151	930	110	1 230	301 000	6 220	1.02
x9.5	9.53	73.9	0.725	9 410	116	719	111	942	233 000	4 710	1.02
x6.4†	6.35	49.7	0.488	6 330	79.9	493	112	640	160 000	3 170	1.02
HSS 273											
x13	12.70	81.6	0.800	10 400	88.3	646	92.2	862	177 000	5 200	0.858
x6.4†	6.35	41.8	0.410	5 320	47.4	347	94.3	452	94 700	2 660	0.858
x4.8†	4.78	31.6	0.310	4 030	36.3	266	94.9	344	72 500	2 020	0.858
HSS 219											
x13	12.70	64.6	0.634	8 230	44.0	402	73.1	542	88 000	4 130	0.688
x9.5	9.53	49.3	0.483	6 270	34.5	315	74.2	419	69 000	3 140	0.688
x6.4†	6.35	33.3	0.327	4 240	24.0	219	75.3	288	48 100	2 120	0.688
x4.8†	4.78	25.3	0.248	3 220	18.5	169	75.8	220	37 000	1 610	0.688
HSS 178											
x13	12.70	51.7	0.507	6 590	22.6	254	58.5	347	45 200	3 310	0.559
x9.5	9.53	39.5	0.388	5 040	17.9	201	59.6	270	35 800	2 520	0.559
x8.0†	7.95	33.3	0.327	4 240	15.3	172	60.1	230	30 700	2 120	0.559
x6.4†	6.35	26.8	0.263	3 420	12.6	142	60.7	187	25 200	1 710	0.559
x4.8†	4.78	20.4	0.200	2 600	9.73	109	61.2	143	19 500	1 300	0.559
HSS 168											
x13	12.70	48.7	0.478	6 210	18.9	225	55.2	308	37 800	3 120	0.529
x9.5	9.53	37.3	0.366	4 750	15.0	179	56.2	241	30 100	2 380	0.529
x8.0†	7.95	31.4	0.308	4 000	12.9	153	56.8	205	25 800	2 010	0.529
x6.4†	6.35	25.4	0.249	3 230	10.6	126	57.3	167	21 200	1 620	0.529
x4.8†	4.78	19.3	0.189	2 460	8.21	97.6	57.8	128	16 400	1 230	0.529
x3.2†	3.18	12.9	0.127	1 650	5.62	66.8	58.4	86.7	11 200	825	0.529
HSS 152											
x9.5	9.53	33.6	0.329	4 280	11.0	144	50.6	195	21 900	2 150	0.479
x8.0†	7.95	28.3	0.278	3 610	9.44	124	51.1	166	18 900	1 810	0.479
x6.4†	6.35	22.9	0.224	2 910	7.78	102	51.7	136	15 600	1 460	0.479
x4.8†	4.78	17.4	0.171	2 220	6.04	79.3	52.2	104	12 100	1 110	0.479
x3.2†	3.18	11.7	0.115	1 490	4.15	54.5	52.8	70.8	8 300	746	0.479

* Diameter x Thickness, see page 6-19.
† Check availability.

Note: C_{rt} is the ratio of applied shear force to maximum shear stress.

HOLLOW STRUCTURAL SECTIONS
G40.20 - Round

PROPERTIES AND DIMENSIONS

Designation*	Wall Thick-ness	Mass	Dead Load	Area	I	S	r	Z	Torsional Constant J	Shear Constant C_rt	Surface Area
mm x mm	mm	kg/m	kN/m	mm²	10^6 mm⁴	10^3 mm³	mm	10^3 mm³	10^3 mm⁴	mm²	m²/m
HSS 141											
x9.5	9.53	31.0	0.304	3 950	8.61	122	46.7	166	17 200	1 980	0.444
x6.4†	6.35	21.1	0.207	2 690	6.14	86.9	47.8	116	12 300	1 350	0.444
x4.8†	4.78	16.1	0.158	2 050	4.78	67.7	48.3	89.1	9 560	1 030	0.444
HSS 127											
x13	12.70	35.8	0.351	4 560	7.54	119	40.7	167	15 100	2 300	0.399
x9.5	9.53	27.6	0.271	3 520	6.11	96.2	41.7	132	12 200	1 770	0.399
x8.0†	7.95	23.3	0.229	2 970	5.29	83.3	42.2	113	10 600	1 490	0.399
x6.4†	6.35	18.9	0.185	2 410	4.39	69.2	42.7	92.5	8 780	1 210	0.399
x4.8†	4.78	14.4	0.141	1 840	3.43	54.1	43.2	71.4	6 860	919	0.399
x3.2†	3.18	9.71	0.095	1 240	2.37	37.4	43.8	48.8	4 740	619	0.399
HSS 114											
x9.5	9.53	24.6	0.242	3 140	4.34	75.9	37.2	105	8 680	1 580	0.359
x4.8†	4.78	12.9	0.127	1 640	2.47	43.2	38.8	57.4	4 940	823	0.359
x3.2†	3.18	8.71	0.086	1 110	1.71	30.0	39.3	39.3	3 430	555	0.359
HSS 102											
x8.0†	7.95	18.4	0.180	2 340	2.58	50.8	33.2	69.9	5 170	1 180	0.319
x6.4†	6.35	14.9	0.146	1 900	2.16	42.6	33.8	57.7	4 330	953	0.319
x4.8†	4.78	11.4	0.112	1 450	1.71	33.6	34.3	44.8	3 420	728	0.319
x3.2†	3.18	7.72	0.076	983	1.19	23.5	34.8	30.8	2 380	492	0.319
HSS 89											
x6.4†	6.35	12.9	0.127	1 650	1.41	31.7	29.3	43.4	2 820	827	0.279
x4.8†	4.78	9.92	0.097	1 260	1.12	25.2	29.8	33.9	2 240	633	0.279
x3.2†	3.18	6.72	0.066	856	0.788	17.7	30.3	23.4	1 580	429	0.279
HSS 76											
x6.4†	6.35	10.9	0.107	1 390	0.857	22.5	24.8	31.1	1 710	701	0.239
x4.8†	4.78	8.42	0.083	1 070	0.687	18.0	25.3	24.4	1 370	538	0.239
HSS 73											
x6.4†	6.35	10.4	0.102	1 330	0.745	20.4	23.7	28.3	1 490	669	0.229
x4.8†	4.78	8.04	0.079	1 020	0.599	16.4	24.2	22.3	1 200	514	0.229
x3.2†	3.18	5.48	0.054	698	0.426	11.7	24.7	15.5	852	349	0.229
HSS 64											
x6.4†	6.35	8.95	0.088	1 140	0.471	14.8	20.3	20.8	942	575	0.199
x4.8†	4.78	6.92	0.068	882	0.383	12.0	20.8	16.5	765	443	0.199
x3.2†	3.18	4.73	0.046	603	0.275	8.66	21.4	11.6	550	302	0.199
HSS 60											
x6.4†	6.35	8.45	0.083	1 080	0.397	13.2	19.2	18.6	794	543	0.189
x4.8†	4.78	6.54	0.064	834	0.324	10.7	19.7	14.8	647	419	0.189
x3.2†	3.18	4.48	0.044	571	0.233	7.74	20.2	10.4	467	286	0.189
HSS 48											
x4.8†	4.78	5.13	0.050	654	0.157	6.48	15.5	9.09	313	329	0.152
x3.2†	3.18	3.54	0.035	451	0.115	4.77	16.0	6.48	231	226	0.152

* Diameter x Thickness, see page 6-19.
† Check availability.

Note: C_{rt} is the ratio of applied shear force to maximum shear stress.

HOLLOW STRUCTURAL SECTIONS
ASTM A500
Rectangular

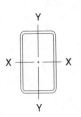

PROPERTIES AND DIMENSIONS

Designation*	Nominal Wall Thickness	Design Wall Thickness	Mass	Dead Load	Area	Axis X-X				Axis Y-Y				Torsional Constant
						I_x	S_x	r_x	Z_x	I_y	S_y	r_y	Z_y	J
mm x mm x mm	mm	mm	kg/m	kN/m	mm^2	$10^6\ mm^4$	$10^3\ mm^3$	mm	$10^3\ mm^3$	$10^6\ mm^4$	$10^3\ mm^3$	mm	$10^3\ mm^3$	$10^3\ mm^4$
HSS 356x254														
x16	15.88	14.29	139	1.36	16 100	279	1 570	132	1 910	165	1 300	101	1 520	337 000
x13	12.70	11.43	113	1.11	13 100	232	1 300	133	1 570	138	1 090	103	1 250	277 000
x9.5	9.53	8.58	86.5	0.849	9 970	181	1 020	135	1 210	108	850	104	965	213 000
HSS 305x203														
x16	15.88	14.29	114	1.11	13 200	161	1 060	111	1 310	85.4	841	80.5	989	184 000
x13	12.70	11.43	93.0	0.912	10 800	135	886	112	1 090	72.0	709	81.8	821	152 000
x9.5	9.53	8.58	71.3	0.700	8 230	106	697	114	843	56.9	560	83.1	638	118 000
x8.0	7.95	7.16	60.1	0.590	6 930	90.6	595	114	715	48.6	479	83.8	542	100 000
x6.4	6.35	5.72	48.6	0.476	5 590	74.1	486	115	581	39.8	392	84.4	441	81 300
HSS 254x152														
x16	15.88	14.29	88.3	0.866	10 300	81.8	644	89.2	820	36.4	478	59.6	572	85 100
x13	12.70	11.43	72.7	0.713	8 430	69.6	548	90.8	686	31.2	410	60.8	480	71 400
x9.5	9.53	8.58	56.1	0.551	6 490	55.4	436	92.4	538	25.0	329	62.1	378	56 100
x8.0	7.95	7.16	47.5	0.466	5 480	47.6	375	93.2	458	21.6	283	62.8	322	47 800
x6.4	6.35	5.72	38.4	0.377	4 430	39.1	308	94.0	374	17.8	234	63.4	263	39 000
HSS 203x152														
x13	12.70	11.43	62.6	0.614	7 270	39.9	393	74.1	486	25.4	334	59.1	398	51 600
x9.5	9.53	8.58	48.5	0.476	5 620	32.1	316	75.6	384	20.5	269	60.5	315	40 600
x8.0	7.95	7.16	41.1	0.403	4 750	27.7	272	76.3	328	17.8	233	61.1	270	34 700
x6.4	6.35	5.72	33.4	0.327	3 850	22.9	225	77.1	269	14.7	193	61.8	221	28 400
x4.8	4.78	4.30	25.5	0.250	2 940	17.8	175	77.8	207	11.5	150	62.4	170	21 800
HSS 203x102														
x13	12.70	11.43	52.4	0.515	6 110	29.2	288	69.2	375	9.63	190	39.7	228	24 800
x9.5	9.53	8.58	40.9	0.401	4 740	23.8	235	70.9	299	7.97	157	41.0	183	20 000
x8.0	7.95	7.16	34.8	0.341	4 030	20.7	204	71.7	257	6.97	137	41.6	158	17 300
x6.4	6.35	5.72	28.3	0.278	3 270	17.2	169	72.5	211	5.84	115	42.2	130	14 200
x4.8	4.78	4.30	21.7	0.213	2 500	13.4	132	73.3	164	4.60	90.5	42.9	101	11 000
HSS 178x127														
x13	12.70	11.43	52.4	0.515	6 110	24.7	278	63.6	350	14.5	228	48.7	276	30 800
x9.5	9.53	8.58	40.9	0.401	4 740	20.1	226	65.1	278	11.9	187	50.0	221	24 600
x8.0	7.95	7.16	34.8	0.341	4 030	17.4	196	65.8	239	10.3	163	50.7	190	21 100
x6.4	6.35	5.72	28.3	0.278	3 270	14.5	163	66.6	197	8.62	136	51.4	156	17 300
x4.8	4.78	4.30	21.7	0.213	2 500	11.3	127	67.3	152	6.76	107	52.0	121	13 400
HSS 152x102														
x13	12.70	11.43	42.3	0.415	4 950	13.9	182	52.9	235	7.26	143	38.3	176	16 400
x9.5	9.53	8.58	33.3	0.327	3 870	11.5	151	54.5	190	6.08	120	39.6	143	13 300
x8.0	7.95	7.16	28.4	0.279	3 300	10.1	132	55.3	164	5.34	105	40.3	124	11 500
x6.4	6.35	5.72	23.2	0.228	2 690	8.44	111	56.0	136	4.50	88.6	40.9	103	9 530
x4.8	4.78	4.30	17.9	0.175	2 060	6.66	87.3	56.8	106	3.56	70.1	41.6	80.0	7 410

* Depth x Width x Thickness, see page 6-19.

Designation*	Nominal Wall Thickness	Design Wall Thickness	Mass	Dead Load	Area	Axis X-X				Axis Y-Y				Torsional Constant
						I_x	S_x	r_x	Z_x	I_y	S_y	r_y	Z_y	J
mm x mm x mm	mm	mm	kg/m	kN/m	mm²	10^6 mm⁴	10^3 mm³	mm	10^3 mm³	10^6 mm⁴	10^3 mm³	mm	10^3 mm³	10^3 mm⁴
HSS 152x76														
x13	12.70	11.43	37.3	0.365	4 370	11.0	144	50.1	194	3.55	93.2	28.5	117	9 430
x9.5	9.53	8.58	29.5	0.290	3 440	9.25	121	51.9	158	3.05	80.0	29.8	96.4	7 860
x8.0	7.95	7.16	25.3	0.248	2 930	8.16	107	52.7	138	2.71	71.2	30.4	84.1	6 880
x6.4	6.35	5.72	20.7	0.203	2 400	6.88	90.3	53.6	114	2.31	60.7	31.0	70.3	5 750
x4.8	4.78	4.30	16.0	0.157	1 850	5.46	71.6	54.4	89.4	1.85	48.6	31.7	55.2	4 520
HSS 127x76														
x9.5	9.53	8.58	25.7	0.252	3 000	5.76	90.7	43.8	117	2.55	66.9	29.1	81.7	6 070
x8.0	7.95	7.16	22.1	0.217	2 570	5.12	80.6	44.6	103	2.28	59.8	29.8	71.6	5 320
x6.4	6.35	5.72	18.2	0.178	2 110	4.35	68.5	45.4	85.7	1.95	51.2	30.4	60.0	4 460
x4.8	4.78	4.30	14.1	0.138	1 630	3.47	54.7	46.2	67.4	1.57	41.2	31.1	47.3	3 510
HSS 102x76														
x9.5	9.53	8.58	21.9	0.215	2 570	3.24	63.8	35.5	82.1	2.05	53.7	28.2	67.0	4 330
x8.0	7.95	7.16	18.9	0.186	2 210	2.91	57.2	36.3	72.2	1.84	48.4	28.9	59.0	3 830
x6.4	6.35	5.72	15.6	0.153	1 820	2.49	49.1	37.0	60.8	1.59	41.7	29.6	49.8	3 220
x4.8	4.78	4.30	12.2	0.119	1 410	2.01	39.6	37.8	48.1	1.29	33.8	30.2	39.5	2 550
x3.2	3.18	2.86	8.35	0.082	964	1.43	28.2	38.5	33.6	0.920	24.1	30.9	27.6	1 770
HSS 102x51														
x9.5	9.53	8.58	18.1	0.178	2 130	2.29	45.2	32.8	61.8	0.736	29.0	18.6	37.1	1 980
x8.0	7.95	7.16	15.8	0.155	1 840	2.10	41.2	33.7	55.1	0.681	26.8	19.2	33.3	1 800
x6.4	6.35	5.72	13.1	0.129	1 530	1.83	36.0	34.6	46.9	0.602	23.7	19.9	28.6	1 550
x4.8	4.78	4.30	10.3	0.101	1 190	1.49	29.4	35.4	37.5	0.499	19.6	20.5	23.0	1 250
x3.2	3.18	2.86	7.09	0.070	818	1.08	21.2	36.3	26.4	0.365	14.4	21.1	16.3	891
HSS 89x64														
x8.0	7.95	7.16	15.8	0.155	1 840	1.77	39.9	31.0	51.4	1.04	32.6	23.7	40.5	2 260
x6.4	6.35	5.72	13.1	0.129	1 530	1.54	34.7	31.8	43.7	0.907	28.6	24.4	34.5	1 930
x4.8	4.78	4.30	10.3	0.101	1 190	1.26	28.3	32.5	34.9	0.744	23.4	25.0	27.6	1 540
x3.2	3.18	2.86	7.09	0.070	818	0.907	20.4	33.3	24.6	0.540	17.0	25.7	19.5	1 080
HSS 76x51														
x8.0	7.95	7.16	12.6	0.124	1 480	0.975	25.6	25.7	34.0	0.506	19.9	18.5	25.4	1 170
x6.4	6.35	5.72	10.6	0.104	1 240	0.867	22.7	26.5	29.3	0.454	17.9	19.1	22.0	1 020
x4.8	4.78	4.30	8.35	0.082	971	0.721	18.9	27.2	23.8	0.381	15.0	19.8	17.9	834
x3.2	3.18	2.86	5.82	0.057	673	0.528	13.9	28.0	17.0	0.282	11.1	20.5	12.8	596
HSS 51x25														
x4.8	4.78	4.30	4.54	0.045	534	0.144	5.65	16.4	7.74	0.046 1	3.63	9.29	4.65	124
x3.2	3.18	2.86	3.28	0.032	382	0.114	4.50	17.3	5.87	0.037 7	2.96	9.92	3.57	97.1

* Depth x Width x Thickness, see page 6-19.

HOLLOW STRUCTURAL SECTIONS
ASTM A500
Square

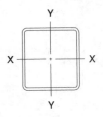

PROPERTIES AND DIMENSIONS

Designation*	Nominal Wall Thickness	Design Wall Thickness	Mass	Dead Load	Area	I	S	r	Z	Torsional Constant J	Surface Area
mm x mm x mm	mm	mm	kg/m	kN/m	mm²	10^6 mm⁴	10^3 mm³	mm	10^3 mm³	10^3 mm⁴	m²/m
HSS 305x305											
x16	15.88	14.29	139	1.36	16 100	222	1 460	118	1 730	358 000	1.17
x13	12.70	11.43	113	1.11	13 100	185	1 210	119	1 430	294 000	1.18
x9.5	9.53	8.58	86.5	0.849	9 970	144	948	120	1 100	226 000	1.19
x8.0	7.95	7.16	72.8	0.714	8 390	123	806	121	931	191 000	1.19
x6.4	6.35	5.72	58.7	0.576	6 750	100	656	122	754	155 000	1.20
HSS 254x254											
x16	15.88	14.29	114	1.11	13 200	124	973	96.8	1 170	202 000	0.967
x13	12.70	11.43	93.0	0.912	10 800	104	817	98.2	968	167 000	0.977
x9.5	9.53	8.58	71.3	0.700	8 230	81.7	643	99.6	751	129 000	0.987
x8.0	7.95	7.16	60.1	0.590	6 930	69.7	549	100	638	109 000	0.991
x6.4	6.35	5.72	48.6	0.476	5 590	57.0	449	101	518	88 600	0.996
HSS 203x203											
x16	15.88	14.29	88.3	0.866	10 300	59.5	585	76.1	714	99 100	0.764
x13	12.70	11.43	72.7	0.713	8 430	50.6	498	77.5	598	82 700	0.774
x9.5	9.53	8.58	56.1	0.551	6 490	40.3	397	78.9	469	64 600	0.783
x8.0	7.95	7.16	47.5	0.466	5 480	34.7	341	79.5	399	54 900	0.788
x6.4	6.35	5.72	38.4	0.377	4 430	28.5	281	80.2	326	44 700	0.793
HSS 178x178											
x16	15.88	14.29	75.6	0.742	8 820	38.1	428	65.7	529	64 300	0.662
x13	12.70	11.43	62.6	0.614	7 270	32.7	368	67.1	446	54 100	0.672
x9.5	9.53	8.58	48.5	0.476	5 620	26.3	296	68.5	352	42 500	0.682
x8.0	7.95	7.16	41.1	0.403	4 750	22.7	256	69.2	301	36 300	0.687
x6.4	6.35	5.72	33.4	0.327	3 850	18.8	211	69.9	247	29 600	0.692
x4.8	4.78	4.30	25.5	0.250	2 940	14.6	164	70.5	190	22 800	0.696
HSS 152x152											
x13	12.70	11.43	52.4	0.515	6 110	19.6	258	56.7	317	32 900	0.570
x9.5	9.53	8.58	40.9	0.401	4 740	16.0	210	58.1	252	26 200	0.580
x8.0	7.95	7.16	34.8	0.341	4 030	13.9	183	58.8	217	22 400	0.585
x6.4	6.35	5.72	28.3	0.278	3 270	11.6	152	59.5	178	18 400	0.590
x4.8	4.78	4.30	21.7	0.213	2 500	9.05	119	60.2	138	14 200	0.595
HSS 127x127											
x13	12.70	11.43	42.3	0.415	4 950	10.6	167	46.3	209	18 100	0.469
x9.5	9.53	8.58	33.3	0.327	3 870	8.82	139	47.7	169	14 600	0.479
x8.0	7.95	7.16	28.4	0.279	3 300	7.73	122	48.4	146	12 600	0.483
x6.4	6.35	5.72	23.2	0.228	2 690	6.49	102	49.1	121	10 400	0.488
x4.8	4.78	4.30	17.9	0.175	2 060	5.12	80.6	49.8	94.2	8 090	0.493

* Depth x Width x Thickness, see page 6-19.

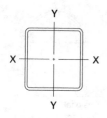

PROPERTIES AND DIMENSIONS

Designation*	Nominal Wall Thickness	Design Wall Thickness	Mass	Dead Load	Area	I	S	r	Z	Torsional Constant J	Surface Area
mm x mm x mm	mm	mm	kg/m	kN/m	mm²	10^6 mm⁴	10^3 mm³	mm	10^3 mm³	10^3 mm⁴	m²/m
HSS 114x114											
x13	12.70	11.43	37.3	0.365	4 370	7.38	129	41.1	164	12 800	0.418
x9.5	9.53	8.58	29.5	0.290	3 440	6.22	109	42.5	134	10 400	0.428
x8.0	7.95	7.16	25.3	0.248	2 930	5.48	95.9	43.2	116	9 040	0.433
x6.4	6.35	5.72	20.7	0.203	2 400	4.63	81.0	43.9	96.5	7 490	0.438
x4.8	4.78	4.30	16.0	0.157	1 850	3.67	64.2	44.6	75.4	5 840	0.442
x3.2	3.18	2.86	10.9	0.107	1 250	2.57	45.0	45.3	52.1	4 020	0.447
HSS 102x102											
x13	12.70	11.43	32.2	0.316	3 790	4.88	96.1	35.9	124	8 570	0.367
x9.5	9.53	8.58	25.7	0.252	3 000	4.18	82.4	37.3	102	7 100	0.377
x8.0	7.95	7.16	22.1	0.217	2 570	3.72	73.2	38.0	89.4	6 200	0.382
x6.4	6.35	5.72	18.2	0.178	2 110	3.16	62.3	38.7	74.7	5 170	0.387
x4.8	4.78	4.30	14.1	0.138	1 630	2.53	49.8	39.4	58.7	4 050	0.392
x3.2	3.18	2.86	9.62	0.094	1 110	1.78	35.1	40.1	40.8	2 800	0.397
HSS 89x89											
x9.5	9.53	8.58	21.9	0.215	2 570	2.65	59.6	32.1	75.2	4 570	0.326
x8.0	7.95	7.16	18.9	0.186	2 210	2.38	53.6	32.8	66.2	4 020	0.331
x6.4	6.35	5.72	15.6	0.153	1 820	2.05	46.0	33.5	55.8	3 380	0.336
x4.8	4.78	4.30	12.2	0.119	1 410	1.65	37.1	34.2	44.1	2 670	0.341
x3.2	3.18	2.86	8.35	0.082	964	1.18	26.5	34.9	30.9	1 850	0.346
HSS 76x76											
x9.5	9.53	8.58	18.1	0.178	2 130	1.55	40.6	26.9	52.2	2 710	0.275
x8.0	7.95	7.16	15.8	0.155	1 840	1.41	37.0	27.6	46.5	2 420	0.280
x6.4	6.35	5.72	13.1	0.129	1 530	1.23	32.2	28.4	39.6	2 060	0.285
x4.8	4.78	4.30	10.3	0.101	1 190	1.00	26.3	29.0	31.6	1 640	0.290
x3.2	3.18	2.86	7.09	0.070	818	0.724	19.0	29.7	22.3	1 150	0.295
HSS 64x64											
x8.0	7.95	7.16	12.6	0.124	1 480	0.746	23.5	22.4	30.2	1 310	0.229
x6.4	6.35	5.72	10.6	0.104	1 240	0.663	20.9	23.2	26.1	1 130	0.234
x4.8	4.78	4.30	8.35	0.082	971	0.553	17.4	23.9	21.2	917	0.239
x3.2	3.18	2.86	5.82	0.057	673	0.406	12.8	24.6	15.1	652	0.244
HSS 51x51											
x6.4	6.35	5.72	8.05	0.079	947	0.305	12.0	18.0	15.5	535	0.184
x4.8	4.78	4.30	6.45	0.063	752	0.262	10.3	18.7	12.8	445	0.188
x3.2	3.18	2.86	4.55	0.045	528	0.198	7.79	19.4	9.35	323	0.193
HSS 38x38											
x4.8	4.78	4.30	4.54	0.045	534	0.096 7	5.08	13.5	6.54	170	0.138
x3.2	3.18	2.86	3.28	0.032	382	0.076 8	4.03	14.2	4.95	129	0.143

* Depth x Width x Thickness, see page 6-19.

HOLLOW STRUCTURAL SECTIONS
ASTM A500 - Round

PROPERTIES AND DIMENSIONS

Designation*	Nominal Wall Thickness	Design Wall Thickness	Mass	Dead Load	Area	I	S	r	Z	Torsional Constant J	Surface Area
mm x mm	mm	mm	kg/m	kN/m	mm²	10^6 mm⁴	10^3 mm³	mm	10^3 mm³	10^3 mm⁴	m²/m
HSS 406											
x13	12.70	11.43	123	1.21	14 200	277	1 360	140	1 780	554 000	1.28
x9.5	9.53	8.58	93.3	0.915	10 700	212	1 040	141	1 360	424 000	1.28
x6.4	6.35	5.72	62.6	0.615	7 190	144	711	142	918	289 000	1.28
HSS 356											
x16	15.88	14.29	133	1.31	15 300	224	1 260	121	1 670	447 000	1.12
x13	12.70	11.43	107	1.05	12 400	183	1 030	122	1 350	366 000	1.12
x9.5	9.53	8.58	81.3	0.798	9 350	141	792	123	1 030	282 000	1.12
x6.4	6.35	5.72	54.7	0.537	6 280	96.2	541	124	700	192 000	1.12
HSS 324											
x13	12.70	11.43	97.5	0.956	11 200	137	847	111	1 120	274 000	1.02
x9.5	9.53	8.58	73.9	0.725	8 500	106	653	112	853	211 000	1.02
x6.4	6.35	5.72	49.7	0.488	5 710	72.3	447	113	579	145 000	1.02
HSS 273											
x13	12.70	11.43	81.6	0.800	9 400	80.6	590	92.6	783	161 000	0.858
x6.4	6.35	5.72	41.8	0.410	4 800	42.9	314	94.6	409	85 800	0.858
x4.8	4.78	4.30	31.6	0.310	3 630	32.8	240	95.0	311	65 600	0.858
HSS 219											
x16	15.88	14.29	79.6	0.781	9 200	48.5	442	72.6	600	96 900	0.688
x13	12.70	11.43	64.6	0.634	7 460	40.3	368	73.5	493	80 600	0.688
x9.5	9.53	8.58	49.3	0.483	5 670	31.5	287	74.5	380	63 000	0.688
x6.4	6.35	5.72	33.3	0.327	3 830	21.8	199	75.5	260	43 600	0.688
x4.8	4.78	4.30	25.3	0.248	2 900	16.7	153	76.0	199	33 500	0.688
HSS 178											
x13	12.70	11.43	51.7	0.507	5 970	20.8	234	59.0	317	41 500	0.559
x9.5	9.53	8.58	39.5	0.388	4 560	16.4	184	59.9	246	32 700	0.559
x8.0	7.95	7.16	33.3	0.327	3 840	14.0	157	60.4	208	28 000	0.559
x6.4	6.35	5.72	26.8	0.263	3 090	11.4	129	60.9	169	22 900	0.559
x4.8	4.78	4.30	20.4	0.200	2 340	8.83	99.3	61.4	130	17 700	0.559
HSS 168											
x13	12.70	11.43	48.7	0.478	5 630	17.4	207	55.6	282	34 800	0.529
x9.5	9.53	8.58	37.3	0.366	4 300	13.8	164	56.6	219	27 500	0.529
x8.0	7.95	7.16	31.4	0.308	3 620	11.8	140	57.0	186	23 600	0.529
x6.4	6.35	5.72	25.4	0.249	2 920	9.66	115	57.5	151	19 300	0.529
x4.8	4.78	4.30	19.3	0.189	2 220	7.46	88.6	58.0	116	14 900	0.529
x3.2	3.18	2.86	12.9	0.127	1 490	5.09	60.5	58.5	78.3	10 200	0.529
HSS 152											
x9.5	9.53	8.58	33.6	0.329	3 880	10.1	132	50.9	178	20 100	0.479
x8.0	7.95	7.16	28.3	0.278	3 260	8.63	113	51.4	151	17 300	0.479
x6.4	6.35	5.72	22.9	0.224	2 630	7.09	93.1	51.9	123	14 200	0.479
x4.8	4.78	4.30	17.4	0.171	2 000	5.49	72.1	52.4	94.4	11 000	0.479
x3.2	3.18	2.86	11.7	0.115	1 340	3.76	49.3	52.9	64.0	7 520	0.479

* Diameter x Thickness, see page 6-19.

PROPERTIES AND DIMENSIONS

Designation*	Nominal Wall Thickness	Design Wall Thickness	Mass	Dead Load	Area	I	S	r	Z	Torsional Constant J	Surface Area
mm x mm	mm	mm	kg/m	kN/m	mm²	10⁶ mm⁴	10³ mm³	mm	10³ mm³	10³ mm⁴	m²/m
HSS 141											
x9.5	9.53	8.58	31.0	0.304	3 580	7.91	112	47.0	151	15 800	0.444
x6.4	6.35	5.72	21.1	0.207	2 430	5.60	79.3	48.0	105	11 200	0.444
x4.8	4.78	4.30	16.1	0.158	1 850	4.35	61.5	48.5	80.8	8 700	0.444
HSS 127											
x13	12.70	11.43	35.8	0.351	4 150	7.00	110	41.1	153	14 000	0.399
x9.5	9.53	8.58	27.6	0.271	3 190	5.62	88.6	42.0	120	11 200	0.399
x8.0	7.95	7.16	23.3	0.229	2 690	4.85	76.4	42.4	103	9 710	0.399
x6.4	6.35	5.72	18.9	0.185	2 180	4.01	63.2	42.9	84.1	8 030	0.399
x4.8	4.78	4.30	14.4	0.141	1 660	3.12	49.2	43.4	64.8	6 250	0.399
x3.2	3.18	2.86	9.71	0.095	1 120	2.15	33.9	43.9	44.1	4 300	0.399
HSS 114											
x9.5	9.53	8.58	24.6	0.242	2 850	4.01	70.1	37.5	96.1	8 010	0.359
x4.8	4.78	4.30	12.9	0.127	1 490	2.25	39.4	38.9	52.1	4 500	0.359
x3.2	3.18	2.86	8.71	0.086	1 000	1.56	27.2	39.4	35.5	3 110	0.359
HSS 102											
x8.0	7.95	7.16	18.4	0.180	2 120	2.38	46.9	33.5	63.9	4 760	0.319
x6.4	6.35	5.72	14.9	0.146	1 720	1.99	39.1	34.0	52.6	3 970	0.319
x4.8	4.78	4.30	11.4	0.112	1 310	1.56	30.7	34.4	40.8	3 120	0.319
x3.2	3.18	2.86	7.72	0.076	888	1.08	21.3	34.9	27.9	2 170	0.319
HSS 89											
x8.0	7.95	7.16	15.9	0.156	1 840	1.55	34.8	29.0	47.9	3 090	0.279
x6.4	6.35	5.72	12.9	0.127	1 490	1.30	29.2	29.5	39.6	2 600	0.279
x4.8	4.78	4.30	9.92	0.097	1 140	1.03	23.1	29.9	30.8	2 050	0.279
x3.2	3.18	2.86	6.72	0.066	774	0.717	16.1	30.4	21.2	1 430	0.279
HSS 76											
x6.4	6.35	5.72	10.9	0.107	1 270	0.791	20.8	25.0	28.5	1 580	0.239
x4.8	4.78	4.30	8.42	0.083	972	0.630	16.5	25.5	22.3	1 260	0.239
HSS 73											
x6.4	6.35	5.72	10.4	0.102	1 210	0.689	18.9	23.9	25.9	1 380	0.229
x4.8	4.78	4.30	8.04	0.079	928	0.550	15.1	24.3	20.3	1 100	0.229
x3.2	3.18	2.86	5.48	0.054	631	0.388	10.6	24.8	14.1	777	0.229
HSS 64											
x6.4	6.35	5.72	8.95	0.088	1 040	0.437	13.8	20.5	19.1	875	0.199
x4.8	4.78	4.30	6.92	0.068	800	0.352	11.1	21.0	15.1	705	0.199
x3.2	3.18	2.86	4.73	0.046	545	0.251	7.91	21.5	10.5	502	0.199
HSS 60											
x6.4	6.35	5.72	8.45	0.083	980	0.369	12.2	19.4	17.1	738	0.189
x4.8	4.78	4.30	6.54	0.064	757	0.298	9.90	19.9	13.5	597	0.189
x3.2	3.18	2.86	4.48	0.044	516	0.214	7.08	20.3	9.45	427	0.189
HSS 48											
x4.8	4.78	4.30	5.13	0.050	595	0.145	6.02	15.6	8.35	291	0.152
x3.2	3.18	2.86	3.54	0.035	409	0.106	4.38	16.1	5.92	212	0.152

* Diameter x Thickness, see page 6-19.

Desig-nation[†]	Outside Dia.	Thick-ness	Weight Class*	Mass	Dead Load	Area	I	S	r	Z	Shear Constant	J	Surface Area
mm	mm	mm		kg/m	kN/m	mm^2	10^6 mm^4	10^3 mm^3	mm	10^3 mm^3	mm^2	10^6 mm^4	m^2/m
DN15	21.3	2.77	STD	1.27	0.012 4	161	0.007 08	0.664	6.62	0.958	81.8	0.014 2	0.066 9
	21.3	3.73	XS	1.62	0.015 9	206	0.008 30	0.780	6.35	1.17	106	0.016 6	0.066 9
	21.3	7.47	XXS	2.55	0.025 0	325	0.010 0	0.941	5.56	1.57	191	0.020 0	0.066 9
DN20	26.7	2.87	STD	1.69	0.016 5	215	0.015 5	1.16	8.49	1.64	108	0.030 9	0.083 9
	26.7	3.91	XS	2.20	0.021 6	280	0.018 7	1.40	8.18	2.05	143	0.037 4	0.083 9
	26.7	7.82	XXS	3.64	0.035 7	464	0.024 2	1.81	7.23	2.95	257	0.048 4	0.083 9
DN25	33.4	3.38	STD	2.50	0.024 5	319	0.036 4	2.18	10.7	3.06	161	0.072 7	0.105
	33.4	4.55	XS	3.24	0.031 8	412	0.044 0	2.63	10.3	3.82	210	0.087 9	0.105
	33.4	9.09	XXS	5.45	0.053 5	694	0.058 5	3.50	9.18	5.62	378	0.117	0.105
DN32	42.2	3.56	STD	3.39	0.033 3	432	0.081 3	3.85	13.7	5.33	217	0.163	0.133
	42.2	4.85	XS	4.47	0.043 8	569	0.101	4.78	13.3	6.80	288	0.202	0.133
	42.2	9.70	XXS	7.77	0.076 3	990	0.142	6.75	12.0	10.5	524	0.285	0.133
DN40	48.3	3.68	STD	4.05	0.039 7	516	0.129	5.35	15.8	7.34	259	0.259	0.152
	48.3	5.08	XS	5.41	0.053 1	690	0.163	6.76	15.4	9.53	348	0.327	0.152
	48.3	10.16	XXS	9.56	0.093 7	1 220	0.237	9.82	14.0	15.1	637	0.474	0.152
DN50	60.3	3.91	STD	5.44	0.053 3	693	0.277	9.18	20.0	12.5	347	0.553	0.189
	60.3	5.54	XS	7.48	0.073 4	953	0.361	12.0	19.5	16.7	480	0.722	0.189
	60.3	11.07	XXS	13.4	0.132	1 710	0.545	18.1	17.8	27.3	884	1.09	0.189
DN65	73.0	5.16	STD	8.63	0.084 7	1 100	0.636	17.4	24.1	23.8	552	1.27	0.229
	73.0	7.01	XS	11.4	0.112	1 450	0.800	21.9	23.5	30.6	732	1.60	0.229
	73.0	14.02	XXS	20.4	0.200	2 600	1.19	32.7	21.4	49.7	1 350	2.39	0.229
DN80	88.9	5.49	STD	11.3	0.111	1 440	1.26	28.3	29.6	38.3	721	2.51	0.279
	88.9	7.62	XS	15.3	0.150	1 950	1.62	36.5	28.9	50.5	979	3.24	0.279
	88.9	15.24	XXS	27.7	0.272	3 530	2.49	56.1	26.6	83.9	1 810	4.99	0.279
DN90	101.6	5.74	STD	13.6	0.133	1 730	1.99	39.2	34.0	52.8	866	3.99	0.319
	101.6	8.08	XS	18.6	0.183	2 370	2.61	51.5	33.2	70.8	1 190	5.23	0.319
DN100	114.3	6.02	STD	16.1	0.158	2 050	3.01	52.7	38.3	70.7	1 030	6.02	0.359
	114.3	8.56	XS	22.3	0.219	2 840	4.00	70.0	37.5	95.9	1 430	8.00	0.359
	114.3	17.12	XXS	41.0	0.403	5 230	6.36	111	34.9	163	2 670	12.7	0.359
DN125	141.3	6.55	STD	21.8	0.214	2 770	6.31	89.3	47.7	119	1 390	12.6	0.444
	141.3	9.52	XS	30.9	0.304	3 940	8.60	122	46.7	166	1 980	17.2	0.444
	141.3	19.05	XXS	57.4	0.563	7 320	14.0	198	43.7	287	3 720	28.0	0.444
DN150	168.3	7.11	STD	28.3	0.277	3 600	11.7	139	57.0	185	1 800	23.4	0.529
	168.3	10.97	XS	42.6	0.418	5 420	16.9	200	55.8	272	2 720	33.7	0.529
	168.3	21.95	XXS	79.2	0.777	10 100	27.6	328	52.3	474	5 120	55.3	0.529
DN200	219.1	8.18	STD	42.5	0.417	5 420	30.2	276	74.6	364	2 710	60.4	0.688
	219.1	12.70	XS	64.6	0.634	8 230	44.0	402	73.1	542	4 130	88.0	0.688
	219.1	22.23	XXS	108	1.06	13 700	67.5	616	70.0	865	6 930	135	0.688
DN250	273.1	9.27	STD	60.3	0.592	7 680	66.9	490	93.3	646	3 840	134	0.858
	273.1	12.70	XS	81.6	0.800	10 400	88.3	646	92.2	862	5 200	177	0.858
	273.1	25.40	XXS	155	1.52	19 800	153	1 120	88.0	1 560	9 950	306	0.858
DN300	323.9	9.52	STD	73.8	0.724	9 400	116	718	111	941	4 700	233	1.02
	323.9	12.70	XS	97.5	0.956	12 400	151	930	110	1 230	6 220	301	1.02
	323.9	25.40	XXS	187	1.83	23 800	267	1 650	106	2 270	12 000	534	1.02

* Class refers to: Standard Weight - STD, Extra Strong - XS, Double Extra Strong - XXS

† This designation has been suggested by the U.S. National Institute of Building Sciences.

COLD-FORMED STEEL C- and Z-SECTIONS

General

While various proprietary cold-formed C- and Z-sections are available from Canadian roll formers, the sections listed on pages 6-114 to 6-123 are representative of typical products. Coated sections refer to products that are supplied with a metallic coating such as zinc or 55% aluminum-zinc alloy. Uncoated products do not have this coating. The metallic coating, if present, does not affect the calculated properties of the section. Both gross and effective section properties are presented in these tables. The calculated values were based on an assumed inside bend radius of twice the steel thickness unless stated otherwise, and the possible effect of cold work of forming was not included. The effective section properties, factored shear and moment resistances for the coated C-sections were computed in accordance with CSA Standard S136-07 with the 2009 Supplement (*North American Specification for the Design of Cold-Formed Steel Structural Members*). The calculated values for the uncoated sections were determined in accordance with CSA S136-01. A yield strength of 345 MPa was used in these calculations since this is the equivalent to Grade 50 material (50 ksi), which is more commonly specified than the metric Grade 340.

Material

For coated sections, steel meets the requirements of ASTM A653/A653M Grade 340 (Grade 50), $F_y = 345$ MPa, and for uncoated sections, steel meets the requirements of ASTM A1011/A1011M Grade 340 (Grade 50), $F_y = 345$ MPa.

Tables

Only some of the noteworthy terms are defined below. All others are self-explanatory.

I_{xe} = effective moment of inertia about X-X axis, (10^6 mm^4)
S_{xe} = effective section modulus about X-X axis, (10^3 mm^3)
y_e = distance from neutral axis to extreme compressive fibre, (mm)
I_{xe} = effective moment of inertia about Y-Y axis assuming lips in tension, (10^6 mm^4)
S_{ye} = effective section modulus about Y-Y axis, (10^3 mm^3)
x_e = distance from neutral axis to extreme compressive fibre, (mm)
M_{rxe} = effective factored moment resistance about X-X axis, (kN·m)
V_r = factored shear resistance, (kN)
L_u = maximum unbraced length of compression flange beyond which appropriate values in Table must be reduced for lateral-torsional buckling, (mm)
t = design base steel thickness, (mm)
x_o = distance from shear centre to centroid of gross area, (mm)
r_o = polar radius of gyration, (mm)
J = Saint-Venant torsion constant, (10^3 mm^4)
j = torsional-flexural buckling parameter, (mm)
C_w = torsional warping constant, (10^9 mm^6)

The minimum base steel thickness is 95% of the design base steel thickness. The design base steel thickness was used to calculate values in the tables.

Dr. R. M. Schuster, Professor Emeritus of Structural Engineering and Director of the Canadian Cold-Formed Steel Research Group at the University of Waterloo has prepared these tables.

COLD-FORMED C-SECTIONS, COATED

Effective Properties

F_y = 345 MPa

Based on CSA S136-07 (including 2009 Supplement)

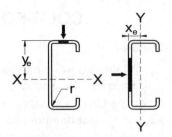

Designation	Mass	Gross Area	Effective Section Properties						M_{rxe}	V_r	L_u
			X-X Axis			Y-Y Axis					
			I_{xe}	S_{xe}	y_e	I_{ye}	S_{ye}	x_e			
	kg/m	mm²	10^6 mm⁴	10^3 mm³	mm	10^6 mm⁴	10^3 mm³	mm	kN·m	kN	mm
1400S300-97	10.9	1 394	22.5	119	189	0.736	14.8	26.5	36.9	39.4	1 538
1400S300-68	7.75	988	14.6	72.1	203	0.460	10.3	31.6	22.4	13.4	1 551
1400S250-97	10.2	1 295	19.8	104	190	0.433	9.68	18.7	32.3	39.4	1 223
1400S250-68	7.21	919	12.6	61.4	205	0.276	6.84	23.1	19.1	13.4	1 238
1400S200-97	9.65	1 230	17.8	93.8	190	0.254	6.89	13.9	29.1	39.4	980
1400S200-68	6.85	873	12.1	60.6	199	0.165	4.95	17.5	18.8	13.4	996
1400S162-97	9.01	1 148	15.4	80.5	191	0.128	3.92	8.70	25.0	39.4	727
1400S162-68	6.40	815	10.4	51.4	202	0.087	2.91	11.3	16.0	13.4	745
1200S300-97	9.91	1 263	16.4	107	153	0.729	14.8	26.8	33.2	46.3	1 561
1200S300-68	7.03	896	10.7	65.6	164	0.457	10.3	31.7	20.4	15.7	1 572
1200S300-54	5.61	715	7.72	43.8	176	0.334	8.03	34.6	13.6	7.80	1 578
1200S250-97	9.14	1 164	13.9	87.1	159	0.429	9.65	19.0	27.1	46.3	1 245
1200S250-68	6.49	827	8.94	52.0	172	0.275	6.83	23.3	16.2	15.7	1 259
1200S250-54	5.18	660	6.81	38.2	178	0.201	5.37	26.0	11.9	7.80	1 265
1200S200-97	8.62	1 099	12.4	78.3	159	0.252	6.87	14.1	24.3	46.3	1 003
1200S200-68	6.13	781	8.53	51.2	166	0.164	4.94	17.7	15.9	15.7	1 018
1200S200-54	4.90	624	6.47	37.3	173	0.120	3.91	20.1	11.6	7.80	1 025
1200S162-97	7.98	1 017	10.7	67.1	160	0.127	3.91	8.90	20.8	46.3	749
1200S162-68	5.68	723	7.29	43.3	168	0.087	2.90	11.4	13.5	15.7	765
1200S162-54	4.54	578	5.50	31.3	176	0.065	2.33	13.3	9.73	7.80	773
1000S300-97	8.88	1 131	10.6	83.0	128	0.720	14.7	27.2	25.8	56.0	1 586
1000S300-68	6.31	804	7.27	55.3	131	0.454	10.3	31.9	17.2	19.0	1 595
1000S300-54	5.04	642	5.22	36.6	142	0.332	8.02	34.7	11.4	9.40	1 601

Designation Example: 800S162-68; where 800 = section depth (in. x 100); S = stud or joist C-section;

162 = flange width (in. x 100); 68 = minimum base steel thickness (mils, in. x 1000)

Dimensions and Gross Properties

Depth	Flange Width	Stiff'r Depth	Design Thickness	Inside Radius	Gross Section Properties										
					X-X Axis			Y-Y Axis			x_o	r_o	J	j	C_w
d	b	D	t	r	I_x	S_x	r_x	I_y	S_y	r_y					
mm	mm	mm	mm	mm	10^6 mm^4	10^3 mm^3	mm	10^6 mm^4	10^3 mm^3	mm	mm	mm	10^3 mm^4	mm	10^9 mm^6
356	76.2	25.4	2.58	3.87	24.0	135	131	0.941	16.0	26.0	45.2	141	3.10	217	24.4
356	76.2	25.4	1.81	2.72	17.2	96.6	132	0.690	11.7	26.4	46.0	142	1.08	213	17.8
356	63.4	19.1	2.58	3.87	21.1	119	128	0.524	10.3	20.1	32.8	133	2.88	252	13.6
356	63.4	19.1	1.81	2.72	15.2	85.3	129	0.389	7.63	20.6	33.6	134	1.00	244	9.99
356	50.8	19.1	2.58	3.87	19.1	107	125	0.299	7.22	15.6	24.4	128	2.74	293	8.04
356	50.8	19.1	1.81	2.72	13.7	77.2	126	0.225	5.41	16.1	25.1	129	0.950	282	5.93
356	41.3	12.7	2.58	3.87	16.7	93.9	121	0.142	4.05	11.1	16.0	122	2.55	383	3.93
356	41.3	12.7	1.81	2.72	12.1	67.8	122	0.109	3.11	11.6	16.6	123	0.890	361	2.94
305	76.2	25.4	2.58	3.87	16.5	108	114	0.904	15.8	26.8	48.6	127	2.81	174	17.4
305	76.2	25.4	1.81	2.72	11.9	77.7	115	0.663	11.6	27.2	49.5	128	0.980	171	12.7
305	76.2	25.4	1.44	2.16	9.51	62.4	115	0.538	9.41	27.4	49.9	129	0.490	169	10.2
305	63.4	19.1	2.58	3.87	14.5	94.9	111	0.506	10.2	20.8	35.5	119	2.59	195	9.63
305	63.4	19.1	1.81	2.72	10.4	68.2	112	0.376	7.55	21.3	36.3	120	0.900	190	7.06
305	63.4	19.1	1.44	2.16	8.36	54.8	113	0.307	6.16	21.5	36.7	120	0.450	188	5.73
305	50.8	19.1	2.58	3.87	13.0	85.0	109	0.290	7.16	16.2	26.6	113	2.44	222	5.69
305	50.8	19.1	1.81	2.72	9.34	61.3	109	0.218	5.37	16.7	27.4	114	0.850	214	4.20
305	50.8	19.1	1.44	2.16	7.52	49.3	110	0.179	4.40	16.9	27.8	115	0.430	210	3.42
305	41.3	12.7	2.58	3.87	11.2	73.6	105	0.138	4.02	11.7	17.6	107	2.26	286	2.77
305	41.3	12.7	1.81	2.72	8.12	53.3	106	0.106	3.09	12.1	18.3	108	0.790	269	2.08
305	41.3	12.7	1.44	2.16	6.55	43.0	106	0.088	2.56	12.3	18.6	109	0.400	262	1.70
254	76.2	25.4	2.58	3.87	10.7	84.1	97.2	0.858	15.6	27.5	52.7	114	2.52	139	11.7
254	76.2	25.4	1.81	2.72	7.68	60.5	97.7	0.630	11.4	28.0	53.6	115	0.880	137	8.52
254	76.2	25.4	1.44	2.16	6.17	48.6	98.0	0.511	9.27	28.2	54.1	115	0.440	136	6.90

COLD-FORMED C-SECTIONS, COATED

Effective Properties

F_y = 345 MPa

Based on CSA S136-07 (including 2009 Supplement)

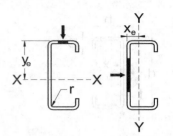

Designation	Mass	Gross Area	Effective Section Properties						M_{rxe}	V_r	L_u
			X-X Axis			Y-Y Axis					
			I_{xe}	S_{xe}	y_e	I_{ye}	S_{ye}	x_e			
	kg/m	mm²	10⁶ mm⁴	10³ mm³	mm	10⁶ mm⁴	10³ mm³	mm	kN·m	kN	mm
1000S250-97	8.11	1 030	9.23	72.5	127	0.423	9.61	19.4	22.5	56.0	1 268
1000S250-68	5.77	735	6.31	47.9	132	0.272	6.81	23.5	14.9	19.0	1 279
1000S250-54	4.61	587	4.68	33.5	140	0.200	5.35	26.1	10.4	9.40	1 285
1000S200-97	7.59	967	8.12	62.9	129	0.248	6.84	14.5	19.5	56.0	1 028
1000S200-68	5.41	689	5.63	41.8	135	0.162	4.92	17.9	13.0	19.0	1 040
1000S200-54	4.32	551	4.30	30.6	140	0.120	3.90	20.2	9.51	9.40	1 047
1000S162-97	6.95	885	6.93	53.6	129	0.125	3.90	9.20	16.6	56.0	771
1000S162-68	4.95	631	4.79	35.3	136	0.086	2.89	11.6	11.0	19.0	786
1000S162-54	3.96	505	3.65	25.7	142	0.065	2.33	13.5	7.99	9.40	794
800S250-97	7.08	902	5.41	53.1	102	0.414	9.54	20.1	16.5	61.9	1 293
800S250-68	5.04	643	3.72	35.4	105	0.269	6.77	23.8	11.0	24.0	1 301
800S250-54	4.04	514	2.91	27.1	107	0.199	5.34	26.3	8.43	11.9	1 306
800S250-43	3.24	412	2.15	18.9	114	0.146	4.19	28.5	5.86	6.00	1 310
800S200-97	6.56	836	4.78	47.1	102	0.243	6.80	15.0	14.6	61.9	1 055
800S200-68	4.68	597	3.47	34.2	102	0.160	4.90	18.2	10.6	24.0	1 065
800S200-54	3.75	478	2.75	26.8	103	0.118	3.89	20.4	8.31	11.9	1 070
800S200-43	3.01	383	1.99	17.9	111	0.087	3.07	22.4	5.54	6.00	1 075
800S200-33	2.32	296	1.34	11.0	122	0.061	2.31	24.5	3.41	2.70	1 079
800S162-97	5.92	754	4.04	39.8	102	0.122	3.87	9.70	12.4	61.9	796
800S162-68	4.23	539	2.86	27.3	105	0.085	2.88	11.9	8.47	24.0	809
800S162-54	3.39	432	2.20	20.1	109	0.064	2.32	13.7	6.25	11.9	815
800S162-43	2.72	347	1.64	14.2	116	0.048	1.85	15.5	4.40	6.00	820
800S162-33	2.10	268	1.21	10.1	120	0.033	1.40	17.4	3.14	2.70	825
600S162-97	4.89	623	2.00	26.2	76.1	0.118	3.82	10.5	8.15	59.7	824
600S162-68	3.51	447	1.47	19.3	76.2	0.083	2.86	12.4	5.98	30.4	833
600S162-54	2.82	359	1.17	15.2	77.0	0.063	2.30	14.0	4.72	16.0	837
600S162-43	2.26	288	0.910	11.6	78.8	0.047	1.84	15.7	3.59	8.00	842
600S162-33	1.75	223	0.660	7.90	83.5	0.033	1.39	17.6	2.45	3.60	846

Designation Example: 800S162-68; where 800 = section depth (in. x 100); S = stud or joist C-section;

162 = flange width (in. x 100); 68 = minimum base steel thickness (mils, in. x 1000)

Depth	Flange Width	Stiff'r Depth	Design Thickness	Inside Radius	Gross Section Properties										
					X-X Axis			Y-Y Axis			x_o	r_o	J	j	C_w
d	b	D	t	r	I_x	S_x	r_x	I_y	S_y	r_y					
mm	mm	mm	mm	mm	10^6 mm^4	10^3 mm^3	mm	10^6 mm^4	10^3 mm^3	mm	mm	mm	10^3 mm^4	mm	10^9 mm^6
254	63.4	19.1	2.58	3.87	9.28	73.1	94.8	0.483	10.0	21.6	38.8	105	2.30	149	6.40
254	63.4	19.1	1.81	2.72	6.69	52.7	95.5	0.359	7.45	22.1	39.7	106	0.800	146	4.70
254	63.4	19.1	1.44	2.16	5.39	42.4	95.8	0.293	6.08	22.3	40.1	106	0.400	144	3.81
254	50.8	19.1	2.58	3.87	8.25	64.9	92.3	0.278	7.07	17.0	29.3	98.0	2.15	163	3.78
254	50.8	19.1	1.81	2.72	5.96	47.0	93.1	0.209	5.31	17.4	30.1	99.0	0.750	158	2.80
254	50.8	19.1	1.44	2.16	4.80	37.8	93.4	0.171	4.35	17.6	30.5	100	0.380	156	2.28
254	41.3	12.7	2.58	3.87	7.06	55.6	89.3	0.133	3.98	12.3	19.5	92.0	1.97	204	1.83
254	41.3	12.7	1.81	2.72	5.13	40.4	90.2	0.103	3.06	12.8	20.3	93.0	0.690	193	1.38
254	41.3	12.7	1.44	2.16	4.14	32.6	90.6	0.085	2.53	13.0	20.6	94.0	0.350	189	1.13
203	63.4	19.1	2.58	3.87	5.44	53.5	77.7	0.454	9.83	22.4	42.9	92.0	2.01	113	3.91
203	63.4	19.1	1.81	2.72	3.94	38.7	78.3	0.337	7.31	22.9	43.8	93.0	0.700	111	2.88
203	63.4	19.1	1.44	2.16	3.17	31.2	78.5	0.275	5.96	23.1	44.2	93.0	0.350	110	2.34
203	63.4	19.1	1.15	1.81	2.56	25.2	78.8	0.224	4.85	23.3	44.6	93.0	0.180	110	1.90
203	50.8	19.1	2.58	3.87	4.78	47.0	75.6	0.262	6.95	17.7	32.7	84.0	1.86	117	2.31
203	50.8	19.1	1.81	2.72	3.47	34.2	76.3	0.197	5.22	18.2	33.5	85.0	0.650	114	1.72
203	50.8	19.1	1.44	2.16	2.80	27.6	76.6	0.161	4.28	18.4	33.9	86.0	0.330	113	1.40
203	50.8	19.1	1.15	1.81	2.26	22.2	76.8	0.132	3.50	18.5	34.3	86.0	0.170	112	1.14
203	50.8	19.1	0.879	1.94	1.75	17.3	77.0	0.103	2.74	18.7	34.6	86.0	0.080	111	0.890
203	41.3	12.7	2.58	3.87	4.04	39.8	73.2	0.127	3.92	13.0	22.0	78.0	1.68	139	1.10
203	41.3	12.7	1.81	2.72	2.95	29.0	74.0	0.098	3.01	13.5	22.8	79.0	0.590	133	0.830
203	41.3	12.7	1.44	2.16	2.39	23.5	74.3	0.081	2.50	13.7	23.2	79.0	0.300	130	0.680
203	41.3	12.7	1.15	1.81	1.93	19.0	74.6	0.067	2.06	13.9	23.5	79.0	0.150	128	0.560
203	41.3	12.7	0.879	1.94	1.50	14.8	74.9	0.053	1.62	14.0	23.8	80.0	0.070	126	0.440
152	41.3	12.7	2.58	3.87	2.00	26.2	56.6	0.118	3.82	13.8	25.3	64.0	1.39	90.0	0.580
152	41.3	12.7	1.81	2.72	1.47	19.3	57.3	0.091	2.94	14.2	26.2	65.0	0.490	87.0	0.440
152	41.3	12.7	1.44	2.16	1.19	15.6	57.6	0.075	2.44	14.5	26.6	65.0	0.250	86.0	0.360
152	41.3	12.7	1.15	1.81	0.960	12.7	57.8	0.062	2.01	14.6	27.0	65.0	0.130	85.0	0.290
152	41.3	12.7	0.879	1.94	0.750	9.90	58.1	0.049	1.59	14.8	27.3	66.0	0.060	84.0	0.230

COLD-FORMED C-SECTIONS, UNCOATED

Effective Properties
F_y = 345 MPa

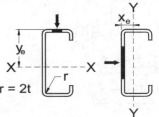

Designation	Mass	Gross Area	Effective Section Properties						M_{rxe}	V_r	L_u
			X-X Axis			Y-Y Axis					
			I_{xe}	S_{xe}	y_e	I_{ye}	S_{ye}	x_e			
	kg/m	mm²	10^6 mm⁴	10^3 mm³	mm	10^6 mm⁴	10^3 mm³	mm	kN·m	kN	mm
406S89-541M	26.8	3 420	74.2	366	203	2.80	41.7	21.9	114	301	1 790
406S89-468M	23.5	2 990	65.7	323	203	2.44	37.4	23.6	100	225	1 800
406S89-396M	20.1	2 550	56.0	272	206	2.05	32.5	26.0	84.4	149	1 810
406S89-326M	16.7	2 120	46.1	219	211	1.63	27.3	29.1	68.0	81.9	1 820
406S89-290M	14.9	1 900	40.8	191	214	1.41	24.4	31.2	59.4	57.2	1 820
406S89-254M	13.1	1 670	35.1	161	218	1.19	21.4	33.5	49.9	38.1	1 830
406S89-218M	11.3	1 440	28.8	127	227	0.966	18.3	36.1	39.5	23.8	1 840
356S89-541M	24.6	3 130	53.4	301	178	2.74	41.5	22.7	93.4	301	1 820
356S89-468M	21.5	2 740	47.3	267	178	2.41	37.2	24.3	82.8	225	1 830
356S89-396M	18.4	2 340	40.9	230	178	2.02	32.4	26.5	71.5	161	1 830
356S89-326M	15.3	1 950	34.4	194	178	1.62	27.2	29.5	60.1	94.3	1 840
356S89-290M	13.7	1 740	30.9	174	178	1.40	24.3	31.5	54.0	65.8	1 850
356S89-254M	12.0	1 530	27.1	152	179	1.18	21.3	33.7	47.1	43.8	1 850
356S89-218M	10.4	1 320	22.3	120	185	0.961	18.3	36.2	37.4	27.4	1 860
356S89-326M	15.0	1 910	32.9	183	180	1.49	24.1	27.1	56.9	94.3	1 760
356S89-290M	13.4	1 700	29.4	163	180	1.29	21.6	29.0	50.6	65.8	1 770
356S89-254M	11.8	1 500	25.5	140	182	1.10	19.0	31.2	43.4	43.8	1 780
356S89-218M	10.1	1 290	20.7	108	191	0.897	16.3	33.7	33.6	27.4	1 780
305S89-541M	22.3	2 840	36.7	241	152	2.65	41.0	24.3	74.9	255	1 850
305S89-468M	19.5	2 490	32.6	214	152	2.35	37.0	25.2	66.5	225	1 860
305S89-396M	16.7	2 130	28.2	185	152	1.99	32.2	27.2	57.5	161	1 860
305S89-326M	13.9	1 780	23.8	156	152	1.59	27.1	30.0	48.5	109	1 870
305S89-290M	12.5	1 590	21.4	140	152	1.38	24.3	31.9	43.6	77.5	1 880
305S89-254M	11.0	1 400	18.8	122	153	1.17	21.3	34.0	38.0	51.5	1 880
305S89-218M	9.50	1 210	15.8	102	156	0.954	18.2	36.5	31.5	32.2	1 890
305S89-326M	13.6	1 730	22.7	148	154	1.47	24.0	27.7	45.8	109	1 790
305S89-290M	12.2	1 550	20.3	131	155	1.28	21.5	29.4	40.7	77.5	1 790
305S89-254M	10.7	1 360	17.6	112	157	1.09	18.9	31.5	34.9	51.5	1 800
305S89-218M	9.20	1 180	14.9	93.4	159	0.891	16.2	33.9	29.0	32.2	1 800
305S89-181M	7.70	986	11.8	71.2	166	0.700	13.4	36.7	22.1	18.5	1 810
254S89-468M	17.6	2 240	21.0	166	127	2.26	36.5	26.8	51.5	183	1 900
254S89-396M	15.1	1 920	18.3	144	127	1.94	32.0	28.3	44.7	158	1 900
254S89-362M	13.9	1 770	16.9	133	127	1.76	29.6	29.4	41.4	135	1 900
254S89-326M	12.6	1 600	15.4	121	127	1.56	26.9	30.8	37.7	109	1 910
254S89-290M	11.2	1 430	13.9	109	127	1.36	24.1	32.5	33.9	86.2	1 910
254S89-254M	9.90	1 260	12.2	95.3	128	1.15	21.2	34.5	29.6	62.5	1 910
254S89-218M	8.50	1 090	10.3	78.9	130	0.945	18.1	36.8	24.5	39.0	1 910

Designation Example: 356S89-254M; where 356 = section depth (mm); S = stud or joist C-section;
89 = flange width (mm); 254 = minimum base steel thickness x 100 (mm); M = metric designation

COLD-FORMED C-SECTIONS, UNCOATED

Dimensions and Gross Properties

Depth	Flange Width	Stiff'r Depth	Thick-ness	Gross Section Properties										
				X-X Axis			Y-Y Axis							
d	b	D	t	I_x	S_x	r_x	I_y	S_y	r_y	x_o	r_o	J	j	C_w
mm	mm	mm	mm	10^6 mm^4	10^3 mm^3	mm	10^6 mm^4	10^3 mm^3	mm	mm	mm	10^3 mm^4	mm	10^9 mm^6
406	89	31.8	5.69	74.2	365	147	2.87	42.0	29.0	51.3	159	36.9	266	104
406	89	31.8	4.93	65.7	323	148	2.60	38.1	29.5	52.1	160	24.2	260	92.6
406	89	31.8	4.17	56.7	279	149	2.30	33.7	30.0	53.0	161	14.8	254	80.8
406	89	31.8	3.43	47.6	234	150	1.97	28.9	30.5	53.8	162	8.32	249	68.6
406	89	31.8	3.05	42.7	210	150	1.79	26.3	30.7	54.3	163	5.88	246	61.9
406	89	31.8	2.67	37.8	186	151	1.60	23.5	30.9	54.7	163	3.96	243	55.0
406	89	31.8	2.29	32.7	161	151	1.40	20.5	31.2	55.1	164	2.50	241	47.9
356	89	31.8	5.69	53.4	301	131	2.77	41.6	29.7	54.7	145	33.8	218	77.0
356	89	31.8	4.93	47.3	266	132	2.51	37.7	30.3	55.6	146	22.2	213	68.9
356	89	31.8	4.17	40.9	230	132	2.22	33.3	30.8	56.5	147	13.6	209	60.2
356	89	31.8	3.43	34.4	194	133	1.90	28.6	31.2	57.4	148	7.64	205	51.1
356	89	31.8	3.05	30.9	174	133	1.73	26.0	31.5	57.8	149	5.40	203	46.2
356	89	31.8	2.67	27.4	154	134	1.54	23.2	31.7	58.2	149	3.63	201	41.1
356	89	31.8	2.29	23.7	133	134	1.35	20.3	31.9	58.7	150	2.30	200	35.8
356	89	25.4	3.43	33.5	188	133	1.71	25.3	30.0	53.7	146	7.47	213	44.8
356	89	25.4	3.05	30.1	169	133	1.56	23.0	30.2	54.1	147	5.28	211	40.5
356	89	25.4	2.67	26.6	150	133	1.39	20.6	30.5	54.6	147	3.55	209	36.0
356	89	25.4	2.29	23.1	130	134	1.22	18.0	30.8	55.0	148	2.25	207	31.4
305	89	31.8	5.69	36.7	241	114	2.65	41.0	30.5	58.7	132	30.6	177	55.0
305	89	31.8	4.93	32.6	214	114	2.40	37.2	31.0	59.6	133	20.2	174	49.3
305	89	31.8	4.17	28.2	185	115	2.12	32.9	31.5	60.6	134	12.3	171	43.1
305	89	31.8	3.43	23.8	156	116	1.82	28.2	32.0	61.4	135	6.96	169	36.6
305	89	31.8	3.05	21.4	140	116	1.65	25.7	32.2	61.9	135	4.92	167	33.1
305	89	31.8	2.67	18.9	124	116	1.47	22.9	32.5	62.4	136	3.31	166	29.5
305	89	31.8	2.29	16.4	108	117	1.29	20.1	32.7	62.8	137	2.10	165	25.7
305	89	25.4	3.43	23.1	152	116	1.64	24.9	30.8	57.6	133	6.79	174	31.8
305	89	25.4	3.05	20.8	136	116	1.49	22.7	31.1	58.0	133	4.80	173	28.8
305	89	25.4	2.67	18.4	121	116	1.34	20.3	31.3	58.5	134	3.23	171	25.6
305	89	25.4	2.29	16.0	105	117	1.17	17.8	31.6	58.9	134	2.05	170	22.3
305	89	25.4	1.91	13.5	88.3	117	0.997	15.2	31.8	59.4	135	1.19	169	18.9
254	89	31.8	4.93	21.0	166	96.9	2.26	36.5	31.8	64.4	121	18.1	142	33.4
254	89	31.8	4.17	18.2	144	97.5	2.00	32.3	32.3	65.4	122	11.1	141	29.3
254	89	31.8	3.81	16.9	133	97.8	1.87	30.2	32.5	65.8	122	8.55	140	27.2
254	89	31.8	3.43	15.4	121	98.1	1.72	27.8	32.8	66.3	123	6.27	139	24.9
254	89	31.8	3.05	13.9	109	98.4	1.56	25.2	33.0	66.7	123	4.44	139	22.6
254	89	31.8	2.67	12.3	96.8	98.7	1.39	22.5	33.2	67.2	124	2.99	138	20.1
254	89	31.8	2.29	10.7	84.0	99.0	1.22	19.7	33.5	67.7	124	1.90	137	17.5

COLD-FORMED C-SECTIONS, UNCOATED
Effective Properties
F_y = 345 MPa

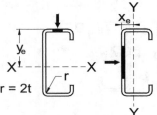

$r = 2t$

Designation	Mass	Gross Area	Effective Section Properties						M_{rxe}	V_r	L_u
			X-X Axis			Y-Y Axis					
			I_{xe}	S_{xe}	y_e	I_{ye}	S_{ye}	x_e			
	kg/m	mm²	10^6 mm⁴	10^3 mm³	mm	10^6 mm⁴	10^3 mm³	mm	kN·m	kN	mm
254S89-468M	17.1	2 180	20.4	161	127	2.04	31.9	25.1	50.0	183	1 800
254S89-396M	14.7	1 870	17.7	140	127	1.77	28.2	26.1	43.4	158	1 810
254S89-362M	13.5	1 720	16.3	128	127	1.62	26.1	27.1	39.8	135	1 810
254S89-326M	12.2	1 560	14.7	115	128	1.44	23.8	28.4	35.7	109	1 810
254S89-290M	10.9	1 390	13.2	102	129	1.26	21.4	30.1	31.7	86.2	1 820
254S89-254M	9.60	1 230	11.4	87.4	131	1.07	18.8	32.0	27.1	62.5	1 820
229S89-326M	11.5	1 470	11.5	99.5	116	1.42	23.7	29.0	30.9	109	1 830
229S89-290M	10.3	1 320	10.3	88.5	116	1.24	21.3	30.5	27.5	86.2	1 830
229S89-254M	9.10	1 160	8.92	75.7	118	1.06	18.8	32.3	23.5	66.0	1 830
229S89-218M	7.90	1 000	7.52	62.7	120	0.875	16.1	34.5	19.5	43.6	1 840
229S89-181M	6.60	841	6.28	52.0	121	0.691	13.4	37.1	16.2	25.0	1 840
203S70-362M	10.8	1 380	8.27	81.6	101	0.866	17.7	21.0	25.3	114	1 500
203S70-326M	9.80	1 250	7.57	74.6	102	0.782	16.3	21.9	23.2	104	1 500
203S70-290M	8.80	1 120	6.84	67.4	102	0.691	14.8	23.0	20.9	86.2	1 500
203S70-254M	7.80	991	6.09	60.0	102	0.594	13.1	24.4	18.6	66.0	1 500
203S70-218M	6.70	857	5.30	52.2	102	0.494	11.3	26.2	16.2	48.5	1 500
203S70-181M	5.70	720	4.35	42.0	104	0.391	9.44	28.4	13.0	28.3	1 510
203S70-144M	4.60	581	3.42	32.4	106	0.292	7.50	30.9	10.1	14.3	1 510
152S70-290M	7.60	968	3.47	45.6	76.1	0.659	14.5	24.4	14.2	67.7	1 550
152S70-254M	6.70	856	3.09	40.6	76.1	0.572	12.9	25.5	12.6	60.2	1 550
152S70-218M	5.80	741	2.70	35.5	76.1	0.479	11.2	27.0	11.0	48.5	1 550
152S70-181M	4.90	623	2.22	28.5	77.9	0.383	9.36	29.0	8.84	33.7	1 550
152S70-144M	4.00	503	1.74	21.9	79.6	0.287	7.45	31.3	6.79	19.4	1 550

Designation Example: 229S70-290M; where 229 = section depth (mm); S = stud or joist C-section;
70 = flange width (mm); 290 = minimum base steel thickness x 100 (mm); M = metric designation

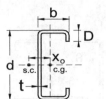

Depth	Flange Width	Stiff'r Depth	Thick-ness	Gross Section Properties										
				X-X Axis			Y-Y Axis			x_o	r_o	J	j	C_w
d	b	D	t	I_x	S_x	r_x	I_y	S_y	r_y					
mm	mm	mm	mm	10^6 mm^4	10^3 mm^3	mm	10^6 mm^4	10^3 mm^3	mm	mm	mm	10^3 mm^4	mm	10^9 mm^6
254	89	25.4	4.93	20.4	161	96.8	2.04	31.9	30.6	60.3	118	17.6	147	28.5
254	89	25.4	4.17	17.7	140	97.5	1.81	28.4	31.1	61.2	119	10.8	145	25.0
254	89	25.4	3.81	16.4	129	97.8	1.69	26.5	31.3	61.7	120	8.32	144	23.3
254	89	25.4	3.43	15.0	118	98.1	1.56	24.5	31.6	62.1	120	6.10	143	21.3
254	89	25.4	3.05	13.5	106	98.4	1.41	22.3	31.9	62.6	121	4.32	142	19.3
254	89	25.4	2.67	12.0	94.2	98.7	1.27	19.9	32.1	63.1	122	2.91	141	17.2
229	89	25.4	3.43	11.7	102	89.2	1.50	24.2	32.0	64.8	115	5.76	130	17.0
229	89	25.4	3.05	10.5	92.2	89.5	1.37	22.0	32.2	65.3	115	4.08	129	15.4
229	89	25.4	2.67	9.35	81.8	89.8	1.22	19.7	32.5	65.7	116	2.75	129	13.7
229	89	25.4	2.29	8.12	71.1	90.1	1.07	17.3	32.7	66.2	117	1.75	128	12.0
229	89	25.4	1.91	6.86	60.0	90.3	0.914	14.7	33.0	66.7	117	1.02	128	10.2
203	70	25.4	3.81	8.27	81.4	77.4	0.866	17.7	25.1	50.6	95.8	6.68	113	8.18
203	70	25.4	3.43	7.57	74.5	77.8	0.801	16.4	25.3	51.1	96.4	4.91	113	7.53
203	70	25.4	3.05	6.84	67.4	78.1	0.732	15.0	25.5	51.5	97.0	3.48	112	6.84
203	70	25.4	2.67	6.09	59.9	78.4	0.658	13.5	25.8	52.0	97.5	2.35	111	6.12
203	70	25.4	2.29	5.30	52.2	78.7	0.580	11.9	26.0	52.5	98.1	1.49	110	5.36
203	70	25.4	1.91	4.49	44.2	79.0	0.496	10.2	26.2	52.9	98.6	0.871	110	4.57
203	70	25.4	1.52	3.65	35.9	79.3	0.407	8.37	26.5	53.4	99.2	0.450	109	3.74
152	70	25.4	3.05	3.47	45.5	59.8	0.663	14.6	26.2	57.4	87.0	3.00	89.8	3.83
152	70	25.4	2.67	3.09	40.6	60.1	0.597	13.1	26.4	57.9	87.5	2.03	89.6	3.44
152	70	25.4	2.29	2.70	35.4	60.4	0.526	11.6	26.6	58.4	88.1	1.29	89.5	3.02
152	70	25.4	1.91	2.29	30.1	60.6	0.450	9.89	26.9	58.8	88.7	0.754	89.4	2.58
152	70	25.4	1.52	1.87	24.5	60.9	0.369	8.13	27.1	59.3	89.2	0.390	89.3	2.11

COLD-FORMED Z-SECTIONS, UNCOATED
Effective Properties
F_y = 345 MPa

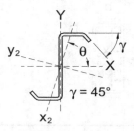

Designation	Mass	Gross Area	Effective Section Properties			M_{rxe}	V_r	L_u
			X-X Axis					
			I_{xe}	S_{xe}	y_e			
	kg/m	mm^2	10^6 mm^4	10^3 mm^3	mm	kN·m	kN	mm
356Z76-326M	14.5	1 850	30.4	171	178	53.1	94.3	1 350
356Z76-290M	12.9	1 650	26.6	146	182	45.3	65.8	1 350
356Z76-254M	11.4	1 450	22.7	121	188	37.5	43.8	1 350
356Z76-218M	9.77	1 240	18.5	94.0	197	29.2	27.4	1 350
305Z76-326M	13.1	1 670	21.3	142	149	44.2	109	1 380
305Z76-290M	11.7	1 490	18.9	125	151	38.8	77.5	1 380
305Z76-254M	10.3	1 310	16.4	107	153	33.4	51.5	1 380
305Z76-218M	8.86	1 130	13.8	88.3	156	27.4	32.2	1 380
305Z76-181M	7.41	944	10.8	65.9	165	20.5	18.5	1 390
254Z76-326M	11.8	1 500	13.7	111	124	34.3	109	1 420
254Z76-290M	10.5	1 340	12.2	97.2	126	30.2	86.2	1 420
254Z76-254M	9.23	1 180	10.6	83.4	128	25.9	62.5	1 420
254Z76-218M	7.95	1 010	8.91	68.3	130	21.2	39.0	1 420
254Z76-181M	6.65	847	7.34	55.4	133	17.2	22.3	1 420
229Z76-326M	11.1	1 410	10.7	95.8	112	29.8	109	1 440
229Z76-290M	9.89	1 260	9.52	84.2	113	26.2	86.2	1 440
229Z76-254M	8.70	1 110	8.30	72.3	115	22.5	66.0	1 440
229Z76-218M	7.49	954	6.95	59.1	118	18.4	43.6	1 440
229Z76-181M	6.27	799	5.72	47.8	120	14.9	25.0	1 440
203Z76-326M	10.4	1 320	8.12	81.8	99.2	25.4	104	1 460
203Z76-290M	9.28	1 180	7.23	72.0	100	22.3	86.2	1 460
203Z76-254M	8.17	1 040	6.30	61.8	102	19.2	66.0	1 460
203Z76-218M	7.03	896	5.27	50.4	105	15.6	48.5	1 460
203Z76-181M	5.89	751	4.34	40.7	107	12.6	28.3	1 460
203Z76-144M	4.74	603	3.43	31.7	108	9.84	14.3	1 460
152Z76-326M	9.02	1 150	4.16	56.1	74.3	17.4	74.9	1 510
152Z76-290M	8.07	1 030	3.71	49.4	75.2	15.3	67.7	1 510
152Z76-254M	7.10	905	3.24	42.4	76.5	13.2	60.2	1 500
152Z76-218M	6.12	780	2.71	34.4	78.8	10.7	48.5	1 500
152Z76-181M	5.13	654	2.23	27.7	80.4	8.60	33.7	1 500
152Z76-144M	4.13	526	1.77	21.7	81.5	6.74	19.4	1 500

Designation Example: 229Z76-290M; where 229 = section depth (mm); Z = Z-section;
76 = flange width (mm); 290 = minimum base steel thickness x 100 (mm); M = metric designation

$r = 2t$

Depth	Flange Width	Stiff'r Depth	Thick-ness	Gross Section Properties											
				X-X Axis		Y-Y Axis		I_{xy}	I_{x2}	I_{y2}	r_{min}	θ	J	C_w
d	b	D	t	S_x	r_x	S_y	r_y							
mm	mm	mm	mm	10^3 mm^3	mm	10^3 mm^3	mm	10^6 mm^4	10^6 mm^4	10^6 mm^4	mm	deg	10^3 mm^4	10^9 mm^6
356	76	24.1	3.43	179	131	21.7	32.8	5.47	1.02	32.8	23.5	79.9	7.24	47.8
356	76	24.1	3.05	160	132	19.5	32.9	4.90	0.917	29.4	23.6	79.9	5.10	43.0
356	76	24.1	2.67	141	132	17.2	33.1	4.33	0.813	25.9	23.7	79.9	3.43	38.1
356	76	24.1	2.29	122	132	14.9	33.2	3.74	0.706	22.4	23.8	79.9	2.17	33.0
305	76	24.1	3.43	144	115	21.7	34.5	4.66	0.952	23.0	23.9	77.5	6.55	34.0
305	76	24.1	3.05	129	115	19.5	34.6	4.18	0.858	20.6	24.0	77.5	4.62	30.6
305	76	24.1	2.67	114	115	17.2	34.7	3.69	0.761	18.2	24.1	77.5	3.11	27.1
305	76	24.1	2.29	98.4	115	14.9	34.9	3.19	0.661	15.7	24.2	77.4	1.97	23.5
305	76	24.1	1.91	82.7	116	12.5	35.0	2.68	0.559	13.2	24.3	77.4	1.14	19.9
254	76	24.1	3.43	112	97.3	21.7	36.4	3.86	0.871	15.3	24.1	73.8	5.87	22.7
254	76	24.1	3.05	100	97.6	19.5	36.6	3.46	0.786	13.7	24.2	73.8	4.14	20.4
254	76	24.1	2.67	88.6	97.8	17.2	36.7	3.06	0.698	12.1	24.4	73.8	2.79	18.1
254	76	24.1	2.29	76.7	98.1	14.9	36.8	2.64	0.607	10.5	24.5	73.8	1.76	15.7
254	76	24.1	1.91	64.5	98.3	12.5	37.0	2.22	0.513	8.83	24.6	73.8	1.03	13.3
229	76	24.1	3.43	96.8	88.6	21.7	37.5	3.46	0.823	12.2	24.1	71.4	5.53	17.9
229	76	24.1	3.05	86.9	88.8	19.5	37.7	3.10	0.742	11.0	24.3	71.4	3.90	16.1
229	76	24.1	2.67	76.8	89.0	17.2	37.8	2.74	0.659	9.71	24.4	71.4	2.63	14.3
229	76	24.1	2.29	66.5	89.3	14.9	37.9	2.37	0.574	8.40	24.5	71.4	1.66	12.4
229	76	24.1	1.91	56.0	89.5	12.5	38.1	1.99	0.485	7.07	24.6	71.4	0.966	10.5
203	76	24.1	3.43	82.6	79.6	21.7	38.8	3.05	0.766	9.61	24.1	68.2	5.19	13.8
203	76	24.1	3.05	74.2	79.8	19.5	38.9	2.74	0.692	8.64	24.2	68.2	3.66	12.4
203	76	24.1	2.67	65.7	80.1	17.2	39.0	2.42	0.615	7.64	24.3	68.2	2.47	11.0
203	76	24.1	2.29	56.9	80.3	14.9	39.1	2.10	0.535	6.62	24.4	68.2	1.56	9.58
203	76	24.1	1.91	47.9	80.5	12.5	39.3	1.76	0.453	5.57	24.6	68.2	0.908	8.10
203	76	24.1	1.52	38.7	80.8	10.1	39.4	1.42	0.368	4.50	24.7	68.2	0.467	6.57
152	76	24.1	3.43	56.4	61.2	21.7	41.6	2.25	0.616	5.67	23.1	58.6	4.51	7.25
152	76	24.1	3.05	50.8	61.4	19.5	41.7	2.02	0.557	5.10	23.3	58.6	3.18	6.55
152	76	24.1	2.67	45.0	61.6	17.2	41.8	1.79	0.496	4.52	23.4	58.7	2.15	5.82
152	76	24.1	2.29	39.1	61.8	14.9	41.9	1.55	0.433	3.92	23.6	58.7	1.36	5.07
152	76	24.1	1.91	33.0	62.0	12.5	42.1	1.30	0.367	3.30	23.7	58.8	0.791	4.29
152	76	24.1	1.52	26.7	62.2	10.1	42.2	1.05	0.299	2.67	23.8	58.8	0.407	3.48

NOTES

BUILT-UP SECTIONS

Built-up sections may be fabricated from plate and shapes in various configurations to produce efficient and economical structural sections. Generally the components are joined by welding, though bolting may also be used for some combinations. Frequently used built-up sections include double angles back-to-back, two channels back-to-back or toe-to-toe, and a channel or C shape in combination with a W shape.

Properties and dimensions of double angles are provided for imperial series angles on pages 6-126 to 6-133. Included are equal-leg angles and unequal-leg angles with long legs back-to-back and with short legs back-to-back. Properties and dimensions of double channels are provided in tables on pages 6-134 and 6-135. Section properties of built-up shapes consisting of W shapes and channels (C shapes) are given on pages 6-136 and 6-137. For more information, the following reference may be consulted: "Buckling properties of monosymmetric I-beams", Kitipornchai, S. and Trahair, N.S., Journal of the Structural Division, ASCE, Vol. 106, No. ST5, May 1980.

Many other combinations of built-up members are possible. Diagrams with expressions and formulae for computing properties of some possible combinations are provided on pages 6-139 to 6-142.

TWO ANGLES EQUAL LEGS
Back-to-Back

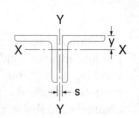

PROPERTIES OF SECTIONS

Designation*	Mass of 2 angles	Dead Load	Area of 2 angles	Axis X-X				Radii of Gyration about Axis Y-Y					
				I	S	r	y	Back-to-back spacing, s, millimetres					
	kg/m	kN/m	mm²	10⁶ mm⁴	10³ mm³	mm	mm	0	8	10	12	16	20
L203x203													
x29	169	1.66	21 600	81.4	574	61.4	61.2	86.7	89.6	90.3	91.0	92.5	94.0
x25	152	1.49	19 300	73.8	517	61.8	60.1	86.2	89.0	89.7	90.5	91.9	93.4
x22	134	1.31	17 000	66.0	458	62.2	58.9	85.7	88.5	89.2	89.9	91.4	92.8
x19	116	1.14	14 800	58.0	399	62.6	57.8	85.2	88.0	88.7	89.4	90.9	92.3
x16	97.4	0.955	12 400	49.4	337	63.1	56.6	84.8	87.5	88.2	88.9	90.3	91.8
x14	87.9	0.863	11 200	44.9	306	63.3	56.0	84.6	87.3	88.0	88.7	90.1	91.5
x13	78.4	0.769	9 990	40.4	274	63.6	55.5	84.4	87.0	87.7	88.4	89.8	91.2
L152x152													
x25	111	1.09	14 200	29.3	279	45.5	47.2	65.6	68.5	69.3	70.0	71.5	73.1
x22	98.2	0.964	12 500	26.3	249	45.9	46.1	65.0	67.9	68.7	69.4	70.9	72.5
x19	85.4	0.838	10 900	23.3	218	46.3	45.0	64.5	67.4	68.1	68.9	70.4	71.9
x16	71.9	0.706	9 160	20.0	185	46.7	43.9	64.1	66.9	67.6	68.3	69.8	71.3
x14	65.0	0.638	8 290	18.2	168	46.9	43.3	63.8	66.6	67.3	68.0	69.5	71.0
x13	58.1	0.570	7 400	16.4	150	47.1	42.7	63.6	66.3	67.1	67.8	69.2	70.7
x11	51.0	0.501	6 500	14.6	133	47.4	42.1	63.4	66.1	66.8	67.5	69.0	70.4
x9.5	44.1	0.432	5 610	12.7	115	47.6	41.5	63.2	65.9	66.6	67.3	68.7	70.1
x7.9	36.9	0.362	4 700	10.8	96.8	47.8	41.0	63.0	65.6	66.3	67.0	68.4	69.9
x6.4	29.7	0.291	3 780	8.73	78.2	48.1	40.4	62.8	65.4	66.1	66.8	68.2	69.6
L127x127													
x22	80.8	0.793	10 300	14.8	169	37.9	39.8	55.0	57.9	58.7	59.4	61.0	62.6
x19	70.4	0.691	8 970	13.1	149	38.3	38.7	54.4	57.3	58.1	58.8	60.4	61.9
x16	59.4	0.583	7 570	11.3	127	38.7	37.6	53.9	56.8	57.5	58.3	59.8	61.3
x13	48.1	0.472	6 130	9.37	103	39.1	36.4	53.4	56.2	57.0	57.7	59.2	60.7
x11	42.3	0.415	5 390	8.33	91.4	39.3	35.8	53.2	56.0	56.7	57.4	58.9	60.4
x9.5	36.6	0.359	4 660	7.28	79.4	39.5	35.3	53.0	55.7	56.4	57.2	58.6	60.1
x7.9	30.7	0.301	3 910	6.18	66.9	39.8	34.7	52.8	55.5	56.2	56.9	58.3	59.8
x6.4	24.7	0.242	3 150	5.03	54.2	40.0	34.1	52.6	55.2	55.9	56.6	58.1	59.5
L102x102													
x19	55.4	0.544	7 060	6.48	93.1	30.3	32.4	44.4	47.4	48.1	48.9	50.5	52.1
x16	47.0	0.461	5 980	5.62	79.5	30.7	31.3	43.8	46.7	47.5	48.3	49.8	51.4
x13	38.1	0.374	4 860	4.69	65.3	31.1	30.2	43.3	46.2	46.9	47.7	49.2	50.8
x11	33.6	0.330	4 280	4.19	57.8	31.3	29.6	43.0	45.9	46.6	47.4	48.9	50.4
x9.5	29.1	0.285	3 710	3.68	50.4	31.5	29.0	42.8	45.6	46.4	47.1	48.6	50.1
x7.9	24.4	0.240	3 110	3.13	42.6	31.7	28.4	42.6	45.4	46.1	46.8	48.3	49.8
x6.4	19.7	0.193	2 510	2.56	34.5	31.9	27.9	42.4	45.1	45.8	46.5	48.0	49.5
L89x89													
x13	32.9	0.323	4 190	3.03	48.8	26.9	26.9	38.0	40.9	41.7	42.4	44.0	45.6
x11	29.1	0.285	3 700	2.71	43.3	27.1	26.3	37.7	40.6	41.4	42.1	43.7	45.3
x9.5	25.2	0.247	3 210	2.39	37.8	27.3	25.7	37.5	40.3	41.1	41.8	43.4	45.0
x7.9	21.2	0.208	2 700	2.04	32.0	27.5	25.2	37.3	40.1	40.8	41.6	43.1	44.6
x6.4	17.1	0.168	2 180	1.67	26.0	27.7	24.6	37.0	39.8	40.5	41.3	42.8	44.3

* Designation consists of nominal leg sizes and thickness.

Note: The properties of angles currently produced by cold forming are up to 7 percent less than the properties shown in the above tables. Check manufacturer's catalog for the exact properties and dimensions.

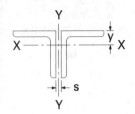

PROPERTIES OF SECTIONS

Designation*	Mass of 2 angles	Dead Load	Area of 2 angles	Axis X-X				Radii of Gyration about Axis Y-Y					
				I	S	r	y	Back-to-back spacing, s, millimetres					
	kg/m	kN/m	mm²	10^6 mm⁴	10^3 mm³	mm	mm	0	8	10	12	16	20
L76x76													
x13	27.9	0.273	3 550	1.85	35.1	22.8	23.7	32.9	35.9	36.6	37.4	39.0	40.7
x11	24.6	0.242	3 140	1.66	31.2	23.0	23.1	32.6	35.5	36.3	37.1	38.7	40.3
x9.5	21.4	0.210	2 720	1.47	27.3	23.2	22.5	32.3	35.3	36.0	36.8	38.4	40.0
x7.9	18.0	0.177	2 290	1.26	23.2	23.4	22.0	32.1	35.0	35.7	36.5	38.0	39.6
x6.4	14.6	0.143	1 850	1.04	18.9	23.6	21.4	31.9	34.7	35.4	36.2	37.7	39.3
x4.8	11.0	0.108	1 410	0.800	14.4	23.9	20.8	31.7	34.4	35.2	35.9	37.4	39.0
L64x64													
x13	22.8	0.224	2 900	1.02	23.7	18.8	20.5	27.8	30.8	31.6	32.4	34.1	35.8
x9.5	17.6	0.172	2 240	0.819	18.6	19.1	19.4	27.2	30.2	31.0	31.8	33.4	35.0
x7.9	14.8	0.146	1 890	0.707	15.8	19.3	18.8	27.0	29.9	30.7	31.4	33.0	34.7
x6.4	12.0	0.118	1 530	0.585	12.9	19.5	18.2	26.7	29.6	30.3	31.1	32.7	34.3
x4.8	9.14	0.089 6	1 160	0.455	9.92	19.8	17.6	26.5	29.3	30.1	30.8	32.4	34.0
L51x51													
x9.5	13.8	0.135	1 750	0.399	11.5	15.1	16.2	22.1	25.2	26.0	26.8	28.5	30.2
x7.9	11.7	0.115	1 490	0.347	9.84	15.3	15.6	21.8	24.8	25.6	26.4	28.1	29.8
x6.4	9.50	0.093 2	1 210	0.289	8.09	15.5	15.0	21.6	24.5	25.3	26.1	27.7	29.4
x4.8	7.24	0.071 0	922	0.227	6.24	15.7	14.5	21.3	24.2	25.0	25.8	27.4	29.1
x3.2	4.91	0.048 2	626	0.158	4.29	15.9	13.9	21.1	23.9	24.7	25.5	27.1	28.7
L44x44													
x6.4	8.24	0.080 8	1 050	0.190	6.11	13.4	13.4	19.0	22.0	22.8	23.6	25.3	27.0
x4.8	6.30	0.061 8	802	0.150	4.73	13.7	12.9	18.8	21.7	22.5	23.3	24.9	26.6
x3.2	4.28	0.042 0	546	0.105	3.26	13.9	12.3	18.5	21.4	22.2	23.0	24.6	26.3
L38x38													
x6.4	6.96	0.068 3	887	0.115	4.39	11.4	11.8	16.4	19.5	20.3	21.2	22.9	24.6
x4.8	5.34	0.052 4	680	0.091 5	3.41	11.6	11.3	16.2	19.2	20.0	20.8	22.5	24.2
x3.2	3.65	0.035 8	464	0.064 8	2.37	11.8	10.7	15.9	18.9	19.6	20.5	22.1	23.8
L32x32													
x6.4	5.71	0.056 0	727	0.064 2	2.98	9.40	10.2	13.9	17.1	17.9	18.8	20.5	22.3
x4.8	4.40	0.043 1	560	0.051 4	2.33	9.58	9.69	13.6	16.7	17.5	18.4	20.1	21.9
x3.2	3.02	0.029 6	384	0.036 8	1.62	9.79	9.12	13.4	16.4	17.2	18.0	19.7	21.5
L25x25													
x6.4	4.43	0.043 5	565	0.030 7	1.83	7.37	8.62	11.3	14.6	15.5	16.4	18.2	20.0
x4.8	3.44	0.033 8	438	0.024 9	1.44	7.54	8.07	11.0	14.2	15.1	16.0	17.8	19.6
x3.2	2.38	0.023 3	303	0.018 1	1.01	7.73	7.52	10.8	13.9	14.7	15.6	17.3	19.1
L19x19													
x3.2	1.75	0.017 2	223	0.007 3	0.55	5.72	5.93	8.2	11.5	12.3	13.2	15.1	16.9

* Designation consists of nominal leg sizes and thickness.

Note: The properties of angles currently produced by cold forming are up to 7 percent less than the properties shown in the above tables. Check manufacturer's catalog for the exact properties and dimensions.

TWO ANGLES UNEQUAL LEGS
Long Legs Back-to-Back

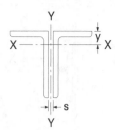

PROPERTIES OF SECTIONS

Designation*	Mass of 2 angles	Dead Load	Area of 2 angles	Axis X-X				Radii of Gyration about Axis Y-Y					
				I	S	r	y	Back-to-back spacing, s, millimetres					
	kg/m	kN/m	mm²	10^6 mm⁴	10^3 mm³	mm	mm	0	8	10	12	16	20
L203x152													
x25	131	1.29	16 700	67.0	494	63.3	67.4	60.6	63.4	64.1	64.9	66.3	67.9
x22	116	1.14	14 800	59.9	438	63.7	66.2	60.1	62.8	63.6	64.3	65.7	67.2
x19	101	0.988	12 800	52.7	382	64.1	65.1	59.6	62.3	63.0	63.7	65.2	66.7
x16	84.6	0.830	10 800	44.9	323	64.6	64.0	59.1	61.8	62.5	63.2	64.6	66.1
x14	76.5	0.750	9 740	40.9	293	64.8	63.4	58.9	61.6	62.3	63.0	64.4	65.8
x13	68.3	0.670	8 690	36.8	262	65.0	62.8	58.7	61.4	62.0	62.7	64.1	65.5
L203x102													
x25	111	1.09	14 200	57.9	460	63.8	77.2	37.4	40.4	41.2	41.9	43.5	45.1
x19	85.7	0.841	10 900	45.7	357	64.7	74.8	36.3	39.1	39.8	40.5	42.1	43.6
x13	58.3	0.572	7 420	32.0	245	65.7	72.4	35.3	37.9	38.6	39.3	40.7	42.2
L178x102													
x19	78.2	0.767	9 970	31.7	277	56.4	63.8	37.8	40.6	41.4	42.1	43.7	45.2
x16	65.9	0.647	8 400	27.1	235	56.8	62.6	37.3	40.0	40.8	41.5	43.0	44.5
x13	53.3	0.523	6 790	22.3	191	57.3	61.4	36.8	39.5	40.2	40.9	42.4	43.9
x11	46.9	0.460	5 970	19.8	169	57.5	60.8	36.6	39.2	39.9	40.6	42.1	43.6
x9.5	40.5	0.397	5 160	17.2	146	57.8	60.2	36.4	39.0	39.7	40.4	41.8	43.3
L152x102													
x22	80.8	0.793	10 300	22.9	233	47.2	53.7	40.2	43.2	43.9	44.7	46.3	47.9
x19	70.4	0.691	8 970	20.3	204	47.6	52.5	39.7	42.6	43.3	44.1	45.6	47.2
x16	59.4	0.583	7 570	17.5	174	48.0	51.4	39.2	42.0	42.7	43.4	44.9	46.5
x14	53.8	0.528	6 860	16.0	158	48.2	50.8	38.9	41.7	42.4	43.1	44.6	46.2
x13	48.1	0.472	6 130	14.4	141	48.5	50.2	38.7	41.4	42.1	42.8	44.3	45.8
x11	42.3	0.415	5 390	12.8	125	48.7	49.6	38.5	41.1	41.9	42.6	44.0	45.5
x9.5	36.6	0.359	4 660	11.2	108	48.9	49.1	38.3	40.9	41.6	42.3	43.7	45.2
x7.9	30.7	0.301	3 910	9.44	91.2	49.2	48.5	38.1	40.7	41.3	42.0	43.5	44.9
L152x89													
x16	56.2	0.551	7 160	16.6	169	48.2	53.9	33.0	35.9	36.6	37.4	38.9	40.5
x13	45.5	0.446	5 800	13.7	138	48.6	52.7	32.5	35.3	36.0	36.7	38.2	39.8
x9.5	34.6	0.340	4 410	10.6	106	49.1	51.6	32.1	34.7	35.4	36.2	37.6	39.1
x7.9	29.0	0.285	3 700	9.01	89.1	49.3	51.0	31.9	34.5	35.2	35.9	37.3	38.8
L127x89													
x19	59.0	0.579	7 520	11.6	140	39.3	44.4	35.5	38.4	39.2	40.0	41.5	43.2
x16	49.9	0.490	6 360	10.0	120	39.7	43.2	34.9	37.8	38.5	39.3	40.8	42.4
x13	40.5	0.397	5 160	8.31	97.9	40.1	42.1	34.4	37.2	37.9	38.7	40.2	41.8
x9.5	30.9	0.303	3 930	6.48	75.2	40.6	40.9	33.9	36.6	37.4	38.1	39.6	41.1
x7.9	25.9	0.254	3 300	5.50	63.5	40.8	40.3	33.7	36.4	37.1	37.8	39.3	40.8
x6.4	20.9	0.205	2 660	4.48	51.4	41.0	39.7	33.5	36.2	36.8	37.5	39.0	40.5

* Designation consists of nominal leg sizes and thickness.

Note: The properties of angles currently produced by cold forming are up to 7 percent less than the properties shown in the above tables. Check manufacturer's catalog for the exact properties and dimensions.

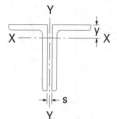

PROPERTIES OF SECTIONS

Designation*	Mass of 2 angles	Dead Load	Area of 2 angles	Axis X-X				Radii of Gyration about Axis Y-Y					
				I	S	r	y	Back-to-back spacing, s, millimetres					
	kg/m	kN/m	mm²	10^6 mm⁴	10^3 mm³	mm	mm	0	8	10	12	16	20
L127x76													
x13	38.0	0.373	4 840	7.87	95.3	40.3	44.5	28.4	31.2	32.0	32.7	34.3	35.9
x11	33.5	0.328	4 260	7.01	84.4	40.6	43.9	28.2	30.9	31.7	32.4	33.9	35.5
x9.5	29.0	0.284	3 690	6.14	73.3	40.8	43.3	27.9	30.6	31.4	32.1	33.6	35.2
x7.9	24.3	0.239	3 100	5.21	61.9	41.0	42.7	27.7	30.4	31.1	31.8	33.3	34.8
x6.4	19.6	0.193	2 500	4.25	50.1	41.2	42.1	27.5	30.1	30.8	31.5	33.0	34.5
L102x89													
x13	35.5	0.349	4 530	4.48	63.9	31.5	31.9	36.6	39.5	40.2	41.0	42.6	44.1
x11	31.3	0.307	3 990	4.00	56.7	31.7	31.3	36.4	39.2	40.0	40.7	42.2	43.8
x9.5	27.1	0.266	3 460	3.52	49.4	31.9	30.8	36.1	38.9	39.7	40.4	41.9	43.5
x7.9	22.8	0.224	2 910	3.00	41.7	32.1	30.2	35.9	38.7	39.4	40.1	41.6	43.2
x6.4	18.4	0.180	2 340	2.45	33.9	32.3	29.6	35.7	38.4	39.1	39.9	41.3	42.9
L102x76													
x16	40.5	0.397	5 160	5.09	75.9	31.4	35.0	30.9	33.9	34.6	35.4	37.0	38.7
x13	33.0	0.324	4 200	4.25	62.4	31.8	33.9	30.3	33.2	34.0	34.8	36.3	37.9
x11	29.1	0.286	3 710	3.80	55.3	32.0	33.3	30.1	32.9	33.7	34.4	36.0	37.6
x9.5	25.2	0.248	3 210	3.34	48.2	32.2	32.7	29.8	32.6	33.4	34.1	35.7	37.2
x7.9	21.2	0.208	2 700	2.85	40.7	32.4	32.1	29.6	32.4	33.1	33.8	35.4	36.9
x6.4	17.1	0.168	2 180	2.33	33.1	32.7	31.6	29.4	32.1	32.8	33.6	35.0	36.6
L89x76													
x13	30.4	0.298	3 870	2.87	47.7	27.3	28.6	31.5	34.5	35.2	36.0	37.6	39.2
x9.5	23.3	0.228	2 970	2.27	36.9	27.7	27.4	31.0	33.9	34.6	35.4	36.9	38.5
x7.9	19.6	0.192	2 500	1.94	31.3	27.9	26.9	30.8	33.6	34.3	35.1	36.6	38.2
x6.4	15.8	0.155	2 020	1.59	25.4	28.1	26.3	30.6	33.3	34.1	34.8	36.3	37.9
L89x64													
x13	27.9	0.273	3 550	2.70	46.2	27.6	30.6	25.3	28.3	29.1	29.8	31.5	33.1
x9.5	21.4	0.210	2 720	2.13	35.9	28.0	29.5	24.8	27.6	28.4	29.2	30.8	32.4
x7.9	18.0	0.177	2 290	1.82	30.4	28.2	28.9	24.5	27.4	28.1	28.9	30.4	32.0
x6.4	14.6	0.143	1 850	1.50	24.7	28.4	28.3	24.3	27.1	27.8	28.6	30.1	31.7
L76x64													
x13	25.3	0.248	3 230	1.73	34.1	23.2	25.4	26.4	29.5	30.2	31.0	32.7	34.4
x9.5	19.5	0.191	2 480	1.38	26.6	23.6	24.3	25.9	28.8	29.6	30.4	32.0	33.6
x7.9	16.4	0.161	2 090	1.18	22.6	23.8	23.7	25.7	28.5	29.3	30.0	31.6	33.3
x6.4	13.3	0.130	1 690	0.977	18.4	24.0	23.1	25.4	28.2	29.0	29.7	31.3	32.9
x4.8	10.1	0.098 9	1 280	0.755	14.1	24.2	22.6	25.2	28.0	28.7	29.4	31.0	32.6

* Designation consists of nominal leg sizes and thickness.

Note: The properties of angles currently produced by cold forming are up to 7 percent less than the properties shown in the above tables. Check manufacturer's catalog for the exact properties and dimensions.

TWO ANGLES UNEQUAL LEGS
Long Legs Back-to-Back

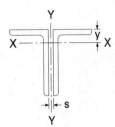

PROPERTIES OF SECTIONS

Designation*	Mass of 2 angles	Dead Load	Area of 2 angles	Axis X-X				Radii of Gyration about Axis Y-Y					
				I	S	r	y	Back-to-back spacing, s, millimetres					
	kg/m	kN/m	mm²	10^6 mm⁴	10^3 mm³	mm	mm	0	8	10	12	16	20
L76x51													
x13	22.8	0.224	2 900	1.60	32.9	23.5	27.5	20.3	23.4	24.2	25.0	26.7	28.4
x9.5	17.6	0.172	2 240	1.28	25.6	23.9	26.4	19.7	22.7	23.5	24.3	25.9	27.6
x7.9	14.8	0.146	1 890	1.10	21.8	24.1	25.8	19.5	22.4	23.1	23.9	25.6	27.2
x6.4	12.0	0.118	1 530	0.905	17.8	24.3	25.2	19.2	22.1	22.8	23.6	25.2	26.8
x4.8	9.14	0.089 6	1 160	0.700	13.6	24.5	24.6	19.0	21.8	22.5	23.3	24.8	26.5
L64x51													
x9.5	15.7	0.154	2 000	0.760	17.9	19.5	21.1	20.8	23.8	24.6	25.4	27.1	28.8
x7.9	13.3	0.130	1 690	0.656	15.3	19.7	20.6	20.5	23.5	24.3	25.1	26.7	28.4
x6.4	10.8	0.106	1 370	0.544	12.5	19.9	20.0	20.3	23.2	23.9	24.7	26.3	28.0
x4.8	8.19	0.080 3	1 040	0.423	9.60	20.1	19.4	20.1	22.9	23.6	24.4	26.0	27.6
L51x38													
x6.4	8.23	0.080 7	1 050	0.263	7.74	15.8	16.9	15.2	18.2	19.0	19.8	21.5	23.3
x4.8	6.29	0.061 7	801	0.206	5.97	16.0	16.3	14.9	17.9	18.6	19.5	21.1	22.8
x3.2	4.28	0.042 0	545	0.144	4.11	16.3	15.7	14.7	17.5	18.3	19.1	20.7	22.4

* Designation consists of nominal leg sizes and thickness.

Note: The properties of angles currently produced by cold forming are up to 7 percent less than the properties shown in the above tables. Check manufacturer's catalog for the exact properties and dimensions.

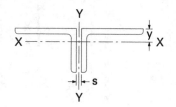

PROPERTIES OF SECTIONS

Designation*	Mass of 2 angles	Dead Load	Area of 2 angles	Axis X-X				Radii of Gyration about Axis Y-Y					
				I	S	r	y	Back-to-back spacing, s, millimetres					
	kg/m	kN/m	mm²	10⁶ mm⁴	10³ mm³	mm	mm	0	8	10	12	16	20
L203x152													
x25	131	1.29	16 700	32.0	291	43.7	41.9	92.4	95.4	96.1	96.9	98.4	100
x22	116	1.14	14 800	28.8	259	44.1	40.7	91.9	94.8	95.6	96.3	97.8	99.3
x19	101	0.988	12 800	25.4	226	44.5	39.6	91.4	94.3	95.0	95.7	97.2	98.8
x16	84.6	0.830	10 800	21.8	192	44.9	38.5	90.9	93.7	94.5	95.2	96.7	98.2
x14	76.5	0.750	9 740	19.9	174	45.2	37.9	90.6	93.5	94.2	94.9	96.4	97.9
x13	68.3	0.670	8 690	17.9	156	45.4	37.3	90.4	93.2	93.9	94.6	96.1	97.6
L203x102													
x25	111	1.09	14 200	9.81	130	26.3	26.7	100	103	104	105	106	108
x19	85.7	0.841	10 900	7.90	102	26.9	24.3	98.9	102	103	104	105	107
x13	58.3	0.572	7 420	5.67	70.9	27.6	21.9	97.8	101	102	102	104	105
L178x102													
x19	78.2	0.767	9 970	7.64	100	27.7	25.8	85.1	88.1	88.9	89.7	91.3	92.8
x16	65.9	0.647	8 400	6.61	85.4	28.1	24.6	84.5	87.5	88.3	89.1	90.6	92.2
x13	53.3	0.523	6 790	5.50	69.9	28.5	23.4	84.0	86.9	87.7	88.5	90.0	91.5
x11	46.9	0.460	5 970	4.90	61.9	28.7	22.8	83.7	86.6	87.4	88.2	89.7	91.2
x9.5	40.5	0.397	5 160	4.30	53.9	28.9	22.2	83.4	86.4	87.1	87.9	89.4	90.9
L152x102													
x22	80.8	0.793	10 300	8.20	112	28.2	28.7	71.5	74.5	75.3	76.1	77.6	79.2
x19	70.4	0.691	8 970	7.32	98.3	28.6	27.5	70.9	73.9	74.7	75.5	77.0	78.6
x16	59.4	0.583	7 570	6.34	83.8	28.9	26.4	70.3	73.3	74.1	74.8	76.4	77.9
x14	53.8	0.528	6 860	5.82	76.4	29.1	25.8	70.1	73.0	73.8	74.5	76.1	77.6
x13	48.1	0.472	6 130	5.28	68.7	29.3	25.2	69.8	72.7	73.5	74.2	75.8	77.3
x11	42.3	0.415	5 390	4.71	60.9	29.6	24.6	69.5	72.4	73.2	73.9	75.5	77.0
x9.5	36.6	0.359	4 660	4.13	53.0	29.8	24.1	69.3	72.2	72.9	73.7	75.2	76.7
x7.9	30.7	0.301	3 910	3.51	44.7	30.0	23.5	69.0	71.9	72.6	73.4	74.9	76.4
L152x89													
x16	56.2	0.551	7 160	4.23	63.6	24.3	22.4	72.3	75.3	76.1	76.9	78.5	80.1
x13	45.5	0.446	5 800	3.54	52.2	24.7	21.2	71.7	74.7	75.5	76.3	77.8	79.4
x9.5	34.6	0.340	4 410	2.78	40.4	25.1	20.0	71.2	74.2	74.9	75.7	77.2	78.7
x7.9	29.0	0.285	3 700	2.37	34.1	25.3	19.4	70.9	73.9	74.6	75.4	76.9	78.4
L127x89													
x19	59.0	0.579	7 520	4.63	72.8	24.8	25.3	59.3	62.3	63.1	63.9	65.5	67.1
x16	49.9	0.490	6 360	4.03	62.2	25.2	24.2	58.7	61.7	62.5	63.2	64.8	66.4
x13	40.5	0.397	5 160	3.37	51.2	25.6	23.0	58.1	61.1	61.9	62.6	64.2	65.7
x9.5	30.9	0.303	3 930	2.65	39.6	26.0	21.9	57.6	60.5	61.3	62.0	63.6	65.1
x7.9	25.9	0.254	3 300	2.26	33.5	26.2	21.3	57.4	60.3	61.0	61.7	63.3	64.8
x6.4	20.9	0.205	2 660	1.86	27.2	26.4	20.7	57.1	60.0	60.7	61.5	63.0	64.5

* Designation consists of nominal leg sizes and thickness.

Note: The properties of angles currently produced by cold forming are up to 7 percent less than the properties shown in the above tables. Check manufacturer's catalog for the exact properties and dimensions.

TWO ANGLES UNEQUAL LEGS
Short Legs Back-to-Back

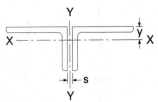

PROPERTIES OF SECTIONS

Designation*	Mass of 2 angles	Dead Load	Area of 2 angles	Axis X-X				Radii of Gyration about Axis Y-Y					
				I	S	r	y	Back-to-back spacing, s, millimetres					
	kg/m	kN/m	mm²	10⁶ mm⁴	10³ mm³	mm	mm	0	8	10	12	16	20
L127x76													
x13	38.0	0.373	4 840	2.15	37.6	21.1	19.1	60.0	63.0	63.8	64.6	66.2	67.8
x11	33.5	0.328	4 260	1.93	33.4	21.3	18.5	59.7	62.7	63.5	64.3	65.8	67.4
x9.5	29.0	0.284	3 690	1.70	29.1	21.5	17.9	59.5	62.4	63.2	64.0	65.5	67.1
x7.9	24.3	0.239	3 100	1.45	24.7	21.7	17.3	59.2	62.1	62.9	63.7	65.2	66.8
x6.4	19.6	0.193	2 500	1.20	20.1	21.9	16.7	58.9	61.9	62.6	63.4	64.9	66.4
L102x89													
x13	35.5	0.349	4 530	3.16	49.7	26.4	25.4	44.8	47.7	48.5	49.3	50.8	52.4
x11	31.3	0.307	3 990	2.83	44.1	26.6	24.8	44.6	47.5	48.2	49.0	50.5	52.1
x9.5	27.1	0.266	3 460	2.49	38.5	26.8	24.2	44.3	47.2	47.9	48.7	50.2	51.8
x7.9	22.8	0.224	2 910	2.13	32.6	27.1	23.6	44.1	46.9	47.6	48.4	49.9	51.4
x6.4	18.4	0.180	2 340	1.74	26.5	27.3	23.1	43.8	46.6	47.4	48.1	49.6	51.1
L102x76													
x16	40.5	0.397	5 160	2.40	44.3	21.6	22.1	47.0	50.1	50.9	51.6	53.2	54.9
x13	33.0	0.324	4 200	2.02	36.6	21.9	21.0	46.5	49.4	50.2	51.0	52.6	54.2
x11	29.1	0.286	3 710	1.81	32.5	22.1	20.4	46.2	49.1	49.9	50.7	52.2	53.8
x9.5	25.2	0.248	3 210	1.60	28.4	22.3	19.8	45.9	48.9	49.6	50.4	51.9	53.5
x7.9	21.2	0.208	2 700	1.37	24.1	22.5	19.2	45.7	48.6	49.3	50.1	51.6	53.2
x6.4	17.1	0.168	2 180	1.13	19.6	22.7	18.7	45.4	48.3	49.0	49.8	51.3	52.9
L89x76													
x13	30.4	0.298	3 870	1.94	35.9	22.4	22.2	39.5	42.5	43.2	44.0	45.6	47.2
x9.5	23.3	0.228	2 970	1.54	27.9	22.8	21.1	39.0	41.9	42.6	43.4	45.0	46.6
x7.9	19.6	0.192	2 500	1.32	23.7	23.0	20.5	38.7	41.6	42.3	43.1	44.6	46.2
x6.4	15.8	0.155	2 020	1.09	19.3	23.2	19.9	38.5	41.3	42.1	42.8	44.3	45.9
L89x64													
x13	27.9	0.273	3 550	1.14	24.9	17.9	17.9	41.2	44.2	45.0	45.8	47.4	49.1
x9.5	21.4	0.210	2 720	0.908	19.4	18.3	16.8	40.6	43.6	44.4	45.2	46.8	48.4
x7.9	18.0	0.177	2 290	0.782	16.5	18.5	16.2	40.4	43.3	44.1	44.9	46.4	48.0
x6.4	14.6	0.143	1 850	0.647	13.5	18.7	15.6	40.1	43.0	43.8	44.5	46.1	47.7
L76x64													
x13	25.3	0.248	3 230	1.08	24.4	18.3	19.1	34.4	37.4	38.2	39.0	40.7	42.3
x9.5	19.5	0.191	2 480	0.868	19.0	18.7	17.9	33.8	36.8	37.6	38.4	40.0	41.6
x7.9	16.4	0.161	2 090	0.748	16.2	18.9	17.4	33.6	36.5	37.3	38.1	39.6	41.3
x6.4	13.3	0.130	1 690	0.619	13.2	19.1	16.8	33.3	36.2	37.0	37.8	39.3	40.9
x4.8	10.1	0.098 9	1 280	0.480	10.2	19.3	16.2	33.1	36.0	36.7	37.5	39.0	40.6

* Designation consists of nominal leg sizes and thickness.

Note: The properties of angles currently produced by cold forming are up to 7 percent less than the properties shown in the above tables. Check manufacturer's catalog for the exact properties and dimensions.

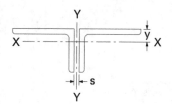

PROPERTIES OF SECTIONS

Designation*	Mass of 2 angles	Dead Load	Area of 2 angles	Axis X-X				Radii of Gyration about Axis Y-Y					
				I	S	r	y	Back-to-back spacing, s, millimetres					
	kg/m	kN/m	mm²	10^6 mm⁴	10^3 mm³	mm	mm	0	8	10	12	16	20
L76x51													
x13	22.8	0.224	2 900	0.559	15.5	13.9	14.8	36.2	39.3	40.1	40.9	42.6	44.3
x9.5	17.6	0.172	2 240	0.452	12.2	14.2	13.7	35.6	38.6	39.4	40.2	41.9	43.5
x7.9	14.8	0.146	1 890	0.392	10.4	14.4	13.1	35.3	38.3	39.1	39.9	41.5	43.2
x6.4	12.0	0.118	1 530	0.326	8.52	14.6	12.5	35.0	38.0	38.8	39.6	41.2	42.8
x4.8	9.14	0.089 6	1 160	0.255	6.56	14.8	11.9	34.8	37.7	38.5	39.3	40.8	42.5
L64x51													
x9.5	15.7	0.154	2 000	0.428	11.9	14.6	14.8	28.7	31.8	32.6	33.4	35.0	36.7
x7.9	13.3	0.130	1 690	0.372	10.2	14.8	14.2	28.5	31.5	32.3	33.1	34.7	36.4
x6.4	10.8	0.106	1 370	0.310	8.34	15.0	13.6	28.2	31.2	32.0	32.7	34.3	36.0
x4.8	8.19	0.080 3	1 040	0.242	6.42	15.2	13.1	28.0	30.9	31.6	32.4	34.0	35.6
L51x38													
x6.4	8.23	0.080 7	1 050	0.126	4.57	11.0	10.5	23.1	26.2	27.0	27.8	29.5	31.2
x4.8	6.29	0.061 7	801	0.100	3.54	11.2	9.93	22.9	25.9	26.6	27.5	29.1	30.8
x3.2	4.28	0.042 0	545	0.071	2.46	11.4	9.35	22.6	25.5	26.3	27.1	28.7	30.4

* Designation consists of nominal leg sizes and thickness.

Note: The properties of angles currently produced by cold forming are up to 7 percent less than the properties shown
in the above tables. Check manufacturer's catalog for the exact properties and dimensions.

TWO CHANNELS
Toe-to-Toe

PROPERTIES OF SECTIONS

Channel Size	For Two Channels			Axis X-X			Axis Y-Y					
	Mass	Dead Load	Area	I_x	S_x	r_x	Toe-to-Toe			c = d		
							I_y	S_y	r_y	I_y	S_y	r_y
	kg/m	kN/m	mm^2	10^6 mm^4	10^3 mm^3	mm	10^6 mm^4	10^3 mm^3	mm	10^6 mm^4	10^3 mm^3	mm
MC460												
x86*	173	1.69	22 000	564	2 460	160	174	1 630	88.9	954	4 170	208
x77.2*	154	1.52	19 700	522	2 280	163	147	1 410	86.3	854	3 740	208
x68.2*	136	1.34	17 400	482	2 100	166	124	1 210	84.4	753	3 300	208
x63.5*	127	1.25	16 200	462	2 020	169	110	1 100	82.4	701	3 070	208
C380												
x74*	149	1.46	19 000	336	1 760	133	112	1 190	76.9	558	2 930	172
x60*	119	1.17	15 100	290	1 520	138	80.2	901	72.8	449	2 360	172
x50*	101	0.990	12 900	262	1 370	143	62.8	730	69.9	381	2 000	172
C310												
x45	89.3	0.876	11 400	135	884	109	49.4	618	65.9	213	1 400	137
x37	74.1	0.727	9 440	120	786	113	37.6	488	63.1	177	1 160	137
x31	61.5	0.604	7 840	107	702	117	28.1	380	59.9	146	956	136
C250												
x45	89.0	0.873	11 300	85.6	674	86.9	43.6	574	62.0	142	1 120	112
x37	74.6	0.731	9 500	75.8	598	89.4	34.0	466	59.8	120	949	113
x30	59.3	0.582	7 560	65.4	514	93.0	24.0	348	56.4	96.5	760	113
x23	45.2	0.443	5 760	55.6	438	98.2	15.7	242	52.3	72.9	574	113
C230												
x30*	59.7	0.585	7 600	51.0	444	81.9	22.7	339	54.7	77.6	677	101
x22	44.6	0.437	5 680	42.6	372	86.6	14.7	233	50.9	57.8	505	101
x20	39.7	0.390	5 060	39.6	346	88.6	12.0	197	48.8	51.3	448	101
C200												
x28	55.9	0.548	7 120	36.4	360	71.6	19.2	299	51.9	55.7	548	88.4
x21	40.8	0.400	5 200	29.8	294	75.8	11.8	200	47.6	41.1	405	88.9
x17	34.1	0.334	4 340	27.0	266	78.7	8.93	157	45.3	33.9	334	88.4
C180												
x22	43.6	0.428	5 560	22.6	254	63.7	12.1	209	46.7	32.8	369	76.8
x18	36.3	0.356	4 620	20.0	226	65.9	9.02	164	44.2	27.5	309	77.1
x15	29.0	0.285	3 700	17.7	199	69.3	6.49	123	41.9	21.7	244	76.6
C150												
x19	38.5	0.377	4 900	14.2	187	53.9	9.13	169	43.2	20.4	268	64.5
x16	31.1	0.305	3 960	12.4	164	56.1	6.54	128	40.6	16.6	219	64.8
x12	24.0	0.236	3 060	10.7	141	59.1	4.33	90.1	37.6	12.7	168	64.5
C130												
x13	26.5	0.260	3 380	7.32	115	46.5	4.64	98.8	37.1	9.47	149	52.9
x10	19.8	0.194	2 520	6.18	97.2	49.5	2.92	66.4	34.1	7.00	110	52.7
C100												
x11	21.5	0.211	2 740	3.82	74.8	37.3	3.07	71.3	33.5	4.62	90.6	41.1
x9	18.7	0.183	2 380	3.54	69.2	38.5	2.52	59.9	32.5	4.01	78.6	41.1
x8	16.0	0.157	2 040	3.22	63.2	39.7	1.91	47.7	30.6	3.43	67.3	41.0
C75												
x9	17.6	0.172	2 240	1.69	44.6	27.4	2.07	51.6	30.4	†	†	†
x7	14.7	0.144	1 870	1.50	39.4	28.3	1.46	39.6	28.0	1.56	41.1	28.9
x6	12.0	0.117	1 530	1.34	35.2	29.6	1.03	29.5	26.0	1.27	33.3	28.8

† The condition c = d cannot be met for this section.

* Not available from Canadian mills

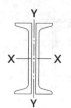

TWO CHANNELS
Back-to-Back

| Channel Size | For Two Channels | | | Axis X-X | | | Radii of Gyration about Axis Y-Y | | | | | |
| | Mass | Dead Load | Area | I_x | S_x | r_x | Back-to-Back Channels, millimetres | | | | | |
	kg/m	kN/m	mm^2	10^6 mm^4	10^3 mm^3	mm	0	8	10	12	16	20
MC460												
x86*	173	1.69	22 000	564	2 460	160	33.9	36.6	37.3	38.0	39.5	41.1
x77.2*	154	1.52	19 700	522	2 280	163	34.2	36.8	37.6	38.3	39.8	41.3
x68.2*	136	1.34	17 400	482	2 100	166	34.5	37.2	37.9	38.6	40.1	41.6
x63.5*	127	1.25	16 200	462	2 020	169	35.0	37.7	38.4	39.1	40.6	42.1
C380												
x74*	149	1.46	19 000	336	1 760	133	30.0	32.8	33.5	34.3	35.9	37.5
x60*	119	1.17	15 100	290	1 520	138	30.0	32.8	33.5	34.2	35.8	37.4
x50*	101	0.990	12 900	262	1 370	143	30.5	33.2	33.9	34.7	36.2	37.8
C310												
x45	89.3	0.876	11 400	135	884	109	25.7	28.5	29.3	30.0	31.6	33.2
x37	74.1	0.727	9 440	120	786	113	26.2	28.9	29.7	30.4	32.0	33.6
x31	61.5	0.604	7 840	107	702	117	26.7	29.5	30.3	31.0	32.6	34.2
C250												
x45	89.0	0.873	11 300	85.6	674	86.9	23.4	26.3	27.1	27.9	29.5	31.2
x37	74.6	0.731	9 500	75.8	598	89.4	23.3	26.1	26.9	27.7	29.3	30.9
x30	59.3	0.582	7 560	65.4	514	93.0	23.3	26.1	26.9	27.7	29.2	30.9
x23	45.2	0.443	5 760	55.6	438	98.2	23.9	26.7	27.5	28.3	29.8	31.5
C230												
x30*	59.7	0.585	7 600	51.0	444	81.9	22.0	24.9	25.6	26.4	28.0	29.7
x22	44.6	0.437	5 680	42.6	372	86.6	22.5	25.4	26.1	26.9	28.5	30.1
x20	39.7	0.390	5 060	39.6	346	88.6	22.7	25.5	26.3	27.1	28.7	30.3
C200												
x28	55.9	0.548	7 120	36.4	360	71.6	21.0	23.9	24.7	25.5	27.1	28.8
x21	40.8	0.400	5 200	29.8	294	75.8	20.9	23.8	24.5	25.3	26.9	28.6
x17	34.1	0.334	4 340	27.0	266	78.7	21.5	24.3	25.1	25.9	27.5	29.2
C180												
x22	43.6	0.428	5 560	22.6	254	63.7	19.7	22.6	23.4	24.2	25.8	27.5
x18	36.3	0.356	4 620	20.0	226	65.9	19.5	22.4	23.2	24.0	25.6	27.3
x15	29.0	0.285	3 700	17.7	199	69.3	20.2	23.1	23.9	24.7	26.3	28.0
C150												
x19	38.5	0.377	4 900	14.2	187	53.9	18.4	21.4	22.2	23.0	24.7	26.4
x16	31.1	0.305	3 960	12.4	164	56.1	18.3	21.3	22.1	22.9	24.5	26.2
x12	24.0	0.236	3 060	10.7	141	59.1	18.7	21.6	22.4	23.2	24.9	26.6
C130												
x13	26.5	0.260	3 380	7.32	115	46.5	17.1	20.1	20.9	21.8	23.4	25.2
x10	19.8	0.194	2 520	6.18	97.2	49.5	17.5	20.5	21.3	22.1	23.8	25.5
C100												
x11	21.5	0.211	2 740	3.82	74.8	37.3	16.1	19.2	20.0	20.8	22.5	24.3
x9	18.7	0.183	2 380	3.54	69.2	38.5	16.4	19.4	20.2	21.0	22.7	24.5
x8	16.0	0.157	2 040	3.22	63.2	39.7	16.2	19.3	20.1	21.0	22.7	24.4
C75												
x9	17.6	0.172	2 240	1.69	44.6	27.4	15.6	18.7	19.5	20.4	22.1	23.9
x7	14.7	0.144	1 870	1.50	39.4	28.3	14.9	18.0	18.9	19.7	21.4	23.2
x6	12.0	0.117	1 530	1.34	35.2	29.6	14.9	18.1	18.9	19.8	21.5	23.3

* Not available from Canadian mills

W SHAPES AND CHANNELS

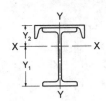

PROPERTIES OF SECTIONS

Beam	Channel	Dead Load	Total Area	Axis X-X					
				I	$S_1 = I/Y_1$	$S_2 = I/Y_2$	r	Y_1	Y_2
		kN/m	mm^2	10^6 mm^4	10^3 mm^3	10^3 mm^3	mm	mm	mm
W920x289	MC460x63.5	3.46	44 900	6 410	11 800	16 300	378	545	393
	C380x50	3.33	43 200	6 180	11 600	15 200	378	531	406
x271	MC460x63.5	3.29	42 700	6 050	11 100	15 600	376	547	387
	C380x50	3.16	41 000	5 830	11 000	14 500	377	532	401
x253	MC460x63.5	3.11	40 400	5 680	10 300	14 900	375	549	381
	C380x50	2.98	38 700	5 460	10 200	13 800	376	534	395
x238	MC460x63.5	2.96	38 500	5 340	9 680	14 200	372	551	375
	C380x50	2.83	36 800	5 120	9 560	13 100	373	536	390
x223	MC460x63.5	2.83	36 700	5 020	9 070	13 600	370	554	369
	C380x50	2.69	35 000	4 810	8 950	12 500	371	537	384
W840x226	MC460x63.5	2.85	37 000	4 490	8 700	13 000	348	516	346
	C380x50	2.72	35 300	4 310	8 600	12 000	349	501	360
x210	MC460x63.5	2.69	34 900	4 170	8 040	12 300	346	519	339
	C380x50	2.56	33 200	4 000	7 950	11 300	347	503	353
x193	MC460x63.5	2.53	32 800	3 800	7 290	11 500	340	521	330
	C380x50	2.39	31 100	3 640	7 210	10 500	342	505	345
W760x196	MC460x63.5	2.56	33 200	3 260	6 840	10 700	313	476	305
	C380x50	2.42	31 500	3 120	6 760	9 790	315	462	319
x185	MC460x63.5	2.43	31 600	3 060	6 400	10 200	311	478	299
	C380x50	2.30	29 900	2 930	6 330	9 360	313	463	313
x173	MC460x63.5	2.32	30 200	2 870	5 980	9 790	308	480	293
	C380x50	2.19	28 500	2 750	5 920	8 940	311	465	308
x161	MC460x63.5	2.19	28 500	2 650	5 480	9 270	305	484	286
	C380x50	2.06	26 800	2 530	5 410	8 410	307	467	301
W690x170	C380x50	2.16	28 000	2 260	5 330	8 090	284	424	279
	C310x31	1.96	25 500	2 070	5 200	6 850	285	398	302
x152	C380x50	1.99	25 800	2 050	4 800	7 560	282	427	271
	C310x31	1.79	23 300	1 870	4 670	6 340	283	400	295
x140	C380x50	1.86	24 200	1 880	4 370	7 120	279	430	264
	C310x31	1.67	21 700	1 710	4 260	5 910	281	402	289
W610x125	C380x50	1.72	22 300	1 390	3 550	6 020	250	391	231
	C310x31	1.52	19 800	1 260	3 460	4 950	252	364	255
x113	C380x50	1.60	20 800	1 260	3 190	5 640	246	395	223
	C310x31	1.41	18 300	1 140	3 110	4 590	250	367	248
W530x101	C380x50	1.49	19 300	904	2 550	4 690	216	355	193
	C310x31	1.29	16 800	817	2 490	3 790	221	329	216
x92	C380x50	1.40	18 200	826	2 310	4 440	213	357	186
	C310x31	1.21	15 700	745	2 260	3 550	218	330	210
W460x74	C380x50	1.22	15 900	516	1 630	3 440	180	317	150
	C310x31	1.03	13 400	465	1 590	2 710	186	292	172
W410x54	C380x50	1.02	13 200	308	1 050	2 600	153	295	119
	C310x31	0.824	10 700	277	1 020	1 990	161	271	139
W360x45	C310x31	0.743	9 650	186	765	1 600	139	243	116
	C250x23	0.663	8 610	175	756	1 380	143	232	127
W310x39	C310x31	0.682	8 860	131	598	1 330	122	219	98.2
	C250x23	0.602	7 820	123	590	1 140	125	208	108
W250x33	C250x23	0.543	7 050	73.1	411	846	102	178	86.4
	C200x17	0.488	6 340	69.5	409	743	105	170	93.5
W200x27	C200x17	0.428	5 560	37.6	268	521	82.2	140	72.2

PROPERTIES OF SECTIONS

Mass	Axis Y-Y			Shear Centre	Torsional Constant	Warping Constant	Monosymmetry Constant †
	I	S	r	Y_0	J	C_w	β_X
kg/m	10^6 mm^4	10^3 mm^3	mm	mm	10^3 mm^4	10^9 mm^6	mm
352.5	387	1 690	92.8	212	9 740	53 500	523
339.1	287	1 510	81.5	156	9 650	48 200	395
335.2	376	1 650	93.8	216	8 210	50 100	538
321.9	276	1 450	82.0	161	8 120	45 100	411
317.1	365	1 600	95.1	220	6 780	46 500	554
303.8	265	1 390	82.7	167	6 690	42 000	428
302.2	354	1 550	95.9	225	5 660	43 200	570
288.9	254	1 330	83.1	173	5 570	39 100	445
288.1	343	1 500	96.7	230	4 730	39 800	586
274.8	243	1 280	83.3	180	4 640	36 100	464
290.5	345	1 510	96.6	214	5 650	35 000	545
277.1	245	1 290	83.3	167	5 560	31 700	430
274.0	334	1 460	97.8	219	4 560	31 800	562
260.6	234	1 230	84.0	174	4 470	28 900	450
257.5	321	1 410	99.0	224	3 560	28 200	581
244.1	221	1 160	84.4	182	3 470	25 800	474
260.6	313	1 370	97.0	215	4 550	21 600	548
247.3	213	1 120	82.2	178	4 460	19 800	452
248.1	306	1 340	98.4	217	3 840	19 900	558
234.7	206	1 080	83.0	182	3 750	18 300	465
237.1	300	1 310	99.6	219	3 200	18 300	568
223.7	200	1 050	83.7	186	3 110	16 900	479
223.7	292	1 280	101	222	2 580	16 300	582
210.4	192	1 010	84.6	192	2 490	15 200	498
219.8	197	1 040	83.9	172	3 470	13 500	442
200.2	120	785	68.5	114	3 200	11 400	292
202.5	189	991	85.5	176	2 620	12 000	460
182.9	111	730	69.1	122	2 350	10 200	314
190.0	183	959	86.9	179	2 090	10 800	474
170.3	105	690	69.6	128	1 820	9 250	331
175.1	170	894	87.4	173	1 960	6 820	457
155.4	92.8	609	68.5	133	1 690	5 910	338
163.3	165	868	89.1	175	1 540	6 000	469
143.7	87.8	576	69.3	139	1 270	5 240	357
151.5	158	829	90.5	162	1 440	3 790	434
131.9	80.4	527	69.2	136	1 170	3 350	347
142.9	155	813	92.2	162	1 180	3 360	439
123.2	77.3	507	70.2	139	914	2 990	360
124.8	148	775	96.3	143	938	1 800	384
105.2	70.1	460	72.3	131	669	1 630	342
103.6	141	741	103	125	647	897	313
84.0	63.6	417	77.1	124	378	831	331
75.8	61.7	404	79.9	111	312	533	287
67.6	36.0	283	64.6	100	246	493	268
69.6	60.8	398	82.8	98.2	278	377	231
61.4	35.1	276	67.0	89.9	212	349	237
55.3	32.5	256	67.9	83.8	185	168	192
49.8	18.2	180	53.6	71.7	152	153	188
43.6	16.8	166	55.0	65.2	125	74.0	147

† β_X is positive when the larger flange is in flexural compression, and negative otherwise.

NOTES

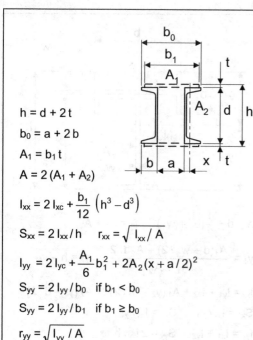

$$h = d + 2t$$
$$b_0 = a + 2b$$
$$A_1 = b_1 t$$
$$A = 2(A_1 + A_2)$$
$$I_{xx} = 2 I_{xc} + \frac{b_1}{12}\left(h^3 - d^3\right)$$
$$S_{xx} = 2 I_{xx} / h \qquad r_{xx} = \sqrt{I_{xx} / A}$$
$$I_{yy} = 2 I_{yc} + \frac{A_1}{6} b_1^2 + 2 A_2 (x + a/2)^2$$
$$S_{yy} = 2 I_{yy} / b_0 \quad \text{if } b_1 < b_0$$
$$S_{yy} = 2 I_{yy} / b_1 \quad \text{if } b_1 \geq b_0$$
$$r_{yy} = \sqrt{I_{yy} / A}$$

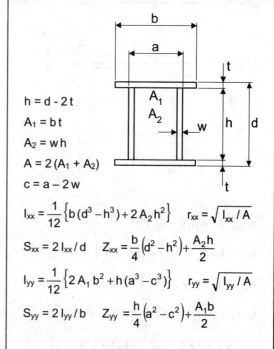

$$h = d - 2t$$
$$A_1 = b t$$
$$A_2 = w h$$
$$A = 2(A_1 + A_2)$$
$$c = a - 2w$$
$$I_{xx} = \frac{1}{12}\left\{ b(d^3 - h^3) + 2 A_2 h^2 \right\} \qquad r_{xx} = \sqrt{I_{xx} / A}$$
$$S_{xx} = 2 I_{xx} / d \qquad Z_{xx} = \frac{b}{4}\left(d^2 - h^2\right) + \frac{A_2 h}{2}$$
$$I_{yy} = \frac{1}{12}\left\{ 2 A_1 b^2 + h(a^3 - c^3) \right\} \qquad r_{yy} = \sqrt{I_{yy} / A}$$
$$S_{yy} = 2 I_{yy} / b \qquad Z_{yy} = \frac{h}{4}\left(a^2 - c^2\right) + \frac{A_1 b}{2}$$

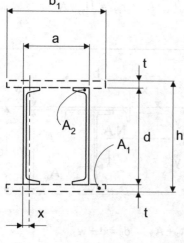

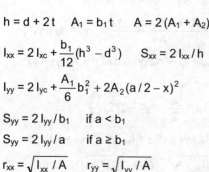

$$h = d + 2t \qquad A_1 = b_1 t \qquad A = 2(A_1 + A_2)$$
$$I_{xx} = 2 I_{xc} + \frac{b_1}{12}(h^3 - d^3) \qquad S_{xx} = 2 I_{xx} / h$$
$$I_{yy} = 2 I_{yc} + \frac{A_1}{6} b_1^2 + 2 A_2 (a/2 - x)^2$$
$$S_{yy} = 2 I_{yy} / b_1 \quad \text{if } a < b_1$$
$$S_{yy} = 2 I_{yy} / a \quad \text{if } a \geq b_1$$
$$r_{xx} = \sqrt{I_{xx} / A} \qquad r_{yy} = \sqrt{I_{yy} / A}$$

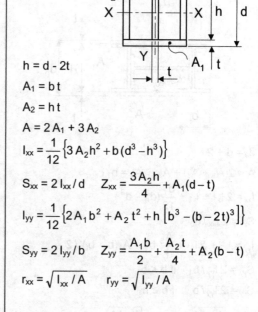

$$h = d - 2t$$
$$A_1 = b t$$
$$A_2 = h t$$
$$A = 2 A_1 + 3 A_2$$
$$I_{xx} = \frac{1}{12}\left\{ 3 A_2 h^2 + b(d^3 - h^3) \right\}$$
$$S_{xx} = 2 I_{xx} / d \qquad Z_{xx} = \frac{3 A_2 h}{4} + A_1(d - t)$$
$$I_{yy} = \frac{1}{12}\left\{ 2 A_1 b^2 + A_2 t^2 + h\left[b^3 - (b - 2t)^3 \right] \right\}$$
$$S_{yy} = 2 I_{yy} / b \qquad Z_{yy} = \frac{A_1 b}{2} + \frac{A_2 t}{4} + A_2 (b - t)$$
$$r_{xx} = \sqrt{I_{xx} / A} \qquad r_{yy} = \sqrt{I_{yy} / A}$$

Elements of the shape which are shown in dotted outline are optional and, if omitted, the variable defining their size should be set equal to zero.

All elements of the shape are assumed to be continuous along the length of the shape.

BUILT-UP SECTIONS

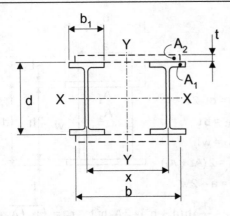

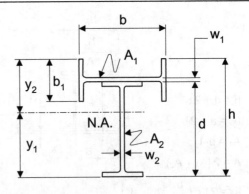

$A = 2(A_1 + A_2)$ $A_2 = bt$

$I_{xx} = 2 I_{xw} + \dfrac{1}{12} b\left[(d + 2t)^3 - d^3\right]$

$S_{xx} = 2 I_{xx} / (d + 2t)$

$I_{yy} = 2 I_{yw} + \dfrac{1}{6} A_2 b^2 + \dfrac{1}{2} A_1 x^2$

For $(x + b_1) > b$: $S_{yy} = 2 I_{yy} / (x + b_1)$

For $(x + b_1) \leq b$: $S_{yy} = 2 I_{yy} / b$

$r_{xx} = \sqrt{I_{xx} / A}$ $r_{yy} = \sqrt{I_{yy} / A}$

$h = d + \dfrac{1}{2}(b_1 + w_1)$ $A = A_1 + A_2$

$y_1 = \dfrac{A_1(d + w_1/2) + A_2 d/2}{A_1 + A_2}$ $y_2 = h - y_1$

$I_{xx} = I_{y1} + I_{x2} + A_1(y_2 - b_1/2)^2 + A_2(y_1 - d/2)^2$

$S_{x1} = I_{xx} / y_1$ $S_{x2} = I_{xx} / y_2$

$I_{yy} = I_{x1} + I_{y2}$ $S_{yy} = 2 I_{yy} / b$

$*I_{yT} = I_{x1} + I_{y2}/2 - (y_1 - d/2)w_2^3/12$

$r_{xx} = \sqrt{I_{xx} / A}$ $r_{yy} = \sqrt{I_{yy} / A}$

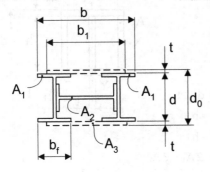

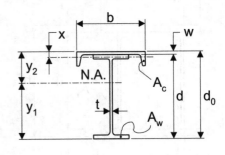

$d_0 = d + 2t$

$A = 2(A_1 + A_3) + A_2$ $A_3 = b_1 t$

$I_{xx} = 2 I_{x1} + I_{y2} + \dfrac{b_1}{12}(d_0^3 - d^3)$

$S_{xx} = 2 I_{xx} / d_0$

$I_{yy} = I_{x2} + 2 I_{y1} + \dfrac{A_3}{6} b_1^2 + A_1(b - b_f)^2/2$

$S_{yy} = 2 I_{yy} / b_1$ if $b < b_1$

$S_{yy} = 2 I_{yy} / b$ if $b \geq b_1$

$r_{xx} = \sqrt{I_{xx} / A}$ $r_{yy} = \sqrt{I_{yy} / A}$

$A = A_c + A_w$ $d_0 = d + w$

$y_1 = \dfrac{A_w d/2 + A_c(d_0 - x)}{A}$ $y_2 = d_0 - y_1$

$I_{xx} = I_{xw} + I_{yc} + A_w(y_1 - d/2)^2 + A_c(y_2 - x)^2$

$I_{yy} = I_{yw} + I_{xc}$

$*I_{yT} = I_{xc} + \dfrac{I_{yw}}{2} - (y_1 - d/2)\dfrac{t^3}{12}$

$S_{x1} = I_{xx} / y_1$ $S_{x2} = I_{xx} / y_2$ $S_{yy} = 2 I_{yy} / b$

$r_{xx} = \sqrt{I_{xx} / A}$ $r_{yy} = \sqrt{I_{yy} / A}$

*I_{yT} is the moment of inertia of the T-section above the neutral axis.

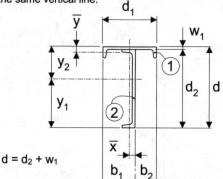

Note: Centres of gravity of both channels are on the same vertical line.

$d = d_2 + w_1$

$A = A_1 + A_2$

$b_1 = (d_1/2) + \overline{x}$

$y_1 = \dfrac{A_1(d - \overline{y}) + \dfrac{A_2}{2}d_2}{A}$

$b_2 = d_1 - b_1$

$y_2 = d - y_1$

$I_{xx} = I_{1y} + I_{2x} + A_1(y_2 - \overline{y})^2 + A_2(y_1 - \dfrac{d_2}{2})^2$

$S_{x1} = I_{xx}/y_1 \qquad S_{x2} = I_{xx}/y_2 \qquad r_{xx} = \sqrt{I_{xx}/A}$

$I_{yy} = I_{x1} + I_{y2} \qquad S_y = 2\,I_{yy}/d_1 \qquad r_{yy} = \sqrt{I_{yy}/A}$

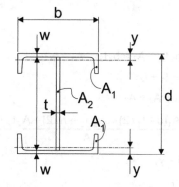

$h = d - 2w$

$A = 2A_1 + A_2 \qquad A_2 = h\,t$

$I_{xx} = 2I_{yc} + \dfrac{1}{12}A_2 h^2 + 2A_1(d/2 - y)^2$

$S_{xx} = 2\,I_{xx}/d$

$I_{yy} = 2\,I_{xc} + \dfrac{1}{12}A_2 t^2 \qquad S_{yy} = 2\,I_{yy}/b$

$r_{xx} = \sqrt{I_{xx}/A} \qquad r_{yy} = \sqrt{I_{yy}/A}$

Note: a and b are the angle leg lengths, and b_1 is the width of the channel flange.

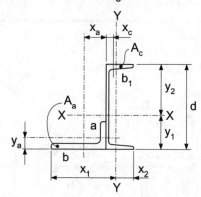

$A = A_a + A_c \qquad y_1 = \dfrac{A_a y_a + A_c d/2}{A} \qquad y_2 = d - y_1$

$x_1 = \dfrac{A_a(b - x_a) + A_c(b + x_c)}{A} \qquad x_2 = b_1 + b - x_1$

$I_{xx} = I_{ya} + I_{xc} + A_a(y_1 - y_a)^2 + A_c(\dfrac{d}{2} - y_1)^2$

$S_{x1} = I_{xx}/y_1 \qquad S_{x2} = I_{xx}/y_2$

$I_{yy} = I_{xa} + I_{yc} + A_a(x_1 - b + x_a)^2 + A_c(b_1 - x_2 - x_c)^2$

$S_{y1} = I_{yy}/x_1 \qquad S_{y2} = I_{yy}/x_2$

$r_{xx} = \sqrt{I_{xx}/A} \qquad r_{yy} = \sqrt{I_{yy}/A}$

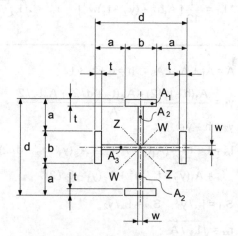

$A = 4A_1 + 2A_2 + A_3 \qquad A_1 = b\,t$

$A_2 = (d - w - 2t)w/2 \qquad A_3 = 2A_2 + w^2$

$I_x = I_y = \dfrac{1}{12}\left\{b(d^3 - E^3) + wE^3 + 2tb^3 + Ew^3 - w^4\right\}$

$E = d - 2t$

$S_x = S_y = 2\,I_x/d$

$r_x = r_y = \sqrt{I_x/A}$

BUILT-UP SECTIONS

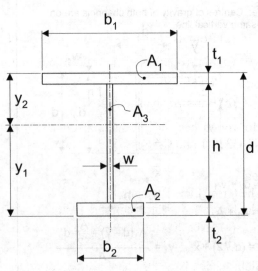

$A_1 = b_1 t_1 \qquad A_2 = b_2 t_2 \qquad A_3 = w h$

$d = h + t_1 + t_2$

$A = A_1 + A_2 + A_3$

$y_1 = \dfrac{A_1(d - t_1/2) + A_3(t_2 + h/2) + A_2 t_2/2}{A}$

$y_2 = d - y_1$

$J = \dfrac{1}{3}\left\{A_1 t_1^2 + A_3 w^2 + A_2 t_2^2\right\}$

$C_w = \dfrac{\left(d - \dfrac{t_1 + t_2}{2}\right)^2 b_1^3 t_1}{12\left[1 + (b_1/b_2)^3 (t_1/t_2)\right]}$

$I_{xx} = \dfrac{1}{12}\left[A_1 t_1^2 + A_2 t_2^2 + A_3 h^2\right] + A_1(y_2 - t_1/2)^2 + A_2(y_1 - t_2/2)^2 + A_3(y_1 - t_2 - h/2)^2$

$S_{x1} = I_{xx}/y_1 \qquad S_{x2} = I_{xx}/y_2$

$I_{yy} = \dfrac{1}{12}\left[A_1 b_1^2 + A_2 b_2^2 + A_3 w^2\right] \qquad S_{yy} = 2 I_{yy}/b_1$

$^* I_{yT} = \dfrac{1}{12}\left[A_1 b_1^2 + (y_2 - t_1)w^3\right] \qquad r_{xx} = \sqrt{I_{xx}/A} \qquad r_{yy} = \sqrt{I_{yy}/A}$

$A = A_1 + A_2 + A_S \qquad h = d + t_1 + t_2$

$y_1 = \dfrac{A_1(h - t_1/2) + A_S(t_2 + d/2) + A_2 t_2/2}{A}$

$y_2 = h - y_1$

$I_{xx} = I_{xS} + \dfrac{1}{12}(A_1 t_1^2 + A_2 t_2^2) + A_S(y_1 - t_2 - d/2)^2$
$\qquad + A_1(y_2 - t_1/2)^2 + A_2(y_1 - t_2/2)^2$

$S_{x1} = I_{xx}/y_1 \qquad S_{x2} = I_{xx}/y_2$

$r_{xx} = \sqrt{I_{xx}/A}$

$I_{yy} = I_{yS} + \dfrac{1}{12}\left[A_1 b_1^2 + A_2 b_2^2\right]$

$S_{yy} = 2 I_{yy}/b_1 \quad \text{if } b_1 > b_2$

$S_{yy} = 2 I_{yy}/b_2 \quad \text{if } b_1 \leq b_2$

$r_{yy} = \sqrt{I_{yy}/A}$

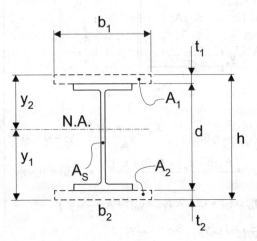

*I_{yT} is the moment of inertia of the T-section above the neutral axis.

BARS AND PLATES

Bars

The term "Bars" means:

    (a) Rounds, squares and hexagons of all sizes;

    (b) Flat-rolled steel up to 200 mm inclusive in width and over 5.0 mm in thickness, except for widths from 150 mm to 200 mm up to 6.0 mm in thickness;

    (c) Bar-size shapes under 75 mm in maximum dimension.

Hot-rolled bar flat products are available in most widths and thicknesses according to CAN3-G312.1 and CAN3-G312.2 Standards.

Plates

The term "Plates" means:

Flat hot-rolled steel, when ordered to thickness;

    (a) Over 200 mm in width and over 6.0 mm in thickness, and

    (b) Over 1200 mm in width and over 4.5 mm in thickness.

Slabs, sheet, bars, strip and skelp, although frequently falling within these size ranges, are not classified as plate. The following table, Standard Product Classification for Flat Hot-Rolled Steel Products and Bars, summarizes the ranges for plate, bar, strip and sheet products.

Plates may be further defined as "Universal Mill Plates" or "Sheared Plates". Sheared plates are rolled on a mill with horizontal rolls only, producing a product with uneven edges which must be sheared (or, at the option of the producer, flame cut) to ordered dimensions.

Universal mill plates are rolled to the ordered width on a mill having side rollers to control the width. Slab or ingot on a universal mill plate are not cross rolled, but are only elongated during the rolling process. The mill order must specify universal mill plate when it is required.

Extreme plate sizes produced by mills vary greatly with the size of various mills, and individual mills should be consulted for this information. Canadian mills can produce sheared and flame cut plate in widths ranging from 200 mm to 3900 mm and in thicknesses ranging from 4.5 mm to 150 mm. First and second preference thicknesses for plate according to CAN3-G312.1 are provided in the table on page 6-145. Where possible, designs should generally be based on first preference thickness for economy.

Standard mill practice is to invoice the purchaser for actual scale weight at point of shipment. Allowable overweight above theoretical that may be charged is limited in accordance with either the CSA-G40.20 or ASTM A6 Standards, depending upon whether the steel is furnished to Canadian or ASTM material specifications.

Various extras for thickness, width, length, cutting, quality, quantity (or quantity discounts), and for other special requirements are added to the base price of plates. Particulars of these extras should be obtained from the producing mills.

Sketch Plates

Sketch plates of special or unusual shape usually require flame cutting, for which flame cutting extras apply. Some mills can supply sketch plates of certain shapes by shearing to size.

Floor Plates

Floor plates in different styles, patterns, and extreme dimensions are produced by different mills. The nominal, or ordered, thickness is that of the flat plate exclusive of the raised pattern. Individual producers should be consulted for more details.

Bearing Plates

Rolled steel bearing plates are used for column bases, and other bearing plates. Depending on the thickness required by design, bearing plates may require additional thickness for machining to ensure proper bearing. Plates up to and including 50 mm in thickness are rolled flat with surfaces sufficiently smooth to receive, without machining or flattening, the milled or machine-cut ends of column shafts. Bearing plates 100 mm and under in thickness can sometimes be flattened by press to within required flatness tolerances. Rolled steel bearing plates greater than 100 mm thick usually require machining of the top surface in contact with the column shaft, but do not require flattening of the bottom surface when bearing on a grouted base. When bearing plates over 100 mm thick bear on a steel surface, both the top and bottom surfaces will require to be machined over the bearing areas.

Tables

The following Tables are included in this section:

Standard Product Classification of Flat Hot-Rolled Steel Products and Bars

Flat Metal Products – Sheet and Plate

Mass (kg/m) for Rectangular Steel Products

SI Wire Size – Wire Gauges Comparison

SI Thickness – Imperial Gauge Comparisons

Mass of Round Bars and Square Bars

STANDARD PRODUCT CLASSIFICATION

Flat Hot-Rolled Steel Products and Bars

Width, w (mm)	Thickness, t (mm)					
	t > 6	6 ≥ t > 5	5 ≥ t > 4.5	4.5 ≥ t > 1.2	1.2 ≥ t > 0.9	0.9 ≥ t > 0.65
w ≤ 100	BAR	BAR	STRIP	STRIP	STRIP	STRIP
100 < w ≤ 150	BAR	BAR	STRIP	STRIP	STRIP	
150 < w ≤ 200	BAR	STRIP	STRIP	STRIP		
200 < w ≤ 300	PLATE	STRIP	STRIP	STRIP		
300 < w ≤ 1200	PLATE	SHEET*	SHEET*	SHEET*		
1200 < w	PLATE	PLATE	PLATE	SHEET		

* For alloy steels, sheet begins at widths over 600 mm.

FLAT METAL PRODUCTS* – Sheet & Plate

Nominal Thickness,** mm		Mass† kg/m²	Dead Load kN/m²	Nominal Thickness,** mm		Mass† kg/m²	Dead Load kN/m²
First preference	Second preference			First preference	Second preference		
0.050		0.393	0.003 85		14	110	1.08
0.060		0.471	0.004 62	16		126	1.23
0.080		0.628	0.006 16		18	141	1.39
0.10		0.785	0.007 70	20		157	1.54
0.12		0.942	0.009 24		22	173	1.69
	0.14	1.10	0.010 8	25		196	1.93
0.16		1.26	0.012 3		28	220	2.16
	0.18	1.41	0.013 9	30		236	2.31
0.20		1.57	0.015 4		32	251	2.46
	0.22	1.73	0.016 9	35		275	2.70
0.25		1.96	0.019 3		38	298	2.93
	0.28	2.20	0.021 6	40		314	3.08
0.30		2.36	0.023 1		45	353	3.47
	0.35	2.75	0.027 0	50		393	3.85
0.40		3.14	0.030 8		55	432	4.24
	0.45	3.53	0.034 7	60		471	4.62
0.50		3.93	0.038 5		70	550	5.39
	0.55	4.32	0.042 4	80		628	6.16
0.60		4.71	0.046 2		90	707	6.93
	0.65	5.10	0.050 1	100		785	7.70
	0.70	5.50	0.053 9		110	864	8.47
0.80		6.28	0.061 6	120		942	9.24
	0.90	7.07	0.069 3		130	1020	10.0
1.0		7.85	0.077 0	140		1100	10.8
	1.1	8.64	0.084 7		150	1180	11.6
1.2		9.42	0.092 4	160		1260	12.3
	1.4	11.0	0.108	180		1410	13.9
1.6		12.6	0.123	200		1570	15.4
	1.8	14.1	0.139	250		1960	19.3
2.0		15.7	0.154	300		2360	23.1
	2.2	17.3	0.169				
2.5		19.6	0.193				
	2.8	22.0	0.216				
3.0		23.6	0.231				
	3.2	25.1	0.246				
3.5		27.5	0.270				
	3.8	29.8	0.293				
4.0		31.4	0.308				
	4.2	33.0	0.323				
4.5		35.3	0.347				
	4.8	37.7	0.370				
5.0		39.3	0.385				
	5.5	43.2	0.424				
6.0		47.1	0.462				
7.0		55.0	0.539				
8.0		62.8	0.616				
	9.0	70.7	0.693				
10		78.5	0.770				
	11	86.4	0.847				
12		94.2	0.924				

* Sizes are those listed in CAN3-G312.1-75

** For coated structural sheet, the nominal thickness applies to the base metal. For metric thickness dimensions for zinc coated structural quality sheet steel, see Part 7, Structural Sheet Steel Products.

† Computed using steel density of 7 850 kg/m³.

MASS (kg/m) for RECTANGULAR STEEL PRODUCTS*

Width (mm)	Thickness, millimetres														
First / Second	5	6	8	10	12	14	16	18	20	22	25	28	30	35	40
25	0.981	1.18	1.57	1.96	2.36	2.75	3.14	3.53	3.93	4.32					
28	1.10	1.32	1.76	2.20	2.64	3.08	3.52	3.96	4.40	4.84	5.50				
30	1.18	1.41	1.88	2.36	2.83	3.30	3.77	4.24	4.71	5.18	5.89	6.59			
35	1.37	1.65	2.20	2.75	3.30	3.85	4.40	4.95	5.50	6.04	6.87	7.69	8.24		
40	1.57	1.88	2.51	3.14	3.77	4.40	5.02	5.65	6.28	6.91	7.85	8.79	9.42	11.0	
45	1.77	2.12	2.83	3.53	4.24	4.95	5.65	6.36	7.07	7.77	8.83	9.89	10.6	12.4	14.1
50	1.96	2.36	3.14	3.93	4.71	5.50	6.28	7.07	7.85	8.64	9.81	11.0	11.8	13.7	15.7
55	2.16	2.59	3.45	4.32	5.18	6.04	6.91	7.77	8.64	9.50	10.8	12.1	13.0	15.1	17.3
60	2.36	2.83	3.77	4.71	5.65	6.59	7.54	8.48	9.42	10.4	11.8	13.2	14.1	16.5	18.8
70	2.75	3.30	4.40	5.50	6.59	7.69	8.79	9.89	11.0	12.1	13.7	15.4	16.5	19.2	22.0
80	3.14	3.77	5.02	6.28	7.54	8.79	10.0	11.3	12.6	13.8	15.7	17.6	18.8	22.0	25.1
90	3.53	4.24	5.65	7.07	8.48	9.89	11.3	12.7	14.1	15.5	17.7	19.8	21.2	24.7	28.3
100	3.93	4.71	6.28	7.85	9.42	11.0	12.6	14.1	15.7	17.3	19.6	22.0	23.6	27.5	31.4
110	4.32	5.18	6.91	8.64	10.4	12.1	13.8	15.5	17.3	19.0	21.6	24.2	25.9	30.2	34.5
120	4.71	5.65	7.54	9.42	11.3	13.2	15.1	17.0	18.8	20.7	23.6	26.4	28.3	33.0	37.7
140	5.50	6.59	8.79	11.0	13.2	15.4	17.6	19.8	22.0	24.2	27.5	30.8	33.0	38.5	44.0
160		7.54	10.0	12.6	15.1	17.6	20.1	22.6	25.1	27.6	31.4	35.2	37.7	44.0	50.2
180		8.48	11.3	14.1	17.0	19.8	22.6	25.4	28.3	31.1	35.3	39.6	42.4	49.5	56.5
200		9.42	12.6	15.7	18.8	22.0	25.1	28.3	31.4	34.5	39.3	44.0	47.1	55.0	62.8
220		10.4	13.8	17.3	20.7	24.2	27.6	31.1	34.5	38.0	43.2	48.4	51.8	60.4	69.1
250		11.8	15.7	19.6	23.6	27.5	31.4	35.3	39.3	43.2	49.1	55.0	58.9	68.7	78.5
300		14.1	18.8	23.6	28.3	33.0	37.7	42.4	47.1	51.8	58.9	65.9	70.7	82.4	94.2

Note: The mass has been computed using a steel density of 7 850 kg/m^3.

* Sizes are those listed in Table 2 of CAN3-G312.2-M76

SI WIRE SIZE – WIRE GAUGES COMPARISON

SI Wire Size Preferred Diam.* (mm)	The United States Steel Wire Gauge	American or Brown & Sharpe Wire Gauge	British Imperial or English Legal Standard Wire Gauge	Birmingham or Stubs Iron Wire Gauge
25.0				
24.0				
23.0				
22.0				
21.0				
20.0				
19.0				
18.0				
17.0				
16.0				
15.0				
		6/0's		
14.0				
		5/0's		
13.0				
			7/0's	5/0's
12.5				
	7/0's			
12.0				
11.8				
	6/0's	4/0's	6/0's	4/0's
11.2				
11.0				
	5/0's		5/0's	3/0's
10.6				
		3/0's	4/0's	
10.0	4/0's			
				2/0's
9.5				
	3/0's	2/0's	3/0's	
9.0				
			2/0's	1/0
8.5				
	2/0's	1/0	1/0	
8.0				
	1/0		1	1
7.5				
	1	1	2	2
7.0				
6.7	2			
		2		3
6.5				
			3	
6.3				
	3			4
6.0				
6.0				
	4	3	4	5
5.6				
			5	
5.3	5			
		4		6
5.0				
	6		6	
4.8				
		5		
4.6				
	7		7	7
4.4				
4.2				
	8	6	8	8
4.0				
3.8				
	9	7	9	9
3.6				
	10			
3.4				
				10
		8	10	
3.2				
	11			11
3.0				
		9	11	
2.8				
	12		12	12
2.6				
		10		13
2.4				
	13	11	13	
2.3				
2.2				
				14
2.1				
	14	12	14	
2.0				
1.90				
	15	13	15	15
1.80				
1.70				
		14	16	16
1.60				
	16			
1.50				

* From CAN3-G312.2-M76

SI THICKNESS – IMPERIAL GAUGE COMPARISONS[†]

SI Preferred Thickness		United States Standard Gauge*				New Birmington Sheet Gauge		
First mm	Second mm	Weight Oz. per sq. ft.	Ga. No.	Approximate Thickness Inches	mm	Gauge Number	Thickness Inches	mm
	18							
						7/0's	0.6666	16.932
16								
						6/0's	0.6250	15.875
						5/0's	0.5883	14.943
	14							
						4/0's	0.5416	13.757
						3/0's	0.5000	12.700
12								
						2/0's	0.4452	11.562
	11							
						0	0.3964	10.069
10								
	9.0							
						1	0.3532	8.971
8.0								
						2	0.3147	7.993
						3	0.2804	7.122
7.0								
		160	3	0.2391	6.073	4	0.2500	6.350
6.0								
		150	4	0.2242	5.695	5	0.2225	5.652
	5.5							
		140	5	0.2092	5.314	6	0.1981	5.032
5.0								
		130	6	0.1943	4.935			
	4.8							
		120	7	0.1793	4.554			
4.5								
						7	0.1764	4.481
	4.2							
		110	8	0.1644	4.176			
4.0								
						8	0.1570	3.988
	3.8	100	9	0.1495	3.797			
						9	0.1398	3.551
3.5								
		90	10	0.1345	3.416			
	3.2							
		80	11	0.1196	3.038	10	0.1250	3.175
3.0								
						11	0.1113	2.827
	2.8							
		70	12	0.1046	2.657	12	0.0991	2.517
2.5								

† Preferred thicknesses are as per CAN3-G312.1-75
* U.S. Standard Gauge is officially a weight gauge, in oz. per sq. ft. as tabulated. The Approx. thickness shown is the "Manufacturers' Standard" of the AISI based on a steel density of 501.81 lb. per ft.[3]

SI THICKNESS – IMPERIAL GAUGE COMPARISONS[†]

SI Preferred Thickness		United States Standard Gauge*				New Birmington Sheet Gauge		
		Weight	Ga. No.	Approximate Thickness		Gauge Number	Thickness	
First mm	Second mm	Oz. per sq. ft.		Inches	mm		Inches	mm
		60	13	0.0897	2.278	13	0.0882	2.240
	2.2							
2.0						14	0.0785	1.994
		50	14	0.0747	1.897			
	1.8							
		45	15	0.0673	1.709	15	0.0699	1.775
1.6								
		40	16	0.0598	1.519	16	0.0625	1.588
						17	0.0556	1.412
	1.4							
		36	17	0.0538	1.367			
		32	18	0.0478	1.214	18	0.0495	1.257
1.2								
						19	0.0440	1.118
	1.1							
		28	19	0.0418	1.062			
1.0						20	0.0392	0.996
		24	20	0.0359	0.912			
	0.90							
		22	21	0.0329	0.836	21	0.0349	0.886
0.80						22	0.0313	0.795
		20	22	0.0299	0.759			
	0.70					23	0.0278	0.706
		18	23	0.0269	0.683			
	0.65							
						24	0.0248	0.630
0.60		16	24	0.0239	0.607			
						25	0.0220	0.559
	0.55							
		14	25	0.0209	0.531			
0.50						26	0.0196	0.498
	0.45	12	26	0.0179	0.455	27	0.0175	0.445
		11	27	0.0164	0.417			
0.40						28	0.0156	0.396
		10	28	0.0149	0.378			
	0.35	9	29	0.0135	0.343	29	0.0139	0.353
						30	0.0123	0.312
0.30		8	30	0.0120	0.305			
	0.28					31	0.0110	0.279
		7	31	0.0105	0.267			
0.25								

[†] Preferred thicknesses are as per CAN3-G312.1-75
* U.S. Standard Gauge is officially a weight gauge, in oz. per sq. ft. as tabulated. The Approx. thickness shown is the "Manufacturers' Standard" of the AISI based on a steel density of 501.81 lb. per ft.[3]

MASS OF BARS
Round Bars

First	Second	Mass* kg/m	Area mm²	First	Second	Mass* kg/m	Area mm²	First	Second	Mass* kg/m	Area mm²
3.0		0.055 5	7.07		21	2.72	346		65	26.0	3 320
	3.5	0.075 5	9.62	22		2.98	380		70	30.2	3 850
4.0		0.098 6	12.6		23	3.26	415		72†	32.0	4 070
	4.5	0.125	15.9		24	3.55	452		75	34.7	4 420
5.0		0.154	19.6	25		3.85	491	80		39.5	5 030
	5.5	0.187	23.8		26	4.17	531		90	49.9	6 360
6.0		0.222	28.3		27†	4.49	573	100		61.7	7 850
	6.5	0.260	33.2		28	4.83	616		110	74.6	9 500
	7.0	0.302	38.5	30		5.55	707	120		88.8	11 300
8.0		0.395	50.3		32	6.31	804		130	104	13 300
	9.0	0.499	63.6	35		7.55	962	140		121	15 400
10		0.617	78.5		36†	7.99	1 020		150	139	17 700
	11	0.746	95.0		38	8.90	1 130	160		158	20 100
12		0.888	113	40		9.86	1 260		170	178	22 700
	13	1.04	133		42	10.9	1 390	180		200	25 400
14		1.21	154	45		12.5	1 590		190	223	28 400
	15	1.39	177		48	14.2	1 810	200		247	31 400
16		1.58	201	50		15.4	1 960		220	298	38 000
	17	1.78	227		55	18.7	2 380	250		385	49 100
18		2.00	254		56†	19.3	2 460		280	483	61 600
	19	2.23	284	60		22.2	2 830	300		555	70 700
20		2.47	314		64†	25.3	3 220		320	631	80 400

† Screw Stock, not listed in CAN3-G312.2-M76

MASS OF BARS
Square Bars

First	Second	Mass* kg/m	Area mm²	First	Second	Mass* kg/m	Area mm²	First	Second	Mass* kg/m	Area mm²
3.0		0.070 7	9.00	25		4.91	625	100		78.5	10 000
4.0		0.126	16.0		28	6.15	784		110	95.0	12 100
5.0		0.196	25.0	30		7.07	900	120		113	14 400
6.0		0.283	36.0		35	9.62	1 230		140	154	19 600
8.0		0.502	64.0	40		12.6	1 600	160		201	25 600
10		0.785	100		45	15.9	2 030		180	254	32 400
12		1.13	144	50		19.6	2 500	200		314	40 000
	14	1.54	196		55	23.7	3 030		220	380	48 400
16		2.01	256	60		28.3	3 600	250		491	62 500
	18	2.54	324		70	38.5	4 900	300		707	90 000
20		3.14	400	80		50.2	6 400				
	22	3.80	484		90	63.6	8 100				

* Computed using a steel density of 7 850 kg/m³

CRANE RAILS

General

Crane rails are designated by their mass in pounds per yard, with bolt sizes, hole diameters, and washer sizes dimensioned in inches. The SI metric dimensions and properties for crane rails and their accessories given on the following pages are soft converted from manufacturers' catalogues.

ASCE 40, 60 and 85 pound rails require special drilling and punching at time of purchase, while all other rail sizes are predrilled and punched by the manufacturer. The manufacturer should be consulted as to the availability of metric fasteners and metric size holes.

Rails listed in this handbook are the most popular sizes used for crane runways. For dimensions and properties not provided in the tables, consult the manufacturer.

ASCE 40 and 60 pound rails are usually supplied in 9140 mm lengths, ASCE 60 and 85 pound rails are available in 10 100 mm lengths and ASCE 85 pound and heavier rails are available in 11 900 mm lengths. If bolted rail bar splices are to be used, the number of rail lengths required, plus one short length in each run should be specified, to permit staggering of the joints. Orders must clearly specify that "THESE RAILS ARE INTENDED FOR CRANE SERVICE".

The ends of rails are often hardened to better resist rail end batter. Most manufacturers will chamfer the top and sides of the rail head at the ends, unless specified otherwise by the purchaser. Chamfering permits mild deformations to occur and minimizes chipping of the running surfaces.

When selecting a rail for crane service, the characteristics of operation must be considered. Some common variables which affect service life are:

- Frequency of operation
- Crane carriage speed and impact – rate of loading and unloading
- Corrosion – acidic mill conditions
- Abrasion
- Alignment of crane and supporting members
- Crane operating procedures

Crane rails are joined together end-to-end by either mechanical fasteners or welding. When bolting is used, special joint bars are employed (as shown on the following pages) and the rails are usually predrilled 1/16-inch larger than the specified bolt size. If welded, manual arc welding is usually used and joint bars are not required. Welding has the advantage of eliminating mechanical joints, thus reducing the problem of aligning the top of rails.

CRANE RAILS – PROPERTIES AND DIMENSIONS

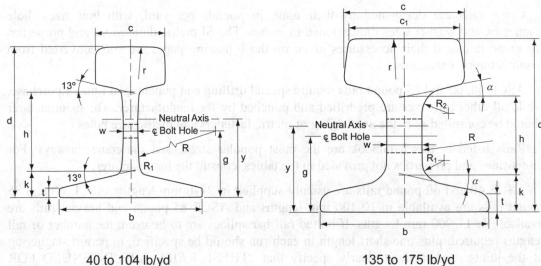

40 to 104 lb/yd   135 to 175 lb/yd

Dimensions

Rail type	Depth	Head		Base		Web								
	d	c	c_1	b	t	w	Gauge g	k	h	r	R	R_1	R_2	α
	mm	mm	mm	mm	mm	mm	mm	mm	mm	mm	mm	mm	mm	deg
ASCE 40	89	48	48	89	5.6	9.9	39	16	47	305	305	6.4	6.4	13
ASCE 60	108	60	60	108	7.1	12	48	19	58	305	305	6.4	6.4	13
ASCE 85	132	65	65	132	7.5	14	58	23	70	305	305	6.4	6.4	13
Beth. 104	127	64	64	127	13	25	62	27	62	305	89	13	13	13
Beth. 135	146	87	76	132	12	32	63	27	71	356	305	19	19	13
Beth. 171	152	109	102	152	16	32	67	32	70	Flat	Vert.	19	22	12
Beth. 175	152	108	102	152	13	38	67	29	79	457	Vert.	29	51	12

Properties

Rail type	Mass	Dead Load	Area	I_x	S_x Head	S_x Base	y
	kg/m	kN/m	mm^2	10^6 mm^4	10^3 mm^3	10^3 mm^3	mm
ASCE 40	19.8	0.195	2 540	2.72	58.8	63.7	42.7
ASCE 60	29.8	0.292	3 830	6.08	109	117	52.1
ASCE 85	42.2	0.414	5 370	12.5	182	200	62.7
Beth. 104	51.6	0.506	6 650	12.4	175	221	56.1
Beth. 135	67.0	0.657	8 580	21.1	283	297	71.4
Beth. 171	84.8	0.832	10 800	30.6	401	400	76.5
Beth. 175	86.8	0.852	11 000	29.3	383	387	75.7

Rail Fasteners

Hook bolts are primarily used when the flange of the crane beam is too narrow to permit the use of rail clamps. Hook bolts are used in groups of 2, located 75 to 100 mm apart, at 600 mm centres, and may be adjusted plus or minus 12 mm. Rails require special preparation either in the fabricator's shop or by the crane rail supplier.

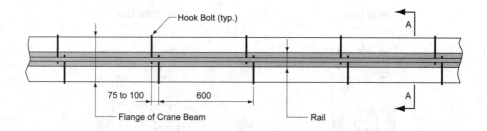

Suggested rail clamp dimensions are shown in Section B-B. For prefabricated rail clamps, reference should be made to Manufacturers' catalogues of track accessories. Two types of clamps are available: the tight clamp and the floating clamp. Floating clamps are used when longitudinal and controlled transverse movement is required for thermal expansion and alignment. Rail clamps are fabricated from pressed or forged steel and usually have single or double bolts.

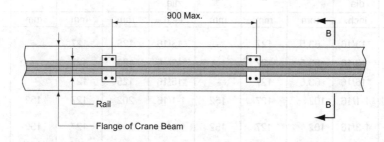

RAIL FASTENERS

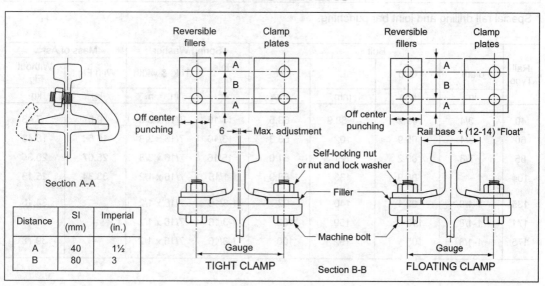

Distance	SI (mm)	Imperial (in.)
A	40	1½
B	80	3

RAIL SPLICES

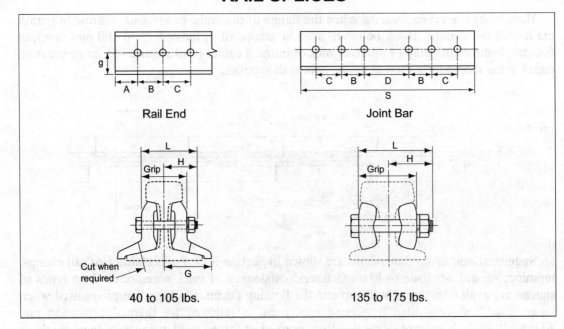

Rail End   Joint Bar

40 to 105 lbs.   135 to 175 lbs.

Cut when required

Rail Type	Rail						Joint Bar					
	g	Hole dia.	A	B	C		Hole dia.	D	B	C	S	G
	mm	inch.	mm	mm	mm		inch.	mm	mm	mm	mm	mm
40	39.5	*13/16	63.5	127	–		*13/16	125	127	–	508	55.6
60	48.2	*13/16	63.5	127	–		*13/16	125	127	–	610	68.3
85	57.5	*15/16	63.5	127	–		*15/16	125	127	–	610	84.9
104	61.9	1-1/16	102	127	152		1-1/16	202	127	152	864	88.9
135	62.7	1-3/16	102	127	152		1-3/16	202	127	152	864	–
171	66.7	1-3/16	102	127	152		1-3/16	202	127	152	864	–
175	67.5	1-3/16	102	127	152		1-3/16	202	127	152	864	–

* Special rail drilling and joint bar punching.

Rail Type	Bolt				Spring Washer		Mass of Ass'y	
	diam.	Grip	L	H	Hole dia.	Thk. & width	With Flg.	Without Flg.
	in.	mm	mm	mm	in.	in. in.	kg.	kg.
40	3/4	49.2	88.9	63.5	13/16	7/16 x 3/8	9.07	7.48
60	3/4	65.9	102	68.3	13/16	7/16 x 3/8	16.56	13.43
85	7/8	80.2	121	81.0	15/16	7/16 x 3/8	25.67	20.55
104	1	88.9	133	88.9	1-1/16	7/16 x 1/2	33.34	25.13
135	1-1/8	92.1	140	93.7	1-3/16	7/16 x 1/2	–	34.16
171	1-1/8	113	159	103	1-3/16	7/16 x 1/2	–	41.19
175	1-1/8	105	152	100	1-3/16	7/16 x 1/2	–	39.78

Splices

Rail drilling and joint bar punching as supplied for track work is not recommended for crane rails, since oversize holes may allow too much movement at the rail ends and result in failure. Tight joints which require special rail and joint bar drilling (see table on previous page) and squaring of the rail ends are recommended.

Light rails are not finished at the mill and are usually finished at the fabricator's shop or at the erection site. This may require reaming of holes for proper fit of bolts if dimensional tolerances are cumulative.

Joint bars are provided for crane service to match the rails ordered, and may be ordered blank. Under no circumstances should these joint bars be used as welding straps. Manufacturer's catalogues should be consulted for joint bar specifications, dimensions and identification necessary to match the crane rail specified.

Joint bar bolts for crane service are readily identified from those used for track work, as they have straight shanks and are manufactured to ASTM A449 specification. Matching nuts are manufactured to ASTM A563 Grade B. The bolted assembly includes an alloy spring washer which is furnished to American Railway Engineers Association (AREA) specification. Bolts and nuts manufactured to ASTM A325 may also be acceptable.

To prolong the life of the runway, bolts should be retightened within 30 days after installation and every 3 months thereafter.

FASTENERS

General

The information on fasteners provided herein is based on standards, specifications and publications of the:

> Canadian Standards Association
>
> American National Standards Institute
>
> Industrial Fasteners Institute
>
> Research Council on Structural Connections

Additional fastener information can be obtained from the various manufacturers and from the Canadian Fasteners Institute.

Availability

The more commonly used fasteners for structural purposes in Canada have included the following:

> ⅝-inch ASTM A307 bolts for light steel framing such as girts, purlins, etc.
>
> ¾-inch ASTM A325 bolts for building structures
>
> ⅞-inch ASTM A325 bolts for bridge structures

While other diameters and types of bolts have been used on specific projects in Canada, larger sizes of ASTM A325 bolts, all sizes of ASTM A490 bolts, and all sizes of metric bolts (A325M and A490M) have not been in common use in Canada, and designers contemplating their use should first check for their availability.

Clause 22.3.5.1 of CSA S16-09 permits the use of matching imperial-size and metric-size bolts in the appropriate metric-size holes for the more commonly used high-strength bolts. Designers and detailers should therefore base their calculations on the smaller size of matching fastener as appropriate, and allow substitutions as dictated by availability of metric or imperial size fasteners at the time of fabrication.

Definitions

Body Length means the distance from the underside of the head bearing surface to either the last scratch of thread or the top of the extrusion angle, whichever is the closest to the head.

Bolt Length means the length from the underside of the head bearing surface to the extreme point.

Finished Fastener means a fastener made to close tolerances and having surfaces other than the threads and bearing surface finished to provide a general high-grade appearance.

Grip means the thickness of material or parts which the fastener is designed to secure when fully assembled.

Height of Bolt Head means the overall distance, measured parallel to the fastener axis, from the extreme top (excluding raised identification marks) to the bearing surface and including the thickness of the washer face where provided.

Natural Finish means the as-processed finish, unplated or uncoated of the bolt or nut.

Nominal Size means the designation used for the purpose of general identification.

Proof Load means a specified test load which a fastener must withstand without any indication of significant deformation or failure.

Thickness of Nut means the overall distance from the top of the nut to the bearing surface, measured parallel to the axis of the nut.

Thread Length of a Bolt means the distance from the extreme point to the last complete thread.

Transition Thread Length means the distance from the last complete thread to either the last scratch of thread or the top of the extrusion angle, whichever is the closest to the head.

Washer Face means a circular boss on the bearing surface of a bolt or nut.

Tables

The following Tables are included in this section:

ASTM A325 and ASTM A490 High-Strength Bolts and Nuts

ASTM A325M and ASTM A490M High-Strength Bolts and Nuts

Bolt Lengths for Various Grips — ASTM A325 and A490 Bolts

Minimum and Maximum Grips for Metric Heavy Hex. Structural Bolts

Weight of ASTM A325 Bolts, Nuts and washers

Mass of ASTM A325M Bolts, Nuts and Washers

ASTM F436M Metric Washer Dimensions

ASTM A307 Bolts and Nuts

Fasteners — Miscellaneous Detailing Data

Usual Gauges — W, M, S, C shapes, Angles

Erection Clearances — Bolt Impact Wrenches

ASTM A325 AND ASTM A490
HIGH-STRENGTH BOLTS AND NUTS

REQUIRED MARKINGS

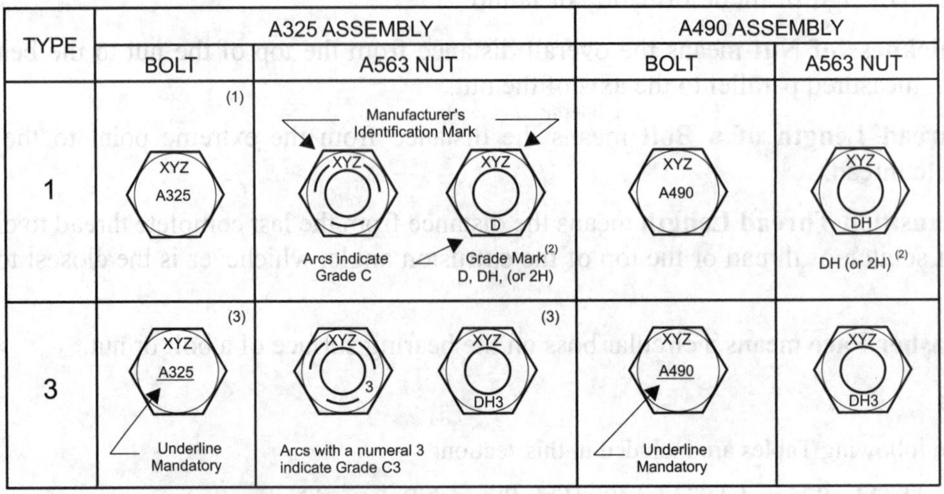

TYPE	A325 ASSEMBLY		A490 ASSEMBLY	
	BOLT	A563 NUT	BOLT	A563 NUT
1	(1) XYZ A325 — Arcs indicate Grade C	Manufacturer's Identification Mark — XYZ ; XYZ D — Grade Mark (2) D, DH, (or 2H)	XYZ A490	XYZ DH — DH (or 2H) (2)
3	(3) XYZ A325 — Underline Mandatory	XYZ 3 ; XYZ DH3 — Arcs with a numeral 3 indicate Grade C3	(3) XYZ A490 — Underline Mandatory	XYZ DH3

(1) Additional Optional 3 Radial Lines at 120° may be added.
(2) Type 3 also acceptable. Nuts according to ASTM A194 Grade 2H, plain finish, may also be used.
(3) Additional Optional Mark indicating Weathering Grade may be added.

DIMENSIONS

Dimensions						Coarse Thread Series — UNC**			
Nominal Bolt Size, Inches D	Bolt Dimensions*, Inches Heavy Hex Structural Bolts			Nut Dimensions*, Inches Heavy Hex nuts		Threads Per Inch	Basic Pitch Dia	Section at Minor Dia	Tensile Stress Area
	Width across flats, F	Height, H	Thread length	Width across flats, W	Height, H		In.	In.²	In.²
½	⅞	⁵⁄₁₆	1	⅞	³¹⁄₆₄	13	0.4500	0.1257	0.1419
⅝	1¹⁄₁₆	²⁵⁄₆₄	1¼	1¹⁄₁₆	³⁹⁄₆₄	11	0.5660	0.202	0.226
¾	1¼	¹⁵⁄₃₂	1⅜	1¼	⁴⁷⁄₆₄	10	0.6850	0.302	0.334
⅞	1⁷⁄₁₆	³⁵⁄₆₄	1½	1⁷⁄₁₆	⁵⁵⁄₆₄	9	0.8028	0.419	0.462
1	1⅝	³⁹⁄₆₄	1¾	1⅝	⁶³⁄₆₄	8	0.9188	0.551	0.606
1⅛	1¹³⁄₁₆	¹¹⁄₁₆	2	1¹³⁄₁₆	1⁷⁄₆₄	7	1.0322	0.693	0.763
1¼	2	²⁵⁄₃₂	2	2	1⁷⁄₃₂	7	1.1572	0.890	0.969
1⅜	2³⁄₁₆	²⁷⁄₃₂	2¼	2³⁄₁₆	1¹¹⁄₃₂	6	1.2667	1.054	1.155
1½	2⅜	¹⁵⁄₁₆	2¼	2⅜	1¹⁵⁄₃₂	6	1.3917	1.294	1.405

* Dimensions according to ANSI B18.2.1

** Thread dimensions according to ANSI B1.1

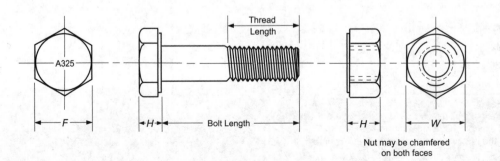

Nut may be chamfered on both faces

ASTM A325M AND ASTM A490M**
HIGH-STRENGTH BOLTS AND NUTS

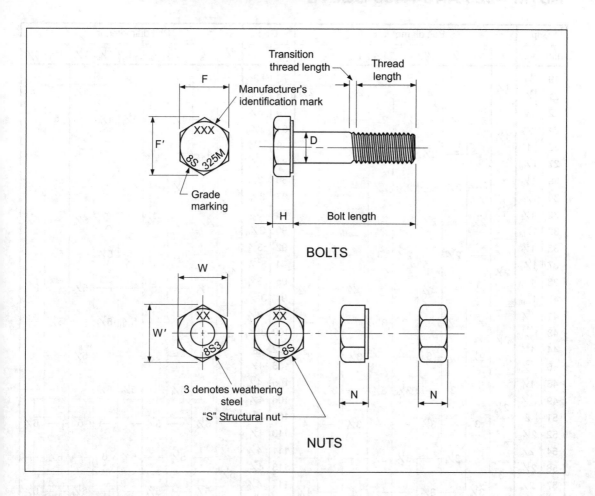

BOLTS

NUTS

3 denotes weathering steel

"S" Structural nut

DIMENSIONS

Nominal Bolt Size	Heavy Hex Bolt or Nut Dimension				Heavy Hex Nut Max. Height	Heavy Hex Structural Bolt			
	Across Flats F or W		Across Corners F′ or W′			Max Head Height	Thread Length*		Max. Transition Thread Length
	Max.	Min.	Max.	Min.	N	H	Bolt Lengths ≤100	Bolt Lengths >100	
mm	mm	mm	mm	mm	mm	mm	mm	mm	mm
M16 x 2	27.00	26.16	31.18	29.56	17.1	10.75	31	38	6.0
M20 x 2.5	34.00	33.00	39.26	37.29	20.7	13.40	36	43	7.5
M22 x 2.5	36.00	35.00	41.57	39.55	23.6	14.90	38	45	7.5
M24 x 3	41.00	40.00	47.34	45.20	24.2	15.90	41	48	9.0
M27 x 3	46.00	45.00	53.12	50.85	27.6	17.90	44	51	9.0
M30 x 3.5	50.00	49.00	57.74	55.37	30.7	19.75	49	56	10.5
M36 x 4	60.00	58.80	69.28	66.44	36.6	23.55	56	63	12.0

* Does not include transition thread length.
** Strength requirements are based on ASTM Specifications A325M and A490M. See page 3—5.
Bolt dimensions conform to those listed in ANSI B18.2.3.7M-1979 (R2001) "Metric Heavy Hex Structural Bolts",
and the nut dimensions conform to those listed in ANSI B18.2.4.6M-1979 (R1998) "Metric Heavy Hex Nuts".

BOLT LENGTHS* FOR VARIOUS GRIPS** ASTM A325 AND A490 BOLTS

Grip (mm)	Grip (in)	1/2	5/8	3/4	7/8	1	1 1/8	1 1/4	1 3/8	1 1/2
19	3/4	1 1/2								
21	13/16		1 3/4		2			2 1/2		2 3/4
22	7/8			2		2 1/4	2 1/2		2 3/4	
24	15/16	1 3/4								
25	1		2		2 1/4			2 3/4		3
27	1 1/16									
29	1 1/8			2 1/4		2 1/2	2 3/4		3	
30	1 3/16	2								
32	1 1/4		2 1/4		2 1/2			3		3 1/4
33	1 5/16									
35	1 3/8			2 1/2		2 3/4	3		3 1/4	
37	1 7/16	2 1/4								
38	1 1/2		2 1/2		2 3/4			3 1/4		3 1/2
40	1 9/16									
41	1 5/8			2 3/4		3	3 1/4		3 1/2	
43	1 11/16	2 1/2								
44	1 3/4		2 3/4		3			3 1/2		3 3/4
46	1 13/16									
48	1 7/8			3		3 1/4	3 1/2		3 3/4	
49	1 15/16	2 3/4								
51	2		3		3 1/4			3 3/4		4
52	2 1/16									
54	2 1/8			3 1/4		3 1/2	3 3/4		4	
56	2 3/16	3								
57	2 1/4		3 1/4		3 1/2			4		4 1/4
59	2 5/16									
60	2 3/8			3 1/2		3 3/4	4		4 1/4	
62	2 7/16	3 1/4								
64	2 1/2		3 1/2		3 3/4			4 1/4		4 1/2
65	2 9/16									
67	2 5/8			3 3/4		4	4 1/4		4 1/2	
68	2 11/16	3 1/2								
70	2 3/4		3 3/4		4			4 1/2		4 3/4
71	2 13/16									
73	2 7/8			4		4 1/4	4 1/2		4 3/4	
75	2 15/16	3 3/4								
76	3		4		4 1/4			4 3/4		5
78	3 1/16									

Grip (mm)	Grip (in)	1/2	5/8	3/4	7/8	1	1 1/8	1 1/4	1 3/8	1 1/2
76	3									
78	3 1/16		4		4 1/4			4 3/4		5
79	3 1/8			4 1/4		4 1/2	4 3/4		5	
81	3 3/16	4								
83	3 1/4		4 1/4		4 1/2			5		5 1/4
84	3 5/16									
86	3 3/8			4 1/2		4 3/4	5		5 1/4	
87	3 7/16	4 1/4								
89	3 1/2		4 1/2		4 3/4			5 1/4		5 1/2
90	3 9/16									
92	3 5/8			4 3/4		5	5 1/4		5 1/2	
94	3 11/16	4 1/2								
95	3 3/4		4 3/4		5			5 1/2		5 3/4
97	3 13/16									
98	3 7/8			5		5 1/4	5 1/2		5 3/4	
100	3 15/16	4 3/4								
102	4		5		5 1/4			5 3/4		6
103	4 1/16									
105	4 1/8			5 1/4		5 1/2	5 3/4		6	
106	4 3/16	5								
108	4 1/4		5 1/4		5 1/2			6		6 1/4
110	4 5/16									
111	4 3/8			5 1/2		5 3/4	6		6 1/4	
113	4 7/16	5 1/4								
114	4 1/2		5 1/2		5 3/4			6 1/4		6 1/2
116	4 9/16									
117	4 5/8			5 3/4		6	6 1/4		6 1/2	
119	4 11/16	5 1/2								
121	4 3/4		5 3/4		6			6 1/2		6 3/4
122	4 13/16									
124	4 7/8			6		6 1/4	6 1/2		6 3/4	
125	4 15/16	5 3/4								
127	5		6		6 1/4			6 3/4		7
129	5 1/16									
130	5 1/8			6 1/4		6 1/2	6 3/4		7	
132	5 3/16	6								
133	5 1/4		6 1/4		6 1/2			7		7 1/2
135	5 5/16									

* Bolt lengths must be specified in inches for ASTM A325 and A490 bolts.

** Grip is thickness of material to be connected exclusive of washers.

For each flat washer, add 4 mm (5/32 inch) to grip.

For each beveled washer, add 8 mm (5/16 inch) to grip.

MINIMUM AND MAXIMUM GRIPS FOR METRIC HEAVY HEX. STRUCTURAL BOLTS, IN MILLIMETRES

Nominal Bolt Size	M16		M20		M22		M24		M27		M30		M36	
L Nominal Length (mm)	Min. Grip	Max. Grip	Min. Grip	Max. Grip	Min. Grip	Max. Grip	Min. Grip	Max. Grip	Min. Grip	Max. Grip	Min. Grip	Max. Grip	Min. Grip	Max. Grip
45	14	26		23		20								
50	19	31	14	28		25		24						
55	24	36	19	32	17	29		29		25				
60	29	41	24	37	22	34	19	34		30		27		
65	34	46	29	42	27	39	24	39	21	35		32		
70	39	51	34	47	32	44	29	44	26	40	21	37		31
75	44	56	39	52	37	49	34	49	31	45	26	42		36
80	49	61	44	57	42	54	39	54	36	50	31	47	24	41
85	54	66	49	62	47	59	44	59	41	55	36	52	29	46
90	59	71	54	67	52	64	49	64	46	60	41	57	34	51
95	64	76	59	72	57	69	54	69	51	65	46	62	39	56
100	69	81	64	77	62	74	59	74	56	70	51	67	44	61
110	72	91	67	87	65	84	62	84	59	80	54	77	47	71
120	82	101	77	97	75	94	72	94	69	90	64	87	57	81
130	92	110	87	107	85	104	82	103	79	100	74	97	67	91
140	102	120	97	117	95	114	92	113	89	110	84	107	77	101
150	112	130	107	127	105	124	102	123	99	120	94	117	87	111
160	122	138	117	135	115	132	112	131	109	128	104	125	97	119
170	132	148	127	145	125	142	122	141	119	138	114	135	107	129
180	142	158	137	155	135	152	132	151	129	148	124	145	117	139
190	152	168	147	165	145	162	142	161	139	158	134	155	127	149
200	162	178	157	175	155	172	152	171	149	168	144	165	137	159
210	172	188	167	185	165	182	162	181	159	178	154	175	147	169
220	182	198	177	195	175	192	172	191	169	188	164	185	157	179
230	192	208	187	205	185	202	182	201	179	198	174	195	167	189
240	202	218	197	215	195	212	192	211	189	208	184	205	177	199
250	212	228	207	225	205	222	202	221	199	218	194	215	187	209
260	222	238	217	235	215	232	212	231	209	228	204	225	197	219
270	232	248	227	245	225	242	222	241	219	238	214	235	207	229
280	242	258	237	255	235	252	232	251	229	248	224	245	217	239
290	252	268	247	265	245	262	242	261	239	258	234	255	227	249
300	262	278	257	275	255	272	252	271	249	268	244	265	237	259

1. This table is based on ANSI B18.2.3.7M-1979 (R2006).
2. Bolts with lengths above the heavy solid line are threaded full length.

WEIGHT OF ASTM A325 BOLTS, NUTS AND WASHERS

WEIGHT IN POUNDS PER 100 UNITS

Length Under Head, Inches	HEAVY HEX STRUCTURAL BOLTS WITH HEAVY HEX NUTS (WITHOUT WASHERS)								
	Bolt Diameter, Inches								
	$\frac{1}{2}$	$\frac{5}{8}$	$\frac{3}{4}$	$\frac{7}{8}$	1	$1\frac{1}{8}$	$1\frac{1}{4}$	$1\frac{3}{8}$	$1\frac{1}{2}$
1	16.5	29.4	47.0						
$1\frac{1}{4}$	17.8	31.1	49.6	74.4	104				
$1\frac{1}{2}$	19.2	33.1	52.2	78.0	109	148	197		
$1\frac{3}{4}$	20.5	35.3	55.3	81.9	114	154	205	261	333
2	21.9	37.4	58.4	86.1	119	160	212	270	344
$2\frac{1}{4}$	23.3	39.8	61.6	90.3	124	167	220	279	355
$2\frac{1}{2}$	24.7	41.7	64.7	94.6	130	174	229	290	366
$2\frac{3}{4}$	26.1	43.9	67.8	98.8	135	181	237	300	379
3	27.4	46.1	70.9	103	141	188	246	310	391
$3\frac{1}{4}$	28.8	48.2	74.0	107	146	195	255	321	403
$3\frac{1}{2}$	30.2	50.4	77.1	111	151	202	263	332	416
$3\frac{3}{4}$	31.6	52.5	80.2	116	157	209	272	342	428
4	33.0	54.7	83.3	120	162	216	280	353	441
$4\frac{1}{4}$	34.3	56.9	86.4	124	168	223	289	363	453
$4\frac{1}{2}$	35.7	59.0	89.5	128	173	230	298	374	465
$4\frac{3}{4}$	37.1	61.2	92.7	133	179	237	306	384	478
5	38.5	63.3	95.8	137	184	244	315	395	490
$5\frac{1}{4}$	39.9	65.5	98.9	141	190	251	324	405	503
$5\frac{1}{2}$	41.2	67.7	102	146	196	258	332	416	515
$5\frac{3}{4}$	42.6	69.8	105	150	201	265	341	426	527
6	44.0	71.9	108	154	207	272	349	437	540
$6\frac{1}{4}$		74.1	111	158	212	279	358	447	552
$6\frac{1}{2}$		76.3	114	163	218	286	367	458	565
$6\frac{3}{4}$		78.5	118	167	223	293	375	468	577
7		80.6	121	171	229	300	384	479	589
$7\frac{1}{4}$		82.8	124	175	234	307	392	489	602
$7\frac{1}{2}$		84.9	127	179	240	314	401	500	614
$7\frac{3}{4}$		87.1	130	183	246	321	410	510	626
8		89.2	133	187	251	328	418	521	639
$8\frac{1}{4}$				192	257	335	427	531	651
$8\frac{1}{2}$				196	262	342	435	542	664
$8\frac{3}{4}$							444	552	676
9							453	563	689
Per inch additional	5.5	8.6	12.4	16.9	22.1	28.0	34.4	42.5	49.7

	$\frac{1}{2}$	$\frac{5}{8}$	$\frac{3}{4}$	$\frac{7}{8}$	1	$1\frac{1}{8}$	$1\frac{1}{4}$	$1\frac{3}{8}$	$1\frac{1}{2}$
Plain round washers	2.1	3.6	4.8	7.0	9.4	11.3	13.8	16.8	20.0
Beveled square washers	23.1	22.4	21.0	20.2	19.2	34.0	31.6	31.2	32.9

MASS OF ASTM A325M BOLTS, NUTS AND WASHERS

MASS IN KILOGRAMS PER 100 UNITS

Length Under Head, mm	HEAVY HEX STRUCTURAL BOLTS WITH HEAVY HEX NUTS (WITHOUT WASHERS)						
	Bolt Diameter, mm						
	M16	M20	M22	M24	M27	M30	M36
45	16.3						
50	17.1	30.4					
55	17.8	31.6	39.2				
60	18.6	32.9	40.7	53.7			
65	19.4	34.1	42.2	55.4	76.8		
70	20.2	35.3	43.7	57.2	79.0	98.0	
75	21.0	36.6	45.2	59.0	81.3	101	
80	21.8	37.8	46.7	60.7	83.5	104	167
85	22.6	39.0	48.1	62.5	85.8	106	171
90	23.4	40.3	49.6	64.3	88.0	109	175
95	24.1	41.5	51.1	66.1	90.2	112	179
100	24.9	42.7	52.6	67.8	92.5	114	183
110	26.3	44.9	55.3	71.0	96.7	120	191
120	27.9	47.4	58.2	74.5	101	125	199
130	29.5	49.8	61.2	78.0	106	131	207
140	31.1	52.3	64.2	81.6	110	136	214
150	32.6	54.7	67.2	85.1	115	142	222
160	34.2	57.2	70.2	88.7	119	147	230
170	35.8	59.7	73.1	92.2	124	153	238
180	37.3	62.1	76.1	95.8	128	158	246
190	38.9	64.6	79.1	99.3	132	164	254
200	40.5	67.0	82.1	103	137	169	262

	M16	M20	M22	M24	M27	M30	M36
Plain round washers	1.8	2.9	3.2	4.3	5.2	5.9	8.6
Beveled square washers	10.5	9.7	9.3	8.8	15.9	14.9	12.8

ASTM F436M METRIC WASHER DIMENSIONS

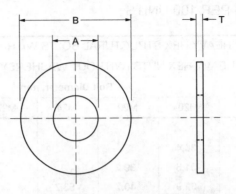

PLAIN CIRCULAR WASHERS

Metric Bolt Size	B Outside Diameter		A Hole Diameter		T Thickness	
	Max	Min	Max	Min	Max	Min
M16 x 2	34.0	32.4	18.4	18.0	4.6	3.1
M20 x 2.5	42.0	40.4	22.5	22.0	4.6	3.1
M22 x 2.5	44.0	42.4	24.5	24.0	4.6	3.4
M24 x 3	50.0	48.4	26.5	26.0	4.6	3.4
M27 x 3	56.0	54.1	30.5	30.0	4.6	3.4
M30 x 3.5	60.0	58.1	33.6	33.0	4.6	3.4
M36 x 4	72.0	70.1	39.6	39.0	4.6	3.4

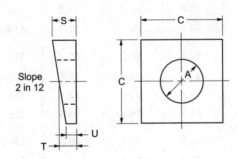

Slope
2 in 12

BEVELLED SQUARE WASHERS

Metric Bolt Size	C Width		A Hole Diameter		S	T Thickness	U
	Max	Min	Max	Min	Thick Side	Mean Nom.	Thin Side
M16 x 2	45.0	43.0	18.4	18.0	11.7	8	4.3
M20 x 2.5	45.0	43.0	22.5	22.0	11.7	8	4.3
M22 x 2.5	45.0	43.0	24.5	24.0	11.7	8	4.3
M24 x 3	45.0	43.0	26.5	26.0	11.7	8	4.3
M27 x 3	58.0	56.0	30.5	30.0	12.8	8	3.3
M30 x 3.5	58.0	56.0	33.6	33.0	12.8	8	3.3
M36 x 4	58.0	56.0	39.6	39.0	12.8	8	3.3

ASTM A307 BOLTS AND NUTS
DIMENSIONS IN IMPERIAL UNITS

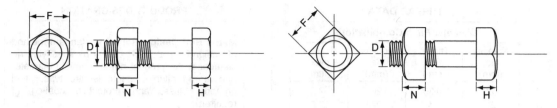

Nominal Diameter of Bolt	Regular Square Bolts		Finished Hex Bolts		Minimum Thread Lengths		Regular Square Nuts		Finished Hex Nuts	
	Nominal Width F	Nominal Height H	Basic Width F	Basic Height H	Length Under Head		Nominal Width F	Nominal Height H	Basic Width F	Basic Height N
					6 In. and under	Over 6 In.				
Inches	Inches	Inches	Inches	Inches	Inches	Inches	Inches	Inches	Inches	Inches
1/4	3/8	11/64	7/16	5/32	3/4	1	7/16	7/32	7/16	7/32
3/8	9/16	1/4	9/16	15/64	1	1 1/4	5/8	21/64	9/16	21/64
1/2	3/4	21/64	3/4	5/16	1 1/4	1 1/2	13/16	7/16	3/4	7/16
5/8	15/16	27/64	15/16	25/64	1 1/2	1 3/4	1	35/64	15/16	35/64
3/4	1 1/8	1/2	1 1/8	15/32	1 3/4	2	1 1/8	21/32	1 1/8	41/64
7/8	1 5/16	19/32	1 5/16	35/64	2	2 1/4	1 5/16	49/64	1 5/16	3/4
1	1 1/2	21/32	1 1/2	39/64	2 1/4	2 1/2	1 1/2	7/8	1 1/2	55/64
1 1/8	1 11/16	3/4	1 11/16	11/16	2 1/2	2 3/4	1 11/16	1	1 11/16	31/32
1 1/4	1 7/8	27/32	1 7/8	25/32	2 3/4	3	1 7/8	1 3/32	1 7/8	1 1/16

The dimensions for Regular Square Bolts conform to those for Square Head Bolts, Regular Series listed in CSA Standard B33.1-1961, "Square and Hexagon Bolts and Nuts, Studs and Wrench Openings", and to those for Square Bolts listed in ANSI Standard B18.2.1-1965, "Square and Hex Bolts and Screws".

The dimensions for Finished Hexagon Bolts (Hex Cap Screws) conform to those for Hexagon Head Bolts, Finished Grade, Regular Series listed in CSA Standard B33.1-1961, and to those for Hex Cap Screws (Finished Hex Bolts) listed in ANSI Standard B18.2.1-1965.

The minimum thread lengths are in agreement with the requirements of CSA Standard B33.1-1961 and with ANSI Standard B18.2.1-1965. In general, these requirements are as follows:

- Bolts 6 inches or less in length – twice diameter plus ¼-inch.
- Bolts longer than 6 inches – twice diameter plus ½-inch.
- Bolts too short for the above thread lengths shall be threaded as close to the head as practicable.

The dimensions for Regular Square Nuts conform to those for Square Nuts, Regular Series listed in CSA Standard B33.1-1961, and to those for Square Nuts listed in ANSI Standard B18.2.2-1965, "Square and Hex Nuts".

The dimensions for Finished Hexagon Nuts conform to those for Hexagon Nuts, Finished Grade, Regular Series listed in CSA Standard B33.1-1961 and to those for Hex Nuts listed in ANSI Standard B18.2.2-1965.

Note: Square head bolts are used with either square or hexagon nuts. However, the use of Finished Hexagon Bolts and Finished Hexagon Nuts is gradually replacing the use of square head bolts and nuts in sizes up to one inch in diameter and six inches in length. A307 bolts and nuts are manufactured in Imperial dimensions only.

FASTENERS – MISCELLANEOUS DETAILING DATA

Metric Fastener Designations

THREAD DATA

Diameter Pitch Combinations			
Nominal dia. (mm)	Thread pitch (mm)	Nominal dia. (mm)	Thread pitch (mm)
1.6	0.35	20	2.5
2	0.4	22	2.5
2.5	0.45	24	3
3	0.5	27	3
3.5	0.6	30	3.5
4	0.7	36	4
5	0.8	42	4.5
6.0	1.0	48	5
8	1.25	56	5.5
10	1.5	64	6
12	1.75	72	6
14	2	80	6
16	2	90	6
		100	6

Basic Metric Thread Designation: Metric screw threads are designated by the letter "M" followed by the nominal size (basic major diameter) in millimetres and the pitch in millimetres separated by the symbol "X".

M12	X	1.75	– 6g
Size (mm)		Thread (pitch in mm)	Standard class of fit

Note: In the metric system, the pitch of the thread is given in mm instead of threads per inch – thus a M12 x 1.75 thread has a nominal diameter of 12 mm and the pitch of the thread is 1.75 mm.

PRODUCT DESIGNATION

Metric Bolt Designation: The standard method of designating a metric bolt is by specifying (in sequence) the product name, nominal diameter and thread pitch, nominal length, type, steel property class, and protective coating (if required).

Heavy Hex Structural Bolt, M22x2.5x160, Type 2, ASTM A325M-09, Zinc Galvanized

Metric Nut Designation: The standard method of designating a metric nut is by specifying (in sequence) the product name, nominal diameter and pitch, steel property class or material identification, and protective coating (if required).

Heavy Hex Nut, M30x3.5, ASTM A563M class 105, hot dipped galvanized

Note: It is common practice to omit the thread pitch from the product designation.

Slotted Hole Dimensions

See S16-09 Clause 22.3.5.2 regarding provisions.

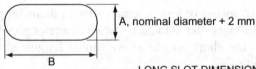

A, nominal diameter + 2 mm

B

SHORT SLOT DIMENSIONS

Nominal Bolt Diameter	Slot Dimensions	
	Width, A	Length, B
mm	mm	mm
16	18	22
20	22	26
22	24	28
24	26	32
27	29	37
30	32	40
36	38	46

LONG SLOT DIMENSIONS

Nominal Bolt Diameter	Slot Dimensions	
	Width, A	Length, B
mm	mm	mm
16	18	40
20	22	50
22	24	55
24	26	60
27	29	67.5
30	32	75
36	38	90

FASTENERS - MISCELLANEOUS DETAILING DATA
Diagonal Distance for Staggered Fasteners

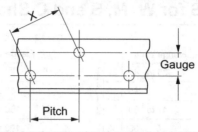

Pitch	Gauge, mm																	
mm	25	30	35	40	45	50	55	60	65	70	75	80	85	90	95	100	105	110
5	25	30	35	40	45	50	55	60	65	70	75	80	85	90	95	100	105	110
10	27	32	36	41	46	51	56	61	66	71	76	81	86	91	96	100	105	110
15	29	34	38	43	47	52	57	62	67	72	76	81	86	91	96	101	106	111
20	32	36	40	45	49	54	59	63	68	73	78	82	87	92	97	102	107	112
25	35	39	43	47	51	56	60	65	70	74	79	84	89	93	98	103	108	113
30	39	42	46	50	54	58	63	67	72	76	81	85	90	95	100	104	109	114
35	43	46	49	53	57	61	65	69	74	78	83	87	92	97	101	106	111	115
40	47	50	53	57	60	64	68	72	76	81	85	89	94	98	103	108	112	117
45	51	54	57	60	64	67	71	75	79	83	87	92	96	101	105	110	114	119
50	56	58	61	64	67	71	74	78	82	86	90	94	99	103	107	112	116	121
55	60	63	65	68	71	74	78	81	85	89	93	97	101	105	110	114	119	123
60	65	67	69	72	75	78	81	85	88	92	96	100	104	108	112	117	121	125
65	70	72	74	76	79	82	85	88	92	96	99	103	107	111	115	119	123	128
70	74	76	78	81	83	86	89	92	96	99	103	106	110	114	118	122	126	130
75	79	81	83	85	87	90	93	96	99	103	106	110	113	117	121	125	129	133
80	84	85	87	89	92	94	97	100	103	106	110	113	117	120	124	128	132	136
85	89	90	92	94	96	99	101	104	107	110	113	117	120	124	127	131	135	139
90	93	95	97	98	101	103	105	108	111	114	117	120	124	127	131	135	138	142

BOLT LENGTH TOLERANCES

Nominal Length	Nominal Bolt Dia.
	M16 through M36
to 50 mm	± 1.2
over 50 to 80 mm	± 1.5
over 80 to 120 mm	± 1.8
over 120 to 150 mm	± 2.0
over 150 mm	± 4.0

MINIMUM EDGE DISTANCE FOR BOLT HOLES

Bolt Diameter mm	At Sheared Edge mm	At Rolled or Gas Cut Edge[†] mm
16	28	22
20	34	26
22	38	28
24	42	30
27	48	34
30	52	38
36	64	46
over 36	1¾ x Diameter	1¼ x Diameter

† Gas cut edges shall be smooth and free from notches. Edge distance in this column may be decreased 3 mm when hole is at a point where computed stress under factored loads is not more than 0.3 of the yield stress.

USUAL GAUGES

USUAL GAUGES for W, M, S and C Shapes, Millimetres

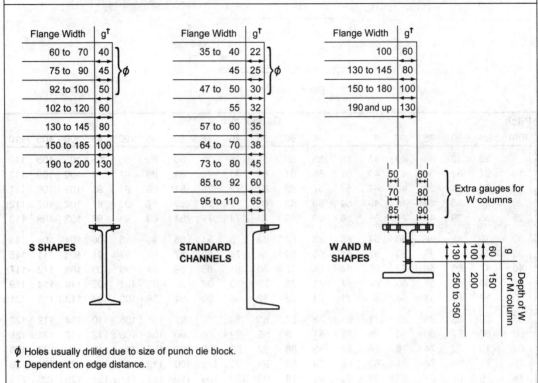

Flange Width	g†
60 to 70	40
75 to 90	45
92 to 100	50
102 to 120	60
130 to 145	80
150 to 185	100
190 to 200	130

S SHAPES

Flange Width	g†
35 to 40	22
45	25
47 to 50	30
55	32
57 to 60	35
64 to 70	38
73 to 80	45
85 to 92	60
95 to 110	65

STANDARD CHANNELS

Flange Width	g†
100	60
130 to 145	80
150 to 180	100
190 and up	130

W AND M SHAPES

Extra gauges for W columns: 50 60 / 70 80 / 85 90

ø Holes usually drilled due to size of punch die block.

† Dependent on edge distance.

USUAL GAUGES for Angles, Millimetres

Notes:

Those values shown above the dashed line allow for full socket wrench clearance requirements.

The bolt sizes shown in italics to the left of g and g_1 are the maximum bolt sizes permissible for the dimensions shown.

$g_2 \geq 2\frac{2}{3}$ bolt diameters.

Gauge Leg	g		g_1		g_2
200	M36	115	M30	80	80
150	M36	90	M24	55	65
125	M30	80	M20	45	54
100	M27	65			
90	M24	60			
80	M24	50			
75	M24	45			
65	M24	35			
60	M24	30			
55	M22	27			
50	M16	28			
45	M16	23			

ERECTION CLEARANCES
Bolt Impact Wrenches

METRIC	IMPERIAL

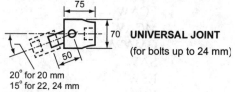

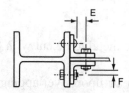

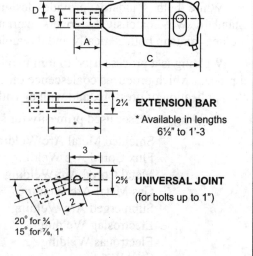

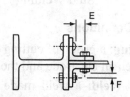

METRIC

EXTENSION BAR
* Available in lengths
160 to 380 mm

UNIVERSAL JOINT
(for bolts up to 24 mm)

20° for 20 mm
15° for 22, 24 mm

MINIMUM CLEARANCES

	Size	C	D
Light Wrenches	16 to 24	337 to 356	54
Heavy Wrenches	24 to 36	375 to 438	64

	Sockets		Min. Clearance	
Bolt size	A	B	E	F
16	80	45	25	28
20	85	54	30	34
22	90	57	32	36
24	95	60	34	38
27	100	70	38	42
30	110	75	41	45
36	130	90	48	52

IMPERIAL

EXTENSION BAR
* Available in lengths
6½" to 1'-3

UNIVERSAL JOINT
(for bolts up to 1")

20° for ¾
15° for ⅞, 1"

MINIMUM CLEARANCES

	Size	C	D
Light Wrenches	⅝ to 1	1-1¼ to 1-2	2⅛
Heavy Wrenches	1 to 1½	1-2¾ to 1-5¼	2½

	Sockets		Min. Clearance	
Bolt size	A	B	E	F
5/8	2-5/8	1-3/4	1-1/8	1-1/4
3/4	3	2-1/4	1-1/4	1-3/8
7/8	3-1/4	2-1/2	1-5/16	1-7/16
1	3-1/2	2-5/8	1-7/16	1-9/16
1-1/8	3-3/4	2-7/8	1-9/16	1-11/16
1-1/4	4	3-1/8	1-5/8	1-3/4
1-3/8	4-1/4	3-1/4	2-1/8	2-1/4
1-1/2	4-3/8	4-1/4		

WELDING

The welding of steel shapes and plates for structural purposes is governed by CAN/CSA-S16, Design of Steel Structures, and CSA Standard W59, Welded Steel Construction (Metal-Arc Welding). In case of conflict between the requirements of CSA W59 and S16, however, S16 shall take precedence (see CSA S16-09 Clause 24.1).

While both standards provide design information on the resistance of welds, CSA Standard W59 extensively covers workmanship, inspection, and acceptance criteria for welded joints in both statically and dynamically loaded structures.

Welding is a process used to join two or more pieces of material together. Arc welding is a process which produces coalescence of metals by heating them with an arc, with or without the application of pressure, and with or without the use of filler metal.

Welding processes used primarily for structural steelwork are:

Shielded Metal Arc Welding	SMAW
Flux Cored Arc Welding	FCAW
Metal Cored Arc Welding	MCAW
Gas Metal Arc Welding	GMAW
Submerged Arc Welding	SAW
Electroslag Welding	ESW
Electrogas Welding	EGW
Stud Welding	SW

Welding Definitions

Arc Cutting: a group of cutting processes which melts the metal to be cut with the heat of an arc between an electrode and the base metal.

Arc Spot Weld: a weld made by arc welding between or upon overlapping members in which coalescence may start and occur on the faying surfaces or may proceed from the surface of one member. This is commonly used for thin materials, such as roof and floor deck attachment.

Base Metal: the metal to be welded or cut.

Bevel Angle: the angle formed between the prepared edge of a member and a plane perpendicular to the surface of the member.

Chain Intermittent Welds: intermittent welds on both sides of a joint in which the weld increments on one side are approximately opposite those on the other side.

Coalescence: the growing together or growth into one body of the material being welded.

Complete Joint Penetration: a joint in which the weld metal completely fills the groove and is fused to the base metal throughout its total thickness.

Edge Joint: a joint between the edge of two or more parallel or nearly parallel members.

Effective Weld Length: the length of weld throughout which the correctly proportioned cross section exists. In a curved weld, it is measured along the axis of the weld.

Effective Throat: the minimum distance from the root of a weld to its face less any reinforcement.

End Return (Boxing): the continuation of a fillet weld around a corner of a member as an extension of the principal weld.

Face of Weld: the exposed surface of a weld on the side from which the welding was done.

Fillet Weld: a weld of approximately triangular cross section joining two surfaces approximately at right angles to each other in a lap joint, T-joint, or corner joint.

Groove Weld: a weld made in a groove between two members to be joined.

Intermittent Weld: a weld in which the continuity is broken by recurring unwelded spaces.

Joint Design: the joint geometry together with the required dimensions of the welded joint.

Joint Penetration: the minimum depth a groove weld extends from its face into a joint, exclusive of reinforcement, but including, if present, root penetration.

Leg of a Fillet Weld: the distance from the root of the joint to the toe of the fillet weld.

Partial Joint Penetration: a joint penetration which is less than complete.

Procedure Qualification: a demonstration that welds made by a specific procedure can meet prescribed standards.

Root of Joint: that portion of a joint to be welded where the members approach closest to each other. In cross section, the root of the joint may be a point, a line or an area.

Root of Weld: the points, as shown in cross section, at which the back of the weld intersects the base metal surfaces.

Root Penetration: the depth that a weld extends into the root of a joint measured on the centreline of the root cross section.

Size of Weld:

It should be noted that weld symbols and sizes used in North America generally comply with American Welding Society A2.4 "Standard Symbols for Welding, Brazing and Nondestructive Examination". Care should be taken when interpreting other symbol systems.

> **Groove Weld**: the joint penetration (depth of bevel plus the root penetration when specified). The size of a groove weld and its effective throat are one and the same.

> **Fillet Weld**:

> For equal-leg fillet welds, the leg lengths of the largest isosceles right triangle which can be inscribed within the fillet weld cross section.

> For unequal-leg fillet welds, the leg lengths of the largest right triangle which can be inscribed within the fillet weld cross section.

> Note: When one member makes an angle with the other member greater than 105 degrees, the leg length (size) is of less significance than the effective throat which is the controlling factor for the strength of a weld.

Tack Weld: a weld made to hold parts of a weldment in proper alignment until the final welds are made. (Care should be taken to ensure the compatibility of weld metals.)

Throat of a Fillet Weld:

> **Theoretical Throat**: the distance from the beginning of the root of the joint perpendicular to the hypotenuse of the largest right triangle that can be inscribed within the fillet weld cross section. This dimension is based on the assumption that the root opening is equal to zero.

> **Actual Throat**: the shortest distance from the root of weld to its face.

> **Effective Throat**: the minimum distance minus any reinforcement from the root of weld to its face.

WELDING PRACTICE

Fillet Welds

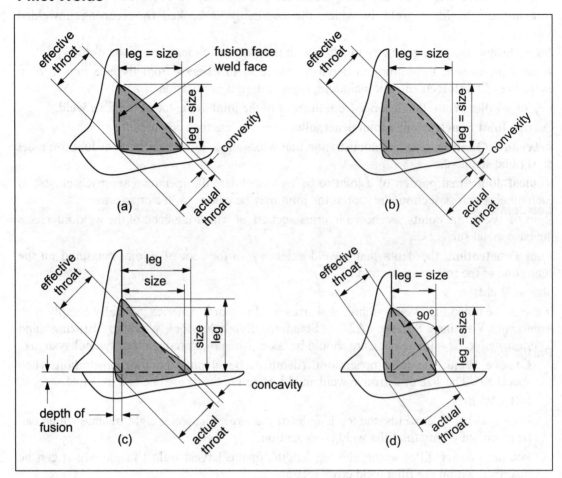

Minimum Size

- The minimum size of a fillet weld as measured should not be less than the values shown on the right, except that it need not exceed the thickness of the thinner part.

  When welding attachments to non-load-carrying members, the values on the right need not apply.

Material thickness of thicker part joined (mm)	Minimum size of fillet weld (mm)
to 6 incl.	3
over 6 to 12	5
over 12 to 20	6
over 20	8

- The minimum effective length of a fillet weld should be 38 mm or 4 times the size of the fillet, whichever is larger.

Maximum Size of Weld

- The maximum fillet weld size, D_{max}, recommended by good practice along a sheared edge is:

  $$D_{max} = t \qquad \text{when } t < 6 \text{ mm}$$
  $$D_{max} = t - 2 \qquad \text{when } t \geq 6 \text{ mm}$$

- Material with rolled edges:

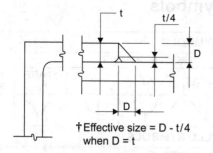 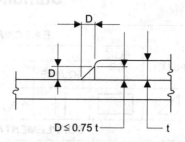

† Effective size = D - t/4
when D = t

$D \leq 0.75\,t$

- When fillet welds are used in holes or slots, the diameter of the hole or the width of the slot should not be less than the thickness (t) of the member containing it plus 8 mm. The maximum width shall be t + 12 mm or 2.25 t, whichever is greater.

Lap Joints

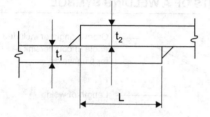

$L_{min} = 5\,t_1 \geq 25$ mm when $t_1 \leq t_2$
$L_{min} = 5\,t_2 \geq 25$ mm when $t_2 < t_1$

Partial Penetration Groove Welds

Minimum Groove Depth for Partial Joint Penetration Groove Welds†

Thickness of Thicker Part Joined (Millimetres)	Minimum Groove Depth, mm	
	Groove Angle, α, at Root $45° \leq \alpha < 60°$ (V-, Bevel Grooves)	Groove Angle, α, at Root $\alpha \geq 60°$ (V-, Bevel, J-, U-Grooves)
Total 12 incl.	8	5
Over 12 – 20	10	6
Over 20 – 40	11	8
Over 40 – 60	12	10
Over 60	16	12

† Not combined with fillet welds

Flare Bevel and Flare V-Welds

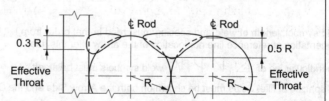

0.3 R   ¢ Rod   ¢ Rod   0.5 R

Effective Throat   R   R   Effective Throat

Solid or hollow sections with weld filled flush to the curved surface:
Not applicable to the GMAW process
Flare Bevel Groove Weld:
The effective throat for a joint between a curved and a planar surface shall be 0.3 R.
Flare Vee Groove Weld:
The effective throat for a joint between two curved surfaces shall be 0.5 R.

WELDED JOINTS
Standard Symbols

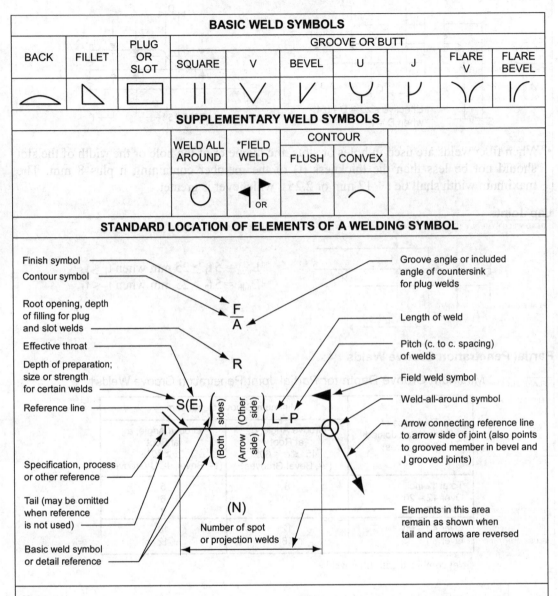

BASIC WELD SYMBOLS										
			GROOVE OR BUTT							
BACK	FILLET	PLUG OR SLOT	SQUARE	V	BEVEL	U	J		FLARE V	FLARE BEVEL

SUPPLEMENTARY WELD SYMBOLS				
	WELD ALL AROUND	*FIELD WELD	CONTOUR	
			FLUSH	CONVEX

STANDARD LOCATION OF ELEMENTS OF A WELDING SYMBOL

Finish symbol

Contour symbol

Root opening, depth of filling for plug and slot welds

Effective throat

Depth of preparation; size or strength for certain welds

Reference line

Specification, process or other reference

Tail (may be omitted when reference is not used)

Basic weld symbol or detail reference

$\dfrac{F}{A}$

R

S(E)

T

(Both sides)   (Arrow side)   (Other side)

L–P

(N)

Number of spot or projection welds

Groove angle or included angle of countersink for plug welds

Length of weld

Pitch (c. to c. spacing) of welds

Field weld symbol

Weld-all-around symbol

Arrow connecting reference line to arrow side of joint (also points to grooved member in bevel and J grooved joints)

Elements in this area remain as shown when tail and arrows are reversed

Notes:

Size, weld symbol, length of weld and spacing must read in that order from left to right along the reference line. Neither orientation of reference line nor location of the arrow alter this rule.

The perpendicular leg of ⊿, V, ⌐, ⟨ weld symbols must be at left.

Size and spacing of fillet welds must be shown on both the Arrow Side and the Other Side Symbol.

Symbols apply between abrupt changes in direction of welding unless governed by the "all around" symbol or otherwise dimensioned.

These symbols do not explicitly provide for the case that frequently occurs in structural work, where duplicate material (such as stiffeners) occurs on the far side of a web or gusset plate. The fabricating industry has adopted this convention: when the billing of the detail material discloses the identity of far side with near side, the welding shown for the near side shall also be duplicated on the far side.

* Pennant points away from arrow.

WELDING SYMBOLS

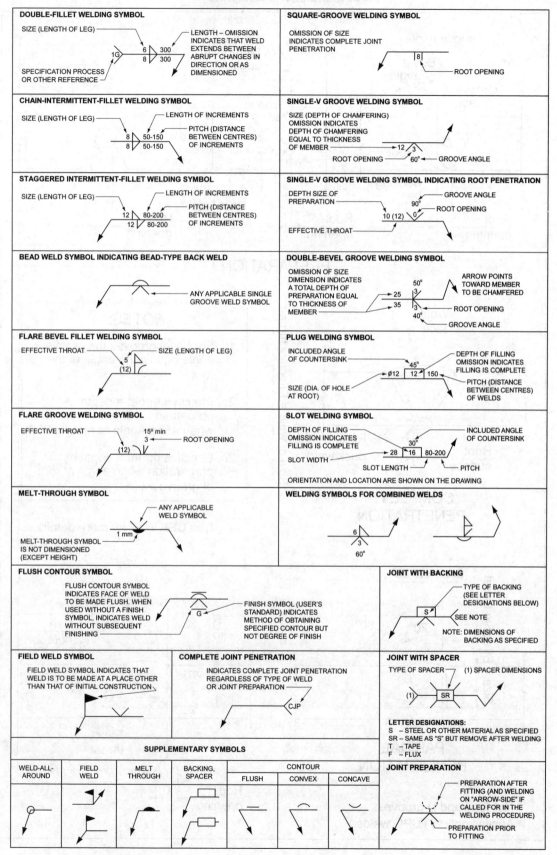

SAMPLE GROOVE WELDS

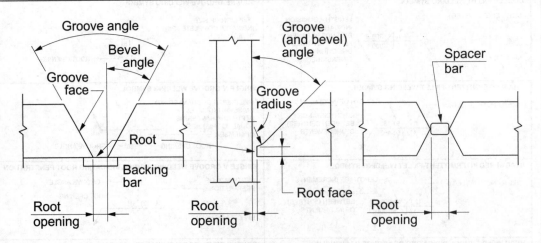

PREPARATION

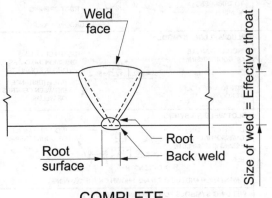

COMPLETE PENETRATION

NOTES:

1. For bevel grooves the groove angle equals the angle at the root.[1]

2a. Effective throat = depth of preparation − 3 mm when $45° \leq$ Angle at root $< 60°$ [2]

2b. Effective throat = depth of preparation when angle at root of groove $\geq 60°$ [2]

See CSA W59 for more details.

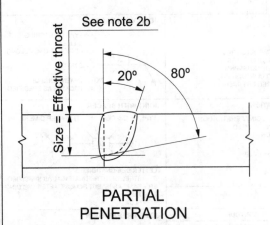

PARTIAL PENETRATION

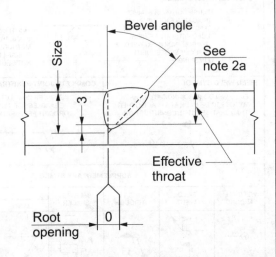

[1] Not for J and U grooves
[2] Applies only to PJPG welds.

STEEL PRODUCTS – RECORD OF CHANGES

Following is a chronological record of changes to the list of steel sections included in the CISC Handbook of Steel Construction since the first printing of the Third Edition.

1983   No longer produced by Algoma are:

        M100x19
        S150x26, 19; S130x22, 15; S100x11; S75x11, 8
        All angles except 8" x 8" leg sizes

1985   No longer produced by Algoma are:

        WWF550x217; WWF350x385

    New shapes and sections produced by Algoma:

        WWF1800x632, 548; WWF1600x579, 495
        WWF1400x491, 407; WWF550x280

    Welded Reduced Flange (WRF) shapes with top flanges narrower than the bottom flanges and intended primarily for composite bridge girders:

        WRF1800x543, 480, 416; WRF1600x491, 427, 362
        WRF1400x413, 348, 284; WRF1200x373, 309, 244
        WRF1000x340, 275, 210

1986   New shapes and sections produced by Algoma:

        W610x91, 84; W530x72; W310x31; W250x24; W200x21

1989   Sections produced by Algoma

    Sections deleted:

        WWF1800x632, 548; WWF1600x579, 495
        WWF1400x491, 407; WWF1200x403, 364
        WWF1100x335, 291, 255, 220; WWF1000x324, 280, 244
        WWF900x293, 249, 213; WWF800x332–154; WWF700x222–141

    Sections added:

        WWF2000x732–542; WWF1800x700–510; WWF1600x622–431
        WWF1400x597–358; WWF1200x418, 380, 333
        WWF1100x351, 304, 273, 234; WWF1000x340, 293, 262, 223
        WWF900x309, 262, 231; WWF800x339–161; WWF700x245–152
        WWF650x864–400; WWF600x793–369

    Sections not available from Canadian mills added:

        W1000–All sizes
        W920x1262–488; W840x922–392; W760x865–350; W760x134
        W690x802–289; W610x732–262; W530x599–248; W460x464–193

1991   Sections no longer available from Canadian mills:

W310x283, 253
C380x74–50; C310x45–31

1993   The following shapes are no longer produced:

HP330x149–89
M150x29.8–6.5; M100x19

1995   Sections deleted:

W1000x488–286, 976, 790–483; W920x1072, 876, 722; W840x922–577
W760x865, 783, 644, 531; W690x735, 605, 500, 419
W610x670, 551, 455; W530x599–331
HP330x149–89
M150x29.8, 6.5; M100x19
S180x30, 22.8; S130x22
C130x17
MC250x9.7; MC180x26.2; MC150x22.8
L152x102x4.8; L127x127x4.8; L127x89x11, 4.8; L127x76x16, 4.8
L102x102x4.8; L102x89x16, 11, 4.8; L102x76x4.8; L89x89x16, 4.8
L89x76x16, 11; L89x64x16, 11; L76x76x16; L76x64x16, 11
L76x51x16, 11; L64x64x3.2; L64x51x3.2; L51x38x9.5, 3.2
L32x32x9.5; L25x25x9.5, 7.9
L200–L25 (All metric angles)

Sections added:

W1100x499–342; W1000x749–478, 259, 693–314; W920x381, 345
W840x251; W760x220; W690x192; W610x153; W360x1202
M310x16.1; M250x11.9; M100x8.9
SLB100x5.4, 4.8; SLB75x4.5, 4.3
L203x102x22, 16, 11; L178x102x11; L19x19x3.2

1997   Sections deleted:

W1000x478, 259, 693; W920x1262; W760x710; W690x667
W610x732, 608; W460x464–286; W360x1202
L203x203x14; L203x152x22, 16, 14; L203x102x22, 16, 14, 11
L152x102x6.4; L152x89x6.4; L89x76x4.8; L89x64x4.8; L64x38x7.9–4.8
L51x38x7.9; L44x44x9.5, 7.9; L38x38x9.5, 7.9, 4.0; L32x32x7.9
HSS51x51x2.5; HSS38x38x2.5; HSS32x32x3.8–2.5; HSS25x25x3.2, 2.5
HSS127x64x9.5–4.8; HSS127x51x9.5–4.8; HSS51x25x2.5
HSS48x2.8; HSS42x3.2, 2.5; HSS33x3.2, 2.5; HSS27x3.2, 2.5

Sections added:

W1000x591, 539, 486, 483; W840x576; W760x531; W690x500, 419
W610x551, 455; W150x13
L152x152x6.4

HSS127x127x13; HSS102x102x3.8, 3.2; HSS89x89x3.8, 3.2
HSS76x76x9.5, 3.8, 3.2
HSS152x102x13; HSS152x76x9.5–4.8; HSS127x76x3.8
HSS102x76x3.8, 3.2; HSS76x51x3.2
HSS610x13–6.4; HSS559x13–6.4; HSS508x13–6.4

2000   Sections deleted:

HP310x174, 152, 132

2004   Sections deleted:

W840x576; W760x531
WT230x33.5, 30.5
L203x152x11
HSS305x305x11; HSS254x254x11; HSS203x203x11; HSS178x178x11
HSS152x152x11; HSS127x127x11; HSS102x102x3.8; HSS89x89x3.8
HSS76x76x3.8; HSS64x64x3.8; HSS51x51x3.8; HSS38x38x3.8
HSS305x203x11; HSS254x152x11; HSS203x152x11; HSS203x102x11
HSS178x127x11; HSS152x102x11; HSS127x76x3.8; HSS102x76x3.8
HSS102x51x3.8; HSS89x64x3.8; HSS76x51x3.8
HSS610x13, 11, 9.5, 8.0, 6.4; HSS559x13, 11, 9.5, 8.0, 6.4
HSS508x13, 11, 9.5, 8.0, 6.4; HSS406x11, 8.0; HSS356x11, 8.0
HSS324x11, 8.0; HSS273x11, 9.5, 8.0; HSS219x11, 8.0; HSS141x8.0
HSS114x8.0, 6.4; HSS102x3.8; HSS89x3.8; HSS73x3.8; HSS60x3.8
HSS48x3.8

Sections added:

M310x14.9; M250x11.2; M200x9.2; M150x6.6, 5.5
SLB100x5.1; SLB75x5.6, 3.8; SLB55x6.4
C100x7, C75x5
MC150x22.8
L203x203x14; L203x152x22, 16, 14; L102x89x11; L51x38x3.2
HSS305x305x16; HSS254x254x16; HSS203x203x16; HSS178x178x16
HSS114x114x13, 9.5, 8.0, 6.4, 4.8, 3.2; HSS102x102x13; HSS64x64x8.0
HSS356x254x16, 13, 9.5; HSS305x203x16; HSS254x152x16
HSS152x76x13; HSS102x51x9.5; HSS51x25x4.8
HSS356x16; HSS273x4.8; HSS219x16; HSS178x13, 9.5, 8.0, 6.4, 4.8
HSS168x13, 3.2; HSS152x9.5, 8.0, 6.4, 4.8, 3.2
HSS127x13, 9.5, 8.0, 6.4, 4.8, 3.2; HSS114x9.5, 3.2; HSS102x3.2
HSS89x3.2; HSS76x6.4, 4.8; HSS64x6.4, 4.8, 3.2

2006   Sections deleted:

W920x1188, 967, 784, 653, 585, 534, 488, 446, 417, 387, 365, 342

Sections added:

W1000x438; W920x1191, 970, 787, 725, 656, 588, 537, 491, 449, 420,
390, 368, 344; W840x576; W760x531; W460x464, 421, 384, 349, 315,
286

2010   Sections deleted:

W920x1191, 970, 787, 725; W690x802; W310x31; W250x24; W200x21
WT460x223, 208.5, 193.5, 182.5, 171
M200x9.2, M150x5.5, M130x28.1

Sections added:

WT460x224.5, 210, 195, 184, 172

PART SEVEN
MISCELLANEOUS

CISC
CODE OF STANDARD PRACTICE
for Structural Steel

Seventh Edition

Published by the
CANADIAN INSTITUTE OF STEEL CONSTRUCTION
3760 14th Avenue ▪ Suite 200
Markham ▪ Ontario ▪ L3R 3T7

cisc ⏚ icca

TABLE OF CONTENTS

CISC CODE OF STANDARD PRACTICE
for Structural Steel

PREFACE

The CISC Code of Standard Practice for Structural Steel is a compilation of usual industry practices relating to the design, fabrication and erection of structural steel. These practices evolve over a period of time and are subject to change as improved methods replace those of an earlier period. The Code is revised whenever a sufficient number of changes have occurred to warrant a new edition.

The first edition of the Code was adopted and published in November 1958. A second edition incorporating minor revisions was published in October 1962. The third edition, published in September 1967 and revised in May 1970, incorporated minor changes throughout with principal changes in Section 2 - Definition of Structural Steel and Section 3 - Computation of Weights for Unit Price Bids.

The fourth edition adopted in June 1980, revised December 1980, broadened the scope to include bridges and other structures. It also incorporated the CISC "Guide to Tendering Procedures" into Section 3 and Appendices B and C. The Code was converted to SI (metric) units and provided conversion factors and Imperial units in Appendix E.

The fifth edition (1991) reflected the steel standard's recognition of the preparation of five types of fabrication and erection documents which may be produced in fulfilling a steel construction contract. These documents may be in the form of drawings, diagrams, sketches, computer output, hand calculations and other data which can be supplied by the fabricator/erector. This data is generally referred to in contract documents as "shop drawings". The computation of mass has been changed by deleting the mass of welds and the allowances for paint and other coatings. Appendix B, Guideline for Unit Price Application for Changes, and Appendix C, A Suggested Format for Price-Per-Unit of Mass or Price-Per-Item Contracts were substantially revised. To foster uniformity, two new appendices were added: Miscellaneous Steel and A Suggested Format for a Monthly Progress Claim Form.

The sixth edition (1999) clarified the role of the fabricator, the information required, and where that information is expected, as stipulated in the governing technical standards. Added were: definitions of Design Drawings and Quotations, clauses on quotations, discrepancies, shims for bearing surfaces, the allowance for return of documents, the information required when painting is specified, and Appendix H - Suggested Definitions for Progress Invoicing and Substantial Performance. Changes were also made to Appendix C, the terminology for Unit Price contracts, connection types, and anchor rods – the latter two to be consistent with the changes in CSA Standard CAN/CSA-S16-01.

This seventh edition adds two new appendices: I - Architecturally Exposed Structural Steel (AESS) and J - Digital Modelling, in order to give guidance to designers, owners, and contractors on these two important topics. As each of these topics involves issues that vary widely and approaches differ, the Code endeavours to identify and clarify the main points that should be addressed by the interested parties to avoid conflicts during actual construction. In addition, definitions of AESS, STEEL DETAILER and WORK, and a time frame for accepting erected steelwork have been added.

Whenever a gender-specific term is used, it shall be read as gender-neutral.

By documenting standard practices the Code aims to promote a clear understanding between the Canadian structural steel fabrication and erection industry and its clients.

Canadian Institute of Steel Construction

Adopted June 6, 2008

CISC CODE OF STANDARD PRACTICE
for Structural Steel

1. General Provisions

1.1 Scope

This Code covers standard industry practice with respect to the furnishing of structural steel. In the absence of provisions to the contrary contained in contracts to which members of the Canadian Institute of Steel Construction are contracting parties, members will abide by the practices described herein.

1.2 Definitions

Approved-for-Construction Drawings	Drawings and other documents approved by the client authorizing work to proceed. (May also be called "Issued-for-Construction Drawings").
Architect	As defined under the appropriate Architect's Act.
Architecturally Exposed Structural Steel	Structural steel which is specifically designated as architecturally exposed and the appearance of which is governed by Appendix I, Architecturally Exposed Structural Steel.
Client	A person, corporation, or authority with whom the fabricator has contracted.
Connection Design Details	Documents which provide details of standard and non-standard connections and other data necessary for the preparation of shop details.
Construction Drawings	Drawings used to govern the construction of the works.
Construction Specifications	Specifications used to govern the construction of the works.
Contract	The agreement between the fabricator and/or erector, and the client.
Contract Documents	The documents which define the responsibilities of the parties involved in tendering, purchasing, supplying, fabricating and erecting structural steel, including tender drawings and tender specifications and applicable revisions in effect and agreed to at the time of contract award.
Cost Plus a Fee Contract	An Agreement whereby the fabricator and/or erector agrees to fulfil the contract for a consideration which is calculated on the basis of the fabricator's costs plus a specified fee as defined in the contract.
Design Drawings	Drawings, including computer output, electronic and other data, as prepared by the designer showing member sizes and dimensions and all required forces for connection design, i.e. shears, axial forces, moments and torsions. (See governing technical standard).

Designer	The designer of the structure. See Engineer of Record.
Engineer	As defined under the appropriate Professional Engineer's Act.
Engineer of Record	Professional Engineer who designs the structure, as defined under the appropriate Professional Engineer's Act.
Erection Bracing	Bracing materials or members which are used to plumb, align and stabilize structural members or the structure during construction and are removed when the structural members or the structure is secured by bolting or welding of structural members.
Erection Diagrams	Are general arrangement drawings showing the principal dimensions and elevations of the steel structure, sizes of the steel members, piece marks, size (diameter) and type of bolts, bolt installation requirements, elevations of column bases, all necessary dimensions and details for setting anchor rods, and all other information necessary for the assembly of the structure.
Erection Procedures	Outline the construction methods, erection sequence, erection and temporary bracing requirements, and other engineering details necessary for shipping, handling, erecting, and maintaining the stability of the structural steel frame.
Erector	Means the party responsible for erection of the steelwork.
Fabricator	Means the party responsible for furnishing the structural steel.
Field Work Details	Are details that provide complete information for modifying fabricated members in the field (e.g. prepare existing steel to receive new steel).
General Contractor, Constructor or Construction Manager	The person or corporation who constructs, coordinates, and supervises the construction of the work.
General Terminology e.g. Beams, Joists, Columns, etc.	These terms have the meanings stated or implied in CAN/CSA-S16 (latest edition), CAN/CSA-S6 (latest edition) and Appendix A of this Code.
Lump Sum Price Contract	Also called Stipulated Price Contract. An agreement whereby the fabricator and/or erector contracts to fulfil the contract terms for a lump sum (stipulated price) consideration.
Miscellaneous Steel	Steel items described and listed in Appendix F of this Code.
Others	Means a party or parties other than the fabricator and/or erector.
Owner	Means the owner of a structure and shall include his authorized agent and any person taking possession of a structure on the owner's behalf. Depending on the circumstances an authorized agent may be the architect, engineer, general contractor, construction manager, public authority or other designated representative of the owner.

Price-per-Unit Contract	Also called Unit-Price Contract. An agreement whereby the fabricator and/or erector contracts to fulfil the contract terms for a consideration which is based on the units of steel calculated in accordance with the CISC Code of Standard Practice for Structural Steel.
Quotations	Proposals by the fabricator based on structural steel as defined in Clause 2.1 and as included in the tender documents, and in accordance with the documents outlined in Clause 3.1.1.
Revision	A change in the contract documents.
Shop Details	Documents which provide complete information for the fabrication of various members and components of the structure, including the required material and product standards; the location, type, and size of all mechanical fasteners; bolt installation requirements; and welds.
Steel Detailer	The skilled technicians responsible for the preparation of shop details and other data necessary for fabrication and/or erection. May also be the fabricator.
Stipulated Price Contract	See Lump Sum Price Contract.
Structural Drawings	Drawings showing the structural steel required.
Structural Steel	Those items listed under Clause 2.1
Structural Steel Frame	An assemblage of structural steel components (beams, columns, purlins, girts, etc.) for the purpose of resisting loads and forces. See Clause 2.1.
Structural Steel Specifications	The portion of the tender specifications containing the requirements for the fabrication and erection of the structural steel.
Temporary Bracing	Members designed by the Engineer of Record to be removed at a later date at his or her instruction.
Tender Documents	Drawings, specifications, general conditions, addenda, etc., used as the basis for preparing a tender.
Tender Drawings	Drawings used as the basis for preparing a tender.
Tender Specifications	Specifications used as the basis for preparing a tender.
Unit-Price Contract	See Price-per-Unit Contract.
Work	Defined as the product or services provided by the steel Fabricator or Erector.

1.3 Governing Technical Standards

The provisions of the latest edition of CAN/CSA-S16 "Limits States Design of Steel Structures" shall govern the design, fabrication and erection of steel structures except bridges. The provisions of the latest edition of CAN/CSA-S6 "Canadian Highway Bridge Design Code", the

"Ontario Highway Bridge Design Code" (in Ontario) or the American Railway Engineering Association's "Specifications for Steel Railway Bridges" shall govern the design, fabrication and erection of structural steel for bridges. The provisions of the latest edition of CSA Standard W59 "Welded Steel Construction (Metal-Arc Welding)" shall govern arc welding design and practice. The provisions of other standards shall be applicable if called for in the tender drawings and tender specifications.

1.4 Responsibility for Design

When the client provides the structural drawings and specifications, the fabricator and the erector shall not be responsible for determining the adequacy of the design nor liable for the loss or damage resulting from an inadequate design. Should the client desire the fabricator to assume any responsibility for design beyond that of proposing adequate connections and details, and, when required, components, members, or assemblies standardized by the fabricator, the client shall state clearly his requirements in the invitation to tender or in the accompanying tender drawings and tender specifications. Even though proposed connections and design details may be prepared by the fabricator's technical staff, the overall behaviour of the structure remains the responsibility of the designer of the structure. (See also Clause 5.6).

1.5 Responsibility for Erection Procedure

When the erection of structural steel is part of his contract, the fabricator shall be responsible for determining the erection procedure, for checking the adequacy of the connections for the uncompleted structure and for providing erection bracing or connection details. When the erection of the structural steel is not part of his contract, the fabricator shall not be responsible for determining the erection procedure, for checking the adequacy of the connections for the uncompleted structure, or for providing erection bracing or connection details not included in the contract documents, nor shall the fabricator be liable for loss or damage resulting from faulty erection. However, the steel fabricator shall be informed by the client of the erection sequence to be used which may influence the sequence and process of the manufacturing. (See also Clauses 5.1 and 5.4).

1.6 Patented Devices

Except when the contract documents call for the design to be furnished by the fabricator or erector, the fabricator and erector assume that all necessary patent rights have been obtained by the client and that the fabricator and erector will be fully protected by the client in the use of patented designs, devices or parts required by the contract documents.

1.7 Scheduling

The client should provide a construction schedule in the tender documents. In the absence of such a schedule, one should be mutually agreed upon between the contracting parties, prior to the contract award.

2. Classification of Material

2.1 Structural Steel

Unless otherwise specified in the tender documents, a contract to supply, fabricate and deliver structural steel shall include only those items from the following list which are clearly indicated as being required by the structural drawings and tender specifications. (See Appendix A).

Anchors for structural steel.

Base plates and bearings for structural steel members.

Beams, purlins, girts forming part of the structural steel frame.

Bearing plates and angles for structural steel members and steel deck.

Bins and hoppers of 6 mm plate or heavier, attached to the structural steel frame.

Bracing for steel members, trusses or frames.

Brackets attached to the structural steel.

Bridge bearings connected to the structural steel members.

Cables for permanent bracing or suspension systems.

Canopy framing if attached to the structural steel frame.

Cold-formed channels when used as structural members as listed in the CISC Handbook of Steel Construction.

Columns.

Conveyor galleries and supporting bents (exclusive of conveyor stringers, deck plate and supporting posts which are normally part of the conveyor assembly).

Crane rails and stops, excluding unless otherwise noted final alignment of the rails.

Curb angles and plates attached to the structural steel frame if shown on the structural steel drawings.

Deck support angles at columns, walls, if shown on the structural steel drawings.

Diaphragms for bridges.

Door frame supports attached to the structural steel frame.

Embedded items connecting structural steel.

Expansion joints connected to the structural steel frame (excluding expansion joints for bridges).

Field bolts to connect structural steel components.

Floor plates, roof plates (raised pattern or plain) and steel grating connected to the structural steel frame.

Girders.

Grillage beams of structural steel.

Hangers supporting structural steel framing.

Jacking girders.

Lintels if attached to steel frame and shown on the structural drawings.

Mechanical roof support and floor opening framing shown on structural drawings.

Monorail beams of standard structural steel shapes.

Open-web steel joists, including anchors, bridging, headers and trimmers; also, when specified to be included in the structural steel contract documents, light-gauge forms and temperature reinforcement.

Sash angles attached to the structural steel frame.

Separators, angles, tees, clips and other detail fittings essential to the structural steel frame.

Shear connectors/studs, except when installed through sheet steel deck by deck installer.

Shelf angles attached to the structural steel frame if shown on structural drawings.

Shop fasteners or welds, and fasteners required to assemble parts for shipment.

Steel tubes or cores for composite columns or braces.

Steel window sills attached to the structural steel frame.

Struts.

Suspended ceiling supports of structural steel shapes at least 75 mm in depth.

Temporary components to facilitate transportation to the site.

Tie, hanger and sag rods forming part of the structural steel frame.

Trusses.

2.1.2 Only if shown on the structural drawings and specifically noted by the structural engineer to be supplied by the structural fabricator:

Steel stairs, walkways, ladders and handrails forming part of the structural steelwork. (See Appendix A).

2.2 Field Connection Material

2.2.1 When the fabricator erects the structural steel, he shall supply all material required for temporary and for permanent connection of the component parts of the structural steel.

2.2.2 When the erection of the structural steel is not part of the fabricator's contract, unless otherwise specified, the fabricator shall furnish appropriate bolts and nuts (plus washers, if required) or special fasteners, of suitable size and in sufficient quantity for all field connections of steel to steel which are specified to be thus permanently connected, plus an over-allowance of two per cent of each size to cover waste.

Unless otherwise specified in the tender documents, welding electrodes, back-up bars, temporary shims, levelling plates, fitting-up bolts and drift pins required for the structural steel shall not be furnished by the fabricator when the erection of the structural steel is not part of the fabricator's contract.

2.3 Items Supplied by Others

Unless otherwise specified in the tender documents, the following steel or other items shall not be supplied by the structural steel fabricator.

Bins and hoppers not covered in Clause 2.1 of this Code.

Bolts for wood lagging.

Bridge bearings not connected to structural steel items.

Canopy framing not attached to structural steel.

Catch basin frames.

Concrete for filling HSS or pipe sections. Concrete is to be supplied and poured by others in the shop or field with the cooperation of the fabricator/erector.

Connection material for other trades.

Conveyor stringers, deck plate and supporting posts.

Drain pipes.

Door and corner guards.

Door frames not covered in Clause 2.1 of this Code.

Drilling of holes into masonry or concrete, including core drilling of anchor rods for bridges and drilling for deck support angles.

Edge forming less than 3.2 mm thick for steel deck and not covered in Clause 2.1 of this code.

Embedded steel parts in precast concrete.

Embedded steel parts not required for structural steel or deck.

Flagpoles and supports.

Floor plates, roof plates and grating not covered in Clause 2.1 of this Code.

Grout.

Hoppers and chutes.

Hose and tire storage brackets.

Installation of embedded parts.

Lag bolts, machine bolts and shields or inserts for attaching shelf angles, trimmer angles and channels to masonry or concrete.

Lintels over wall recesses.

Lintels which are either an integral part of door frames or not attached to the structural steel frame.

Machine bases, rollers and pulleys.

Members made from gauge material except cold-formed channels indicated in Clause 2.1.

Metal-clad doors and frames.

Miscellaneous Steel; see Appendix F.

Shear connectors through sheet steel deck by deck installer.

Sheet steel cladding.

Sheet steel deck.

Sheet steel flashing.

Shelf angles not covered in Clause 2.1 of this Code.

Shoring under composite floors and stub girders.

Steel doors.

Steel sash.

Steel stacks.

Steel stairs, landings, walkways, ladders and handrails, not covered in Clause 2.1.2 of this Code.

Steel tanks and pressure vessels.

Steel window sills not covered in Clause 2.1 of this Code.

Support for sheet steel deck at column cutouts and for openings not requiring framing connected to structural steel.

Temporary bracing for other trades.

Trench covers.

Trim angles, eave angles or fascia plates not directly attached to the structural steel frame.

3. Quotations and Contracts

3.1 Standard Form of Contract

Unless otherwise agreed upon, a contract to fabricate, deliver and/or erect structural steel shall be the appropriate Standard Construction Documents approved by the Canadian Construction Documents Committee, or the Canadian Construction Association.

3.1.1 Quotations

Quotations from fabricators are based on the following documents:

(1) *A Standard Form of Contract.* The generally accepted standard form of contract is the CCA 1-2008 Stipulated Price Subcontract Form, and

(2) Canadian Institute of Steel Construction (CISC) Code of Standard Practice for Structural Steel, latest edition

3.1.2 Progress Payment Claim Form

A suggested format for a progress payment claim form is provided in Appendix G.

3.1.3 Progress Invoicing and Substantial Completion

For suggested definitions, see Appendix H.

3.2 Types of Contracts

3.2.1 For contracts stipulating a "lump sum price", the work required to be performed by the fabricator and/or erector must be completely defined by the contract documents.

3.2.2 For contracts stipulating a "price per unit", the scope of the work, type of materials, character of fabrication, and conditions of erection are based upon the contract documents which must be representative of the work to be performed. For methods of computing mass, area, or quantity, see Clause 3.5. Also see Appendix C of this Code.

3.2.3 For contracts stipulating "cost plus fee", the work required to be performed by the fabricator and/or erector is indefinite in nature at the time the contract documents are prepared. Consequently the contract documents should define the method of measurement of work performed, and the fee to be paid in addition to the fabricator's costs.

3.3 Revisions to Contract Documents

3.3.1 Revisions to the contract shall be made by the issue of dated new or revised documents. All revisions shall be clearly indicated. Such revisions should be issued by a Detailed Change Notice.

3.3.2 The fabricator shall advise the client or client representative of any impact such revision or change will have on the existing agreement between the two parties.

3.3.3 Upon agreement between the fabricator and the client or client representative as to the revision's impact, the client or his representative shall issue a change order or extra work order for the revisions.

3.3.4 Unless specifically stated to the contrary, the issue of revision documents or changes indicated on drawing approvals is authorization by the client to release these revisions for construction.

3.4 Discrepancies

In case of discrepancies between the structural drawings and specifications for buildings, the specifications govern. In case of discrepancies between the structural drawings and specifications for bridges, the structural drawings govern. In case of discrepancies between scale dimensions on the structural drawings and figures written on them, the figures govern. In case of discrepancies between the structural drawings and plans for other trades or disciplines, the structural drawings govern.

3.5 Computation of Units

Unless another method is specified and fully described at the time tenders are requested, the computed mass of steel required for the structure shall be determined by the method of computation described herein. (Although the method of computation described does not result in the actual mass of fabricated structural steel and other items, its relative simplicity results in low computational cost and it is based on quantities which can be readily computed and checked by all parties involved to establish the basis of payment). No additional mass for welds, or mass allowance for painting, galvanizing, and metallizing is to be included in the computation of mass.

a) *Mass Density.* The mass density of steel is assumed to be 7850 kilograms per cubic metre.

b) *Shapes, Bars and Hollow Structural Sections.* The mass of shapes, bars and hollow structural sections is computed using the finished dimensions shown on shop details. No deductions shall be made for holes created by cutting, punching or drilling, for material removed by coping or clipping, or for material removed by weld joint preparation. No cutting, milling or planing allowance shall be added to the finished dimensions. The mass per metre of length for shapes and hollow structural sections is the published mass. The mass per metre of length for bars is the published mass, or if no mass is published, the mass computed from the specified cross-sectional area.

c) *Plates and Slabs.* The mass/area of plates and slabs is computed using the rectangular dimensions of plates or slabs from which the finished plate or slab pieces shown on the shop details can be cut. No burning, cutting, trimming or planing allowance shall be added. When it is practical and economical to do so, several irregularly-shaped pieces may be cut from the same plate or slab. In this case, the mass shall be computed using the rectangular dimensions of the plate or slab from which the pieces can be cut. No cutting or trimming allowance shall be added. In all cases, the specified plate or slab thickness is to be used to compute the mass. The mass of raised-pattern rolled plate is that published by the manufacturer.

d) *Bolts.* The mass of shop and field bolts, nuts and washers is computed on the basis of the shop details and the nominal published mass of the applicable types and sizes of fastener.

e) *Studs.* If not included in the contract on a "price-per-unit basis", the mass of studs is computed on the basis of the shop details and/or erection diagrams and the published mass of the studs.

f)   *Grating.* The mass/area of grating is computed on the basis of the shop details and/or erection diagrams and published mass of the grating. The area to be used is the minimum rectangular area from which the piece of grating can be cut.

g)   Where supplied, such items as shims, levelling plates, temporary connection material, back-up bars and certain field "consumables" shall be considered as part of the structural steel whether or not indicated specifically in the contract documents. Such items then will be added to, and become a part of, computed mass of steel for the structure.

3.6 Contract Price Adjustments

3.6.1 When the responsibility of the fabricator and/or erector is changed from that previously established by the contract documents, an appropriate modification of the contract price shall be made. In computing the contract price adjustment, the fabricator and/or erector shall consider the quantity of work added or deleted, modifications in the character of the work, the timeliness of the change with respect to the status of material ordering, the detailing, fabrication and erection operations and related impact costs.

3.6.2 Requests for contract price adjustments shall be presented by the fabricator and/or erector and shall be accompanied by a description of the change in sufficient detail to permit evaluation and prompt approval by the client.

3.6.3 Price-per-Unit Contracts
Generally they provide for minor revisions to the quantity of work prior to the time work is approved for construction. Minor revisions to the quantity of work should be limited to an increase or decrease in the quantity of any category not exceeding ten percent. Should the quantity of steel of any category vary by more than ten percent, then the contract unit price of that category may require adjustment. Changes to the character of the work or the mix of the work, at any time or changes to the quantity of the work after the work is approved for construction, may require a contract price adjustment.

3.6.4 A suggested format for accommodating contract price adjustments is contained in Appendix B.

3.7 Scheduling

3.7.1 The contract documents should specify the schedule for the performance of the work. This schedule should state when the approved-for-construction drawings will be issued and when the job site, foundations, cores, walls, piers and abutments will be ready, free from obstructions and accessible to the erector, so that erection can start at the designated time and continue without interference or delay caused by the client or other trades.

3.7.2 The fabricator and/or erector has the responsibility to advise the client of the effect any revision may have on the contract schedule.

3.7.3 If the fabrication and erection schedule is significantly delayed due to revisions, or for other reasons which are the client's responsibility, the fabricator and erector shall be compensated for additional costs incurred. Changes to the scope of the work shall provide additional time to the schedule, if required.

4. Contract Documents

4.1 Tender Documents – Tender Drawings and Tender Specifications

4.1.1 At the time tenders are called, the steel fabricator shall receive a complete set of structural drawings and a complete set of tender specifications. In order to ensure adequate and complete tenders for Lump Sum Price Contracts[1], these documents shall include complete structural drawings, conforming to the requirements for design drawings of the governing technical standard. Structural steel specifications should include any special requirements controlling the fabrication and erection of the structural steel, surface preparation and coating, and should indicate the extent of non-destructive examination, if any, to be carried out.

4.1.2 Design drawings shall be drawn to a scale adequate to convey the required information. The drawings shall show a complete design of the structure with members suitably designated and located, including such dimensions and detailed description as necessary to permit the preparation of fabrication and erection documents. Floor levels, column centres, and offsets shall be dimensioned. The term "drawings" may include computer output and other data. Stiffeners and doubler plates required to maintain stability and which are an integral part of the main member shall be shown and dimensioned.

4.1.3 Design drawings shall designate the design standards used, shall show clearly the type or types of construction to be employed, shall show the category of the structural system used for seismic design, and shall designate the material or product standards applicable to the members and details depicted. Drawings shall give the governing combinations of shears, moments, pass-through forces, and axial forces to be resisted by the connections.

4.1.4. Where connections are not shown, the connections shall be assumed to be in accordance with the requirements of the governing technical standard (see Clause 1.3).

4.2 Architectural, Electrical and Mechanical Drawings

Architectural, electrical and mechanical drawings may be used as a supplement to the structural drawing to define detail configurations and construction information, provided all requirements for the structural steel are noted on the structural drawings.

4.3 Construction Drawings and Construction Specifications

4.3.1 At the time specified in the tender documents or pre-award negotiations (if different), the client shall furnish the fabricator with a plot plan of the construction site, and a set of complete drawings and specifications approved for construction consistent with the tender drawings and tender specifications. These construction drawings and specifications are required by the fabricator for ordering the material and for the preparation and completion of fabrication and erection documents. The approved-for-construction drawings shall show:

a) all changes or revisions to the tender drawings, clearly indicated on the construction drawings;

b) the complete design of the structure with members suitably designated and located, including such dimensions and detailed description as necessary to permit preparation of the fabrication and erection documents. Floor levels, column centres, and offsets shall be dimensioned;

---

[1] *For other types of contracts, it is desirable for the contract documents to be as complete as possible.*

CISC Code of Standard Practice

c) all materials to be furnished by the fabricator, together with sufficient information to prepare fabrication and erection documents, including the design standards used, the type or types of construction to be employed, the category of the system used for seismic design, the applicable material or product standards, and the governing combinations of shears, moments and axial forces to be resisted by connections.

The fabricator shall receive a complete set of the tender drawings and tender specifications.

4.4 Architecturally Exposed Structural Steel

In addition to the preceding requirements, all structural elements, or parts thereof, to be treated as Architecturally Exposed Structural Steel must be in accordance with the requirements of Appendix I and clearly shown on the structural drawings.

4.5 Digital Modelling

4.5.1 When a project utilizes digital project models to convey a substantive portion of the project information, Appendix J shall be used as a guide.

4.5.2 The owner of the digital model shall be responsible for the accuracy and maintenance of the digital model unless otherwise stated in the contract documents.

4.5.3 The contract documents shall clearly stipulate the party designated as the owner of the digital model.

5. Fabrication and Erection Documents

NOTE: *The term "shop drawings", frequently used in the construction industry, is replaced in this Code of Standard Practice by the terms "fabrication and erection documents". These terms more correctly describe the following five separate and distinct documents that may be prepared by a fabricator/erector. See also Clause 1.2 for definitions. Not all of these documents will be required for every project.*

5.1 Erection Diagrams

Unless provided by the client, the fabricator will prepare erection diagrams from the approved construction drawings. In this regard, the fabricator may request reproducible copies of the structural drawings which may be altered for use as erection diagrams. When using reproducible copies of the structural drawings, the structural engineer's name and seal shall be removed. Erection diagrams shall be submitted to the designer for review and approval. Erection diagrams are general arrangement drawings showing the principal dimensions of the structure, piece marks, sizes of the members, size (diameter) and type of bolts, bolt installation requirements, elevations of column bases, all necessary dimensions and details for setting anchor rods, and all other information necessary for the assembly of the structure. Only one reproducible copy, or electronic file, of each diagram will be submitted for review and approval unless a larger number of copies is required by the client as part of the tender documents.

5.2 Connection Design Details

Connection design details shall be prepared in advance of preparing shop details and submitted to the designer for confirmation that the intent of the design is met. Connection design details shall provide details of standard and non-standard connections, and other data necessary for the preparation of shop details. Connection design details shall be referenced to the design drawings, and/or erection drawings.

5.3 Shop Details

Unless provided by the client, shop details shall be prepared in advance of fabrication from the information on the approved construction drawings, the connection design details, and the erection diagrams. Shop details shall provide complete information for the fabrication of various members and components of the structure, including the required material and product standards; the location, type, and size of all attachments, mechanical fasteners, and welds. When shop details are required to be submitted for review and approval, only one reproducible copy of each shop detail will be submitted, unless a larger number of copies is required by the client as part of the tender specifications.

5.3.1 Shop Details Furnished by the Client

When the shop details are furnished by the client, he shall deliver them in time to permit fabrication to proceed in an orderly manner according to the time schedule agreed upon. The client shall prepare these shop details, insofar as practicable, in accordance with the detailing standards of the fabricator. The client shall be responsible for the completeness and accuracy of shop details so prepared.

5.3.2 Clipped Double Connections

Where two beams or girders, framing at right angles from opposite sides of a supporting member, share the same bolts, a clipped double connection shall be used unless a seated connection or other detail is used to facilitate safe erection of the beams or girders. A clipped double connection is not applicable to a two-bolt connection or when the beams are equal to or deeper than half the depth of the girder. For a description of a clipped double connection, see Appendix A.

5.4 Erection Procedures

Erection procedures shall outline the construction methods, erection sequence, erection bracing, temporary bracing if required, and other engineering details necessary for shipping, erecting, and maintaining the stability of the steel frame. Erection procedures shall be supplemented by drawings and sketches to identify the location of stabilizing elements. Erection procedures shall be submitted for review when so specified.

5.5 Field Work Details

Field work details shall be submitted to the designer for review and approval. Field work details shall provide complete information for modifying fabricated members on the job site. All operations required to modify the member shall be shown on the field work details. If extra materials are necessary to make modifications, shop details may be required.

5.6 Review and Approval

Erection diagrams, non-standard connection design details, shop details and field work details are normally submitted for review and approval. The fabricator includes a maximum allowance of fourteen (14) calendar days in his schedule for the return of all documents submitted for approval. Approval, by the designer, of shop details submitted by the fabricator indicates that the fabricator has interpreted correctly the contract requirements. Approval by the designer of shop details submitted by the fabricator does not relieve the fabricator of the responsibility for accuracy of the detail dimensions on shop details, nor of the general fit-up of parts to be assembled.

The preparation of fabrication and erection documents is governed by the following sequence of procedures.

a) Sufficient information must be indicated in the construction drawings as stipulated in Clause 4.3 of this Code to permit the completion of fabrication and erection documents.

b) The fabrication and erection documents are prepared by steel detailers using industry and company standards, and represent the fabricator's interpretation of intent of the contract documents, particularly as described by the construction drawings. Connection design details are reviewed by the fabricator's technical staff prior to submission to the designer.

c) The connection design details, shop details, erection diagrams and field work details are submitted to the designer for review and approval. Erection procedures are submitted when so specified.

d) It is assumed by the fabricator that the fabrication and erection documents, when approved, have been reviewed by the client for accuracy in the interpretation of the contract requirements. Connection design details and shop details are reviewed and approved by the designer for structural adequacy and to ensure conformance with the loads, forces and special instructions contained in the contract documents.

e) Shop details are prepared from the approved connection design details and erection diagrams.

If the client does not wish to review and approve the fabricator's fabrication and erection documents, the basis for interpreting the contract requirements, as well as the adequacy of connection details, is limited to the information contained in the structural steel specifications and shown on the structural drawings. This information shall be sufficient, as indicated in Clause 4.3, to permit proper execution of the work. However, the Engineer of Record is ultimately responsible for the structural integrity of the structure and the connections.

5.7 Additions, Deletions or Changes

Additions, deletions or changes, when approved, will be considered as contract revisions and constitute the client's authorization to release the additions, deletions or revisions for construction. See also Clauses 3.3 and 3.6.

6. Material, Fabrication, Inspection, Painting and Delivery

6.1 Material

Materials used by the fabricator for structural use shall conform to structural steel material standards of the Canadian Standards Association, or the American Society for Testing and Materials, or to other published material specifications, in accordance with the requirements of the construction drawings and construction specifications.

6.2 Identification

6.2.1 The method of identification stipulated in CAN/CSA-S16 shall form the basis for a fabricator's identification of material. Control and identification procedures may differ to some extent from fabricator to fabricator.

6.3 Preparation of Material

6.3.1 Flame cutting of structural steel may be by hand or mechanically guided means.

6.3.2 Surfaces noted as "finished" on the drawings are defined as having a roughness height rating not exceeding 500 (12.5 μm) as defined in CSA Standard B95, Surface Texture (Roughness, Waviness and Lay), unless otherwise specified. Any fabricating technique that produces such a finish may be used.

6.4 Fitting and Fastening

6.4.1 Projecting elements of connection attachments need not be straightened in the connecting plane if it can be demonstrated that installation of the connectors or fitting aids will provide adequate contact between faying surfaces.

6.4.2 When runoff tabs are used, the fabricator or erector need not remove them unless specified in the contract documents, required by the governing technical standard or the steel is exposed to view. When their removal is required, they may be hand flame-cut close to the edge of the finished member with no more finishing required, unless other finishing is specifically called for in the contract documents or governing technical standard.

6.5 Dimensional Tolerances

Tolerances on fabricated members shall be those prescribed in the applicable governing technical standard. Tolerances on steel material supplied by the fabricator shall meet those prescribed in Canadian Standards Association Standard G40.20.

6.6 Inspection of Steelwork

Should the client wish to have an independent inspection and non-destructive examination of the steelwork, he shall reserve the right to do so in the tender documents. Arrangements should be made with the fabricator for inspection of steelwork at the fabrication shop by the client's inspectors. The cost of this inspection and testing is the responsibility of the client. Inspectors are to be appointed prior to start of fabrication, and the client is to advise the fabricator of the arrangement made.

6.7 Surface Preparation

If paint is specified, the fabricator shall clean all steel surfaces to be painted of loose rust, loose mill scale, prominent spatter, slag or flux deposit, oil, dirt and other foreign matter by wire brushing or other suitable means. Unless specified, the fabricator shall not be obliged to blast-clean, pickle or perform any specific surface preparation operation aimed at total or near-total removal of tight mill scale, rust or non-deleterious matter.

6.8 Paint

When structural steel is specified to receive a shop coat of paint, the fabricator shall be responsible only to the extent of performing the surface preparation and painting in the specified manner. The painting requirements specified in the tender documents for the shop coat should include the identification of the members to be painted, surface preparation, paint specification, if applicable, the manufacturer's product identification, and the required minimum and maximum dry film thickness. Unless otherwise agreed upon as part of the contract documents, the fabricator shall not be responsible for the deterioration of the paint that may result from exposure to the weather for more than ninety days after completion of the painting.

6.9 Marking and Shipping

6.9.1 Except for weathering steel surfaces exposed to view and for architecturally exposed structural steel (AESS) (see also Appendix I), erection marks shall be painted or otherwise legibly marked on the members. Preferably, members which are heavy enough to require special erection equipment shall be marked to indicate the computed or scale mass and the centre of gravity for lifting.

6.9.2 Bolts of the same length and diameter, and loose nuts and washers of each size shall be packaged separately. Pins, bolts, nuts, washers and other small parts shall be shipped in boxes, crates, kegs or barrels, none of which exceed 135 kg gross mass. A list and description of material contained therein shall be marked plainly on the outside of each container.

6.9.3 When requested by the erector, long girders shall be loaded and marked so that they will arrive at the job site in position for handling without turning. Instructions for such delivery shall be given to the carrying agency when required.

6.9.4 For each shipment, the fabricator shall furnish a shipping bill listing the items in the shipment. Such bill shall show the erection mark, the approximate length, the description (whether beam, column, angle, etc.) of each item. Such bill shall be signed by the receiver and returned to the fabricator within 48 hours of receipt of the shipment with a note regarding shortages or damages, if any, and the bill shall act as a receipt for the shipment. When the shipments are made by truck transport, the bills should accompany the shipment. When shipments are made by rail or water, the bills shall be sent to the receiver to arrive on or before receipt of the shipment.

6.9.5 Unless otherwise specified at time of tender, steel during shipment will not be covered by tarpaulins or otherwise protected. When such protection is specified, the shipper is to notify the carrier of the protection requirements.

6.10 Delivery of Materials

6.10.1 Fabricated structural steel shall be delivered in a sequence which will permit the most efficient and economical performance of shop fabrication and erection. If the client contracts separately for delivery and erection, he must coordinate planning between the fabricator, erector and general contractor.

6.10.2 Anchor rods, washers and other anchorages, grillages, or materials to be built into masonry or concrete should be shipped so that they will be on hand when needed. The client must give the fabricator sufficient notice to permit fabrication and shipping of materials before they are needed.

6.10.3 The quantities of material shown by the shipping bill are customarily accepted by the client, fabricator and erector as correct. If any shortage or damage is claimed, the client or erector should, within 48 hours, notify the carrier and the fabricator in order that the claim may be investigated.

6.10.4 The size and mass of structural steel assemblies may be limited by the shop capabilities, the permissible mass and clearance dimensions of available transportation or government regulations and the job site conditions. The fabricator determines the number of field splices consistent with economy.

6.10.5 On supply-only contracts the unloading of steel is the responsibility of others. Unless stated otherwise, the unloading of steel is part of the steel erection.

7. Erection

7.1 Method of Erection

Unless otherwise specified or agreed upon, erection shall proceed according to the most efficient and economical method available to the erector on the basis of continuous operation consistent with the drawings and specifications.

7.1.1 Temporary Bracing
Temporary bracing of the steel frame shall only be removed on instruction from the Engineer of Record.

7.2 Erection Safety

Erection shall be done in a safe manner and in accordance with applicable provincial legislation.

7.3 Site Conditions

The client shall provide and maintain adequate, all-weather access roads cleared of snow and ice and other material that impedes entry into and through the site for the safe delivery of derricks, cranes, other necessary equipment, and the material to be erected. The client shall provide for the erector a firm, properly graded, drained, convenient and adequate space and laydown area for steel of sufficient load-carrying capacity at the site for the operation of erection equipment and shall remove at the client's cost all overhead obstructions such as power lines, telephone lines, etc., in order to provide a safe and adequate working area for erection of the steelwork. The erector shall provide and install the safety protection required for his own operations or for his work forces to meet the safety requirements of applicable Acts or Codes. The general contractor shall install protective covers to all protruding rebar, machinery, anchor rods, etc., which are a hazard to workers. Any protection for pedestrians, property, other trades, etc., not essential to the steel erection activity is the responsibility of the client. When the structure does not occupy the full available site, the client shall provide adequate storage space to enable the fabricator and erector to operate at maximum practicable speed and efficiency. Cleaning of steelwork required because of site conditions, mud, site worker traffic, etc., shall not be to the fabricator's/erector's account.

7.4 Foundations

The tender specifications preferably shall specify the time that foundations will be ready, free from obstruction and accessible to the erector. Unless otherwise agreed upon, the work of erection shall be tendered on the basis that it will start at the time designated in the tender specifications without interference or delay caused by others. Neither the fabricator nor the erector shall be responsible for the accurate location, strength and suitability of foundations.

7.5 Bearing Surfaces

Levelling plates shall be set by others true, level and to the correct elevation.

7.6 Building Lines and Bench Marks

The erector shall be provided with a plot plan accurately locating building lines and bench marks at the site of the structure.

7.7 Installation of Anchor Rods and Embedded Items

7.7.1 Anchor rods and foundation rods shall be set by the client in accordance with the erection diagrams. They must not vary from the dimensions shown on the erection diagrams by more than the following (see also Appendix D):

    a)   3 mm centre-to-centre of any two rods within an anchor rod group, where an anchor rod group is defined as the set of anchor rods which receives a single fabricated steel shipping piece;

    b)   6 mm centre-to-centre of adjacent anchor rod groups;

    c)   Maximum accumulation of 6 mm per 30 000 mm along the established column line of multiple anchor rod groups, but not to exceed a total of 25 mm. The established column line is the actual field line most representative of the centres of the as-built anchor rod groups along a line of columns;

    d)   6 mm from the centre of any anchor rod group to the established column line through that group.

    e)   Shims: the finished tops of all footings shall be at the specified level which will not exceed the maximum specified grouting allowance to predetermine the amount of shimming that will be required.

The tolerances of paragraphs (b), (c), and (d) also apply to offset dimensions, shown on the construction drawings, measured parallel and perpendicular to the nearest established column line for individual columns shown on the drawings to be offset from established column lines.

7.7.2 Unless shown otherwise, anchor rods shall be set perpendicular to the theoretical bearing surface, threads shall be protected, free of concrete, and nuts should run freely on the threads. Shear pockets shall be cleaned of debris, formwork, ice and snow by the client prior to steel erection.

7.7.3 Other embedded items or connection materials between the structural steel and the work of others shall be located and set by the client in accordance with approved erection diagrams. Accuracy of these items must satisfy the erection tolerance requirements of Clause 7.12.

7.7.4 All work performed by the client shall be completed so as not to delay or interfere with the erection of the structural steel.

7.8 Bearing Devices

The client shall set to lines and grades all levelling plates and loose bearing plates which can be handled without a derrick or crane. All other bearing devices supporting structural steel shall be set and wedged, shimmed or adjusted with levelling screws by the erector to lines and grades established by the client. The fabricator and/or erector shall provide the wedges, shims or levelling screws that are required, and shall scribe clearly the bearing devices with working lines to facilitate proper alignment. Promptly after the setting of any bearing devices, the client shall check lines and grades, and grout as required. The final location and proper grouting of bearing devices are the responsibility of the client.

When steel columns, girders or beams which will be supported on concrete or masonry have base plates or bearing plates fabricated as an integral part of the member, the bearing area of the support shall be suitably prepared by others so as to be at exact grade and level to receive the steelwork.

7.9 Examination by Erector

Prior to field erection, the erector shall do a random check to examine the work of all others on which his work is in any way dependent and shall report to the client any errors or discrepancies as discovered that may affect erection of structural steel before or during erection. The accurate placement and integrity of all anchor rods /embedment etc., remains the responsibility of the client.

7.10 Adjustable Shelf Angles and Sash Angles

The erector shall position at time of erection all adjustable shelf angles and sash angles attached to the steel frame true and level within the tolerances permitted by the governing technical standard. Any subsequent adjustment that may be necessary to accommodate the work of others shall be performed by others.

7.11 Loose Lintels, Wall-Bearing Members and Other Pieces

Unless otherwise specified, loose lintels, shelf angles, wall-bearing members and other pieces not attached to the structural steel frame shall be received and set by others.

7.12 Tolerances

Unless otherwise specified, tolerances on erected structural steel shall be those prescribed in the applicable governing technical standard.

7.13 Checking Erected Steelwork

Prior to placing or applying any other materials, the owner is responsible for determining that the location of the structural steel is acceptable for plumbness, level and alignment within tolerances with bolts correctly installed and welds inspected. The erector is given timely notice of acceptance by the owner or a listing of specific items to be corrected in order to obtain acceptance. Such notice is rendered immediately upon completion of any part of the work and prior to the start of work by other trades that may be supported, attached or applied to the structural steelwork. Should such notice not be received within 14 days, the erected steel work is taken to have been accepted.

7.14 Removal of Bracing

7.14.1 Removal of Erection Bracing

Guys, braces and falsework or cribbing supplied by the erector shall remain the property of the erector. The erector shall remove them when the steel structure is otherwise adequately braced unless other arrangements are made. Guys and braces temporarily left in place under such other arrangements shall be removed by others provided prior permission by the erector for their removal has been given, and returned to the erector in good condition. See Clause 7.14.2.

7.14.2 Removal of Temporary Bracing

Temporary bracing required by the designer shall only be removed on instruction from the Engineer of Record.

7.15 Correction of Errors When Material Is Not Erected by the Fabricator

Correction of minor misfits and a moderate amount of cutting, welding, and reaming shall be considered a part of the erection; in the same manner as if the Fabricator were erecting the work. Any major rework required due to incorrect shop work shall be immediately reported to the Fabricator, before rework commences. The Fabricator shall then either correct the error, resupply the item within a reasonable time period, or approve the method of correction including applicable costs, whichever is the most economical.

7.16 Field Assembly

Unless otherwise specified, the fabricator shall provide for suitable field connections that will, in his opinion, afford the greatest overall economy.

7.17 Accommodation of Other Trades

Neither the fabricator nor the erector shall cut, drill or otherwise alter the work of others or his own work to accommodate other trades unless such work is clearly defined in the tender drawings and tender specifications and unless detailed information is provided before the erection diagrams are approved. Any subsequent cutting, drilling or other alteration of the structural steel performed by the fabricator or the erector for the accommodation of other trades, shall be specifically agreed upon and authorized by the client before such work is commenced.

7.18 Temporary Floors and Access Stairs

Unless otherwise required by law, all temporary access stairs shall be provided by others, except for the floor upon which erecting equipment is located. On this floor the erector shall provide such temporary flooring as he requires, moving his planking, etc., as the work progresses.

7.19 Touch-Up of Shop Paint

Unless so specified, the fabricator/erector will not spot-paint field fasteners and field welds nor touch-up abrasions to the shop paint.

7.20 Final Painting

Unless so specified, the fabricator/erector will not be responsible for cleaning the steel after erection in preparation for field painting, nor for any general field painting that may be required.

7.21 Final Cleanup

Except as provided in Clause 7.14, upon completion of erection and before final acceptance, the erector shall remove all falsework, rubbish and temporary building furnished by him.

APPENDIX A – Structural Steel in Buildings

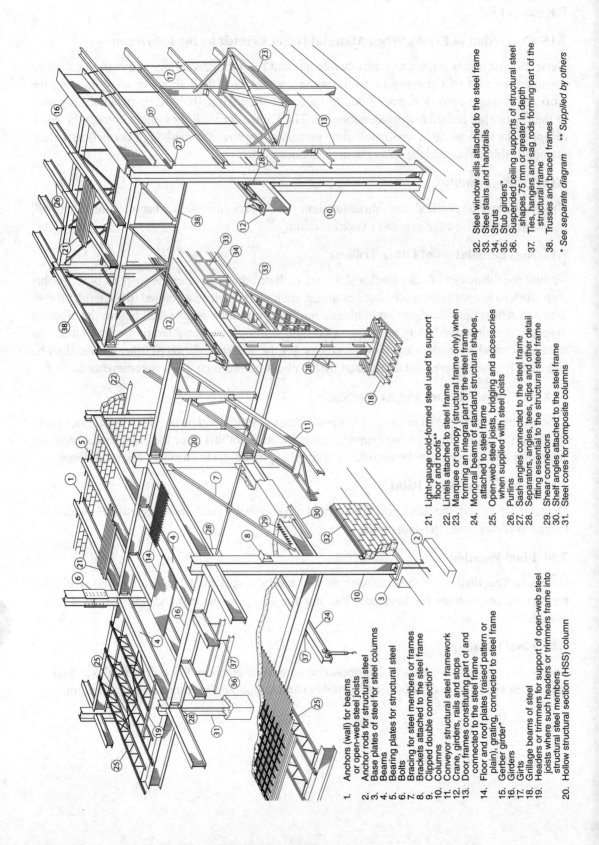

1. Anchors (wall) for beams or open-web steel joists
2. Anchor rods for structural steel
3. Base plates of steel for steel columns
4. Beams
5. Bearing plates for structural steel
6. Bolts
7. Bracing for steel members or frames
8. Brackets attached to the steel frame
9. Clipped double connection*
10. Columns
11. Conveyor structural steel framework
12. Crane, girders, rails and stops
13. Door frames constituting part of and connected to the steel frame
14. Floor and roof plates (raised pattern or plain), grating, connected to steel frame
15. Gerber girder**
16. Girders
17. Girts
18. Grillage beams of steel
19. Headers or trimmers for support of open-web steel joists where such headers or trimmers frame into structural steel members
20. Hollow structural section (HSS) column

21. Light-gauge cold-formed steel used to support floor and roofs**
22. Lintels attached to steel frame
23. Marquee or canopy (structural frame only) when forming an integral part of the steel frame
24. Monorail beams of standard structural shapes, attached to steel frame
25. Open-web steel joists, bridging and accessories when supplied with steel joists
26. Purlins
27. Sash angles connected to the steel frame
28. Separators, angles, tees, clips and other detail fitting essential to the structural steel frame
29. Shear connectors
30. Shelf angles attached to the steel frame
31. Steel cores for composite columns

32. Steel window sills attached to the steel frame
33. Steel stairs and handrails
34. Struts
35. Stub girders*
36. Suspended ceiling supports of structural steel shapes 75 mm or greater in depth
37. Ties, hangers and sag rods forming part of the structural frame
38. Trusses and braced frames

*See separate diagram   **Supplied by others

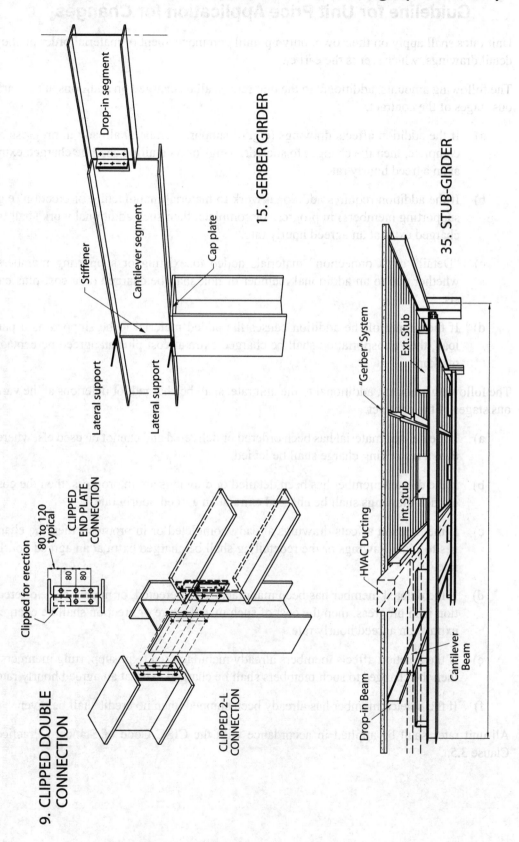

15. GERBER GIRDER

Drop-in segment

Cantilever segment

Stiffener

Cap plate

Lateral support

Lateral support

9. CLIPPED DOUBLE CONNECTION

Clipped for erection

80 to 120 typical

80 | 80

CLIPPED END PLATE CONNECTION

CLIPPED 2-L CONNECTION

35. STUB-GIRDER

"Gerber" System

Ext. Stub

Int. Stub

HVAC Ducting

Drop-in Beam

Cantilever Beam

APPENDIX B
Guideline for Unit Price Application for Changes

1. Unit rates shall apply on their own, only up until commencement of material order or shop detail drawings, whichever is the earlier.

2. The following amounts, additional to the unit rate, shall be charged on additions at the various stages of the contract.

   a) If the addition affects drawings (e.g. of support members) already in progress or complete, then the changes to such drawings or redetailing shall be charged extra at an agreed hourly rate.

   b) If the addition requires additional work to material manufacture or erection (e.g. supporting members) in progress or complete, then such additional work shall be charged extra at an agreed hourly rate.

   c) "Detail" or "Connection" materials added to existing or supporting members, whether due to an additional member or not, shall be charged on a cost-plus basis.

   d) If the timing of the addition causes the added material to be shipped as a part load, then transportation shall be charged extra at cost plus an agreed percentage markup.

3. The following amounts, additional to the unit rate, shall be charged for deletions at the various stages of the contract.

   a) If the deleted material has been ordered or delivered and cannot be used elsewhere, then a restocking charge shall be levied.

   b) If the deleted member has been detailed or drawings are in progress, then the cost of such drawings shall be charged extra at an agreed hourly rate.

   c) If the deletion affects drawings already completed or in progress, then the changes to such drawings or the redetailing shall be charged extra at an agreed hourly rate.

   d) If the deleted member has been manufactured or erected, or manufacture or erection is in progress, then the cost of such manufacture or erection shall be charged extra at an agreed hourly rate.

   e) If the deletion affects members already manufactured (e.g. supporting members), then the changes to such members shall be charged extra at an agreed hourly rate.

   f) If the deleted member has already been shipped, then no credit shall be given.

4. All unit rates shall be applied in accordance with the CISC Code of Standard Practice, Clause 3.5.

5. Hourly Rates are as follows:

    a) Engineering Design – $ / labour hour

    b) Detailing Labour – $ / labour hour

    c) Shop Labour – $ / labour hour

    d) Field Labour – $ / labour hour

    e) Equipment used for revisions will be charged at negotiated rental rates, according to Canadian Construction Association standard practice.

6. Revisions involving the use of grades of steel, sources of supply, or types of sections other than specified will be subject to price adjustments.

7. Units will be computed in accordance with Clause 3.5 of the CISC Code of Standard Practice for Structural Steel.

APPENDIX C
A Suggested Format for Price-per-Unit Contracts

The following is a list of suggested categories for which unit prices could be tendered, such categories being selected or added to, depending upon the nature of the project.

For payment purposes, the connection material required to connect an individual member to its supporting member is assumed to be part of the member to which it is attached for shipping purposes.

A. Structural Steel

1. Columns

a) Rolled Shapes
1. Up to and including 30 kg/m
2. Over 30 — up to and including 60 kg/m
3. Over 60 — up to and including 90 kg/m
4. Over 90 — up to and including 150 kg/m
5. Over 150 kg/m

b) WWF or Plate Fabricated
1. Up to and including 90 kg/m
2. Over 90 — up to and including 150 kg/m
3. Over 150 kg/m

c) Hollow Structural Sections
1. Up to and including 30 kg/m
2. Over 30 — up to and including 60 kg/m
3. Over 60 — up to and including 90 kg/m
4. Over 90 — up to and including 150 kg/m
5. Over 150 kg/m

2. Beams

a) Rolled Shapes
1. Up to and including 30 kg/m
2. Over 30 — up to and including 60 kg/m
3. Over 60 — up to and including 90 kg/m
4. Over 90 — up to and including 150 kg/m
5. Over 150 kg/m

b) WWF or Plate Fabricated
1. Up to and including 90 kg/m
2. Over 90 — up to and including 150 kg/m
3. Over 150 kg/m

c) Stud Shear Connectors
___ diam. ___ mm long

3. Crane Rails

   a) Rail Complete with Rail Clips

      1. Up to and including 30 kg/m

      2. Over 30 kg/m

   b) Stops

   c) Monorails

      1. Straight

      2. Curved

4.1 Trusses – Where Principal Members Are:

   a) Tees, Angles or W-Shapes

   b) Hollow Structural Sections

4.2 Open-Web Steel Joists

5. Bracing

   a) Rolled Shapes

      1. Up to and including 30 kg/m

      2. Over 30 kg/m

   b) Hollow Structural Sections

      1. Up to and including 30 kg/m

      2. Over 30 kg/m

   c) WT Sections

      1. Up to and including 30 kg/m

      2. Over 30 kg/m

6. Purlins, Girts and Sag Rods

   a) Rolled Shapes

      1. Up to and including 30 kg/m

      2. Over 30 kg/m

   b) Cold-Formed Sections

      1. Up to and including 5.75 kg/m

      2. Over 5.75 kg/m

   c) Hollow Structural Sections

      1. Up to and including 30 kg/m

      2. Over 30 kg/m

   d) Sag Rods

7. Framing

   Wall and Roof Openings

8. Stair Stringers

9. **Ladders (Galvanized or Painted)**

    a) Without safety cage

    b) With safety cage

10. **Utility Bridges (Plus Interior Framing)**

    a) Tees, Angles or W-Shapes

    b) Hollow Structural Sections

11. **Conveyor Galleries**

    a) Tees, Angles or W-Shapes

    b) Hollow Structural Sections

    c) Open Conveyor Trusses

12. **Miscellaneous Platforms (Tees, Angles or W-Shapes)**

        1. Up to and including 30 kg/m

        2. Over 30 kg/m

B. Miscellaneous Steel & Grating

1. **Grating**

    a) Floors

        1. Galvanized

        2. Painted

    b) Stair Landings

        1. Galvanized

        2. Painted

2. **Checkered Plate (6 mm Thick)**

    a) Steel – Galvanized

    b) Steel – Painted

3. **Stair Treads (Maximum 1000 mm Long)**

    a) Grating – Galvanized

    b) Grating – Painted

4. **Handrail (Without Kickplate)**

    a) Horizontal

        1. Steel – Galvanized

        2. Steel – Painted

    b) Sloping

        1. Steel – Galvanized

        2. Steel – Painted

5. **Kickplate**

    a) Plate attached to handrail
        1. Steel – Galvanized
        2. Steel – Painted
    b) Banding – attached to grating
        1. Steel – Galvanized
        2. Steel – Painted

C. Mobilization and Demobilization

1. Mobilization for erection and demobilization

D. Unit Rates for Extra Work

1. For extra engineering design _____ /hr.
2. For extra detailing work _____ /hr. all inclusive (composite rate)
3. For extra shop labour _____ /hr. all inclusive (composite rate)
4. For extra field erection _____ /hr. all inclusive (composite rate)
5. Field labour work week _____ /hrs. per week

NOTE: "All inclusive" shall mean all labour cost including overheads and profits, and in the field all small tools (up to $1000 value).

APPENDIX D
Tolerances on Anchor Rod Placement

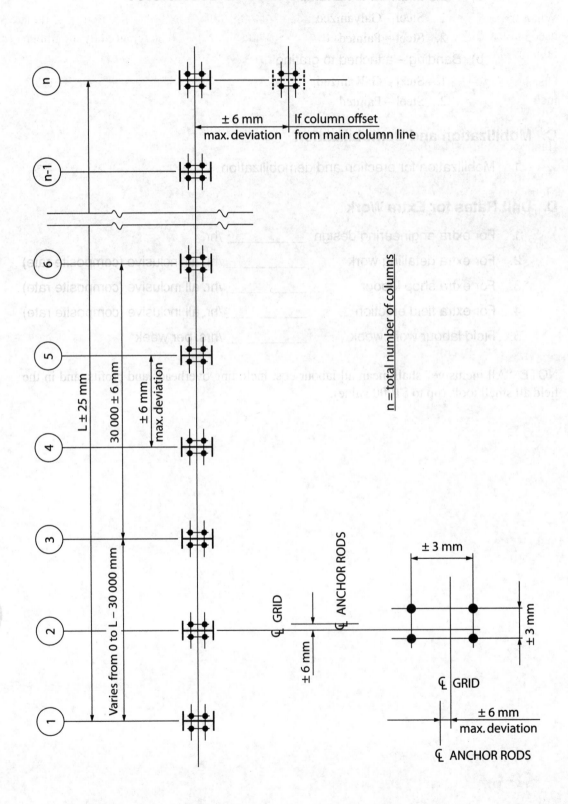

APPENDIX E
Conversion of SI Units to Imperial Units

When Imperial units are used in contract documents, unless otherwise stipulated, the SI units used in the CISC Code of Standard Practice for Structural Steel shall be replaced by the Imperial units shown, for the clause as noted.

Clause 3.5 (a). Unit Weight. The unit weight of steel is assumed to be 0.2833 pounds per cubic inch.

For other clauses, the standard conversion factors (for length, mass, etc.) stipulated in CISC Handbooks should be used.

Note: Imperial projects should be entirely in the imperial designation including shape sizes. Metric projects should be entirely in the SI designation, including shape sizes. Units should not be intermixed on the same project.

APPENDIX F
Miscellaneous Steel

Unless otherwise specified in the tender documents, the following items are considered miscellaneous steel of ferrous metal only, fabricated from 2.0 mm (14 ga.) and more of metal, including galvanizing, cadmium and chrome plating, but not stainless steel and cast iron items.

This list of items is to be read in conjunction with Clause 2.1 Structural Steel and Clause 2.3 Items Supplied by Others, and shall include all steel items not included in Clauses 2.1 and 2.3 unless specified otherwise.

Access doors and frames — except trade-name items and those required for servicing mechanical and electrical equipment.

Angles and channel frames for doors and wall openings — drilling and tapping to be specified as being done by others.

Benches and brackets.

Bollards, bumper posts and rails

Bolts — only includes those bolts and anchors required for anchoring miscellaneous steel supplied under this list.

Burglar/security bars.

Clothes line poles, custom-fabricated types only.

Coat rods, custom-fabricated types only.

Corner protection angles.

Expansion joint angles, plates custom-fabricated, etc., including types made from steel, or a combination of steel and non-ferrous metal.

Fabricated convector frames and enclosures.

Fabricated items where clearly detailed or specified and made from 2.0 mm (14 ga.) and heavier steel, except where included in another division.

Fabricated steel framing for curtain walls and storefronts where not detailed on structural drawings and not enclosed by architectural metal.

Fabricated wire mesh and expanded metal partitions and screens.

Fire escapes.

Flag poles — steel custom-fabricated. (Excluding hardware)

(Custom-fabricated) Footscrapers, mud and foot grilles, including pans, but less drains.

Frames, grating and plate covers for manholes, catch basins, sumps, trenches, hatches, pits, etc., except cast iron, frames and covers and trade-name floor and roof drains.

Gates, grilles, grillwork and louvres, excluding baked enamel or when forming part of mechanical system.

Grating-type floors and catwalks — excluding those forming part of mechanical system.

Handrails, balusters and any metal brackets attached to steel rail including plastic cover, excluding steel handrails forming part of structural steel framing.

Joist hangers, custom-fabricated types only.

Joist strap anchors.

Lintels, unless shown on structural drawings.

Mat recess frames, custom-fabricated types only.

Mobile chalk and tackboard frames, custom-fabricated types only.

Monorail beams of standard shapes, excluding trade-name items, unless shown on structural drawings.

Shop drawings and/or erection diagrams.

Shop preparation and/or priming.

Sleeves if specified, except for mechanical and electrical division.

Stair nosings, custom-fabricated types only.

Steel ladders and ladder rungs not forming part of structural steel or mechanical work.

Steel stairs and landings not forming part of structural steel.

Table and counter legs, frames and brackets, custom-fabricated types only.

Thresholds and sills, custom-fabricated types only.

Vanity and valance brackets, custom-fabricated types only.

Weatherbars — steel.

Miscellaneous Steel Items Excluded

Bases and supports for mechanical and electrical equipment where detailed on mechanical or electrical drawings.

Bolts other than for anchoring items of miscellaneous steel.

Cast iron frames and covers for manhole and catch basins.

Chain link and woven wire mesh.

Glulam connections and anchorages.

Joist hangers, trade-name types.

Metal cladding and covering, less than 2.0 mm (14 ga.).

Precast concrete connections and anchorages in building structure.

Reinforcing steel or mesh.

Roof and floor hatches when trade-name items.

Sheet metal items, steel decking and siding and their attachments, closures, etc., less than 2.0 mm (14 ga.).

Shoring under composite floors and stub-girders.

Steel reinforcement for architectural metal storefronts, curtainwalls and windows.

Steel stacks.

Stone anchors.

Stud shear connectors when used with steel deck.

Temporary bracing for other trades.

Thimbles and breeching, also mechanical fire dampers.

Window and area wells.

When miscellaneous steel fabricator erects miscellaneous steel, all material required for temporary and/or permanent connections of the component parts of the miscellaneous steel shall be supplied.

APPENDIX G
A Suggested Format for a
Monthly Progress Payment Claim Form

MONTHLY PROGRESS CLAIM FORM

FIRM NAME: _____

PROJECT: _____

CONTRACT NO: _____

PROGRESS CLAIM NO: _____

DATE: _____

ITEM	ORIGINAL BASE CONTRACT	APPROVED CHANGES TO DATE	REVISED BASE CONTRACT	PROGRESS TO DATE	PREVIOUS AMOUNT CLAIMED	THIS PROGRESS CLAIM	% COMPLETE
1. ENGINEERING & DETAILING							
2. RAW MATERIALS IN YARD							
3. FABRICATION							
4. FREIGHT TO SITE							
5. ERECTION							
6. PLUMB / BOLT / CLEANUP							
7. TOTAL GROSS AMOUNT							
8. HOLDBACK _____ %							
9. NET AMOUNT							
10. GST _____ % OF LINE 9							
11. TOTAL AMOUNT DUE							

APPROVED CHANGE ORDER(S) TO DATE: _____

APPENDIX H
Suggested Definitions for Progress Invoicing and Substantial Performance

1. Progress Invoicing

a) The submission of erection diagrams and/or shop details will initiate progress invoicing. Payments of invoices will be in accordance with the terms of the contract.

b) Any and all materials fabricated will initiate additional progress invoicing with payment as per contract.

c) Any and all materials shipped to the site and/or erected in place will initiate additional progress invoicing with payment as per contract.

d) Final invoicing will be made after all steel has been delivered to site, erected and all work completed.

e) Substantial completion is based on the completion of the WORK of the steel Fabricator or Erector, and therefore release of holdback will be 41 days (or as per applicable lien legislation) after issuance of the Certificate of Completion of this WORK.

2. Substantial Performance

a) The word "WORK" shall be defined as the product or services provided by the steel Fabricator or Erector.

b) Substantial performance and total performance shall be directly related to product or services provided by the steel Fabricator or Erector.

c) Certification of completion by the owner's representative applies to the WORK performed by the steel Fabricator or Erector.

d) Payment shall be governed by certified completion of the WORK.

APPENDIX I
Architecturally Exposed Structural Steel (AESS)

I1. Scope and Requirements

I1.1 General Requirements. When members are specifically designated as "Architecturally Exposed Structural Steel" or "AESS" in the Contract Documents, the requirements in Sections 1 through 7 shall apply as modified by this Appendix. AESS members or components shall be fabricated and erected with the care and dimensional tolerances that are stipulated in Sections 1.2 through 1.5.

I1.2 Definition of Categories. Categories are listed in the AESS Matrix shown in Table I1 where each Category is represented by a set of Characteristics. The following Categories shall be used when referring to AESS:

AESS 1: **Basic Elements**

Suitable for "basic" elements which require enhanced workmanship.

AESS 2: **Feature Elements Viewed at a Distance > 6 m**

Suitable for "feature" elements viewed at a distance greater than six metres. The process involves basically good fabrication practices with enhanced treatment of weld, connection and fabrication detail, tolerances for gaps, and copes.

AESS 3: **Feature Elements Viewed at a Distance ≤ 6 m**

Suitable for "feature" elements – where the designer is comfortable allowing the viewer to see the art of metalworking. Welds are generally smooth but visible; some grind marks are acceptable. Tolerances are tighter than normal standards. The structure is normally viewed closer than six metres and is frequently subject to touching by the public.

AESS 4: **Showcase Elements**

Suitable for "showcase or dominant" elements – where the designer intends the form to be the only feature showing in an element. All welds are ground, and filled edges are ground square and true. All surfaces are sanded/filled. Tolerances of fabricated forms are more stringent – generally one-half of the standard tolerance. All surfaces are to be "glove" smooth.

AESS C: **Custom Elements**

Suitable for elements which require a different set of Characteristics than specified in Categories 1, 2, 3 or 4.

I1.3 Additional Information. The following additional information shall be provided in the Contract Documents when AESS is specified:

a) Specific identification of members or components that are AESS using the AESS Categories listed in I1.2. Refer to Table I1;

b) Fabrication and/or erection tolerances that are to be more restrictive than provided for in this Appendix;

c) For Categories AESS 2, 3, 4 requirements, if any, of a visual sample or first-off component for inspection and acceptance standards prior to the start of fabrication;

d) For Category AESS C, the AESS Matrix included in Table I1 shall be used to specify the required treatment of the element.

I2. Shop Detail, Arrangement and Erection Drawings

I2.1 Identification. All members designated as AESS members are to be clearly identified with a Category, either AESS 1, 2, 3, 4 or C, on all shop detail, arrangement and erection drawings.

I2.2 Variations. Any variations from the AESS Categories listed must be clearly noted. These variations could include machined surfaces, locally abraded surfaces, and forgings. In addition:

a) If a distinction is to be made between different surfaces or parts of members, the transition line/plane must be clearly identified/defined on the shop detail, arrangement and erection drawings;

b) Tack welds, temporary braces and fixtures used in fabrication are to be indicated on shop drawings;

c) All architecturally sensitive connection details will be submitted for approval by the Architect/Engineer prior to completion of shop detail drawings.

I3. Fabrication

I3.1 General Fabrication. The fabricator is to take special care in handling the steel to avoid marking or distorting the steel members.

a) All slings will be nylon-type or chains with softeners or wire rope with softeners.

b) Care shall be taken to minimize damage to any shop paint or coating.

c) If temporary braces or fixtures are required during fabrication or shipment, or to facilitate erection, care must be taken to avoid and/or repair any blemishes or unsightly surfaces resulting from the use or removal of such temporary elements.

d) Tack welds shall be ground smooth.

I3.2 Unfinished, Reused or Weathering Steel. Members fabricated of unfinished, reused or weathering steel that are to be AESS may still have erection marks, painted marks or other marks on surfaces in the completed structure. Special requirements shall be specified as Category AESS C.

I3.3 Tolerances for Rolled Shapes. The permissible tolerances for depth, width, out-of- square, camber and sweep of rolled shapes shall be as specified in CSA G40.20/21 and ASTM A6. The following exceptions apply:

a) For Categories AESS 3 and 4: the matching of abutting cross-sections shall be required;

b) For Categories AESS 2, 3 and 4: the as-fabricated straightness tolerance of a member is one-half of the standard camber and sweep tolerance in CSA G40.20/21.

I3.4 Tolerances for Built-up Members. The tolerance on overall section dimensions of members made up of plates, bars and shapes by welding is limited to the accumulation of permissible tolerances of the component parts as provided by CSA W59 and ASTM A6. For Categories AESS 2, 3 and 4, the as-fabricated straightness tolerance for the built-up member is one-half of the standard camber and sweep tolerances in CSA W59.

I3.5 Joints. For Categories AESS 3 and 4, all copes, miters and butt cuts in surfaces exposed to view are made with uniform gaps, if shown to be open joint, or in uniform contact if shown without gap.

I3.6 Surface Appearance. For Categories AESS 1, 2 and 3, the quality surface as delivered by the mills will be acceptable. For Category AESS 4, the steel surface imperfections should be filled and sanded.

I3.7 Welds. For corrosive environments, all joints should be seal welded. In addition:

a) For Categories AESS 1, 2 and 3, a smooth uniform weld will be acceptable. For Category AESS 4, the weld will be contoured and blended.
b) For Categories AESS 1, 2, 3 and 4, all weld spatter is to be avoided/removed where exposed to view.
c) For Categories AESS 1 and 2, weld projection up to 2 mm is acceptable for butt and plug-welded joints. For Categories AESS 3 and 4, welds will be ground smooth/filled.

I3.8 Weld Show-through. It is recognized that the degree of weld show-through, which is any visual indication of the presence of a weld or welds on the opposite surface from the viewer, is a function of weld size and material thickness.

a) For Categories AESS 1, 2 and 3, the members or components will be acceptable as produced.
b) For Category AESS 4, the fabricator shall minimize the weld show-through.

I3.9 Surface Preparation for Painting. Unless otherwise specified in the Contract Documents, the Fabricator will clean AESS members to meet the requirement of SSPC-SP 6 "Commercial Blast Cleaning" (sandblast or shotblast). Prior to blast cleaning:

a) Any deposits of grease or oil are to be removed by solvent cleaning, SSPC-SP 1;
b) Weld spatter, slivers and surface discontinuities are to be removed;
c) Sharp edges resulting from flame cutting, grinding and especially shearing are to be softened.

I3.10 Hollow Structural Sections (HSS) Seams

a) For Categories AESS 1 and 2, seams of hollow structural sections shall be acceptable as produced.
b) For Category AESS 3, seams shall be oriented away from view or as indicated in the Contract Documents.
c) For Category AESS 4, seams shall be treated so that they are not apparent.

I4. Delivery of Materials

I4.1 General Delivery. The Fabricator shall use special care to avoid bending, twisting or otherwise distorting the Structural Steel. All tie-downs on loads will be either nylon strap or chains with softeners to avoid damage to edges and surfaces of members.

I4.2 Standard of Acceptance. The standard for acceptance of delivered and erected members shall be equivalent to the standard employed at fabrication.

I5. Erection

I5.1 General Erection. The Erector shall use special care in unloading, handling and erecting the AESS to avoid marking or distorting the AESS. The Erector must plan and execute all operations in a manner that allows the architectural appearance of the structure to be maintained.

a)   All slings will be nylon-strap or chains with softeners.
b)   Care shall be taken to minimize damage to any shop paint or coating.
c)   If temporary braces or fixtures are required to facilitate erection, care must be taken to avoid and/or repair any blemishes or unsightly surfaces resulting from the use or removal of such temporary elements.
d)   Tack welds shall be ground smooth and holes shall be filled with weld metal or body filler and smoothed by grinding or filling to the standards applicable to the shop fabrication of the materials.
e)   All backing bars shall be removed and ground smooth.
f)   All bolt heads in connections shall be on the same side, as specified, and consistent from one connection to another.

I5.2 Erection Tolerances. Unless otherwise specified in the Contract Documents, members and components are plumbed, leveled and aligned to a tolerance equal to that permitted for structural steel.

I5.3 Adjustable Connections. When more stringent tolerances are specifically required for erecting AESS, the Owner's plans shall specify/allow adjustable connections between AESS and adjoining structural elements, in order to enable the Erector to adjust and/or specify the method for achieving the desired dimensions. Adjustment details proposed by the Erector shall be submitted to the Architect and Engineer for review.

TABLE I1 - AESS Category Matrix

ID	Characteristics	AESS C Custom Elements	AESS 4 Showcase Elements	AESS 3 Feature Elements Viewed at a distance ≤ 6 m	AESS 2 Feature Elements Viewed at a distance > 6 m	AESS 1 Basic Elements	SSS Standard Structural Steel CSA S16
1.1	Surface preparation to SSPC-SP 6		✓	✓	✓	✓	
1.2	Sharp edges ground smooth		✓	✓	✓	✓	
1.3	Continuous weld appearance		✓	✓	✓	✓	
1.4	Standard structural bolts		✓	✓	✓	✓	
1.5	Weld spatter removed		✓	✓	✓	✓	
2.1	Visual samples		optional	optional	optional		
2.2	One-half standard fabrication tolerances		✓	✓	✓		
2.3	Fabrication marks not apparent		✓	✓	✓		
2.4	Welds uniform and smooth		✓	✓	✓		
3.1	Mill marks removed		✓	✓			
3.2	Butt and plug welds ground smooth and filled		✓	✓			
3.3	HSS weld seam oriented for reduced visibility		✓	✓			
3.4	Cross-sectional abutting surface aligned		✓	✓			
3.5	Joint gap tolerances minimized		✓	✓			
3.6	All welded connections		optional	optional			
4.1	HSS seam not apparent		✓				
4.2	Welds contoured and blended		✓				
4.3	Surfaces filled and sanded		✓				
4.4	Weld show-through minimized		✓				
C.1							
C.2							
C.3							
C.4							
C.5							

TABLE I1 - AESS Category Matrix (Cont'd)

	Notes
1.1	Prior to blast cleaning, any deposits of grease or oil are to be removed by solvent cleaning, SSPC-SP 1.
1.2	Rough surfaces are to be deburred and ground smooth. Sharp edges resulting from flame cutting, grinding and especially shearing are to be softened.
1.3	Intermittent welds are made continuous, either with additional welding, caulking or body filler. For corrosive environments, all joints should be seal welded. Seams of hollow structural sections shall be acceptable as produced.
1.4	All bolt heads in connections shall be on the same side, as specified, and consistent from one connection to another.
1.5	Weld spatter, slivers and surface discontinuities are to be removed. Weld projection up to 2 mm is acceptable for butt and plug-welded joints.
2.1	Visual samples are either a 3-D rendering, a physical sample, a first-off inspection, a scaled mock-up or a full-scale mock-up, as specified in Contract Documents.
2.2	These tolerances are required to be one-half of those of standard structural steel as specified in CSA S16.
2.3	Members marked with specific numbers during the fabrication and erection processes are not to be visible.
2.4	—
3.1	All mill marks are not to be visible in the finished product.
3.2	Caulking or body filler is acceptable.
3.3	Seams shall be oriented away from view or as indicated in the Contract Documents.
3.4	The matching of abutting cross-sections shall be required.
3.5	This characteristic is similar to 2.2 above. A clear distance of 3 mm between abutting members is required.
3.6	Hidden bolts may be considered.
4.1	HSS seams shall be treated so that they are not apparent.
4.2	In addition to a contoured and blended appearance, welded transitions between members are also required to be contoured and blended.
4.3	Steel surface imperfections should be filled and sanded.
4.4	The back face of a welded element caused by the welding process can be minimized by hand grinding the back side of the weld. The degree of weld show-through is a function of weld size and material.
C.	Additional characteristics may be added for custom elements.

APPENDIX J
Digital Modelling

This Appendix is intended to facilitate the understanding and use of digital modelling technology in the design and construction of steel structures. No long-established standard of practice exists; therefore, it is the intent of this Appendix to provide guidance when its use is contemplated.

J1. Digital Building Product Models

When the contract documents indicate that a three-dimensional digital Building Product Model (BPM – sometimes referred to as a Building Information Model (BIM)) replaces contract drawings and is to be used as the primary means of designing, representing, and exchanging structural steel data for the project, the provisions in this Appendix shall apply. In this case, all references to the Design Drawings in this Code shall instead apply to the Design Model, and all references to Fabrication (Shop Details – formerly Shop Drawings) and Erection Documents in the Code shall instead apply to the Manufacturing Model. The CIS/2 Logical Product Model (LPM) shall be used as the Building Product Model for structural steel. The CIS/2 LPM for structural steel may exist solely as the project's BPM or may be integrated into a multi-disciplinary BPM for projects adopting greater digital model design application. Refer to the Electronic Data Interchange Project Flowchart at the end of this Appendix to understand this interoperability. In the context of the structural discipline, the BIM is sometimes referred to as the SBIM (Structural Building Information Model).

If the primary means of project communication reverts from a model-based (electronic) system to a paper-based system, the requirements in this Code other than in this Appendix shall apply.

J2. Definitions

Building Product Model A digital information structure of the objects making up a building or structure, capturing the form, function, behaviour and relations of the parts and assemblies within one or more building systems, such as architectural, structural and mechanical. The data in the model is created, manipulated (edited), evaluated, reviewed and presented using computer-based design, engineering and manufacturing applications. Traditional two-dimensional drawings may be one of many reports generated by the Building Product Model.

CIS/2 (CIM Steel Integration Standards/ Version 2) The specification providing the Building Product Model for structural steel and format for Electronic Data Interchange (EDI) among software applications dealing with steel design, analysis, and manufacturing.

Logical Product Model (LPM)	The CIS/2 Building Product Model which supports the engineering of low-, medium-, and high-rise construction in domestic, institutional, commercial and industrial contexts. All elements of the structure are covered, including main and secondary framing and connections. The connections used can be of a variety of structural shape or element. The LPM addresses the exchange of data between structural steel software applications. It is meant to support a heterogeneous set of software applications over a broad portion of the steel information development conveyance life cycle. It is organized around the three different sub-models: the Analysis Model (data represented in structural analysis), the Design Model (data represented in frame design layout) and the Manufacturing Model (data represented in detailing for fabrication).
Data Management Conformance (DMC)	The capability of the CIS/2 BPM (or LPM) to include optional data entities for managing and tracking additions, deletions and modifications to a model, including who made the change and when the change was made for all editing instances.

J3. Standards

Where three-dimensional digital Building Product Model data is specified for information conveyance between the design and construction teams of a project, the CIM Steel Integration Standards Release 2: Second Edition P265: CIS/2.1: Volumes 1 through 4 shall be followed.

J4. Contract Documents

In addition to the requirements in Clause 4, the following requirements shall apply to the Design Model.

J4.1 The Design Model shall:

a) Consist of Data Management Conformance Classes.
b) Contain Analysis Model data so as to include load calculations as indicated in the Contract Specifications referencing jurisdictional codes.
c) Include entities that fully define each steel element, and the extent of detailing of each element, as would be recorded on an equivalent set of structural steel design drawings (see Clause 4.1.2).
d) Include all steel elements (primary and secondary structural), as well as any other entities required for strength and stability of the completely erected structure.
e) Govern over all other forms of information, including drawings, sketches, etc.

J4.2 The Owner shall designate an Administrator for the LPM, who shall:

a) Control the LPM by providing appropriate access privileges (read, write, etc.) to all relevant parties.
b) Maintain the security of the LPM.
c) Guard against data loss of the LPM.

d) Be responsible for updates and revisions to the LPM as they occur and archive all versions with appropriate annotations.

e) Inform all involved parties regarding changes to the LPM.

NOTE: When a project is designed and constructed using EDI, it is imperative that an individual entity on the team be responsible for maintaining the LPM. This is to assume protection of data through proper back-up, storage and security and to provide coordination of the flow of information to all team members when information is added to the model. Team members exchange information to revise the model with this Administrator. The Administrator will validate all changes to the LPM. This ensures proper tracking and control of revisions. The Administrator can be one of the design team members such as an Architect, Structural Engineer, or a separate entity on the design team serving this purpose who is well experienced with applicable (sophisticated) software. The Administrator can also be the Fabricator's Detailer or a separate entity on the construction team serving this purpose. Currently, numerous firms within the Detailer Industry in Canada are well versed in this model management and information protocol for steel-framed structures.

J5. Fabrication and Erection Documents

In addition to the requirements in Clause 5, the following requirements shall apply:

When the Design Model is used to develop the Manufacturing Model, the Fabricator shall accept the information under the following conditions:

a) When the design information is to be conveyed to the Fabricator by way of the Design Model, in the event of a conflict between the model and any Design Drawings, the Design Model will govern.

b) The ownership of the information added to the LPM in the Manufacturing Model should be defined in the Contract Documents. In the absence of terms for ownership regarding the information added by the Fabricator to the LPM in the Contract Documents, the ownership will belong to the Fabricator, dependent on which party provided the expertise for the information to be incorporated to the LPM. See Note below.

c) During the development of the Manufacturing Model, as member locations are adjusted to convert the modelled parts from a Design Model, these relocations will only be done with approval of the Designer.

d) The Fabricator and Erector shall accept the use of the LPM and Design Model under the same conditions as set forth in Clause 4.3.1, except as modified in J5.

e) When approval of the detailed material is to be done by using the Manufacturing Model, the version of the submitted model shall be identified. Comments attached to the individual elements as specified in the CIS/2 Standard shall be used to annotate the Manufacturing Model. The Fabricator will issue the revised Manufacturing Model for review, and the version of the model submitted will be tracked as previously defined.

NOTE: Approval of the Manufacturing Model by the Designer can replace the approval of actual Fabrication and Erection Documents. For this method to be effective, a system must be in place to record review, approval, correction and final release of the

Manufacturing Model for fabrication of structural steel. The versions of the model must be tracked with review comments and approvals permanently attached to the versions of the model to the same extent as such data is maintained with conventional hard copy approvals. The CIS/2 Standard provides this level of tracking.

Electronic Data Interchange Project Flowchart

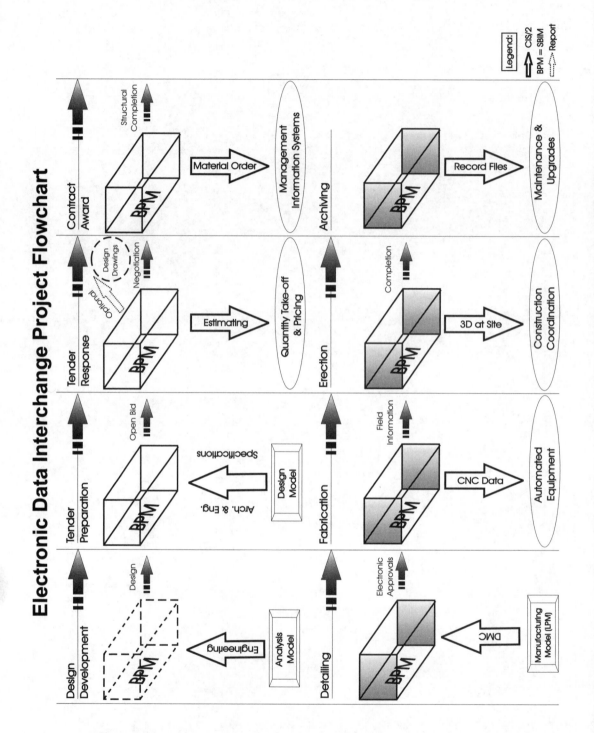

CISC Code of Standard Practice

STRUCTURAL SHEET STEEL PRODUCTS

General

Structural sheet steel products such as roof deck, floor deck and cladding complement the structural steel frame of a building. These large-surface elements often

TYPICAL STEEL DECK AND CLADDING PROFILES

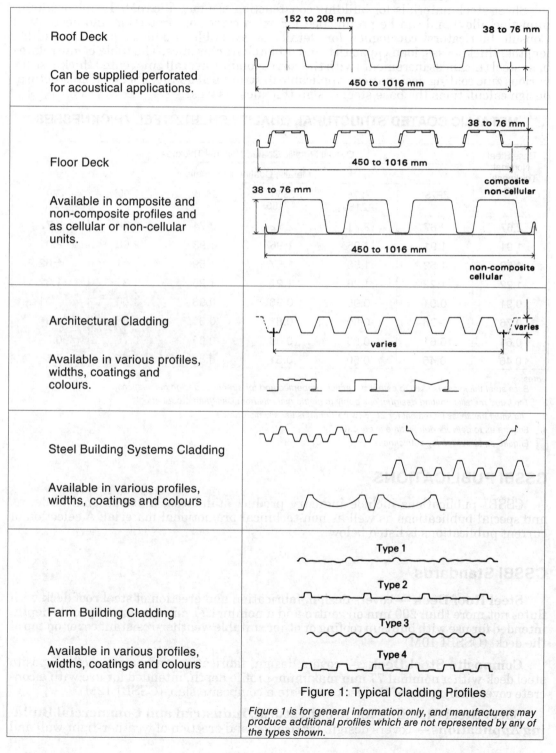

Roof Deck Can be supplied perforated for acoustical applications.	152 to 208 mm, 38 to 76 mm, 450 to 1016 mm
Floor Deck Available in composite and non-composite profiles and as cellular or non-cellular units.	38 to 76 mm, 450 to 1016 mm, composite non-cellular, 38 to 76 mm, 450 to 1016 mm, non-composite cellular
Architectural Cladding Available in various profiles, widths, coatings and colours.	varies, varies
Steel Building Systems Cladding Available in various profiles, widths, coatings and colours	
Farm Building Cladding Available in various profiles, widths, coatings and colours	Type 1, Type 2, Type 3, Type 4

Figure 1: Typical Cladding Profiles

Figure 1 is for general information only, and manufacturers may produce additional profiles which are not represented by any of the types shown.

perform both structural and non-structural functions, thereby enhancing the overall economy of the design.

Many of the sheet steel products used in Canada are supplied by members of the Canadian Sheet Steel Building Institute, a national association of steel producers, zinc producers, coil coaters, fastener manufacturers and fabricators of steel building products, steel building systems and lightweight steel framing components. The Institute promotes the use of sheet steel in building construction by encouraging good design, pleasing form and greater economy.

Sheet steel materials for building construction are metallic coated (zinc or aluminum-zinc alloy) and can be prefinished for extra corrosion protection and aesthetics. Consult fabricators' catalogues for details of available products, profiles, widths, lengths, thicknesses, load capacities and other characteristics. The table below relates base steel thickness increments with the corresponding overall zinc coated thickness for various zinc coating designations applicable to structural quality sheets. For structural design calculations the base steel design thickness is used.

METALLIC COATED STRUCTURAL QUALITY SHEET STEEL THICKNESSES

Base Steel Nominal Thickness[1], mm	Overall Metallic Coated Nominal Thickness, mm					
	Metallic Coating Designation[2]					
	ZF75[3]	Z275 AZ150	Z350[4] AZ180	Z450[4]	Z600[4]	Z700[4]
2.67	2.67	2.71	2.72	2.74	2.76	2.77
1.91	1.91	1.95	1.96	1.98	2.00	2.01
1.52	1.52	1.56	1.57	1.59	1.61	1.62
1.22	1.22	1.26	1.27	1.29	1.31	1.32
0.91	0.91	0.95	0.96	0.98	1.00	1.01
0.76	0.76	0.80	0.81	0.83	0.85	0.86
0.61	0.61	0.65	0.66	0.68	0.70	0.71
0.46	0.46	0.50	0.51	0.53	0.55	0.56

Notes:
1. Base steel thickness is used to establish section properties and for structural design calculations.
2. The listed metallic coating designations apply to metric material from Canadian producers.
3. The small thickness increment for ZF75 (wiped coat) is usually disregarded.
4. Enquire as to delivery date, if time is critical.
■ Enquire as to availability of thickness.

CSSBI PUBLICATIONS

CSSBI publications include industry product standards, informational bulletins and special publications as well as non-technical promotional material. A selection of current publications is listed below.

CSSBI Standards

Steel Roof Deck — covers design, fabrication and erection of steel roof deck with flutes not more than 200 mm on centre and a nominal 77 mm maximum profile depth, intended for use with built-up roofing or other suitable weather-resistant cover on top of the deck. (CSSBI 10M)

Composite Steel Deck — covers design, fabrication and erection of composite steel deck with a nominal 77 mm maximum profile depth, intended for use with a concrete cover slab on top of the deck to create a composite slab. (CSSBI 12M)

Sheet Steel Cladding for Architectural, Industrial and Commercial Building Applications — covers design, fabrication and erection of weather-tight wall and roof cladding made from metallic coated, prefinished sheet steel for use on buildings with low internal humidity. (CSSBI 20M)

Steel Building Systems — covers the design, fabrication and erection of steel building systems (SBS). Includes definitions, classification of SBS by type, checklist of items normally furnished, criteria for load combinations, design standards, and certification by a registered engineer. (CSSBI 30M)

Steel Farm Roofing and Siding — covers the manufacture, load carrying capacity, handling and installation of sheet steel cladding intended for application to walls and/or roofs of farm buildings. (CSSBI 21M)

Bulletins and Special Publications

Criteria for the Testing of Composite Slabs — provides the criteria for conducting a series of shear-bond tests necessary to determine the structural capacity of a composite slab. (CSSBI S2)

Criteria for the Design of Composite Slabs — contains design criteria, based on limit states design, for composite slabs made of a structural concrete placed permanently over a composite steel deck. (CSSBI S3)

Design of Steel Deck Diaphragms — offers a simple and practical approach to the design of steel deck diaphragms supported by horizontal steel framing. (CSSBI B13)

Lightweight Steel Framing Design Manual — shows through examples how to design lightweight steel framing structural systems. Detailed calculations are shown for curtain walls, infill walls, and axial load bearing systems as well as all connections. (CSSBI 51M)

How-To Series: Insulated Sheet Steel Wall Assemblies — describes the various stages in the selection of sheet steel wall assembly components, architectural and structural design issues, as well as building science topics and material selection. (CSSBI S10)

How-To Series: Insulated Sheet Steel Roof Assemblies — describes the various stages in the selection of the sheet steel roof assembly components, architectural and structural design issues, as well as building science topics and material selection. (CSSBI S11)

How-To Series: Steel Roof and Floor Deck — describes the various stages in the selection of steel deck products, the different types of deck products, structural design issues and material selection. (CSSBI S15)

How To Series: Lightgauge Steel Roofing and Siding — offers simple and practical recommendations for the selection, application and installation of lightgauge steel cladding. (CSSBI S14)

Barrier Series Prefinished Sheet Steel: Product Performance & Applications — presents the features and benefits of the Barrier Series prefinished paint system for sheet steel building products in more aggressive environments. (CSSBI B17)

Lightweight Steel Framing Architectural Design Guide — provides information to the architect about the uses and specification of Lightweight Steel Framing (LSF) systems, including details on design, building science, acoustic and fire ratings, as well as extensive references. (CSSBI 57)

Contact CSSBI at the address below for a complete listing of publications, copies of publications, or other information concerning sheet steel in construction.

Canadian Sheet Steel Building Institute
652 Bishop St. N., Unit 2A, Cambridge, Ontario N3H 4V6
Tel (519) 650-1285   Fax (519) 650-8081   Website: www.cssbi.ca

MASS AND FORCES FOR MATERIALS

MATERIAL	Mass (kg/m³)	Force (kN/m³)	MATERIAL	Mass (kg/m³)	Force (kN/m³)
METALS, ALLOYS, ORES			**TIMBER, AIR-DRY**		
Aluminum	2 640	25.9	Birch	689	6.76
Brass	8 550	83.8	Cedar	352	3.45
Bronze, 7.9-14% tin	8 150	79.9	Fir, Douglas, seasoned	545	5.34
Bronze, aluminum	7 700	75.5	Fir, Douglas, unseasoned	641	6.29
Copper	8 910	87.4	Fir, Douglas, wet	801	7.86
Copper ore, pyrites	4 200	41.2	Fir, Douglas, glue laminated	545	5.34
Gold	19 300	189	Hemlock	481	4.72
Iron, cast, pig	7 210	70.7	Larch, tamarack	561	5.50
Iron, wrought	7 770	76.2	Larch, western	609	5.97
Iron, spiegel-eisen	7 500	73.5	Maple	737	7.23
Iron, ferro-silicon	7 000	68.6	Oak, red	689	6.76
Iron ore, hematite	5 210	51.1	Oak, white	753	7.38
Iron ore, hematite in bank	2 560-2 880	25.1-28.2	Pine, jack	481	4.72
Iron ore, hematite, loose	2 080-2 560	20.4-25.1	Pine, ponderosa	513	5.03
Iron ore, limonite	3 800	37.3	Pine, red	449	4.40
Iron ore, magnetite	5 050	49.5	Pine, white	416	4.08
Iron slag	2 760	27.1	Poplar	481	4.72
Lead	11 400	112	Spruce	449	4.40
Lead ore, galena	7 450	73.1	For pressure treated timber add retention to mass of air-dry material.		
Magnesium	1 790	17.6			
Manganese	7 610	74.6			
Manganese ore	4 150	40.7			
Mercury	13 600	133	**LIQUIDS**		
Monel	8 910	87.4	Alcohol, pure	785	7.70
Nickel	9 050	88.8	Gasoline	673	6.60
Platinum	21 300	209	Oils	929	9.11
Silver	10 500	103	Water, fresh at 4°C (max. density)	1 000	9.81
Steel, rolled	7 850	77.0			
Tin	7 350	72.1	Water, fresh at 100°C	961	9.42
Tin ore, cassiterite	6 700	65.7	Water, salt	1 030	10.1
Zinc	7 050	69.1			
Zinc ore, blende	4 050	39.7	**EARTH, ETC. EXCAVATED**		
			Earth, wet	1 600	15.7
MASONRY			Earth, dry	1 200	11.8
Ashlar	2 240-2 560	22.0-25.1	Sand and gravel, wet	1 920	18.8
Brick, soft	1 760	17.3	Sand and gravel, dry	1 680	16.5
Brick, common	2 000	19.6			
Brick, pressed	2 240	22.0	**VARIOUS BUILDING MATERIALS**		
Clay tile, average	961	9.42			
Rubble	2 080-2 480	20.4-24.3	Cement, Portland, loose	1 510	14.8
Concrete, cinder, haydite	1 600-1 760	15.7-17.3	Cement, Portland, set	2 930	28.7
Concrete, slag	2 080	20.4	Lime, gypsum, loose	849-1 030	8.33-10.1
Concrete, stone	2 310	22.7	Mortar, cement-lime, set	1 650	16.2
Concrete, stone, reinforced	2 400	23.5	Quarry stone, piled	1 440-1 760	14.1-17.3
SOLID FUELS			**MISCELLANEOUS**		
Coal, anthracite, piled	753-929	7.38-9.11	Asphaltum	1 300	12.7
Coal, bituminous, piled	641-865	6.29-8.48	Tar, bituminous	1 200	11.8
Coke, piled	368-513	3.61-5.03	Glass, common	2 500	24.5
Charcoal, piled	160-224	1.57-2.20	Glass, plate or crown	2 580	25.3
Peat, piled	320-416	3.14-4.08	Glass, crystal	2 950	28.9
			Paper	929	9.11
ICE AND SNOW					
Ice	897	8.80			
Snow, dry, fresh fallen	128	1.26			
Snow, dry, packed	192-400	1 .88-3.92			
Snow, wet	432-641	4.24-6.29			

DESIGN DEAD LOADS (kPa) OF MATERIALS

STEEL DECKS	
Steel deck* 38 mm deep	
(up to 0.91 mm thick)	0.10
(1.22 to 1.52 mm thick)	0.15
Steel deck* 76 mm deep (Narrow-Rib)	
(up to 0.91 mm thick)	0.15
(1.22 to 1.91 mm thick)	0.30
Steel deck* 76 mm deep (Wide-Rib)	
(up to 0.91 mm thick)	0.10
(1.22 to 1.52 mm thick)	0.15
* for cellular deck, add	0.08
CONCRETE, per 100 mm	
- 2350 kg/m^3 (N.D.)	2.31
- 2000 kg/m^3 (slag aggregate)	1.96
-1850 kg/m^3 (S.L.D.)	1.82
HOLLOW CORE PRECAST (no topping)	
- 200 mm deep (N.D.)	2.60
- 300 mm deep (N.D.)	3.50
WOOD JOISTS (at 400 mm centres)	
- 38 mm x 184 mm joists	0.09
- 38 mm x 235 mm joists	0.12
- 38 mm x 286 mm joists	0.14
PLYWOOD	
- 11 mm thick	0.06
- 14 mm thick	0.08
- 19 mm thick	0.11
CHIPBOARD	
- 12.7 mm thick	0.07
- 15.9 mm thick	0.09
- 19.0 mm thick	0.11
WALLS AND CLADDING	
- Solid brick wall (concrete)	
- 100 mm thick (S.L.D.)	1.40
- 100 mm thick (N.D.)	1.90
- Hollow block (S.L.D.)	
- 100 mm thick	1.10
- 200 mm thick	1.60
- 300 mm thick	2.30
- Hollow block (N.D.)	
- 100 mm thick	1.40
- 200 mm thick	2.10
- 300 mm thick	2.90
- P.C. wall plus glazing	2.40 - 3.80
- Metal curtain wall	0.74 - 1.50
- Insulated sheet steel wall	
(exclude girts)	0.25 - 0.40
- 38 x 89 wood studs @ 400 mm	0.05
- Gypsum wallboard per 10 mm	0.08
- Stone veneer per 25 mm	0.40

FLOOR FINISHING	
- Vinyl, linoleum or asphalt tile	0.07
- Softwood subfloor per 10 mm	0.06
- Hardwood per 10 mm	0.08
- Carpeting	0.10
- Asphaltic concrete per 10 mm	0.23
- 20 mm Ceramic or quarry tiles on	
12 mm mortar bed	0.80
- Terrazzo per 10 mm	0.24
- Mastic floor (20 mm)	0.45
ROOFING	
- 3 ply asphalt, no gravel	0.15
- 4 ply asphalt, no gravel	0.20
- 3 ply asphalt and gravel	0.27
- 4 ply asphalt and gravel	0.32
- Asphalt strip shingles	0.15
- Gypsum wallboard per 10 mm	0.08
INSULATION (per 100 mm thick)	
- Glass fibre, batts	0.05
- Glass fibre, blown	0.04
- Glass fibre, rigid	0.07
- Urethane, rigid foam	0.03
- Insulating concrete	0.06
CEILINGS	
- Gypsum wallboard per 10 mm	0.08
- Tiled ceiling & suspension system,	
with fixtures, average	0.20
- 20 mm plaster on lath/furring	0.40
- Sprayed fire protection, average	0.07
- Ducts/pipes/wiring allowance	0.25
(average condition)	
DECK-SLABS (average condition)	
- 38 mm deck with	
- 65 mm N.D. cover#	1.95
- 90 mm N.D. cover#	2.55
- 65 mm S.L.D. cover##	1.55
- 85 mm S.L.D. cover##	1.90
- 75 mm (or 76 mm) "wide-rib" deck with	
- 65 mm N.D. cover#	2.55
- 90 mm N.D. cover#	3.15
- 65 mm S.L.D. cover##	2.15
- 85 mm S.L.D. cover##	2.50
- 76 mm "narrow-rib" deck with	
- 65 mm N.D. cover#	2.20
- 90 mm N.D. cover#	2.80
- 65 mm S.L.D. cover##	1.90
- 85 mm S.L.D. cover##	2.25
# assume 2350 kg/m^3 concrete	
## assume 1850 kg/m^3 concrete	

M/D Ratios

How *M/D* Ratios are Calculated

M/D ratios are used to measure the thermal mass resistance of a member under fire. Typically, the higher the *M/D* ratio, the greater the fire resistance. The numbers given in the following table were calculated by dividing the steel member mass per unit length, *M* (kg/m) by the heated perimeter, *D* (m). The resulting units are (kg/m)/m in the Metric system and (lb/ft)/in in the Imperial system.

The *D* value is based on the heated perimeter following the contour of the shape, including all flange and web surfaces, and is applicable to fire protection with spray-applied fire-resistive materials. Two separate *M/D* ratios are given for each steel section: (1) one for columns based on the entire perimeter (fire exposure from all sides), and (2) one for beams which typically have the top surface of its top flange shielded from the fire, hence having one less exposed surface.

This heated perimeter (*D*) calculation corresponds to the "contour protection", as described by Gewain *et al* (2006), and is distinct from the "box protection" based on members being boxed up with gypsum board.

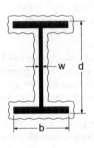

$$D \approx 4b + 2d - 2w$$

(1) Heated perimeter, *D*
for steel columns

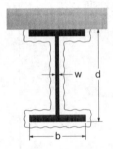

$$D \approx 3b + 2d - 2w$$

(2) Heated perimeter, *D*
for steel beams

Note: The above formulas for the heated perimeter are approximate and do not include the flange-to-web fillets. These have been taken into account when calculating the M/D ratios given in the following pages.

Reference

GEWAIN, R.G., IWANKIW, N.R., ALFAWAKHIRI, F., AND FRATER, G. 2006. Fire Facts for Steel Buildings, Canadian Institute of Steel Construction, American Institute of Steel Construction.

M/D RATIOS FOR CONTOUR PROTECTION

Designation	SI (kg/m)/m		Imperial (lb./ft.)/in.		Designation	SI (kg/m)/m		Imperial (lb./ft.)/in.	
	Beam	Column	Beam	Column		Beam	Column	Beam	Column
WWF2000					WWF800				
x732	131		2.24		x339	111		1.89	
x648	116		1.98		x300	98.3		1.68	
x607	109		1.85		x253	91.9		1.57	
x542	99.6		1.70		x223	80.8		1.38	
					x184	74.7		1.27	
WWF1800					x161	65.4		1.12	
x700	135		2.30						
x659	127		2.17		WWF700				
x617	119		2.03		x245	95.7		1.63	
x575	111		1.89		x214	83.7		1.43	
x510	101		1.73		x196	76.4		1.30	
					x175	77.5		1.32	
WWF1600					x152	67.4		1.15	
x622	130		2.21						
x580	121		2.06		WWF650				
x538	112		1.91		x864		230		3.92
x496	103		1.76		x739		194		3.30
x431	92.5		1.58		x598		156		2.66
					x499		130		2.22
WWF1400					x400		104		1.78
x597	136		2.32						
x513	117		1.99		WWF600				
x471	107		1.82		x793		229		3.91
x405	95.3		1.63		x680		193		3.30
x358	90.6		1.55		x551		156		2.66
					x460		130		2.22
WWF1200					x369		104		1.78
x487	122		2.08						
x418	108		1.85		WWF550				
x380	98.7		1.68		x721		229		3.90
x333	93.8		1.60		x620		193		3.29
x302	85.1		1.45		x503		156		2.66
x263	80.9		1.38		x420		130		2.22
					x280		86.0		1.47
WWF1100									
x458	121		2.06		WWF500				
x388	106		1.82		x651		228		3.89
x351	96.0		1.64		x561		193		3.29
x304	90.6		1.55		x456		156		2.66
x273	81.5		1.39		x381		130		2.22
x234	76.6		1.31		x343		117		2.00
					x306		104		1.78
WWF1000					x276		93.7		1.60
x447	125		2.13		x254		86.0		1.47
x377	109		1.87		x223		75.8		1.29
x340	98.4		1.68		x197		66.8		1.14
x293	92.9		1.58						
x262	83.1		1.42		WWF450				
x223	78.1		1.33		x503		192		3.28
x200	70.4		1.20		x409		155		2.65
					x342		130		2.22
WWF900					x308		117		2.00
x417	123		2.09		x274		104		1.78
x347	107		1.82		x248		93.6		1.60
x309	94.9		1.62		x228		85.9		1.47
x262	88.6		1.51		x201		75.7		1.29
x231	78.3		1.34		x177		66.7		1.14
x192	72.3		1.23						
x169	63.8		1.09						

M/D RATIOS FOR CONTOUR PROTECTION

Designation	SI (kg/m)/m		Imperial (lb./ft.)/in.		Designation	SI (kg/m)/m		Imperial (lb./ft.)/in.	
	Beam	Column	Beam	Column		Beam	Column	Beam	Column
WWF400					W920				
x444		192		3.27	x656	208		3.56	
x362		155		2.65	x588	189		3.22	
x303		130		2.21	x537	173		2.95	
x273		117		2.00	x491	159		2.72	
x243		104		1.78	x449	146		2.50	
x220		93.6		1.60	x420	137		2.35	
x202		85.9		1.47	x390	128		2.18	
x178		75.7		1.29	x368	121		2.06	
x157		66.9		1.14	x344	114		1.95	
WWF350					W920				
x315		155		2.64	x381	139		2.37	
x263		129		2.21	x345	126		2.16	
x238		117		1.99	x313	115		1.96	
x212		104		1.78	x289	107		1.82	
x192		93.5		1.60	x271	101		1.72	
x176		85.8		1.46	x253	94.3		1.61	
x155		75.7		1.29	x238	89.1		1.52	
x137		66.7		1.14	x223	84.1		1.44	
					x201	75.7		1.29	
W1100					W840				
x499	148		2.53		x576	195		3.32	
x433	129		2.21		x527	180		3.07	
x390	117		2.00		x473	163		2.77	
x343	103		1.77		x433	150		2.56	
					x392	136		2.33	
W1000					x359	125		2.14	
x883	268		4.57		x329	116		1.97	
x748	230		3.92		x299	106		1.80	
x642	200		3.41						
x591	185		3.16		W840				
x554	174		2.98		x251	99.1		1.69	
x539	170		2.90		x226	90.1		1.54	
x483	153		2.62		x210	83.9		1.43	
x443	141		2.41		x193	77.7		1.33	
x412	132		2.25		x176	70.8		1.21	
x371	119		2.04						
x321	104		1.77		W760				
x296	96.4		1.64		x582	211		3.59	
					x531	193		3.30	
W1000					x484	178		3.04	
x584	199		3.40		x434	161		2.74	
x494	171		2.92		x389	145		2.48	
x486	168		2.88		x350	132		2.25	
x438	153		2.60		x314	119		2.03	
x415	146		2.49		x284	108		1.85	
x393	138		2.36		x257	98.5		1.68	
x350	124		2.11						
x314	112		1.91		W760				
x272	97.4		1.66		x220	96.3		1.64	
x249	89.7		1.53		x196	86.4		1.47	
x222	80.6		1.38		x185	81.2		1.39	
					x173	76.6		1.31	
					x161	71.0		1.21	
					x147	65.4		1.12	
					x134	59.7		1.02	

M/D RATIOS FOR CONTOUR PROTECTION

Designation	SI (kg/m)/m		Imperial (lb./ft.)/in.		Designation	SI (kg/m)/m		Imperial (lb./ft.)/in.	
	Beam	Column	Beam	Column		Beam	Column	Beam	Column
W690					**W530**				
x548	215		3.67		x138	81.9		1.40	
x500	198		3.38		x123	73.6		1.26	
x457	183		3.12		x109	65.6		1.12	
x419	168		2.87		x101	61.1		1.04	
x384	156		2.65		x92	56.2		0.959	
x350	143		2.44		x82	50.3		0.858	
x323	133		2.26		x72	44.0		0.751	
x289	119		2.03						
x265	110		1.88		**W530**				
x240	100		1.71		x85	55.6		0.950	
x217	91.7		1.56		x74	49.4		0.843	
					x66	43.7		0.746	
W690									
x192	91.0		1.55		**W460**				
x170	81.0		1.38		x464	238		4.07	
x152	73.2		1.25		x421	219		3.75	
x140	67.3		1.15		x384	202		3.45	
x125	60.9		1.04		x349	186		3.17	
					x315	169		2.89	
W610					x286	156		2.66	
x551	234		3.99		x260	143		2.45	
x498	214		3.65		x235	131		2.23	
x455	197		3.36		x213	119		2.04	
x415	182		3.10		x193	109		1.87	
x372	165		2.81		x177	101		1.72	
x341	152		2.59		x158	90.3		1.54	
x307	138		2.36		x144	83.0		1.42	
x285	129		2.20		x128	74.4		1.27	
x262	119		2.03		x113	65.8		1.12	
x241	110		1.88						
x217	100		1.71		**W460**				
x195	90.2		1.54		x106	71.9		1.23	
x174	81.0		1.38		x97	65.8		1.12	
x155	72.3		1.23		x89	61.3		1.05	
					x82	56.2		0.960	
W610					x74	51.4		0.877	
x153	82.0		1.40		x67	46.7		0.797	
x140	75.2		1.28		x61	42.0		0.716	
x125	67.1		1.15						
x113	61.1		1.04		**W460**				
x101	55.4		0.946		x68	51.1		0.873	
x91	49.4		0.842		x60	44.8		0.764	
x84	45.6		0.779		x52	39.5		0.674	
W610					**W410**				
x92	54.7		0.934		x149	93.2		1.59	
x82	48.5		0.828		x132	83.1		1.42	
					x114	72.8		1.24	
					x100	63.8		1.09	
W530									
x300	146		2.49		**W410**				
x272	133		2.28		x85	63.6		1.09	
x248	122		2.08		x74	56.6		0.966	
x219	109		1.86		x67	51.2		0.875	
x196	98.4		1.68		x60	45.4		0.775	
x182	91.2		1.56		x54	41.1		0.702	
x165	83.9		1.43						
x150	76.6		1.31		**W410**				
					x46	38.8		0.663	
					x39	33.1		0.565	

M/D RATIOS FOR CONTOUR PROTECTION

Designation	SI (kg/m)/m		Imperial (lb./ft.)/in.		Designation	SI (kg/m)/m		Imperial (lb./ft.)/in.	
	Beam	Column	Beam	Column		Beam	Column	Beam	Column
W360					**W310**				
x1086		395		6.75	x283		146		2.49
x990		365		6.23	x253		132		2.26
x900		339		5.79	x226		120		2.05
x818		312		5.33	x202		108		1.85
x744		289		4.93	x179		96.7		1.65
x677		267		4.56	x158		86.1		1.47
					x143		78.3		1.34
W360					x129	86.2	71.5	1.47	1.22
x634		253		4.31	x118	78.8	65.4	1.34	1.12
x592		238		4.07	x107	71.8	59.5	1.22	1.02
x551		224		3.82	x97	65.2	54.1	1.11	0.923
x509		209		3.57					
x463		192		3.28	**W310**				
x421		177		3.02	x86	64.7	54.3	1.10	0.927
x382		162		2.77	x79	59.7	50.1	1.02	0.855
x347		148		2.53					
x314		135		2.31	**W310**				
x287		125		2.13	x74	62.2	53.1	1.06	0.906
x262		115		1.96	x67	56.2	47.9	0.959	0.818
x237		104		1.78	x60	50.4	42.9	0.860	0.733
x216		96.2		1.64					
					W310				
W360					x52	47.5		0.811	
x196		90.5		1.54	x45	40.9		0.699	
x179		82.9		1.41	x39	35.8		0.611	
x162	91.1	75.3	1.55	1.29					
x147	83.5	69.1	1.43	1.18	**W310**				
x134	76.4	63.1	1.30	1.08	x33	36.3		0.620	
					x28	31.6		0.540	
W360					x24	26.9		0.460	
x122	84.5	71.7	1.44	1.22	x21	23.9		0.408	
x110	76.6	65.0	1.31	1.11					
x101	70.9	60.2	1.21	1.03	**W250**				
x91	64.2	54.4	1.10	0.929	x167		106		1.81
					x149		95.8		1.63
W360					x131		85.2		1.45
x79	62.2	53.6	1.06	0.915	x115		75.3		1.28
x72	56.5	48.6	0.964	0.830	x101	80.9	67.1	1.38	1.15
x64	50.8	43.8	0.867	0.747	x89	72.0	59.7	1.23	1.02
					x80	64.9	53.8	1.11	0.918
W360					x73	59.4	49.2	1.01	0.840
x57	47.5		0.810						
x51	42.7		0.728		**W250**				
x45	38.1		0.650		x67	61.9	52.1	1.06	0.889
					x58	54.3	45.6	0.927	0.779
W360					x49	46.2	38.8	0.789	0.663
x39	37.0		0.632						
x33	31.3		0.534		**W250**				
					x45	47.6		0.812	
W310					x39	41.3		0.706	
x500		239		4.08	x33	35.4		0.604	
x454		220		3.76					
x415		204		3.49	**W250**				
x375		187		3.19	x28	35.7		0.610	
x342		173		2.96	x25	32.0		0.547	
x313		160		2.73	x22	28.5		0.486	
					x18	22.9		0.390	

Designation	SI (kg/m)/m		Imperial (lb./ft.)/in.		Designation	SI (kg/m)/m		Imperial (lb./ft.)/in.	
	Beam	Column	Beam	Column		Beam	Column	Beam	Column
W200					S380				
x100	96.1	79.9	1.64	1.36	x74	67.8		1.16	
x86	84.4	70.1	1.44	1.20	x64	58.2		0.994	
x71	70.9	58.8	1.21	1.00					
x59	59.6	49.4	1.02	0.844	S310				
x52	52.9	43.8	0.903	0.748	x74	79.9		1.36	
x46	47.0	38.9	0.802	0.664	x60.7	65.6		1.12	
W200					S310				
x42	47.6	40.0	0.812	0.683	x52	56.9		0.972	
x36	41.4	34.7	0.706	0.593	x47	51.8		0.885	
W200					S250				
x31	39.5	33.8	0.675	0.577	x52	65.0		1.11	
x27	33.8	28.9	0.578	0.494	x38	47.5		0.811	
W200					S200				
x22	32.5		0.555		x34	52.3		0.892	
x19	28.4		0.485		x27	42.1		0.718	
x15	22.1		0.376		S150				
W150					x26	49.6		0.846	
x37	49.1	40.8	0.839	0.697	x19	36.5		0.623	
x30	39.9	33.1	0.681	0.565					
x22	30.5	25.2	0.520	0.431	S130				
					x15	34.0		0.580	
W150									
x24	40.1	34.3	0.685	0.585	S100				
x18	30.7	26.1	0.523	0.446	x14.1	38.7		0.660	
x14	23.5	20.1	0.402	0.342	x11	31.6		0.539	
x13	22.0	18.8	0.376	0.320	S75				
W130					x11	37.7		0.644	
x28		37.7		0.644	x8	28.8		0.491	
x24		32.2		0.549					
W100					M310				
x19		32.6		0.556	x17.6	21.3		0.364	
					x16.1	19.7		0.336	
S610					x14.9	17.9		0.305	
x180	104		1.77		M250				
x158	91.2		1.56		x13.4	19.4		0.331	
					x11.9	17.4		0.296	
S610					x11.2	16.1		0.275	
x149	90.1		1.54						
x134	81.2		1.39		M200				
x119	72.3		1.23		x9.7	17.2		0.293	
S510					M150				
x143	97.6		1.67		x6.6	15.1		0.258	
x128	88.3		1.51						
S510					M100				
x112	79.7		1.36		x8.9		15.9		0.272
x98.2	70.3		1.20						
S460									
x104	81.1		1.38						
x81.4	63.8		1.09						

COEFFICIENTS OF THERMAL EXPANSION

(Linear, per degree $\times 10^{-6}$)

METALS	c per °C	c per °F	NON-METALS	c per °C	c per °F
Aluminum	23	13	Cement, Portland	13	7
Brass	19	10.4	Concrete, Stone	10	5.7
Bronze	18	10.1	Glass	7	4
Copper	16.7	9.3	Granite	8.3	4.6
Iron, Gray Cast	11	5.9	Limestone	7.9	4.4
Iron, Wrought	12	6.7	Marble	9	5
Lead	28.7	15.9	Masonry, Ashlar	6.3	3.5
Magnesium	28.8	16	Masonry, Brick	6.1	3.4
Nickel	12.6	7	Masonry, Rubble	6.3	3.5
Steel, Cast	11.3	6.3	Plaster	16	9
Steel, Stainless	17.8	9.9	Sandstone	11	6
Steel, Structural	11.7	6.5	Slate	10	5.8
Zinc, Rolled	31	17.3	Fir (parallel to fibre)	3.8	2.1
			Fir (perpendicular to fibre)	58	32

NOTE: Coefficients of thermal expansion indicated are average values from various sources. Minor variations may be expected in metals. Large variations may be expected in concrete and masonry due to the many combinations of constituents possible.

Coefficients apply in general to a temperature range from 0 to 100 degrees Celsius.

The coefficient of linear thermal expansion (c) is the change in length per unit of length for a change of one degree of temperature. The coefficient for surface expansion is approximately two times, and the coefficient of volume expansion is approximately three times, the linear coefficient.

Change in length = $c\,L$ × change in temperature, if member is free to elongate or contract.

Change in unit stress = $c\,E$ × change in temperature, if member is not permitted to elongate or contract (E = modulus of elasticity).

ELECTRONIC AIDS

Internet

The Canadian Institute of Steel Construction maintains a website on the Internet at the following address: *www.cisc-icca.ca*. Since this is a very dynamic area of information transfer, a full description of the site's contents is unwarranted in this publication. In general terms, however, the site provides information on CISC's members, publications, videos, seminars, and technical information.

Structural Section Tables (SST)

The SST database contains the North American structural steel sections listed in this publication. All dimensions and section properties are given in Metric units, with the exception of the section designation, nominal depth and nominal mass, which are given in both Metric and Imperial units. The following steel shapes are included:

W, S, M, HP, WWF, C, MC, L, WT, WWT, 2L short legs back-to-back, 2L long legs back-to-back, 2L equal legs back-to-back, WRF, HSS square, HSS rectangular, and HSS round.

The database includes two sets of HSS shapes: those produced in accordance with CSA G40.20 and those produced in accordance with ASTM A500.

The Structural Section Tables (SST) database is available in Excel spreadsheet format at this link: *http://www.cisc-icca.ca/publications/software/sst/*

CHECKLIST FOR DESIGN DRAWINGS

General

A design does not provide a satisfactory structure unless sufficient information is conveyed to the builder so that the designer's intentions are clearly understood. Furthermore, attempting to prepare an estimate for a structure from plans and specifications which contain insufficient information involves risks which tend to increase the tendered price. Clause 4.2 of CSA S16-09 governs the minimum requirements of design drawings. In addition, the following items are suggested as a check list of information to be included on design drawings to avoid unnecessary and costly uncertainty at the time of bidding:

1. The type or types of design as defined in CSA S16-09. If plastic analysis is employed, it should be stated. Show the category of the structural system used for seismic design.

2. The grade(s) of structural steel, grade(s) and diameters of bolts.

3. All structural drawings to be adequately dimensioned, preferably in SI metric units. Do not intermix Metric and Imperial systems of units.

4. Centre-to-centre distances for all columns.

5. Outside dimensions of rigid frames and offset dimensions from grid lines to outside of rigid frames.

6. Out-to-out dimension of trusses and offset dimensions from centre line of chords to outside of chords—include any camber requirements.

7. Offset dimensions from centre of column lines to centre of beams for all beams that are not on the grid lines.

8. Relation of outside of exterior walls to centre lines of columns.

9. Relation of the top surfaces of beams to finished floor elevations.

10. Length of bearing for all beams bearing on exterior walls, including the dimension from the outside of the wall to the end of the steel beam and size of bearing plate.

11. Elevations of underside of column base plates.

12. Dimensions of all clear openings for doorways, ducts, stair wells, roof openings, etc., and their relation to adjacent steel members.

13. Indicate whether loads and forces shown on drawings are factored or unfactored.

14. Axial loads in beams, columns and bracing members and joint pass-through forces.

15. Forces in truss members including moments when members are loaded between panel points.

16. Minimum end reactions required for all connections.

17. Moments for restrained beams and cantilevers. Governing combinations of shears, moments, and axial forces to be resisted by the connections.

18. All information necessary to design and manufacture the open-web steel joists and steel deck to suit the loading conditions.

19. When a particular type of connection is required, the location and type of connection.

20. Type of beam-to-column connection when beams frame over top of columns, including type and location of stiffeners.

21. Any bearing-type connections that are required to be pretensioned.

22. For composite beams, the size and location of shear studs and which beams, if any, must be shored.

23. Size of column base plates and size and location of anchors. (Column bases require a minimum of four anchor rods unless special precautions are taken.)

24. Size and location of stiffeners, web doubler plates, reinforcement, and bracing required for stability of compression elements.

25. Details and location of built-up lintels.

26. Identify roof cladding systems that do not provide lateral restraint to the roof structure.

27. Reinforcement, where necessary, for openings through beam webs.

28. Ledger angles complete with method of attachment.

29. Members requiring prime paint or galvanizing.

30. Identify architecturally exposed structural steel elements requiring special tolerances and finishes. (Also refer to the CISC Code of Standard Practice in Part 7, Appendix I.)

31. Treatment of steel encased in concrete.

32. Fabrication and erection tolerances if other than those specified in CSA S16-09. Special tolerances when interfacing with other materials, i.e., steel attached to concrete.

33. A note that all structural welding is to be performed only by companies certified to Division 1 or 2.1 of CSA W47.1.

34. When weld symbols are shown, refer to "WELDED JOINTS Standard Symbols" from Part 6.

Allow as much time as possible (three weeks for an average job) for preparing bids. During the time allotted for preparing tenders, only those changes necessary to clarify bidding instructions should be issued by addendum. If major changes are included in an addendum, an extension of the tender closing should be considered.

PROPERTIES OF GEOMETRIC SECTIONS
Definitions

Neutral Axis

The line, in any given section of a member subject to bending, on which there is neither tension nor compression.

For pure elastic bending of a straight beam, the neutral axis at any cross-section is coincident with the centroidal axis of the cross-section.

In the case of fully plastic bending, the neutral axis divides the sectional area equally. Therefore, the neutral axis for elastic and plastic bending coincide only in the case of sections symmetrical about the neutral axis.

Moment of Inertia I

The sum of the products obtained by multiplying each of the elementary areas, of which the section is composed, by the square of its perpendicular distance from the axis about which the moment of inertia is being calculated.

Elastic Section Modulus S

The moment of inertia divided by the perpendicular distance from the axis about which the moment of inertia has been calculated to the most remote part of the section.

The elastic section modulus is used to determine the bending stress in the extreme fibre of a section by dividing the bending moment by the section modulus, referred to the neutral axis perpendicular to the plane of bending, both values being expressed in like units of measure.

Radius of Gyration r

The perpendicular distance from a neutral axis to the centre of gyration (i.e., the point where the entire area is considered to be concentrated so as to have the same moment of inertia as the actual area). The square of the radius of gyration of a section is equal to the moment of inertia (referred to the appropriate axis) divided by the area.

The radius of gyration of a section is used to ascertain the load this section will sustain when used in compression as a strut or column. The ratio of the effective unsupported length of the section divided by the least radius of gyration applicable to this length is called the slenderness ratio.

Plastic Modulus Z

The modulus of resistance to bending of a completely yielded cross-section, calculated by taking the combined statical moment, about the neutral axis, of the cross-sectional areas above and below that axis.

In general, the plastic modulus is calculated by simple statics and has been included for only a few of the shapes listed.

PROPERTIES OF GEOMETRIC SECTIONS

SQUARE

Axis of moments through centre

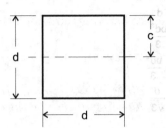

$$A = d^2$$

$$c = \frac{d}{2}$$

$$I = \frac{d^4}{12}$$

$$S = \frac{d^3}{6}$$

$$r = \frac{d}{\sqrt{12}}$$

$$Z = \frac{d^3}{4}$$

SQUARE

Axis of moments on base

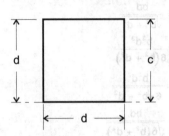

$$A = d^2$$

$$c = d$$

$$I = \frac{d^4}{3}$$

$$S = \frac{d^3}{3}$$

$$r = \frac{d}{\sqrt{3}}$$

SQUARE

Axis of moments on diagonal

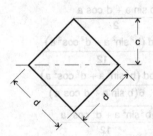

$$A = d^2$$

$$c = \frac{d}{\sqrt{2}}$$

$$I = \frac{d^4}{12}$$

$$S = \frac{d^3}{6\sqrt{2}}$$

$$r = \frac{d}{\sqrt{12}}$$

$$Z = \frac{2c^3}{3} = \frac{d^3}{3\sqrt{2}}$$

RECTANGLE

Axis of moments through centre

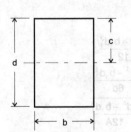

$$A = bd$$

$$c = \frac{d}{2}$$

$$I = \frac{bd^3}{12}$$

$$S = \frac{bd^2}{6}$$

$$r = \frac{d}{\sqrt{12}}$$

$$Z = \frac{bd^2}{4}$$

PROPERTIES OF GEOMETRIC SECTIONS

RECTANGLE

Axis of moments on base

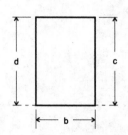

$$A = bd$$

$$c = d$$

$$I = \frac{bd^3}{3}$$

$$S = \frac{bd^2}{3}$$

$$r = \frac{d}{\sqrt{3}}$$

RECTANGLE

Axis of moments on diagonal

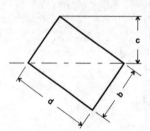

$$A = bd$$

$$c = \frac{bd}{\sqrt{b^2 + d^2}}$$

$$I = \frac{b^3d^3}{6(b^2 + d^2)}$$

$$S = \frac{b^2d^2}{6\sqrt{b^2 + d^2}}$$

$$r = \frac{bd}{\sqrt{6(b^2 + d^2)}}$$

RECTANGLE

Axis of moments any line through centre of gravity

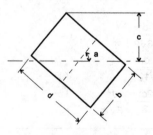

$$A = bd$$

$$c = \frac{b \sin a + d \cos a}{2}$$

$$I = \frac{bd\left(b^2\sin^2 a + d^2\cos^2 a\right)}{12}$$

$$S = \frac{bd\left(b^2\sin^2 a + d^2\cos^2 a\right)}{6(b \sin a + d \cos a)}$$

$$r = \sqrt{\frac{b^2\sin^2 a + d^2\cos^2 a}{12}}$$

HOLLOW RECTANGLE

Axis of moments through centre

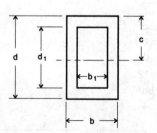

$$A = bd - b_1 d_1$$

$$c = \frac{d}{2}$$

$$I = \frac{bd^3 - b_1 d_1^3}{12}$$

$$S = \frac{bd^3 - b_1 d_1^3}{6d}$$

$$r = \sqrt{\frac{bd^3 - b_1 d_1^3}{12A}}$$

$$Z = \frac{1}{4}\left(bd^2 - b_1 d_1^2\right)$$

PROPERTIES OF GEOMETRIC SECTIONS

EQUAL RECTANGLES

Axis of moments through
centre of gravity

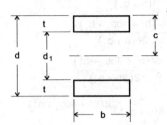

$$A = b(d - d_1)$$

$$c = \frac{d}{2}$$

$$I = \frac{b(d^3 - d_1^3)}{12}$$

$$S = \frac{b(d^3 - d_1^3)}{6d}$$

$$r = \sqrt{\frac{d^3 - d_1^3}{12(d - d_1)}}$$

$$Z = \frac{b}{4}(d^2 - d_1^2) = bt(d - t)$$

UNEQUAL RECTANGLES

Axis of moments through
centre of gravity

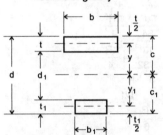

$$A = bt + b_1 t_1$$

$$c = \frac{\frac{1}{2}bt^2 + b_1 t_1 (d - \frac{1}{2}t_1)}{A}$$

$$I = \frac{bt^3}{12} + bty^2 + \frac{b_1 t_1^3}{12} + b_1 t_1 y_1^2$$

$$S = \frac{I}{c} \qquad S_1 = \frac{I}{c_1}$$

$$r = \sqrt{\frac{I}{A}}$$

TRIANGLE

Axis of moments through
centre of gravity

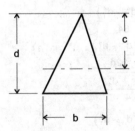

$$A = \frac{bd}{2}$$

$$c = \frac{2d}{3}$$

$$I = \frac{bd^3}{36}$$

$$S = \frac{bd^2}{24}$$

$$r = \frac{d}{\sqrt{18}}$$

TRIANGLE

Axis of moments on base

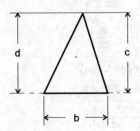

$$A = \frac{bd}{2}$$

$$c = d$$

$$I = \frac{bd^3}{12}$$

$$S = \frac{bd^2}{12}$$

$$r = \frac{d}{\sqrt{6}}$$

PROPERTIES OF GEOMETRIC SECTIONS

TRAPEZOID

Axis of moments through
centre of gravity

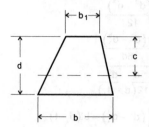

$$A = \frac{d(b + b_1)}{2}$$

$$c = \frac{d(2b + b_1)}{3(b + b_1)}$$

$$I = \frac{d^3(b^2 + 4bb_1 + b_1^2)}{36(b + b_1)}$$

$$S = \frac{d^2(b^2 + 4bb_1 + b_1^2)}{12(2b + b_1)}$$

$$r = \frac{d}{6(b + b_1)}\sqrt{2(b^2 + 4bb_1 + b_1^2)}$$

CIRCLE

Axis of moments
through centre

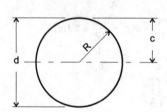

$$A = \frac{\pi d^2}{4} = \pi R^2$$

$$c = \frac{d}{2} = R$$

$$I = \frac{\pi d^4}{64} = \frac{\pi R^4}{4}$$

$$S = \frac{\pi d^3}{32} = \frac{\pi R^3}{4}$$

$$r = \frac{d}{4} = \frac{R}{2}$$

$$Z = \frac{d^3}{6}$$

HOLLOW CIRCLE

Axis of moments
through centre

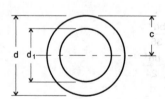

$$A = \frac{\pi(d^2 - d_1^2)}{4}$$

$$c = \frac{d}{2}$$

$$I = \frac{\pi(d^4 - d_1^4)}{64}$$

$$S = \frac{\pi(d^4 - d_1^4)}{32d}$$

$$r = \frac{\sqrt{d^2 + d_1^2}}{4}$$

$$Z = \frac{1}{6}(d^3 - d_1^3)$$

HALF CIRCLE

Axis of moments through
centre of gravity

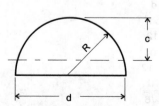

$$A = \frac{\pi R^2}{2}$$

$$c = R\left(1 - \frac{4}{3\pi}\right)$$

$$I = R^4\left(\frac{\pi}{8} - \frac{8}{9\pi}\right)$$

$$S = \frac{R^3}{24}\frac{(9\pi^2 - 64)}{(3\pi - 4)}$$

$$r = R\frac{\sqrt{9\pi^2 - 64}}{6\pi}$$

PROPERTIES OF GEOMETRIC SECTIONS

PARABOLA

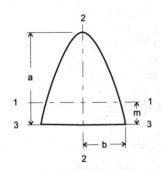

$$A = \frac{4}{3}ab$$

$$m = \frac{2}{5}a$$

$$I_1 = \frac{16}{175}a^3L$$

$$I_2 = \frac{4}{15}ab^3$$

$$I_3 = \frac{32}{105}a^3b$$

HALF PARABOLA

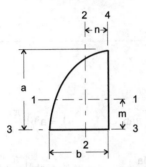

$$A = \frac{2}{3}ab$$

$$m = \frac{2}{5}a$$

$$n = \frac{3}{8}b$$

$$I_1 = \frac{8}{175}a^3b$$

$$I_2 = \frac{19}{480}ab^3$$

$$I_3 = \frac{16}{105}a^3b$$

$$I_4 = \frac{2}{15}ab^3$$

COMPLEMENT OF HALF PARABOLA

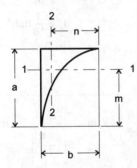

$$A = \frac{1}{3}ab$$

$$m = \frac{7}{10}a$$

$$n = \frac{3}{4}b$$

$$I_1 = \frac{37}{2100}a^3b$$

$$I_2 = \frac{1}{80}ab^3$$

PARABOLIC FILLET IN RIGHT ANGLE

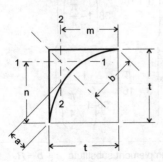

$$a = \frac{t}{2\sqrt{2}}$$

$$b = \frac{t}{\sqrt{2}}$$

$$A = \frac{1}{6}t^2$$

$$m = n = \frac{4}{5}t$$

$$I_1 = I_2 = \frac{11}{2100}t^4$$

PROPERTIES OF GEOMETRIC SECTIONS

* HALF ELLIPSE

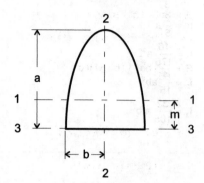

$$A = \frac{1}{2}\pi ab$$

$$m = \frac{4a}{3\pi}$$

$$I_1 = a^3b\left(\frac{\pi}{8} - \frac{8}{9\pi}\right)$$

$$I_2 = \frac{1}{8}\pi ab^3$$

$$I_3 = \frac{1}{8}\pi a^3b$$

* QUARTER ELLIPSE

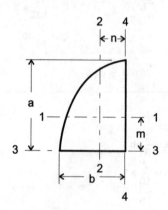

$$A = \frac{1}{4}\pi ab \qquad\qquad I_1 = a^3b\left(\frac{\pi}{16} - \frac{4}{9\pi}\right)$$

$$m = \frac{4a}{3\pi} \qquad\qquad I_2 = ab^3\left(\frac{\pi}{16} - \frac{4}{9\pi}\right)$$

$$n = \frac{4b}{3\pi} \qquad\qquad I_3 = \frac{1}{16}\pi a^3b$$

$$I_4 = \frac{1}{16}\pi ab^3$$

* ELLIPTIC COMPLEMENT

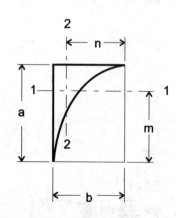

$$A = ab\left(1 - \frac{\pi}{4}\right), \qquad m = \frac{a}{6\left(1 - \frac{\pi}{4}\right)}, \qquad n = \frac{b}{6\left(1 - \frac{\pi}{4}\right)}$$

$$I_1 = a^3b\left(\frac{1}{3} - \frac{\pi}{16} - \frac{1}{36\left(1 - \frac{\pi}{4}\right)}\right)$$

$$I_2 = ab^3\left(\frac{1}{3} - \frac{\pi}{16} - \frac{1}{36\left(1 - \frac{\pi}{4}\right)}\right)$$

* To obtain properties of half circle, quarter circle and circle complement substitute $a = b = R$.

PROPERTIES OF GEOMETRIC SECTIONS AND STRUCTURAL SHAPES

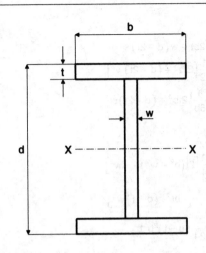

$$A = 2bt + (d - 2t)w$$

$$I = \frac{1}{12}\left[bd^3 - (b - w)(d - 2t)^3\right]$$

$$S = \frac{1}{6d}\left[bd^3 - (b - w)(d - 2t)^3\right]$$

$$r = \sqrt{\frac{I}{A}}$$

$$Z = \frac{1}{4}\left[bd^2 - (b - w)(d - 2t)^2\right]$$

$$J = \frac{1}{3}\left[2bt^3 + (d - t)w^3\right]$$

$$C_w = \frac{1}{24}(d - t)^2 b^3 t$$

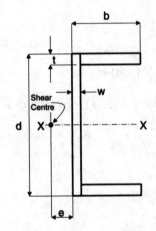

$$A = dw + 2(b - w)t$$

$$I = \frac{1}{12}\left[bd^3 - (b - w)(d - 2t)^3\right]$$

$$S = \frac{1}{6d}\left[bd^3 - (b - w)(d - 2t)^3\right]$$

$$r = \sqrt{\frac{I}{A}}$$

$$e = \frac{3t(b - w/2)^2}{6t(b - w/2) + (d - t)w} - \frac{w}{2}$$

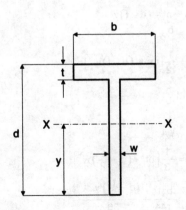

$$A = bt + w(d - t)$$

$$y = \frac{1}{2}\left(\frac{bdt}{A} + d - t\right)$$

$$I = \frac{1}{12}\left[bt^3 + w(d - t)^3 + \frac{3bwtd^2(d - t)}{A}\right]$$

$$S_1 = \frac{I}{y}; \quad S_2 = \frac{I}{d - y}$$

$$r = \sqrt{\frac{I}{A}}$$

$$J = \frac{1}{3}\left[bt^3 + \left(d - \frac{t}{2}\right)w^3\right]$$

$$C_w = \frac{b^3 t^3}{144} + \frac{\left(d - \frac{t}{2}\right)^3 w^3}{36}$$

PROPERTIES OF GEOMETRIC SECTIONS
AND STRUCTURAL SHAPES

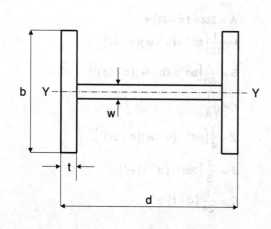

$$A = 2bt + w(d - 2t)$$

$$I = \frac{1}{12}\left[2tb^3 + (d - 2t)w^3\right]$$

$$S = \frac{1}{6b}\left[2tb^3 + (d - 2t)w^3\right]$$

$$r = \sqrt{\frac{I}{A}}$$

$$Z = \frac{1}{4}\left[2t(b^2 - w^2) + dw^2\right]$$

$$J = \frac{1}{3}\left[2bt^3 + (d - t)w^3\right]$$

$$C_w = \frac{1}{24}(d - t)^2 b^3 t$$

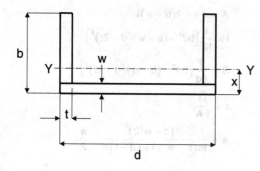

$$A = dw + 2(b - w)t$$

$$x = \frac{1}{2A}\left[(d - 2t)w^2 + 2tb^2\right]$$

$$I = \frac{1}{3}\left[dx^3 + 2t(b - x)^3 - (d - 2t)(x - w)^3\right]$$

$$S_1 = \frac{I}{b - x} \; ; \qquad S_2 = \frac{I}{x}$$

$$r = \sqrt{\frac{I}{A}}$$

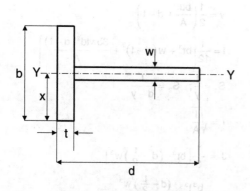

$$A = bt + (d - t)w$$

$$x = \frac{b}{2}$$

$$I = \frac{1}{12}\left[tb^3 + (d - t)w^3\right]$$

$$S = \frac{2I}{b}$$

$$r = \sqrt{\frac{I}{A}}$$

$$J = \frac{1}{3}\left[bt^3 + \left(d - \frac{t}{2}\right)w^3\right]$$

$$C_w = \frac{b^3 t^3}{144} + \frac{\left(d - \frac{t}{2}\right)^3 w^3}{36}$$

PROPERTIES OF GEOMETRIC SECTIONS AND STRUCTURAL SHAPES

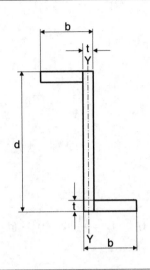

$$J = \frac{1}{3}\left[2b + d - 2t\right]t^3$$

$$C_w = \frac{(d-t)^2(b-t/2)^3 t}{12}\left[\frac{b+2d-5t/2}{d+2b-2t}\right]$$

See next page for other section properties.

ANGLE

Axis of moments through
Centre of gravity

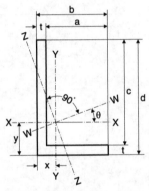

Z-Z is axis of minimum I

$$\tan 2\theta = \frac{2K}{I_y - I_x}$$

$$A = t(b+c) \qquad x = \frac{b^2 + ct}{2(b+c)} \qquad y = \frac{d^2 + at}{2(b+c)}$$

K = Product of Inertia about X-X & Y-Y

$$= \mp \frac{abcdt}{4(b+c)}$$

$$I_x = \frac{1}{3}\left[t(d-y)^3 + by^3 - a(y-t)^3\right]$$

$$I_y = \frac{1}{3}\left[t(b-x)^3 + dx^3 - c(x-t)^3\right]$$

$$I_z = I_x \sin^2\theta + I_y \cos^2\theta + K\sin 2\theta$$

$$I_w = I_x \cos^2\theta + I_y \sin^2\theta - K\sin 2\theta$$

K is negative when heel of angle, with respect to c.g., is in 1st or 3rd quadrant, positive when in 2nd or 4th quadrant.

BEAMS AND CHANNELS

Transverse force oblique
through centre of gravity

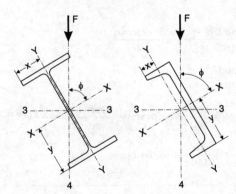

$$I_3 = I_x \sin^2\phi + I_y \cos^2\phi$$

$$I_4 = I_x \cos^2\phi + I_y \sin^2\phi$$

$$f = M\left(\frac{y}{I_x}\sin\phi + \frac{x}{I_y}\cos\phi\right)$$

where M is bending moment due to force F.

PROPERTIES OF GEOMETRIC SECTIONS
AND STRUCTURAL SHAPES

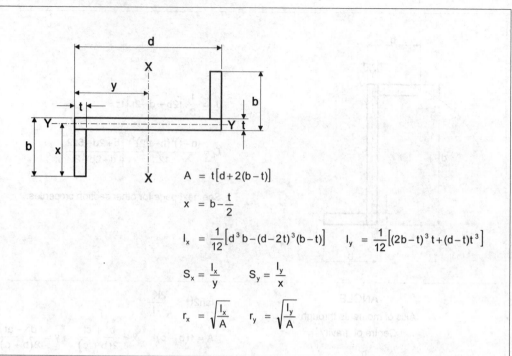

$$A = t[d + 2(b - t)]$$

$$x = b - \frac{t}{2}$$

$$I_x = \frac{1}{12}[d^3 b - (d - 2t)^3(b - t)] \qquad I_y = \frac{1}{12}[(2b - t)^3 t + (d - t)t^3]$$

$$S_x = \frac{I_x}{y} \qquad S_y = \frac{I_y}{x}$$

$$r_x = \sqrt{\frac{I_x}{A}} \qquad r_y = \sqrt{\frac{I_y}{A}}$$

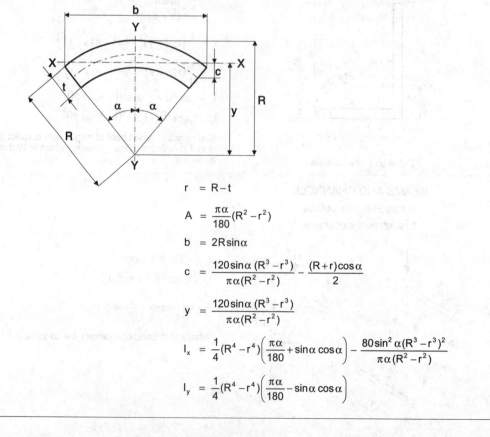

$$r = R - t$$

$$A = \frac{\pi \alpha}{180}(R^2 - r^2)$$

$$b = 2R \sin \alpha$$

$$c = \frac{120 \sin \alpha (R^3 - r^3)}{\pi \alpha (R^2 - r^2)} - \frac{(R + r) \cos \alpha}{2}$$

$$y = \frac{120 \sin \alpha (R^3 - r^3)}{\pi \alpha (R^2 - r^2)}$$

$$I_x = \frac{1}{4}(R^4 - r^4)\left(\frac{\pi \alpha}{180} + \sin \alpha \cos \alpha\right) - \frac{80 \sin^2 \alpha (R^3 - r^3)^2}{\pi \alpha (R^2 - r^2)}$$

$$I_y = \frac{1}{4}(R^4 - r^4)\left(\frac{\pi \alpha}{180} - \sin \alpha \cos \alpha\right)$$

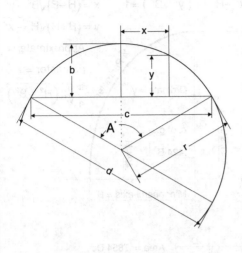

Circumference = 6.28318 r = 3.14159 d
Diameter = 0.31831 circumference
Area = 3.14159 r²

Arc $\quad$ a $\quad = \dfrac{\pi r A°}{180°} = 0.017453 r A°$

Angle A° $\quad = \dfrac{180° a}{\pi r} = 57.29578 \dfrac{a}{r}$

Radius r $\quad = \dfrac{4b^2 + c^2}{8b}$

Chord c $\quad = 2\sqrt{2br - b^2} = 2r \sin \dfrac{A}{2}$

Rise b $\quad = r - \dfrac{1}{2}\sqrt{4r^2 - c^2} = \dfrac{c}{2} \tan \dfrac{A}{4}$

$\quad = 2r \sin^2 \dfrac{A}{4} = r + y - \sqrt{r^2 - x^2}$

y $\quad = b - r + \sqrt{r^2 - x^2}$

x $\quad = \sqrt{r^2 - (r + y - b)^2}$

Diameter of circle of equal periphery as square = 1.27324 side of square
Side of square of equal periphery as circle = 0.78540 diameter of circle
Diameter of circle circumscribed about square = 1.41421 side of square
Side of square inscribed in circle = 0.70711 diameter of circle

CIRCULAR SECTOR

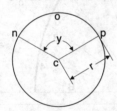

r = radius of circle, $\quad$ y = angle ncp in degrees

Area of Sector ncpo $= \frac{1}{2}$(length of arc nop × r)

$\quad$ = Area of Circle $\times \dfrac{y}{360}$

$\quad$ = 0.0087266 × r² × y

CIRCULAR SEGMENT

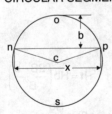

r = radius of circle, $\quad$ x = chord, $\quad$ b = rise

Area of Segment nop = Area of Sector ncpo − Area of triangle ncp

$\quad = \dfrac{(\text{Length of arc nop} \times r) - x(r - b)}{2}$

Area of Segment nsp = Area of Circle − Area of Segment nop

PROPERTIES OF PARABOLA AND ELLIPSE

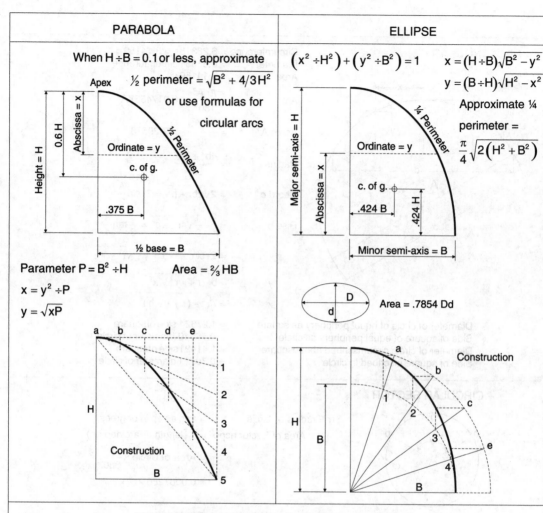

PARABOLA

When $H \div B = 0.1$ or less, approximate

$$\tfrac{1}{2}\text{ perimeter} = \sqrt{B^2 + 4/3\,H^2}$$

or use formulas for circular arcs

Apex

Abscissa = x

0.6 H

Height = H

Ordinate = y

½ Perimeter

c. of g.

.375 B

½ base = B

Parameter $P = B^2 \div H$ \qquad Area $= \tfrac{2}{3}HB$

$x = y^2 \div P$

$y = \sqrt{xP}$

a b c d e

H

1
2
3
4
5

Construction

B

ELLIPSE

$$\left(x^2 \div H^2\right) + \left(y^2 \div B^2\right) = 1 \qquad x = (H \div B)\sqrt{B^2 - y^2}$$

$$y = (B \div H)\sqrt{H^2 - x^2}$$

Approximate ¼ perimeter $=$

$$\frac{\pi}{4}\sqrt{2\left(H^2 + B^2\right)}$$

Major semi-axis = H

Abscissa = x

¼ Perimeter

Ordinate = y

c. of g.

.424 B

.424 H

Minor semi-axis = B

D

d

Area $= .7854\, Dd$

a
b
1
2
c
H
B
3
e
4

Construction

B

AREA BETWEEN PARABOLIC CURVE AND SECANT

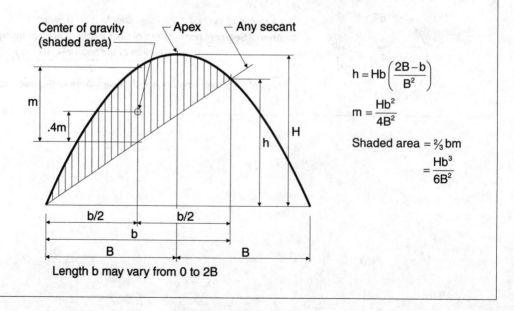

Center of gravity (shaded area)

Apex

Any secant

m

.4m

H

h

b/2   b/2

b

B   B

Length b may vary from 0 to 2B

$$h = Hb\left(\frac{2B - b}{B^2}\right)$$

$$m = \frac{Hb^2}{4B^2}$$

Shaded area $= \tfrac{2}{3}bm$

$$= \frac{Hb^3}{6B^2}$$

RECTANGULAR PARALLELEPIPED

Volume = abc

Surface area = $2(ab + ac + bc)$

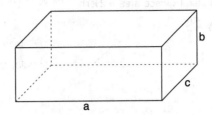

PARALLELEPIPED

Volume = $Ah = abc \sin\theta$

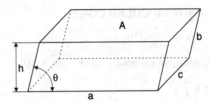

PYRAMID

Volume = $\frac{1}{3}Ah$

The centroid of a pyramid is located y-distance from the base on the line joining the centre of gravity of area A and the apex.

$y = \frac{h}{4}$

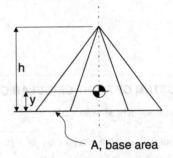

A, base area

FRUSTUM OF PYRAMID

$V = \frac{h}{3}\left(A_1 + A_2 + \sqrt{A_1 A_2}\right)$

The centroid is located y-distance up from area A_1 on the line joining the centres of gravity of areas A_1 and A_2.

$y = \frac{h\left(A_1 + 2\sqrt{A_1 A_2} + 3A_2\right)}{4\left(A_1 + \sqrt{A_1 A_2} + A_2\right)}$

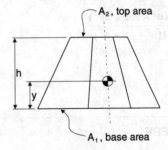

A_2, top area

A_1, base area

WEDGE

$V = \frac{(2a + c)\,bh}{6}$

The centroid is located y-distance from the base on the line joining the centre of gravity of the base area and the mid point of edge, c.

$y = \frac{h(a + c)}{2(2a + c)}$

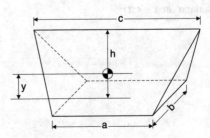

PROPERTIES OF SOLIDS

RIGHT CIRCULAR CYLINDER

Volume = $\pi r^2 h$

Lateral surface area = $2\pi rh$

$y = \dfrac{h}{2}$

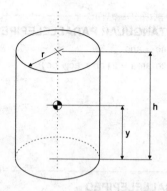

RIGHT CIRCULAR CONE

Volume = $\dfrac{1}{3}\pi r^2 h$

Lateral surface area = $\pi r\sqrt{r^2 + h^2} = \pi rl$

$y = \dfrac{h}{4}$

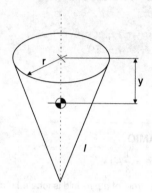

FRUSTUM OF RIGHT CIRCULAR CONE

Volume = $\dfrac{1}{3}\pi h\left(a^2 + ab + b^2\right)$

Lateral surface area = $\pi(a+b)\sqrt{h^2 + (b-a)^2}$
$\qquad\qquad\qquad = \pi(a+b)l$

$y = \dfrac{h\left(b^2 + 2ab + 3a^2\right)}{4\left(b^2 + ab + a^2\right)}$

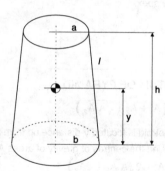

SPHERE

Volume = $\dfrac{4}{3}\pi r^3$

Surface area = $4\pi r^2$

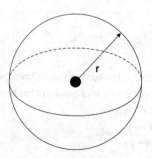

TRIGONOMETRIC FUNCTIONS

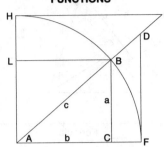

Radius AF $= 1$

$= \sin^2 A + \cos^2 A = \sin A \csc A$

$= \cos A \sec A = \tan A \cot A$

Sine A $= \dfrac{\cos A}{\cot A} = \dfrac{1}{\csc A} = \cos A \tan A = \sqrt{1 - \cos^2 A}$ $= BC$

Cosine A $= \dfrac{\sin A}{\tan A} = \dfrac{1}{\sec A} = \sin A \cot A = \sqrt{1 - \sin^2 A}$ $= AC$

Tangent A $= \dfrac{\sin A}{\cos A} = \dfrac{1}{\cot A} = \sin A \sec A$ $= FD$

Cotangent A $= \dfrac{\cos A}{\sin A} = \dfrac{1}{\tan A} = \cos A \csc A$ $= HG$

Secant A $= \dfrac{\tan A}{\sin A} = \dfrac{1}{\cos A}$ $= AD$

Cosecant A $= \dfrac{\cot A}{\cos A} = \dfrac{1}{\sin A}$ $= AG$

RIGHT ANGLED TRIANGLES

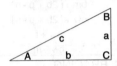

$a^2 = c^2 - b^2$
$b^2 = c^2 - a^2$
$c^2 = a^2 + b^2$

Known	Required					
	A	B	a	b	c	Area
a, b	$\tan A = \dfrac{a}{b}$	$\tan B = \dfrac{b}{a}$			$\sqrt{a^2 + b^2}$	$\dfrac{ab}{2}$
a, c	$\sin A = \dfrac{a}{c}$	$\cos B = \dfrac{a}{c}$		$\sqrt{c^2 - a^2}$		$\dfrac{a\sqrt{c^2 - a^2}}{2}$
A, a		$90° - A$		$a \cot A$	$\dfrac{a}{\sin A}$	$\dfrac{a^2 \cot A}{2}$
A, b		$90° - A$	$b \tan A$		$\dfrac{b}{\cos A}$	$\dfrac{b^2 \tan A}{2}$
A, c		$90° - A$	$c \sin A$	$c \cos A$		$\dfrac{c^2 \sin 2A}{4}$

OBLIQUE ANGLED TRIANGLES

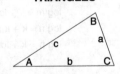

$s = \dfrac{a + b + c}{2}$

$K = \sqrt{\dfrac{(s-a)(s-b)(s-c)}{s}}$

$a^2 = b^2 + c^2 - 2bc \cos A$
$b^2 = a^2 + c^2 - 2ac \cos B$
$c^2 = a^2 + b^2 - 2ab \cos C$

Known	Required					
	A	B	C	b	c	Area
a, b, c	$\tan\dfrac{1}{2}A = \dfrac{K}{s-a}$	$\tan\dfrac{1}{2}B = \dfrac{K}{s-b}$	$\tan\dfrac{1}{2}C = \dfrac{K}{s-c}$			$\sqrt{s(s-a)(s-b)(s-c)}$
a, A, B			$180° - (A+B)$	$\dfrac{a \sin B}{\sin A}$	$\dfrac{a \sin C}{\sin A}$	
a, b, A		$\sin B = \dfrac{b \sin A}{a}$			$\dfrac{b \sin C}{\sin B}$	
a, b, C	$\tan A = \dfrac{a \sin C}{b - a \cos C}$				$\sqrt{a^2 + b^2 - 2ab \cos C}$	$\dfrac{ab \sin C}{2}$

BRACING FORMULAE

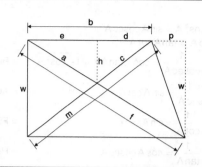

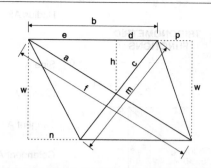

Given	To Find	Formula
bpw	f	$\sqrt{(b+p)^2 + w^2}$
bw	m	$\sqrt{b^2 + w^2}$
bp	d	$b^2 \div (2b + p)$
bp	e	$b(b+p) \div (2b + p)$
bfp	a	$bf \div (2b + p)$
bmp	c	$bm \div (2b + p)$
bpw	h	$bw \div (2b + p)$
afw	h	$aw \div f$
cmw	h	$cw \div m$

Given	To Find	Formula
bpw	f	$\sqrt{(b+p)^2 + w^2}$
bnw	m	$\sqrt{(b-n)^2 + w^2}$
bnp	d	$b(b-n) \div (2b + p - n)$
bnp	e	$b(b+p) \div (2b + p - n)$
bfnp	a	$bf \div (2b + p - n)$
bmnp	c	$bm \div (2b + p - n)$
bnpw	h	$bw \div (2b + p - n)$
afw	h	$aw \div f$
cmw	h	$cw \div m$

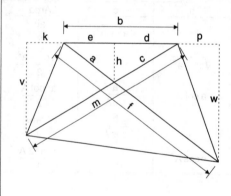

Given	To Find	Formula
bpw	f	$\sqrt{(b+p)^2 + w^2}$
bkv	m	$\sqrt{(b+k)^2 + v^2}$
bkpvw	d	$bw(b+k) \div [v(b+p) + w(b+k)]$
bkpvw	e	$bv(b+p) \div [v(b+p) + w(b+k)]$
bfkpvw	a	$fbv \div [v(b+p) + w(b+k)]$
bkmpvw	c	$bmw \div [v(b+p) + w(b+k)]$
bkpvw	h	$bvw \div [v(b+p) + w(b+k)]$
afw	h	$aw \div f$
cmv	h	$cv \div m$

PARALLEL BRACING

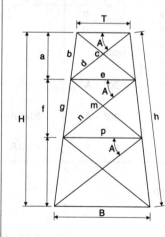

$k = (\log B - \log T) \div$ no. of panels. Constant k plus the logarithm of any line equals the log of the corresponding line in the next panel below.

$$a = TH \div (T + e + p)$$
$$b = Th \div (T + e + p)$$
$$c = \sqrt{(\tfrac{1}{2}T + \tfrac{1}{2}e)^2 + a^2}$$
$$d = ce \div (T + e)$$

$$\log e = k + \log T$$
$$\log f = k + \log a$$
$$\log g = k + \log b$$
$$\log m = k + \log c$$
$$\log n = k + \log d$$
$$\log p = k + \log e$$

The above method can be used for any number of panels.
In the formulas for "a" and "b" the sum in parenthesis, which in the case shown is $(T + e + p)$, is always composed of all the horizontal distances except the base.

LENGTH OF CIRCULAR ARCS
FOR UNIT RADIUS

By the use of this table, the length of any arc may be found if the length of the radius and the angle of the segment are known.

Example: Required the length of arc of segment 32° 15' 27" with radius of 8 000 mm.

From table: Length of arc (Radius 1) for
32°	=	.5585054
15'	=	.0043633
27"	=	.0001309
		.5629996

.5629996 X 8 000 (length of radius) = 4504 mm

For the same arc but with the radius expressed as 24 feet 3 inches, the length of arc would be 0.5629996 X 24.25 = 13.65 feet

DEGREES						MINUTES		SECONDS	
1	.017 4533	61	1.064 6508	121	2.111 8484	1	.000 2909	1	.000 0048
2	.034 9066	62	1.082 1041	122	2.129 3017	2	.000 5818	2	.000 0097
3	.052 3599	63	1.099 5574	123	2.146 7550	3	.000 8727	3	.000 0145
4	.069 8132	64	1.117 0107	124	2.164 2083	4	.001 1636	4	.000 0194
5	.087 2665	65	1.134 4640	125	2.181 6616	5	.001 4544	5	.000 0242
6	.104 7198	66	1.151 9173	126	2.199 1149	6	.001 7453	6	.000 0291
7	.122 1730	67	1.169 3706	127	2.216 5682	7	.002 0362	7	.000 0339
8	.139 6263	68	1.186 8239	128	2.234 0214	8	.002 3271	8	.000 0388
9	.157 0796	69	1.204 2772	129	2.251 4747	9	.002 6180	9	.000 0436
10	.174 5329	70	1.221 7305	130	2.268 9280	10	.002 9089	10	.000 0485
11	.191 9862	71	1.239 1838	131	2.286 3813	11	.003 1998	11	.000 0533
12	.209 4395	72	1.256 6371	132	2.303 8346	12	.003 4907	12	.000 0582
13	.226 8928	73	1.274 0904	133	2.321 2879	13	.003 7815	13	.000 0630
14	.244 3461	74	1.291 5436	134	2.338 7412	14	.004 0724	14	.000 0679
15	.261 7994	75	1.308 9969	135	2.356 1945	15	.004 3633	15	.000 0727
16	.279 2527	76	1.326 4502	136	2.373 6478	16	.004 6542	16	.000 0776
17	.296 7060	77	1.343 9035	137	2.391 1011	17	.004 9451	17	.000 0824
18	.314 1593	78	1.361 3568	138	2.408 5544	18	.005 2360	18	.000 0873
19	.331 6126	79	1.378 8101	139	2.426 0077	19	.005 5269	19	.000 0921
20	.349 0659	80	1.396 2634	140	2.443 4610	20	.005 8178	20	.000 0970
21	.366 5191	81	1.413 7167	141	2.460 9142	21	.006 1087	21	.000 1018
22	.383 9724	82	1.431 1700	142	2.478 3675	22	.006 3995	22	.000 1067
23	.401 4257	83	1.448 6233	143	2.495 8208	23	.006 6904	23	.000 1115
24	.418 8790	84	1.466 0766	144	2.513 2741	24	.006 9813	24	.000 1164
25	.436 3323	85	1.483 5299	145	2.530 7274	25	.007 2722	25	.000 1212
26	.453 7856	86	1.500 9832	146	2.548 1807	26	.007 5631	26	.000 1261
27	.471 2389	87	1.518 4364	147	2.565 6340	27	.007 8540	27	.000 1309
28	.488 6922	88	1.535 8897	148	2.583 0873	28	.008 1449	28	.000 1357
29	.506 1455	89	1.553 3430	149	2.600 5406	29	.008 4358	29	.000 1406
30	.523 5988	90	1.570 7963	150	2.617 9939	30	.008 7266	30	.000 1454
31	.541 0521	91	1.588 2496	151	2.635 4472	31	.009 0175	31	.000 1503
32	.558 5054	92	1.605 7029	152	2.652 9005	32	.009 3084	32	.000 1551
33	.575 9587	93	1.623 1562	153	2.670 3538	33	.009 5993	33	.000 1600
34	.593 4119	94	1.640 6095	154	2.687 8070	34	.009 8902	34	.000 1648
35	.610 8652	95	1.658 0628	155	2.705 2603	35	.010 1811	35	.000 1697
36	.628 3185	96	1.675 5161	156	2.722 7136	36	.010 4720	36	.000 1745
37	.645 7718	97	1.692 9694	157	2.740 1669	37	.010 7629	37	.000 1794
38	.663 2251	98	1.710 4227	158	2.757 6202	38	.011 0538	38	.000 1842
39	.680 6784	99	1.727 8760	159	2.775 0735	39	.011 3446	39	.000 1891
40	.698 1317	100	1.745 3293	160	2.792 5268	40	.011 6355	40	.000 1939
41	.715 5850	101	1.762 7825	161	2.809 9801	41	.011 9264	41	.000 1988
42	.733 0383	102	1.780 2358	162	2.827 4334	42	.012 2173	42	.000 2036
43	.750 4916	103	1.797 6891	163	2.844 8867	43	.012 5082	43	.000 2085
44	.767 9449	104	1.815 1424	164	2.862 3400	44	.012 7991	44	.000 2133
45	.785 3982	105	1.832 5957	165	2.879 7933	45	.013 0900	45	.000 2182
46	.802 8515	106	1.850 0490	166	2.897 2466	46	.013 3809	46	.000 2230
47	.820 3047	107	1.867 5023	167	2.914 6999	47	.013 6717	47	.000 2279
48	.837 7580	108	1.884 9556	168	2.932 1531	48	.013 9626	48	.000 2327
49	.855 2113	109	1.902 4089	169	2.949 6064	49	.014 2535	49	.000 2376
50	.872 6646	110	1.919 8622	170	2.967 0597	50	.014 5444	50	.000 2424
51	.890 1179	111	1.937 3155	171	2.984 5130	51	.014 8353	51	.000 2473
52	.907 5712	112	1.954 7688	172	3.001 9663	52	.015 1262	52	.000 2521
53	.925 0245	113	1.972 2221	173	3.019 4196	53	.015 4171	53	.000 2570
54	.942 4778	114	1.989 6753	174	3.036 8729	54	.015 7080	54	.000 2618
55	.959 9311	115	2.007 1286	175	3.054 3262	55	.015 9989	55	.000 2666
56	.977 3844	116	2.024 5819	176	3.071 7795	56	.016 2897	56	.000 2715
57	.994 8377	117	2.042 0352	177	3.089 2328	57	.016 5806	57	.000 2763
58	1.012 2910	118	2.059 4885	178	3.106 6861	58	.016 8715	58	.000 2812
59	1.029 7443	119	2.076 9418	179	3.124 1394	59	.017 1624	59	.000 2860
60	1.047 1976	120	2.094 3951	180	3.141 5927	60	.017 4533	60	.000 2909

SI SUMMARY

General

The following information on SI units is provided to assist those involved in the planning, design, fabrication and erection of steel structures prepared in SI units. Information related to the metric system in general is to be found in CAN3-Z234.1-79, "Canadian Metric Practice Guide" and for terms related to the steel industry in the "Industry Practice Guide for SI Metric Units in the Canadian Iron and Steel Industry". The latter is available from the Task Force for Metric Conversion in the Canadian Iron and Steel Industry, P.O. Box 4248, Station "D", Hamilton, Ontario, L8V 4L6.

The eleventh General Conference of Weights and Measures, in 1960, adopted the name International System of Units for a coherent system which includes the metre as the base unit of length and the kilogram as the base unit of mass. The international abbreviation of the name of this system, in all languages, is SI.

Canada is a signatory to the General Conference on Weights and Measures, and in 1970, the Canadian government stated that the eventual conversion to the metric system is an objective of Canadian policy. Since that time, metric conversion activity in Canada has developed to the point where material and design standards, building codes and technical literature are available in SI units.

The SI system is based on the seven base units listed in Table 7-1. Decimal multiples and sub-multiples of the SI base units are formed by the addition of the prefixes given in Table 7-2.

SI BASE UNITS
Table 7-1

Quantity	Name	Symbol
length	metre	m
mass	kilogram	kg
time	second	s
electric current	ampere	A
thermodynamic temperature	kelvin	K
amount of substance	mole	mol
luminous intensity	candela	cd

SI PREFIXES
Table 7-2

Multiplying Factor	Prefix	Symbol
$1\ 000\ 000\ 000\ 000 = 10^{12}$	tera	T
$1\ 000\ 000\ 000 = 10^{9}$	giga	G
$1\ 000\ 000 = 10^{6}$	mega	M
$1\ 000 = 10^{3}$	kilo	k
$100 = 10^{2}$	hecto	h
$10 = 10^{1}$	deca	da
$0.1 = 10^{-1}$	deci	d
$0.01 = 10^{-2}$	centi	c
$0.001 = 10^{-3}$	milli	m
$0.000\ 001 = 10^{-6}$	micro	μ
$0.000\ 000\ 001 = 10^{-9}$	nano	n
$0.000\ 000\ 000\ 001 = 10^{-12}$	pico	p
$0.000\ 000\ 000\ 000\ 001 = 10^{-15}$	femto	f
$0.000\ 000\ 000\ 000\ 000\ 001 = 10^{-18}$	atto	a

In choosing the appropriate decimal multiple or sub-multiple, the Canadian Metric Practice Guide recommends the use of prefixes representing 10 raised to a power that is a multiple of 3, a ternary power. Thus, common structural steel design units would be:

Force - newton (N), kilonewton (kN)

Stress - pascal (Pa), kilopascal (kPa), megapascal (MPa)

Length - millimetre (mm), metre (m)

Mass - kilogram (kg), megagram (Mg)

The tonne is a special unit, equal to 1 000 kg (or 1 Mg) that will be used in the basic steel industry, but should not be used in structural design calculations.

Designers using SI units must transform loads given in mass (kilograms) to forces, using the relationship force = mass times acceleration. In the design of structures on earth, acceleration is the acceleration due to gravity, designated by "g" and established as 9.806 65 metres per second per second at the third General Conference on Weights and Measures in 1901.

The unit of force to be used in design is the newton (N) (or multiples thereof) where a newton is defined as the force that, when applied to a body having a mass of one kilogram (kg), gives the body an acceleration of one metre (m) per second squared (s^2). The unit of stress is the pascal (Pa), which is one newton per square metre (m^2). Since this is a very small unit, designers of steel structures will generally use megapascals (MPa), where one megapascal is one million pascals and equals one newton per square millimetre (N/mm^2). See also "Structural Loads, Mass and Force".

Properties and dimensions of steel sections are given, in this book, in millimetre units, tabulated to an appropriate ternary power of 10, and millimetres should be used for dimensioning steel structures. Some relationships and values of interest to steel designers are shown below:

SI PREFIXES
Table 7-3

Density of Steel		7 850	kg/m³
Modulus of Elasticity	E	200 000	MPa
Shear Modulus of Steel	G	77 000	MPa
Coefficient of Thermal Expansion		11.7 x10⁻⁶	/°C
Acceleration due to Earth's Gravity	g	9.806 65	m/s²

For a more complete description of SI, the Canadian Metric Practice Guide should be consulted; however, Table 7-4 provides a convenient summary listing selected SI units, the quantity represented, the unit name and typical application.

Structural Loads, Mass and Force

Since most civil engineers have been accustomed to designing structures on earth to withstand loads more variable than the acceleration due to gravity, the pound-force and the kilogram-force have been used as standard units of force. These units were assumed to be numerically equal to their mass counter-parts, the pound-mass and the kilogram-mass respectively.

In SI, the units of mass and force, the kilogram and the newton respectively, are distinctly different both in name and in value. The two are related through the famous Newtonian equation, force = mass times acceleration, or

$$F = ma$$

Thus a newton (N) is defined as the force required to give one kilogram (kg) mass an acceleration of one metre (m) per second (s) squared, or

$$1 \text{ N} = 1 \text{ kg·m/s}^2$$

The standard international value of acceleration due to gravity is 9.806 65 m/s². However, for hand calculations in Canada a value of

$$g = 9.81 \text{ m/s}^2$$

may be more acceptable as it retains three significant figures (adequate for most structural design) and produces a numerical value of force distinctly different from the value of mass. Thus, whether or not the mass has been converted to a force will be readily apparent, and errors will tend to be reduced.

SELECTED SI UNITS
Table 7-4

Quantity	Preferred Units	Unit Name	Typical Applications	Remarks
Area	mm²	square millimetre	Area of cross section for structural sections	Avoid cm²
	m²	square metre	Areas in general	
Bending Moment	kN·m	kilonewton metre	Bending moment in structural sections	
Coating mass	g/m²	gram per square metre	Mass of zinc coating on steel deck	
Coefficient of Thermal Expansion	$1/°C$ *	reciprocal (of) degree Celsius	Expansion of materials subject to temperature change (generally expressed as a ratio per degree Celsius)	$11.7 \times 10^{-6}/°C$ for steel
Density, mass	kg/m³	kilogram per cubic metre	Density of materials in general; mass per unit volume	$7\,850$ kg/m³ for steel
Force	N	newton	Unit of force used in structural calculations	$1N = 1 kg·m/s^2$
	kN	kilonewton	Force in structural elements such as columns; concentrated forces; axial forces; reactions; shear force; gravitational force	
Force per Unit Length	N/m	newton per metre	Unit for use in calculations	1 kg/m $\times$ 9.81 m/s² = (9.81 kg·m/s²) $\times \dfrac{1}{m}$ = 9.81 N/m
	kN/m	kilonewton per metre	Transverse force per unit length on a beam, column etc.; dead load of a beam for stress calculations	(1 kg/m $\times$ 9.81 m/s²) $\times \dfrac{1\,000}{1\,000}$ = (9.81 kg·m/s²) $\times \dfrac{1}{m} \times \dfrac{1\,000}{1\,000}$ = (9.81 N/m) $\times \dfrac{1\,000}{1\,000}$ = 9.81 kN/m $\times$ 1/1 000 = 0.009 81 kN/m
Force per Unit Area (See Pressure)				
Frequency	Hz	hertz	Frequency of vibration	1 Hz = 1/s = s⁻¹ replaces cycle per second (cps)
Impact energy	J	joule	Charpy V-notch test	1 N·m = 1 J
Length	mm	millimetre	Dimensions on all drawings; dimensions of sections, spans, deflection, elongations, eccentricity	
	m	metre	Overall dimensions; in calculations; contours; surveys	
	km	kilometre	Distances for transportation purposes	
	μm	micrometre	Thickness of coatings (paint)	
Mass	kg	kilogram	Mass of materials, structural elements and machinery	A metric tonne, t 1t = 10³ kg = 1Mg = 1 000 kg
Mass per Unit Length	kg/m	kilogram per metre	Mass per unit length of section, bar, or similar items of uniform cross section.	Also known as "linear density"
Mass per Unit Area	kg/m²	kilogram per square metre	Mass per unit area of plates, slabs, or similar items of uniform thickness; rating for load-carrying capacities on floors (display on notices only)	DO NOT USE IN STRESS CALCULATION
Mass Density	kg/m³	kilogram per cubic metre	Density of materials in general; mass per unit volume	7 850 kg/m³ for steel
Modulus of Elasticity (Young's)	MPa	megapascal	Modulus of elasticity; Young's modulus	200 000 MPa for carbon, high-strength low alloy and low-alloy wrought steels
Modulus, Shear	MPa	megapascal	Shear Modulus	77 000 MPa assumed for steel
Modulus, Section	mm³	millimetre to third power	First moment of area of cross section of structural section, such as plastic section modulus, elastic section modulus	

* The preferred unit is 1/K, however $1/°C$ is an acceptable unit for the construction industry

SELECTED SI UNITS
Table 7-4

Quantity	Preferred Units	Unit Name	Typical Applications	Remarks
Moment of Inertia	mm⁴	millimetre to fourth power	Second moment of area; moment of inertia of a section; torsional constant of cross section	
Moment of Force	kN·m	kilonewton metre	Bending moment (in structural sections); overturning moment	
	N·m	newton metre		
Pressure (see also Stress)	Pa	pascal	Unit used in calculation	1 Pa = 1 N/m²
	kPa	kilopascal	Uniformly distributed loads on floors; soil pressure, wind loads; snow loads; dead loads; live loads.	1 kPa = 1 kN/m²
Section Modulus (see Modulus)				
Stress	MPa	megapascal	Stress (yield, ultimate, permitted, calculated) in structural steel	1 MPa = 1 MN/m² = 1 N/mm²
Structural Load (see Force)				
Temperature	°C	degree Celsius	Ambient temperature	0°C ≈ 273.15K However, for temperature intervals 1°C = 1K
Thickness	mm	millimetre	Thickness of web, flange, plate, etc.	
	μm	micrometre	Thickness of paint	
Torque	kN·m	kilonewton metre	Torsional moment on a cross section	
Volume	m³	cubic metre	Volume; volume of earthworks, excavation, concrete, sand, all bulk materials.	1 m³ = 1 000 L The cubic metre is the preferred unit of volume for engineering purposes
	L	litre	Volume of fluids and containers for fluids	
Work, Energy	J	joule	Energy absorbed in impact testing of materials; energy in general	1 kWh = 3.6 MJ where kWh is a kilowatt hour.

There are two common areas where the designer of a structure must be alert to the distinction between mass and force:

1. dead loads due to the mass of the structural elements, permanent equipment etc.,

2. superimposed, or live loads due to storage of materials.

In these and other cases where mass is well known since it is the unit of commerce, the designer must convert mass to force by multiplying by g.

COMMON CONVERSION FACTORS
Table 7-5

Item	Imperial – SI	SI – Imperial
Acceleration	1 ft./s² = 0.304 8 m/s²	1 m/s² = 3.2808 ft./s²
Area	1 acre = 0.404 685 6 ha 1 ft.² = 0.092 903 04 m² 1 in.² = 645.16 mm² 1 mi.² = 2.589 988 km² 1 yd.² = 0.836 127 4 m²	1 ha = 2.471 acres 1 m² = 10.764 ft.² 1 mm² = 1.55 x 10⁻³ in.² 1 km² = 0.3861 mi.² 1 m² = 1.20 yd.²
Capacity (Canadian Legal Units)	1 oz. = 28.413 062 mL 1 gal. = 4.546 090 L 1 pt. = 0.568 261 L 1 qt. = 1.136 522 L	1 mL = 35.2 x 10⁻³ oz. 1 L = 0.220 gal. 1 L = 1.76 pt. 1 L = 0.880 qt.
Density, Mass	1 lb./ft. = 1.488 16 kg/m 1 lb./yd. = 0.496 055 kg/m 1 oz./ft.² = 305.152 g/m² 1 lb./ft.² = 4.882 43 kg/m² 1 lb./in.² = 703.069 6 kg/m² 1 lb./ft.³ = 16.018 46 kg/m³ 1 lb./in.³ = 27.679 90 Mg/m³	1 kg/m = 0.672 lb./ft. 1 kg/m = 2.016 lb./yd. 1 g/m² = 3.277 x 10⁻³ oz./ft.² 1 kg/m² = 0.205 lb./ft.² 1 kg/m² = 1.42 x 10⁻³ lb./in.² 1 kg/m³ = 62.4 x 10⁻³ lb./ft.³ 1 Mg/m³ = 0.0361 lb./in.³
Force	1 kip = 4.448 222 kN	1 kN = 0.225 kip
Length	1 ft. = 0.304 8 m = 304.8 mm 1 in. = 25.4 mm 1 mile = 1.609 344 km 1 yd. = 0.914 4 m	1 m = 3.28 ft. 1 mm = 0.0394 in. 1 km = 0.622 mi. 1 m = 1.09 yd.
Mass	1 lb. = 0.453 592 37 kg 1 ton (2000 lb.) = 0.907 184 74 Mg	1 kg = 2.205 lb. 1 Mg = 1.10 ton = 2205 lb.
Mass per Unit Area	1 lb./ft.² = 4.882 43 kg/m²	1 kg/m² = 0.205 lb./ft.²
Mass per Unit Length	1 lb./ft. = 1.488 16 kg/m	1 kg/m = 0.672 lb./ft.
Moment of Inertia a) Second Moment of Area b) Section Modulus	1 in.⁴ = 416 231.4 mm⁴ 1 in.³ = 16 387.064 mm³	1 mm⁴ = 2.4 x 10⁻⁶ in.⁴ 1 mm³ = 0.061 x 10⁻³ in.³
Pressure or Stress	1 ksi = 6.894 757 MPa 1 psf = 47.880 26 Pa 1 psi = 6.894 757 kPa	1 MPa = 0.145 ksi 1 Pa = 0.0209 psf 1 kPa = 0.145 psi
Torque or Moment of Force	1 ft.·kipf = 1.355 818 kN·m	1 kN·m = 0.738 ft.·kipf
Volume	1 in.³ = 16 387.064 mm³ 1 ft.³ = 28.316 85 dm³ 1 yd.³ = 0.764 555 m³	1 mm³ = 0.061 x 10⁻³ in.³ 1 dm³ = 0.0353 ft.³ 1 m³ = 1.308 yd.³
Costs	1 $/ft. = 3.28 $/m 1 $/ft.² = 10.764 $/m² 1 $/yd.² = 1.20 $/m² 1 $/ft.³ = 35.34 $/m³ 1 $/yd.³ = 1.307 $/m³	1 $/m = 0.305 $/ft. 1 $/m² = 0.0929 $/ft.² 1 $/m² = 0.836 $/yd.² 1 $/m³ = 0.0283 $/ft.³ 1 $/m³ = 0.765 $/yd.³

MILLIMETRE EQUIVALENTS
DECIMALS AND EACH 64TH OF AN INCH

FRACTIONS	INCHES	mm		FRACTIONS	INCHES	mm
1/64	.015625	.397			.51181	**13**
1/32	.03125	.794		33/64	.515625	13.097
	.03937	**①**		17/32	.53125	13.494
3/64	.046875	1.191		35/64	.546875	13.891
1/16	.0625	1.588			.55118	**14**
5/64	.078125	1.984		9/16	.5625	14.288
	.07874	**②**		37/64	.578125	14.684
3/32	.09375	2.381			.59055	**⑮**
7/64	.109375	2.778		19/32	.59375	15.081
	.11811	**③**		39/64	.609375	15.478
1/8	.125	3.175		5/8	.625	15.875
9/64	.140625	3.572			.62992	**16**
5/32	.15625	3.969		41/64	.640625	16.272
	.15748	**④**		21/32	.65625	16.669
11/64	.171875	4.366			.66929	**17**
3/16	.1875	4.763		43/64	.671875	17.066
	.19685	**⑤**		11/16	.6875	17.463
13/64	.203125	5.159		45/64	.703125	17.859
7/32	.21875	5.556			.70866	**18**
15/64	.234375	5.953		23/32	.71875	18.256
	.23622	**6**		47/64	.734375	18.653
¼	.25	6.350			.74893	**19**
17/64	.265625	6.747		¾	.75	19.050
	.27559	**7**		49/64	.765625	19.447
9/32	.28125	7.144		25/32	.781250	19.844
19/64	.296875	7.541			.7874	**⑳**
5/16	.3125	7.938		51/64	.796875	20.241
	.31496	**8**		13/16	.8125	20.638
21/64	.328125	8.334			.82677	**21**
11/32	.34375	8.731		53/64	.828125	21.034
	.35433	**9**		27/32	.84375	21.431
23/64	.359375	9.128		55/64	.859375	21.828
3/8	.375	9.525			.86614	**22**
25/64	.390625	9.922		7/8	.875	22.225
	.3937	**⑩**		57/64	.890625	22.622
13/32	.40625	10.319			.90551	**23**
27/64	.421875	10.716		29/32	.90625	23.019
	.43307	**11**		59/64	.921875	23.416
7/16	.4375	11.113		15/16	.9375	23.813
29/64	.453125	11.509			.94488	**24**
15/32	.46875	11.906		61/64	.953125	24.209
	.47244	**12**		31/32	.96875	24.606
31/64	.484375	12.303			.98425	**㉕**
½	.5	12.700		63/64	.984375	25.003
				①	1.000	25.4

MISCELLANEOUS CONVERSION FACTORS

Area
1 acre	= 0.404 685 6 ha
1 hectare	= 1 hm²
1 legal subdivision (40 acres)	= 0.161 874 2 km²
1 section (1 mile square, 640 acres)	= 2.589 988 km²
1 square foot	= **929.0304 cm²**
1 square inch	= **645.16 mm²**
1 square mile	= 2.589 988 km²
1 square yard	= 0.836 127 4 m²
1 township (36 sections)	= 93.239 57 km²

Linear Density (Mass per Unit Length)
1 pound per inch	= 17.858 kg/m
1 pound per foot	= 1.488 16 kg/m
1 pound per yard	= 0.496 055 kg/m

Area Density (Mass per Unit Area)
1 ounce per square foot	= 305.152 g/m²
1 pound per square foot	= 4.882 43 kg/m²
1 pound per square inch	= 703.0696 kg/m²

Mass Density (Mass per Unit Volume)
1 pound per cubic foot	= 16.018 46 kg/m³
1 pound per cubic inch	= 27.679 90 Mg/m³
1 ton (long) per cubic yard	= 1.328 939 Mg/m³
1 ton (short) per cubic yard	= 1.186 553 Mg/m³

Energy
1 British thermal unit (Btu) (International Table)	= **1.055 056 kJ**
1 foot pound-force	= 1.355 818 J
1 horsepower hour	= 2.684 52 MJ
1 kilowatt hour	= **3.6 MJ**

Force
1 kilogram-force	= **9.806 65 N**
1 kip (thousand pounds force)	= 4.448 222 kN
1 pound-force	= 4.448 222 N

Heat
1 Btu *foot per (square foot hour °F)	= 1.730 74 W/(m·K)	k-value
1 Btu per (square foot hour °F)	= 5.678 29 W/(m²·K)	U-value
1 square foot hour °F per Btu	= 0.176 109 m²·K/W	R-value

Based on the Btu IT.

Length
1 chain (66 feet)	= **20.1168 m**
1 foot	= **0.3048 m**
1 inch	= **25.4 mm**
1 microinch	= **25.4 nm**
1 micron	= 1 µm
1 mil (0.001 inch)	= **25.4 µm**
1 mile	= **1.609 344 km**
1 mile (International nautical)	= **1.852 km**
1 mile (UK nautical)	= **1.853 184 km**
1 mile (US nautical)	= **1.852 km**
1 yard	= **0.9144 m**

MISCELLANEOUS CONVERSION FACTORS

Mass

1 hundredweight (100 lb)	= **45.359 237** kg
1 hundredweight (long) (112 lb, UK)	= 50.802 345 kg
1 pennyweight	= 1.555 174 g
1 pound (avoirdupois)	= **0.453 592 37** kg
1 ton (long, 2240 lb, UK)	= **1.016 046 908 8** Mg
1 ton (short, 2000 lb)	= **0.907 184 74** Mg

Mass Concentration

1 pound per cubic foot	= 16.018 46 kg/m³

Second Moment of Area (Moment of Inertia)

1 inch⁴	= 0.416 231 4 ×10⁶ mm⁴

Section Modulus

1 inch³	= **16.387 064 × 10³** mm³

Momentum

1 pound foot per second	= 0.138 255 kg·m/s

Power. See also Energy.

1 Btu (IT)* per hour	= 0.293 072 W
1 foot pound-force per hour	= 0.376 616 1 mW
1 foot pound-force per minute	= 22.596 97 mW
1 foot pound-force per second	= 1.355 818 W
1 horsepower (550 ft·lbf/s)	= 745.6999 W
*International Tables.	

Pressure or Stress (Force per Area)

1 atmosphere, standard	= **101.325** kPa
1 inch of mercury (conventional, 32°F)	= 3.386 39 kPa
1 inch of water (conventional)	= 249.089 Pa
1 ksi (1000 lbf/in²)	= 6.894 757 MPa
1 mm mercury (conventional, 0°C)	= 133.322 Pa
1 pound-force per square foot	= 47.880 26 Pa
1 pound-force per square inch (psi)	= 6.894 757 kPa
1 ton-force per square inch	= 13.789 514 MPa
1 ton-force (UK) per square inch	= 15.4443 MPa

Temperature

Scales

Celsius * temperature	= temperature in kelvins − **273.15**
Fahrenheit temperature	= **1.8** (Celsius temperature) + **32**
Fahrenheit temperature	= **1.8** (temperature in kelvins) − **459.67**
Rankine temperature	= **1.8** (temperature in kelvins)

Intervals

1 degree Celsius*	= **1** K
1 degree Fahrenheit	= **5/9** K
1 degree Rankine	= **5/9** K

* "Celsius" replaced "Centigrade" in 1948 to eliminate confusion with the word centigrade, associated with centesimal angular measure.

MISCELLANEOUS CONVERSION FACTORS

Time

1 day (mean solar)	= **86.4** ks
1 hour (mean solar)	= **3.6** ks
1 minute (mean solar)	= **60** s
1 month (mean calendar, 365/12 days)	= **2.628** Ms
1 year (calendar, 365 days)	= **31.536** Ms

Torque (Moment of Force)

1 pound-force foot	= 1.355 818 N·m
1 pound-force inch	= 0.112 985 N·m

Volume

1 acre foot	= 1233.482 m³
1 barrel (oil, 42 US gallons)	= **0.158 987 3** m³
1 board foot*	= 2.359 737 dm³
1 cubic foot	= 28.316 85 dm³
1 cubic inch	= **16.387 064** cm³
1 cubic yard	= 0.764 555 m³
1 gallon	= **4.546 09** dm³
1 gallon (UK) §	= 4.546 092 dm³
1 gallon (US)	= 3.785 412 dm³

*The board foot is nominally
$1 \times 12 \times 12 = 144$ in³.
However, the actual volume of wood is about
2/3 of the nominal quantity.
§ Also referred to as the "Imperial gallon."

Volume Rate of Flow

1 cubic foot per minute	= 0.471 947 4 dm³/s
1 cubic foot per second	= 28.316 85 dm³/s
1 cubic yard per minute	= 12.742 58 dm³/s
1 gallon per minute	= 75.768 17 cm³/s
1 gallon (UK) per minute	= 75.7682 cm³/s
1 gallon (US) per minute	= 63.0902 cm³/s
1 million gallons per day	= 52.6168 dm³/s

Notes:

1. The conversion factors give the relationship between SI units and other Canadian legal units as well as commonly encountered units of measure of United Kingdom and USA origin. The yard and the pound are the same throughout the world; by definition they are specified fractions of the metre and the kilogram. The gallons of Canada and Australia, which are identical, differ by a relatively insignificant amount from the gallon of the United Kingdom, whereas that of the USA is a much smaller measure.
2. The conversion factors given in tables apply to Canadian units unless stated otherwise.
3. Conversion factors that are exact are shown in boldface type. Other factors are given to more than sufficient accuracy for most general and scientific work.
4. Conversions are those listed in CAN3-Z234.1-79

PART EIGHT
GENERAL INDEX